PRENTICE HALL

Teacher's

SCIENCE EXPLORER

Edition

Grade 6

Prentice Hall

Needham, Massachusetts
Upper Saddle River, New Jersey
Glenview, Illinois

ISBN 0-13-053481-1

3 4 5 6 7 8 9 10   08 07 06 05 04 03 02

Table of Contents

Grade 6

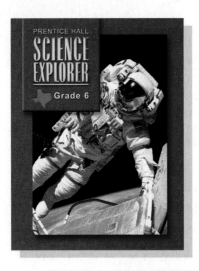

TEXAS SCIENCE EXPLORER

Get ready for a content-rich, hands-on exploration

Dear Texas Science Educator:

Welcome to the world of *Texas Science Explorer!*

Once again, Prentice Hall is offering Texas students and teachers the best in educational textbooks and software. Continuing our commitment to publishing materials that align with the TEKS and support the 11th grade Exit Exam, we are proud to introduce *Texas Science Explorer*.

Each grade level was developed exclusively for Texas, with accessible content and a rich assortment of hands-on activities—providing numerous opportunities for investigations, inquiry, and experimentation.

In addition to rich content and hands-on activities, the texts contain a variety of ways to attract and maintain your students' attention. A student-friendly writing style, integrated reading strategies, ongoing assessment, and an unsurpassed art program make the texts accessible to all students.

I am very excited about our new Texas middle grades science program, and I think you and your students will be too!

Sincerely,

Michael J Padilla

Michael Padilla
Lead Author of
Texas Science Explorer

Created exclusively for Texas educators and students

TEKS integrated throughout

Texas Science Explorer has been developed specifically to match the **Texas Essential Knowledge and Skills.** Complete correlation of the text to the <u>TEKS</u> **assures you are adhering to the state Guidelines.** For your convenience the <u>TEKS</u> are referenced at each chapter opener and in the Teacher's Edition at point-of-use.

Solid content with built-in reading support

A superior writing style, combined with **reading support <u>before</u>, <u>during</u>, and <u>after</u> every section,** builds student confidence, helping them grasp and retain important ideas. **The Guide for Reading, boldfaced sentences,** and **section review questions** provide a consistent, comfortable, framework encouraging students to read with purpose. **Visual Essays** present major concepts in a clear and understandable format. **Reading Strategies** and **Checkpoint Questions** help students access content and reflect back and remember what they read.

Rich assortment of labs and activities

Student and teacher tested activities reinforce key concepts and motivate students to explore science for themselves. **Six types of labs/activities in every chapter with step by step teacher instruction.**

TEKS-based assessment

Texas Science Explorer gives you all the resources you need to diagnose, monitor and regularly assess student progress. Includes traditional, self assessment, portfolio, and performance assessment.

Integrated Technology

From video tapes to the new **iText, interactive, online student edition,** *Texas Science Explorer* provides a complete range of technology components to help you plan, teach, manage and assess.

An exciting, full-featured program

A comprehensive array of components organized to help maximize learning

Core Resources

- **Texas Science Explorer Teacher's Edition**
Contains a three-step lesson plan—Engage/Explore, Facilitate, and Assess—that is ideal for reaching all students. Chapter planning charts make it easy to find resources, as well as to plan for block scheduling and team teaching.

- **Texas Unit Resources**
Includes Chapter Project Support, Lesson Plans, Section summaries, Review & Reinforce Worksheets, Enrich Worksheets, Student Edition Lab Worksheets, and complete Answer Keys.

- **Texas Color Transparencies**
Vibrant color transparencies bring difficult-to-understand concepts to life.

 = Texas-specific component

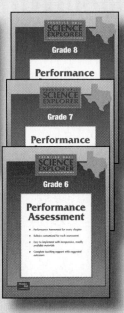

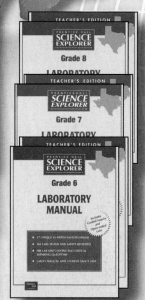

Assessment Resources

- **Texas Science Explorer Assessment System**
  Preparation for the 11th Grade Exit Exam with
  content diagnosis and prescriptions, review and
  remediation, and TAAS test practice for middle
  school students.

- **Texas Performance Assessment**
  Performance Assessment for every chapter, easy to
  implement with inexpensive, readily available materials.

- **Texas Chapter and Unit Tests**
  Contains test strategies, abundant sample problems,
  and blackline master practice worksheets and tests.

- **How to Assess Student Work**
  Articles and activities on integrating assessment,
  using rubrics, and establishing a portfolio program.

- **Texas Computer Test Bank Book with CD-ROM**
  Correlated to the Texas Essential Knowledge and
  Skills Standards, this comprehensive assessment
  package contains Computer Test Bank software
  and chapter tests with correlations to the Texas
  Science Content Standards.

Skills Development

Reading and Study Skills

- **Texas Guided Reading and Study Workbook**
  Section-by-section questions encourage active reading
  and build study skills.

- **Reading in the Content Area with Literature Connections**
  Provides additional strategies for successful reading.

- **Teacher's ELL Handbook**
  Provides multiple strategies for reaching students who lack
  fluency in English. Select appropriate activities to meet the needs
  of individual students.

Lab/Activity Skills

- **Texas Laboratory Manual**
  In-depth labs, covering the entire curriculum, with complete
  teaching support.

- **Probeware Lab Manual**
  Provides exciting opportunities for high-tech lab work and
  encourages students to analyze and interpret data.

- **Inquiry Skills Activity Book**
  Contains additional activities that introduce basic and advanced
  inquiry skills and reinforce skills on an as-needed basis

- **Student Centered Science Activity Book for the Southwest**
  Regional activity book that includes topics from Life, Earth, and
  Physical science, focused on the Southwest.

Texas Technology Components

Texas iText

Provides an online interactive version of the Student Edition.

Contains:

- Animations
- Simulations
- Videos to enhance student understanding and retention of concepts
- Point and click navigation
- Self-assesment with instant feedback
- Learning links right at point of use

Texas Student Edition on Audio CD

Complete student edition is read to students on Audio CD—section by section. Provides support to student of all learning abilities. CDs are available in English and Spanish.

Texas Resource Pro®
CD-ROM with Planning Express®

The ultimate lesson planning and scheduling tool, with electronic access to worksheets. Lets you plan by the day, week, month, or year!

Texas Science Explorer Web site

Activities and teaching resources for every chapter of the text at www.phschool.com

Science News Connection

Weekly science content updates on the Web keep you and your students current!

Texas Computer Test Bank Book with CD-ROM

Correlated to the Texas Essential Knowledge and Skills Standards, this comprehensive assessment package contains Computer Test Bank software and chapter tests, with correlations to the Texas Science Content Standards.

Texas Lab Activity Video Library

Provides step-by-step instruction, with students performing activities from every chapter. Promotes and teaches proper lab techniques, inquiry, and safety skills.

Texas Science Explorer Videotapes and Videodiscs

Explore and visualize concepts through spectacular short documentaries containing computer animations. Videotapes are also available in Spanish.

TEKS	Chapters															
	1	2	3	4	5	6	7	8	9	10	11	12	13	14	15	16
(6.1) Scientific processes. The student conducts field and laboratory investigations using safe, environmentally appropriate, and ethical practices. The student is expected to:																
(A) demonstrate safe practices during field and laboratory investigations; and	■	■	■	■	■	■	■	■	■	■	■	■	■	■		■
(B) make wise choices in the use and conservation of resources and the disposal or recycling of materials.	■			■		■						■	■			
(6.2) Scientific processes. The student uses scientific inquiry methods during field and laboratory investigations. The student is expected to:																
(A) plan and implement investigative procedures including asking questions, formulating testable hypotheses, and selecting and using equipment and technology;	■	■	■	■	■	■	■	■			■		■	■		■
(B) collect data by observing and measuring;	■	■	■	■	■	■	■	■	■	■	■	■	■	■	■	■
(C) analyze and interpret information to construct reasonable explanations from direct and indirect evidence;	■	■	■	■	■	■	■	■	■	■	■	■	■	■	■	■
(D) communicate valid conclusions; and	■	■	■	■	■	■	■	■	■	■	■	■	■	■		
(E) construct graphs, tables, maps, and charts using tools including computers to organize, examine, and evaluate data.	■	■	■	■	■	■	■	■	■	■	■	■	■	■	■	■
(6.3) Scientific processes. The student uses critical thinking and scientific problem solving to make informed decisions. The student is expected to:																
(A) analyze, review, and critique scientific explanations, including hypotheses and theories, as to their strengths and weaknesses using scientific evidence and information;				■												■
(B) draw inferences based on data related to promotional materials for products and services;	■					■										
(C) represent the natural world using models and identify their limitations;	■	■		■	■	■	■	■	■	■	■	■		■	■	■
(D) evaluate the impact of research on scientific thought, society, and the environment; and						■			■		■	■	■		■	■
(E) connect Grade 6 science concepts with the history of science and contributions of scientists.	■	■		■					■			■	■		■	■
(6.4) Scientific processes. The student knows how to use a variety of tools and methods to conduct science inquiry. The student is expected to:																
(A) collect, analyze, and record information using tools including beakers, petri dishes, meter sticks, graduated cylinders, weather instruments, timing devices, hot plates, test tubes, safety goggles, spring scales, magnets, balances, microscopes, telescopes, thermometers, calculators, field equipment, compasses, computers, and computer probes; and	■	■	■	■	■	■	■	■	■	■	■	■	■	■	■	■
(B) identify patterns in collected information using percent, average, range, and frequency.			■			■		■					■	■	■	■

TEKS	Chapters															
	1	2	3	4	5	6	7	8	9	10	11	12	13	14	15	16
(6.5) Scientific concepts. The student knows that systems may combine with other systems to form a larger system. The student is expected to:																
(A) identify and describe a system that results from the combination of two or more systems such as in the solar system; and																■
(B) describe how the properties of a system are different from the properties of its parts.												■				
(6.6) Science concepts. The student knows that there is a relationship between force and motion. The student is expected to:																
(A) identify and describe the changes in position, direction of motion, and speed of an object when acted upon by force;			■													■
(B) demonstrate that changes in motion can be measured and graphically represented; and			■								■					
(C) identify forces that shape features of the Earth including uplifting, movement of water, and volcanic activity.			■													
(6.7) Science concepts. The student knows that substances have physical and chemical properties. The student is expected to:																
(A) demonstrate that new substances can be made when two or more substances are chemically combined and compare the properties of the new substances to the original substances; and	■															
(B) classify substances by their physical and chemical properties.	■	■														
(6.8) Science concepts. The student knows that complex interactions occur between matter and energy. The student is expected to:																
(A) define matter and energy;	■															
(B) explain and illustrate the interactions between matter and energy in the water cycle and in the decay of biomass such as in a compost bin; and								■				■				
(C) describe energy flow in living systems including food chains and food webs.								■								
(6.9) Science concepts. The student knows that obtaining, transforming, and distributing energy affects the environment. The student is expected to:																
(A) identify energy transformations occurring during the production of energy for human use such as electrical energy to heat energy or heat energy to electrical energy;	■								■							
(B) compare methods used for transforming energy in devices such as water heaters, cooling systems, or hydroelectric and wind power plants; and									■							
(C) research and describe energy types from their source to their use and determine if the type is renewable, non-renewable, or inexhaustible.									■							

TEKS Correlation at a Glance

TEKS	1	2	3	4	5	6	7	8	9	10	11	12	13	14	15	16
(6.10) Science concepts. The student knows the relationship between structure and function in living systems. The student is expected to:																
(A) differentiate between structure and function;				■	■	■	■									
(B) determine that all organisms are composed of cells that carry on functions to sustain life; and				■	■	■	■									
(C) identify how structure complements function at different levels of organization including organs, organ systems, organisms, and populations.				■		■	■	■								
(6.11) Science concepts. The student knows that traits of species can change through generations and that the instructions for traits are contained in the genetic material of the organisms. The student is expected to:																
(A) identify some changes in traits that can occur over several generations through natural occurrence and selective breeding;					■											
(B) identify cells as structures containing genetic material; and				■	■	■										
(C) interpret the role of genes in inheritance.				■												
(6.12) Science concepts. The student knows that the responses of organisms are caused by internal or external stimuli. The student is expected to:																
(A) identify responses in organisms to internal stimuli such as hunger or thirst;				■		■	■									
(B) identify responses in organisms to external stimuli such as the presence or absence of heat or light; and				■		■	■									
(C) identify components of an ecosystem to which organisms may respond.								■								
(6.13) Science concepts. The student knows components of our solar system. The student is expected to:																
(A) identify characteristics of objects in our solar system including the Sun, planets, meteorites, comets, asteroids, and moons; and																■
(B) describe types of equipment and transportation needed for space travel.																■
(6.14) Science concepts. The student knows the structures and functions of Earth systems. The student is expected to:																
(A) summarize the rock cycle;										■						
(B) identify relationships between groundwater and surface water in a watershed; and												■				
(C) describe components of the atmosphere, including oxygen, nitrogen, and water vapor, and identify the role of atmospheric movement in weather change.													■	■	■	

Options for Pacing Grade 6

The Pacing Chart below suggests one way to schedule your instructional time. The *Science Explorer* program offers many other aids to help you plan your instructional time, whether regular class periods or **block scheduling.** Refer to the Chapter Planning Guide before each chapter to view all program resources with suggested times for Student Edition activities.

Pacing Chart

Title and TEKS	Days	Blocks	Title and TEKS	Days	Blocks
Introduction to Science	2–3	$1-1\frac{1}{2}$	**Chapter 4 Cells: The Building Blocks of Life** 6.1A; 6.2B, C, D	Ongoing	Ongoing
Chapter 1 Matter and Energy 6.1A; 6.2A, B, C, D; 6.3B	Ongoing	Ongoing	**1** What Is Life? 6.1A; 6.2A, B, C, D, E; 6.3A, D, E; 6.4A; 6.12A, B	2–3	$1-1\frac{1}{2}$
1 Describing Matter and Energy 6.1A; 6.4A; 6.7A, B; 6.8A; 6.9A	3	$1\frac{1}{2}$	**2** Integrating Technology: Discovering Cells 6.1A, B; 6.2B, C; 6.3D, E; 6.4A; 6.10B	1–2	$\frac{1}{2}-1$
2 Measuring Matter 6.2A, B, C, D, E; 6.3E; 6.4A; 6.7B	3	$1\frac{1}{2}$	**3** Looking Inside Cells 6.1A; 6.2B, C; 6.3C; 6.4A; 6.10A, B, C; 6.11B	3–4	$1\frac{1}{2}-2$
3 Particles of Matter 6.3C, E	2	1	**4** Introduction to Genetics 6.2B, C; 6.11A, B, C	2	1
4 Integrating Earth Science: Elements from Earth 6.1A, B; 6.2A, B, C, D; 6.4A; 6.7B	2	1	Chapter 4 Review and Assessment	1	$\frac{1}{2}$
Chapter 1 Review and Assessment	1	$\frac{1}{2}$	**Chapter 5 Cell Processes and Energy** 6.1A; 6.2B, C, D, E; 6.3C; 6.10B	Ongoing	Ongoing
Chapter 2 Solids, Liquids, and Gases 6.2D, 6.3C	Ongoing	Ongoing	**1** The Cell in Its Environment 6.2A, B, C; 6.10A, B	2–3	$1-1\frac{1}{2}$
1 States of Matter 6.2D, 6.7B	2	1	**2** Integrating Chemistry: The Cell and Energy 6.1A; 6.2B, C, D, E; 6.4A; 6.10B	2–3	$1-1\frac{1}{2}$
2 Gas Behavior 6.1A; 6.2A, B; 6.3E; 6.4A; 6.7B	3	$1\frac{1}{2}$	**3** Cell Division 6.1A; 6.2A, B, C, D, E; 6.3C; 6.4A; 6.10B; 6.11B	2–3	$1-1\frac{1}{2}$
3 Integrating Mathematics: Graphing Gas Behavior 6.1A; 6.2A, B, C, E; 6.3C; 6.4A; 6.7B	2	1	Chapter 5 Review and Assessment	1	$\frac{1}{2}$
4 Changes in State 6.1A; 6.2A, B, C, E; 6.4A; 6.7B	2	1	**Chapter 6 From Bacteria to Plants** 6.2B; 6.10C	Ongoing	Ongoing
Chapter 2 Review and Assessment	1	$\frac{1}{2}$	**1** Classifying Living Things 6.2C; 6.10B; 6.11B	2–3	$1-1\frac{1}{2}$
Chapter 3 Relating Force and Motion 6.1A; 6.2B, C, D, E; 6.4A, B	Ongoing	Ongoing	**2** Bacteria 6.1A, B; 6.2A, B, C, D, E; 6.3B, C; 6.4A; 6.10A, B, C; 6.11B	2–3	$1-1\frac{1}{2}$
1 Describing, Measuring, and Graphing Motion 6.1A; 6.2A, B, C, D, E; 6.4A, B; 6.6A, B	4	2	**3** Protists and Fungi 6.1A, B; 6.2B, C; 6.4A; 6.10A, B, C; 6.12B	2–3	$1-1\frac{1}{2}$
2 Force and Acceleration 6.1A; 6.2A, B, C, D, E; 6.4A, B; 6.6A, B	4	2	**4** The Plant Kingdom 6.1A; 6.2A, B, C, D; 6.4A, B; 6.10A, B, C; 6.11B; 6.12A, B	3–4	$1\frac{1}{2}-2$
3 Integrating Earth Science: Water in Motion 6.2B; 6.6A, C	2	1	Chapter 6 Review and Assessment	1	$\frac{1}{2}$
Chapter 3 Review and Assessment	1	$\frac{1}{2}$			
Nature of Science: Understanding Nature's Designs	1	$\frac{1}{2}$			

Options for Pacing Grade 6

Pacing Chart

Title and TEKS	Days	Blocks	Title and TEKS	Days	Blocks
Chapter 7 Animals 6.2C; 6.3C; 6.10A, C	Ongoing	Ongoing	**Chapter 10 Solid Earth** 6.3C; 6.14	Ongoing	Ongoing
1 What Is an Animal? 6.2B, C; 6.10A, B, C; 6.12A, B	2	1	**1** Inside Earth 6.2B, C, D, E; 6.3C; 6.14	2–3	$1-1\frac{1}{2}$
2 Integrating Mathematics: Symmetry 🌀 6.2B; 6.10A, B, C	1	$\frac{1}{2}$	**2** Minerals 6.2B, C, D, E; 6.3C; 6.4A; 6.14A	3	$1\frac{1}{2}$
3 Sponges, Cnidarians, Worms, and Mollusks 6.1A; 6.2A, B, C, D; 6.4A; 6.10A, B, C; 6.12B	4–5	$2-2\frac{1}{2}$	**3** Rocks and the Rock Cycle 6.1A; 6.2B, C, D, E; 6.4A; 6.14A	2	1
4 Arthropods and Echinoderms 6.2A, B, C; 6.3C; 6.10A, C; 6.12A, B	3–4	$1\frac{1}{2}-2$	Chapter 10 Review and Assessment	1	$\frac{1}{2}$
5 Fishes, Amphibians, and Reptiles 6.1A; 6.2B, C, D; 6.3D; 6.4A; 6.10A, C; 6.12B	4–5	$2-2\frac{1}{2}$	**Chapter 11 Earthquakes and Volcanoes** 6.2E; 6.3D; 6.6C	Ongoing	Ongoing
6 Birds and Mammals 6.1A; 6.2A, B, C, D, E; 6.3D; 6.4A; 6.10A, C; 6.12A, B	2–3	$1-1\frac{1}{2}$	**1** Plate Tectonics 6.2B, C; 6.4A; 6.6C	2	1
Chapter 7 Review and Assessment	1	$\frac{1}{2}$	**2** Earth's Crust in Motion 6.1A; 6.2B, C, E; 6.3C; 6.4A; 6.6C	3	$1\frac{1}{2}$
Nature of Science: Unlocking the Secrets of Cells	2	1	**3** Measuring Earthquakes 6.2B, C; 6.6C	2–3	$1-1\frac{1}{2}$
Chapter 8 Ecosystems 6.1A, 6.2A, B, C, D, E	Ongoing	Ongoing	**4** Volcanic Activity 6.2A, B, C, D, E; 6.3C; 6.4A; 6.6C	4	2
1 Components of an Ecosystem 6.1A; 6.2B, C, D, E; 6.4A; 6.10C; 6.12C	2	1	**5** Volcanic Landforms 6.2B, C, E; 6.3C; 6.6C	2	1
2 Integrating Mathematics: Studying Populations 🌀 6.2A, B, C, D, E; 6.3C; 6.4A, B; 6.8C; 6.12C	3	$1\frac{1}{2}$	Chapter 11 Review and Assessment	1	$\frac{1}{2}$
3 Energy in an Ecosystem 6.2B, C; 6.4A; 6.8B, C	2	1	**Chapter 12 Fresh Water** 6.1B; 6.2B, C, D, E; 6.14B	Ongoing	Ongoing
Chapter 8 Review and Assessment	1	$\frac{1}{2}$	**1** The Water Cycle 6.1A; 6.2B, C, D, E; 6.3C, D; 6.4A; 6.8B; 6.14B	2	1
Chapter 9 Energy Resources 6.2A, B, D; 6.9	Ongoing	Ongoing	**2** Surface Water 6.2B, C; 6.3C; 6.4A; 6.14B	3	$1\frac{1}{2}$
1 Energy and Fossil Fuels 6.2B, E; 6.4A; 6.9A, B, C	3	$1\frac{1}{2}$	**3** Groundwater 6.1A; 6.2B, C, D, E; 6.3C; 6.14B	3	$1\frac{1}{2}$
2 Renewable Sources of Energy 6.2A, B, C, D; 6.3D; 6.4A; 6.9A, B, C	2	1	**4** Wetland Systems 6.2B, C, E; 6.3C; 6.5B	2	1
3 Integrating Chemistry: Nuclear Energy 🌀 6.2B, C, D, E; 6.3C; 6.4A; 6.9A, C	3	$1\frac{1}{2}$	**5** Water Resources 6.2B, C; 6.3C, D, E; 6.4A; 6.14B	1	$\frac{1}{2}$
4 Energy Conservation 6.1A; 6.2B, C; 6.3E; 6.4A; 6.9A	2–3	$1-1\frac{1}{2}$	Chapter 12 Review and Assessment	1	$\frac{1}{2}$
Chapter 9 Review and Assessment	1	$\frac{1}{2}$	**Chapter 13 Earth's Atmosphere** 6.2B, C, D, E; 6.4B; 6.14C	Ongoing	Ongoing
Nature of Science: Protecting Desert Wildlife	2	1	**1** The Air Around You 6.1A; 6.2A, B, C, D, E; 6.4A; 6.14C	2	1
			2 Integrating Environmental Science: Air Quality 🌀 6.1B; 6.2B, C; 6.3D; 6.14C	2	1
			3 Air Pressure 6.2B, C, D, E; 6.4A; 6.14C	3	$1\frac{1}{2}$
			4 Layers of the Atmosphere 6.2B, C; 6.3E; 6.14C	2	1
			Chapter 13 Review and Assessment	1	$\frac{1}{2}$

Pacing Chart

Title and TEKS	Days	Blocks	Title and TEKS	Days	Blocks
Chapter 14 Weather Factors 6.2A, B, C, D, E; 6.4A, B; 6.14C	Ongoing	Ongoing	**Chapter 16 Components of the Solar System** 6.2E; 6.3C	Ongoing	Ongoing
1 Energy in the Atmosphere 6.1A; 6.2A, B, C, D, E; 6.4A; 6.14C	3–4	$1\frac{1}{2}$–2	**1** Describing the Solar System 6.1A; 6.2C; 6.3A, C, D, E; 6.5A; 6.13A	2	1
2 Integrating Physics: Heat Transfer 🔵 6.2B, C, E; 6.4A; 6.14C	1	$\frac{1}{2}$	**2** Characteristics of the Sun 6.1A; 6.2B, C, E; 6.4A; 6.13A	2–3	1–$1\frac{1}{2}$
3 Winds 6.2B, C, E; 6.3C; 6.4A; 6.14C	3	$1\frac{1}{2}$	**3** Characteristics of the Inner Planets 6.1A; 6.2E; 6.3C; 6.4A; 6.13A	2	1
4 Water in the Atmosphere 6.1A; 6.2A, B, C, D; 6.3C; 6.14C	2–3	1–$1\frac{1}{2}$	**4** Characteristics of the Outer Planets 6.1A; 6.2A, B, C, E; 6.3C; 6.4A; 6.13A	3	$1\frac{1}{2}$
5 Precipitation 6.2C; 6.14C	1–2	$\frac{1}{2}$–1	**5** Comets, Asteroids, and Meteors 6.1A; 6.3C; 6.4B; 6.5A; 6.13A	2	1
Chapter 14 Review and Assessment	1	$\frac{1}{2}$	**6** Integrating Technology: Traveling in Space 🔵 6.1A; 6.4A; 6.6A; 6.13B	1	$\frac{1}{2}$
Chapter 15 Weather Patterns 6.2B, C, E; 6.4B; 6.14C	Ongoing	Ongoing	Chapter 16 Review and Assessment	1	$\frac{1}{2}$
1 Air Masses and Fronts 6.2B, C; 6.14C	2–3	1–$1\frac{1}{2}$	Interdisciplinary Exploration: The Mississippi	2	1
2 Storms 6.2B, C, D; 6.3C, D, E; 6.14C	3	$1\frac{1}{2}$			
3 Integrating Health: Floods 🔵 6.2B, C; 6.3C; 6.4A; 6.14C	1	$\frac{1}{2}$			
4 Predicting Weather Change 6.2B, C, D; 6.14C	3	$1\frac{1}{2}$			
Chapter 15 Review and Assessment	1	$\frac{1}{2}$			

RESOURCE⊙ PRO®

The Resource Pro® CD-ROM is the ultimate scheduling and lesson planning tool. Resource Pro® allows you to preview all the resources in the *Science Explorer* program, organize your chosen materials, and print out any teaching resource. You can follow the suggested lessons or create your own, using resources from anywhere in the program.

Science TAAS Handbook

The *Science Explorer* program provides a strong foundation for the 10th Grade Science Texas Assessment of Academic Skills (TAAS) and the 11th Grade Exit Level Science TAAS. The Exit Level TAAS assesses knowledge of science process and content. Mastery of science process and content will lead to scientific literacy in Texas students, and to success on the TAAS.

Use these pages for an overview of the:
- major content strands
- TEKS related to the content strands
- concepts introduced in Grades 1–5 that relate to the content strands
- 6th, 7th, and 8th Grade TEKS that develop the concepts of the content strands
- *Science Explorer* objectives that relate to the content strands
- concepts in Grades 9–10 that complete the mastery of the content strands

---

Content strand

Organization of Living Systems

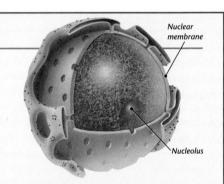

Nuclear membrane

Nucleolus

States the Biology TEKS and the Integrated Physics and Chemistry TEKS related to the content strand

BIOLOGY TEKS 4   The student knows that cells are the basic structures of all living things and have specialized parts that perform specific functions, and that viruses are different from cells and have different properties and functions.

 For graduation, students are expected to investigate and identify cellular processes including homeostasis, permeability, energy production, transportation of molecules, disposal of wastes, function of cellular parts, and synthesis of new molecules. **(BIO TEKS 4B)** and they are expected to compare the structures and functions of viruses to cells and describe the role of viruses in causing diseases and conditions such as acquired immune deficiency syndrome, common colds, smallpox, influenza, and warts. **(BIO TEKS 4C)**

Summarizes the Grades 1–5 concepts that relate to the content strand

Progression of Science Knowledge

Grades 1–5

Students described and compared life cycles of plants and animals. They have identified characteristics that allow members within a species to survive and reproduce.

Grades 6–8

Identifies the Grades 6–8 TEKS related to the content strand

Grade 6	Grade 7	Grade 8
TEKS 6.10B Students determine that all organisms are composed of cells that carry on functions to sustain life.	**TEKS 7.10A** Students identify that sexual reproduction results in more diverse offspring and asexual reproduction results in more uniform offspring.	**TEKS 8.11C** Students make predictions about possible outcomes of various genetic combinations of inherited characteristics.
In *Science Explorer*, students will	**In *Science Explorer*, students will**	**In *Science Explorer*, students will**
■ determine that all organisms are composed of cells and state the three points of the cell theory. ■ identify the cell wall, cell membrane, and nucleus, and describe their functions. ■ identify other organelles in the cell.	■ contrast the offspring of sexual reproduction with the offspring of asexual reproduction.	■ explain what multiple alleles are. ■ explain why some human traits show a large variety of phenotypes. ■ describe the causes and symptoms of four human genetic disorders.
	Sample Assessment Question Which of these is a form of asexual reproduction? **A** fertilization **B** binary fission **C** meiosis **D** homeostasis	
Sample Assessment Question Which part of the cell controls what substances enter and leave the cell? **A** ribosomes **B** mitochondria **C** cell membrane **D** nucleus		**Sample Assessment Question** Chromosomes function to **A** produce energy. **B** carry on photosynthesis. **C** transport materials within the cell. **D** carry genes from parents to offspring.

Highlights the *Science Explorer* objectives that lead to mastery of the content strand

Shows a sample question that illustrates how content emphasis might be assessed

Describes the concepts to be mastered in Grades 9–10 (When this section is absent, content mastery is expected in Grade 8.)

Grades 9–10

Students investigate and identify cellular processes including homeostasis, permeability, energy production, transportation of molecules, disposal of wastes, function of cellular parts, and synthesis of new molecules. They compare the structures and functions of viruses to cells and describe the role of viruses in causing diseases and conditions such as acquired immune deficiency syndrome, common colds, smallpox, influenza, and warts.

Organization of Living Systems

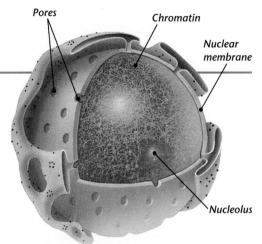

Pores Chromatin Nuclear membrane Nucleolus

BIOLOGY TEKS 4   The student knows that cells are the basic structures of all living things and have specialized parts that perform specific functions, and that viruses are different from cells and have different properties and functions.

For graduation, students are expected to investigate and identify cellular processes including homeostasis, permeability, energy production, transportation of molecules, disposal of wastes, function of cellular parts, and synthesis of new molecules. **(BIO TEKS 4B)** and they are expected to compare the structures and functions of viruses to cells and describe the role of viruses in causing diseases and conditions such as acquired immune deficiency syndrome, common colds, smallpox, influenza, and warts. **(BIO TEKS 4C)**

Progression of Science Knowledge

Grades 1–5
Students described and compared life cycles of plants and animals. They have identified characteristics that allow members within a species to survive and reproduce.

Grades 6–8

Grade 6
TEKS 6.10B Students determine that all organisms are composed of cells that carry on functions to sustain life.

In *Science Explorer,* students will
- determine that all organisms are composed of cells and state the three points of the cell theory.
- identify the cell wall, cell membrane, and nucleus, and describe their functions.
- identify other organelles in the cell.

Sample Assessment Question
Which part of the cell controls what substances enter and leave the cell?
A ribosomes
B mitochondria
C cell membrane
D nucleus

Grade 7
TEKS 7.10A Students identify that sexual reproduction results in more diverse offspring and asexual reproduction results in more uniform offspring.

In *Science Explorer,* students will
- contrast the offspring of sexual reproduction with the offspring of asexual reproduction.

Sample Assessment Question
Which of these is a form of asexual reproduction?
A fertilization
B binary fission
C meiosis
D homeostasis

Grade 8
TEKS 8.11C Students make predictions about possible outcomes of various genetic combinations of inherited characteristics.

In *Science Explorer,* students will
- explain what multiple alleles are.
- explain why some human traits show a large variety of phenotypes.
- describe the causes and symptoms of four human genetic disorders.

Sample Assessment Question
Chromosomes function to
A produce energy.
B carry on photosynthesis.
C transport materials within the cell.
D carry genes from parents to offspring.

Grades 9–10
Students investigate and identify cellular processes including homeostasis, permeability, energy production, transportation of molecules, disposal of wastes, function of cellular parts, and synthesis of new molecules. They compare the structures and functions of viruses to cells and describe the role of viruses in causing diseases and conditions such as acquired immune deficiency syndrome, common colds, smallpox, influenza, and warts.

Organization of Living Systems

BIOLOGY TEKS 6 The student knows the structures and functions of nucleic acids in the mechanism of genetics.

    For graduation, students are expected to describe components of DNA and illustrate how information for specifying the traits of an organism is carried in the DNA. **(BIO TEKS 6A)**; they are expected to explain replication, transcription, and translation using models of DNA and ribonucleic acid (RNA) **(BIO TEKS 6B)**; and they are expected to identify and illustrate how changes in DNA cause mutations and evaluate the significance of these changes. **(BIO TEKS 6C)**

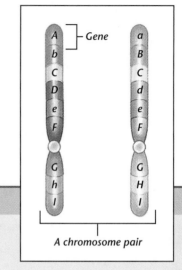

A chromosome pair

Progression of Science Knowledge

Grades 1–5
Students identify traits that are inherited from parents to offspring in plants and animals.

Grades 6–8

Grade 6

TEKS 6.11B Students identify cells as structures containing genetic material.
TEKS 6.11C Students interpret the role of genes in inheritance.

In *Science Explorer,* students will
- determine that all organisms are composed of cells and state the three points of the cell theory.
- identify cells as structures containing genetic material, and interpret the role of genes in inheritance.
- identify some changes in traits that can occur over several generations through natural occurrence and selective breeding.
- differentiate between sexual and asexual reproduction.

Sample Assessment Question
Which of these is the smallest unit that contains all of the instructions for the traits of an organism?
A organ system
B organ
C tissue
D cell

Grade 7

TEKS 7.10B Students compare traits of organisms of different species that enhance their survival and reproduction.
TEKS 7.10C Students distinguish between dominant and recessive traits and recognize that inherited traits of an individual are contained in genetic material.

In *Science Explorer,* students will
- compare traits of organisms of different species that enhance their survival and reproduction.
- distinguish between dominant and recessive alleles.
- explain what a gene is.

Sample Assessment Question
How are genes and DNA related?
A There are six genes in every DNA molecule.
B Genes are proteins coded by DNA.
C There are the same number of genes and DNA molecules in a cell.
D A gene is a segment of a DNA molecule.

Grade 8

TEKS 8.11B Students distinguish between inherited traits and other characteristics that result from interactions with the environment.
TEKS 8.11C Students make prediction about possible outcomes of various genetic combinations of inherited characteristics.

In *Science Explorer,* students will
- explain how environmental factors can alter the effects of a gene.
- explain what multiple alleles are.
- describe how geneticists use pedigrees.
- identify the factors that control the inheritance of traits in organisms.

Sample Assessment Question
Which of these is a goal of the Human Genome Project?
A to map every gene on the human genome
B to find how genes determine gender
C to list traits for selective breeding
D to find out how traits are passed on

Grades 9–10
Students describe components of deoxyribonucleic acid (DNA) and illustrate how information for specifying the traits of an organism is carried in the DNA. They will explain replication, transcription, and translation using models of DNA and ribonucleic acid (RNA) and they will identify and illustrate how changes in DNA cause mutations and evaluate the significance of these changes.

Organization of Living Systems

BIOLOGY TEKS 6 The student knows the structures and functions of nucleic acids in the mechanism of genetics.

For graduation, students are expected to compare genetic variations observed in plants and animals. (**BIO TEKS 6D**)

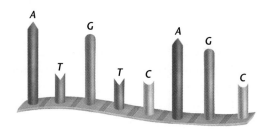

Progression of Science Knowledge

Grades 1–5
Students identify traits that are inherited from parents to offspring in plants and animals.

Grades 6–8

Grade 6

TEKS 6.11A Students identify some changes in traits that can occur over several generations through natural occurrence and selective breeding.
TEKS 6.11C Students interpret the role of genes in inheritance.

In *Science Explorer*, students will
- identify cells as structures containing genetic material, and interpret the role of genes in inheritance.
- differentiate between asexual and sexual reproduction.
- identify some changes in traits that can occur over several generations through natural occurrence and selective breeding.
- describe the structure of DNA and DNA replication.

Sample Assessment Question
The study of the passing of traits from parents to offspring is
A genetics.
B dominant gene.
C cloning.
D DNA.

Grade 7

TEKS 7.10B Students compare traits of organisms of different species that enhance their survival and reproduction.
TEKS 7.10C Students distinguish between dominant and recessive traits and recognize that inherited traits of an individual are contained in genetic material.

In *Science Explorer*, students will
- contrast the offspring of sexual reproduction with the offspring of asexual reproduction.
- distinguish between dominant and recessive alleles.
- define adaptations and explain the role of genes in adaptations.
- compare traits of organisms of different species that enhance their survival and reproduction.

Sample Assessment Question
If two black Labrador retrievers mate and have a yellow Lab puppy, what can you infer about the traits for coat color?
A The yellow allele is dominant.
B The yellow allele is recessive.
C Coat color is determined by the environment.
D Coat color is not inherited.

Grade 8

TEKS 8.11B Students distinguish between inherited traits and other characteristics that result from interactions with the environment.
TEKS 8.11C Students make predictions about possible outcomes of various genetic combinations of inherited characteristics.

In *Science Explorer*, students will
- identify what determines sex, and explain why some sex-linked traits are more common in males than in females.
- describe how geneticists use pedigrees.
- describe the causes and symptoms of four human genetic disorders.

Sample Assessment Question
In Labrador retrievers, the genes for coat color are B, for black and b, for yellow coat color. If two heterozygous black Labs are mated, what are the chances that yellow pups will be in the litter?
A 0%
B 25%
C 50%
D 100%

Grades 9–10
Students compare genetic variations observed in plants and animals.

Organization of Living Systems

BIOLOGY TEKS 8 The student knows applications of taxonomy and can identify its limitations.

For graduation, students are expected to identify characteristics of kingdoms including monerans, protists, fungi, plants, and animals. **(BIO TEKS 8C)**

Family Strigidae

Progression of Science Knowledge

Grades 1–5
Students describe and compare life cycles of plants and animals.

Grades 6–8

Grade 6	Grade 7	Grade 8
In *Science Explorer*, students will ■ list the six kingdoms into which all organisms are classified. ■ describe the characteristics of fungi. ■ identify the characteristics that all plants share. ■ describe four major characteristics of animals. **Sample Assessment Question** Which of these is a characteristic of fungi? **A** Fungi move from place to place. **B** Fungi make their own food. **C** Fungi are often many-celled organisms. **D** All fungi are one-celled organisms.	In *Science Explorer*, students will ■ identify the levels of organization in complex organisms. **Sample Assessment Question** Why are humans classified as mammals? **A** They nurture their young with milk. **B** They have a backbone. **C** They have a heart. **D** They have a brain.	In *Science Explorer*, students will ■ describe the factors that affect where ocean organisms live. ■ describe conditions in the open ocean and identify where algae live. ■ explain how hydrothermal vents support organisms. **Sample Assessment Question** Marine organisms that are microscopic and drift with the ocean currents are **A** plankton. **B** benthos. **C** plants. **D** viruses.

Grades 9–10
Students identify characteristics of kingdoms including monerans, protists, fungi, plants, and animals.

Organization of Living Systems

BIOLOGY TEKS 10   The student knows that, at all levels of nature, living systems are found within other living systems, each with its own boundary and limits.

For graduation, students are expected to interpret the functions of systems in organisms including circulatory, digestive, nervous, endocrine, reproductive, integumentary, skeletal, respiratory, muscular, excretory, and immune **(BIO TEKS 10A)** and they are expected to compare the interrelationships of organ systems to each other and to the body as a whole. **(BIO TEKS 10B)**

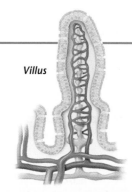

Villus

Progression of Science Knowledge

Grades 1–5
Students know that a system is a collection of cycles, structures, and processes that interact. They describe some interactions that occur in a simple system.

Grades 6–8

Grade 6

TEKS 6.10A Students differentiate between structure and function.
TEKS 6.10C Students identify how structure complements function at different levels of organization including organs, organ systems, organisms, and populations.

In *Science Explorer*, students will
- describe the relationship between animal body structures and functions.
- relate structure and function in sponges and cnidarians.
- describe the structure of a mollusk.
- describe the structures characteristic of arthropods.
- describe the structures that characterize insects.
- identify the characteristics of echinoderms.
- explain the function of a vertebrate's skeletal system.
- describe the characteristics of fishes, amphibians and reptiles.
- identify the common characteristics of birds.
- describe the characteristics all mammals share.

Sample Assessment Question
Which of these is a function of the skeletal system?
A to support the body
B to fight infections
C to aid digestion
D to regulate water balance in the body

Grade 7

TEKS 7.9A Students identify the systems of the human organism and describe their functions.
TEKS 7.9B Students describe how organisms maintain stable internal conditions while living in changing external environments.

In *Science Explorer*, students will
- explain the importance of maintaining stable internal conditions (homeostasis).
- list the functions of the skeleton.
- identify the three types of muscles, describe the function of each, and relate force to the action of muscles.
- describe the functions of skin.
- describe the general functions carried out by the digestive system and the specific functions of the mouth, esophagus, and stomach.
- explain the structure and function of the small intestine.
- explain the function of the large intestine in digestion.
- describe the function of the cardiovascular system.
- identify the functions of the respiratory system.

Sample Assessment Question
Which system controls body processes by means of chemicals?
A circulatory
B respiratory
C nervous
D endocrine

Grade 8

TEKS 8.6A Students describe interactions among systems in the human organism.

In *Science Explorer*, students will
- describe the levels of organization in multicellular organisms and explain what a system is.
- describe interactions among systems in the human organism.
- identify and describe feedback mechanisms that maintain equilibrium of systems such as body temperature, turgor pressure, and chemical reactions.
- describe the major types of interactions among organisms in an ecosystem.

Sample Assessment Question
Which of the following body systems work together to transport oxygen to cells?
A endocrine and digestive systems
B respiratory and circulatory systems
C respiratory and immune systems
D circulatory and digestive systems

Grades 9–10
Students interpret the functions of systems in organisms including circulatory, digestive, nervous, endocrine, reproductive, integumentary, skeletal, respiratory, muscular, excretory, and immune. They compare the interrelationships of organ systems to each other and to the body as a whole.

Interdependence of Organisms and the Environment

BIOLOGY TEKS 7   The student knows the theory of biological evolution.

For graduation, students are expected to identify evidence of change in species using fossils, DNA sequences, anatomical similarities, physiological similarities, and embryology **(BIO TEKS 7A)** and they are expected to illustrate the results of natural selection in speciation, diversity, phylogeny, adaption, behavior, and extinction. **(BIO TEKS 7B)**

Finches on the Galapagos Islands

Progression of Science Knowledge

Grades 1–5
Students compare the characteristics of species that improve their ability to survive and reproduce in an ecosystem. They predict some adaptive characteristics required for survival and reproduction by an organism in an ecosystem.

Grades 6–8

Grade 6

TEKS 6.11A Students identify some changes in traits that can occur over several generations through natural occurrence and selective breeding.
TEKS 6.11C Students interpret the roles of genes in inheritance.

In *Science Explorer*, students will
- identify cells as structures containing genetic material, and interpret the role of genes in inheritance.
- identify some changes in traits that can occur over several generations through natural occurrence and selective breeding.
- determine that all organisms are composed of cells and state the three points of cell theory.
- differentiate between asexual and sexual reproduction.

Sample Assessment Question
Strawberries grown today may have improved resistance to disease because of which process?
A radiation
B selective breeding
C photosynthesis
D changes in the ozone layer

Grade 7

TEKS 7.10B Students compare traits of organisms of different species that enhance their survival and reproduction.
TEKS 7.10C Students distinguish between dominant and recessive traits and recognize that inherited traits of an individual are contained in genetic material.

In *Science Explorer*, students will
- compare traits of organisms of different species that enhance their survival and reproduction.
- distinguish between dominant and recessive alleles.
- contrast the offspring resulting from asexual and sexual reproduction.
- explain what a gene is.

Sample Assessment Question
Suppose that both red and green frogs live on a riverbed covered with grass. Which statement would be true?
A Red and green frogs have equal chances of survival.
B Red frogs will have more offspring.
C Green frogs will have a better chance of survival.
D Red frogs will have a better chance of survival.

Grade 8

TEKS 8.11A Students identify that change in environmental conditions can affect the survival of individuals and of species.
TEKS 8.11C Students make predictions about possible outcomes of various genetic combinations of inherited characteristics.
TEKS 8.14B Students analyze how natural or human events may have contributed to the extinction of some species.

In *Science Explorer*, students will
- identify what determines sex, and explain why some sex-linked traits are more common in males than in females.
- describe how geneticists use pedigrees.
- describe the causes and symptoms of four human genetic disorders.
- describe three ways in which people have developed organisms with desired traits.

Sample Assessment Question
In modern times, among finches natural selection was seen on one of the Galapagos Islands when a drought occurred and only large seed pods were produced. Some finches had a beak type that allowed them to open these seed pods easier than other beak types, and they survived better than the other finches. This beak type would be a
A homologous structure
B variation
C stage of development
D genetically engineered trait

Grades 9–10
Students identify evidence of change in species using fossils, DNA sequences, anatomical similarities, physiological similarities, and embryology. They illustrate the results of natural selection in speciation, diversity, phylogeny, adaption, behavior, and extinction.

Interdependence of Organisms and the Environment

BIOLOGY TEKS 9   The student knows metabolic processes and energy transfers that occur in living organisms.

For graduation, students are expected to analyze the flow of matter and energy through different trophic levels and between organisms and the physical environment. **(BIO TEKS 9D)**

Carbon dioxide   *Water*   *Sunlight*   *Oxygen*   *Sugar*

Progression of Science Knowledge

Grades 1–5

Students observe and describe the habitats of organisms within an ecosystem. They observe and identify organisms with similar needs that compete with one another for resources such as oxygen, water, food, or space.

Grades 6–8

Grade 6	Grade 7	Grade 8
TEKS 6.8A Students define matter and energy. **TEKS 6.8B** Students explain and illustrate the interactions between matter and energy in the water cycle and in the decay of biomass such as in a compost bin. **TEKS 6.8C** Students describe energy flow in living systems including food chains and food webs. **TEKS 6.12C** Students identify components of an ecosystem to which organisms may respond. **In *Science Explorer*, students will** ▪ define matter and energy. ▪ explain how energy flows in living systems. ▪ describe what happens when biomass decays. ▪ identify the components of an ecosystem to which organisms respond, including biotic and abiotic parts of an ecosystem. **Sample Assessment Question** Where does photosynthesis occur in plant cells? **A** in chloroplasts **B** in chromosomes **C** in mitochondria **D** in ribosomes	**TEKS 7.5B** Students observe and describe the role of ecological succession in maintaining an equilibrium in an ecosystem. **TEKS 7.8B** Students identify that radiant energy from the sun is transferred into chemical energy through the process of photosynthesis. **In *Science Explorer*, students will** ▪ describe the differences between primary and secondary succession and explain the role of succession in maintaining equilibrium in an ecosystem. ▪ describe the energy conversion that occurs during photosynthesis. ▪ list and describe Earth's major freshwater and ocean biomes and describe the varieties of organisms they support. **Sample Assessment Question** The source of energy in most ecosystems is **A** water. **B** the sun. **C** consumers. **D** decomposers.	**TEKS 8.6C** Students describe interactions within ecosystems. **In *Science Explorer*, students will** ▪ describe the factors that affect where ocean organisms live. ▪ describe conditions in the open ocean and identify where algae live. ▪ explain how hydrothermal vents support organisms. ▪ describe the major types of interactions among organisms in an ecosystem. **Sample Assessment Question** During the oxygen-carbon dioxide cycle, what returns oxygen to the air? **A** consumers **B** producers **C** symbiosis **D** respiration

Grades 9–10

Students analyze the flow of matter and energy through different trophic levels and between organisms and the physical environment.

Interdependence of Organisms and the Environment

BIOLOGY TEKS 12   The student knows that interdependence and interactions occur within an ecosystem.

For graduation, students are expected to interpret interactions among organisms exhibiting predation, parasitism, commensalism, and mutualism. **(BIO TEKS 12B).**

Progression of Science Knowledge

Grades 1–5

Students know that living organisms need food, water, light, air, a way to dispose of waste, and an environment in which to live. They are expected to observe and describe the habitats of organisms within an ecosystem.

Grades 6–8

Grade 6

TEKS 6.8C Students describe energy flow in living systems including food chains and food webs.
TEKS 6.12C Students identify components of an ecosystem to which organisms may respond.

In *Science Explorer*, students will
- explain what causes populations to change in size.
- identify factors that limit population growth.
- explain how energy flows in living systems.
- identify the needs that are met by an organism's habitat.
- identify the components of an ecosystem to which organisms respond, including biotic and abiotic parts of an ecosystem.
- describe the levels of organization within an ecosystem.

Sample Assessment Question
Which of these things are biotic factors in an ecosystem?
A water
B trees
C air
D rocks

Grade 7

TEKS 7.5B Students observe and describe the role of ecological succession in maintaining an equilibrium in an ecosystem.
TEKS 7.12A Students identify components of an ecosystem.
TEKS 7.12B Students observe and describe how organisms including producers, consumers, and decomposers live together in an environment and use existing resources.
TEKS 7.12C Students describe how different environments support different varieties of organisms.
TEKS 7.12D Students observe and describe the role of ecological succession in ecosystems.

In *Science Explorer*, students will
- describe the differences between primary and secondary succession and explain the role of succession in maintaining equilibrium in an ecosystem.
- identify the components of an ecosystem and describe the energy roles that organisms play.
- identify the factors that affect biodiversity and describe how different environments support different varieties of organisms.

Sample Assessment Question
A food chain always begins with a
A producer.
B first level consumer.
C second level consumer.
D decomposer.

Grade 8

TEKS 8.6C Students describe interaction within ecosystems.

In *Science Explorer*, students will
- describe the factors that affect where ocean organisms live.
- describe conditions in the open ocean and identify where algae live.
- explain how hydrothermal vents support organisms.
- describe the major types of interactions among organisms in an ecosystem.

Sample Assessment Question
A predator and prey are part of a _____.
A parasitic relationship
B decomposer
C succession
D food web

Grades 9–10

Students interpret interactions among organisms exhibiting predation, parasitism, commensalism, and mutualism.

Interdependence of Organisms and the Environment

BIOLOGY TEKS 12   The student knows that interdependence and interactions occur within an ecosystem.

For graduation, students are expected to investigate and explain the interactions in an ecosystem including food chains, food webs, and food pyramids. **(BIO TEKS 12E)**

Energy pyramid

Progression of Science Knowledge

Grades 1–5

Students know that living organisms need food, water, light, air, a way to dispose of waste, and an environment in which to live. They are expected to observe and describe the habitats of organisms within an ecosystem.

Grades 6–8

Grade 6	Grade 7	Grade 8
TEKS 6.8C Students describe energy flow in living systems including food chains and food webs.	**TEKS 7.5B** Students observe and describe the role of ecological succession in maintaining an equilibrium in an ecosystem.	**TEKS 8.6C** Students describe interaction within ecosystems.

Grade 6

TEKS 6.8C Students describe energy flow in living systems including food chains and food webs.

In *Science Explorer,* students will
- explain how energy flows in living systems.
- identify the needs that are met by an organism's habitat.
- identify the components of an ecosystem to which organisms respond, including biotic and abiotic parts of an ecosystem.
- describe the levels of organization within an ecosystem.

Sample Assessment Question
Decomposers get energy by
A making their own food.
B eating other things.
C eating both plants and animals.
D breaking down dead organisms.

Grade 7

TEKS 7.5B Students observe and describe the role of ecological succession in maintaining an equilibrium in an ecosystem.
TEKS 7.12A Students identify components of an ecosystem.
TEKS 7.12B Students observe and describe how organisms including producers, consumers, and decomposers live together in an environment and use existing resources.
TEKS 7.12C Students describe how different environments support different varieties of organisms.
TEKS 7.12D Students observe and describe the role of ecological succession in ecosystems.

In *Science Explorer,* students will
- describe the differences between primary and secondary succession and explain the role of succession in maintaining equilibrium in an ecosystem.
- identify the components of an ecosystem and describe the energy roles that organisms play.
- explain the roles of producers, consumers, and decomposers in food chains and food webs.

Sample Assessment Question
How does the amount of energy change as you move up the food chain?
A It increases.
B It decreases.
C It stays the same.
D It doubles.

Grade 8

TEKS 8.6C Students describe interaction within ecosystems.

In *Science Explorer,* students will
- describe the major types of interactions among organisms in an ecosystem.

Sample Assessment Question
In which type of interaction do both species benefit?
A predation
B mutualism
C commensalism
D parasitism

Grades 9–10

Students investigate and explain the interactions in an ecosystem including food chains, food webs, and food pyramids.

Interdependence of Organisms and the Environment

BIOLOGY TEKS 13   The student knows the significance of plants in the environment. For graduation, students are expected to evaluate the significance of structural and physiological adaptations of plants to their environments. (BIO TEKS 13A)

Flower parts

Progression of Science Knowledge

Grades 1–5
Students describe and compare life cycles of plants and animals.

Grades 6–8

Grade 6

In *Science Explorer,* students will
- identify the characteristics that all plants share.
- explain how energy flows in living systems.
- identify the needs that are met by an organism's habitat.
- identify the components of an ecosystem to which organisms respond, including biotic and abiotic parts of an ecosystem.
- describe the levels of organization within an ecosystem.

Sample Assessment Question
Which of these is a characteristic of plants?
A They are simple one-cell organisms.
B They make their own food.
C They do not make their own food, but absorb food from other living things.
D They move from place to place.

Grade 7

TEKS 7.8B Students identify that radiant energy from the Sun is transferred into chemical energy through the process of photosynthesis.

In *Science Explorer,* students will
- state that energy enters most ecosystems through photosynthesis, and relate available energy to the levels of an energy pyramid.

Sample Assessment Question
What substances are needed for photosynthesis?
A nitrogen and water
B oxygen and nitrogen
C water and carbon dioxide
D oxygen and carbon dioxide

Grade 8

TEKS 8.6B Students identify feedback mechanisms that maintain equilibrium of systems such as body temperature, turgor pressure, and chemical reactions.

In *Science Explorer,* students will
- describe the characteristics of a system in equilibrium.
- identify and describe feedback mechanisms that maintain equilibrium of systems such as body temperature, turgor pressure, and chemical reactions.

Sample Assessment Question
If a plant cell does not have enough water to maintain turgor pressure, the plant will begin to _____.
A grow
B wilt
C make nitrogen
D convert carbon dioxide and water into sugar and oxygen

Grades 9–10
Students evaluate the significance of structural and physiological adaptations of plants to their environments.

Structure and Properties of Matter

INTEGRATED PHYSICS AND CHEMISTRY TEKS 7 The student knows relationships exist between properties of matter and its components.

For graduation, students are expected to investigate and identify properties of fluids including density, viscosity, and buoyancy **(IPC TEKS 7A)** and they are expected to relate the chemical behavior of an element including bonding, to its placement on the periodic table. **(IPC TEKS 7D)**

Particles of a gas

Progression of Science Knowledge

Grades 1–5

Students classify matter based on its physical properties including magnetism, physical state, and the ability to conduct or insulate heat, electricity, and sound. They study mixtures and demonstrate that some mixtures maintain the physical properties of their ingredients. They observe and measure characteristic properties of substances that remain constant such as boiling points and melting points.

Grades 6–8

Grade 6	Grade 7	Grade 8
TEKS 6.7A Students demonstrate that new substances can be made when two or more substances are chemically combined and compare the properties of the new substances to the original substances.	**TEKS 7.7B** Students describe physical properties of elements and identify how they are used to position an element on the periodic table.	**TEKS 8.9A** Students demonstrate that substances may react chemically to form new substances. **TEKS 8.9B** Students interpret information on the periodic table to understand that physical properties are used to group elements.
In *Science Explorer,* students will ■ explain that substances can be identified or classified by their physical and chemical properties. ■ explain the differences among elements, compounds, and mixtures. ■ distinguish between physical and chemical change.	**In *Science Explorer,* students will** ■ describe the organization of the periodic table. ■ identify the groups within the periodic table and state what properties elements in a group have in common. ■ locate nonmetals and metalloids in the periodic table.	**In *Science Explorer,* students will** ■ state key events in the historical development of the periodic table. ■ list the information in the periodic table, and describe how it is organized. ■ compare the valence electrons in a period and in a group, and explain how they influence the properties of elements.
Sample Assessment Question Which of these describe a physical change? **A** a change in size **B** the rusting of iron **C** the burning of wood **D** the production of a new gas	**Sample Assessment Question** The atomic number of helium is 2. How many protons does it have? **A** one **B** two **C** three **D** four	**Sample Assessment Question** What does the atomic number tell you about an element? **A** the number of neutrons in the nucleus of the atoms **B** the order of its discovery **C** the number of protons in the nucleus of the atoms **D** the number of atoms in the element

Grades 9–10

Students investigate and identify properties of fluids including density, viscosity, and buoyancy. They relate the chemical behavior of an element including bonding, to its placement on the periodic table.

Structure and Properties of Matter

INTEGRATED PHYSICS AND CHEMISTRY TEKS 7   The student knows relationships exist between properties of matter and its components.

For graduation, students are expected to classify samples of matter from everyday life as being elements, compounds, or mixtures. **(IPC TEKS 7E)**

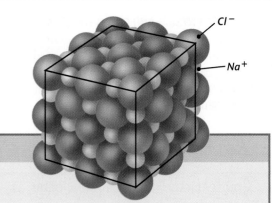

Cl $^-$

Na $^+$

Progression of Science Knowledge

Grades 1–5

Students classify matter based on its physical properties, including magnetism, physical state, and the abilitly to conduct or insulate heat, electricity, and sound.

Grades 6–8

Grade 6	Grade 7	Grade 8
TEKS 6.7B Students classify substances by their physical and chemical properties.	**TEKS 7.7C** Students recognize that compounds are composed of elements.	**TEKS 8.9A** Students demonstrate that substances may react chemically to form new substances. **TEKS 8.9B** Students interpret information on the periodic table to understand that physical properties are used to group elements. **TEKS 8.9C** Students recognize the importance of formulas and equations to express what happens in a chemical reaction.

In *Science Explorer,* students will

Grade 6:
- explain that substances can be identified or classified by their physical and chemical properties.
- explain the differences among elements, compounds, and mixtures.
- explain that a chemical reaction is needed to obtain an element from one of its compounds.

Sample Assessment Question
Which of these describes a compound?
A Elements can be changed into a simpler substance.
B Elements are combined as a mixture.
C Elements are combined through a chemical reaction.
D Compounds are made up of only one element.

In *Science Explorer,* students will

Grade 7:
- define and compare elements, compounds, and mixtures.
- compare chemical changes to physical changes.
- explain how valence electrons are related to the reactions of atoms.
- identify the properties of ionic compounds.
- describe how covalent bonds form.
- identify the properties of molecular compounds.

Sample Assessment Question
Which best describes what is listed in the periodic table?
A molecules
B elements
C compounds
D mixtures

In *Science Explorer,* students will

Grade 8:
- explain that the production of new substances having different properties shows that a chemical reaction has occurred.
- describe compounds as the result of the chemical combination of two or more elements.
- compare the valence electrons in a period and in a group, and explain how they influence the properties of elements.
- identify and describe three classes of chemical reactions.

Sample Assessment Question
The formula for sucrose (table sugar) is $C_{12}H_{22}O_{11}$. How many atoms are in a molecule of sucrose?
A 12
B 22
C 2,904
D 45

Grades 9–10

Students classify samples of matter from everyday life as being elements, compounds, or mixtures.

Structure and Properties of Matter

INTEGRATED PHYSICS AND CHEMISTRY TEKS 8 The student knows that changes in matter affect everyday life.

For graduation, students are expected to distinguish between physical and chemical changes in matter such as oxidation, digestion, changes in states, and stages in the rock cycle **(IPC TEKS 8A)** and they are expected to investigate and identify the law of conservation of mass. **(IPC TEKS 8C)**

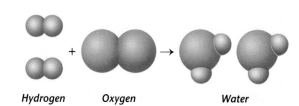

Hydrogen   Oxygen   Water

Progression of Science Knowledge

Grades 1–5
Students identify changes that can occur in the physical properties of the ingredients of solutions such as dissolving sugar in water.

Grades 6–8

Grade 6

TEKS 6.7A Students demonstrate that new substances can be made when two or more substances are chemically combined and compare the properties of the new substances to the original substances.

In *Science Explorer*, students will
- distinguish between physical and chemical changes.
- explain that a chemical reaction is needed to obtain an element from one of its compounds.
- define and differentiate among solids, liquids, and gases in terms of shape and volume.
- compare the particle motion in solids, liquids, and gases.

Sample Assessment Question
Which indicates a chemical change?
A browning of a cut apple left out in the air
B ice melting
C peeling an apple
D cutting a piece of wood

Grade 7

TEKS 7.7A Students identify and demonstrate everyday examples of chemical phenomena such as rusting and tarnishing of metals and burning of wood.

In *Science Explorer*, students will
- identify physical and chemical properties of matter.
- describe chemical and physical properties of metals.
- describe the ions formed when acids and bases are dissolved in water.
- explain the function of the digestive system.
- describe what happens to particles of a solute when a solution forms.
- describe the pH scale and tell how it is used.
- identify what causes chemical weathering.

Sample Assessment Question
During digestion, the chewing of food in the mouth and the churning of food in the stomach are examples of which type of change?
A chemical
B physical
C fission
D decomposition

Grade 8

TEKS 8.9A Students demonstrate that substances may react chemically to form new substances.
TEKS 8.9B Students interpret information on the periodic table to understand that physical properties are used to group elements.
TEKS 8.9C Students recognize the importance of formulas and equations to express what happens in a chemical reaction.
TEKS 8.12A Students analyze and predict the sequence of events in the lunar and rock cycles.

In *Science Explorer*, students will
- list the information in the periodic table and describe how it is organized.
- describe the information conveyed in a chemical equation.
- apply the principle of conservation of mass to chemical reactions.
- explain that the production of new substances having different properties shows that a chemical reaction has occurred.
- describe compounds as the result of the chemical combination of two or more elements.
- identify the characteristics of a mineral.
- identify the physical and chemical properties that can be used to identify minerals.
- describe the processes by which minerals form.

Sample Assessment Question
In a chemical reaction, how does the sum of the masses of the atoms in the reactants compare with the sum of the masses of the atoms in the products?
A They double.   **C** They are the same.
B They triple.   **D** They are less.

Grades 9–10
Students distinguish between physical and chemical changes in matter such as oxidation, digestion, changes in states, and stages in the rock cycle. They investigate and identify the law of conservation of mass.

Structure and Properties of Matter

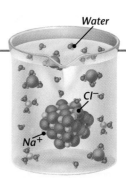

INTEGRATED PHYSICS AND CHEMISTRY TEKS 9 The student knows how solution chemistry is a part of everyday life.

For graduation, students are expected to relate the concentration of ions in a solution to physical and chemical properties such as pH, electrolytic behavior, and reactivity; **(IPC TEKS 9B)** and they are expected to demonstrate how various factors influence solubility including temperature, pressure, and nature of the solute and solvent. **(IPC TEKS 9D)**

Progression of Science Knowledge

Grades 1–5
Students demonstrate that some mixtures maintain the physical properties of their ingredients. They identify changes that can occur in the physical properties of the ingredients of solutions such as dissolving sugar in water. They observe and measure characteristic properties of substances that remain constant such as boiling points and melting points.

Grades 6–8

Grade 6	Grade 7	Grade 8
In *Science Explorer*, students will ■ identify different forms of energy, and give examples of energy transformations that affect matter. ■ identify chemical bonds as the force holding atoms together in molecules. ■ explain that a chemical reaction is needed to obtain an element from one of its compounds. **Sample Assessment Question** What is an ion? **A** something that holds two or more things together **B** a chemical reaction **C** a particle that has a charge **D** sharing electrons	In *Science Explorer*, students will ■ explain the differences between an atom and an ion. ■ describe what happens to particles of a solute when a solution forms. ■ identify the factors that affect the solubility of substances. ■ describe how solutes affect the freezing and boiling points of solvents. ■ identify and describe the properties of acids and bases. ■ describe the ions formed when acids and bases are dissolved in water. ■ describe the pH scale and tell how it is used. ■ explain what happens in a neutralization reaction. **Sample Assessment Question** For what is the pH scale used? **A** to neutralize acids and bases **B** to separate mixtures **C** to make solutions **D** to represent the concentration of hydrogen ions in a solution	In *Science Explorer*, students will ■ explain the role of valance electrons in forming chemical bonds. ■ compare the valence electrons in a period and in a group, and explain how they influence the properties of elements. ■ explain that the production of new substances having different properties shows that a chemical reaction has occurred. ■ describe compounds as the result of the chemical combination of two or more elements. ■ describe the information conveyed in a chemical equation. ■ identify and describe three classes of chemical reactions. ■ list factors that control the rate of chemical reactions. ■ identify the major sources of water pollution. **Sample Assessment Question** What is the role of valence electrons in a chemical reaction? **A** They determine how atoms will react with one another. **B** They always form an ionic bond. **C** They always form a covalent bond. **D** They all have a positive charge.

Grades 9–10
Students relate the concentration of ions in a solution to physical and chemical properties such as pH, electrolytic behavior, and reactivity; and they demonstrate how various factors influence solubility including temperature, pressure, and nature of the solute and solvent.

Motion, Forces, and Energy

INTEGRATED PHYSICS AND CHEMISTRY TEKS 4   The student knows concepts of force and motion evident in everyday life.

For graduation, students are expected to calculate speed, momentum, acceleration, work, and power in systems such as in the human body, moving toys, and machines **(IPC TEKS 4A)**, they are expected to investigate and describe applications of Newton's laws such as in vehicle restraints, sports activities, geological processes, and satellite orbits **(IPC TEKS 4B)** and they are expected to investigate and demonstrate mechanical advantage and efficiency of various machines such as levers, motors, wheels and axles, pulleys, and ramps. **(IPC TEKS 4D)**

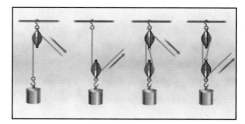

Types of pulleys

Progression of Science Knowledge

Grades 1–5

Students measure and record changes in the position and direction of the motion of an object to which a force such as a push or pull has been applied.

Grades 6–8

Grade 6

TEKS 6.6A Students identify and describe the changes in position, direction of motion, and speed of an object when acted upon by force.
TEKS 6.6B Students demonstrate that changes in motion can be measured and graphically represented.
TEKS 6.6C Students identify forces that shape features of the Earth including uplifting, movement of water, and volcanic activity.

In *Science Explorer,* **students will**
- explain when an object is in motion and how motion is relative to a reference point.
- calculate an object's speed and velocity using SI units of distance.
- graph motion showing changes in distance as a function of time.
- describe how moving water shapes the land.
- explain the theory of plate tectonics.
- describe what happens when a volcano erupts.

Sample Assessment Question
What is difference between speed and acceleration?
A They are the same.
B Acceleration is the rate of change in speed or direction.
C Acceleration is the distance traveled over a given amount of time.
D Acceleration is only an increase in speed.

Grade 7

TEKS 7.6A Students demonstrate basic relationships between force and motion using simple machines including pulleys and levers.
TEKS 7.6B Students demonstrate that an object will remain at rest or move at a constant speed and in a straight line if it is not being subjected to an unbalanced force.

In *Science Explorer,* **students will**
- identify when work is done on an object.
- explain what machines do and how they make work easier.
- explain the basic relationship between force and motion, using the six types of simple machines.
- relate forces to basic processes in living organisms by explaining how the body uses levers and wedges.
- state Newton's first law of motion and define inertia.
- state Newton's second law of motion and explain how force and mass are related to acceleration.
- state Newton's third law of motion.

Sample Assessment Question
How does an inclined plane make work easier?
A It changes the direction of the force.
B It increases the strength of the force.
C It increases the distance over which the force is applied.
D It increases the magnitude of the force.

Grade 8

TEKS 8.7A Students demonstrate how unbalanced forces cause changes in the speed or direction of an object's motion.

In *Science Explorer,* **students will**
- describe the process of sea-floor spreading.
- explain the theory of plate tectonics.
- describe how plate movement changes Earth's surface.

Sample Assessment Question
In an earthquake, plates move because of _____.
A convection currents in the mantle
B convergence
C seismographs
D Richter scale

Grades 9–10

Students calculate speed, momentum, acceleration, work, and power in systems such as in the human body, moving toys, and machines. They investigate and describe applications of Newton's laws such as in vehicle restraints, sports activities, geological processes, and satellite orbits. They investigate and demonstrate mechanical advantage and efficiency of machines such as levers, motors, wheels and axles, pulleys, and ramps.

Motion, Forces, and Energy

INTEGRATED PHYSICS AND CHEMISTRY TEKS 5   The student knows the effects of waves on everyday life.

For graduation, students are expected to demonstrate wave types and their characteristics through a variety of activities such as modeling with ropes and coils, activating tuning forks, and interpreting data on seismic waves. **(IPC TEKS 5A)**

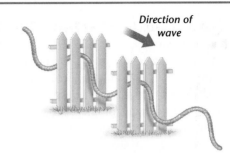

Direction of wave

Progression of Science Knowledge

Grades 1–5

Students identify and demonstrate everyday examples of how light is reflected, such as from tinted windows, and refracted, such as in cameras, telescopes, and eyeglasses. They verify that vibrating an object can produce sound.

Grades 6–8

Grade 6

In *Science Explorer*, students will
- identify the different kinds of seismic waves.
- explain what seismic waves are and how geologists use them to study Earth's structure.

Sample Assessment Question
The fastest-moving type of seismic waves are _____.
A surface waves
B P waves
C S waves
D mercalli waves

Grade 7

In *Science Explorer*, students will
- identify what gives ocean waves their energy.

Sample Assessment Question
Which of these controls the size of ocean waves?
A acceleraton of waves
B Earth's rotation
C distance over which the wind blows
D temperature of the water

Grade 8

TEKS 8.7B Students recognize that waves are generated and can travel through different media.

In *Science Explorer*, students will
- explain how matter and energy interact when waves are generated.
- identify and compare the three main types of waves.
- list and describe the basic properties of waves.
- describe how a wave's speed is related to its wavelength and frequency, and calculate a wave's speed.
- define sound and explain how it travels.
- identify the factors that affect the speed of sound through a medium.
- describe an electromagnetic wave and its properties.
- list and compare different types of electromagnetic waves.
- explain what happens when light waves enter a new medium at an angle.
- describe the images formed by concave and convex lenses.
- describe how light waves are sensed and interpreted as images in humans.

Sample Assessment Question
Objects reflected in a convex mirror look _____.
A smaller   C the same
B larger   D upside down

Grades 9–10

Students demonstrate wave types and their characteristics through a variety of activities such as modeling with ropes and coils, activating tuning forks, and interpreting data on seismic waves.

Motion, Forces, and Energy

INTEGRATED PHYSICS AND CHEMISTRY TEKS 6   The student knows the impact of energy transformations in everyday life.

For graduation, students are expected to describe the law of conservation of energy. **(IPC TEKS 6A)** They are expected to investigate and demonstrate the movement of heat through solids, liquids, and gases by convection, conduction, and radiation. **(IPC TEKS 6B)** They are expected to investigate and compare economic and environmental impacts of using various energy sources such as rechargeable or disposable batteries and solar cells. **(IPC TEKS 6D)**

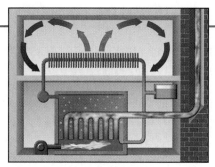

Convection currents

Progression of Science Knowledge

Grades 1–5

Students differentiate among forms of energy including light, heat, electrical, and solar energy.

Grades 6–8

Grade 6

TEKS 6.9C Students research and describe energy types from their source to their use and determine if the type is renewable, non-renewable, or inexhaustible.

In *Science Explorer*, students will
- identify different forms of energy, and give examples of energy transformations that affect matter.
- explain how fuels provide energy.
- explain how the sun provides energy and describe ways to collect this energy.
- identify and describe various sources of renewable energy.
- explain how a nuclear power plant produces electricity.

Sample Assessment Question
Which of these is a renewable energy source?
A gas
B coal
C water power
D oil

Grade 7

TEKS 7.8A Students illustrate examples of potential and kinetic energy in everyday life such as objects at rest, movement of geologic faults, and running water.
TEKS 7.8B Students identify that radiant energy from the Sun is transferred into chemical energy through the process of photosynthesis.

In *Science Explorer*, students will
- define and calculate potential and kinetic energy.
- list different forms of energy.
- describe conversions between different forms of energy.
- explain how fossil fuels contain energy that came from the sun.

Sample Assessment Question
Which of these is an example of potential energy?
A a ball placed on the edge of a table
B a boat moving
C lightning
D playing a drum

Grade 8

TEKS 8.10A Students illustrate interactions between matter and energy including specific heat.
TEKS 8.10C Students identify and demonstrate that loss or gain of heat energy occurs during exothermic and endothermic chemical reactions.

In *Science Explorer*, students will
- compare endothermic and exothermic reactions.

Sample Assessment Question
Which of these can cause an endothermic reaction?
A furnace
B car engine
C coolant in air conditioner
D toaster

Grades 9–10

Students describe the law of conservation of energy. They investigate and demonstrate the movement of heat through solids, liquids, and gases by convection, conduction, and radiation. They investigate and compare economic and environmental impacts of using various energy sources such as rechargeable or disposable batteries and solar cells.

Motion, Forces, and Energy

INTEGRATED PHYSICS AND CHEMISTRY TEKS 6 The student knows the impact of energy transformations in everyday life.

For graduation, students are expected to investigate and compare series and parallel circuits. **(IPC TEKS 6F)**

Energy transformations

Progression of Science Knowledge

Grades 1–5
Students differentiate among forms of energy including light, heat, electrical, and solar energy. They demonstrate that electricity can flow in a circuit and can produce heat, light, sound, and magnetic effects.

Grades 6–8

Grade 6	Grade 7	Grade 8
In *Science Explorer*, students will ■ identify different forms of energy, and give examples of energy transformations that affect matter. ■ define matter and energy. ■ identify different forms of energy, and give examples of energy transformations that affect matter. ■ explain how fuels provide energy.	**In *Science Explorer*, students will** ■ explain the differences between an atom and an ion. ■ list different forms of energy. ■ describe conversions between different forms of energy.	**In *Science Explorer*, students will** ■ describe the structure of an atom, and define protons, neutrons, and electrons. ■ explain why atoms are neutral. ■ explain the role of valence electrons in forming chemical bonds.
Sample Assessment Question What energy transformation allows a TV to work? **A** Solar energy changes into light and sound energy. **B** Electrical energy changes into light and sound energy. **C** A TV emits electrical and light energy. **D** Mechanical energy is changed to light energy.	**Sample Assessment Question** Why do atoms in a compound containing ionic bonds have an electrical attraction for each other? **A** They have different numbers of electrons. **B** Some atoms have positive charges and other atoms have negative charges. **C** All of the atoms have positive charges, and like charges attract. **D** All of the atoms have negative charges, and like charges attract.	**Sample Assessment Question** If you know the number of protons an atom has, how many electrons does it have? **A** The number can vary. **B** There are always more protons than electrons. **C** There are always more electrons than protons. **D** There are the same number of protons and electrons.

Grades 9–10
Students investigate and compare series and parallel circuits.

Earth Sciences

GRADE 8 TEKS 8.10 The student knows that complex interactions occur between matter and energy.

For graduation, students are expected to describe interactions among solar, weather, and ocean systems. **(TEKS 8.10B)** They are expected to relate the role of oceans to climatic changes. **(TEKS 8.12B)**

Sea Breeze

Progression of Science Knowledge

Grades 1–5

Students describe the characteristics of the Sun and summarize the effects of the oceans on land. They identify the Sun as the major source of energy for the Earth and understand its role in the growth of plants, in the creation of winds, and in the water cycle.

Grades 6–8

Grade 6

TEKS 6.5A Students identify and describe a system that results from the combination of two or more systems such as in the solar system.

TEKS 6.14C Students describe components of the atmosphere, including oxygen, nitrogen, and water vapor, and identify the role of atmospheric movement in weather change.

In *Science Explorer*, students will
- state how the atmosphere is important to living things.
- identify the gases that are present in Earth's atmosphere.
- identify some of the properties of air.
- identify and classify the main layers of the atmosphere.
- state in what form energy travels from the sun to Earth.
- explain what happens to energy from the sun when it reaches Earth.
- explain what causes winds.
- describe how relative humidity is measured.
- explain how clouds form.
- identify the main types of precipitation.

Sample Assessment Question
Which of these causes air pressure?
A temperature   C wind
B weight of air   D humidity

Grade 7

In *Science Explorer*, students will
- identify what gives ocean waves their energy.
- state that energy enters most ecosystems through photosynthesis, and relate available energy to the levels of an energy pyramid.
- list and describe Earth's major land biomes and describe the varieties of organisms they support.
- list and describe Earth's major freshwater and ocean biomes and describe the varieties of organisms they support.
- describe the differences between primary and secondary succession and explain the role of succession in maintaining equilibrium in an ecosystem.

Sample Assessment Question
Organisms that can make their own food through photosynthesis are the _____ in an ecosystem.
A producers
B scavengers
C herbivores
D consumers

Grade 8

TEKS 8.10B Students describe interactions among solar, weather, and ocean systems.
TEKS 8.12B Students relate the role of oceans to climatic changes.

In *Science Explorer*, students will
- identify factors used to define climates.
- describe the different types of climate regions.
- explain the theories that have been proposed to explain natural climate change.

Sample Assessment Question
Temperature and _____ are the two most important conditions that determine climate.
A wind
B altitude
C sunlight
D precipitation

Earth Sciences

GRADE 8 TEKS 8.12 The student knows that cycles exist in Earth systems.
For graduation, students are expected to predict the results of modifying the Earth's nitrogen, water, and carbon cycles. **(TEKS 8.12C)**

The water cycle

Progression of Science Knowledge

Grades 1–5

Students identify the significance of the water, carbon, and nitrogen cycles.

Grades 6–8

Grade 6

TEKS 6.8B Students explain and illustrate the interactions between matter and energy in the water cycle and in the decay of biomass such as in a compost bin.
TEKS 6.12C Students identify components of an ecosystem to which organisms may respond.
TEKS 6.14B Students identify relationships between groundwater and surface water in a water shed.
TEKS 6.14C Students describe components of the atmosphere, including oxygen, nitrogen, and water vapor, and identify the role of atmospheric movement in weather change.

In *Science Explorer,* students will
- explain how photochemical smog and acid rain form.
- identify some of the properties of air.
- identify and classify the characteristics of the main layers of the atmosphere.
- state in what form energy travels from the sun to Earth.
- describe how relative humidity is measured.
- explain how clouds form.
- identify the main types of precipitation.

Sample Assessment Question
What is the most important cause of smog in the United States?
A automobile emissions **C** recyling
B waste water **D** landfills

Grade 7

In *Science Explorer,* students will
- state that energy enters most ecosystems through photosynthesis, and relate available energy to the levels of an energy pyramid.
- describe the processes that wear down and build up Earth's surface.
- explain how water erosion is mainly responsible for shaping Earth's land surface.
- compare energy and power.

Sample Assessment Question
Runoff from rainfall is one cause of _____.
A evaporation
B ice ages
C sand dunes
D erosion

Grade 8

TEKS 8.12C Students predict the results of modifying the Earth's nitrogen, water, and carbon cycles.

In *Science Explorer,* students will
- identify and describe the nitrogen cycle.
- name and describe three ways of dealing with solid waste.
- identify methods for managing hazardous wastes.
- identify and explain the water cycle.
- explain the theories that have been proposed to explain natural climate change.
- identify and describe outdoor and indoor air pollutants.
- describe ways that technology can help control air pollution.
- describe ways that technology can help control water pollution.
- describe the greenhouse effect and how humans are affecting it.

Sample Assessment Question
Pollutants in the air react chemically to produce nitrous oxide and sulfuric oxide. These combine with moisture in the air and fall to Earth as _____.
A acid rain
B hydrocarbons
C salt water
D ground water

Earth Sciences

GRADE 8 TEKS 8.14 The student knows that natural events and human activities can alter Earth systems.

For graduation, students are expected to predict land features resulting from gradual changes such as mountain building, beach erosion, land subsidence, and continental drift. **(TEKS 8.14A)**

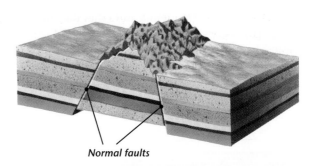

Normal faults

Progression of Science Knowledge

Grades 1–5
Students identify the physical characteristics of the Earth and compare them to the physical characteristics of the moon.

Grades 6–8

Grade 6	Grade 7	Grade 8
TEKS 6.6C Students identify forces that shape features of the Earth including uplifting, movement of water, and volcanic activity.	**TEKS 7.14B** Students analyze effects of regional erosional deposition and weathering.	**TEKS 8.14A** Students predict land features resulting from gradual changes such as mountain building, beach erosion, land subsidence, and continental drift.

Grade 6

In *Science Explorer,* students will
- explain how a flood affects the land near a river and how floods can be controlled.
- explain the theory of plate tectonics.
- describe what happens when a volcano erupts.
- identify landforms formed from magma that hardens beneath the surface.
- identify landforms that lava and other volcanic material create on Earth's surface.

Sample Assessment Question
A _____ forms when molten lava builds up and hardens on Earth's surface.
A dome mountain
B volcano
C sill
D batholith

Grade 7

In *Science Explorer,* students will
- identify what causes mechanical and chemical weathering.
- describe the factors that determine how fast weathering occurs.
- explain how soil is formed and how soil horizons develop.
- describe the processes that wear down and build up Earth's surface.
- explain how water erosion shapes Earth's land surface.
- describe some of the land features formed by water erosion.
- describe land features formed when rivers and streams deposit sediment.
- list the factors that affect a river's ability to erode.
- describe two processes by which glaciers erode the land.
- describe how ocean waves shape a coast.
- describe the process by which wind causes erosion.

Sample Assessment Question
Which of these is a way that glaciers erode land?
A deflation
B pressure
C plucking and abrasion
D chemical weathering

Grade 8

In *Science Explorer,* students will
- identify the two main forces that change Earth's surface.
- describe the theory of continental drift.
- describe the process of sea-floor spreading.
- explain the theory of plate tectonics.
- identify and describe outdoor and indoor air pollutants.
- explain why fresh water is a limited resource.

Sample Assessment Question
Where do most earthquakes occur?
A along plate boundaries
B on the ocean floor
C in California
D in the middle of plates

Earth Sciences

GRADE 8 TEKS 8.14 The student knows that natural events and human activities can alter Earth systems.

For graduation, students are expected to describe how human activities have modified soil, water, and air quality. **(TEKS 8.14C)**

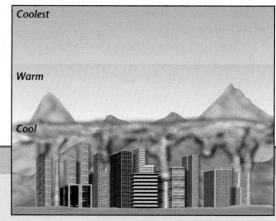

Temperature inversion

Progression of Science Knowledge

Grades 1–5

Students describe environmental changes in which some organisms would thrive, become ill, or perish.

Grades 6–8

Grade 6	Grade 7	Grade 8
In *Science Explorer,* **students will** ■ explain why fossil fuels are considered nonrenewable resources. ■ list two ways to ensure that there will be enough energy for the future. ■ identify things that individuals can do to conserve energy. ■ describe conditions that can result in a water shortage and list sources of fresh water for the future. ■ explain how water can be conserved. ■ name the main sources of air pollution. ■ explain how photochemical smog and acid rain form.	**TEKS 7.14C** Students make inferences and draw conclusions about effects of human activity on Earth's renewable, non-renewable, and inexhaustible resources. In *Science Explorer,* **students will** ■ explain why soil is a valuable resource. ■ identify some ways that soil can be conserved. ■ explain how human activities can increase the impact of catastrophic events. ■ identify the main types of environmental issues; explain the effects of human activity on Earth's resources. ■ name some human activities and catastrophic events that threaten biodiversity.	**TEKS 8.14C** Students describe how human activities have modified soil, water, and air quality. In *Science Explorer,* **students will** ■ identify problems that occur when soil is not properly managed. ■ name and describe three ways of dealing with solid waste. ■ list the four major types of recyclable waste. ■ list and describe the categories of hazardous wastes. ■ identify methods of managing hazardous wastes. ■ identify and describe outdoor and indoor air pollutants. ■ identify the major sources of water pollution. ■ describe ways that technology can help control air and water pollution. ■ describe the greenhouse effect and how humans are affecting it.
Sample Assessment Question Which of these is a way to conserve water? **A** don't let the water run when you brush your teeth **B** take showers instead of baths **C** only use cold water **D** only use hot water	**Sample Assessment Question** Which of these is a cause of nutrient depletion in soil? **A** decaying plants **B** planting the same crops every year **C** weathering rock **D** nitrogen-fixing bacteria	**Sample Assessment Question** Which of these are causes of water pollution? **A** damage to the ozone layer **B** evaporation **C** disposing of paint, oil, and toxic materials on the ground **D** condensation

Earth Sciences

GRADE 8 TEKS 8.13 The student knows characteristics of the universe.

For graduation, students are expected to describe characteristics of the universe such as stars and galaxies. **(TEKS 8.13A)**

Star formation

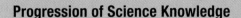
Progression of Science Knowledge

Grades 1–5
Students describe the characteristics of the Sun. They identify the Sun as the major source of energy for the Earth and understand its role in the growth of plants, in the creation of winds, and in the water cycle.

Grades 6–8

Grade 6
TEKS 6.5A Students identify and describe a system that results from the combination of two or more systems such as in the solar system.
TEKS 6.14C Students describe components of the atmosphere, including oxygen, nitrogen, and water vapor, and identify the role of atmospheric movement in weather change.

In *Science Explorer,* students will
- state in what form energy travels from the sun to Earth.
- explain what happens to energy from the sun when it reaches Earth.
- explain two factors that keep planets in their orbits.
- describe what combines to form our solar system.
- identify features of the sun's surface.
- identify the main characteristics of the inner planets.
- identify the main characteristics of the gas giant planets.
- identify the characteristics of comets and asteroids.
- describe the formation of meteoroids.

Sample Assessment Question
Earth is 150,000,000 kilometers from the sun. Light travels at 300,000 kilometers per second. How long does it take the sun's light to reach Earth?
A 5 seconds
B 50 seconds
C 500 seconds
D 5,000 seconds

Grade 7
TEKS 7.13A Students identify and illustrate how the tilt of the Earth on its axis as it rotates and revolves around the Sun causes changes in seasons and the length of a day.

In *Science Explorer,* students will
- identify the effects of Earth's rotation and revolution.
- describe the causes of the moon's phases.
- describe what causes solar and lunar eclipses.
- describe the origin and structure of the moon.
- explain the causes of the seasons on Earth.

Sample Assessment Question
What causes the changing phases of the moon?
A the seasons
B the moon's revolution around the earth
C eclipses
D Earth's rotation

Grade 8
TEKS 8.13A Students describe characteristics of the universe such as stars and galaxies.

In *Science Explorer,* students will
- explain the main purpose of a telescope.
- describe how astronomers measure distances to nearby stars.
- explain how stars are classified.
- describe a star system.
- identify and describe three types of galaxies.
- explain the big bang theory of how the universe was formed.
- describe one theory about how the solar system was formed.

Sample Assessment Question
What is a group of stars that seem to form a picture or pattern?
A a constellation
B a protostar
C a galaxy
D a star cloud

Inquiry Skills Chart

The Prentice Hall *Science Explorer* program provides comprehensive teaching, practice, and assessment of science skills, with an emphasis on the process skills necessary for inquiry. The chart lists the skills covered in the program and cites the page numbers where each skill is covered.

	Basic Process SKILLS		
	Student Text: Projects and Labs	Student Text: Activities	Student Text: Caption and Review Questions
Observing	48–49, 120, 148, 157, 178, 183, 194, 212, 229, 338–339, 348, 384–385, 403, 416–417, 433, 461	26, 31, 88, 108, 131, 149, 151, 158, 163, 167, 170, 192, 196, 200, 205, 208, 223, 224, 238, 247, 250, 280, 292, 326, 330, 333, 348, 354, 358, 359, 368, 370, 374, 375, 386, 388, 396, 398, 404, 405, 412, 414, 418, 440, 465, 473, 503, 519, 532, 538, 540, 544, 549, 562, 566, 568	236, 345, 355, 489, 509, 521, 553, 556, 563
Inferring	48–49, 106–107, 157, 194, 272, 348, 366–367, 403	24, 35, 41, 86, 90, 98, 101, 138, 158, 160, 163, 167, 190, 200, 204, 230, 237, 253, 266, 280, 307, 313, 333, 396, 434, 447, 468, 487, 515, 550, 562	27, 52, 79, 82, 114, 147, 151, 152, 168, 180, 181, 202, 205, 215, 225, 252, 258, 275, 300, 329, 347, 350, 351, 378, 415, 431, 441, 443, 468, 539, 555, 559, 569
Predicting	229, 272, 279, 305, 461, 512–513	34, 61, 99, 101, 108, 355, 358, 423, 425, 442, 451, 532, 535	62, 67, 70, 75, 83, 105, 111, 141, 154, 155, 159, 162, 177, 180, 304, 316, 346, 350, 351, 365, 392, 393, 431, 436, 446, 450, 458, 480, 484, 518, 525, 559, 565
Classifying	338–339, 348, 353, 366–367	24, 26, 56, 124, 184, 221, 280, 342, 359, 404, 501, 552	21, 45, 27, 102, 147, 154, 176, 185, 189, 203, 211, 214, 311, 318, 319, 350, 392, 430, 458, 486, 492, 502, 528
Making Models	217, 272, 325, 366–367, 384–385, 531	144, 172, 277, 308, 359, 370, 375, 386, 388, 398, 405, 414, 421, 472, 552, 555, 562, 568	172, 529, 573
Communicating	23, 85, 120, 178, 183, 217, 259, 264, 325, 352, 395, 433, 495	37, 44, 238, 282, 309, 486, 516, 550	21, 52, 53, 114, 214, 215, 288, 289, 318, 458, 528
Measuring	40, 80, 85, 96–97, 106–107, 157, 256, 265, 416–417, 438–439; 448–449; 466–467; 474–475	34, 86, 98, 99, 277, 354, 363, 397, 423, 425, 462, 535, 544, 552, 555	89, 115, 373, 469
Calculating	40, 96–97, 106–107, 178, 279, 395, 403, 531	28, 43, 93, 104, 274, 276, 309, 335, 397, 459, 489, 504, 552	53, 115, 136, 319, 459, 493
Creating Data Tables	40, 85, 96–97, 194, 256, 338–339, 348, 395, 433, 461, 466–467	540	
Graphing	96–97, 157, 256, 264, 279, 395, 461, 543	8, 295, 459, 547	83, 181, 259, 289, 459, 493

Advanced Process SKILLS

	Student Text: Projects and Labs	Student Text: Activities	Student Text: Caption and Review Questions
Posing Questions	23, 183	326	10, 327, 329, 529
Developing Hypotheses	17, 121, 212, 229, 384–385, 466–467, 560–561	62, 64, 74, 158, 170, 178, 299, 374, 436, 481, 496	12, 155, 289, 390, 425
Designing Experiments	23, 73, 80, 97, 121, 130, 195, 212, 229, 256, 264, 305, 312, 385, 439, 561	46, 128, 234	155
Controlling Variables	23, 130, 169, 256, 264		155
Forming Operational Definitions	305	122, 218, 273, 340, 354	476
Interpreting Data	23, 40, 169, 178, 256, 325, 395, 416–417, 438–349, 448–449, 495, 512–513, 526, 543	31, 90, 173, 193, 470, 483, 522, 540	53, 83, 115, 181, 259, 289, 319, 435, 459, 477, 522, 529, 573
Drawing Conclusions	23, 48–49, 72, 96–97, 121, 130, 157, 194, 305, 312, 352, 416–417, 446–467, 474–475	31, 34, 59, 243, 268, 333, 351, 413, 436, 445	53, 215, 259, 319, 333, 351, 383, 393, 431, 456, 493573

Critical Thinking SKILLS

	Student Text: Projects and Labs	Student Text: Activities	Student Text: Caption and Review Questions
Comparing and Contrasting	23, 148, 217, 531, 543	26, 149, 151, 172, 205, 246, 276, 330, 363, 374, 532, 544, 549	52, 58, 81, 82, 87, 91, 124, 132, 154, 180, 193, 197, 214, 215, 236, 238, 254, 257, 258, 267, 286, 288, 298, 318, 331, 350, 387, 392, 419, 430, 492, 528, 542, 572
Applying Concepts	48–49, 85, 106–107, 217, 256, 279, 325, 238, 384–385, 403, 416–417, 438–439, 466–467, 512–513, 543	46	16, 25, 33, 42, 47, 52, 67, 77, 79, 82, 100, 114, 128, 129, 137, 145, 154, 162, 163, 164, 166, 168, 171, 180, 193, 201, 214, 220, 221, 228, 234, 239, 242, 245, 248, 251, 258, 271, 281, 288, 316, 334, 337, 347, 350, 371, 392, 427, 437, 452, 458, 465, 471, 478, 480, 490, 497, 504, 511, 517, 528, 537, 569, 572
Interpreting Diagrams, Graphs, Photographs, and Maps	48–49, 495, 526	110, 388	13, 14, 30, 32, 45, 69, 71, 161, 167, 172, 187, 189, 191, 209, 226, 232, 241, 268, 276, 285, 289, 294, 302, 309, 310, 329, 347, 361, 369, 393, 405, 410, 413, 415, 422, 440, 459, 463, 477, 500, 502, 508, 511, 524, 529, 533, 536, 545, 567
Relating Cause and Effect			21, 60, 65, 82, 99, 112, 154, 222, 250, 258, 286, 288, 318, 343, 350, 357, 359, 373, 390, 392, 402, 411, 424, 430, 458, 492, 528, 533, 542, 551, 572

Critical Thinking SKILLS continued

	Student Text: Projects and Labs	Student Text: Activities	Student Text: Caption and Review Questions
Making Generalizations			38, 103, 112, 114, 123, 210, 231, 255, 288, 392, 407, 430, 572
Making Judgments		246	21, 50, 318, 422, 427, 528
Problem Solving		104, 246, 426	21, 39, 52, 95, 105, 114, 180, 214, 278, 288, 430, 492, 569

Information Organizing SKILLS

	Student Text: Projects and Labs	Student Text: Activities	Student Text: Caption and Review Questions
Concept Maps			51, 113, 153, 213, 287, 429, 457, 491
Compare/ Contrast Tables			81, 257, 317, 391, 527, 571
Venn Diagrams		307	
Flowcharts			
Cycle Diagrams			179, 349

Master Materials List

The Master Materials list cross-references items to activities and defines the quantities needed for a class of 30 students working in 5 groups of 6. To make obtaining supplies convenient and easy, Science Kit & Boreal Laboratories has developed this materials list. You can download a materials list from www.sciencekit.com. You can also request a materials list and order materials directly by calling Science Kit & Boreal Laboratories at 1-800-828-7777.

Science Kit & Boreal Laboratories

Consumable Materials

Description	Qty	Textbook Section(s)	Description	Qty	Textbook Section(s)
Acetate Sheet 8 1/2" x 11" Each	10	11-5 (TT), 16-4 (TT)	Cardboard Strip, 10 cm x 25 cm	5	13-3 (Lab)
Air Freshener	1	5-1 (DIS)	Cardboard Strip, 15 cm x 20 cm	5	14-3 (Lab)
Alcohol, Isopropyl, 500 mL	1	6-2 (Lab)	Cardboard, 30 cm x 45 cm	5	7-4 (DIS)
Antacid Tablets, Pkg/24	1	1-1 (SYS), 2-1 (DIS), 16-6 (TT)	Cardboard, Corrugated 32 cm x 32 cm	10	3-1 (Lab), 7-3 (Lab), 15-1 (DIS), 16-1 (TT)
Aluminum Foil, Roll 12" x 25'	1	9-2 (Lab)			
Bag, Plastic Small (Sandwich)	15	12-1 (Lab)	Cardboard, White 8-1/2" x 11"	10	16-2 (DIS), 16-2 (TT)
Bag, Plastic Zip Lip 6 x 8" (1 qt)	40	1-1 (SYS), 4-1 (Lab), 6-2 (LAB), 9-2 (DIS), 13-4 (DIS)	Cards, Index Blank 3" x 5", Pkg/100	2	INT, 1-4 (Lab), 8-2 (Lab)
			Chalk, White, Pkg/12	2	2-2 (DIS)
Bag, Plastic Zip Lip 9 x 12"	5	14-1 (DIS)	Charcoal (Activated Carbon), 16 oz	1	8-1 (Lab)
Baking Powder 7 oz (200 g)	1	1-1 (TT)	Cheesecloth, 2 m Piece	1	12-3 (Lab)
Baking Soda 454 g	1	11-4 (TT), 16-4 (TT)	Chlorella, Live, Pyrenoidosa, 30 Students	1	6-3 (TT)
Balloons, Round 13", Pkg/10	2	11-5 (DIS), 13-3 (Lab), 16-6 (DIS),	Clay, 4 Colors (Water Resistent), lb	45	1-2 (Lab), 2-3 (Lab), 6-4 (Lab), 10-2 (DIS), 11-2 (Lab), 11-5 (TT), 12-3 (TT), 13-1 (DIS), 13-2 (DIS), 13-3 (TT), 13-3 (Lab), 16-5 (DIS)
Balloons, Round 9", Pkg/35	1	2-1 (DIS), 2-2 (TT), 13-3 (DIS)			
Battery, 6 V, Lantern	5	1-4 (Lab)			
Battery, Size D	10	7-3 (Lab)	Clay, Powder, 1 lb	1	12-3 (Lab)
Bottle, 1 L, Plastic	10	2-1 (DIS), 12-1 (SYS)	Cornstarch, 500 g	1	1-1 (TT)
Bottle, Clear, Plastic, Pre-Cut	5	8-1 (Lab)	Cotton Balls, Pkg/300	1	6-3 (TT)
Bottle, Plastic , 1 L or 2 L	5	11-4 (TT)	Crayons, Pkg/16	1	1-2 (Lab)
Bottle, Plastic, 2 L	10	13-3 (TT), 14-4 (DIS)	Crickets, Live Adult, (12)	1	7-1 (DIS)
Box, Oameal, Empty	15	11-4 (Lab)	Cup, Paper, 100 mL	5	16-6 (TT)
Bread without Preservatives, Slice	20	4-1 (Lab)	Cup, Paper, 200 mL	5	9-3 (Lab)
Brine Shrimp Eggs, Live, 6 Dram Vial	1	8-1 (TT)	Cup, Paper, 360 mL, Pkg/25	2	6-2 (DIS), 12-4 (DIS)
Bromothymol Blue, 500 mL	4	1-1 (SYS), 5-2 (Lab)	Cup, Plastic, 9 oz, Pkg/50	2	1-1 (TT), 1-2 (DIS), 1-2 (TT), 2-2 (TT), 2-4 (Lab), 5-1 (TT), 11-4 (Lab), 12-1 (SYS), 15-3 (DIS)
Bulb, 100 W, Incandescent	10	INT, 14-1 (Lab)			
Bulb, 15 W, Flourescent	5	9-4 (DIS)			
Bulb, 60 W, Incandescent	5	9-4 (DIS)	Cup, Plastic Clear, 300 mL	5	9-3 (Lab)
Candle, White 10 cm x 1.75 cm	5	14-2 (DIS)	Cup, Styrofoam, 180 mL	5	9-3 (Lab)
Candles, Birthday, Pkg/36	1	13-1 (DIS), 13-2 (DIS)	Cupric Chloride Crystals, 100 g	1	1-4 (Lab)

KEY: **DIS**: Discover; **SYS**: Sharpen Your Skills; **TT**: Try This; **Lab**: Lab; **INT**: Introduction Lab

Master Materials List

Consumable Materials (continued)

Description	Qty	Textbook Section(s)	Description	Qty	Textbook Section(s)
Detergent, Household 14.7 oz	1	2-2 (SYS), 15-2 (DIS)	Marshmallows, Miniature, 10 oz	1	9-2 (Lab)
Disinfectant, Lysol 15 oz	1	6-2 (Lab)	Masking Tape, 3/4" x 60 yards	5	1-2 (TT), 3-1 (Lab), 3-2 (DIS), 6-4 (Lab), 7-4 (DIS), 8-2 (TT), 9-2 (Lab), 11-1 (DIS), 11-2 (SYS), 11-5 (DIS), 13-3 (Lab), 14-3 (DIS), 14-3 (Lab), 16-2 (DIS), 16-2 (TT), 16-3 (TT), 16-6 (TT)
Dropper, Disposable, Polyethylene, Pkg/500	1	INT, 1-1 (SYS), 4-1 (Lab), 4-2 (SYS), 4-3 (Lab), 5-1 (TT), 5-3 (DIS), 6-2 (TT), 6-2 (Lab), 6-3 (DIS), 6-3 (TT), 6-4 (TT), 7-3 (TT), 7-3 (Lab), 10-2 (Lab), 12-1 (SYS), 12-2 (DIS), 12-5 (DIS)			
Eggs, Chicken	5	7-6 (TT)	Matches, Wood Safety, Box/30	5	13-1 (DIS), 13-2 (DIS)
Elodea Anacharis, Live, 12 Plants	2	4-3 (Lab), 5-2 (Lab)	Materials that Resemble Cell Organelles, Set	5	4-3 (TT)
Emery Boards, Pkg/10	1	10-2 (SYS)	Methylene Blue BIOstain, 100 mL	1	5-3 (DIS), 6-2 (TT)
Earthworms, Live, (12)	2	7-1 (DIS), 7-3 (Lab)	Minnows	5	7-1 (DIS)
Filters, Coffee Box/100	1	13-1 (Lab)	Moss Plants	5	8-1 (Lab)
Food Coloring, Dark Red, 30 mL	1	11-4 (Lab)	Newspaper	5	4-2 (DIS), 12-3 (TT)
Food Coloring, Pkg/4 Colors, 8 mL	1	5-1 (TT), 11-5 (TT), 15-1 (DIS)	Newspaper, Local, Weather Report	1	15-4 (DIS)
Gelatin, Box of 4 Packets	4	4-3 (TT), 11-4 (Lab)	Nutrient Agar Plates, Pkg/6	3	6-2 (Lab)
Glue, School White, 4 oz	5	9-2 (Lab), 13-3 (Lab)	Oil, Vegetable, 16 oz	2	2-1 (TT)
Glycerin, 50 mL	1	2-2 (SYS)	Pan, Aluminum Foil, 22.5 cm Diam	5	14-2 (DIS)
Graph Paper, Metric Coordinates, Pkg/100	1	2-3 (DIS), 2-3 (Lab), 7-6 (Lab), 8-2 (Lab), 14-1 (Lab), 14-2 (TT), 16-2 (Lab), 16-3 (SYS)	Pan, Pizza, Aluminum, with holes punched at 2.5 cm intervals	5	11-4 (Lab)
			Paper Clips, Box/100	1	1-4 (Lab)
Gravel, Aquarium, 1 kg	2	8-1 (Lab)	Paper Clips, Jumbo, Box/100	2	1-1 (DIS), 10-2 (SYS)
Honey, Jar	1	2-1 (TT), 11-1 (DIS)	Paper Clips, Plastic, Pkg/100	1	1-1 (DIS)
Hydra, Live Brown, 30 Students	1	7-3 (TT)	Paper Towel, Roll	5	INT, 1-2 (Lab), 1-4 (DIS), 6-4 (Lab), 7-3 (Lab), 12-2 (TT)
Ice Cubes, Bucket	4	2-4 (Lab), 9-3 (Lab), 12-1 (DIS), 14-4 (DIS)			
Ice, Crushed, Bucket	1	14-5 (DIS)	Paper, Construction, Assorted, Pkg/50	1	5-3 (TT), 14-3 (TT)
Knives, Plastic, Pkg/24	1	10-2 (DIS), 11-2 (Lab), 11-4 (Lab)	Paper, Oaktag, Sheet	15	9-2 (Lab)
Leaf, Lettuce	5	6-4 (TT)	Paper, Sheet	65	3-1 (TT), 3-2 (TT), 4-3 (TT), 6-2 (TT), 6-4 (TT), 7-2 (DIS), 7-5 (SYS), 8-1 (DIS), 8-1 (TT), 8-3 (DIS), 11-4 (Lab), 14-1 (DIS), 16-1 (TT), 16-2 (DIS), 16-2 (TT), 16-3 (DIS), 16-3 (TT), 16-4 (DIS), 16-6 (TT)
Leaves, Average Rainfall Environment	5	6-4 (DIS)			
Leaves, Desert Environment	5	6-4 (DIS)			
Lemon, Slice	5	4-1 (TT)			
Lid, For Paper Cup	5	9-3 (Lab)	Paper, Tracing 9" x 12", Sheet	5	15-2 (Lab)
Lid, For Plastic Cup	5	9-3 (Lab)	Paramecium Caudatum, Live	1	6-3 (TT)
Lid, for Styrofoam Cup	5	9-3 (Lab)	Pebbles, 1-2 cm, 1 lb	1	12-1 (Lab)
Limewater Solution, 500 mL	2	13-1 (TT)	Pebbles/Gravel, 1 kg	5	3-3 (DIS), 12-3 (DIS), 12-3 (Lab)
Marker, Black, Permanent	5	11-2 (Lab), 14-3 (DIS)	Pen, Marking, Black Ink	5	11-3 (TT), 14-3 (Lab)

KEY: **DIS**: Discover; **SYS**: Sharpen Your Skills; **TT**: Try This; **Lab**: Lab; **INT**: Introduction Lab

Consumable Materials (continued)

Description	Qty	Textbook Section(s)
Pencil, Wax Marking, Black	5	5-2 (Lab), 6-2 (Lab), 6-4 (Lab), 8-1 (TT), 11-5 (TT), 12-1 (SYS)
Pencil, Hex w/Eraser	35	1-2 (DIS), 11-3 (TT), 13-3 (Lab), 14-3 (DIS), 16-1 (TT), 16-2 (Lab), 16-5 (DIS)
Pencils, Colored, Pkg/12	5	4-3 (Lab), 5-3 (Lab), 8-1 (DIS), 15-2 (Lab)
Peppercorns, Black, 1 oz	1	16-4 (TT)
Perch - Under 7", Vac/5	1	7-5 (SYS)
Petri Dish, Disposable Polystyrene, Pkg/20	1	INT, 6-4 (Lab), 7-3 (TT)
Photos, Variety of Mammals	5	7-6 (SYS)
Picture, Nature Scene	5	8-1 (DIS)
Pill Bugs, Live, (24)	2	7-1 (DIS), 7-4 (SYS)
Pipe Cleaners, Asst Colors 6", Pkg/110	1	5-3 (TT)
Pipe Cleaners, White 12", Pkg/30	1	2-2 (SYS)
Plants, Vascular	10	8-1 (Lab)
Plastic Foam Sphere	5	16-4 (TT)
Plastic Wrap, Roll, 50 sq ft	1	2-2 (DIS), 8-1 (Lab), 12-1 (TT)
Plates, Paper 9", Pkg/50	1	4-1 (Lab), 11-1 (DIS)
Pond Culture, Live, Mixed	3	4-2 (SYS), 6-3 (DIS), 12-2 (DIS)
Potato, Slice	5	4-1 (SYS)
Raisins, Small Box	1	11-4 (TT)
Rubber Bands, Assorted, 4 oz	5	8-1 (Lab), 12-1 (TT), 12-3 (Lab), 13-1 (Lab), 13-3 (Lab), 13-4 (DIS)
Sand, Fine 2.5 kg (5.5 lbs)	10	1-4 (DIS), 3-3 (DIS), 11-5 (DIS), 12-1 (TT), 12-3 (DIS), 12-3 (TT), 12-3 (Lab), 14-1 (Lab)
Sandpaper, Medium, 9" x 11" Sheet	3	11-2 (SYS)
Seeds, Brown Bean, 30 g	1	6-4 (TT)
Seeds, Corn, 30 g	1	6-4 (TT), 6-4 (Lab)
Seeds, Pinto Bean, lb	6	6-2 (DIS), 8-2 (DIS)
Silly Putty	5	11-2 (TT)
Sodium Chloride, Iodized Table Salt, 737 g	2	1-1 (TT), 14-5 (DIS), 15-1 (DIS)
Sodium Chloride, Non-Iodized Table Salt, 500 g	1	8-1 (TT)
Soil and Grass Clump	5	3-3 (DIS)
Soil, Potting, 4 lb	1	8-1 (Lab), 12-4 (SYS)
Sponge, Cellulose, 3" x 3"	5	7-3 (DIS), 12-4 (SYS)
Sponge, Natural, 3" x 3", Pkg/6	1	7-3 (DIS)
Spoons, Plastic, Pkg/24	3	1-1 (TT), 1-1 (SYS), 8-1 (TT), 8-1 (Lab), 11-1 (DIS), 12-2 (TT), 12-5 (DIS), 14-5 (DIS)
Spring Water	5	8-1 (TT)
Sticks, Craft, Pkg/30	1	1-2 (Lab), 11-2 (DIS)
Straws, Plastic (Wrapped), Pkg/50	1	1-2 (TT), 5-2 (Lab), 11-5 (DIS), 12-3 (TT), 13-1 (TT), 13-3 (Lab), 14-3 (TT)
Straws, Plastic 10", Pkg/50	1	13-3 (TT)
String, Cotton, 200 ft	1	14-1 (Lab), 14-2 (DIS), 16-1 (TT), 16-4 (Lab), 16-5 (DIS)
Sugar, Granulated, 454 g	1	5-2 (TT)
Sugar, Powdered, 454 g	1	1-1 (TT)
Syringe, Disposable, 10 cc	5	11-4 (Lab)
Syringe, Disposable, 60 cc	5	2-3 (Lab)
Tape, Adding Machine Roll, 3-7/16"	1	11-3 (TT)
Tape, Brown Packing, 60 ft	1	4-1 (Lab)
Tape, Transparent Dispenser Roll, 27.1 ft	5	6-2 (Lab), 14-3 (TT), 16-4 (TT)
Thin Section of Tomato, Onion, or Lettuce	5	4-2 (SYS)
Toothpicks, Flat, Box/750	1	7-3 (TT), 16-4 (TT)
Toothpicks, Round, Box/250	1	14-3 (Lab)
Twist Tie, 10 cm, Plastic	15	12-1 (Lab)
Vinegar, 500 mL	2	1-1 (TT), 1-1 (SYS), 10-2 (Lab), 11-4 (TT)
Wax Paper, Roll, 75 sq ft	1	2-2 (DIS)
Wooden Splints, 15 cm, Pkg/25	1	14-3 (Lab)
Woodland Fern, Live	5	7-1 (DIS)
Wool Socks, Pair	5	7-6 (Lab)
Yeast, Dry, Baking, 7g Pkg	6	5-2 (TT), 5-3 (DIS)
Yogurt, Plain	1	6-2 (TT)

KEY: **DIS**: Discover; **SYS**: Sharpen Your Skills; **TT**: Try This; **Lab**: Lab; **INT**: Introduction Lab

Master Materials List

Nonconsumable Materials

Description	Qty	Textbook Section(s)	Description	Qty	Textbook Section(s)
Ball, Large, Smooth	5	14-3 (DIS)	Container, Cardboard w/Lid, 500 mL	5	7-3 (Lab)
Beaker, Pyrex Low Form, 250 mL	15	1-4 (Lab), 8-2 (DIS), 12-3 (Lab), 13-1 (TT), 14-5 (DIS)	Container, Plastic	5	11-5 (DIS), 11-5 (TT), 15-1 (DIS), 15-3 (DIS)
Beaker, Pyrex Low Form, 400 mL	10	14-1 (Lab)	Cup, Plastic Measuring, 500 mL	5	12-5 (DIS), 12-5 (SYS), 15-1 (DIS)
Beaker, Pyrex Low Form, 600 mL	20	8-1 (TT), 9-3 (Lab)	Dominoes, Box of 28	3	9-3 (DIS)
Beaker, Pyrex Low Form, 1000 mL	10	7-6 (Lab)	Dowel, Wood, 12" x 1/4"	15	9-2 (Lab)
Board, Flat, about 1.5 m long	5	3-1 (Lab)	Dump Truck, Toy	5	16-1 (DIS)
Bolt	15	1-4 (DIS)	Eye Hooks	10	3-2 (SYS)
Books	25	3-1 (Lab), 3-3 (DIS), 9-2 (Lab), 11-3 (TT)	Faucet	5	12-5 (SYS)
Books, Uniform Weight	20	2-3 (Lab)	Feather, White, 12-20 cm	5	7-6 (DIS)
Bottle, Spray Trigger, 16 oz	5	8-1 (Lab)	Field Guides, Assorted	5	8-3 (DIS)
Bowl, Plastic Small, 20 oz	10	7-3 (TT), 7-6 (TT), 11-4 (Lab), 12-1 (SYS), 12-5 (DIS)	Film Canister	5	16-6 (TT)
			Flashlight, Plastic (Size D)	5	7-3 (Lab)
Bowl, Plastic, Large, 40 oz	5	11-4 (Lab), 12-1 (TT)	Flask, Pyrex Erlenmeyer, 250mL	15	5-2 (Lab)
Bowl, White, 2 L	5	1-2 (TT), 1-4 (DIS)	Forceps, 115 mm, Straight	5	4-3 (Lab)
Box	5	1-3 (DIS), 8-2 (Lab)	Funnel, Plastic, 3.25"	5	12-3 (TT), 15-3 (DIS)
Bubble Wrap, 6 x 12"	5	2-2 (DIS)	Funnel, Plastic, 5"	15	12-3 (Lab), 14-5 (SYS)
Can, Aluminum	5	1-2 (DIS)	Glass, Drinking	5	7-2 (DIS), 12-1 (DIS)
Checkers, Pkg/32	5	1-1 (DIS)	Graduated Cylinder, Borosilicate, 10 mL	5	12-1 (SYS)
Cloth, Cotton White, 18" x 22"	1	2-4 (DIS)	Graduated Cylinder, Borosilicate, 100 mL	5	1-2 (Lab), 9-2 (DIS), 11-4 (TT), 12-1 (SYS), 12-3 (Lab), 14-5 (DIS)
Coin	5	3-2 (TT)			
Compass, Directional	5	14-3 (TT)	Graduated Cylinder, Polypropylene, 100 mL	5	5-2 (Lab)
Compass, with Pencil	5	16-3 (DIS), 16-4 (TT)	Hairdryer	5	4-1 (SYS)
Container and Lid, Glass	5	9-3 (Lab)	Hardness Scale, Point Kit	5	10-2 (Lab)
Container and Lid, Metal	5	9-3 (Lab)	Items, Desk, Assortment	5	6-1 (DIS)

KEY: **DIS**: Discover; **SYS**: Sharpen Your Skills; **TT**: Try This; **Lab**: Lab; **INT**: Introduction Lab

Nonconsumable Materials (continued)

Description	Qty	Textbook Section(s)	Description	Qty	Textbook Section(s)
Jar, 16 oz	5	13-1 (DIS)	Nails, 9 cm 16D, Pkg/15	1	10-2 (Lab)
Jar, 4 oz	5	13-1 (DIS), 13-2 (DIS)	Nut, 1/4"	15	1-4 (DIS)
Jar, 8 oz	15	7-6 (Lab), 13-3 (Lab), 13-4 (DIS)	Object, Spherical	5	7-2 (DIS), 10-1 (DIS)
Jar, Glass, Storage, Gallon	5	15-2 (DIS)	Objects, Assorted	5	1-3 (DIS)
Jar, Plastic	10	8-2 (DIS)	Pan, Aluminum, 7-3/8" x 3-5/8" x 2-1/4"	5	12-3 (TT), 12-4 (SYS)
Jar, Plastic, Clear, 4 oz	10	2-1 (TT), 12-1 (TT)	Pan, Aluminum Foil,11 x 21 x 6 cm	5	4-3 (TT)
Jar, Polystyrene, 12 oz	5	12-3 (DIS), 14-5 (SYS)	Pan, Aluminum Foil, 13 x 10 x 2"	5	3-3 (DIS), 12-4 (DIS)
Lid, For 4 oz Jar	10	2-1 (TT)	Pan, Aluminum Foil, 22.5 cm Diam	5	1-4 (DIS), 2-2 (SYS), 4-3 (TT), 11-4 (Lab), 13-1 (DIS), 13-2 (DIS)
Lid, For 8 oz Jar	15	7-6 (Lab)			
Light Socket, Clamp on w/Shade	5	INT, 14-1 (Lab)	Pan, Aluminum Foil, 31 x 22 x 3 cm	5	7-3 (Lab)
Light Socket, Porcelain w/Cord	5	9-4 (DIS)	Penny	5	10-2 (SYS), 10-2 (Lab), 15-2 (DIS)
Light Source	1	5-2 (Lab)	Pins, Pushpins, Plastic, Pkg/100	1	14-3 (TT), 16-1 (TT)
Magnet, Bar Alnico w/Marked Poles	5	10-2 (Lab)	Plants, Potted	5	7-1 (DIS)
Magnifier, 3x & 6x	5	1-1 (TT), 4-2 (DIS), 6-4 (DIS), 6-4 (TT), 7-3 (DIS), 7-3 (TT), 7-5 (SYS), 7-6 (DIS), 7-6 (TT), 8-3 (DIS), 9-1 (DIS), 10-2 (Lab), 10-3 (DIS), 10-3 (TT), 10-3 (Lab), 11-4 (DIS), 12-2 (DIS), 12-3 (Lab)	Protractor, 6" Plastic,180 degrees	5	3-1 (Lab)
			Puzzle, Jigsaw	5	8-2 (TT)
			Quarter	5	16-4 (DIS)
			Rock	5	1-2 (DIS), 12-1 (TT), 16-1 (DIS)
Marbles, 5/8", Pkg/20	3	9-3 (TT)	Rock Classification Set, Igneous	1	10-3 (TT)
Marbles, Glass(5 colors) 3/4", Pkg/30	1	1-1 (DIS), 10-2 (SYS), 15-2 (DIS)	Rock Specimen Kit	1	10-3 (Lab)
Marbles, Glass(5 Colors) 5/8", Pkg/30	1	1-1 (DIS)	Rock, Coal (Bituminous) Specimen Pak	1	9-1 (DIS)
Meter Stick w/Plain Ends, Wood	5	3-1 (DIS), 3-1 (Lab), 3-2 (DIS), 3-2 (Lab), 8-2 (TT), 14-2 (TT), 14-3 (Lab), 16-4 (Lab)	Rock, Obsidian Specimen Pak	1	11-4 (DIS)
			Rock, Pumice Specimen Pak	1	11-4 (DIS)
			Rocks, Three Different Kinds	15	10-3 (DIS)
Mineral Collection	1	10-2 (Lab)	Rolling Pin, Wood	5	10-2 (DIS)
Mineral, Hematite Specimen Pak	1	10-2 (Lab)	Rubber Stopper, Size 2, Solid, lb	1	5-2 (TT)
Mirror, Hand	5	2-4 (DIS)	Rubber Stopper, Size 3, 1-Hole Each	5	16-4 (Lab)
Mirror, Plastic, 7.5 x 12.5 cm	5	4-1 (TT)	Rubber Stopper, Size 6, Solid, lb	1	5-2 (Lab)

KEY: **DIS**: Discover; **SYS**: Sharpen Your Skills; **TT**: Try This; **Lab**: Lab; **INT**: Introduction Lab

Master Materials List

Nonconsumable Materials (continued)

Description	Qty	Textbook Section(s)	Description	Qty	Textbook Section(s)
Ruler, Plastic, 12"/30 cm	5	4-3 (DIS), 8-2 (DIS), 10-2 (DIS), 11-1 (DIS), 12-3 (DIS), 13-3 (Lab), 14-1 (Lab), 14-2 (DIS), 14-4 (DIS), 15-2 (Lab), 16-1 (TT), 16-2 (Lab), 16-3 (DIS), 16-4 (DIS), 16-5 (DIS)	Streak Plates, 2 x 2", Pkg/8	1	10-2 (Lab)
			Tape Measure, 1.5 m Metric/English	5	3-2 (Lab)
			Test Tube Support, Wood	5	1-1 (TT), 5-2 (TT)
			Test Tube, 18 x 150 mm, 27mL	10	1-1 (TT), 5-2 (TT), 14-5 (DIS)
Scissors, General Purpose, 6"	5	4-2 (DIS), 6-4 (TT), 6-4 (Lab), 7-2 (DIS), 7-3 (DIS), 7-6 (Lab), 9-2 (Lab), 10-2 (Lab), 12-3 (TT), 13-3 (Lab), 14-2 (DIS), 14-3 (TT), 16-2 (DIS), 16-2 (TT), 16-4 (TT), 16-5 (DIS), 16-6 (TT)	Thermometer, Red Liquid, 20°C to 110°C	15	2-4 (Lab), 7-6 (Lab), 9-2 (DIS), 9-2 (Lab), 9-3 (Lab), 9-4 (DIS), 13-1 (Lab), 14-1 (DIS), 14-1 (Lab)
			Thermometer, −30°C to 110°C; −20°F to 230°F	5	14-2 (TT)
Screw, Machine, 1/2", 6-32	15	1-4 (DIS)	Tile, Porcelin	5	3-3 (DIS)
Skateboard	5	3-1 (Lab)	Toy, Wind-Up	5	4-1 (DIS)
Slide, Allium (Onion) Root Tip, ls	5	5-3 (Lab)	Tube, Clear Plastic 3/8" x 8"	5	16-4 (Lab)
Slide, Animal Cell, General Type	5	4-3 (Lab)	Umbrella	5	7-5 (DIS)
Slide, Cork Section	5	4-2 (SYS)	Washer, Metal 1-1/2" OD 5/8 ID"	15	16-4 (Lab)
Slides, Plastic & Coverglass Set (72 Slides/ 100 Coverslips)	1	4-2 (SYS), 4-3 (Lab), 5-3 (DIS), 6-2 (TT), 6-3 (DIS), 6-3 (TT), 6-4 (TT), 12-2 (DIS)	Watering Can	5	3-3 (DIS), 12-3 (DIS), 12-4 (SYS)
			Weather Station, Student	1	13-1 (Lab)
Slinky Spring	5	11-3 (DIS)	Weight, Hook, 200g	5	11-2 (SYS)
Sponge, 15 x 7.5 x 1.8 cm	10	12-4 (DIS), 12-4 (SYS)	Wind Vane	5	14-3 (Lab)
Sponge, Natural, 3 x 3" Pkg/6	1	7-1 (DIS)	Wire Lead w/Alligator Clips (red)	10	1-4 (Lab)
Stirring Rod, 10", Polypropylene	10	2-4 (Lab), 5-2 (TT)	Wood, Block 2 x 4 x 6"	5	3-2 (SYS)

KEY: **DIS**: Discover; **SYS**: Sharpen Your Skills; **TT**: Try This; **Lab**: Lab; **INT**: Introduction Lab

Equipment

Description	Qty	Textbook Section(s)	Description	Qty	Textbook Section(s)
Apron, Vinyl	30	many activities	Gloves, Medium Latex, Laboratory Box/100	several	many activities
Balance, Triple Beam, Single Pan	5	1-2 (DIS), 1-2 (Lab), 4-1 (SYS), 12-1 (Lab), 13-3 (DIS), 14-5 (DIS)	Goggles, Chemical Splash, Class Set	1	16-3 (TT), many activities
Binoculars, 8 x 21 mm Compact	5	8-3 (DIS), 16-2 (DIS), 16-2 (TT)	Microscope, Compound	5	4-2 (DIS), 4-2 (SYS), 4-3 (Lab), 5-3 (DIS), 5-3 (Lab), 6-2 (TT), 6-3 (DIS), 6-3 (TT), 6-4 (TT), 7-3 (DIS), 12-2 (DIS), 13-1 (Lab)
Buret Clamp Symmetrical Round Jaws	10	14-1 (Lab), 16-2 (DIS), 16-2 (TT)			
Calculator, Light-Powered	5	5-3 (Lab), 8-2 (Lab)			
Calculator, Solar Powered, No Battery Backup	5	5-2 (DIS)	Mitten, Oven Mitt	10	many activities
Clock or Watch	5	6-2 (Lab), 7-3 (Lab), 7-6 (Lab), 8-2 (DIS), 8-2 (TT), 9-2 (Lab), 9-3 (Lab), 9-4 (DIS), 12-1 (TT), 12-5 (SYS)	Probeware: Temperature Probe (optional)	5	2-4 (Lab), 9-3 (Lab), 14-1 (Lab)
			Spring Scale, 500 g / 5 N, Green	10	3-2 (SYS), 11-2 (SYS)
Computer (Optional)	1	3-1 (Lab), 4-1 (Lab), 5-3 (Lab), 6-2 (Lab), 7-6 (Lab), 9-1 (SYS), 10-3 (Lab), 12-1 (Lab), 13-1 (Lab), 14-3 (Lab), 15-3 (SYS), 16-2 (Lab)	Stopwatch, Electronic LED	10	INT, 2-4 (Lab), 3-1 (DIS), 3-1 (Lab), 3-2 (DIS), 3-2 (Lab), 11-1 (DIS), 12-3 (Lab), 12-5 (DIS), 13-1 (DIS), 14-1 (Lab), 16-4 (Lab)
Computer w/ Graphing Software (Optional)	1	2-3 (Lab)	Support Base with 51 cm Rod	5	14-1 (Lab), 16-2 (DIS), 16-2 (TT)
Computer w/Spreadsheet Program (Optional)	1	1-2 (Lab), 8-2 (Lab)	Telescope, 525X Refracting	5	16-3 (SYS)
Fan	1	16-5 (DIS)	Vacuum Cleaner w/ Intake Hose	1	13-1 (Lab)

KEY: **DIS**: Discover; **SYS**: Sharpen Your Skills; **TT**: Try This; **Lab**: Lab; **INT**: Introduction Lab

PRENTICE HALL SCIENCE EXPLORER

Grade 6

Program Resources

Student Edition
Annotated Teacher's Edition
Unit Resource Books, including:
- Chapter Project Support
- Lesson Plans
- Section Summaries
- Review and Reinforce Worksheets
- Enrich Worksheets
- Student Edition Lab Worksheets
- Answer Keys
Lesson Plans
Chapter and Unit Tests
Performance Assessments
Color Transparencies
Laboratory Manual, Student Edition
Laboratory Manual, Teacher's Edition
Guided Reading and Study Workbook
Guided Reading and Study Workbook, Teacher's Edition
Prentice Hall Assessment System

Program-Wide Components

Inquiry Skills Activity Book
Student-Centered Science Activity Book
  for the Southwest
Reading in the Content Area With
  Literature Connections
Probeware Laboratory Manual with
  CD-ROM
How to Assess Student Work
How to Manage Instruction in the Block
Teacher's ELL Handbook

Media/Technology

Science Explorer iText
Resource Pro CD-ROM
Science Explorer Web site
  at **www.phschool.com**
Computer Test Bank Book with CD-ROM
Student Edition on Audio CD
Student Edition on Audio CD—Spanish
Lab Activity Videotape Library
Science Explorer Videodiscs
Science Explorer Videotape Library
Science Explorer Videotape Library—Spanish

Acknowledgments

The activity on page 568 is from *Exploring Planets in the Classroom.* Copyright by Hawaii Space Grant Consortium, based on a concept developed by Dale Olive.

The activity on pages 384–385 is from *Exploring Planets in the Classroom.* Copyright by Hawaii Space Grant Consortium, based on experiments done by R. Fisk and D. Jackson, U.S. Geological Survey.

ISBN 0-13-053478-1
2 3 4 5 6 7 8 9 10   06 05 04 03 02

Astronaut Jerry Ross works outside the Space Shuttle *Endeavor* during a mission.

Teacher's Edition ISBN 0-13-053481-1

Program Authors

Michael J. Padilla, Ph.D.
Professor
Department of Science Education
University of Georgia
Athens, Georgia

Michael Padilla is a leader in middle school science education. He has served as an editor and elected officer for the National Science Teachers Association. He has been principal investigator of several National Science Foundation and Eisenhower grants and served as a writer of the National Science Education Standards.

As lead author of *Science Explorer,* Mike has inspired the team in developing a program that meets the needs of middle grades students, promotes science inquiry, and is aligned with the National Science Education Standards.

Ioannis Miaoulis, Ph.D.
Dean of Engineering
College of Engineering
Tufts University
Medford, Massachusetts

Martha Cyr, Ph.D.
Director, Engineering
    Educational Outreach
College of Engineering
Tufts University
Medford, Massachusetts

Science Explorer was created in collaboration with the College of Engineering at Tufts University. Tufts has an extensive engineering outreach program that uses engineering design and construction to excite and motivate students and teachers in science and technology education.

Faculty from Tufts University participated in the development of *Science Explorer* chapter projects, reviewed the student books for content accuracy, and helped coordinate field testing.

Series Authors

Elizabeth Coolidge-Stolz, M.D.
Medical Writer
North Reading, Massachusetts

Linda Cronin-Jones, Ph.D.
Professor, College of Education
University of Florida
Gainesville, Florida

Donald Cronkite, Ph.D.
Professor of Biology
Hope College
Holland, Michigan

Joseph D. Exline, M.A., Ed.D.
President
Exline Consulting Services, Inc.
Beaverdam, Virginia

David V. Frank, Ph.D.
Physical Science Department Head
Ferris State University
Big Rapids, Michigan

Fred Holtzclaw
Science Instructor
Oak Ridge High School
Oak Ridge, Tennessee

Jan Jenner, Ph.D.
Science Writer
Talladega, Alabama

Steve Miller
Science Writer
State College, Pennsylvania

Jay M. Pasachoff, Ph.D.
Professor of Astronomy
Williams College
Williamstown, Massachusetts

Barbara Brooks Simons
Science Writer
Boston, Massachusetts

Carole Garbuny Vogel, M.A.T.
Science Writer
Lexington, Massachusetts

Jonathan Gitlin, M.D.
School of Medicine
Washington University
St. Louis, Missouri

Dawn Graff-Haight, Ph.D.
Department of Health, Human
    Performance, and Athletics
Linfield College
McMinnville, Oregon

Deborah L. Gumucio, Ph.D.
Associate Professor
Department of Anatomy and
    Cell Biology
University of Michigan
Ann Arbor, Michigan

William S. Harwood, Ph.D.
Dean of University Division and
    Associate Professor of Education
Indiana University
Bloomington, Indiana

Cyndy Henzel, Ph.D.
Department of Geography
    and Regional Development
University of Arizona
Tucson, Arizona

Greg Hutton
Science and Health
    Curriculum Coordinator
School Board of Sarasota County
Sarasota, Florida

Susan K. Jacobson, Ph.D.
Department of Wildlife Ecology
    and Conservation
University of Florida
Gainesville, Florida

Judy Jernstedt, Ph.D.
Department of Agronomy and
    Range Science
University of California, Davis
Davis, California

John L. Kermond, Ph.D.
Office of Global Programs
National Oceanographic and
    Atmospheric Administration
Silver Spring, Maryland

David E. LaHart, Ph.D.
Institute of Science and
    Public Affairs
Florida State University
Tallahassee, Florida

Joe Leverich, Ph.D.
Department of Biology
St. Louis University
St. Louis, Missouri

Dennis K. Lieu, Ph.D.
Department of Mechanical
    Engineering
University of California
Berkeley, California

Desiree A. Jackson, Ph.D.
Department of Biology
Texas Southern University
Houston, Texas

Akhtar H. Mahmood, Ph.D.
Assistant Professor
University of Texas-Pan American
Edinburg, Texas

Cynthia J. Moore, Ph.D.
Science Outreach Coordinator
Washington University
St. Louis, Missouri

Joseph M. Moran, Ph.D.
Department of Earth Science
University of Wisconsin–Green Bay
Green Bay, Wisconsin

José L. Panero
Assistant Professor of Botany
University of Texas
Austin, Texas

Doris Rosenbaum, Ph.D.
Scholar in Residence, Physics
    Department
Southern Methodist University
Dallas, Texas

Ronald L. Sass, Ph.D.
Professor of Chemistry and Biology
Rice University
Houston, Texas

Eric S. Schmitt, Ph.D., M.S., C.G.C.
Genetic Counselor
Baylor College of Medicine
Houston, Texas

John M. Sharp, Jr., Ph.D.
Chevron Centennial Professor of
    Geology
University of Texas
Austin, Texas

Joseph Stukey, Ph.D.
Department of Biology
Hope College
Holland, Michigan

Seetha Subramanian
Lexington Community College
University of Kentucky
Lexington, Kentucky

Carl L. Thurman, Ph.D.
Department of Biology
University of Northern Iowa
Cedar Falls, Iowa

Edward D. Walton, Ph.D.
Department of Chemistry
California State Polytechnic
    University
Pomona, California

Susan D. Wiediger, Ph.D.
Research Associate
Department of Chemistry
Rice University
Houston, Texas

Aaron S. Yoshinobu, Ph.D.
Assistant Professor
Department of Geosciences
Texas Technical University
Lubbock, Texas

Robert S. Young, Ph.D.
Department of Geosciences and
    Natural Resource Management
Western Carolina University
Cullowhee, North Carolina

Edward J. Zalisko, Ph.D.
Department of Biology
Blackburn College
Carlinville, Illinois

Rosie L. Leno
Krueger Middle School
San Antonio, Texas

Carol Ann Lionello
Kraemer Middle School
Placentia, California

Alison Minish-Ford
Ysleta Middle School
El Paso, Texas

Jaime A. Morales
Henry T. Gage Middle
    School
Huntington Park,
    California

Rebecca Morton
Wedgwood Sixth Grade
    School
Fort Worth, Texas

Patsy Partin
Cameron Middle School
Fort Worth, Texas

Deedra H. Robinson
Newport News Public
    Schools
Newport News, Virginia

Rick Robinson
Medina Valley Middle
    School
San Antonio, Texas

Charles M. Sears
Belzer Middle School
Indianapolis, Indiana

Shirley Simon
South Park Middle
    School
Beaumont, Texas

Barbara M. Strange
Ferndale Middle School
High Point, North
    Carolina

Denzial Tittle
Thornton Middle
    School
Katy, Texas

Kathy Usina
Belzer Middle School
Indianapolis, Indiana

Heidi M. von Oetinger
L'Anse Creuse Public
    School
Harrison Township,
    Michigan

Pam Watson
Hill Country Middle
    School
Austin, Texas

Laurie Westphal
Thornton Middle School
Katy, Texas

Activity Field Testers

Nicki Bibbo
Russell Street School
Littleton, Massachusetts

Connie Boone
Fletcher Middle School
Jacksonville Beach,
    Florida

Rose-Marie Botting
Broward County
    School District
Fort Lauderdale, Florida

Colleen Campos
Laredo Middle School
Aurora, Colorado

Elizabeth Chait
W. L. Chenery Middle
    School
Belmont, Massachusetts

Holly Estes
Hale Middle School
Stow, Massachusetts

Laura Hapgood
Plymouth Community
    Intermediate School
Plymouth, Massachusetts

Sandra M. Harris
Winman Junior High
    School
Warwick, Rhode Island

Jason Ho
Walter Reed Middle
    School
Los Angeles, California

Joanne Jackson
Winman Junior High
    School
Warwick, Rhode Island

Mary F. Lavin
Plymouth Community
    Intermediate School
Plymouth, Massachusetts

James MacNeil, Ph.D.
Concord Public Schools
Concord, Massachusetts

Lauren Magruder
St. Michael's Country Day
    School
Newport, Rhode Island

Warren Phillips
Plymouth Community
    Intermediate School
Plymouth, Massachusetts

Carol Pirtle
Hale Middle School
Stow, Massachusetts

Kathleen M. Poe
Kirby-Smith Middle
    School
Jacksonville, Florida

Cynthia B. Pope
Ruffner Middle School
Norfolk, Virginia

Anne Scammell
Geneva Middle School
Geneva, New York

Karen Riley Sievers
Callanan Middle School
Des Moines, Iowa

David M. Smith
Howard A. Eyer Middle
    School
Macungie, Pennsylvania

Derek Strohschneider
Plymouth Community
    Intermediate School
Plymouth, Massachusetts

Gene Vitale
Parkland Middle School
McHenry, Illinois

Zenovia Young
Meyer Levin Junior
    High School (IS 285)
Brooklyn, New York

Contents

Grade 6

Unit 1   Properties of Physical Systems

Unit 2 Structure and Function in Living Systems

Unit 3 Matter and Energy in the Environment

Unit 4 Earth and Space Systems—Structure and Function

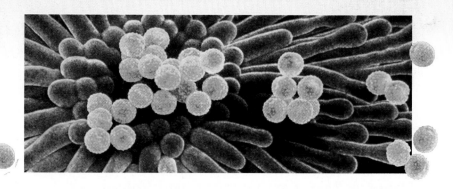

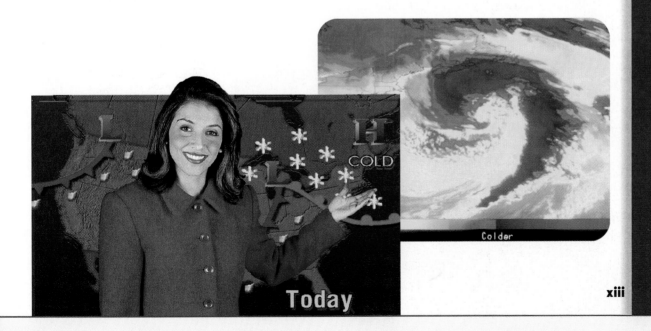

Reference Section

Mt. Monadnock, N.H.
— Roads
- - Trails
  Forest
  Exposed rock
Contour interval 200 feet

0   1   2 mi
0   1   2   3 km

Activities

DISCOVER
Exploration and inquiry before reading

Sharpen your *Skills*

Practice of specific science inquiry skills

TRY THIS

Reinforcement of key concepts

Skills Lab

In-depth practice of inquiry skills

Science at Home

EXPLORING

Visual exploration of concepts

Interdisciplinary Activities

Texas Essential Knowledge and Skills for Science

To Parents and Students:

The State of Texas has established standards describing science knowledge and skills for which all students are responsible. These standards are known as the Texas Essential Knowledge and Skills, or TEKS. State assessments of student achievement in science are based on these TEKS. The Grade 6 TEKS are listed below. The chapter references show where the content and skills are addressed in this textbook. A TEKS may be addressed in more than one chapter. Some chapters address only part of a TEKS.

To check for mastery of the content and process TEKS, students may use the Chapter Assessments at the end of each chapter and the *Science Explorer* iText at: **www.phschool.com**

(6.1) Scientific processes. The student conducts field and laboratory investigations using safe, environmentally appropriate, and ethical practices. *(Chapters 1–14, 16)*
The student is expected to:
(A) demonstrate safe practices during field and laboratory investigations; and
(B) make wise choices in the use and conservation of resources and the disposal or recycling of materials.

(6.2) Scientific processes. The student uses scientific inquiry methods during field and laboratory investigations. *(Chapters 1–16)*
The student is expected to:
(A) plan and implement investigative procedures including asking questions, formulating testable hypotheses, and selecting and using equipment and technology;
(B) collect data by observing and measuring;
(C) analyze and interpret information to construct reasonable explanations from direct and indirect evidence;
(D) communicate valid conclusions; and
(E) construct graphs, tables, maps, and charts using tools, including computers to organize, examine, and evaluate data.

(6.3) Scientific processes. The student uses critical thinking and scientific problem solving to make informed decisions. *(Chapters 1–2, 4–16)*
The student is expected to:
(A) analyze, review, and critique scientific explanations, including hypotheses and theories, as to their strengths and weaknesses using scientific evidence and information;

(B) draw inferences based on data related to promotional materials for products and services;
(C) represent the natural world using models and identify their limitations;
(D) evaluate the impact of research on scientific thought, society, and the environment; and
(E) connect Grade 6 science concepts with the history of science and contributions of scientists.

(6.4) Scientific processes. The student knows how to use a variety of tools and methods to conduct science inquiry. *(Chapters 1–16)*
The student is expected to:
(A) collect, analyze, and record information using tools including beakers, petri dishes, meter sticks, graduated cylinders, weather instruments, timing devices, hot plates, test tubes, safety goggles, spring scales, magnets, balances, microscopes, telescopes, thermometers, calculators, field equipment, compasses, computers, and computer probes; and
(B) identify patterns in collected information using percent, average, range, and frequency.

(6.5) Science concepts. The student knows that systems may combine with other systems to form a larger system. *(Chapters 12, 16)*
The student is expected to:
(A) identify and describe a system that results from the combination of two or more systems such as in the solar system; and
(B) describe how the properties of a system are different from the properties of its parts.

(6.6) Science concepts. The student knows that there is a relationship between force and motion. *(Chapters 3, 11, 16)*
The student is expected to:
(A) identify and describe the changes in position, direction of motion, and speed of an object when acted upon by force;
(B) demonstrate that changes in motion can be measured and graphically represented; and
(C) identify forces that shape features of the Earth, including uplifting, movement of water, and volcanic activity.

(6.7) Science concepts. The student knows that substances have physical and chemical properties. *(Chapters 1, 2)*
The student is expected to:
(A) demonstrate that new substances can be made when two or more substances are chemically combined and compare the properties of the new substances to the original substances; and
(B) classify substances by their physical and chemical properties.

(6.8) Science concepts. The student knows that complex interactions occur between matter and energy. *(Chapters 1, 8, 12)*
The student is expected to:
(A) define matter and energy
(B) explain and illustrate the interactions between matter and energy in the water cycle and in the decay of biomass, such as in a compost bin; and
(C) describe energy flow in living systems, including food chains and food webs.

(6.9) Science concepts. The student knows that obtaining, transforming, and distributing energy affects the environment. *(Chapters 1, 9)*
The student is expected to:
(A) identify energy transformations occurring during the production of energy for human use, such as electrical energy to heat energy or heat energy to electrical energy;
(B) compare methods used for transforming energy in devices such as water heaters, cooling systems, or hydroelectric and wind power plants; and
(C) research and describe energy types from their source to their use and determine if the type is renewable, nonrenewable, or inexhaustible.

(6.10) Science concepts. The student knows the relationship between structure and function in living systems. *(Chapters 4–8)*
The student is expected to:
(A) differentiate between structure and function;
(B) determine that all organisms are composed of cells that carry on functions to sustain life; and
(C) identify how structure complements function at different levels of organization, including organs, organ systems, organisms, and populations.

(6.11) Science concepts. The student knows that traits of species can change through generations and that the instructions for traits are contained in the genetic material of the organisms. *(Chapters 4, 5, 6)*
The student is expected to:
(A) identify some changes in traits that can occur over several generations through natural occurrence and selective breeding;
(B) identify cells as structures containing genetic material; and
(C) interpret the role of genes in inheritance

(6.12) Science concepts. The student knows that the responses of organisms are caused by internal or external stimuli. *(Chapters 4, 6–8)*
The student is expected to:
(A) identify responses in organisms to internal stimuli, such as hunger or thirst;
(B) identify responses in organisms to external stimuli, such as the presence or absence of heat or light; and
(C) identify components of an ecosystem to which organisms may respond.

(6.13) Science concepts. The student knows components of our solar system. *(Chapter 16)*
The student is expected to:
(A) identify characteristics of objects in our solar system, including the sun, planets, meteorites, comets, asteroids, and moons; and
(B) describe types of equipment and transportation needed for space travel.

(6.14) Science concepts. The student knows the structures and functions of Earth systems. *(Chapters 10, 12–15)*
The student is expected to:
(A) summarize the rock cycle;
(B) identify relationships between groundwater and surface water in a watershed; and
(C) describe components of the atmosphere, including oxygen, nitrogen, and water vapor; and identify the role of atmospheric movement in weather change.

Introduction to Science

Objectives	Time	Student Edition Activities	Other Activities
0.0.1 Explain the nature of scientific inquiry. 0.0.2 Identify and describe the skills used by scientists in their work. 0.0.3 Explain how scientific hypotheses can be tested through controlled experiments. 0.0.4 Distinguish among a scientific hypothesis, theory, and law. 0.0.5 Explain the importance of laboratory safety.	2–3 periods/ 1–1$\frac{1}{2}$ blocks	**Skills Lab: Developing Hypotheses** Speeding Up Evaporation, p. 17	TE Addressing Naive Conceptions, p. 11 TE Building Inquiry Skills; Developing Hypotheses, p. 12 TE Demonstration, p. 19

Key: **CTB** Computer Test Bank
       CUT Chapter and Unit Tests
       ELL Teacher's ELL Handbook

Student Edition Activities Planner

ACTIVITY	Time (minutes)	Materials *Quantities for one work group*	Skills
Skills Lab, p. 17	40	**Consumable** water, paper towels **Nonconsumable** 2 plastic petri dishes, 1 petri dish cover, plastic dropper, 3 index cards, stopwatch, lamp	Developing Hypotheses

A list of all materials required for the Student Edition activities can be found on pages T43–T49. You can obtain information about ordering materials by calling 1-800-848-9500 or by accessing the Science Explorer Internet site at **www.phschool.com**.

CHAPTER PLANNING GUIDE

 The Resource Pro® CD-ROM provides flexibility for planning the instruction for any type of schedule.

Program Resources	Assessment Strategies	Media and Technology
UR Introduction Lesson Plan, p. 2	**TE** Ongoing Assessment, pp. 11, 13, 15	Science Explorer at www.phschool.com
UR Introduction Section Summary, p. 3	**TE** Performance Assessment, p. 19	Student Edition on Audio CD, English-Spanish, Introduction
UR Introduction Review and Reinforce, p. 4	**SE** Study Guide/Assessment, pp. 20–21	
UR Introduction Enrich, p. 5	**PA** Introduction Performance Assessment, pp. 2–4	Lab Activity Videotapes, Tape 1
UR Introduction Skills Lab, pp. 6–7	**CUT** Introduction Test, pp. 2–3	Introduction
	CTB Introduction Test	Computer Test Bank, Introduction Test
	PHAS Provides standardized test preparation	

GRSW Guided Reading and Study Workbook
ISAB Inquiry Skills Activity Book
LM Laboratory Manual

PA Performance Assessment
PHAS Prentice Hall Assessment System
PLM Probeware Lab Manual

RCA Reading in the Content Area
SE Student Edition

TE Teacher's Edition
UR Unit Resources

Take It to the Net

 Interactive text at www.phschool.com

Science Explorer comes alive with iText.

- **Complete student text** is accessible from any computer with Internet access or a CD-ROM drive.

- **Animations, simulations, and videos** enhance student understanding and retention of concepts.

- **Self-tests and online study tools** assess student understanding.

- **Teacher management tools** help you make the most of this valuable resource.

STAY CURRENT with

Find out the latest research and information about the nature of science at **www.phschool.com**.

Go to **www.phschool.com**. Select Texas on the navigation bar. Click on the Science icon. Then click on <u>Science Explorer</u> under PH@school.

In the Path of a Hurricane

Focus on Weather

This article introduces students to the dangers of hurricanes and how hurricane preparedness changed during the last century. Students will read about the hurricane that devastated Galveston, Texas in 1900. Hurricanes can be incredibly destructive and claim many lives. Although scientists have not found a method of controlling weather, they have learned to predict when severe storms are on their way so precautions can be taken.

Students will learn more about weather factors in Chapter 14, and weather patterns in Chapter 15. They do not need that knowledge to understand and appreciate the information in this article.

Starting Out

◆ The night before you introduce this lesson, gather several weather reports for your area for the following day from television stations, radio stations, newspapers, and the Internet. Post these on the board. Ask: **How are these forecasts alike? How are they different?** *(Responses will vary. General conditions might be very similar, but such details as predicted high temperatures may be different.)* **Why do you think that not all the predictions are the same?** *(Students should understand that making exact predictions about the weather is difficult for a variety of reasons.)*

◆ Inform students that not all severe storms are hurricanes. Have a volunteer look up the term cyclone in the dictionary and read the meteorological definition aloud. Students should hear that a cyclone is a storm with very high winds that rotates about a center of low atmospheric pressure. In the northern hemisphere, the rotation is counter-clockwise. A hurricane is a warm-core tropical cyclone. The term hurricane is used to describe a cyclone in the Northern hemisphere, east from the International Dateline to the Prime Meridian. Have students locate these longitude lines on a globe or world map.

TEXAS
Field Trip

IN THE PATH OF A HURRICANE

At dawn, it was raining. By noon, the wind was blowing across the island at more than 48 kilometers per hour. Cottages near the beach began washing out to sea. Many streets on the eastern and southern sides of the city were waist-deep in water. The bridge to the mainland was also flooded. It was too late to leave the island. By evening, the entire city was flooded. The water was 5 meters above street level. The wind was whipping at 190 kilometers per hour. It peeled tin roofs off houses and toppled telephone poles. Around midnight, the floodwaters finally began to recede, and the wind died down. The deadliest hurricane to ever strike the shores of the United States had passed, leaving the city of Galveston in ruins.

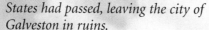

Scenes from Galveston after the hurricane of 1900.

2

Background

History In 1900, the highest point above sea level in Galveston was 2.6 m. The hurricane that hit land there had a storm surge of 4.5 m. Why wasn't the entire city's population wiped out? Because of Isaac Cline.

Dr. Isaac M. Cline was the manager of Galveston's Weather Bureau. Cline and the Weather Bureau knew about the hurricane as it passed over Cuba. At that point, it was on a northern track, and warnings were issued for the eastern Gulf states, Florida, and the southern Atlantic coast.

As the storm failed to follow its predicted path and turned towards Texas, Cline became suspicious of the weather. Cline was convinced that a major storm was nearing, and he raised the hurricane warning flags a full day before the storm struck. He patrolled the beach, warning people to head for higher ground. Had it not been for Cline, many more Galveston residents may have died.

Galveston lies on an island just off the Texas coast, putting it at risk for water and wind damage when hurricanes hit.

Taking a Close Look

◆ Have students read the article about the Galveston hurricane. Students who have visited Galveston may be interested to share their impression of the seawall that now protects the town.

◆ Television stations and meteorological companies often make speakers available for educational purposes. Contact your local weather person and invite him or her to speak to the class. Have students prepare questions about the Galveston hurricane and hurricanes in general before the speaker arrives.

◆ From the article, students know that during the Galveston hurricane, winds reached 190 kph. Have students calculate that speed in miles per hour by dividing 190 by 1.6093. *(about 118 mph)* Inform students that the highest winds ever recorded in Texas was estimated to be 190 kph. The speed had to be estimated because the anemometer blew away when it read 190 kph. The highest wind ever recorded in the United States was at Mt. Washington, New Hampshire, where the wind speed reached 370 kph.

A Record-Setting Hurricane

On September 8, 1900, a forceful hurricane pounded the city of Galveston, Texas. The destruction it left behind was astonishing. A mound of wreckage 5 kilometers long formed a semicircle around the city's business district. Outside this area, there was nothing—not a single home, not a single building, not a single tree. The bay was jammed with debris and dead bodies. The hurricane had destroyed more than 3,600 buildings and killed approximately 6,000 of the city's 37,000 residents.

The Galveston hurricane of 1900 is the deadliest hurricane that has ever hit the United States. No other hurricane since then has caused such terrible damage or loss of life. Were the later hurricanes less powerful? Not at all. The difference now is that people plan for hurricanes, predict their arrival, and get out of their way.

What Is a Hurricane?

A hurricane is a huge storm. It begins when water in a warm ocean evaporates and forms clouds in the atmosphere. Wind develops among the clouds. As the evaporation continues, the clouds become thicker. The wind speed increases, too. When the wind speed reaches 119 kilometers per hour, the storm is called a hurricane. It can take a week or more for a hurricane to develop.

A hurricane grows even stronger as it moves over warm water. When it reaches land, its powerful winds can devastate the shore. The wind blows down trees and telephone poles. It turns branches and pieces of metal into flying objects that crash into windows and cars. Sheets of rain can cause flooding.

The hurricane's wind pushes ocean water ahead of the storm, too. This action creates huge waves that crash onto the shore. Pounding waves can drag the land out from under buildings, causing them to collapse. The pieces of shattered buildings can then batter other buildings, causing even more damage.

3

Background

Facts and Figures Ranking hurricanes historically depends on the criteria chosen. In terms of deaths, the Galveston hurricane of 1900 was the worst hurricane ever to reach the U.S mainland. The death toll for that hurricane is generally given as about 6,000 people, although estimates as high as 12,000 have also been made. The second-deadliest hurricane in the U.S. mainland occurred in Florida in 1928, when 1,826 people died.

Ranking hurricanes in terms of damage is difficult because of changes in the value of the dollar. Even if the value of hurricane damage is "adjusted" to compensate for changes in the dollar, Hurricane Andrew (1992) is by far the most costly hurricane in U.S. history. Andrew caused 25 billion dollars in damage in south Florida. This is more than three times the damage of the second-place hurricane, Hugo (1989), which struck South Carolina.

◆ A hurricane has very low atmospheric pressure, especially in the eye of the storm. Higher pressure outside the hurricane causes air to rush in toward the center of the storm. This demonstration will show students how much force differences in air pressure can exert. **CAUTION:** *Wear safety goggles and heat-resistant gloves.* Find a metal can with a lid, such as those used for syrup or paint thinner. Clean it thoroughly, and fill it with water to a depth of about one inch. Heat the can, using a hot plate, until the water is at a full boil. Have students note that the steam is coming out of the can because the pressure in the can is greater than the pressure outside the can. Ask: **Why is the pressure greater in the can?** *(The pressure is greater because of the heat.)* Remove the can from the heat source and carefully tighten the lid in place using heat-resistant gloves. Place the closed can in a cool place, or pour some cool water on the can to cool it more quickly. The can will collapse inward, as the pressure in the can decreases as it cools. Ask: **After the can was cooled, where was the pressure greater?** *(Outside the can)* **Why didn't air rush into the can?** *(The can was sealed.)* Point out that, just as differences in air pressure pushed on the can and crushed it, differences in air pressure can push air masses in to motion, causing winds.

◆ Ask students who have visited or lived in coastal areas if they have ever seen signs marking certain roads as evacuation routes. Discuss with students why it is important that these routes be established and clearly marked.

(A) A radar image shows a hurricane over the Texas coast. (B) and (C) Storm preparations often include boarding up windows and evacuation.

Protecting Lives and Property

The hurricane that hit Galveston in September of 1900 gained power as it stormed toward the city. Meanwhile, the people in Galveston didn't know that a storm was on its way.

Hurricane Warnings

In 1900, two changes signaled an approaching hurricane: the sky turning the color of "brick-dust," and a decrease in barometer readings. (A barometer is a device that measures air pressure.) Air pressure is lower before and during a storm than it is during clear weather. Unfortunately, the sky in Galveston never changed color before the storm hit that September. And, by the time the barometer started to drop, it was too late to get people out of the island city.

Today, technology helps meteorologists—scientists who study weather—locate and track storms that develop over the ocean. Radar and weather satellites provide data about the location and wind speed of a potential hurricane. Meteorologists at the National Hurricane Center begin tracking its motion. They use the data to predict the power and movement of the storm.

A Plan of Action

Cities facing a major hurricane usually receive an evacuation order. This notice means that everyone is supposed to move inland, away from the coast, where the winds are strongest and flooding is most likely. Cities plan in advance for evacuations. Certain roads are marked as evacuation routes, and people who live in the area know where these routes are. Emergency shelters are set up in safe places so that evacuated families have somewhere to go.

Preventing Damage

When a hurricane strikes, people can move to safer ground, but very little can be done to protect buildings from wind damage. Many people who live where a hurricane is likely to strike have sturdy shutters or pieces of plywood to cover windows.

Flood damage is hard to prevent. After the destruction from the storm in 1900,

4

Background

Facts and Figures Hurricanes are assigned categories according to the Saffir-Simpson Hurricane Scale. While several factors are considered, the hurricane's wind speed is the determining factor for the scale.

A Category One hurricane has winds of 119–153 kph, with a storm surge of about 1.3 m above normal. Damage is limited to signs, shrubs, trees, and unanchored mobile homes.

A Category Two hurricane has winds of 154–177 kph, and a storm surge of about 2.3 m above normal. Damage may be expected to trees and mobile homes, with some flooding along coastal and low-lying areas.

A Category Three hurricane has winds of 178–209 kph, and a storm surge of about 3.3 m above normal. Damage may occur to small residences and utility buildings, with some flooding 3–5 hours before the hurricane arrives.

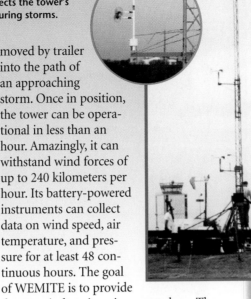

The WEMITE tower is more than 10 meters high. Instruments on the tower collect wind data. A waterproof steel box protects the tower's computer from damage during storms.

the city of Galveston built a sea wall that would hold back the strong waves of a hurricane. The sea wall was tested in 1915, when an equally severe hurricane hit Galveston. Although the sea wall was battered and damaged, fewer than ten people died and there was very little property damage.

Wind Research at Texas Tech

In the past century, Texas was hit with more hurricanes than any other state except Florida. Because wind damage during a hurricane is a great concern, scientists at Texas Tech University at Lubbock are studying how buildings respond to the strong winds that come with hurricanes and tornadoes.

Among the university's research programs is the Wind Engineering Mobile Instrumented Tower Experiment (WEMITE). This project makes use of a tower that can be moved by trailer into the path of an approaching storm. Once in position, the tower can be operational in less than an hour. Amazingly, it can withstand wind forces of up to 240 kilometers per hour. Its battery-powered instruments can collect data on wind speed, air temperature, and pressure for at least 48 continuous hours. The goal of WEMITE is to provide data to wind engineering researchers. They use the information to design and test plans for buildings that will be able to withstand severe wind conditions.

- ◆ **Preparing for an Emergency** As an extension of this activity, have students draw up an emergency plan for their town or city. Help them note the differences between individual or family plans and plans that must take into account thousands or hundreds of thousands of people. Students can also contact the Chamber of Commerce or the Department of Public Safety to see if such a plan exists for their community.
- ◆ **Defining the Term** Students may be surprised to learn that the eye of a hurricane, instead of having the most violent weather, is actually quite calm. As the eye of a hurricane passes over an area, winds decrease and the sky may even clear. However, it is the center of the storm, and after the eye passes, the high winds and danger resume.
- ◆ **Naming a Hurricane** Encourage students also to locate a list of retired hurricane names and to see why each name was retired. Students can place pins in a map to show where these disastrous storms struck and look for patterns.
- ◆ **Visiting the Wind Engineering Research Center** Students who express an interest in wind may also investigate other kinds of wind research and the instruments used. They may find articles and information on wind tunnels, wind farms, wind turbines, wind-chill factors, and wind shear.

TEXAS
Field Trip
SCIENCE ROUNDUP

Find out more about hurricanes and ways to prevent their damage.

Knowing what to do in advance can help keep you safe during an emergency situation. Discuss with your family what to do in case of a fire, hurricane, or tornado. Then write a plan your family can use for one of these emergencies.

Have you ever heard people talk about the "eye of a storm"? Do some research to find out what this phrase means, and how it applies to hurricanes.

Meteorologists give each hurricane a different name. Use library and other resources to find out more about how and why hurricanes are named. You may even be able to find out whether a hurricane will ever be named after you.

If you live in the Lubbock area, plan a visit to the Wind Research Center at Texas Tech University. At the center, you will be able to see wind research projects in progress and learn more about how hurricanes damage buildings.

5

Background

Facts and Figures The most severe hurricanes are rated as Category Four and Category Five on the Saffir-Simpson Hurricane Scale. A Category Four hurricane has winds of 210–249 kph, and storm surges of 4–5.5 m above normal. Damage includes house roofs and trees, with the complete destruction of mobile homes.

A Category Five hurricane has winds in excess of 249 kph, and storm surges more than 5.5 m above normal. Damage to buildings is extensive, and many shrubs and trees are blown away. Low-lying areas flood 3–5 hours before the arrival of the hurricane.

Classifying the Galveston hurricane of 1900 is difficult. Wind speeds during this hurricane could only be estimated. As a result, some meteorologists consider the Galveston hurricane a Category Three storm, while others consider it a Category Four storm.

Reducing Hurricane Damage

Focus on Weather

This four-page article features Kishor Mehta, a civil engineer working and teaching at the University of Texas in Austin. Dr. Mehta works primarily on wind research, and the article describes some of the projects he and his team have tackled. Using Dr. Mehta's research, the article focuses on experimentation as a scientific tool.

Students will learn more about weather factors in Chapter 14, and weather patterns in Chapter 15. They do not need that knowledge to understand and appreciate the information in this article.

Scientific Inquiry

◆ Ask students to think of ways that the wind is helpful, and ways that it can be destructive. *(Responses might include: (helpful) powers windmills, useful for sailboats, flying kites, helps disperse seeds of plants; (destructive) breaks limbs off trees, damages structures, blows topsoil away.)* Keep a list on the board as students make suggestions, dividing the list into appropriate categories.

◆ Ask students why a structural engineer would need to understand the effects of wind on buildings and other structures. *(They need to know how strong a building must be to withstand winds.)*

REDUCING HURRICANE DAMAGE

▲ Kishor Mehta grew up in India, and moved to the United States to go to college. He remembers that his greatest challenge in learning English was learning how to think in a new language. After college, he received his Ph.D. in civil engineering from the University of Texas in Austin.

Hurricane winds roar through a coastal city, tearing off roof tiles and metal sidings from houses. An entire roof rips into the air. Flying tree limbs, street signs, and debris from broken houses crash into the windows and doors of other buildings, opening them to even more damage by wind and water. What can be done to change the fate of buildings in the path of heavy winds? At the Wind Engineering Research Center at Texas Tech University in Lubbock, people are trying to answer this question.

Kishor Mehta (KEE-shour MEH-tah) is the center's director and an expert on the effects of hurricane winds. "Hurricanes cause damage. We can't stop them, but we can learn to live with them. We can prevent them from disrupting the life of the community. That's our goal."

Studying the Wind

Kishor started his studies in the field of civil engineering—which focuses on the design and construction of public buildings, bridges, and other structures. He later became more interested in structural engineering—the branch of civil engineering that concentrates on design. A few years after arriving at Texas Tech, Kishor started to think about doing wind research. He thought that he and his colleagues might investigate wind power, but a tornado gave them an even better idea.

Background

Facts and Figures The Swiss scientist Daniel Bernoulli (1700–1782) studied the flow of fluids, both liquids and gases. He formulated the theory that the pressure exerted by a fluid is inversely proportional to its rate of flow. This is the basis of the Bernoulli effect, or Bernoulli's Principle. According to Bernoulli's Principle, a fast-moving fluid causes an area of low pressure. For example, gusts of wind moving past a building can decrease the air pressure outside the building, which can cause the glass panes to pop out of large windows. When this happens, the relatively higher air pressure inside the building presses outward on walls and windows. If the Bernoulli effect created by the wind outside is strong enough, the air pressure inside the building can push the glass out of the windows.

◄ High winds can rip apart buildings, leaving them battered or destroyed. The instrumented movable test building (shown below) at the Texas Tech Field Laboratory helps researchers study the effects of high winds on buildings.

Starting an Investigation

A devastating tornado had just torn through downtown Lubbock. "We began to study how structures perform under high wind conditions," explains Kishor. "At the time, very little research had been done in this area." Kishor and his team analyzed how the tornado had affected local buildings. Then they traveled to other towns and cities that had been struck by tornadoes or hurricanes to study damage that had happened in those places.

Their early data showed that the winds from tornadoes and hurricanes affect buildings in very similar ways. Once the engineers understood how and why damage was occurring, they began to think about ways to design buildings that could withstand high winds.

Broadening the Research

Lubbock is in a very windy part of Texas, so it is a good place to study how wind affects the structure of a building. Currently, under Kishor's leadership, students and teachers at the university's

Wind Engineering Research Field Laboratory carry out a wide variety of wind experiments. In addition to the WEMITE tower described on page 5, the center has another instrumented tower that is used to measure weather conditions. Nearby, there is even a movable building! Depending on the direction of the wind, researchers can turn the building to orient the instruments in the direction of the wind and see how the roof and walls are affected.

Lubbock

WIND ENGINEERING RESEARCH
CIVIL ENGINEERING

♦ Have students look at the photograph at the top of page 7. Ask students to describe the damage that is shown. Then invite students to suggest changes in construction that might have reduced the damage.

♦ The shape of a building can affect the flow of air around it. To demonstrate how air flows over smooth contours, place a lighted candle on the desk. CAUTION: *Tie back loose hair and clothing, wear safety goggles, and exercise care in lighting and extinguishing the candle.* Hold a small paper, such as a note card, in front of the candle and blow from a distance of about 8 to 10 inches. Students should see that the candle flame bends towards the back of the note card. As you blow on the card, air flows towards the card, but has to shift direction and go around the card. Since the air pressure of the moving air is less than the pressure of the still air, the moving air flows backward to balance the pressure. Now bend the note card into a teardrop shape, and use tape to hold the ends together. Hold the card in front of the candle, with the closed end facing the candle. Again, blow toward the card. Students should see that the flame bends away from the card. Air flow is much smoother, and the pressure is generally balanced without major points of backdraft.

7

Background

Facts and Figures The instrumented tower at Wind Engineering Research Field Laboratory is about 50 m tall. The tower has groups of instruments at intervals from near the ground to its top. These instruments measure and record the wind profile, wind turbulence level, density of the air, ground roughness, and the stability of the atmosphere.

The field laboratory's test building is mounted on a circular track. The building can be rotated to face the wind at a desired angle. The surface of the building has taps that record pressures using differential pressure transducers.

Scientists at the laboratory study the effects of wind pressures on buildings and roofing, and wind flow around buildings. They also use the site to gain field data during high winds and thunderstorms.

- Have students reread the last paragraph under "Working in Teams." Discuss with students the concept of cost-benefit analysis. Ask students what sort of information the team might need before they can recommend specific building standards. *(They would need to know what typical "normal" winds are like in the area, and they would need wind data for severe storms that have occurred in that area. This information would help the team understand the forces that would affect a building in the area.)*

- In the Northern hemisphere, wind generally blows from west to east. Differences in air pressure and temperatures, as well as surrounding terrain, may change this direction slightly. Winds are named for the direction from which the wind is blowing. Have students keep a record of the wind direction around the school for two weeks. Using a compass, select a place that is as open as possible, and chalk the positions of the compass on the ground. Always take the wind direction in this same place, and as close as possible to the same time every day. Ask: **How can you determine the direction of the wind?** *(Responses may include suggestions such as wetting a finger and holding it in the air, tossing light objects to see which way they blow, or holding a handkerchief by one end to see which way it blows.)* **How can you compare the speed of the wind from one day to another?** *(Students might suggest measuring the distance a tossed object is carried, how close to horizontal a handkerchief or ribbon becomes when held in the wind.)* Allow small groups of students to decide how they will determine the direction and speed of the wind. Groups can compare their records at the end of two weeks.

Working in Teams

Kishor sometimes works with researchers from other fields. For example, he and a professor from Texas Tech's economics department conducted a study of property damage from hurricanes in Galveston. "I like working in teams," Kishor explains. "Each person brings a different set of skills, a different point of view. Keeping costs in mind, we can work together to decide where to put the most effort into design."

Designing buildings that resist severe weather is not a problem. Engineers know how, and they do just that for nuclear power plants. "But when it comes to building houses, the costs are too high" says Kishor "So what we do is sit down with a group of people— economists, architects, city planners—and decide how we can do the most good with the resources available."

Solving a Problem

While the Texas Tech researchers spend quite a bit of time in the field, they also use equipment and devices at the school's Wind Engineering Research Field Laboratory to solve specific problems.

A few years ago, the Texas Department of Transportation noticed something troubling about certain traffic lights. Some of the lights that were attached to horizontal poles hanging over the street would vibrate. State officials were concerned about the danger to cars passing under the lights. "They wanted to know what kind of wind was causing the problem and why it affected some poles but not others," says Kishor. Was there any way to reinforce the poles or the lights?

The school's field laboratory was set up to test how wind affects traffic light poles. Kishor and his colleagues discovered that serious

Kishor and another researcher watch as wind data from the instrumented tower and test building are recorded by computer. ▶

8

Background

Facts and Figures Steady winds can cause problems, if engineers do not consider the effects of wind on a structure. The classic example of such a problem was the Tacoma Narrows Bridge near Seattle, Washington. While the bridge was still under construction, people noticed that it swayed in the wind. Engineers were called in to study the problem. Months before the bridge's completion in 1940, winds of 64 kph caused the bridge to undulate and twist violently.

The bridge was literally torn apart by its own movements. Fortunately, the bridge had been closed to traffic before it collapsed.

The designers of the bridge had not considered the possibility of wind damage, and they had not done any wind-tunnel tests on the design. Engineers designed the second Tacoma Narrows Bridge to resist swaying. The bridge's structure was strengthened sand a grating in the bridge's deck allowed wind to pass through.

(A) A traffic light was erected at the field laboratory to test vibration of the pole in natural wind. (B) The solution to the problem was a metal plate above the traffic lights to prevent dangerous vibrations of the pole.

vibrations occur when the backs of the lights face into steady winds blowing from about 15 to 50 kilometers per hour. The team looked for a way to reduce the vibrations. They found that attaching a horizontal metal plate to the pole on top of the light eased the problem. Grateful for the suggestion, the state added the plates to the traffic lights. They also passed the study results on to other parts of the United States where high winds pose risks.

Reaching His Goals

Early in his career, Kishor realized that he enjoyed teaching. The opportunity to teach and do research led him to Texas Tech. In recent years, Kishor has spent more than half his time teaching.

He also continues to direct the overall research and management of the center, work with colleagues, and speak publicly about how wind affects buildings and other structures. As a result of the efforts of Kishor and his colleagues, the Texas Tech Wind Engineering Research Field Laboratory has become recognized as a place where people can find out how to live more safely.

In Your Journal

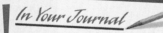

Kishor Mehta changed his plan for studying the wind when a tornado gave him another idea. Think about an example in your life when you switched to another plan for a project, trip, social event, or other activity. How did you feel about giving up your idea for a new one? What factors convinced you to change?

9

◆ Have students look at the photographs on page 9. Ask volunteers to describe the shape, size, and position of the metal plate on top of the horizontal pole. Encourage students to suggest other shapes, sizes, or positions that might have been tested. Point out that scientists do not necessarily find the best design on the first test. Help students understand that testing a design that does not have the desired effect is still a valuable learning experience.

In Your Journal Encourage students to think of a time when the change in plans was dramatic, or at least serious. You may want to discuss what kinds of changes are appropriate for this journal entry before allowing students to proceed with their assignment.

READING STRATEGIES

Further Reading

◆ *Do Tornadoes Really Twist?: Questions and Answers About Tornadoes and Hurricanes* Melvin Berger, et al. (Scholastic, 2000)
◆ *Eye of the Storm: Inside the World's Deadliest Hurricanes, Tornadoes, and Blizzards* Jeffery P. Rosenfield (Plenum Press, 1999)
◆ *Galveston and the 1900 Storm* Patricia Bellis Bixel Elizabeth Hayes Turner (University of Texas Press, 2000)
◆ *Hurricanes and Tornadoes (Natural Disasters)* Neil Morris (Barron's, 1999)
◆ *Hurricanes (Disasters in Nature)* Catherine Chambers (Heineman Library)
◆ *Isaac's Storm: A Man, a Time, and the Deadliest Hurricane in History* Erik Larson, (G. K. Hall & Co., 2000)

What is Science?

Objectives

After completing this introduction, students will be able to

♦ explain the nature of scientific inquiry;
♦ describe the skills used by scientists in their work;
♦ explain how scientific hypotheses can be tested through controlled experiments;
♦ distinguish among a scientific hypothesis, theory, and law;
♦ explain the importance of laboratory safety.

1 Engage/Explore

Activating Prior Knowledge

Ask students what they think scientists do. Students will likely say that scientists work in a laboratory and carry out experiments. Have students preview pages 18–19. Then discuss that scientists work in many kinds of places.

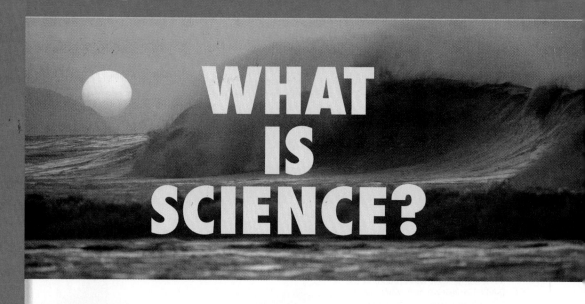

WHAT IS SCIENCE?

GUIDE FOR READING

♦ What skills do scientists use?

♦ How can you work safely in the laboratory?

Reading Tip Before you begin reading, make a list of the boldfaced terms. As you read, write the definition for each term.

Key Terms science
• scientific inquiry
• observation
• inference
• hypothesis
• variable
• manipulated variable
• responding variable
• controlled experiment
• data
• scientific law
• scientific theory

As a structural engineer, Kishor Mehta asks a lot of questions. Is the pole that holds up a traffic signal sturdy enough to stand up to strong winds? How can we design buildings so that they can withstand tornadoes and hurricanes? Asking questions is an important part of science.

Science is a way of learning about the natural world. Science also includes all the knowledge gained through the process of exploring the natural world. This body of knowledge is always growing and changing as scientists ask new questions and explore new ideas.

Another term for the many ways in which scientists study the world around them is **scientific inquiry.** Scientific inquiry is used every day by the engineers at the Wind Engineering Research Center at Texas Tech University.

You do not have to be a scientist to use scientific inquiry. In fact, you may not realize that you probably have used the process of scientific inquiry. If you have tried to find the best conditions for fish in a fish tank or the correct way to throw a curve ball, you have used scientific inquiry.

Figure 1 This student is using the skills of scientific inquiry as she monitors conditions in this fish tank. *Posing Questions What questions would you have about the conditions needed to keep fish alive and healthy in a fish tank?*

READING STRATEGIES

Reading Tip Have students write a question for each of the terms they list. They may combine terms in a compare-and-contrast statement. Sample answer: How does a manipulated variable differ from a responding variable?

Program Resources

♦ **Unit 1 Resources** Introduction Lesson Plan, p. 2; Introduction Section Summary, p. 3
♦ **Guided Reading and Study Workbook** Introduction

Thinking Like a Scientist

Kishor Mehta uses many skills as he investigates the effects of strong winds on buildings. You may have used some of these skills, while others will be new to you.

Some of the skills that scientists use are posing questions, making observations and inferences, developing hypotheses, designing experiments, collecting data and making measurements, interpreting data, and drawing conclusions. Sometimes scientists make models to help them understand the problem they are trying to solve. Scientists also must use the skill of communication in their work.

Posing Questions In the 1800s, scientists used scientific inquiry to study glaciers. Glaciers are huge masses of ice. They are usually found on and around high mountains, such as the Alps in Switzerland.

Two hundred years ago, scientists knew very little about glaciers. Some scientists thought that glaciers could move. Others doubted that these huge masses of ice could move at all. So some scientists in Switzerland decided to investigate.

Scientists usually begin an investigation with a question about something that is unexplained. The Swiss scientists studying glaciers asked, "Do glaciers move?"

Making Observations and Inferences Look at the glacier in Figure 2. What color is it? What does its surface look like? As you answer these questions, you are using a science skill. You are making observations. The skill of **observation** involves using one or more of your senses—sight, hearing, smell, and sometimes taste—to gather information. In this case, you used your sense of sight to gather information about glaciers.

You may have observed a dark band in the glacier. If you could travel to this glacier and make more-detailed observations, you would find that this dark band is due to rocks in the ice. Where did the rocks come from? You might think that they came from nearby mountains. This statement is an **inference,** an interpretation based on observations and prior knowledge.

✓ *Checkpoint* *What is the difference between an observation and an inference?*

Figure 2 The Gorner glacier winds down from high peaks in the Swiss Alps. The dark bands in the glacier are pieces of rock broken off and picked up by the moving ice.

Thinking Like a Scientist

Addressing Naive Conceptions

Materials *beaker, water, hot plate*

Help students distinguish between making observations and inferences. Heat a beaker of water on a hot plate until the water boils. When the water has reached the boiling point, ask students to describe what they see. Students will likely say that the water is boiling. Ask them to describe what they see without using the word *boiling*. Students should describe observing bubbles forming inside the water, rising, and breaking at the surface. Students may also be able to observe a fog-like layer above the surface of the water. Point out that these are observations, and the statement that the water is boiling is an inference based on observing the hot, bubbling water and using what they know about boiling. **learning modality: visual**

Using the Visuals: Figure 2

Have students identify the glacier and the dark bands in the photograph. Ask how the glacier differs from the mountains around it. **learning modality: visual**

Background

For students, the most important task is learning to distinguish *observations* (evidence gathered through the senses) from *inferences* (logical thinking about those observations). Students often mistake one for the other. By making the distinction, they take a major step in modeling the way scientists think. Use the Addressing Naive Conceptions activity on this page to help students practice making the distinction.

Answers to Self-Assessment

Caption Question

Figure 1 Questions may include, "What do fish need to eat?", "Is the temperature of the water important?", and similar questions.

✓ *Checkpoint*

An observation is information that is gathered by the senses. An inference is an interpretation of an observation and involves a person's prior knowledge.

Ongoing Assessment

Skills Check Place a glass of ice water on a table at the front of the class. Have students write 3 observations and 3 inferences about it.

11

Thinking Like a Scientist, continued

Building Inquiry Skills: Developing Hypotheses

Materials *beaker, water, hot plate, ice cube, tongs*

Heat water in a beaker on a hot plate. When the water is boiling, ask students: **What does boiling water feel like?** *(Very hot)* Show students an ice cube. Ask: **What does an ice cube feel like?** *(Very cold)* On the board write, "When an ice cube is placed into boiling water…" and invite students to suggest endings for the sentence. List the endings on the board. Tell students that these statements are hypotheses. Discuss how the hypotheses can be tested. Then use the tongs to place the ice cube into the boiling water so that students can see if their hypotheses are supported. **learning modality: visual**

Including All Students

At the time that the first humans landed on the moon, several areas of the United States had heavy rains. Some people said that the rain was caused by the moon landing. Ask students if this is a valid hypothesis. *(No, because it is based on a coincidence, and even if the observation was repeated, this would not support the hypothesis. Also, this is not a testable hypothesis because all the relevant variables could never be controlled in a way that would establish a causal relationship between moon landings and rain.)* **learning modality: logical/ mathematical**

Building Inquiry Skills: Communicating

Divide students into two groups. Have one group take the part of the Swiss scientists who believed that glaciers did not move. Have the other group take the part of the Swiss scientists who believed that glaciers did move. Have each group list observations that led to its point of view. **learning modality: verbal**

Developing Hypotheses After posing a question, scientists often gather information or make observations. They then use this information to form a hypothesis. A **hypothesis** is a possible explanation for a set of observations or answer to a scientific question. In science, a hypothesis must be something that can be tested. A hypothesis can be tested by observation or experimentation. Scientists do not accept a hypothesis after just one test. Repeated tests must provide evidence that supports the hypothesis.

People in the Alps had long observed boulders in the valleys below glaciers. Did that mean that moving ice had carried the boulders? Such observations led scientists to propose the following hypothesis: *Glaciers move slowly over the land.*

Designing Controlled Experiments

How do scientists test a hypothesis? In many cases, they carry out experiments. In setting up an experiment, scientists think about all the factors that could affect the outcome of the experiment. These factors are called **variables.** The scientists change one variable, called the **manipulated variable,** or independent variable. They then observe how this change affects another variable. The variable that changes as a result is called the **responding variable,** or dependent variable.

There can be many variables in an experiment. To be sure that changes in the manipulated variable alone are responsible for any changes in the responding variable, scientists must test only one variable at a time. They control all of the other variables so that they do not change. An experiment in which there is only one manipulated variable and all other variables are kept constant is called a **controlled experiment.**

Figure 3 shows an example of a controlled experiment. The student is investigating whether the shape of an ice block affects how quickly it melts. The manipulated variable in the experiment is the shape of the ice. The responding variable is the time it takes for the ice to melt. Notice that all other variables are kept constant. The two blocks of ice are exposed to identical sources of heat, contain the same volume of water, and are on identical surfaces. Because all other variables have been controlled, any difference in melting times must be due to the difference in shape.

Figure 3 In this controlled experiment, the shape of the ice block is the manipulated variable. The time it takes for melting to occur is the responding variable. *Developing Hypotheses What hypothesis is being investigated?*

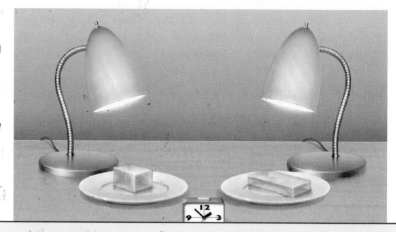

12

Background

The term *hypothesis* refers to a proposed explanation that can be tested. In science, many hypotheses are developed as inferences, that is, through logical thinking. But some hypotheses have resulted from imagination, creative leaps, chance events, and even dreams. The key characteristic of a hypothesis is that it is testable. Use the Building Inquiry Skills and the Including All Students activities on this page to help students practice identifying a valid hypothesis.

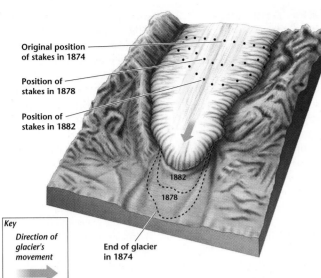

Original position
of stakes in 1874

Position of
stakes in 1878

Position of
stakes in 1882

1882

1878

Key
Direction of
glacier's
movement

End of glacier
in 1874

Figure 4 To measure the movement of a glacier, scientists drove a row of stakes into the glacier. They then measured how much the stakes moved in relation to the rocky sides of the valley. *Interpreting Diagrams* Which part of the glacier appears to be moving the fastest? How can you tell?

Ask students: **How did the edge of the glacier change from 1874 to 1882?** (*The glacier's edge appeared to move back.*) **Suggest hypotheses that could explain this observation.** (*Possible hypotheses: the glacier is moving backward; the glacier is melting at its edge.*) Then direct students to look at the stakes in the glacier. Ask: **How have the positions of the stakes in the glacier changed?** (*They moved downhill.*) **How does this observation affect hypotheses about the change at the edge of the glacier?** (*If the stakes moved downhill, the hypothesis that the glacier moved uphill is unlikely.*) **learning modality: visual**

In the real world, conducting a controlled experiment can be difficult or impossible. The objects studied by some scientists can be very large. And some processes that scientists study can take millions of years. In cases like these, scientists test hypotheses through observation and measurement, as did the scientists who studied glaciers.

Figure 4 shows how the Swiss scientists investigated the movement of a glacier. They placed a row of stakes across the glacier, and went back over time to see if the stakes moved.

☑ *Checkpoint* *What is a variable?*

Collecting Data and Making Measurements The facts, figures, and other evidence collected in an experiment are called **data.** Scientists know that it is important to record all data carefully. That way they have a permanent account of what happened in an experiment.

Some data can be in the form of descriptions. For example, the scientists studying glaciers may have examined rocks and compared them with rocks from nearby mountains.

Much of the data collected in experiments is in the form of measurements. The scientists studying the glacier noted the original positions of the stakes in the glacier and then measured how far the stakes moved from these positions.

Scientists around the world all use the same system of measurement. This system is called the International System of Units. The name is abbreviated as SI, which comes from the French name for the system (*Système International d'Unités*).

SI is based on the metric system of measurements. If you have ever measured length in meters, you have used SI units. To learn about making measurements in science, see pages 582–583 in the Skills Handbook.

Answers to Self-Assessment

Caption Questions

Figure 3 Thin ice melts faster than thick ice.

Figure 4 The area just to the right of center appears to be moving fastest because the stakes moved farther in that location.

☑ *Checkpoint*

A variable is one of the factors in an experiment that can change.

Thinking Like a Scientist, continued

Using the Visuals: Figure 5

Have students look at the data table and line graph. Ask: **What kind of information is shown?** (*How the size of the glacier changed.*) **How is the size of the glacier recorded?** (*Its area is recorded in hectares.*) **How did the area change?** (*It decreased.*) **Was the rate of change always the same?** (*No*) **How can you tell?** (*The line on the graph falls more steeply between 1900 and 1945 than it does in any other time span.*)

Addressing Naive Conceptions

Ask students: **Do you think every experiment allows the scientist to draw a conclusion?** (*Responses may vary, but most students may believe this is true.*) Help students understand that not all experiments or data collections will lead to a firm conclusion. Some can be labeled as "inconclusive." This, as well as negative support of a hypothesis, can be a good result. Scientists must then look for other factors and other ways to test their hypotheses. Sometimes a different approach can lead to a new discovery.
learning modality: verbal

Interpreting Data After scientists collect their data, they then need to interpret, or find the meaning of, these data. Finding a way to display the data is part of interpreting it. One way to display data is in the form of a diagram, such as the one in Figure 4. Another way to display data is in data tables and graphs, as in Figure 5.

Interpreting data involves looking for patterns, or trends. The study of the Swiss glacier produced two sets of data. The positions of the stakes at three different times make up one set of data. Look back at Figure 4. What pattern do you see in these positions?

The other set of data is the three positions of the lower end of the glacier. There's a pattern here, too. How did the end of the glacier change over the years of the study?

Drawing Conclusions Once scientists have reviewed their data, they are ready to draw a conclusion. The data may support the hypothesis.

Or the data may show that the hypothesis was incorrect. Sometimes, no conclusion can be reached, and more data must be collected.

The Swiss scientists studying glaciers concluded that their data supported their hypothesis. But the data also revealed a surprise. As the glacier was moving downhill, it was also getting shorter at its lower end. A surprising find like this one can lead scientists to form new hypotheses and try new experiments. What hypothesis could you propose to explain the change at the lower end of the glacier?

In the example of the glacier, the evidence collected by the scientists supported their hypothesis. But what if it hadn't supported the hypothesis? Would that mean the experiment was a failure? Definitely not! Eliminating a false hypothesis is as important as supporting another hypothesis. And what may seem like a failure often turns out to be the first step on the path to a new discovery.

Change in Size of a Glacier Over Time

Year	Area of Glacier (hectares*)
1850	380
1900	370
1927	240
1945	160
1993	135

*1 hectare = 10,000 square meters

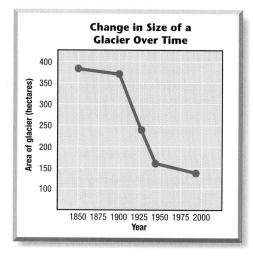

Figure 5 The data in this data table were collected by scientists studying a glacier in Glacier National Park in Montana. When the data are graphed, the graph reveals a pattern or trend. *Interpreting Graphs* What pattern do you see in the graph?

Background

The words *inference* and *conclusion* have the same meaning in everyday language, and one term is often used to define the other. In science, however, *inference* is often used as the broader term, while *conclusion* is used for the culminating, formal inference of an experiment. In keeping with this distinction, *drawing a conclusion* refers here to making a statement that summarizes how experimental data relates to the hypothesis tested.

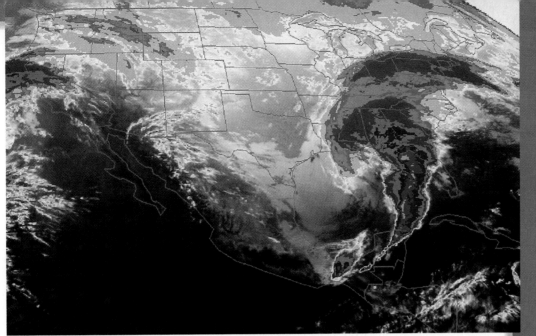

Including all Students

Ask students to list objects that are too large to study in the classroom. *(Answers will vary, but may include skyscrapers, airplanes, ships, the moon, or planets.)* Than ask what kinds of models might help students to study these objects? *(Three-dimensional models, drawings, maps, blueprints of buildings, ships, or planes.)* **learning modality: verbal**

Cultural Diversity

Ask students why studying one or more languages other than English might be useful to scientists. *(Possible answers: To communicate with scientists from other places in the world, to study work done by scientists in other languages, to facilitate field work or research in another country.)* **learning modality: verbal**

Making Models and Simulations What would you do if you wanted to show your classmates what a glacier looks like? You can't take a glacier into your classroom, but you can use a model to show what the glacier looks like. The model could be a three-dimensional scale model. It could also be a diagram or a map. Many scientists today use computers to make models of complex objects or events.

Sometimes scientists use simulations to test a hypothesis. A simulation is a model that imitates a real-world situation.

Scientists working in modern laboratories have used simulations to study how glaciers move. The scientists studied samples of hot metal to see how the metal changes shape when under great pressure. The changes in the metal simulate the movement of the slowly flowing ice in a glacier. Using such simulations helps scientists develop new hypotheses and new ways of testing them.

Communicating Information

For scientists, communicating information is an important part of scientific inquiry. By sharing ideas and experimental findings, scientists learn from each other.

Scientists communicate with each other by writing articles for scientific journals. Scientists also go to scientific meetings. There they talk about their own research and listen to talks about the research of other scientists. Scientists also use the Internet to communicate with one another.

Scientific discoveries also are shared with the general public—people who are not scientists. In these communications, scientists must use simpler terms that can be easily understood by everyone. Communicating with nonscientists is especially important in areas that affect people's health and safety.

☑ *Checkpoint* **What are some ways in which scientists communicate information?**

Figure 6 A weather map is a model of changing conditions in Earth's atmosphere. This map, based on satellite data, shows a storm over the eastern United States.

Answers to Self-Assessment

Caption Question

Figure 5 The size of the glacier decreased over time.

☑ *Checkpoint*

Scientists communicate by writing articles, attending scientific meetings, and by using the Internet.

Ongoing Assessment

Skills Check Have students draw flowcharts that show how scientists test a hypothesis. *(Sample flowchart: design a controlled experiment → collect data → interpret data → draw conclusions)*

Scientific Laws and Theories

Scientific Laws and Theories

Scientific inquiry often begins with observations. Scientists have noticed that some events in nature always happen the same way. What happens if you hold a ball in your hand and let go of it? Has this happened every time you've tried it? You have made the same observation over and over again—the ball falls to the ground.

When scientists have observed an event so often that they are sure it will always happen, they call the observation a scientific law. A **scientific law** is a statement that describes what scientists expect to happen every time under a particular set of conditions. In the case of the falling ball, the scientific law has to do with gravity.

Sometimes a large body of related information can be explained by a single major idea. If that idea is supported by many tests, it may develop into a scientific theory. A **scientific theory** is a well-tested scientific concept that explains a wide range of observations. An accepted scientific theory has withstood repeated tests. However, it is possible that additional tests could contradict the theory. If that happens, scientists will change the theory or abandon it.

Have you ever heard someone say, "Well, my theory is . . ."? In everyday language, people often use the word *theory* to refer to any explanation or personal opinion. Remember that, in science, a theory is an explanation that has been thoroughly tested. It is not merely a guess.

☑ *Checkpoint* **What is a scientific theory?**

Laboratory Safety

An important part of scientific inquiry is carrying out experiments. Scientists don't just go into a laboratory and start experimenting. They plan their steps carefully and make sure their procedures are safe.

As you use this textbook, you will conduct many experiments. As you do this, it is very important to think about safety. Always follow your teacher's instructions. Follow the steps you are given and use only the materials your teacher tells you to use. **Safe laboratory practices protect both you and your classmates from injury. In addition, your lab investigations will be more successful if you follow safety guidelines.**

Before conducting any experiments, review Appendix A on pages 597–599. Be sure that you understand the safety symbols and rules.

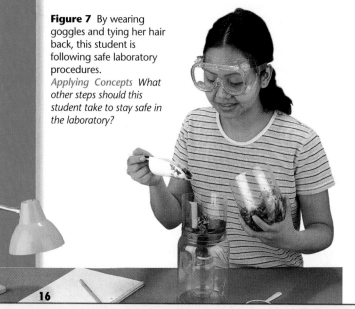

Figure 7 By wearing goggles and tying her hair back, this student is following safe laboratory procedures. *Applying Concepts What other steps should this student take to stay safe in the laboratory?*

16

Speeding Up Evaporation

Evaporation is the process by which water vapor enters Earth's atmosphere from the ocean and other surface waters. Rates of evaporation determine the amount of moisture in the atmosphere. Atmospheric moisture in turn affects the formation of clouds and helps to determine whether it will rain.

Problem

What factors increase the rate at which water evaporates?

Materials

water	plastic dropper
2 plastic petri dishes	1 petri dish cover
3 index cards	paper towels
stopwatch	lamp

Procedure

Part 1 Effect of Heat

1. How do you think heating a water sample will affect how fast it evaporates? Record your hypothesis.
2. Place each petri dish on an index card.
3. Add a single drop of water to each of the petri dishes. Try to make the two drops the same size.
4. Position the lamp over one of the dishes as a heat source. Turn on the light. Make sure the light does not shine on the other dish. **CAUTION:** *The light bulb will become very hot. Avoid touching the bulb or getting water on it.*
5. Observe the dishes every 3 minutes to see which sample evaporates faster. Record your result.

Part 2 Effect of Wind

6. How do you think fanning the water will affect how fast it evaporates? Record your hypothesis.
7. Dry both petri dishes and place them over the index cards. Add a drop of water to each dish as you did in Step 3.
8. Use an index card to fan one of the dishes for 5 minutes. Be careful not to fan the other dish.
9. Observe the dishes to see which sample evaporates faster. Record your result.

Analyze and Conclude

1. Did the evidence support both hypotheses? If not, which hypothesis was not supported?
2. Make a general statement about factors that increase the rate at which water evaporates.
3. **Think About It** What everyday experiences helped you make your hypotheses at the beginning of each experiment? Explain how hypotheses differ from guesses.

Design an Experiment

How do you think increasing the surface area of a water sample will affect how fast it evaporates? Write your hypothesis and then design an experiment to test it. Check your plan with your teacher before you begin.

17

---

3. **Think About It** Sample response: how quickly a puddle dries in the sun or wind. Hypotheses are based on information gathered through study or experience, whereas guesses are based only on feelings.

Safety

Caution students to be careful when handling a lamp, because the bulb gets hot and can explode if splashed with water. Review the safety guidelines in Appendix A.

Design an Experiment

A typical hypothesis might suggest that increasing the surface area of a water sample increases the rate of evaporation. A typical design might suggest pouring equal amounts of water into a deep bowl and a shallow pan and then exposing both to the same amount of heat or wind.

Speeding Up Evaporation

Preparing for Inquiry

Key Concept Various factors influence the rate at which water evaporates, including exposure to a heat source and the presence of wind.

Skills Objectives Students will be able to:
◆ develop hypotheses about factors affecting the evaporation of water;
◆ control variables to determine the effect of different factors;
◆ draw conclusions about how various factors affect evaporation.

Time 40 minutes

Advance Planning Choose locations for each group's dishes for each part.

Guiding Inquiry

Invitation Ask: **Do you think evaporation occurs faster in a desert or a forest?** *(In a desert)* **Does it occur faster on a windy day or a calm day?** *(On a windy day)*

Introducing the Procedure
Have students read through the complete procedure. Then ask: **What variable is being tested in each part?** *(In Part 1, exposure to a heat source; in Part 2, the presence of wind)*

Troubleshooting the Experiment
Emphasize that in each part, both dishes should contain drops of water that are the same size.

Expected Outcome
In Part 1, water under a lamp evaporates faster. In Part 2 water fanned by the index card evaporates faster.

Analyze and Conclude
1. Answers will vary. Some students may have foreseen the results correctly in each case and confirmed their hypothesis through the experiment.
2. Factors that increase the rate of evaporation of water include exposure to a heat source and exposure to wind.

Branches of Science

Building Inquiry Skills: Inferring

Have students look at the photographs of the scientists on pages 18 and 19, and ask them to identify the branch of science for each career. Ask volunteers to describe the activites shown and infer the purpose of each activity. **learning modality: visual**

Addressing Naive Conceptions

The names of various careers may be misleading to some students. Point out that a meteorologist, for example, does not study meteors, but weather and weather patterns. An oceanographer may not study the ocean at all, but rather fresh water and climate. Ask students to name some careers and what scientists in that field study. Be sure to correct any misconceptions. **learning modality: auditory/verbal**

Technology and the Internet

Demonstration

Demonstrate, or have a computer teacher or math teacher demonstrate, how a computer can be used to plot the points of a scatter plot graph and draw the line of best fit. Before the actual demonstration, give students the coordinates of the points and have them make their own scatter plots on graph paper. Then ask them to draw the line of best fit themselves. Later they can compare their graphs to the graph drawn by the computer. Discuss also the relative ease of obtaining the results by hand and through the computer. Which was faster? Which was more reliable? **learning modality: logical/mathematical**

ACTIVITY

Branches of Science

There are four main branches of science—physical science, Earth science, life science, and environmental science. Physical science includes the study of motion, energy, sound, light, electricity, magnetism, and the matter that makes up everything around you.

Earth science is the study of Earth and its place in the universe. This includes studying landforms, oceans, rocks and minerals, weather, and the planets that make up the solar system.

Life science is the study of living things, including plants, animals, and microscopic life forms. Life scientists also study how living things interact with each other and with their surroundings.

Environmental science is the study of how human activities affect Earth's land, air, water, and living things. Environmental scientists try to find solutions for problems that result from the use of Earth's natural resources. Some problems that environmental scientists study are pollution and global warming.

The branches of science are not separate from one another. For example, Kishor Mehta and the other engineers he works with are mainly physical scientists. They study the effects of the force of wind on various objects. But to understand wind, they have to study weather, which is part of Earth science.

In Figure 8, you can see some of the work that scientists do. You may think of scientists as people who work in laboratories. But as you can see, scientists work in all kinds of places—from the bottom of the ocean to outer space. Scientists test water supplies to make sure the water is clean enough to drink. They design safer cars and buildings. They search the rain forests to find new plants and animals. Wherever people are asking questions and searching for answers, they are using the skills of scientific inquiry.

☑ *Checkpoint* *Which branch of science would be involved in studying volcanoes and earthquakes?*

Figure 8 Scientists seek answers to questions in a wide variety of places using diverse skills and tools.

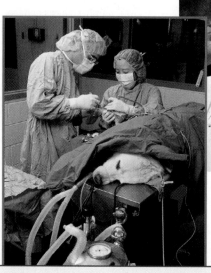

Veterinarians ▶
Veterinarians are doctors that treat animals. They care for animals ranging from house pets to farm and zoo animals.

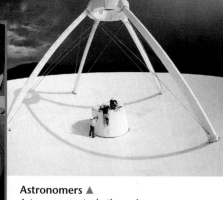

Astronomers ▲
Astronomers study the universe. These astronomers are using a radio telescope to detect radio signals from distant stars and galaxies.

18

Technology and the Internet

Today, many scientists use the latest technology in their research. From high-powered microscopes that can look at tiny viruses to huge telescopes that search the sky for faraway stars, scientists have many tools that they can use.

Most modern scientific instruments are connected to computers, which allow scientists to quickly record, store, and analyze the data they collect. You have already read how important computers are for creating models and simulations of scientific events.

Computers also help scientists communicate information to each other and to the public. You can find large amounts of information about current research and discoveries in science on the Internet. Many government agencies maintain Web sites that are excellent sources of scientific information. Hospitals and universities that have research centers often have Web sites, too. The publisher of this textbook maintains a Web site, **www.phschool.com**. This site includes links to other Web sites that may help you as you study science.

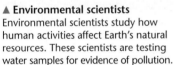

▲ Environmental scientists
Environmental scientists study how human activities affect Earth's natural resources. These scientists are testing water samples for evidence of pollution.

▼ Research chemists
Research chemists study the compositon and structure of matter as well as matter's physical and chemical properties. Their applied research is often aimed at developing new materials for a wide range of uses.

Including All Students

Have students form four groups and assign each group one of the careers highlighted on the pages. Encourage each group to list what they know about the work "their" scientist does and what they would like to learn about the career. Have groups share their knowledge and questions with the whole class. Some questions might be: What kind of education is needed by each scientist? Where might each scientist work? What is the pay scale for jobs in this type of science? Have each group prepare a notebook with information about their scientist's career. **cooperative learning**

Answers to Self-Assessment

☑ *Checkpoint*
The study of volcanoes and earthquakes is included in Earth science.

Performance Assessment

Writing Have students select a scientific career, name the branch of science, and list the scientific skills needed for that career. Be sure students give examples for each skill, such as: observing—the chemist would observe the reaction of the chemicals to the tested substance.

Reviewing Content

Multiple Choice

1. b **2.** d **3.** a **4.** d **5.** b

True or False

6. inference **7.** true **8.** true
9. simulation **10.** true

Checking Concepts

11. Students should describe science as a way of knowing about the natural world based on observations and logical reasoning.

12. Scientists cannot always use controlled experiments because some of the things that they study are very large, or are located in space, or may involve processes that take a very long time or happened millions of years ago.

13. A hypothesis is a possible explanation for an observation or an answer to a scientific question. A hypothesis can be tested by observation or experiment. A scientific theory is a concept that explains a wide range of observations. If scientists test a hypothesis repeatedly and find that the evidence supports the hypothesis, that hypothesis may be accepted as a scientific theory.

14. Scientists interpret the data collected during an experiment to determine whether the data support their hypothesis. Scientists can then draw a conclusion about the hypothesis.

15. Following safety rules ensures that nobody involved in the experiment will be injured. It also protects equipment from damage.

16. The four main branches of science are Earth science, life science, physical science, and environmental science. Earth scientists study Earth and its place in the universe. Life scientists study all living things. Physical scientists study motion, energy, sound, light, and particles. Environmental scientists study how human activity affects the Earth.

17. Answers may vary. An example might be: I saw baby geese flapping their wings before they could fly. I think they do this to build up strength in their flying muscles, so when they can start to fly they will be able to.

Study Guide

Key Ideas

◆ Science is both a way of learning about the natural world and the knowledge gained from that process.

◆ Scientific methods generally include posing questions, making observations and inferences, developing hypotheses, designing experiments, collecting data and making measurements, interpreting data, and drawing conclusions. Scientists also may make models and use the skill of communication in their work.

◆ The System of International Units (SI) is the standard system of measurement in science.

◆ A scientific law describes what scientists expect to happen every time under a particular set of conditions. A scientific theory is a well-tested scientific concept that explains a wide range of observations.

◆ In experiments and activities, it is very important to think about safety. Always follow your teacher's instructions on safety in the laboratory.

Key Terms

science	manipulated variable
scientific inquiry	responding variable
observation	controlled experiment
inference	scientific law
hypothesis	scientific theory
variable	

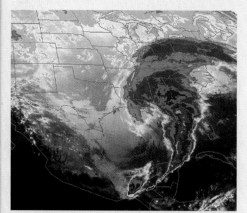

Reviewing Content

 Review key concepts online using iText at www.phschool.com

Multiple Choice

Choose the letter of the best answer.

1. Scientists seek to answer questions about the natural world in a process of
　a. modeling.　　　**b.** scientific inquiry.
　c. predicting.　　　**d.** developing hypotheses.

2. An explanation that can be tested by observation or experimentation is a(n)
　a. experiment.　　　**b.** scientific theory.
　c. scientific fact.　　**d.** hypothesis.

3. One of the factors that can change in an experiment is called a(n)
　a. variable.　　　**b.** theory.
　c. hypothesis.　　**d.** observation.

4. One way in which scientists test a hypothesis is by
　a. asking questions.
　b. drawing conclusions.
　c. interpreting data.
　d. conducting a controlled experiment.

5. A scientist who studies weather and climate is a(n)
　a. life scientist.
　b. Earth scientist.
　c. physical scientist.
　d. environmental scientist.

True or False

If the statement is true, write true. If it is false, change the underlined word or words to make the statement true.

6. A <u>variable</u> is an interpretation of an observation.

7. The facts and figures that a scientist collects in an experiment are called <u>data</u>.

8. If an experiment fails to support a <u>scientific theory</u>, scientists will change the theory or abandon it.

9. A <u>hypothesis</u> is a model that imitates a real-world situation.

10. <u>Environmental scientists</u> study the effects of human activities on Earth's land, air, water, and living things.

Checking Concepts

11. In your own words, explain briefly what science is.
12. Why is it sometimes difficult to use controlled experiments to test hypotheses?
13. What is the difference between a hypothesis and a scientific theory?
14. Explain how a scientist would use the data gathered through a controlled experiment.
15. Explain the importance of following safety rules in laboratory experiments.
16. What are the four main branches of science? Briefly describe what each type of scientist studies.
17. **Writing to Learn** Give an example of an observation of the natural world that you have made. Then give an example of an inference that you made based on that observation. Explain.

Thinking Critically

18. **Problem Solving** You may have heard the saying, "Red sky at night/Sailor's delight." This expression is a hypothesis: A colorful red sunset means there will be fair weather the next day. Describe a scientific method of testing this hypothesis.
19. **Relating Cause and Effect** In a controlled experiment, why do scientists try to control all of the variables except one?
20. **Making Judgments** As a result of just one experiment, a scientist finds evidence that supports a hypothesis. Should other scientists around the world accept this hypothesis? Explain your answer.
21. **Classifying** Which branch of science would investigate the surface temperature of a star? Which branch would investigate the chemical makeup of a food?

Read the passage. Then answer Questions 22–25.

It may surprise you to learn that the climate in a large city can be different from the climate just outside the city. Climate is the average, year-to-year weather conditions in a region. Meteorologists have collected data on these climate differences. The data show that the climate in a city is often warmer and wetter than the climate in the nearby countryside. Cities are also less sunny and less windy than the country around them.

Why are cities warmer? One reason is that buildings and paved surfaces absorb and store more of the sun's energy than do grass, crops, and trees. Another reason is that cars, factories, heating, and air conditioning in cities all give off heat.

Scientists think several factors cause increased rainfall in cities. One hypothesis is that the built-up areas of a city form an obstacle to passing storms. As a result, the storms take longer to move over the city, allowing more rain to fall.

22. The best title for this reading selection is
    A Sunny Weather Ahead
    B Meteorologists at Work
    C City Climates
    D What Causes Storms?
23. Meteorologists found that the climate in a city differs from the climate in the country by
    F asking city residents.
    G collecting data.
    H observing clouds.
    J performing controlled experiments.
24. How would you predict a city could lower its outdoor temperature in the summer?
    A by building more factories
    B by having more parks with grass and trees
    C by putting more cars on the road
    D by adding more air conditioners
25. The idea that a city's buildings can increase rainfall by slowing down a passing storm is an example of a
    F variable.   G scientific theory.
    H determining factor. J hypothesis.

Thinking Critically

18. Answers may vary. Students may say that you would need to observe the color of sunsets over time and then record what kinds of weather occurred on each following day. If fair weather consistently followed a colorful sunset, then you could conclude that the evidence supported the hypothesis.
19. By controlling all variables but one, scientists can draw a valid conclusion. If more than one variable is changing, scientists cannot tell which variable is the cause of the results that are observed.
20. Other scientists should not accept the hypothesis. For a hypothesis to be accepted, other scientists must be able to repeat the experiment many times and obtain the same results.
21. Investigating the temperature of a star involves Earth science; the chemical make up of a food is a subject for life science.

Test Preparation
22. C 23. G 24. B 25. J

Matter and Energy

Sections	Time	Student Edition Activities	Other Activities	
CHAPTER PROJECT **Comparing Brands X, Y, and Z** p. 23	Ongoing (2 weeks)	TEKS: 6.1A; 6.2A, B, C, D; 6.3B Check Your Progress, pp. 33, 45, 50 Present Your Project, p. 53	TE	Chapter 1 Project Notes, pp. 22–23
1 Describing Matter and Energy pp. 24–33 TEKS: 6.7A, B; 6.8A; 6.9A 1.1.1 Define matter and energy. 1.1.2 Explain that substances can be identified or classified by their physical and chemical properties. 1.1.3 Explain the differences among elements, compounds, and mixtures. 1.1.4 Distinguish between physical and chemical changes. 1.1.5 Identify different forms of energy, and give examples of energy transformations that affect matter.	3 periods/ 1½ blocks	TEKS: 6.1A; 6.4A **Discover** What is a Mixture?, p. 24 **Try This** Alike or Different?, p. 26 **Sharpen Your Skills** Inferring, p. 31	TE TE TE TE	Real-Life Learning, pp. 27, 32 Building Inquiry Skills: Inferring, p. 28, Demonstration, p. 30 Including All Students, pp. 30, 31
2 Measuring Matter pp. 34–40 TEKS: 6.7B 1.2.1 Explain the difference between weight and mass. 1.2.2 Calculate the density of substances using SI units for mass and volume.	3 periods/ 1½ blocks	TEKS: 6.2A, B, C, D, E; 6.3E; 6.4A **Discover** Which Has More Mass?, p. 34 **Try This** Bubble Time, p. 35 **Science at Home,** p. 39 **Skills Lab: Interpreting Data** Making Sense of Density, p. 40	TE TE TE LM	Building Inquiry Skills: Applying Concepts, p. 35; Making Measurements, p. 38 Integrating Mathematics, p. 36 Including All Students, p. 37 1, "Determining the Density of Liquids"
3 Particles of Matter pp. 41–45 1.3.1 Identify atoms as the smallest particles of an element. 1.3.2 Describe Dalton's theory of atoms. 1.3.3 Identify chemical bonds as the force holding atoms together in molecules.	2 periods/ 1 block	TEKS: 6.3C, E **Discover** What's in the Box?, p. 41	TE	Demonstration, p. 43
4 INTEGRATING EARTH SCIENCE Elements From Earth pp. 46–50 TEKS: 6.7B 1.4.1 Describe how the density of gold allows it to be panned. 1.4.2 Explain that a chemical reaction is needed to obtain an element from one of its compounds.	2 periods/ 1 block	TEKS: 6.1A, B; 6.2A, B, C, D; 6.4A **Discover** How Can You Separate Bolts From Sand?, p. 46 **Real-World Lab: How It Works** Isolating Copper, pp. 48–49	TE	Demonstration, p. 50
Study Guide/Chapter Assessment pp. 51–53	1 period/ ½ block	PLM Provides blackline masters for Probeware labs	ISAB	Provides teaching and review of all inquiry skills

Key: **CTB** Computer Test Bank
CUT Chapter and Unit Tests
ELL Teacher's ELL Handbook

CHAPTER PLANNING GUIDE

 The Resource Pro® CD-ROM provides flexibility for planning the instruction for any type of schedule.

Program Resources	Assessment Strategies	Media and Technology
UR Chapter 1 Project Teacher Notes, pp. 8–9 UR Chapter 1 Project Overview and Worksheets, pp. 10–13	SE Performance Assessment: Present Your Project, p. 53 TE Check Your Progress, pp. 33, 45, 50 UR Chapter 1 Project Scoring Rubric, p. 14	Science Explorer at www.phschool.com Student Edition on Audio CD, English-Spanish, Chapter 1
UR 1-1 Section Lesson Plan, p. 15 UR 1-1 Section Summary, p. 16 UR 1-1 Review and Reinforce, p. 17 UR 1-1 Enrich, p. 18	SE Section 1 Review, p. 33 TE Ongoing Assessment, pp. 25, 27, 29, 31 TE Performance Assessment, p. 33	
UR 1-2 Section Lesson Plan, p. 19 UR 1-2 Section Summary, p. 20 UR 1-2 Review and Reinforce, p. 21 UR 1-2 Enrich, p. 22 UR Skills Lab blackline masters, pp. 31–32	SE Section 2 Review, p. 39 TE Ongoing Assessment, pp. 35, 37 TE Performance Assessment, p. 39	Physical Science Videodisc Unit 6, Side 1, "Density" Life Science Videodisc Unit 1, Side 1, "The Metric System" Videotape Grade 6, Unit 1, "Density"; "The Metric System" Lab Activity Videotapes, Tape 1
UR 1-3 Section Lesson Plan, p. 23 UR 1-3 Section Summary, p. 24 UR 1-3 Review and Reinforce, p. 25 UR 1-3 Enrich, p. 26	SE Section 3 Review, p. 45 TE Ongoing Assessment, p. 43 TE Performance Assessment, p. 45	Physical Science Videodisc Unit 1, Side 1, "Rutherford's Experiment" Videotape Grade 6, Unit 1, "Rutherford's Experiment" Transparency 1, "Models of Molecules"
UR 1-4 Section Lesson Plan, p. 27 UR 1-4 Section Summary, p. 28 UR 1-4 Review and Reinforce, p. 29 UR 1-4 Enrich, p. 30 UR Real-World Lab blackline masters, pp. 33–35	SE Section 4 Review, p. 50 TE Ongoing Assessment, p. 47 TE Performance Assessment, p. 50	Physical Science Videodisc Unit 1, Side 1, "Ore What?" Videotape Grade 6, Unit 1, "Ore What?" Lab Activity Videotapes, Tape 1
ELL Provides multiple strategies for English language learners GRSW Provides worksheets to promote student comprehension of content RCA Provides strategies to improve science reading skills	SE Chapter 1 Study Guide/Assessment, pp. 51–53 PA Chapter 1 Assessment, pp. 5–7 CUT Chapter 1 Test, pp. 4–7 CTB Chapter 1 Test PHAS Provides standardized test preparation	Chapter 1 Computer Test Bank, Chapter 1 Test

GRSW Guided Reading and Study Workbook
ISAB Inquiry Skills Activity Book
LM Laboratory Manual

PA Performance Assessment
PHAS Prentice Hall Assessment System
PLM Probeware Lab Manual

RCA Reading in the Content Area
SE Student Edition

TE Teacher's Edition
UR Unit Resources

Student Edition Activities Planner

ACTIVITY	Time (minutes)	Materials — Quantities for one work group	Skills
Section 1			
Discover, p. 24	15	**Nonconsumable** small objects such as checkers, marbles, and paper clips of different colors and sizes	Inferring
Try This, p. 26	20	**Consumable** powdered sugar, salt, cornstarch, baking powder, water, vinegar **Nonconsumable** hand lens, plastic cup or test tube	Classifying
Sharpen your Skills, p. 31	15	**Consumable** vinegar, bromthymol blue indicator, antacid tablet, resealable plastic bag **Nonconsumable** plastic spoon	Inferring
Section 2			
Discover, p. 34	15	**Nonconsumable** triple-beam balance; objects of different weights such as rocks, plastic drinking cups, aluminum cans, pencils	Drawing Conclusions
Try This, p. 35	10	**Consumable** water, tape, flexible drinking straw **Nonconsumable** large container, clear plastic cup	Inferring
Science at Home, p. 39	home	**Consumable** water, salt, food coloring, clear plastic straw **Nonconsumable** two cups with flat bottoms	Communicating
Skills Lab, p. 40	30	**Consumable** water, paper towels **Nonconsumable** balance; wooden stick, approximately 6 cm long; ball of modeling clay, approximately 5 cm wide; crayon with paper covering removed; graduated cylinder, 100 mL, computer and spreadsheet program (optional)	Interpreting Data
Section 3			
Discover, p. 41	10	**Nonconsumable** shoe box containing one or more objects such as a candle, pencil, empty soda can, sock, marble, sponge	Inferring
Section 4			
Discover, p. 46	15	**Consumable** water, paper towels **Nonconsumable** dry sand, metal bolts, plastic tray or pie pan, bowl	Designing an Experiment
Real-World Lab, pp. 48–49	30	**Consumable** two paper clips; copper chloride solution (0.6 M), 50–100 mL; index card **Nonconsumable** glass jar, about 250 mL; wires with alligator clips or battery holder with wires; 6-volt battery	Observing, Inferring

A list of all materials required for the Student Edition activities can be found on pages T43–T49. You can obtain information about ordering materials by calling 1-800-848-9500 or by accessing the Science Explorer Internet site at **www.phschool.com**.

Texas Essential Knowledge and Skills

(6.1) Scientific processes. The student conducts field and laboratory investigations using safe, environmentally appropriate, and ethical practices. *(Project; Sections 1, 4)*
The student is expected to:
(A) demonstrate safe practices during field and laboratory investigations; and
(B) make wise choices in the use and conservation of resources and the disposal or recycling of materials.

(6.2) Scientific processes. The student uses scientific inquiry methods during field and laboratory investigations. *(Project; Sections 2, 4)*
The student is expected to:
(A) plan and implement investigative procedures including asking questions, formulating testable hypotheses, and selecting and using equipment and technology;
(B) collect data by observing and measuring;
(C) analyze and interpret information to construct reasonable explanations from direct and indirect evidence;
(D) communicate valid conclusions; and
(E) construct graphs, tables, maps, and charts using tools including computers to organize, examine, and evaluate data.

(6.3) Scientific processes. The student uses critical thinking and scientific problem solving to make informed decisions. *(Project; Sections 2, 3)*
The student is expected to:
(B) draw inferences based on data related to promotional materials for products and services;
(C) represent the natural world using models and identify their limitations;
(E) connect Grade 6 science concepts with the history of science and contributions of scientists.

(6.4) Scientific processes. The student knows how to use a variety of tools and methods to conduct science inquiry. *(Sections 1, 2, 4)*
The student is expected to:
(A) collect, analyze, and record information using tools including beakers, petri dishes, meter sticks, graduated cylinders, weather instruments, timing devices, hot plates, test tubes, safety goggles, spring scales, magnets, balances, microscopes, telescopes, thermometers, calculators, field equipment, compasses, computers, and computer probes.

(6.7) Science concepts. The student knows that substances have physical and chemical properties. *(Sections 1, 2, 4)*
The student is expected to:
(A) demonstrate that new substances can be made when two or more substances are chemically combined and compare the properties of the new substances to the original substances; and
(B) classify substances by their physical and chemical properties.

(6.8) Science concepts. The student knows that complex interactions occur between matter and energy. *(Section 1)*
The student is expected to:
(A) define matter and energy.

(6.9) Science concepts. The student knows that obtaining, transforming, and distributing energy affects the environment. *(Section 1)*
The student is expected to:
(A) identify energy transformations occurring during the production of energy for human use such as electrical energy to heat energy or heat energy to electrical energy.

Take It to the Net

 Interactive text at www.phschool.com

Science Explorer comes alive with iText.

- **Complete student text** is accessible from any computer with Internet access or a CD-ROM drive.
- **Animations, simulations, and videos** enhance student understanding and retention of concepts.
- **Self-tests and online study tools** assess student understanding.
- **Teacher management tools** help you make the most of this valuable resource.

STAY CURRENT with **SCIENCE NEWS**®

Find out the latest research and information about properties of matter at **www.phschool.com**.

Go to **www.phschool.com**. Select Texas on the navigation bar. Click on the Science icon. Then click on <u>Science Explorer</u> under PH@school.

Comparing Brands X, Y, and Z

TEKS: 6.1A; 6.2A, B, C, D; 6.3B

Many students consider chemistry and chemicals as divorced from everyday matter. They can see in this project how properties of matter can be investigated by comparing household products.

Purpose In this project, students design experiments to test a chosen property of three similar brands of a consumer product. The emphasis is on designing experiments that are easily duplicated and have reproducible results. The project should help students recognize the physical properties of everyday consumer products.

Skills Focus After completing the Chapter 1 Project, students will be able to
- pose questions about the properties of matter;
- design experiments in which they control variables, interpret data, and draw conclusions;
- compare results from having two people follow the same procedure;
- communicate their findings about their product to their classmates.

Project Time Line This project will take approximately two weeks to complete. During the first week, students brainstorm a list of products they might select to study, then design experiments and develop procedures to study a physical property of their products. Students should consult with a first partner to get advice about their experimental designs. During the beginning of the second week, students conduct their experiments, collect data, and draw conclusions. At this time, assign students new partners with whom they can exchange procedures and materials. Students then conduct their partners' experiments. At the end of the second week, students complete their projects, compare their results with those of their second partner, and present their work to the class.

Before beginning the project, see the Chapter 1 Project Teacher Notes on pages 8–9 in Unit 1 Resources for more details on carrying out the project. Distribute to students the Chapter 1 Project Overview,

CHAPTER 1
Matter and Energy

WEB ACTIVITY
www.phschool.com

22

Worksheets, and Scoring Rubric on pages 10–14 in Unit 1 Resources.

Possible Materials Possible materials include paper towels, batteries, tomato sauces, adhesive tapes, and laundry detergents. Encourage students to suggest and use other materials, but make sure they consider the cost of the products when they design their experiments. Students should also obtain enough materials so they and their partners can conduct experiments with repeated trials.

Launching the Project To introduce the project, bring two brands of a product into the classroom, for example, two brands of paper towels. Ask: **How could you determine which product works better?** *(Sample: Conduct an experiment that measures a physical property, such as the absorbency of the paper towels.)*

Allow time for students to read the description of the project in their text and the Chapter Project Overview on pages 10–11 in Unit 1 Resources. Then discuss the physical properties of matter and materials that could

Review experimental design with the class, as outlined in the Skills Handbook. Make sure students understand their results should be measurable. They should record their data in a data table, and may present the data in a graph at the end of the project. Students should be able to interpret their data and draw conclusions they can discuss in their class presentation.

CHAPTER 1 PROJECT

Comparing Brands X, Y, and Z

Before you get dressed, you probably spend time picking out clothes that go together. Clothes can come in a huge variety of colors. That's because researchers have developed many different dyes. Fibers, cloth, dyes, and water are just some examples of the materials that make up our world. The scientific name for these materials is matter. Every object in this photograph—actually, every object in the world—is an example of matter. Also, materials have different properties, such as color, shape, and hardness. It's the properties of a particular material that determine whether it is useful for a specific purpose.

Your Goal Compare a property of matter in three different brands of a consumer product.

To complete the project you will
◆ design a comparison test of a consumer-product property
◆ conduct the comparison test designed by a partner
◆ analyze the data you and a partner obtained
◆ follow the safety guidelines in Appendix A

Get Started As a class, brainstorm a list of different products to compare. For each product, write down several properties that could be compared, including those related to promotional claims of manufacturers. For example, paper towels may absorb different amounts of water. Review Designing an Experiment in the Skills Handbook.

Check Your Progress You'll be working on this project as you study this chapter. To keep your project on track, look for Check Your Progress boxes at the following points.
Section 1 Review, page 33: Design an experiment.
Section 3 Review, page 45: Perform the procedure.
Section 4 Review, page 50: Trade procedures with your partner.

Present Your Project At the end of the chapter (page 53), you and your second partner will try to repeat each other's procedures.

Dyes give fibers and other materials their distinctive colors.

TEKS

In addition to process TEKS, this chapter addresses these concept TEKS as they relate to the chapter's topics.

(6.7) The student knows that substances have physical and chemical properties. The student is expected to:
(A) demonstrate that new substances can be made when two or more substances are chemically combined and compare the properties of the new substances to the original substances; and
(B) classify substances by their physical and chemical properties.

(6.8) The student knows that complex interactions occur between matter and energy. The student is expected to:
(A) define matter and energy.

(6.9) The student knows that obtaining, transforming , and distributing energy affects the environment. The student is expected to:
(A) identify energy transformations occuring during the production of energy for human use such as electrical energy to heat energy or heat energy to electrical energy.

23

Program Resources

◆ **Unit 1 Resources** Chapter 1 Project Teacher Notes, pp. 8–9; Chapter 1 Project Overview and Worksheets, pp. 10–13

Media and Technology

🎧 **Student Edition on Audio CD**
English-Spanish, Chapter 1

WEB ACTIVITY www.phschool.com

You will find an Internet activity, chapter self-tests for students, and links to other chapter topics at this site.

Performance Assessment

The Chapter 1 Project Scoring Rubric on page 14 of Unit 1 Resources will help you evaluate how well students complete the Chapter 1 Project. Students are assessed on
◆ how well their procedures test the properties chosen to study and allow for conclusive tests in the time allowed;
◆ whether their experimental procedures are clearly written, easy to follow, and allow for repeated trials and quantifiable results;
◆ whether their presentations and data comparisons are thorough and well organized;
◆ how well they work with other students in exchanging procedures.
By sharing the Chapter 1 Project Scoring Rubric with students at the beginning of the project, you will make it clear to them what they are expected to do.

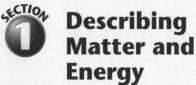

TEKS: 6.1A; 6.4A; 6.7A, B; 6.8A; 6.9A

Objectives

After completing the lesson, students will be able to
◆ define matter and energy;
◆ explain that substances can be identified or classified by their physical and chemical properties;
◆ explain the differences among elements, compounds, and mixtures;
◆ distinguish between physical and chemical changes;
◆ identify different forms of energy, and give examples of energy transformations that affect matter.

1 Engage/Explore

Activating Prior Knowledge

Ask students to describe how they identify unfamiliar objects. Challenge them to make a list of qualities they observe, such as size, color, shape, texture, smell, and weight. Then ask a volunteer to describe a common object to the class using descriptions from each category on the list. The other students should listen to the description and identify the object.

DISCOVER

Skills Focus inferring
Materials *small objects such as checkers, marbles, and paper clips of different colors and sizes*
Time 15 minutes
Tips Encourage students to think about the properties of objects as they sort the objects.
Think It Over Students will likely group objects of the same type together, for example checkers in one group, paper clips in another group. Students may infer that a substance has one set of properties, while a mixture may be made of parts that have different properties.

SECTION 1 Describing Matter and Energy

DISCOVER · ACTIVITY

What Is a Mixture?

1. Your teacher will give you a handful of objects, such as checkers, marbles, and paper clips of different sizes and colors.

2. Examine the objects. Then sort them into at least three groups. Each item should be grouped with other similar items.

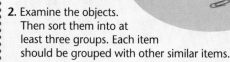

3. Describe the differences between the unsorted handful and the sorted groups of objects. Then make a list of the characteristics of each sorted group.

Think It Over
Inferring The handful of objects represents a mixture. Your sorted groups represent substances. Using your observations, infer what the terms *mixture* and *substance* mean.

GUIDE FOR READING

◆ Why is it useful to know the physical and chemical properties of matter?
◆ What happens when elements combine?
◆ How do physical and chemical changes differ?
◆ How are energy and changes in matter related?

Reading Tip Before you read, use the headings to outline the section. As you read, add information to your outline.

Key Terms matter • energy
• chemistry • substance
• physical property
• chemical property • element
• compound • mixture
• physical change
• chemical change

Y ou're watching a soccer game on an autumn afternoon. There's the whistle. The player kicks the ball, and it moves straight down the field into the net! You've just seen a goal. You've also just seen an example of the interaction of matter and energy. People use the words *matter* and *energy* in different ways. How often have you heard someone say, "As a matter of fact, . . ." or "Hey, what's the matter?" Maybe you've heard, "That team plays with a lot of energy!" Are these phrases familiar? What do the words mean in science?

Defining Matter and Energy

Scientists define **matter** as anything that has mass and takes up space. Mass is how much of something you have. As you learn more about matter and mass in this chapter, these terms will become more meaningful to you. Thinking about examples of matter is an easy way to get an idea of what matter is.

Examples of matter ▶

24

READING STRATEGIES

Reading Tip Help students preview the section and locate the blue-green main headings and purple sub-headings. Remind students to leave space below headings so that they can add information as they read. Students' outlines might begin like this:

I. Describing Matter and Energy
   A. Defining Matter and Energy
   B. Classifying Matter
      1. Physical Properties
      2. Chemical Properties
   C. Kinds of Matter
      1. Elements
      2. Compounds
      3. Mixtures

Matter is the "stuff" that makes up everything in the universe. Fruit, softballs, tools, animals, rain, flowers—all these are examples of matter. Even air is matter. It may be invisible, but you know it is there when you feel a cool breeze on your face or watch bubbles rise in a fish tank.

Energy is the ability to do work or cause change. Change can sometimes mean motion, that is, moving matter from one place to another. When you pound a nail, energy moves the hammer that drives the nail into a board. Energy even moves your hand. Change can also mean a change in form. A kettle of water that goes from room temperature to boiling on the stove tells you something about energy. Energy is always involved when changes in matter occur. The study of the properties of matter and how matter changes is called **chemistry.**

Classifying Matter by Its Physical and Chemical Properties

In addition to having mass and taking up space, matter has a variety of characteristics, or properties, that can differ. For example, matter can be solid, liquid, or gas. In turn, solid matter can be hard or soft, rough or smooth, square or round. Some kinds of matter catch fire easily. Others don't. The properties of matter usually fall into two groups—physical properties and chemical properties. **Physical and chemical properties are used to identify, describe, and classify matter.** A single kind of matter that has distinct physical and chemical properties is called a **substance.**

Figure 1 Fuel burning in the engines of this boat provides energy that turns the paddle wheel.

Chapter 1　**25**

2 *Facilitate*

Defining Matter and Energy

Inquiry Challenge

ACTIVITY

Students can learn more about matter and energy by using the five senses of smell, sight, taste, hearing, and touch. Have students list the five senses and then describe examples of matter and energy that they might detect using each sense. For example, if students hear a thunderstorm, they are detecting electrical energy and the matter that makes up clouds and rain. **learning modality: logical/mathematical**

Language Arts Connection

Have students use dictionaries to compare the meanings of the terms *matter, material, mass,* and *substance.* Have students share the various definitions they found. Help them distinguish between scientific and everyday meanings of the terms. **learning modality: verbal**

Classifying Matter by Its Physical and Chemical Properties

Including All Students

Point out that both matter and energy have properties, or characteristics, and that these can be used to classify matter and energy into different types. Have students describe three types of matter; for example, solids, liquids, and gases. Then ask for three types of energy. Students may mention heat, light, motion, and nuclear. Explain that, as students learn more about matter and energy, they will be able to create more comprehensive classification systems. **learning modality: logical/ mathematical**

Ongoing Assessment

Writing Ask students to briefly define matter and energy in their own words.

Classifying Matter by Its Physical and Chemical Properties, continued

Addressing Naive Conceptions

List common substances such as wood, plastic, or metals on the board, and have student describe properties of each. Write the properties next to the items. Ask: **Which of these properties do you think could be used to identify a substance?** (*Sample answer: color, size, shape, odor*) Help students understand that properties such as size or weight refer to an individual object and not to the substance of which it is made.
learning modality: logical/mathematical

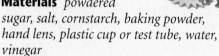

Skills Focus classifying
Materials *powdered sugar, salt, cornstarch, baking powder, hand lens, plastic cup or test tube, water, vinegar*
Time 20 minutes
Tips Have students make five-column data tables to record and compare their observations. The column titles can be: Substance, Appearance, Texture, With Water, and With Vinegar.
Expected Outcome In Steps 1 and 2, students are looking for physical properties such as color and texture. The sugar and salt will look like crystals when examined with the hand lens; the cornstarch and baking powder will appear dusty. In Steps 3 and 4 students observe another physical property—how easily each substance dissolves in water or vinegar. In addition, the baking powder will fizz, or create bubbles. This is evidence of a chemical property because a new substance—the gas—has been produced. (*The gas is carbon dioxide.*)
Extend Have students choose several other common kitchen substances such as corn syrup, lemon juice, and cooking oil. Students can look for physical and chemical properties of these substances and add them to their data tables.
learning modality: tactile/kinesthetic

Alike or Different?

1. Examine samples of powdered sugar, salt, cornstarch, and baking powder.

2. With a hand lens, look closely at each substance. Then rub a little of one substance between your fingers. Repeat with each of the other substances. Record your observations. Wash your hands.

3. Place one spoonful of each substance in a different plastic cup or test tube. Add two spoonfuls of water to each substance. Record any changes.

4. Repeat Step 3, using vinegar instead of water. Record any changes.

Classifying Make a list of properties for each of the substances. Based on your observations, can you group any of the substances together? Explain.

Physical Properties Have you ever smelled a bottle of vinegar? Whew! You can't miss its sharp odor. You wouldn't mistake its taste for the sweet taste of sugar, either. Odor and taste are physical properties. A **physical property** is a characteristic of a substance that can be observed without changing the substance into something else.

Other physical properties include hardness, texture, color, and the temperature at which a solid melts or a liquid boils. Every diamond, for example, is hard enough to scratch glass. Every sample of pure water boils at 100°C. Even when you describe a substance as a solid, a liquid, or a gas, you are stating one of its physical properties. Some types of matter can be easily classified based on their physical properties. Iron, copper, and aluminum may be different substances, but you know by looking at them that they are all metals.

Chemical Properties Some properties can't be determined just by looking at or touching a substance. Instead, you must change the substance to find out about such properties. A **chemical property** is a characteristic that is observed when a substance interacts with another substance. Like physical properties, chemical properties are used to classify substances. If you hold a toothpick and an iron rod in a candle flame, the toothpick will burn, but the rod will not. Burning, or flammability, is a chemical property of the substances in wood but is not a property of iron. Another chemical property involves rusting. Suppose you place an iron rod and a toothpick on a paper towel moistened with salt water. In a few days, the toothpick will remain unchanged, but the iron will react with water to form rust. Still other chemical properties determine whether a substance will explode like fireworks or tarnish like a piece of silverware.

☑ *Checkpoint* What is an example of a physical property of a candle? What is an example of a chemical property of a candle?

Figure 2 These medals are made of different substances but share many physical properties that classify them as metals.

Background

Integrating Science In chemistry, water is discussed as a pure compound, H_2O. In nature, water is found not as a pure compound, but as a mixture. Sea water contains a mixture of salts, mostly sodium chloride. The water in lakes and rivers contains varying amounts of dissolved minerals. After a heavy rain, river water also contains particles of silt in suspension. Drinking water is not pure H_2O. Water from a well contains dissolved minerals. Water from a city water distribution system often contains dissolved minerals and also small amounts of chlorine or other chemicals added to reduce the amount of bacteria.

For laboratory use, chemists often need pure water. Water can be purified for lab use by distillation. Tap water is boiled and the water vapor that is given off is condensed. The condensed water is pure H_2O.

Figure 3 A geodesic dome, a bridge, and a skyscraper are all made from steel, but their uses are very different. *Inferring Based on the uses shown in these photos, what properties of steel make it useful for a variety of construction projects?*

Kinds of Matter

Take an imaginary walk through your city or town and notice all the buildings. Their shapes, sizes, and uses are very different. You would never confuse a doghouse with an airport terminal, or a gas station with a 50-story office tower. But they are all constructed of a few kinds of materials. Bricks, wood, glass, stone, concrete, and steel are some of the most common forms of matter used in building. Using these forms of matter, people have built many different structures.

Elements Just as many different buildings are made from a few kinds of materials, all the different kinds of matter in the universe are made from a few more than 100 different substances, called elements. An **element** is a substance that cannot be broken down into any other substances by chemical or physical means. Each element can be identified by its specific physical and chemical properties.

You have experience with some elements in the world around you. Examples include aluminum foil and copper coatings on pennies. Oxygen and nitrogen gases are two elements in the air you breathe.

Answers to Self-Assessment

Caption Question

Figure 3 Steel is strong and it resists rusting.

☑ *Checkpoint*

Examples of physical properties of a candle may be: solid, smooth texture; soft enough to cut with a knife. Flammability is an example of a chemical property.

Kinds of Matter

Real-Life Learning

Have students collect samples of items around **ACTIVITY** their homes that are made of common elements. Encourage students to look for items made of iron, copper, aluminum, and carbon. Make a display of the items students find. You may wish to have students use periodic tables of elements to check that their choices are elements rather than compounds or mixtures. **learning modality: tactile/ kinesthetic**

Addressing Naive Conceptions

Students may think that familiar substances such as glass, wood, and steel must be elements because they are so common. Emphasize the definition— that an element is not made of other substances. Point out that students may not be able to identify whether a substance is an element by looking at it. They may need to check books or other reference sources to find out what a substance is made of. For example, steel is an alloy of iron and carbon. **learning modality: verbal**

Building Inquiry Skills: Classifying

Materials *worksheets with simplified periodic table of element*
Time 20 minutes

Introduce the periodic table of the elements to students. Explain that it is a way of organizing all the known elements. Point out that each element has a chemical symbol—usually one or two letters that stand for the element. Have students find familiar elements such as iron, gold, silver, and oxygen. Have each student choose three familiar elements, name one or two properties of each, and state whether each element ordinarily exists as a solid, a liquid, or a gas. **learning modality: visual**

Ongoing Assessment

Oral Presentation Ask students to give examples of properties that would help them identify water.

Kinds of Matter, continued

Math TOOLBOX

Ratios

A ratio compares two numbers. It tells you how much you have of one item in comparison to how much you have of another. For example, a recipe for cookies calls for 2 cups of flour for every 1 cup of sugar. You can write the ratio of flour to sugar as:

2 to 1 or 2 : 1

The elements in a compound are present in a specific ratio. If two compounds contain the same elements in different ratios, such as CO and CO_2, they are different compounds.

Figure 4 The element silver (above) is sometimes found in a wiry, tree-shaped form. The paints (right) are mixtures of several compounds. The compounds that give paints their colors are called pigments.

Compounds Most elements are found in nature combined with other elements. A **compound** is a substance made of two or more elements chemically combined in a set ratio, or proportion. For example, the carbon dioxide gas you breathe out is a compound made of carbon and oxygen. Any sample of carbon dioxide will always be made of one part carbon to two parts oxygen (CO_2). Table salt (sodium chloride) is made of one part sodium to one part chlorine (NaCl).

You use many compounds every day. The fruit sugar that makes juice taste sweet, the water that you drink when you are thirsty, and the cavity-fighting ingredient in your toothpaste are all compounds made from different combinations of elements. Each compound has its own specific properties. Water at room temperature, for example, is a clear, colorless liquid.

When elements are combined to make a compound, the new substance has properties different from those of the original elements. Consider table sugar, for example. It is a compound made from three elements—carbon, oxygen, and hydrogen. The sugar crystals do not resemble the carbon you see in charcoal or the colorless gases oxygen and hydrogen.

Mixtures Most matter that you find in the environment occurs as mixtures. A **mixture** is made from two or more substances—elements, compounds, or both—that are in the same place but are not chemically combined. Mixtures differ from compounds in two ways. First, the substances in a mixture keep their individual properties. Second, the parts of a mixture are not necessarily present in set ratios.

Consider a handful of moist soil. If you look at the soil through a hand lens, you will find particles of sand, tiny bits of clay, maybe even pieces of decaying plants. If you squeeze the soil, you might force out a few drops of water. Another sample of soil won't necessarily contain the same amount of water or any other material. Soil from a flowerpot in your home may be very different from the soil in a nearby park.

☑ *Checkpoint* **Why is soil a mixture and not a compound?**

EXPLORING *Matter at the Beach*

You can find all sorts of matter at an ocean beach, including sand, seashells, grasses and other plants, and sea water. Many types of beach sand are made up of small rocks and other particles that are washed ashore by the ocean's waves.

Mixture
Some beach sand is a mixture of a substance called quartz and tiny fragments of seashells. Different types of shells cause different colors of beach sand.

Compounds
Seashells contain different calcium compounds, including calcium carbonate. Quartz is formed from a compound called silicon dioxide.

Calcium carbonate

Silicon dioxide

Elements
The compounds in beach sand are made mostly of four elements: silicon, oxygen, calcium, and carbon. Like most substances, beach sand shares few properties with the elements that make it up!

Silicon   *Oxygen*   *Calcium*   *Carbon*

Answers to Self-Assessment

☑ *Checkpoint*

The substances that make up soil are not chemically combined, and they may not be present in the same ratio in two different samples of soil.

EXPLORING

Matter at the Beach

Direct students' attention to the photos of the compounds that compose sand and to the photos of the elements that make up those compounds. Inform students that silicon dioxide, SiO_2, is a compound containing silicon and oxygen. Then ask a volunteer to explain how silicon dioxide is different from its elements, silicon and oxygen. (*Silicon is a solid, and oxygen is a gas. The compound is a solid.*) Ask students to explain how calcium carbonate, $CaCO_3$, is different from its elements, calcium, carbon, and oxygen. (*Calcium is a gray solid, carbon is a black solid, and oxygen is a colorless gas. The compound is a white solid.*) Then ask: **How do the properties of the beach sand, which is a mixture, compare to the properties of the compounds it contains?** (*Different samples of beach sand may have different properties, depending on the individual parts (or compounds) it contains. The individual parts of the sand mixture keep their separate properties.*) Refer to the **ELL Handbook** for additional teaching strategies.
Extend Obtain several different samples of sand and allow students to examine the samples with a hand lens. Ask students how the mixtures are similar and how they are different. **learning modality: visual**

Building Inquiry Skills: Classifying

Encourage students to think about the objects around them, at home, and at places they may have visited. Suggest they classify some of the materials around them first as mixtures, elements, or compounds. Encourage them to find at least two examples of each type. Have the class share their classifications and come to an agreement on each object, then compose a master list. **learning modality: verbal**

Ongoing Assessment

Oral Presentation Ask students to give examples of mixtures and compounds.

Changes in Matter

Demonstration

Materials *tin can, matches, paper*

Time 10 minutes

 Tear some of the paper into small pieces, dropping them into the can. Ask: **Is this a physical or chemical change? Why?** *(Physical; the appearance changed but the original substances are still present.)* Next, carefully burn a piece of paper in the can. Again, ask students to identify the change as chemical or physical and to give a reason. *(Chemical; a new substance—ash—is now in the can and the paper is gone.)* **limited English proficiency**

Including All Students

Materials *small paper cups, ice cubes*

Time 10 minutes

To give extra help to students who have difficulty understanding how matter can change properties, distribute ice cubes in small paper cups to each student. Ask them to describe the ice cube using terms in the text, such as *smooth, hard, soft, colorless, cold,* or other appropriate terms. As the ice cube melts, have students use new terms to describe the new properties of water. Ask them which properties changed and which stayed the same as the ice cube melted. **learning modality: tactile/kinesthetic**

Figure 5 Wood can be chopped into different shapes (above). The bubble below is a thin film of liquid that changes shape around a body of air.
Interpreting Photographs How can you tell that these changes are physical changes?

Changes in Matter

Try to think of a world where nothing ever changes. Pretty boring, isn't it? Actually, you couldn't even survive in such a world because changes must occur inside your body if you are to remain alive. A sandwich that you eat for lunch must be changed by your body into muscle, blood, and other things you need. Chemists study both physical and chemical changes.

Physical Change Think of going to a costume party and seeing someone dressed as a clown. Could it be someone you know? How can you tell? Putting on a costume can make someone look quite different, but the person hasn't changed. So it is with some changes in matter. A change that alters the form or appearance of a material but does not make the material into another substance is called a **physical change.** Examples of physical changes include chopping wood, bending copper wire into new shapes, or molding clay.

As you probably know, matter has three principal states—solid, liquid, and gas. A change in state is another example of physical change. Matter can change from one state to another when the temperature changes. For example, ice cubes are made of solid (frozen) water. They will melt in a tray left on your kitchen table, forming liquid water. If you return the tray to the freezer, the water will become ice again. But if you leave the tray on the table overnight, some of the water will escape into the air as a gas. Water remains the same substance whether it's in the form of a solid, a liquid, or a gas. It is still made of two parts hydrogen and one part oxygen (H_2O).

☑ *Checkpoint* Why is a change in state considered to be a physical change?

Background

Facts and Figures Four physical states of matter are solid, liquid, gas, and plasma. While the first three are familiar, the fourth is quite rare on Earth. The sun and other stars consist of plasma, gas-like matter made of bare atomic nuclei and free electrons.

Five changes in the physical state of matter are melting, freezing, vaporization, condensation, and sublimation. (In sublimation, a substance goes directly from a solid to a gas without passing through the liquid state.) Energy changes are always involved when a change of state occurs. Energy is lost by a substance when it changes from a gas to a liquid or from a liquid to a solid. A change from a solid to a liquid or from a liquid to a gas requires the addition of energy.

Figure 6 Unlike a physical change, a chemical change alters the identity of a substance. In a forest fire, wood is changed into gases and other substances, and energy is released.

Chemical Change A change in matter that produces new substances is called a **chemical change,** or a chemical reaction. In a chemical change, elements may combine to form compounds, or compounds may be broken down into elements, or compounds may change into other compounds. **Unlike a physical change, a chemical change produces new substances with properties different from the original substances.**

Some familiar examples of chemical changes include the souring of milk and the burning of wood. When wood burns, the compounds of the wood combine with oxygen in the air to make new substances. These new substances include carbon dioxide, water, and other compounds. The element carbon is left in the ashes. Each of these new substances can be identified by its properties, which are different from those of the original wood.

Energy and Matter

As you learned earlier, energy and changes in matter go hand-in-hand. Recall that energy may be defined as the ability to do work or cause change. Energy can have different forms, and it can be transformed from one form to another. The idea of energy becomes easier to understand if you remember that what you often observe is the *effects* of energy on matter. Soup boiling on a stove and the sound of clapping hands both result from energy affecting matter. You can detect the effects of energy when matter is moved, when it reacts, or when energy is transformed from one form to another. **Energy is always involved when physical and chemical changes occur in matter.** The following pages describe some forms of energy and its interactions with matter.

Inferring

1.  Put a large spoonful of vinegar into a large resealable plastic bag. As instructed by your teacher, carefully smell the contents.

2. Add a drop of bromthymol blue indicator to the bag. (Bromthymol blue has a different color in different types of some water mixtures.)

3. Add an antacid tablet and seal the bag. Note any changes to the matter in the bag.

4. Based on the changes you observed, do you think there was a physical change to the matter in the bag? Explain.

Chapter 1 **31**

Energy and Matter, continued

Addressing Naive Conceptions

Some students may think that energy cannot change form. Show students a flashlight with the batteries next to it. Ask them to identify the form of energy stored in the batteries. (chemical) Then place the batteries in the flashlight and turn it on. Ask: **What form of energy do you see?** (electromagnetic) Allow students to place their hands near the bulb of the flashlight. Ask: **What form of energy do you feel?** (thermal) **learning modality: visual**

Building Inquiry Skills: Applying Concepts

Encourage students to describe each type of energy in their own words. Challenge students to think of one or two examples of each type of energy. **limited English proficiency**

Real Life Learning

Materials *wintergreen candies, small mirrors*
Time 15 minutes

Not all wintergreen candies work. Test different brands to see which do work.

CAUTION: *Since small pieces of candy can stick in the throat, give students access to a water fountain. Some students may find the wintergreen flavor unpleasant.* Pass out candies to each student. Darken the room. (Note: The room must be very dark and time must be allowed for eyes to adjust.) Have students chew the candies with their lips open as they watch themselves in the mirrors. As each piece of candy is crushed, they will see tiny flashes of white or bluish-white light. Ask: **What kind of energy did the mints have?** (chemical) **What kind of energy did your teeth add?** (mechanical) **What kind of energy did you see?** (electromagnetic) Explain that this is an example of triboluminescence, luminescence induced by friction. **learning modality: visual**

Figure 7 A tornado strikes buildings in Pampa, Texas. *Interpreting Diagrams Will the houses in the path of this tornado undergo a physical or a chemical change? Explain your answer.*

Mechanical Energy Mechanical energy is related to the motion or position of matter. When you shoot a basketball, energy is transferred from your hands to the ball. If you transfer just the right amount of mechanical energy in just the right way, the ball flies into the basket. A skateboard rolling down a hill is another example of mechanical energy.

Thermal Energy One of the most familiar forms of energy is thermal energy, which you sense as heat. All matter is made of small particles that are constantly in motion. If thermal energy is added to matter, the particles move faster, and the matter feels warmer than it did before the energy was added. If thermal energy is lost, the particles move more slowly, and the matter feels cooler than before. Remember the ice cube tray mentioned earlier? To make ice, you would put liquid water into the tray and leave it in the freezer. Thermal energy is lost from the water to the surroundings, and the water freezes. On a hot day, thermal energy in your surroundings will quickly melt the ice if you take the tray out and forget to put it back.

Electromagnetic Energy A familiar form of electromagnetic energy is light. X-rays, microwaves, radio and TV signals, and ultraviolet rays are also forms of electromagnetic energy. When electromagnetic energy interacts with matter, it can produce physical or chemical changes. For example, a microwave oven can change a frozen block of spaghetti and tomato sauce into a piping hot meal—a physical change. This change occurs with the transformation of electromagnetic energy to thermal energy. A similar kind of transformation can produce chemical changes, too. Without sunblock, people at a beach who are exposed to electromagnetic energy from the sun can experience painful chemical changes to the matter that makes up their skin. You know this effect as sunburn.

Electrical Energy A moving electric charge produces electricity. The energy of these moving charges is electrical energy. Electrical energy becomes useful when it is transformed into other forms of energy. In factories, for example, electrical energy is transformed into mechanical energy that turns the large motors

32

Background

Integrating Science As the sun warms Earth's land and water, water evaporates and thermal energy is stored in the air containing the evaporated water. When this stored thermal energy is released, it can cause violent storms. The thermal energy is released when warm air cools and condenses, forming liquid water. An average thunderstorm releases about 36 terajoules of energy. Severe storms can release up to 100 times more energy.

The thermal energy stored in warm air also forms tornadoes and hurricanes. A tornado may have wind speeds that exceed 800 km per hour. Hurricanes, which are much larger than tornadoes, release even more energy. They form over warm ocean waters where evaporation takes place. Winds near the eye may be as high as 300 kilometers per hour, and a hurricane may be over 2,000 km in diameter.

of manufacturing equipment. In a light bu...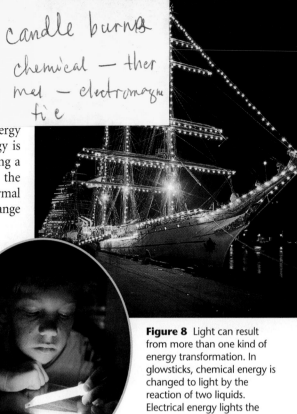
trical energy is transformed as it interacts ...
metal wire in the bulb. With the flick of a...
electrical energy is transformed into t...
energy and light.

Chemical Energy Matter itself contains energy
known as chemical energy. Chemical energy is
transformed to other forms of energy during a
chemical reaction. When a candle burns, the
chemical energy in candle wax becomes thermal
and electromagnetic energy. You detect the change
as heat and light.

 INTEGRATING LIFE SCIENCE One of the most
important energy
transformations on Earth involves
chemical energy. Plants transform
electromagnetic energy from the
sun into chemical energy. These
plants, and animals and other
living things that eat plants, then
transform this chemical energy
once again. It becomes the
mechanical, electrical, and thermal
energy needed to carry out life activities. The potato you have for dinner
might supply the energy you need to go
for a walk or read this book!

handwritten note: candle burns / chemical — ther / mal — electromagne / tic

Figure 8 Light can result
from more than one kind of
energy transformation. In
glowsticks, chemical energy is
changed to light by the
reaction of two liquids.
Electrical energy lights the
bulbs on this ship's rigging.

 ## Section 1 Review

1. Name several properties used to classify matter.
   Tell whether each is a physical property or a
   chemical property.
2. How are compounds formed?
3. Explain the difference between a physical
   change and a chemical change.
4. In what way are energy and matter related?
5. Describe a change in matter that you observed
   today. Tell what kind of energy change you
   think was involved.
6. **Thinking Critically** **Applying Concepts**
   You see a solid that looks like an ice cube, but
   it does not melt at room temperature. Can the
   solid be frozen water? Explain.

Check Your Progress
CHAPTER PROJECT

Choose which product and
property you will test. Design a
procedure to test the property you have
selected. Decide which variables you will
keep constant. Describe how you will
measure and organize the data you
collect. Discuss ideas for your procedure
with a partner. Answer your partner's
questions about the procedure, listen to
any comments offered, and incorporate
appropriate comments into your plan.

Chapter 1 **33**

Program Resources

◆ **Unit 1 Resources** 1-1 Review and
  Reinforce, p. 17; 1-1 Enrich, p. 18

Answers to Self-Assessment
Caption Question

Figure 7 The houses will undergo
physical changes. Their appearance will
change but no new substances will be
produced unless a fire starts or an
explosion occurs.

 Integrating Life Science

Invite students to brainstorm a list of
energy transformations in animals.
Motion (mechanical energy) and body
heat (thermal energy) are likely
responses. Prompt students to think of
other kinds of energy, such as light
(firefly) or electricity (electric eel)

3 Assess

Section 1 Review Answers

1. Sample: Physical properties—taste,
odor, hardness, texture, color, melting
temperature, and boiling temperature.
Chemical properties—how easily a
substance burns, reacts with water to
form rust, explodes, or tarnishes.
2. A compound forms when two or
more elements are chemically combined.
3. Physical change: matter may change
form or appearance, but no new
substances are formed. Chemical change:
one or more new substances are produced.
4. Energy is involved when matter
undergoes a physical or a chemical change.
5. Accept all answers in which students
correctly identify changes as physical or
chemical.
6. No. If the solid was frozen water, it
would melt at room temperature because
the melting temperature of ice is 0°C.

Check Your Progress
CHAPTER PROJECT

Students can work with
their first partner to design their
procedures. The written procedures
should tell how to test the chosen
property of the consumer products.
The procedure should indicate that
students have made predictions
about results they will obtain. You
may want to require students to
include a summary of their partner's
comments with their plans. Check
students' procedures for safety.

Performance Assessment

Writing Have students use the major
headings in the section to write brief
summaries. Students' summaries
should include examples.

SECTION
2 Measuring Matter
TEKS: 6.2A, B, C, D, E; 6.3E; 6.4A; 6.7B

Objectives

After completing the lesson, students will be able to

◆ explain the difference between weight and mass;

◆ calculate the density of substances using SI units for mass and volume.

1 Engage/Explore

Activating Prior Knowledge

Obtain two bars of hand soap, one that floats (such as Ivory) and one that does not. Remove the packaging. Show students the two bars, and ask: **What will happen when I place the two bars in a pan of water about 10 cm deep?** *(One will float and one will sink.)* Put the bars in the water. Let students observe the results and try to explain them.

DISCOVER

Skills Focus drawing conclusions

Materials *triple-beam balance, objects of different weights such as rocks, plastic drinking cups, aluminum cans, pencils*

Time 15 minutes

Tips Choose objects that are small but heavy (lead weights, small rocks, bolts, or paperweights), and objects that are larger but lightweight (plastic drinking cups, pieces of plastic foam, empty aluminum cans).

Think It Over Students may predict that the larger objects are heavier, but should conclude that small objects can be heavier than large objects, depending on density (although they may not know the term yet).

DISCOVER ••••••••••••••••••••••••••••••••• ACTIVITY

Which Has More Mass?

1. Your teacher will provide you with some small objects, such as a rock, a plastic cup, an aluminum can, and a pencil. Look at the objects, but do not touch them.

2. Predict which object is lightest, which is second lightest, and so on. Record your predictions.

3. Use a triple-beam balance to find the mass of each object.

4. Based on your results, list the objects from lightest to heaviest.

Think It Over

Drawing Conclusions How did your predictions compare to your results? Are bigger objects always heavier than smaller objects? Why or why not?

GUIDE FOR READING

◆ What is the difference between weight and mass?

◆ How is density calculated?

Reading Tip Before you read, define *mass, volume,* and *density* in your own words. Then revise your definitions as you read.

Key Terms weight • mass
• International System of Units
• volume • density

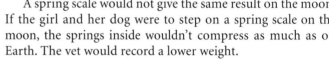

Figure 9 A spring scale measures the weight of an object.

Here's a riddle for you: Which weighs more, a pound of feathers or a pound of bricks? If you answered "the pound of bricks," think again. Both weigh exactly the same—one pound!

There are all sorts of ways of measuring matter, and you use these measurements every day. Scientists rely on measurements as well. In fact, scientists work hard to make sure that their measurements are as accurate as possible.

Mass

A veterinarian wants an updated weight for a dog at its annual checkup. To find the weight, the owner steps on a spring scale, holding the dog. Their combined body weight presses down on springs inside the scale. The more the girl and her dog weigh, the more the springs compress, and the higher the reading. When the owner's weight is subtracted from the total, the vet has an answer.

A spring scale would not give the same result on the moon. If the girl and her dog were to step on a spring scale on the moon, the springs inside wouldn't compress as much as on Earth. The vet would record a lower weight.

34

READING STRATEGIES

Reading Tip Have students write their definitions in their notebooks, leaving space for additions or corrections. Before reading the section, students may define *density* as "how heavy something is." After students have read the section and revised their definitions, call on volunteers to read their revised definitions. Make sure that all incorrect preliminary definitions are revised accurately.

Background

Facts and Figures Weight is a measure of the force of gravity on an object, and is measured using a scale. Mass is a measure of the amount of matter in an object, and is measured using a balance.

Weight and Mass Your **weight** is a measure of the force of gravity on you. On Earth, all objects are attracted downward by Earth's gravity. On other planets, the force of gravity may be more or less. On the moon, the force of gravity is much weaker than on Earth. You would weigh less on the moon.

In everyday life, weight is a useful measurement of how much matter you have. But scientists rely on a property that is constant wherever the object may be. The **mass** of an object is the measurement of how much matter it contains. **Unlike weight, an object's mass will not change if the force of gravity on it changes.** For this reason, mass is a useful physical property for describing and measuring matter.

Units of Mass To measure the properties of matter, scientists use a system of units called the **International System of Units.** The system is abbreviated "SI," after its French name, Système International. For mass, the SI unit is the kilogram (kg). If you weigh 90 pounds on Earth, then your mass is approximately 40 kilograms.

Although you sometimes will see kilograms used in this textbook, usually you will see a smaller unit—the gram (g). There are exactly 1,000 grams in a kilogram. A nickel has a mass of about 5 grams, the mass of a baseball is about 150 grams, and the water in a medium-sized glass has a mass of about 200 grams.

✓ *Checkpoint* What is the SI unit for mass?

Volume

The amount of space that matter occupies is called its **volume.** It's easy to see the volume that solid and liquid objects take up. But gases have volume, too. Watch a balloon as you blow into it. You're actually increasing its volume with your breath.

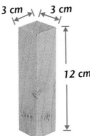
3 cm | 3 cm
12 cm

Figure 10 Volume is measured in several units. Those that scientists commonly use include liters (L), milliliters (mL), and cubic centimeters (cm³).

Bubble Time
Do gases have volume?

1. Fill a large container with water. Completely submerge a clear plastic cup, right-side up, in the container.
2. Mark the water level with a piece of tape on the outside of the container.
3. Turn the cup upside-down under water, without letting any air bubbles enter the cup.
4. Insert the short end of the straw into the water and up into the cup. Then blow into the straw.

Inferring Did blowing air into the cup change the water level in the container? Explain your observations.

Answers to Self-Assessment

✓ *Checkpoint*
Kilogram

---

2 Facilitate

Mass

Building Inquiry Skills: Applying Concepts

Materials *spring scale, objects from Discover activity, string*
Time 20 minutes

Have students weigh the objects on the spring scale. Be sure students zero the spring scales. Challenge students to infer how a spring scale measures the weight of an object. (*It measures the force required to resist gravity.*) Have students list the items in order of weight. Compare this list with the list from the Discover. Ask: **How are mass and weight related?** (*Objects with greater mass have greater weight.*) **What would happen if you weighed the objects using the same spring scale on the moon?** (*The objects would weigh less.*) **learning modality: logical/mathematical**

Volume

Skills Focus inferring
Materials *water, large container, clear plastic cup, tape, flexible drinking straw*
Time 10 minutes
Tips Use a container large enough for students to invert the cup without lifting it out of the water.
Expected Outcome The water level in the container will rise because the air blown into the cup will push water out of the cup and into the container.
Extend Have students develop a method to determine whether the increase in the water's volume is equal to the volume of gas in the cup. (*Students can use graduated containers to measure the volumes.*)
learning modality: tactile/kinesthetic

Ongoing Assessment

Writing Ask students to give brief definitions of weight and mass.

Volume, continued

Integrating Mathematics

Students often have difficulty recognizing how to convert units of area or volume. Have students calculate how many cubic centimeters are in a cubic meter. Remind students that 1 m = 100 cm.

$1 \text{ m}^3 = 100 \text{ cm} \times 100 \text{ cm} \times 100 \text{ cm}$

$1 \text{ m}^3 = 1{,}000{,}000 \text{ cm}^3$

SCIENCE & History

Time 20 minutes

Tips To determine whether students are reading the time line correctly, ask: **How many years are represented by this time line?** *(3,500)* Ask: **Were the early systems of measurement as accurate as those we use today? Why?** *(No, because they depended on things that are not the same for all people at all times, such as the length of a person's arm or how much land oxen can plow in two days)* Then ask students to infer why people still use units of measurement that are not part of the SI system. *(Sample: Because they are familiar with them; because the units are traditionally used in some fields)*

Extend Have students list SI units they use in their everyday lives. Refer to the **ELL Handbook** for additional teaching strategies.

In Your Journal Encourage students to define and explain the units they choose. For example, a *carat*, a unit of weight for precious gems, is equal to 200 milligrams. Horses are measured in *hands*, a unit of height equal to about 10 centimeters. In sailing, a *fathom* (about 2 meters) is used to measure the depth of water. **learning modality: verbal**

INTEGRATING MATHEMATICS For rectangular objects such as a block of wood, the volume is found by multiplying the measurements of length, width, and height.

Volume = Length × Width × Height

When you multiply the three measurements, you must multiply the units as well as the numbers. So, just as $2 \times 2 \times 2 = 2^3$, $\text{cm} \times \text{cm} \times \text{cm} = \text{cm}^3$. If a block of wood has a length of 3 centimeters, a width of 3 centimeters, and a height of 12 centimeters, then the volume would equal the product of those values.

Volume = 3 cm × 3 cm × 12 cm = 108 cm³

Measurement Systems

Like so much else in science, systems of measurement developed gradually over time in different parts of the world.

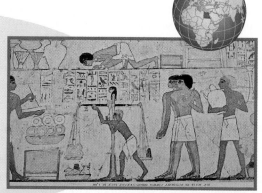

1400 B.C.
Egypt
The ancient Egyptians developed the first known weighing instrument, a simple balance with a pointer. Earlier, they had been the first to standardize a measure of length. The length, called a cubit, was originally defined as the distance between the elbow and the tip of the middle finger.

| 1500 B.C. | 1000 B.C. | 500 B.C. | A.D. 1 |

640 B.C.
Lydia
Merchants in the Middle East and Mediterranean used units of weight to be sure that they received the correct amount of gold and silver in trade and to check the purity of the metal. A *talent* was about 25 kilograms and a *mina* about 500 grams. The Lydians minted the first true coins to have standard weight and value.

200 B.C.
China
Shih Huang Ti, the first emperor of China, set standards for weight, length, and volume. Even earlier, the Chinese were the first to use decimal notation, the number system based on 10 digits. This is the system most people use today.

36

Background

Facts and Figures Students may be interested in hearing more about units of measurement.

◆ A *furlong*, a distance now used only in horse racing, is approximately equal to 200 meters. It comes from an old English unit of length that was based on the length of an average furrow in a plowed field.

◆ The *knot*, a measure of speed at sea, is approximately equal to 1.15 miles per hour, or 1.85 km per hour. The term probably originated because of knots made in a length of rope which were used to measure the speed of a ship through water.

◆ A *fathom* is a measure of depth of water. A fathom is 6 feet, or 1.83 meters. Originally, a fathom was the distance between the tips of the middle fingers of a large man holding his arms fully outstretched.

The abbreviation "cm³" is read as *cubic centimeter(s)*, which is a common unit of volume. Other units of volume include the liter (L) and the milliliter (mL), both of which are often used to measure liquids. A milliliter is exactly 1 cubic centimeter. There are 1,000 milliliters in one liter.

How can you measure the volume of an object with an irregular shape, such as a piece of fruit or a rock? One way is to put the object in a graduated cylinder containing water and measure the change in the volume of the water.

☑ *Checkpoint* *How can you calculate the volume of a rectangular object like a shoe box?*

In Your Journal

Although scientists rely on SI units, people use other measurement units for many different purposes. Research the units used in diamond cutting, horse breeding, sailing, or other activities that interest you. Write a brief essay describing your findings.

A.D. 789

Central Europe

The foot of Charlemagne, emperor of most of central Europe, was set as the standard unit of length. The standard unit of weight was the *Karlspfund*, translated as "Charlemagne's pound."

A.D. 1714

Germany

Gabriel Fahrenheit invented the thermometer, a temperature-measuring device that relies on the expansion of mercury with heat. His name later came to be used as the name for a temperature scale.

| A.D. 500 | A.D. 1000 | A.D. 1500 | A.D. 2000 |

A.D. 700   England

During the reign of Ethelbert II in England, the term *acre* was in common use as a measurement of area. An acre was defined as the amount of land two oxen could plow in one day.

A.D. 1983

France

The International Bureau of Weights and Measures defines a single set of units that is the same everywhere. Scientists throughout the world use these units in their work.

Chapter 1 **37**

Including All Students

Materials *unit cubes (manipulatives used in math class)*

Time 10 minutes

Students who need extra challenges may enjoy visualizing how a small increase in the dimensions of an object can cause a large change in the volume of the object. Ask: **If you make a cube that is 1 cm longer, 1 cm wider, and 1 cm taller than another cube, how much more volume does the bigger cube have?** (*Some students may say the cube will be 1 cm larger.*) Suggest students use unit cubes to model three cubes, the first with one unit cube, the second with dimensions of 2 × 2 × 2, and the third with dimensions of 3 × 3 × 3. Ask students to compare the volume (in unit cubes) of the 2 × 2 × 2 cube (*8*) and the 3 × 3 × 3 cube (*27*). Have students calculate the volume in unit cubes of a cube that is 4 units tall, 4 units wide, and 4 units long. (*64*) **learning modality: logical/mathematical**

Ongoing Assessment

Skills Check Have students calculate the volumes of several rectangular items such as a textbook, a shoe box, and the classroom. For each item, students should draw diagrams that explain how they arrived at their answers.

Density—A Physical Property of Matter

Content Mastery

Materials *assorted small irregularly shaped objects, 1,000-mL graduated cylinder, water, balance, string*

ACTIVITY

Time 15 minutes

To show students how to find the density of irregular objects, first have them find the masses of the objects. They can then use the graduated cylinder, filled with water to the 50-mL line, to find their volumes. (If they are available, you can use an overflow can or a 1,000-mL graduated cylinder to measure the density of larger objects.) To do this, students can tie the string around each object, then slowly lower the object into the cylinder. Each object will displace a certain volume of water, and students can measure how much the water level rises by noting the graduations on the cylinder. Ask: **How can you use the new water level to find the volume of the object?** *(New level − 50 mL = volume of solid)* Finally, have students calculate the density of each object. **learning modality: tactile/kinesthetic**

Sample Problem

Reproduce the sample problem on the board, and work through the steps with students. Point out that density is a ratio of two quantities, mass and volume. Show students how to check their answers by checking the units. The units of density are always expressed in mass per unit volume (so the answer is read as "grams per cubic centimeter"). If students find other units, they are not doing the problem correctly. **learning modality: logical/mathematical**

Practice Problems
1. 24 g ÷ 16 mL = 1.5 g/mL
2. 43.5 g ÷ 15 cm³ = 2.9 g/cm³

Figure 11 This table lists commonly used units of mass, volume, and distance. *Making Generalizations Which units show the amount of space an object occupies? Which units show the amount of matter in an object?*

Common Units and Conversions			
Quantity	**SI/Metric Units**	**Other Units**	**Conversions**
Mass	Kilogram (kg) Gram (g)		1 kilogram = 1,000 grams
Volume	Cubic meter (m³) Liter (L) Milliliter (mL) Cubic centimeter (cm³)	Quart Gallon	1 liter = 1,000 milliliters 1 milliliter = 1 cm³
Distance	Meter (m) Kilometer (km) Centimeter (cm)	Foot Mile Inch	1 kilometer = 1,000 meters 1 centimeter = 0.01 meter

Density—A Physical Property of Matter

Different substances may have the same mass, but they don't necessarily fill the same volume. Remember the riddle about the bricks and the feathers? A kilogram of bricks takes up a much smaller volume than the same mass of feathers. This is because bricks and feathers have different densities—a very important property of matter. **Density** is a physical property that relates the mass and volume of an object or material. **To calculate the density of a sample, divide its mass by its volume.**

$$Density = \frac{Mass}{Volume}$$

A unit of density is always a unit of mass, such as grams, divided by a unit of volume, such as cubic centimeters. One typical unit of density is written as "g/cm³," which is read as "grams per cubic centimeter." The word *per* means "for each," which in mathematics is the same as "divided by." For liquids, density is often stated in grams per milliliter, or g/mL. The density of water is 1.0 g/mL, which is the same as 1.0 g/cm³.

Sometimes you can compare the densities of substances just by observing them. For example, suppose you have a solid block of wood and a solid block of gold. When you drop each block into a tub of water, the wood floats and the gold sinks. You know the density of water is 1.0 g/cm³. You can conclude that the density of wood is less than 1.0 g/cm³. In contrast, the density of the gold is greater than 1.0 g/cm³. In the same way, you can conclude that the density of the solid stone statue in Figure 12 is greater than the density of the water around it.

Figure 12 An object sinks or floats in water depending, in part, on its density. This stone statue remains on the sea floor where it was placed. A statue of solid wood, with a density less than that of water, would float.

38

Background

History of Science A popular legend about the Greek scientist Archimedes offers a useful application of density. King Hieron II of Syracuse suspected a goldsmith of using a mix of metals rather than pure gold to make his crown. Archimedes reasoned that the density of a lump of pure gold and a crown of pure gold would be the same. He then reasoned that a lump of pure gold with the same mass as the crown should have the same volume. To test the trustworthiness of the goldsmith, he placed that lump of pure gold and then the crown in water. The crown displaced more water than the lump of gold with the same mass, indicating that it had a greater volume. Therefore, Archimedes could say with certainty that the crown was not made of pure gold because its density was less than the density of pure gold.

Sample Problem

A small block of wood floats on water. It has a volume of 25 cubic centimeters and a mass of 20 grams. What is the density of the wood?

Analyze. You know the mass and the volume. You want to find the density.

Write the formula. $\text{Density} = \dfrac{\text{Mass}}{\text{Volume}}$

Substitute and solve. $\text{Density} = \dfrac{20 \text{ g}}{25 \text{ cm}^3}$

$\text{Density} = 0.8 \text{ g/cm}^3$

Think about it. The answer shows mass per unit volume.

Practice Problems
1. A sample of liquid has a mass of 24 grams and a volume of 16 milliliters. What is the density of the liquid?
2. A metal sample has a mass of 43.5 grams and a volume of 15 cubic centimeters. What is its density?

Watch a bottle of oil-and-vinegar salad dressing after it's been shaken. You will see oil droplets rise toward the top of the bottle. Eventually, the oil forms a separate layer above the other ingredients. What can you conclude? You're right if you said that the oil is less dense than the rest of the liquid dressing.

Density is a physical property of a substance. As a result, density can be used to help identify a substance. For example, all samples of pure gold at a certain temperature have a density of 19.3 g/cm³. Finding the density of a shiny yellow material is one way to test whether or not that material is gold.

 Section 2 Review

 Science at Home

1. Why is mass more useful than weight for measuring matter?
2. What two quantities do you need to know in order to calculate density?
3. Describe how you could measure the volume of an object with an irregular shape.
4. **Thinking Critically Problem Solving** The density of aluminum is 2.7 g/cm³. A metal sample has a mass of 52.0 grams and a volume of 17.1 cubic centimeters. Could the sample be aluminum? Explain your answer.

Density Demonstration Label two cups A and B and place a cup of water in each. Stir 3 small spoonfuls of salt and several drops of food coloring into Cup B. Dip a clear straw into Cup A to a depth of about 2 cm. Place your finger on the end of the straw and transfer the straw into Cup B to a depth of about 4 cm. Remove your finger from the straw and then replace it. Remove the straw from the cup. Explain to your family what density has to do with the results.

Program Resources

◆ **Unit 1 Resources** 1-2 Review and Reinforce, p. 21; 1-2 Enrich, p. 22

Media and Technology

 Life Science Videodisc
Unit 1, Side 1,
"The Metric System"

Chapter 7

Answers to Self-Assessment

Caption Question

Figure 11 Amount of space—liters, milliliters, cubic meters, and cubic centimeters, as well as quarts and gallons; amount of matter—kilograms and grams

3 Assess

Section 2 Review Answers

1. Unlike weight, mass does not change if the force of gravity changes.
2. Mass and volume
3. Fill a container with enough water to submerge the object. Measure the volume of the water. Place the object in the water and find the increase in volume. The increase in volume is equal to the volume of the object.
4. The density of the metal sample is 52.0 g ÷ 17.1 cm³ = 3.04 g/cm³. This density is greater than the density of aluminum, so the sample is not aluminum.

 Science at Home

Materials *two cups with flat bottoms, water, salt, food coloring, clear plastic straw*

ACTIVITY

Have students predict what will happen before they try this activity. When students have dipped the straw into both cups, the water in the straw will be in two bands. Water from cup A will be at the top, and water from cup B will be at the bottom. Students should explain that the water from cup A is less dense, so it floats on the water from cup B without mixing. This activity can also be performed with three solutions of different densities.

Performance Assessment

Skills Check Have students prepare presentations that explain how to find the density of a small, irregularly shaped solid. Students can use illustrations to explain one or all of the steps.

Portfolio Students can include their illustrations in their portfolios.

Making Sense of Density

Preparing for Inquiry

Key Concept The density of a substance is a property that can be used to identify that substance.

Skills Objectives Students will be able to
- measure mass using a balance;
- measure volume using the method of water displacement;
- calculate density.

Time 30 minutes

Advance Planning
- Make sure the objects to be tested can be broken easily and will fit into graduated cylinders.
- Make sure students know the proper procedure for using the balance.
- *Computer use is optional.*

Guiding Inquiry

Introducing the Procedure
Review the procedure briefly. Students should record each object's initial and new volume in Steps 2 and 3 in case they need to check their calculations.

Troubleshooting the Experiment
Have students develop a method for submerging objects that might float, such as some wood and crayons, in order to measure their volumes. Encourage students to examine what effect this will have on the accuracy of their results.

Expected Outcome
Density values for all samples of each object should be approximately equal.

Analyze and Conclude
1. The density of the whole object should equal the density of each piece.
2. Because every sample of a substance has the same density, density can be used to identify that substance.
3. If the object were wet, then the mass measurements would include water, introducing a source of error into the calculations.

MAKING SENSE OF DENSITY

In this lab you will find out if an object's density changes when its size changes.

Problem

Does the density of a substance change if it is broken into pieces?

Materials

balance   water   paper towels
wooden stick, approximately 6 cm long
ball of modeling clay, approximately 5 cm wide
crayon with paper covering removed
graduated cylinder, 100 mL
computer and spreadsheet program (optional)

Procedure

1. Use a balance to find the mass of the wooden stick. Record the mass in a data table like the one at the right or in a computer spreadsheet.
2. Add enough water to a graduated cylinder so that the stick can be completely submerged. Measure the initial volume of the water.
3. Place the stick in the graduated cylinder. Measure the new volume of the water.
4. The volume of the stick is the difference between the water levels in Steps 2 and 3. Calculate this volume and record it.
5. The density of the stick equals its mass divided by its volume. Calculate and record its density.
6. Thoroughly dry the stick with a paper towel. Then carefully break the stick into two pieces. Repeat Steps 1 through 5 to calculate the density of each of the two pieces.
7. Repeat Steps 1 through 6 using the clay rolled into a rope.
8. Repeat Steps 1–6 again using the crayon.

Analyze and Conclude

1. For each of the three objects you tested, compare the density of the whole object with the densities of the pieces of the object.
2. Use your results to explain how density can be used to identify a substance.
3. Why did you dry the objects in Step 6?
4. **Think About It** Predict the results of this experiment if you had used a pencil with an eraser on one end instead of a wooden stick. Explain your prediction.

More to Explore

Wrap the modeling clay around the wooden stick and predict the density of the object you created. Then measure mass and volume and calculate the density to see if your prediction was correct.

DATA TABLE

Object	Mass (g)	Volume Change (cm³)	Density (g/cm³)
Wooden Stick			
Whole			
Piece 1			
Piece 2			
Modeling Clay			
Whole			
Piece 1			
Piece 2			
Crayon			
Whole			
Piece 1			
Piece 2			

---

4. The density of the eraser would most likely differ from the density of the rest of the pencil. Thus, the density of pencil pieces would differ from the density of the whole pencil.

Extending the Inquiry

More to Explore Students should discover that the density of a mixture falls in between the highest and lowest densities of the substances in the mixture.

Program Resources

- **Unit 1 Resources** Chapter 1 Skills Lab blackline masters, pp. 31–32
- **Inquiry Skills Activity Book** Provides teaching and review of all inquiry skills

Media and Technology

Lab Activity Videotapes
Grade 6, Tape 1

SECTION 3 Particles of Matter

DISCOVER •••••••••••••••••••••••••••••••••••••• ACTIVITY••••

What's in the Box?

1. Your teacher will give you a sealed box that contains one or more objects. Without opening the box, try to find out as much as you can about the contents. Try tilting, turning, shaking, or tapping the box.

2. Ask yourself questions such as these: Are the objects inside round or flat? Do they slide or roll? How many objects are there?

3. Make a list of your observations about the objects in the box.

4. Trade boxes with another group of students and repeat the activity.

Think It Over

Inferring Try to imagine what familiar objects would fit your observations. Make a sketch showing what you think the contents look like. How is it possible to make an inference from indirect evidence?

Glance at the painting below and you see people enjoying an afternoon in the park. Look again and notice that some people are in the sunlight and others are in the shade. How did the artist make your eyes see bright light, dark shadows, and shades in between? You can find the answer by looking closely at the circled detail of the painting. The artist used thousands of small spots of color.

Are you surprised that such a rich painting can be created from lots of small spots? Matter is like that too. The properties you can observe are produced by tiny objects and events that you cannot observe.

◀ "Sunday Afternoon on the Island of La Grande Jatte," by Georges Seurat, at the Art Institute of Chicago

Chapter 1 **41**

GUIDE FOR READING

◆ What did Dalton conclude about atoms?

◆ What are molecules made of?

Reading Tip As you read, take notes on the main points under each heading.

Key Terms atom
• chemical bond • molecule

Objectives

After completing the lesson, students will be able to

◆ identify atoms as the smallest particles of an element;
◆ describe Dalton's theory of atoms;
◆ identify chemical bonds as the force holding atoms together in molecules.

1 Engage/Explore

Activating Prior Knowledge

Distribute hand lenses and sections from the Sunday comics. Have students examine the comics with the hand lenses and describe what they see. Ask students to describe how a whole picture can be made up of many tiny parts.

•••••••• **DISCOVER** ••••••••

Skills Focus inferring
Materials *shoe box containing one or more objects such as a candle, pencil, empty soda can, sock, marble, sponge*
Time 10 minutes
Tips Have students work in pairs or groups of 3. Make certain each shoe box is opaque and taped firmly closed. When students exchange shoe boxes, encourage them to evaluate each other's observations and inferences.
Think It Over Students' answers should be appropriate to their observations. Emphasize to students that they may not have enough information to draw precise conclusions. Students should realize that they can make inferences from indirect evidence by making repeated observations and revising their inferences to fit the observations.

Early Ideas About Atoms

Including All Students

Many students have difficulty when scientific concepts deal with things that cannot be directly observed. Divide the class into small groups, and have students consider the way a crime is solved when there is no direct evidence, such as an eyewitness. Crime solvers make careful measurements and collect as much indirect evidence as possible. Eventually, the evidence can be enough to convince a jury. Have a reporter from each group share the group's finding with the class. Then explain that scientists also collect indirect evidence until they are convinced a particular theory is correct. **cooperative learning**

Using the Visuals: Figure 13

While mercury is a liquid at room temperature, small amounts of mercury vaporize, so mercury vapor is always present. Mercury vapor can be inhaled and can then accumulate in body tissues until concentrations are high enough to cause serious health problems, even brain damage and death. Ask students if they think the smallest droplets of mercury pictured contain just a few atoms of mercury or many atoms. *(many)* Tell students that the smallest droplets pictured, which might have a mass of 0.01 g, still contain around 3 billion billion atoms (3.0×10^{18}). **learning modality: visual**

Figure 13 A drop of spilled mercury breaks into smaller droplets. (Don't do this at home. The element mercury is poisonous and can cause brain damage.) Although these droplets are small, they are not the smallest particles of mercury possible.
Applying Concepts What is the smallest particle of an element?

Early Ideas About Atoms

What's the smallest possible piece of an element? Think of tearing a sheet of aluminum foil in half, and then tearing the halves into quarters, and the quarters into eighths. Could you keep tearing forever, producing smaller and smaller pieces? Or would you eventually reach the smallest possible piece of aluminum? And if matter is made of such tiny pieces, what are those pieces like? How can they explain the properties of matter that you observe? Philosophers and scientists have asked these kind of questions for more than 2,000 years.

One of the first people known to have thought that matter is formed of small pieces was Democritus, a Greek philosopher who lived about 440 B.C. He thought that you could cut matter into ever smaller pieces until you got to its smallest piece, which couldn't be divided any further. Democritus called this smallest piece *atomos*, which is Greek for "uncuttable." Does that word look familiar? Of course! It's where the word *atom* comes from. An **atom** is the smallest particle of an element.

Dalton's Ideas About Atoms

A major step in understanding atoms occurred in 1802 when a British school teacher, John Dalton, proposed an atomic theory. No one knows how much Dalton was influenced by the ideas of Democritus. Unlike Democritus and the ancient Greeks, Dalton used experiments to test his ideas.

42

Background

History of Science John Dalton (1766–1844) began teaching in a Quaker school at the age of 12. At 21, Dalton began his first scientific work, a diary recording the meteorological changes of the district in which he lived. Ultimately, the diary contained 200,000 entries. In 1793, Dalton published his *Meteorological Observations and Essays*.

Dalton preferred to make his own observations and draw his conclusions from them. He also built his own instruments.

Dalton investigated the behavior of gases and discovered that for a mixture of gases, the total pressure equals the sum of the pressures of the individual gases. He also studied color blindness, a condition that he had. Although his theory was later discarded, his work was so influential that color blindness was referred to as *Daltonism*.

Based on evidence from experiments, Dalton inferred that atoms had certain characteristics. Here are his main conclusions.

◆ *Atoms can't be broken into smaller pieces.* **Dalton thought of atoms as similar to tiny marbles, or rigid spheres that are impossible to break.**

◆ *In any element, all the atoms are exactly alike.* This idea explains why an element always has the same properties.

◆ *Atoms of different elements are different.* This idea explains why different elements have their own set of properties.

◆ *Atoms of two or more elements can combine to form compounds.* Compounds can be broken down into elements, so Dalton concluded that compounds had to be made of atoms as well.

◆ *Atoms of each element have a unique mass.* Dalton and other scientists of his day were not actually able to measure the mass of individual atoms, however.

◆ *The masses of the elements in a compound are always in a constant ratio.* Water is made up of hydrogen atoms and oxygen atoms. In any two samples of pure water, the ratio of the mass of hydrogen to the mass of oxygen is always the same.

Today, scientists have identified some important exceptions to Dalton's statements. Even so, Dalton's ideas form the basis of our understanding of atoms.

 Checkpoint What were two of Dalton's ideas about atoms?

Figure 14 The compound calcium oxide is part of mortar, the "glue" that holds bricks together. In this compound, the ratio of the mass of calcium to the mass of oxygen is always 5 to 2.

Math TOOLBOX

Constant Ratios

When two pairs of numbers produce the same ratio, the ratio is said to be constant. Suppose you wanted to increase the recipe in the Math Toolbox on page 28. To double the recipe, you would need 4 cups of flour and 2 cups of sugar. The ratio 4:2 reduces to 2:1 by dividing each number by 2.

$$\frac{4}{2} = \frac{2}{1}$$

To triple the recipe you would need 6 cups of flour and 3 cups of sugar. The ratio 6:3 reduces to 2:1 by dividing each number by 3.

$$\frac{6}{3} = \frac{2}{1}$$

The two ratios are constant because they both reduce to 2:1.

Similarly, for any quantity of a compound, the ratio of the masses of the elements in the compound is constant.

Answers to Self-Assessment

Caption Question

Figure 13 An atom

☑ *Checkpoint*

Any two: Atoms of one element are exactly alike; atoms are indivisible; atoms of each element have a unique mass; atoms of two or more elements can combine to form compounds; the masses of the elements in a compound always have the same ratio.

Dalton's Ideas About Atoms

Demonstration

Materials *two glasses of water, a few drops of milk, bright flashlight with a narrow beam* **ACTIVITY**
Time 10 minutes

Out of sight of the students, place a few drops of milk into one glass of water and stir thoroughly. Be careful not to use too much. The two glasses of water should appear to be the same under room lights. Now darken the room lights, and from the side shine a powerful flashlight beam into each glass. Have students write down their observations. Return the room lights to normal and tell the students that you placed a few drops of milk in one glass. Can they tell which? Have students describe the observations that allowed them to distinguish. (*The beam from the flashlight was clearly visible in the glass with the milk droplets but was invisible in the other.*) Explain that this process shows one way to detect tiny particles that cannot be seen under normal conditions. Point out that what students saw were not individual atoms, but were particles from the milk mixed into the water. **learning modality: visual**

Math TOOLBOX

Review the concepts of writing ratios as fractions and the steps for reducing fractions to their smallest whole-number values. Point out that in the first example, both the numerator and denominator are divisible by 2. Ask: **In the second example, what was done to reduce the fraction $\frac{6}{3}$ to its smallest whole-number values?** (*The numerator and denominator were divided by 3.*) Stress the importance of performing the same operation on both numerator and denominator if ratios are to be kept constant. **learning modality: logical/ mathematical**

Ongoing Assessment

Writing Ask students to briefly describe atoms in their own words.

Ideas About Atoms Today

Language Arts
CONNECTION

Encourage students to think of other stories or movies about people becoming very small. Point out that a person who is the size of a cell in the human body would be visible only under a microscope. Remind students that atoms are much smaller than cells.

In Your Journal If students have trouble writing their stories, encourage them to imagine that they are the size of an atom in or on a specific object, such as a flower or tennis ball. Encourage students to be creative and to remember how small atoms are as they write.
learning modality: verbal

Atoms and Molecules

Using the Visuals: Figure 16

It is very difficult to accurately represent molecules. Scientists and teachers have traditionally used two approaches, known as the "ball-and-stick" model and the "space-filling" model. Figure 16 shows space-filling models of water, oxygen, acetic acid, and part of a DNA molecule. The ball-and-stick model can better show angles and distances between atomic centers, while the space-filling model is better at showing sizes of atoms and shapes of molecules. Direct student's attention to the water molecule and ask them which is hydrogen and which is oxygen. (*Small spheres are hydrogen.*) **How do the sizes of the atoms compare?** (*Oxygen is much larger.*) Point out that the DNA molecule and water molecule are not shown to the same scale.
learning modality: visual

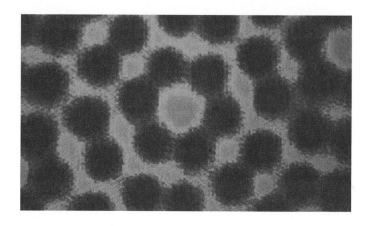

Figure 15 Here you can see something scientists once thought no one would ever see—atoms! This image of silicon atoms was produced by a scanning tunneling microscope.

Language Arts
CONNECTION

In Isaac Asimov's science fiction story *Fantastic Voyage*, people are shrunk down to the size of a single cell. Their experiences inside the body of a full-sized person are "fantastic" reading. Imagine what it would be like to shrink down to the size of a single atom!

In Your Journal

Write a one-page story about what you would see and experience as you shrink down to the size of an atom. Explore your new world, describing the other atoms and molecules around you. What happens as you grow back to normal size?

Ideas About Atoms Today

Atoms are so small that for many years no one expected to see them. Just how small are they? Compare the size of an atom to that of some everyday objects.

> One grain of sand on a typical beach contains more atoms than there are grains of sand on the entire beach.

> Newspaper pictures are made from tiny dots of ink. Each dot contains about a billion billion atoms! (That's a 1 followed by 18 zeros!)

> There are 2,000,000,000,000,000,000,000 (that's 2,000 billion billion) atoms of oxygen in one drop of water—and twice as many atoms of hydrogen!

Despite their tiny size, there is now a tool that gives a glimpse of what atoms look like. A scanning tunneling microscope can magnify matter so much that it can actually capture images of atoms. Figure 15 shows an example of what this microscope can reveal.

Atoms and Molecules

An atom can frequently be linked with one or more other atoms. The force that holds two atoms together is a **chemical bond.** Often, two or more atoms that are bonded together form a particle called a **molecule.** Some molecules are made of atoms that are alike, as in the oxygen gas (O_2) that you breathe. **Most molecules are made of two or more different types of atoms bonded together.** Water molecules have 2 hydrogen atoms combined with 1 oxygen atom (H_2O). Acetic acid, the compound that gives vinegar its sharp odor and sour taste, has 2 carbon atoms, 4 hydrogen atoms, and 2 oxygen atoms ($C_2H_4O_2$). Molecules can be huge. Some molecules in your body contain millions of atoms.

Background

Facts and Figures The scanning tunneling microscope was first developed in 1981 by Gerd Binnig and Heinrich Rohrer in Zurich, Switzerland. Its operation is based on the phenomenon known as tunneling, which occurs when electrons "jump" out of a surface to a conductor that is very close to the surface. The sharp tip of a tungsten needle is positioned about one billionth of a meter above the surface and slowly moved across the surface in a regular pattern. The tunneling current is read at each position, and a computer is used to build up a three-dimensional image of the surface. When the image is displayed on a television monitor, precisely arranged layers of atoms and even individual atoms can clearly be seen. For their discovery, Binnig and Rohrer were awarded the Nobel Prize in physics in 1986.

Oxygen

Water

Acetic acid

Figure 16 Each diagram on the left is a model of a molecule made of atoms bonded together. The molecule on the right shows a small part of the DNA in living cells. (This computer image of DNA was made using a color code for atoms different from the code used in this book.) *Classifying Which one of these models shows a molecule of an element? How do you know?*

The Atom as a Model

Look at the atoms in Figure 15 again. From that image, you cannot really see what atoms look like or how they might work. Like a person trying to imagine what's in a box by shaking it, scientists studying atoms must make inferences about them based on observations.

In this way, atoms act as models. In science, a model may be a diagram, a mental picture, a mathematical statement, or an object that helps explain ideas about the natural world. Scientists use models to make and test predictions. In chemistry, models of atoms and molecules are often used to explain how matter behaves. Dalton's description of atoms was one of the first atomic models. Ideas about atoms have changed greatly since Dalton's time, but models continue to be valuable tools in science. You will see models many times in this book. In the next chapter, for example, simple models of atoms and molecules will be used to help explain the nature of solids, liquids, and gases.

 Section 3 Review

1. What images did Dalton use to help describe atoms?
2. How are atoms and molecules related?
3. An ice cube consists of molecules of water (H_2O). Could you continue, forever, to break an ice cube into smaller and smaller pieces of ice? Explain your answer.
4. **Thinking Critically Interpreting Diagrams** Examine the model of acetic acid ($C_2H_4O_2$) in Figure 16. Which elements are represented by each of the three colors? How do you know? What does the model tell you about the way the different atoms are arranged?

Check Your Progress CHAPTER PROJECT
Get your teacher's approval of your procedure for testing your product. Then obtain the materials you need and perform the test. If you alter the procedure, change the instructions to reflect your alterations. (*Hint:* A good experimental procedure should be reliable—repeatable. Test more than one sample to see if your results are repeated.)

Program Resources

◆ **Unit 1 Resources** 1-3 Review and Reinforce, p. 25; 1-3 Enrich, p. 26

Media and Technology

📽 **Transparencies** "Models of Molecules," Transparency 1

Answers to Self-Assessment

Caption Question

Figure 16 Oxygen, because it is the only molecule made from one kind of atom.

The Atom as a Model

Including All Students

Review with students the use of a model to represent something that can't be easily viewed. Models can be used to study atoms, which are too tiny to see, or the solar system, which is to huge to view all at once. **learning modality: logical/mathematical**

3 Assess

Section 3 Review Answers

1. Tiny marbles or spheres that are impossible to break.
2. A molecule is made of two or more atoms joined together with a chemical bond.
3. No, the smallest possible piece of ice is one molecule of H_2O.
4. Blue—hydrogen, red—oxygen, black—carbon; the four blue spheres must represent the four hydrogen atoms; if oxygen is red, as in the two other models, the black spheres are carbon. The model shows which atoms are connected to other atoms.

Check Your Progress CHAPTER PROJECT
After students obtain their materials and begin to conduct their experiments, ask whether they have had to modify their procedures. If so, make sure their instructions reflect these changes. Also, make sure students are conducting multiple trials with the same product. Encourage students to average the results of their trials.

Performance Assessment

Skills Check Have students model atoms with small clay balls, then use their models to illustrate one of Dalton's ideas. (*Sample: Several identical clay balls together— all atoms of a given element are identical.*)

SECTION 4 Elements From Earth

TEKS: 6.1A, B; 6.2A, B, C, D; 6.4A; 6.7B

Objectives

After completing the lesson, students will be able to

◆ describe how the density of gold allows it to be panned;

◆ explain that a chemical reaction is needed to obtain an element from one of its compounds.

1 Engage/Explore

Activating Prior Knowledge

Supply students with samples of rocks that contain metals or metal compounds, such as iron pyrite or galena. Samples can probably be borrowed from the earth science teacher. Ask students to speculate how engineers could identify what kind of metal is in the rock and how they could extract it.

DISCOVER

Skills Focus designing an experiment

Materials *wet sand, metal bolts and screws, plastic tray or pie pan, water, bowl, paper towels*

Time 15 minutes

Tips One way to separate the mixture is to use a stream of water to wash the sand off the bolts. The sand can be collected in a bowl, then dried on paper towels.

Think It Over Procedures and their successes will vary. The suggested procedure separates the bolts from the sand by taking advantage of the difference in their masses. The lightweight sand particles are carried away by the stream of water, while the heavier bolts sink.

SECTION 4 Elements From Earth

DISCOVER ·················· ACTIVITY

How Can You Separate Bolts From Sand?

1. Mix wet sand with a few small metal bolts and screws. Place the mixture in a tray or pie pan.

2. Think of a way to separate the sand from the bolts. You may not use a magnet, but you may use water, a bowl, paper towels, and other supplies available in your classroom.

3. With your teacher's permission, try your procedure.

Think It Over

Designing an Experiment What properties of matter did you use to separate the sand and the bolts? How successful was your procedure?

GUIDE FOR READING

◆ What physical property of gold allows it to be panned?

◆ What must be done to obtain an element from one of its compounds?

Reading Tip As you read, list the ways that people obtain elements from the forms in which they are found in nature.

Key Terms electrolysis
• electrode

Gold! In 1848, several gold nuggets were found in the American River in northern California near a mill owned by John Sutter. Thousands of people rushed to California with pans, pickaxes, and shovels. They searched the riverbanks and stream beds hoping to find more nuggets or even gold flakes.

Some people got rich, but many went home empty-handed. Perhaps the most disappointed of all were those who found pyrite, a substance that looks like gold. Pyrite is actually a compound of iron and sulfur. Can you tell why pyrite is also called "fool's gold"?

◄ A miner pans for gold in northern California

READING STRATEGIES

Reading Tip Before students begin reading, have them preview the photographs and captions in the section. Then challenge students to describe or speculate about ways that people take matter out of the earth. List students' responses on the board. Then have students read the section and follow directions for the Reading Tip. Students should list panning, electrolysis, and heating. Revise or add to the items on the board after students have read the section.

Gold and Density

During the California gold rush, miners needed a way to remove the precious metal from a mixture that also contained dirt and sand. **Gold can be separated from other materials in a mixture because of its density.** As you read in Section 2, gold has a density of 19.3 g/cm³. This density is much higher than that of most other materials, including fool's gold, which has a density of only 5.0 g/cm³.

The miners used a technique called panning. They put the mixture of gold, dirt, and sand into a shallow pan and covered it with water. They then swirled the contents around and carefully poured off the water. The water carried the less dense dirt and sand with it. The more dense gold sank and was left behind. The miners repeated this process until only gold remained in the pan.

Today, gold mining is done on a much larger scale using machines called dredges. But the basic process of separating gold by its density is the same. The dredge scrapes up large amounts of dirt and sand, washes the mixture, and separates the gold in a way that's similar to panning.

☑ *Checkpoint* *What could you do to tell the difference between real gold and fool's gold?*

Copper and Electrolysis

In nature, finding an element that's not part of a compound is unusual. Most elements, including those that people use for industrial purposes in great amounts, are usually found as compounds. For example, copper compounds are most often found in a certain kind of ore. An ore is any rock that contains a metal or other economically useful material.

The process of obtaining copper from one of its compounds is more complicated than panning for gold. **To obtain an element from its compound, it is necessary to cause a chemical reaction to take place.** In that chemical change, the copper atoms must be separated from the other atoms in the compound.

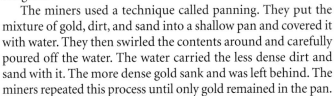

Figure 17 Gold nuggets contain the element gold.

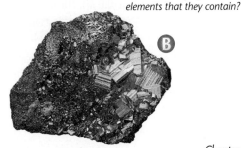

Figure 18 Ores contain useful elements that are combined with other substances. **A.** Malachite contains copper. **B.** Iron pyrite contains iron.
Applying Concepts Why do ores have different properties from the elements that they contain?

Chapter 1 **47**

Program Resources

◆ **Unit 1 Resources** 1-4 Lesson Plan, p. 27; 1-4 Section Summary, p. 28
◆ **Guided Reading and Study Workbook** 1-4

Answers to Self-Assessment

Caption Question

Figure 18 Ores are mixtures of many substances, often including the useful element in the form of a compound.

☑ *Checkpoint*

Find the density of the sample. Real gold has a density of 19.3 g/cm³ and fool's gold has a density of 5.0 g/cm³.

---

2 Facilitate

Gold and Density

Real-Life Learning

Materials *bunch of fresh spinach, large bowl of water*
Time 5 minutes

Tell students that many cooks rely on the same principle used to pan for gold to clean spinach. Because spinach grows in sandy soil, the leaves are often full of sand and can be difficult to clean. Place a bunch of spinach in the water so it is completely submerged and swirl it around. Ask students to predict what will happen. After a few minutes, lift the spinach out of the water and allow students to observe the water in the bowl. The bottom of the bowl should be covered with the sand that was in the spinach. Ask students to explain what happened. (*The sand is more dense than the water, and so it sank to the bottom, allowing you to lift out the clean spinach.*)
learning modality: visual

Copper and Electrolysis

Addressing Naive Conceptions

Some students may think that the process of electrolysis separates copper from the *rock* that contains it. The copper compounds are separated from the rock first. Then electrolysis separates copper from other *elements* in the copper compound by breaking the chemical bonds between them. **learning modality: verbal**

Ongoing Assessment

Oral Presentation Ask students to describe ways metals are found in nature. (*Some metals, such as gold, are found as elements. Other metals, such as copper, are found in compounds*)

Isolating Copper

Preparing for Inquiry

Key Concept Elements can be isolated from some compounds by passing an electric current through a solution containing the compound.

Skills Objectives Students will be able to
- observe the outcome of electrolysis;
- infer the changes occurring in a copper chloride solution during electrolysis.

Time 30 minutes

Advance Planning

- To make the 0.6 M copper (II) chloride (cupric chloride) solution, add 9.5 g of copper (II) chloride dihydrate, $CuCl_2 \cdot 2H_2O$, to 100 mL of distilled water. For 12 pairs of students, you will need about 600–1,200 mL of the solution.
- The electrodes can be used repeatedly, but the tips must be cleaned with #0000 steel wool between uses to remove plated copper.
- To make wire connections, any small leads with alligator clips on both ends will work for this lab. A length of at least 8 cm is easier for students to handle.

Alternative Materials

You may also use a copper sulfate solution.

Guiding Inquiry

Invitation

Show students a bright new penny. Ask students how the copper in the penny was found. *(Many will say the copper was in the ground in the pure elemental state).* Point out that most elements are not found in their elemental states, and they have to be processed to extract the pure element.

Introducing the Procedure

- Set up a sample apparatus for students to look at as they set up their own.
- Point out the positive and negative poles on the 9-volt battery. Remind students that they will be asked which electrode (+ or −) collected the copper.

Many steps are involved in obtaining copper from its ores. The last step in the process is called **electrolysis.** This term literally means "electric cutting." In one kind of electrolysis, a copper compound is dissolved in water, forming a mixture called a solution. Two metal strips called **electrodes** are placed in the copper compound solution. Each electrode is attached to a wire, and the wires are connected to a source of electric current such as a battery.

Real-World Lab

How It Works

Isolating Copper

I n nature, copper is usually found in compounds with other elements. In this investigation, you will perform an electrolysis procedure to isolate copper from a compound called copper chloride.

Problem

How can copper be isolated from a compound by electrolysis?

Skills Focus

observing, inferring

Materials

glass jar, about 250 mL
two paper clips
wires with alligator clips or battery holder with wires
copper chloride solution (0.6 *M*), 100 mL
6-volt battery
index card

Procedure

1. Unbend a paper clip and make a hook shape. Push the long end through an index card until the hooked part touches the card.

2. Repeat Step 1 with another paper clip so that the clips are about 2–3 cm apart. The paper clips serve as your electrodes.

3. Pour enough copper chloride solution into a jar to cover at least half the length of the paper clips when the index card is set on top of the jar. **CAUTION:** *Copper chloride solution can be irritating to the skin and eyes. Do not touch it with your hands or get it in your mouth. The solution can stain your skin and clothes.*

4. Place the index card on top of the jar. If the straightened ends of the paper clips are not at least half-covered by the copper chloride solution, add more solution.

Troubleshooting the Experiment

- Caution students to avoid breaking the electrodes.
- Some students may have difficulty detecting chlorine gas in Step 7. There may not be enough produced to be noticeable, or students may be unfamiliar with the odor.

Expected Outcome

- The pale yellow-gold or pinkish color on the tip of the negative electrode shows that copper has been deposited there.

- The faint odor of chlorine tells students that another substance was also produced by this reaction. They may see small bubbles being produced at the positive electrode. They may or may not be able to identify this substance.

Analyze and Conclude

1. Check students' diagrams. Make sure labels are correct.

2. Copper forms on the negative electrode, and chlorine gas bubbles at the positive electrode.

When the electric current is turned on, one electrode in the solution becomes coated with copper metal. At the same time, other materials form on the second electrode. In a laboratory, electrolysis produces only small amounts of copper metal. In industry, the isolation of copper from its ores happens on a huge scale and involves several complex steps. Because many copper compounds do not dissolve in water, the method of electrolysis used in the last step can vary.

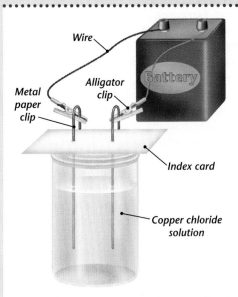

Wire

Battery

Alligator clip

Metal paper clip

Index card

Copper chloride solution

5. Attach a wire to each pole of a battery. Attach the other ends of the wires to a separate paper clip. (See the drawing.) Prevent the paper clips from touching each other.

6. Predict what you think will happen if you allow the current to run for 2–3 minutes. (*Hint:* What elements are present in the copper chloride solution?)

7. Let the setup run for 2–3 minutes or until you see a deposit forming on one of the electrodes. Also look for bubbles.

8. Disconnect the wires. Remove the index card. Bring your face close to the jar and gently wave your hand toward your nose. Note any odor.

9. Note whether the color of the solution has changed since you began the procedure.

10. Note the color of the tips of the electrodes.

11. Discard the solution as directed by your teacher, and wash your hands.

Analyze and Conclude

1. Make a labeled diagram of your experimental setup. Indicate which electrode is connected to the positive side of the battery and which is connected to the negative side.

2. On which electrode was the copper produced? On which electrode was the chlorine produced?

3. If the color of the solution changed, how can you explain the change?

4. Compare the properties of copper, chlorine, and copper chloride solution.

5. Describe the changes in matter that you observed. Classify them as physical changes or chemical changes.

6. **Apply** Using your observations during this lab as evidence, explain why you think copper chloride is a compound, not a mixture.

More to Explore

Suppose you were to reconnect the wires with the positive and negative sides reversed. Predict how your results would differ under these conditions. With your teacher's permission, carry out the electrolysis with the connections reversed. Was your prediction correct?

3. The color changed because the copper compound producing the color was changed during a chemical reaction.

4. Copper is a shiny, gold-colored metal. Chlorine is a dense, green, irritating gas. Copper chloride solution is a clear green liquid.

5. The dissolved copper chloride underwent a chemical change to form new substances, copper and chlorine. As the chemical change took place, the copper became a solid and the chlorine became a gas through physical changes.

6. Copper chloride must be a compound because the electrolysis caused a chemical change by breaking its chemical bonds, and two elements—copper and chlorine—were produced.

Extending the Inquiry

More to Explore Students may predict that the copper and chlorine will form on the opposite electrodes when the polarity is reversed.

Program Resources

◆ **Unit 1 Resources** Chapter 1 Real-World Lab blackline masters, pp. 33–35

Media and Technology

 Lab Activity Videotapes Grade 6, Tape 1

Iron and the Blast Furnace

Demonstration

ACTIVITY

Use gumdrops and toothpicks to show students how iron oxide is changed in a blast furnace. Connect one "iron atom" with two "oxygen atoms". Show students a single "carbon atom". Move the "oxygen atoms" to the "carbon atom". Ask students if the carbon atom is an element or a compound. (*element*)

3 Assess

Section 4 Review Answers

1. Gold is more dense than sand and dirt. When the mixture is swirled with water, the gold sinks. When the water is poured off, it carries away the sand and dirt.

2. A chemical change (chemical bonds must be broken)

3. The carbon in coke reacts with the oxygen that is bonded with the iron and leaves pure iron behind.

4. Recycling programs will probably become more important because more metals will be needed by Earth's growing population.

Check Your Progress

CHAPTER PROJECT

Assign students a new partner and have them exchange procedures and materials. After students conduct each other's experiments, set aside class time for them to discuss their results and to share ways they could make their procedures easier to follow.

Performance Assessment

Writing Have students create two flowcharts for the processes of removing metal from its ore by using heating and electrolysis.

Figure 19 Industry uses large-scale chemical reactions to produce useful materials. This blast furnace is used to make carbon react with iron ore to produce iron metal. The source of the carbon is coke, a substance produced from coal.

Iron and the Blast Furnace

Industry uses huge amounts of the element iron. Like copper, iron is usually found in an ore in the form of a compound. And also like copper, the element iron must be separated from its compounds by a chemical reaction.

Iron ores usually contain compounds formed of iron and oxygen. In order to release the iron, chunks of iron ore are placed in a hot fire along with coke, a source of carbon. In the intense heat of a blast furnace like the one in Figure 19, the carbon reacts with the oxygen. The element iron is left behind.

After leaving the blast furnace, iron is often used with other materials to produce mixtures having specific properties. For example, iron may be mixed with carbon and other metals to produce steel, which is stronger than iron alone. Adding chromium and nickel makes stainless steel, which resists rusting. Iron, copper, and gold are just three examples of useful elements that are extracted from Earth's surface.

Section 4 Review

1. Describe how panning for gold takes advantage of a specific property of gold.
2. What kind of change must take place to remove an element from its compound? Explain.
3. What happens to the elements in iron ore when the ore is mixed with carbon and heated?
4. **Thinking Critically** **Making Judgments** Planet Earth contains a limited supply of all metals. Predict whether programs to recycle aluminum, iron, and other metals will become more important in the future.

Check Your Progress

CHAPTER PROJECT

Trade your written procedure and product samples with a new partner. Repeat this partner's procedure, following the directions as exactly as you can. Share your results with your new partner. Think of ways to improve both your procedure and your partner's procedure to make them clearer to follow.

Program Resources

◆ **Unit 1 Resources** 1-4 Review and Reinforce, p. 29; 1-4 Enrich, p. 30

Media and Technology

Physical Science Videodisc Unit 1, Side 1, "Ore What?"

Chapter 8

Describing Matter and Energy

Key Ideas
- Each specific substance has its own physical and chemical properties. These properties can be used to identify the substance.
- Matter is made up of elements. Elements can be chemically combined in compounds.
- Physical changes alter the form of a substance, but not its identity. Chemical changes result in one or more new substances.
- Energy is needed for both physical and chemical changes. There are different types of energy, which interact with matter in different ways.

Key Terms

matter	physical property	mixture
energy	chemical property	physical change
chemistry	element	chemical change
substance	compound	

 Measuring Matter

Key Ideas
- Mass is a measurement of how much matter an object contains. If you move an object away from Earth, its weight changes, but its mass stays the same.
- The density of an object equals its mass divided by its volume. A unit of density is always a mass unit divided by a volume unit, such as grams per cubic centimeter (g/cm^3).

Key Terms

weight	volume
mass	density
International System of Units (SI)	

 Particles of Matter

Key Ideas
- Atoms are the smallest particles of an element.
- Dalton stated that atoms are unbreakable, rigid spheres. He also said that atoms of different elements are different from one another.
- Atoms can be combined into molecules, which are held together by chemical bonds.

Key Terms

atom	chemical bond	molecule

Elements From Earth

INTEGRATING EARTH SCIENCE

Key Ideas
- Gold, which is usually found in nature as an element, can be separated from other materials because of its density.
- Earth contains deposits of many elements in the form of compounds. A chemical reaction is needed to remove an element from its compound.

Key Terms

electrolysis	electrode

Organizing Information

Concept Map Copy the concept map about classifying matter onto a separate sheet of paper. Then complete the map and add a title. (For more on concept maps, see the Skills Handbook.)

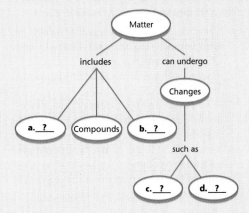

Concept Map Sample title: Classifying Matter; **a.** Elements **b.** Mixtures **c.** Physical changes **d.** Chemical changes

Program Resources
- **Unit 1 Resources** Chapter 1 Project Scoring Rubric, p. 14
- **Performance Assessment** Chapter 1, pp. 5–7
- **Chapter and Unit Tests** Chapter 1 Test, pp. 4–7

Media and Technology

Computer Test Bank
Chapter 1 Test

Reviewing Content
Multiple Choice
1. a 2. b 3. d 4. a 5. a

True or False
6. Elements 7. true 8. mass
9. density 10. true

Checking Concepts
11. When a piece of paper is torn into two pieces, its parts have the same kinds of properties as the original piece of paper. Thus, the paper has undergone a physical change.
12. Place a small amount of water in the graduated cylinder. Record the volume. Submerge the rock and record the new volume. The difference between the new and old volumes is the volume of the rock.
13. Its density is less than that of water (1.0 g/cm^3).
14. The water releases energy as it changes from a liquid to a solid.
15. Encourage students to think creatively about observing properties of matter and writing about them. Challenge students to describe each object so that others can identify it from the description.

Thinking Critically
16. Salt is a solid, water is a liquid, but salt water is a solution, or mixture. Students may suggest boiling the solution to produce water vapor and solid salt.
17. Atoms and molecules are both extremely small particles of matter. Molecules are made up of two or more atoms bonded together. For example, a carbon atom alone is the smallest piece of the element carbon. In the molecule CO_2, a carbon atom is bonded to two oxygen atoms.
18. Dalton reasoned that since every atom of an element is identical and unique to that element, every sample of a substance has the same properties.
19. Since the density of the gold decreases but the mass stays the same, the volume must increase.

Reviewing Content

 Review key concepts online using iText at www.phschool.com

Multiple Choice
Choose the letter of the answer that best completes the statement or answers the question.

1. Matter made of two or more substances is a(n)
   a. mixture.   b. element.
   c. compound.   d. property.
2. One form of electromagnetic energy is
   a. motion.   b. light.
   c. electricity. d. energy in matter.
3. The density of an object equals
   a. the product of its length, width, and height.
   b. its volume divided by its mass.
   c. the product of the mass and volume.
   d. its mass divided by its volume.
4. Dalton imagined atoms to be
   a. rigid, unbreakable spheres.
   b. all exactly alike.
   c. always joined together in compounds.
   d. of equal mass.
5. A method used to release iron metal from its ore involves
   a. heating the ore and carbon together.
   b. cooling the ore in an ice bath.
   c. breaking the ore into small pieces.
   d. panning.

True or False
If the statement is true, write true. If it is false, change the underlined word to make it true.

6. <u>Compounds</u> are substances that cannot be broken down into other substances by any chemical means.
7. <u>Energy</u> is always involved when changes in matter occur.
8. If you move an object from place to place in the universe, the <u>weight</u> of the object will stay the same.
9. Grams per milliliter (g/mL) is an example of a unit of <u>volume</u>.
10. One of Dalton's principles is that each element is made of its own kind of <u>atom</u>.

Checking Concepts
11. When a piece of paper is torn into two pieces, has it undergone a chemical change or a physical change? Explain.
12. How could you find the volume of a small rock, using only a graduated cylinder and water?
13. What can you infer about the density of a substance if a block of that substance floats in water?
14. In terms of energy, describe what happens to water in a freezer.
15. Writing to Learn In a novel or short story, the author describes the properties of objects he or she is writing about. These details add interest to the story. Select at least six different kinds of objects. You might include objects from nature as well as objects made by people. List the properties of each object. Now use that list to write the first paragraph of a story.

Thinking Critically
16. Problem Solving How can you show that salt water is a mixture and not a compound? First compare the properties of the solution to the properties of the individual components. Then come up with a plan to separate the solution into its components.
17. Comparing and Contrasting Compare and contrast atoms and molecules. What do the two kinds of particles have in common? How are they related? Give an example that shows this relationship.
18. Applying Concepts How can you use Dalton's atomic theory to explain why every sample of a particular substance has the same properties?
19. Inferring Solid gold has a greater density than liquid gold. What must happen to the volume of a given mass of solid gold when it becomes a liquid? Explain.

Applying Skills
20. A: 7.6 g/cm³; B: 8.0 g/cm³;
C: 7.2 g/cm³; D: 8.4 g/cm³;
E: 8.9 g/cm³; F: 7.5 g/cm³
21. Coin D
22. The density of Coin E (8.9 g/cm³) is very close to 8.92 g/cm³, so Coin E very likely could be pure copper. The density of Coin C (7.2 g/cm³) is close enough to 7.14 (g/cm³) that there is a good chance Coin C could be pure zinc.

Applying Skills

Use the table below to answer Questions 20–22. The table lists the mass and volume of six coins.

Coin	Mass (g)	Volume (cm³)
A	3.1	0.41
B	4.0	0.50
C	8.6	1.2
D	8.0	0.95
E	9.8	1.1
F	5.0	0.67

20. Calculating Based on the data in the table, calculate the density of Coins A–F.

21. Interpreting Data In Altrusia, all coins are made of a mixture of copper and zinc that has a density of 8.42 g/cm³. Which coins could be from Altrusia?

22. Drawing Conclusions The density of copper is 8.92 g/cm³ and the density of zinc is 7.14 g/cm³. If you assume that only copper and zinc were used to make the coins, can any of the coins be pure copper? Can any be pure zinc? Explain.

Test Preparation

Use these questions to prepare for standardized tests.

Use the diagram to answer Questions 23–26.

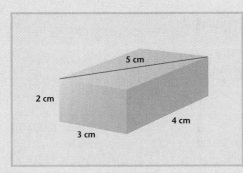

Alexander found a solid block of an unknown material. He used a metric ruler to measure the size of the block. The measurements he recorded are shown in the diagram.

23. What is the volume of the block?
A 9 cm **B** 24 cm²
C 24 cm³ **D** 60 cm³

24. Which measurement shown in the diagram was not needed to find the volume of the box?
F length (4 cm) **G** height (2 cm)
H width (3 cm) **J** diagonal (5 cm)

25. Alexander knows that the density of the material from which the block is made is 2 g/cm³. Knowing this, what is the mass of the block?
A 4.8 g **B** 48 g
C 480 g **D** 4,800 g

26. If the block could be molded into a flatter and longer shape, then the
F mass, volume, and density all would change.
G volume would change, but the mass and density would remain the same.
H mass and volume would change, but the density would remain the same.
J mass, volume, and density all would remain the same.

Test Preparation

23. C **24.** J **25.** B **26.** J

2 Solids, Liquids, and Gases

Sections	Time	Student Edition Activities	Other Activities	
CHAPTER PROJECT **A Story of Changes in Matter** p. 55	Ongoing (2–3 weeks)	TEKS: 6.2D; 6.3C Check Your Progress, pp. 67, 79 Present Your Project, p. 83	TE	Chapter 2 Project Notes, pp. 54–55
1 States of Matter pp. 56–60 TEKS: 6.7B 2.1.1 Define and differentiate among solids, liquids, and gases in terms of shape and volume. 2.1.2 Compare the particle motion in solids, liquids, and gases.	2 periods/ 1 block	TEKS: 6.2D **Discover** What Are Solids, Liquids, and Gases?, p. 56 **Try This** As Thick as Honey, p. 59 **Science at Home,** p. 60	TE	Using the Visuals: Figure 5, p. 58
2 Gas Behavior pp. 61–67 TEKS: 6.7B 2.2.1 Define the relationship between volume and pressure of a gas and state Boyle's law. 2.2.2 Define the relationship between pressure and temperature of a gas. 2.2.3 Define the relationship between volume and the temperature of a gas and state Charles's Law.	3 periods/ $1\frac{1}{2}$ blocks	TEKS: 6.1A; 6.2A, B; 6.3E; 6.4A **Discover** How Can Air Keep Chalk From Breaking?, p. 61 **Sharpen Your Skills** Developing Hypotheses, p. 62 **Try This** Balloon Test, p. 64	TE TE TE TE TE	Including All Students, p. 62 Demonstration, p. 63 Including All Students, p. 63 Real-Life Learning, p. 65 Inquiry Challenge, p. 66
3 **INTEGRATING MATHEMATICS** **Graphing Gas Behavior** pp. 68–73 TEKS: 6.7B 2.3.1 Construct and interpret graphs for Charles's Law and Boyle's Law.	2 periods/ 1 block	TEKS: 6.1A; 6.2A, B, C, E; 6.3C; 6.4A **Discover** What Does a Graph of Pressure and Temperature Show?, p. 68 **Science at Home,** p. 71 **Skills Lab: Drawing Conclusions** It's a Gas, pp. 72–73		
4 Changes in State pp. 74–80 TEKS: 6.7B 2.4.1 Explain that thermal energy always flows from a warmer substance to a cooler substance. 2.4.2 Identify examples of changes in state and explain how thermal energy is involved in each example.	2 periods/ 1 block	TEKS: 6.1A; 6.2A, B, C, E; 6.4A **Discover** What Happens When You Breathe on a Mirror?, p. 74 **Skills Lab: Measuring** Melting Ice, p. 80 (Probeware version available)	TE TE LM	Demonstration, p. 75, 76 Addressing Naive Conceptions, p. 77 2, "Comparing How Liquids Cool"
Study Guide/Chapter Assessment pp. 81–83	1 period/ $\frac{1}{2}$ block	PLM Provides blackline masters for Probeware labs	ISAB	Provides teaching and review of all inquiry skills

Key: **CTB** Computer Test Bank
CUT Chapter and Unit Tests
ELL Teacher's ELL Handbook

CHAPTER PLANNING GUIDE

 The Resource Pro® CD-ROM provides flexibility for planning the instruction for any type of schedule.

Program Resources	Assessment Strategies	Media and Technology
UR Chapter 2 Project Teacher Notes, pp. 36–37 **UR** Chapter 2 Project Overview and Worksheets, pp. 38–41	**SE** Performance Assessment: Present Your Project, p. 83 **TE** Check Your Progress, pp. 67, 79 **UR** Chapter 2 Project Scoring Rubric, p. 42	Science Explorer at www.phschool.com Student Edition on Audio CD, English-Spanish, Chapter 2
UR 2-1 Section Lesson Plan, p. 43 **UR** 2-1 Section Summary, p. 44 **UR** 2-1 Review and Reinforce, p. 45 **UR** 2-1 Enrich, p. 46	**SE** Section 1 Review, p. 60 **TE** Ongoing Assessment, pp. 57, 59 **TE** Performance Assessment, p. 60	Physical Science Videodisc Unit 1, Side 1, "Viscosity Derby" Videotape Grade 6, Unit 1, "Viscosity Derby" Transparency 2, "Particle View of Solids, Liquids, and Gases"
UR 2-2 Section Lesson Plan, p. 47 **UR** 2-2 Section Summary, p. 48 **UR** 2-2 Review and Reinforce, p. 49 **UR** 2-2 Enrich, p. 50	**SE** Section 2 Review, p. 67 **TE** Ongoing Assessment, pp. 63, 65 **TE** Performance Assessment, p. 67	Physical Science Videodisc Unit 1, Side 1, "Racing Hot Air Balloons" Videotape Grade 6, Unit 1, "Racing Hot Air Balloons" Transparencies 3, "Boyle's Law"; 4, "Relationship of Pressure and Temperature"; 5, "Charles's Law"
UR 2-3 Section Lesson Plan, p. 51 **UR** 2-3 Section Summary, p. 52 **UR** 2-3 Review and Reinforce, p. 53 **UR** 2-3 Enrich, p. 54 **UR** Skills Lab blackline masters, pp. 59–61	**SE** Section 3 Review, p. 71 **TE** Ongoing Assessment, p. 69 **TE** Performance Assessment, p. 71	Lab Activity Videotapes, Tape 1 Transparency 6, "Graphs of Charles's Law and Boyle's Law"
UR 2-4 Section Lesson Plan, p. 55 **UR** 2-4 Section Summary, p. 56 **UR** 2-4 Review and Reinforce, p. 57 **UR** 2-4 Enrich, p. 58 **UR** Skills Lab blackline masters, pp. 62–63	**SE** Section 4 Review, p. 79 **TE** Ongoing Assessment, p. 77 **TE** Performance Assessment, p. 79	Physical Science Videodisc Unit 4, Side 2, "The Disappearing Ice Cube" Videotape Grade 6, Unit 1, "The Disappearing Ice Cube" Lab Activity Videotapes, Tape 1
ELL Provides multiple strategies for English language learners **GRSW** Provides worksheets to promote student comprehension of content **RCA** Provides strategies to improve science reading skills	**SE** Chapter 2 Study Guide/Assessment, pp. 81–83 **PA** Chapter 2 Assessment, pp. 8–10 **CUT** Chapter 2 Test, pp. 8–11 **CTB** Chapter 2 Test **PHAS** Provides standardized test preparation	Chapter 2 Computer Test Bank, Chapter 2 Test

GRSW Guided Reading and Study Workbook
ISAB Inquiry Skills Activity Book
LM Laboratory Manual

PA Performance Assessment
PHAS Prentice Hall Assessment System
PLM Probeware Lab Manual

RCA Reading in the Content Area
SE Student Edition

TE Teacher's Edition
UR Unit Resources

Student Edition Activities Planner

ACTIVITy	Time (minutes)	Materials Quantities for one work group	Skills
Section 1			
Discover, p. 56	10	**Consumable** fizzing antacid tablet, large balloon, water **Nonconsumable** 1-L plastic soda bottle	Classifying
Try This, p. 59	10	**Consumable** honey, vegetable oil **Nonconsumable** 2 clear glass jars with screw-top lids	Drawing Conclusions
Science at Home, p. 60	home	**Consumable** water **Nonconsumable** turkey baster	Communicating
Section 2			
Discover, p. 61	10	**Consumable** sheet of wax paper or plastic wrap, plastic bubble wrap, tape **Nonconsumable** 3 pieces of chalk	Inferring
Sharpen Your Skills, p. 62	15	**Consumable** wire or pipe cleaner, soap solution (made from liquid dish soap and glycerin, if available) **Nonconsumable** large pan	Developing Hypotheses
Try This, p. 64	10	**Nonconsumable** balloon, paper or plastic cup	Developing Hypotheses
Section 3			
Discover, p. 68	15	**Consumable** graph paper **Nonconsumable** pencil	Graphing
Science at Home, p. 71	home	**Nonconsumable** newspapers or magazines	Interpreting Graphs
Skills Lab, pp. 72–73	20	**Nonconsumable** strong plastic syringe (with no needle), at least 35 cm^3 capacity; modeling clay; 4 books of uniform weight, computer and graphing software (optional)	Drawing Conclusions
Section 4			
Discover, p. 74	15	**Nonconsumable** hand mirrors, soft cloths	Developing Hypotheses
Skills Lab, p. 80	30	**Consumable** ice cubes, about 2 cm on each side; warm water (about 40°C–45°C), water at room temperature **Nonconsumable** thermometer or temperature probes and CBL procedure (optional); stopwatch or timer; 2 plastic cups, about 200 mL each; 2 stirring rods, preferably plastic	Measuring

A list of all materials required for the Student Edition activities can be found on pages T43–T49. You can obtain information about ordering materials by calling 1-800-848-9500 or by accessing the Science Explorer Internet site at **www.phschool.com**.

Texas Essential Knowledge and Skills

(6.1) Scientific processes. The student conducts field and laboratory investigations using safe, environmentally appropriate, and ethical practices. *(Sections 2, 3, 4)*
The student is expected to:
(A) demonstrate safe practices during field and laboratory investigations.

(6.2) Scientific processes. The student uses scientific inquiry methods during field and laboratory investigations. *(Project; Sections 1, 2, 3, 4)*
The student is expected to:
(A) plan and implement investigative procedures including asking questions, formulating testable hypotheses, and selecting and using equipment and technology;
(B) collect data by observing and measuring;
(C) analyze and interpret information to construct reasonable explanations from direct and indirect evidence;
(D) communicate valid conclusions; and
(E) construct graphs, tables, maps, and charts using tools including computers to organize, examine, and evaluate data.

(6.3) Scientific processes. The student uses critical thinking and scientific problem solving to make informed decisions. *(Project; Sections 2, 3)*
The student is expected to:
(C) represent the natural world using models and identify their limitations;
(E) connect Grade 6 science concepts with the history of science and contributions of scientists.

(6.4) Scientific processes. The student knows how to use a variety of tools and methods to conduct science inquiry. *(Sections 2, 3, 4)*
The student is expected to:
(A) collect, analyze, and record information using tools including beakers, petri dishes, meter sticks, graduated cylinders, weather instruments, timing devices, hot plates, test tubes, safety goggles, spring scales, magnets, balances, microscopes, telescopes, thermometers, calculators, field equipment, compasses, computers, and computer probes.

(6.7) Science concepts. The student knows that substances have physical and chemical properties. *(Sections 1, 2, 3, 4)*
The student is expected to:
(B) classify substances by their physical and chemical properties.

Take It to the Net

 Interactive text at www.phschool.com

Science Explorer comes alive with iText.

- **Complete student text** is accessible from any computer with Internet access or a CD-ROM drive.
- **Animations, simulations, and videos** enhance student understanding and retention of concepts.
- **Self-tests and online study tools** assess student understanding.
- **Teacher management tools** help you make the most of this valuable resource.

STAY CURRENT with **SCIENCE NEWS®**

Find out the latest research and information about properties of matter at **www.phschool.com**.

Go to **www.phschool.com**. Select Texas on the navigation bar. Click on the Science icon. Then click on Science Explorer under PH@school.

A Story of Changes in Matter

TEKS: 6.2D; 6.3C

When matter changes state from solid to liquid or from liquid to gas, changes also occur on the level of the particles that make up the material. In each state, particles are arranged in a characteristic way and have particular amounts of energy.

Purpose In this project, students will use the concepts from the chapter to prepare a skit or cartoon that demonstrates what happens at the particle level of matter during a physical change.

Skills Focus After completing the Chapter 2 Project, students will be able to
- pose questions about how physical change affects the particles of matter;
- form operational definitions relating changes of state to volume, temperature, and pressure;
- communicate their understanding of changes of state through skits or cartoons.

Project Time Line This project should be completed in two stages. First, Section 1 in the text introduces students to the physical states of matter, and Section 2 discusses the behavior of gases in relation to volume, temperature, and pressure. Following the completion of Section 2, students should begin working on their storyboards, applying the concepts they have just learned. Then, after learning about changes of state in Section 4, they may revise their storyboards, work with peer editors, and complete their final presentations. Before beginning the project, see Chapter 2 Project Teacher Notes on pages 36–37 in Unit 1 Resources for more details.

Possible Materials Materials will vary depending on whether students do skits or cartoons. Encourage students to be creative in selecting props for their skits. Students who choose to do cartoons will need large sheets of paper or poster board so that their cartoons can be large enough to be seen by the entire class during presentations. They also need paint, markers, or dark ink to draw their cartoons.

CHAPTER

2 Solids, Liquids, and Gases

WEB ACTIVITY www.phschool.com

54

Launching the Project Show students some examples of cartoons that present science concepts. Talk about how these cartoons use exaggeration, slapstick humor, and puns to make scientific ideas easier to remember. Discuss how a skit is similar to a cartoon in that they both are visually oriented and involve humor. Organize students into groups and have them list the properties of solids, liquids, and gases. To introduce the project, ask: **How could you use cartoons and skits to model the properties of solids, liquids, and gases?**

(Sample Answer: In a skit, individual people could represent particles.)

Allow time for students to read the description of the project in their text, then distribute the Chapter 2 Project Overview and Worksheets on pages 38–41 in Unit 1 Resources. Encourage discussions on cartoon designs, skit plans, and materials that could be used in the skits. Answer any initial questions students may have.

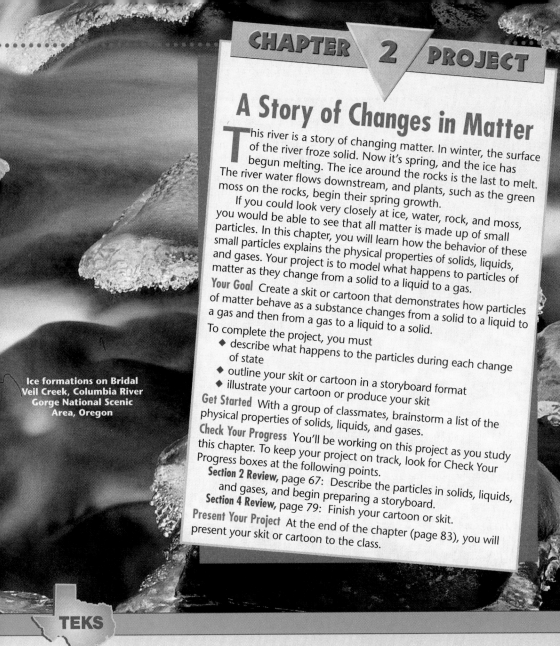

CHAPTER 2 PROJECT

A Story of Changes in Matter

This river is a story of changing matter. In winter, the surface of the river froze solid. Now it's spring, and the ice has begun melting. The ice around the rocks is the last to melt. The river water flows downstream, and plants, such as the green moss on the rocks, begin their spring growth.

If you could look very closely at ice, water, rock, and moss, you would be able to see that all matter is made up of small particles. In this chapter, you will learn how the behavior of these small particles explains the physical properties of solids, liquids, and gases. Your project is to model what happens to particles of matter as they change from a solid to a liquid to a gas.

Your Goal Create a skit or cartoon that demonstrates how particles of matter behave as a substance changes from a solid to a liquid to a gas and then from a gas to a liquid to a solid.

To complete the project, you must
- describe what happens to the particles during each change of state
- outline your skit or cartoon in a storyboard format
- illustrate your cartoon or produce your skit

Get Started With a group of classmates, brainstorm a list of the physical properties of solids, liquids, and gases.

Check Your Progress You'll be working on this project as you study this chapter. To keep your project on track, look for Check Your Progress boxes at the following points.

Section 2 Review, page 67: Describe the particles in solids, liquids, and gases, and begin preparing a storyboard.

Section 4 Review, page 79: Finish your cartoon or skit.

Present Your Project At the end of the chapter (page 83), you will present your skit or cartoon to the class.

Ice formations on Bridal Veil Creek, Columbia River Gorge National Scenic Area, Oregon

TEKS

In addition to process TEKS, this chapter addresses these concept TEKS as they relate to the chapter's topics.

(6.7) The student knows that substances have physical and chemical properties. The student is expected to:
(B) classify substances by their physical and chemical properties.

55

Program Resources

- **Unit 1 Resources** Chapter 2 Project Teacher Notes, pp. 36–37; Chapter 2 Project Overview and Worksheets, pp. 38–41

Media and Technology

Student Edition on Audio CD
English-Spanish, Chapter 2

WEB ACTIVITY www.phschool.com

You will find an Internet activity, chapter self-tests for students, and links to other chapter topics at this site.

Performance Assessment

The Chapter 2 Project Scoring Rubric on page 42 of Unit 1 Resources will help you evaluate how well students complete the Chapter 2 Project. Students will be assessed on
- how they describe what happens to particles during changes of state;
- how they organize the story outline in storyboard format;
- how thoroughly their cartoons or skits illustrate the science concepts;
- their ability to work cooperatively with others.

By sharing the Chapter 2 Project Scoring Rubric with students at the beginning of the project, you will make it clear to them what they are expected to do.

TEKS: 6.2D; 6.7B

Objectives

After completing the lesson, students will be able to

◆ define and differentiate among solids, liquids, and gases in terms of shape and volume;

◆ compare the particle motion in solids, liquids, and gases.

1 Engage/Explore

Activating Prior Knowledge

Ask students: **Which is easier to hold in your hands—a small rock or 100 mL of water? Why?** *(A rock, because it is solid and keeps its shape. The water is liquid and flows out of your hands.)* Explain that students will learn more about the way solids and liquids hold their shapes in this section.

DISCOVER

Skills Focus classifying
Materials *fizzing antacid tablet, large balloon, 1-L plastic soda bottle, water*
Time 10 minutes
Tips Use only seltzer antacid tablets. Have some students try the activity using two antacid tablets. Challenge them to predict what will happen. Tell students the gas formed is carbon dioxide.
Expected Outcome The balloon inflates with the gas produced by the reaction of the antacid tablet and water.
Think It Over Solid—antacid tablet; liquid—water; gas—bubbles produced. Definitions will vary. Sample: *A gas can form bubbles in water; a liquid can change its shape to fit its container; and a solid has a definite shape.*

DISCOVER · ACTIVITY

What Are Solids, Liquids, and Gases?

1. Break an antacid tablet (fizzing type) into three or four pieces. Place the pieces inside a large, uninflated balloon.

2. Fill a 1-liter plastic bottle about halfway with water. Stretch the mouth of the balloon over the top of the bottle, taking care to keep the pieces inside the balloon.

3. Jiggle the balloon so that the pieces fall into the bottle. Observe what happens for about two minutes.

4. Remove the balloon and examine its contents.

Think It Over

Classifying Identify examples of the different states of matter—solids, liquids, and gases—that you observed in this activity. Define each of the three states in your own words.

GUIDE FOR READING

◆ How do shape, volume, and particle motion help classify solids, liquids, and gases?

Reading Tip Before you read, list properties that you think classify substances as solids, liquids, or gases. Revise your list as you read.

Key Terms solid
• crystalline solid
• melting point
• amorphous solid
• liquid • viscosity
• gas

If you visit the annual Winter Carnival in St. Paul, Minnesota, you will see some unusual structures. To celebrate the cold winter weather, people carve huge sculptures out of ice. Over the years, the carnival has featured giant snow figures and ice palaces like the one shown here.

Even in Minnesota, anything made of snow and ice won't last beyond winter. When the temperature rises, snow figures and ice palaces melt into liquid water. And unlike frozen water, liquid water is a poor building material.

Your world is full of materials that can be classified as solids, liquids, or gases. Those materials may be elements, compounds, or mixtures. Gold is an element. Air is a mixture of gases. Water is a compound you've seen as both a solid and a liquid. The states of matter are not defined by what they are made of, but mainly by whether or not they hold their volume and shape.

Figure 1 Each year ice palaces like this one delight visitors to the Winter Carnival in St. Paul, Minnesota.

READING STRATEGIES

Reading Tip Help students think of properties that characterize a solid, a liquid, and a gas by writing questions such as these on the board: *Does it have a definite shape? Does it have a definite volume? How are its particles arranged? How do its particles move?*

Students should be able to characterize the states of matter by shape and volume, but may not be able to answer questions about particles until they have read the section.

Study and Comprehension Have students write brief summaries of the information under each heading. Remind them to include only main ideas and key details. Write each heading from the section on a note card. Place the note cards face down on a table. Then invite a volunteer to select one card and use his or her notes to give a brief oral report on the subject.

Figure 2 In the tanks on their backs, these scuba divers carry air to breathe. *Classifying Find an example of each state of matter in this photograph.*

Solids

What if you were to pick up a solid object, such as a pen or a comb, and move it from place to place around the room? What would you observe? Would the object ever change its size or shape as you moved it? Would a pen become larger if you put it in a bowl? Would a comb become flatter when you place it on a tabletop? Of course not. A **solid** has a definite volume and a definite shape. If your pen has a volume of 6 cm^3 and a cylindrical shape, then it will keep that volume and shape in any position and in any container.

Particles in a Solid The particles that make up a solid are packed very closely together, as shown in Figure 3A. In addition, each particle is tightly fixed in one position. This makes it hard to separate them. **Because the particles in a solid are packed tightly together and stay in fixed positions, a solid has a definite shape and volume.**

Are the particles in a solid completely motionless? No, not really. The particles vibrate, meaning they move back and forth slightly. This motion is similar to a person running in place. Or, you can think of the particles in a solid as something like a group of balls connected by tight springs. Like the balls in Figure 3B, the particles that make up a solid stay in about the same position. However, the individual pieces are still able to vibrate back and forth in their places.

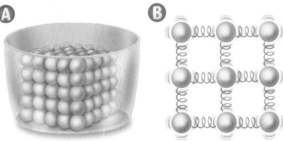

Figure 3 The balls represent the particles in a solid. **A.** A solid keeps its own shape. It doesn't take the shape of a container. **B.** The particles vibrate back and forth within the solid.

Program Resources

◆ **Unit 1 Resources** 2-1 Lesson Plan, p. 43; 2-1 Section Summary, p. 44
◆ **Guided Reading and Study Workbook** 2-1

Answers to Self-Assessment

Caption Question

Figure 2 The scuba tanks are solids, the ocean water is a liquid, and the exhaled air in the bubbles is a gas.

2 Facilitate

Solids

Using the Visuals: Figure 3

Ask students to use their fingers to trace the shape of the solid shown in 3A and compare it to the shape of the container. Ask: **What part of the diagram represents how the solid vibrates?** (*The springs shown in 3B*) Direct students to place a finger on the particle in the center of 3B. Ask: **If the particle vibrates to the left, what will happen to the springs and particles next to it?** (*The spring on the left will coil more tightly and the spring on the right will stretch. The particles in a solid move slightly, but stay attached to each other.*) **learning modality: visual**

Ongoing Assessment

Writing Have students briefly explain how the arrangement of the particles in a solid determines the properties of the solid.

Solids, continued

Language Arts Connection

Explain that the Greek prefix *a-* means "without" and the root word *morph-* means "shape." Ask: **How do the Greek meanings combine to describe an *amorphous* solid?** (*The Greek words mean "without shape," and the particles of an amorphous solid lack a regular pattern or shape.*) **learning modality: verbal**

Liquids

Figure 4 When you heat an amorphous solid such as this butter, it softens before it melts. *Comparing and Contrasting How are the particles in an amorphous solid different from the particles in a crystalline solid?*

Types of Solids In many solids, the particles form a regular, repeating pattern. These patterns create crystals. Solids that are made up of crystals are classified as **crystalline solids** (KRIS tuh lin). Salt, sugar, sand, and snow are examples of crystalline solids. When a crystalline solid such as snow is heated, it melts at a distinct temperature called its **melting point.**

In other solids the particles are not arranged in a regular pattern. These solids are classified as **amorphous solids** (uh MAWR fus). Plastics, rubber, and glass are amorphous solids. Unlike a crystalline solid, an amorphous solid does not have a distinct melting point. Instead, when it is heated it becomes softer and softer as its temperature rises. You have probably noticed this physical property in plastic items that have been out in the sun on a hot day. The plastic gradually melts. In fact, the word *plastic* means "able to be molded into many shapes."

☑ *Checkpoint* How do crystalline and amorphous solids differ?

Liquids

Unlike a solid, a **liquid** has no shape of its own. Instead, a liquid takes on the shape of its container. Without a container, a liquid spreads into a wide, shallow puddle.

However, liquids are like solids in that they do not easily compress or expand. If you gently squeezed on a water-filled plastic bag, for example, the water might change its shape, but its volume would not decrease or increase.

What if you have 100 mL of water? If you pour it into another container, the water still occupies 100 mL. It has the same volume no matter what shape its container has.

Figure 5 Although a liquid's volume does not change, it takes the shape of whatever container you pour it into.

Background

Facts and Figures Space scientists study a fourth state of matter—*plasma.* Atoms of plasma behave differently from atoms in solids, liquids, and gases. In these three states of matter, the nucleus of each atom is surrounded by its rapidly moving electrons. The negatively charged electrons are attracted to the positively charged nucleus. In plasma, which forms at very high temperatures, electrons break free of this attraction and flow freely around the positively charged nuclei of other atoms. Plasma conducts electricity and has strong magnetic fields. As the major component of stars, plasma makes up about 99 percent of the matter in the universe. On Earth, plasma exists in lightning and neon lights.

Figure 6 You can think of the particles of a liquid as somewhat like the people in this train station. They remain near one another but move from place to place.

Particles in a Liquid The particles in a liquid are packed almost as closely as in a solid. However, the particles in a liquid move around one another freely. **Because its particles are free to move, a liquid has no definite shape. However, it does have a definite volume.** You can compare a liquid to the rush-hour crowd at a train station. Like particles in a liquid, the people in the crowd move around the platform that contains them, but they stay in close contact with one another.

Viscosity Because particles in a liquid are free to move around one another, a liquid can flow from place to place. Some liquids flow more easily than others. The resistance of a liquid to flowing is a physical property called **viscosity** (vis KAHS uh tee). Liquids with high viscosity flow slowly. For example, cold molasses has a particularly high viscosity. Liquids with low viscosity flow quickly. Water, rubbing alcohol, and vinegar have relatively low viscosities.

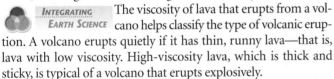 **INTEGRATING EARTH SCIENCE** The viscosity of lava that erupts from a volcano helps classify the type of volcanic eruption. A volcano erupts quietly if it has thin, runny lava—that is, lava with low viscosity. High-viscosity lava, which is thick and sticky, is typical of a volcano that erupts explosively.

Gases

Gases can change volume more easily than either solids or liquids. If you put a gas in a sealed container, the gas particles will spread apart or squeeze together to fill that container. The volume and shape of a gas is the volume and shape of its container. To illustrate this principle, take a deep breath. Your chest expands. Can you feel the air coming through your nose and mouth? Air is a mixture of

As Thick as Honey

Here's how you can compare the viscosity of two liquids.

1. Place on a table a clear plastic jar almost filled with honey and another clear plastic jar almost filled with vegetable oil. Make sure that the tops of both jars are tightly closed.
2. Turn the jars upside-down at the same time. Observe what happens.
3. Turn the two jars right-side up and again watch what happens.

Drawing Conclusions Which liquid has a greater viscosity? What evidence leads you to this conclusion?

Skills Focus drawing conclusions ACTIVITY

Materials *2 clear jars with screw-top lids, honey, vegetable oil, paper towels*

Time 10 minutes

Tips If possible, use clear plastic jars to avoid broken glass. Make sure the jars are tightly sealed before the activity. Have paper towels on hand to wipe up spills.

Drawing Conclusions Honey has the greater viscosity. The bubble in the vegetable oil jar rose faster than the bubble in the honey jar.

Extend Suggest students compare the viscosities of a variety of liquids such as maple syrup, water, and shampoo. **limited English proficiency**

Integrating Earth Science

Students may incorrectly visualize all volcanoes as high, cone-shaped mountains. Explain that the shape of the volcano depends in part on the viscosity of the lava. Shield volcanoes and lava plateaus are produced by low-viscosity lava that spreads out. Ask students to predict what happens if the lava has a high viscosity. (*Lava builds up near the opening.*) **learning modality: verbal**

Gases

Building Inquiry Skills: Observing

Point out that many gases, like air, are not visible. Challenge students to design an experiment that would show that a gas is not just empty space. (*Sample: Using a sensitive balance, measure the mass of a balloon; fill it with air and measure the mass again.*) **learning modality: visual**

Answers to Self-Assessment

Caption Question

Figure 4 Particles in a crystalline solid are arranged in a regular repeating pattern while the particles in an amorphous solid are not in a regular pattern.

☑ *Checkpoint*

Crystalline solid—particles arranged in regular, repeating pattern, has distinct melting point. Amorphous solid—particles not in regular pattern, does not have distinct melting point.

Ongoing Assessment

Oral Presentation Have students compare and contrast the motion of particles in high- and low-viscosity liquids.

3 Assess

Section 1 Review Answers

1. A substance can be classified as a solid if it has a definite volume and definite shape.

2. Particles in a liquid are almost as tightly packed as in a solid, and they stay in close contact, so a liquid has a definite volume. Because the particles can freely move around each other, a liquid does not have a definite shape.

3. Gas particles spread apart from one another easily and fill the space available. Thus, a gas has neither a definite shape nor a definite volume.

4. Because glass is an amorphous solid, it does not have a distinct melting point. Instead, it becomes softer and softer as it is heated. This is why heated glass may be soft enough to bend.

Science at Home

Materials *turkey baster, water*

Students should be sure that the family member does not squeeze the bulb too hard when the baster is filled with water, because it could leak where the bulb fits on the tube. It will be easier to squeeze the bulb filled with air than the bulb filled with water. Students should explain their observations by stating that water, as a liquid, has a definite volume. Air, as a gas, has an indefinite volume.

Figure 7 The particles of a gas can be squeezed into a small volume (left). If allowed to, they will spread out without limit, somewhat like the flock of gulls on the right.

gases that acts as one gas. When you breathe in, air moves from your mouth to your windpipe to your lungs. In each place, the air changes shape and volume. When you breathe out, the changes happen in reverse. If you hold your hand in front of your mouth, you can feel the air move around and past your fingers.

If you could see the individual particles that make up a gas, you would see tiny particles flying at high speeds in all directions. **Gas particles spread apart, filling all the space available to them. Thus, a gas has neither definite shape nor volume.** You can compare a gas to the flock of gulls shown in Figure 7. Like gas particles, these gulls fly very quickly in different directions. They can spread out to "fill" any available space.

 ## Section 1 Review

1. Describe properties you would use to classify a substance as a solid.

2. How does the movement of particles in a liquid help to explain the shape and volume of liquids?

3. Use what you know about the particles in a gas to explain why a gas has no definite shape and no definite volume.

4. Thinking Critically Relating Cause and Effect Glass is an amorphous solid. How can you use that information to help explain why a glassblower can bend and shape a piece of glass that has been heated?

Science at Home

What Gives? Show your family how liquids and gases differ. Completely fill the bulb and cylinder of a turkey baster with water. Hold it over the sink. While you seal the end with your finger, have a family member squeeze the bulb. Now let the water out of the turkey baster. Again, seal the end with your finger and have a family member squeeze the bulb. Was there a difference? Use what you know about liquids and gases to explain the observations.

60

DISCOVER · ACTIVITY

How Can Air Keep Chalk From Breaking?

1. Standing on a chair or table, drop a piece of chalk onto a hard floor. Observe what happens to the chalk.

2. Wrap a second piece of chalk in wax paper or plastic food wrap. Drop the chalk from the same height used in Step 1. Observe the results.

3. Wrap a third piece of chalk in plastic bubble wrap. Drop the chalk from the same height used in Step 1. Observe the results.

Think It Over

Inferring Compare the results from Steps 1, 2, and 3. What properties of the air in the bubble wrap accounted for the results in Step 3?

Every Thanksgiving, the people of New York City gather to watch a big parade. Maybe you have seen this parade on television, or even in person. The parade is famous for its large, floating balloons, like the one shown on this page. The balloons float because they are filled with helium, a gas that is less dense than air.

If you were in charge of a parade balloon, you would be faced with many different questions. How large is the balloon? How much helium should you put inside the balloon? Does the balloon behave differently in warm weather than in cold weather? To answer these questions and others like them, you would need to understand the properties of gases.

GUIDE FOR READING

◆ How are the volume, temperature, and pressure of a gas related?

Reading Tip Before you read, change each heading into a question. Write a brief answer to each question as you read.

Key Terms temperature
• pressure • Boyle's Law
• Charles's Law

Figure 8 A helium balloon of Clifford, the Big Red Dog, floats past Central Park in New York City.

Objectives

After completing the lesson, students will be able to
◆ define the relationship between volume and pressure of a gas and state Boyle's law;
◆ define the relationship between pressure and temperature of a gas;
◆ define the relationship between volume and the temperature of a gas and state Charles's law.

1 Engage/Explore

Activating Prior Knowledge

Allow students to take turns pumping air into a bicycle tire using a bicycle pump. Ask: **What happens if there is too little or too much air in the tire?** (*Too little air leaves the tire flat. Too much air can burst the tire.*) Explain that students learn more about pressure and gases in this section.

· · · · · · · · · DISCOVER · · · · · · · ·

Skills Focus inferring
Materials *3 pieces of chalk, sheet of wax paper or plastic wrap, plastic bubble wrap, tape*
Time 10 minutes
Tips Each student should have a "spotter" to keep him or her from falling off the chair.
Expected Outcome The chalk will break when dropped by itself and when dropped wrapped in wax paper or plastic wrap. It will not break when wrapped in bubble wrap.
Think It Over The chalk did not break when wrapped with the plastic bubble wrap. Therefore, the air bubbles in the wrap must have compressed to absorb the force and cushion the chalk.

READING STRATEGIES

Reading Tip Suggest students write questions that begin with *How, What,* and *Why.* As students change the headings to questions, instruct them to leave several lines of space so that they can add an answer to each question. Sample question: How are gases measured?

Program Resources

◆ **Unit 1 Resources** 2-2 Lesson Plan, p. 47; 2-2 Section Summary, p. 48
◆ **Guided Reading and Study Workbook** 2-2

Measuring Gases

Sharpen your *Skills*

Developing Hypotheses

Materials *wire or pipe cleaner, soap solution (made from liquid dish soap and glycerin, if available), large pan*

Time 15 minutes

Tips Ideally, take students outdoors to experiment with bubbles. Students with respiratory problems can make bubbles by moving the loop through the air at different speeds. Factors that contribute to the size of the bubbles include the size of the wire circle (a larger circle produces a larger bubble) and the amount of air blown into the bubble (the volume of the bubble increases as more air is blown in).

Extend Have students experiment with the composition of the bubble solution by combining different amounts of soap, glycerin, and water. Students should find the combination that allows them to make bubbles of the greatest volume.

Including All Students

Materials *ball bearings, round rubber balloon*

Time 5 minutes

To help students who have difficulty envisioning how gas particles behave at high and low temperatures, place a few ball bearings inside a balloon and inflate the balloon. Have students shake the balloon at different speeds. Ask: **When you shake the balloon quickly, what do the bearings behave like?** (*Gas particles at high temperatures*) **limited English proficiency**

Figure 9 The helium gas in this tank is kept under high pressure within the volume set by the thick steel walls. *Predicting What happens to the helium atoms as they move into the balloons?*

Sharpen your Skills

Developing Hypotheses

1. Pour soapy water into a large pan. Add a little glycerin, if available.

2. Bend the ends of a wire or long pipe cleaner into a circle.

3. Dip the wire circle into the soapy water and then blow into the wire shape to make several bubbles. Observe the bubbles that you produce.

4. What factors seem to change the volume of the soap bubbles? How could you test your hypothesis?

Measuring Gases

How much helium is in the tank in Figure 9? You may think that measuring the volume of the tank will give you an answer. But gases easily contract or expand. To fill the tank, helium was compressed, or pressed together tightly. When the helium is used, it fills a total volume of inflated balloons much greater than the volume of the tank. The actual volume you get, however, depends on the temperature and air pressure that day. So what exactly do measurements of volume, pressure, and temperature mean?

Volume   You know volume is the amount of space that matter fills. Volume is measured in cubic centimeters, milliliters, liters, and other units. Because gases fill the space available, the volume of a gas is the same as the volume of its container.

Temperature   Hot soup, warm hands, cool breezes—you should be familiar with matter at different temperatures. But what exactly does temperature show? Recall that in any substance—solid, liquid, or gas—the particles are constantly moving. **Temperature** is a measure of the average energy of motion of the particles of a substance. The faster the particles are moving, the greater their energy and the higher the temperature. You might think of a thermometer as a speedometer for molecules.

Even at ordinary temperatures, the average speed of particles in a gas is very fast. At 20°C, which is about room temperature, the particles in a typical gas travel about 500 meters per second!

History of Science   In 1738, Daniel Bernoulli suggested that gas particles are in continuous motion. As the particles move, they collide with other particles and the walls of the container holding the gas. Bernoulli attributed the pressure of a gas to collisions of the particles with the container walls.

In 1857, Rudolf Clausius published his kinetic-molecular theory, stating that gases are made up of small, widely separated particles in constant motion. The particles are not attracted to each other and do not gain or lose energy in collisions.

The kinetic-molecular theory can be used to explain Boyle's law. The pressure of a gas is determined by the number of particles hitting the walls of a container and the force with which they hit. If the volume of the container is halved, twice as many collisions occur in a given time and the pressure is doubled.

Pressure The motion of gas particles is related to the force, or push, of the particles against the walls of their container. Because gas particles are moving, they constantly collide with one another. They also collide with the walls of their container. As a result, the gas exerts an outward push on the walls of the container. The **pressure** of the gas is the force of its outward push divided by the area of the walls of the container. Pressure is measured in units of kilopascals (kPa).

INTEGRATING PHYSICS

$$\text{Pressure} = \frac{\text{Force}}{\text{Area}}$$

The firmness of an object inflated with a gas, such as a soccer ball, comes from the pressure of the gas. If the gas (in this case, air) leaks out of the ball, the pressure decreases, and the ball becomes softer. But why does an inflated ball leak when punctured? A gas flows from an area of high pressure to an area of low pressure. The air inside the ball is at a higher pressure than the air outside. Gas particles inside the ball hit the hole more often than gas particles outside the hole. Because more inside particles hit the hole, they have a better chance of getting out of the ball. Thus, many more particles go out than in. The pressure inside drops until it is equal to the pressure outside.

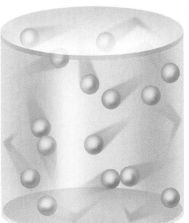

Figure 10 The gas particles are in constant motion, colliding with each other and with the walls of their container.

☑ *Checkpoint* *What are three properties of a gas that you can measure?*

Relating Pressure and Volume

Pressure is also related to the volume of a container. For example, imagine that you are operating a bicycle pump. By pressing down on the plunger, you force the gas inside the pump through the rubber tube and out the nozzle into the tire. What will happen if you close the nozzle and then push down on the plunger?

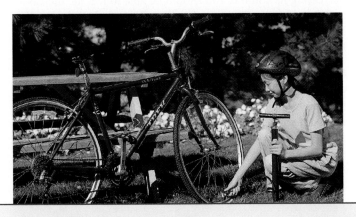

Figure 11 What will happen when this bicyclist operates the pump she is attaching? She will decrease the volume of air in the cylinder and increase its pressure. As a result, air will be forced into the bicycle tire and the tire will inflate.

Integrating Physics

Ask students to predict what would happen to the pressure if the area over which a force is exerted decreased. *(The pressure would increase.)* **learning modality: logical/mathematical**

Demonstration

ACTIVITY

Materials *round rubber balloon*
Time 10 minutes

Inflate the balloon and knot the end. Ask students if the pressure is higher inside or outside the balloon. *(inside)* Then use a push pin to carefully prick a hole in the balloon. Ask students to explain what they observe. *(The higher pressure inside forces more gas particles to leave rather than enter the balloon through the hole. Thus, the balloon deflates slowly.)* **learning modality: visual**

Relating Pressure and Volume

Including All Students

ACTIVITY

Materials *plastic syringe without needle*
Time 10 minutes

Allow students who have difficulty seeing to feel how pressure increases as volume decreases. Group students and give them a syringe. Students can take turns placing a finger over the hole and pushing on the plunger. Ask: **What happens when you push down the plunger?** *(The gas decreases in volume as the pressure increases until the plunger becomes too hard to push.)* **learning modality: tactile/kinesthetic**

Media and Technology

Physical Science Videodisc
Unit 1, Side 1, "Racing Hot Air Balloons"
Chapter 3

Answers to Self-Assessment

Caption Question

Figure 9 The helium atoms will spread farther apart.

☑ *Checkpoint*

Volume, temperature, and pressure

Ongoing Assessment

Writing Have students describe what happens to a gas particle as it moves through a bicycle pump into a flat tire that becomes fully inflated.

Relating Pressure and Volume, continued

Using the Visuals: Figure 12

 Content Mastery

Have students compare the height of the plunger in each drawing. Ask: **As the plunger goes down, what happens to the space between the particles?** (*It decreases.*) Ask students to predict what a fourth drawing would look like if two more weights were added to the plunger top. (*The gas particles would be closer together.*) **learning modality: visual**

TRY THIS

 ACTIVITY

Skills Focus developing hypotheses
Materials *balloon, paper or plastic cup*
Time 10 minutes
Tips As the balloon inflates, the portion inside the cup becomes flatter. This increases the volume of air inside the cup, thereby reducing the pressure. The lower pressure in the cup creates a suction that holds the cup to the balloon.
Developing Hypotheses Sample: The volume of the gas inside the cup increased (pressure decreased). The greater pressure in the balloon pushed it against the cup. Students could test their hypotheses by punching a hole in the bottom of the cup and noting the direction of air flow. (*Into the cup*)
Extend Challenge students to predict the outcome if they repeat the experiment and then slowly deflate the balloon. Have students test their predictions. **learning modality: tactile/kinesthetic**

 Integrating Earth Science

Assuming that soap bubbles burst because of a difference in air pressure inside and outside the bubbles, challenge students to use Boyle's law to explain why bubbles burst when they float too high. (*At greater heights, the atmospheric air pressure decreases; higher pressure inside the bubble causes it to burst.*)
learning modality: logical/ mathematical

Figure 12 As weights are added, the same number of gas particles occupies a smaller volume. The pressure of the gas increases. This relationship is called Boyle's law.

TRY THIS

Balloon Test ACTIVITY

What happens when you change the volume of a gas?

1. Hold the open end of a paper cup on the side of a partly inflated balloon.
2. Inflate the balloon until it presses against the cup and then let go of the cup. What happens?

Developing Hypotheses Use what you know about pressure and volume to write a hypothesis that explains the behavior of the cup after you let it go. How could you test your hypothesis?

64

The answer to this question comes from experiments with gases done by the English scientist Robert Boyle. In the 1600s, Boyle measured the volumes of gases at different pressures as he experimented with ways to improve air pumps. He saw that gases behave in a predictable way. **Boyle found that when the pressure of a gas is increased at constant temperature, the volume of the gas decreases. When the pressure is decreased, the volume increases.** This relationship between the pressure and volume of a gas is named **Boyle's law.**

INTEGRATING EARTH SCIENCE Boyle's law plays an important role in research done with some high-altitude balloons. These balloons are made from lightweight plastic. They are filled with only a small fraction of the helium they could hold. Why is that? As a balloon rises through the atmosphere, the air pressure around it decreases steadily. As the air pressure decreases, the helium inside the balloon expands, stretching the balloon to a greater and greater volume. If the balloon were fully filled at takeoff, it would burst before it got very high.

Boyle's law also applies to situations in which the *volume* of a gas is changed. Then the *pressure* changes in the opposite way. For example, if you squeeze an inflated balloon, you are decreasing its volume. You should be able to feel the increased pressure of the gas inside it. The bicycle pump described earlier is a similar case. As you push on the plunger, the volume of air inside the pump gets smaller and the pressure increases.

✓ *Checkpoint* What is Boyle's law?

Relating Pressure and Temperature

If you pour a bucket of sand onto your skin, it will not hurt at all. But suppose you are caught in a sandstorm. Because the sand grains are flying very fast, they will hurt a great deal! The faster the grains are traveling, the harder they will hit your skin.

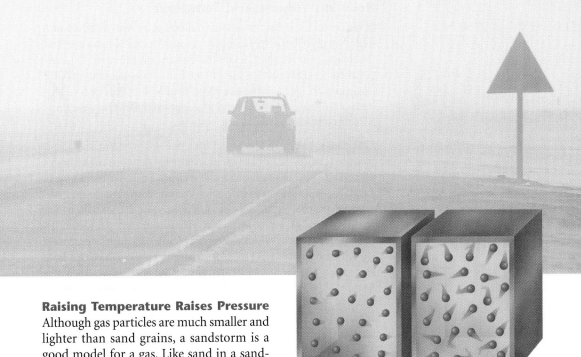

Raising Temperature Raises Pressure

Although gas particles are much smaller and lighter than sand grains, a sandstorm is a good model for a gas. Like sand in a sandstorm, gas particles travel individually and at high speeds. Remember that pressure is a measure of how much gas particles push on the walls of a container. The greater the speed of the gas particles, the more collisions will occur. The more collisions there are, the greater the pressure will be.

Temperature is a measure of the average speed of the particles of a gas. The higher the temperature of a gas, the faster the gas particles are moving. Now you can state a relationship between temperature and pressure. **When the temperature of a gas at constant volume is increased, the pressure of the gas increases. When the temperature is decreased, the pressure of the gas decreases.** A constant volume means a closed, rigid container.

Pressure and Temperature in Action Have you ever looked at the tires of an 18-wheel truck? Because these tires need to support a lot of weight, they are large, heavy, and stiff. The inside volume of these tires doesn't vary much.

On long trips, especially in the summer, a truck's tires can get very hot. As the temperature increases, so does the pressure of the air inside the tire. If the pressure becomes higher than the tire can hold, the tire will burst apart. For this reason, truck drivers need to monitor and adjust tire pressure on long trips.

Figure 13 Particles of a heated gas are like the sand blown by the wind in this sandstorm. When a gas is heated, the particles move faster and collide more with one another and the sides of their container. *Relating Cause and Effect Why does the pressure of the gas increase when the number of collisions increases?*

Answers to Self-Assessment

Caption Question

Figure 13 More collisions mean more particles are pushing on the walls of the container, which makes the pressure higher.

✓ Checkpoint

Boyle's law states that when the pressure of a gas increases at constant temperature, the volume decreases. When the pressure of a gas decreases, the volume increases.

Relating Pressure and Temperature

Real-Life Learning

Materials *tire pressure gauge*

Time 15 minutes

Allow students to examine the markings on a tire pressure gauge. Explain that a standard tire gauge is marked in units of pressure. The customary unit of pressure in the United States is called psi, which stands for pounds per square inch. Newer tire gauges are also marked in kPa, or kilopascals, the SI unit of pressure. If possible, take students to a parking lot and demonstrate how the tire gauge works. Ask: **What makes the gauge move when it is put onto the valve of the tire?** *(The air pressure inside the tire)* Ask students why the same tire might give different pressure readings at different times of the day. *As the temperature inside the tire rises after a long trip or during the hot part of the day, the pressure inside the tire will rise, too.)*

learning modality: visual

Ongoing Assessment

Writing Have students restate Boyle's law in their own words.

Relating Volume and Temperature

Inquiry Challenge

Materials *round balloon, freezer, metric tape measure*

Time 20 minutes, plus overnight freezer time

Have students design and conduct experiments to test Charles's law. Place students in groups and have each assume a key role, such as data collector, hypothesis writer, and freezer monitor. Have groups predict what will happen to the volume of air in a sealed balloon that is placed in a freezer. Then encourage them to create clear experimental designs. Ask: **What two measurements must you make?** *(The circumference of the balloon at room temperature, and its circumference after being in the freezer)* Approve students' designs, then allow them to test their predictions. The change in volume should be about 10 percent—a noticeable but not dramatic difference. Conclude by asking students to explain whether their results confirm Charles's law. **cooperative learning**

Using the Visuals: Figure 14

Ask students to compare the pressure of the gas shown in the two diagrams. *(It is the same.)* Some students may think the pressure is higher on the left, because of the decreased volume. Others may think it is higher on the right, because of the increased speed of the particles. Remind students that pressure is equal to the force exerted over a certain area. Point out that in the smaller volume, the particles are colliding with a smaller area, while in the larger container, the same number of particles are colliding with a much larger area, but they are moving much faster so each particle exerts more force. **learning modality: logical/mathematical**

Relating Volume and Temperature

If the temperature of the gas in a balloon is increased, its volume will change. Will the volume increase or decrease? If you answered "increase," you are right. Gases increase in volume when the temperature increases. On the other hand, as the temperature decreases, the gas volume decreases. People in charge of the large balloons used for parades need to understand the effect temperature has on volume so that the balloons can be inflated properly.

Charles's Law In the late 1700s, a French scientist named Jacques Charles examined the relationship between the temperature and volume of a gas kept at a constant pressure. He measured the volume of a gas at various temperatures in a container whose volume could change. **Charles found that when the temperature of a gas is increased at constant pressure, its volume increases. When the temperature of a gas is decreased its volume decreases.** This principle is called **Charles's law.** Remember that at higher temperatures, the particles move faster. As a result, they collide more often with the walls around them. As long as the volume of the container can change, the pressure stays constant, and the total push of the collisions results in the gas taking up more space. The volume of the gas increases.

Charles's Law in Action You can see Charles's law demonstrated using air contained in a party balloon. Look at Figure 15 on the next page. The left photograph shows the balloon in a beaker of water, resting on a tub of ice. (A smaller beaker of water keeps the balloon submerged in the larger beaker.) In the next photograph, the beaker has been heated on a hot plate. When you compare the photos, you should notice a change. The balloon in the right photograph is larger. This difference is the result of an increase in the volume of the air as it is heated.

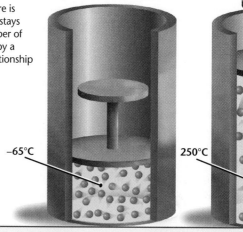

Figure 14 If temperature is increased while pressure stays constant, the same number of particles of gas will occupy a greater volume. This relationship is called Charles's law.

−65°C   250°C

Background

History of Science During the nineteenth century, scientists developed technologies based on new understandings of the way gases behave. One area of interest was constructing airships. The first successful airship was built in 1852 by a French engineer, Henri Giffard. This airship was powered by a steam engine and could travel a distance of about 30 km. Airships usually consisted of a large gas-filled balloon, a section to hold the crew, an engine, and a steering mechanism. They were lifted by gases, such as hydrogen or helium, that were less dense than air. Airships built during the early twentieth century could travel over oceans, but were slow, expensive to build and maintain, and the gases that lifted them were extremely flammable. Like the *Hindenburg*, which contained hydrogen, several airships exploded when their gases ignited.

Figure 15 By heating a gas at constant pressure, you can increase its volume. A sample of air that is chilled (left) has a smaller volume than it does after it is heated (right). *Predicting What will happen to the balloon if the beaker is returned to an ice bath?*

In this example, pressure remains more or less constant because the expanding air is in a flexible container. But what would happen if heating were to continue, and the balloon reached its limit in size? You might guess it would pop, but can you figure out why? When the balloon can no longer expand, the continued increase in temperature would cause an increase in pressure. Eventually, the pressure would be great enough to break the balloon.

Boyle, Charles, and others often described gas behavior two factors at a time. In the real world, however, gases can show changes in pressure, temperature, and volume all at once. Scientists, tire manufacturers, engineers, and others who work with gases must consider these combined effects.

Section 2 Review

1. Describe the relationship between the pressure and volume of a gas.
2. If you change the temperature of a gas but keep the volume the same, how does the pressure change?
3. What is Charles's law?
4. **Thinking Critically** **Applying Concepts** Suppose it is the night before Thanksgiving, and you are in charge of inflating a balloon for the Thanksgiving Day parade. You just learned that the temperature will rise 15°C by the time the parade starts. How will this information affect the way you inflate your balloon?

Check Your Progress
CHAPTER PROJECT

With the members of your group, write a description of how particles behave in each of the three states of matter. Next, think of different ways to model each state, using drawings and words. Decide whether you want to demonstrate a change of state as cartoon pictures or by acting out the motion of particles in a skit. (*Hint:* Prepare a storyboard. A storyboard is a series of simple drawings and captions that outline the action of a story.)

Answers to Self-Assessment
Caption Question
Figure 15 If the beaker is returned to an ice bath, the balloon will shrink.

3 Assess

Section 2 Review Answers
1. As pressure increases at constant temperature, volume decreases. As pressure decreases, volume increases.
2. As the temperature increases at constant volume, the pressure will increase. As the temperature decreases, the pressure will decrease.
3. Charles's law states that for gas held at a constant pressure, volume increases as temperature increases, and volume decreases as temperature decreases.
4. Because you know that the temperature will increase, the volume of gas in the balloon will also increase. To prevent the balloon from bursting, you should underinflate the balloon.

Check Your Progress
CHAPTER PROJECT

Check students' written descriptions of particle behavior. Make sure students' basic understanding of the concept is correct. Review students' storyboards. Make sure they understand a storyboard is not a final product, so they only need to make rough sketches with notes. Encourage students to brainstorm and be creative. Have students exchange storyboards so peer reviewers can check them for clarity and completeness.

Performance Assessment

Writing Have students describe how a balloon may be used to demonstrate Charles's and Boyle's laws. (*Charles's law—A partially filled balloon will expand when heated, showing that the volume of a gas increases with increased temperature when the pressure is constant. Boyle's law—If temperature is constant and the pressure outside the balloon decreases, the balloon will expand as the volume of the gas increases.*)

SECTION 3 Graphing Gas Behavior

TEKS: 6.1A; 6.2A, B, C, E; 6.3C; 6.4A; 6.7B

Objective

After completing the lesson, students will be able to

♦ construct and interpret graphs for Charles's Law and Boyle's Law.

1 Engage/Explore

Activating Prior Knowledge

Show students a graph of daily high or low temperatures for the last week in your area. Ask them to determine at a glance whether the temperature has risen or fallen (or stayed the same) over the last few days. Explain that graphs can also show at a glance how scientific data changes.

•••••• DISCOVER ••••••

Skills Focus graphing
Materials *graph paper, pencil*
Time 15 minutes
Tips Ask: **What intervals will you use for the horizontal axis?** *(Sample: intervals of 5°C)* **What intervals will you use for the vertical axis?** *(Sample: intervals of 2.0 kPa)*
Expected Outcome Students' graphs should show a line that slants upward to the right.
Think It Over The graph shows that as temperature increases, pressure increases.

SECTION 3 Graphing Gas Behavior

DISCOVER •••••••••••••••••••••••••••••••• ACTIVITY

What Does a Graph of Pressure and Temperature Show?

Temperature (°C)	Pressure (kPa)
0	8
5	11
10	14
15	17
20	20
25	23

1. In an experiment, the temperature was varied for a constant volume of gas. Gas pressure was measured after each 5°C change. You now need to graph the data in this table.

2. Show temperature on the horizontal axis with a scale from 0°C to 25°C. Show pressure on the vertical axis with a scale equally spaced from 0 kPa to 25 kPa.

3. For each pair of measurements, draw a point on the graph.

4. Draw a line to connect the points.

Think It Over
Graphing Use the graph to describe the relationship between the pressure and temperature of a gas.

GUIDE FOR READING

♦ What do graphs for Charles's law and Boyle's law look like?

Reading Tip As you read about the experiments in this section, refer to the graphs in Figures 19 and 21.

Key Terms graph
• directly proportional
• vary inversely

The population of a town is increasing. The schools are becoming more crowded, and the people need to decide whether to build more schools. Newspapers illustrate their articles about the problem with graphs.

How could a graph help tell this story? A **graph** is a diagram that tells how two variables, or factors, are related. Graphs show how changes in one variable result in changes in a second variable. You can use graphs to make predictions. For example, according to the graph in Figure 16, the town might have a population of 32,000 in 2020. That assumes, of course, that population continues to grow by the same amount yearly. In this section, you will learn how to interpret graphs that relate properties of gases.

Figure 16 This graph shows that the population in the town is growing steadily. The dashed line predicts what the population would be if the current growth trend were to continue.

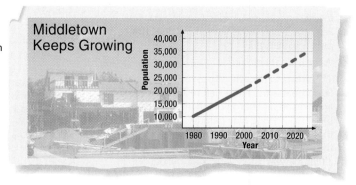

Middletown Keeps Growing

READING STRATEGIES

Reading Tip As students refer to the graphs, ask them to describe what the *x*-axes and *y*-axes show. Have students check the numbers in the tables against those on the graphs. Then ask them to summarize what the graphs reveal. Have students suggest other relationships in science that can be described using graphs.

Study and Comprehension Have students preview the section by reading the headings, subheadings, and captions and by looking at the pictures and graphs. Encourage students to suggest questions they have about interpreting graphs and about graphing gas behavior. Write the questions on the board. After students read the section, have them work as a class to answer the questions on the board.

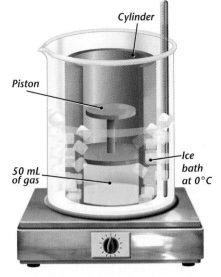

Cylinder

Piston

Ice bath at 0°C

50 mL of gas

Temperature		Volume
(°C)	(K)	(mL)
0	273	50
10	283	52
20	293	54
30	303	56
40	313	58
50	323	60
60	333	62
70	343	63
80	353	66
90	363	67
100	373	69

Figure 17 As the temperature of the water bath increases, the gas inside the cylinder is warmed by the water. The data from the experiment are recorded in the table. Celsius values can be converted to kelvins by adding 273 to the Celsius value.

Temperature and Volume

Recall from Section 2 that Charles's law relates the temperature and volume of a gas that is kept at a constant pressure. You can examine this relationship by doing an experiment in which you change the temperature of a gas and measure its volume. Then you can graph the data you have recorded and look for a relationship. Recall, also, that the motion of particles increases as their temperature increases.

Collecting Data As you can see from the cutaway view in Figure 17, the gas in the experiment is in a cylinder that has a movable piston. The piston moves up and down freely, which allows the gas to change volume and keep the same pressure. To control the temperature, the cylinder is placed in a water bath.

The experiment begins with an ice-water bath at 0°C and the gas volume at 50 mL. Then the water bath is slowly heated. Very gradually, the temperature increases from 0°C to 100°C. Each time the temperature increases by 10 degrees Celsius, the volume of the gas in the cylinder is recorded.

You'll notice a second set of temperatures listed in the table in Figure 17. Scientists often work with gas temperatures in units called kelvins. To convert from Celsius degrees to kelvins, you add 273. The kelvin temperatures will be used to graph the data.

Graphing the Results A graph consists of a grid set up by two lines—one horizontal and one vertical. Each line, or axis, is divided into equal units. The horizontal, or x-, axis shows the manipulated variable, in this case, temperature. The vertical,

Figure 18 The horizontal, or x-, axis and the vertical, or y-, axis are the "backbone" of a graph. *Interpreting Diagrams Which variable is placed on the x-axis?*

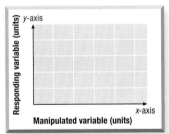

y-axis

Responding variable (units)

x-axis

Manipulated variable (units)

Temperature and Volume

Building Inquiry Skills: Posing Questions

Have students analyze the experimental setup shown in Figure 17. Ask: **What is inside the cylinder, beneath the piston?** *(A gas)* Ask students to identify the manipulated variable in the experiment. *(The temperature of the gas)* Then have students generate two or three questions that could be answered using the setup. *(Sample: How does the volume of air change when temperature increases? How much does the volume of the gas change between 0°C and 100°C?)* Have students use the data table in the figure to answer the questions. **learning modality: logical/mathematical**

Building Inquiry Skills: Interpreting Data

Challenge students to prove that the data table in Figure 17 was used to generate the graph on page 70. Ask students to identify the subject of the graph, the manipulated variable, and the responding variable. **learning modality: logical/ mathematical**

Program Resources

◆ **Unit 1 Resources** 2-3 Lesson Plan, p. 51; 2-3 Section Summary, p. 52
◆ **Guided Reading and Study Workbook** 2-3

Answers to Self-Assessment

Caption Question

Figure 18 The manipulated variable is on the x-axis.

Ongoing Assessment

Skills Check Have students draw a grid for a graph in which the x-axis shows time in 5-minute intervals for 30 minutes and the y-axis shows temperature in 2°C intervals for 10 degrees starting at 0°C.

Temperature and Volume, continued

Using the Visuals: Figure 19

Challenge students to explain how the dotted portion of the graph was made. *(The straight line made through the data points was extended downward.)* Ask: **Is it reasonable to extend the graph in this manner? Explain.** *(Yes. The temperature of the gas could be lowered, and the volumes could be measured.)* Challenge students to determine the volume at specific temperatures along the dotted line. Finally, have students describe what a directly proportional relationship looks like on a graph. *(A straight line that passes through point (0, 0))* **learning modality: logical/mathematical**

Pressure and Volume

Building Inquiry Skills: Interpreting Diagrams

Have students examine the set-up in Figure 20. Ask: **What units are on the pressure gauge?** *(kPa)* Ask students to identify what variable must be controlled for this experiment to show that the pressure increase is due to a change in volume. *(temperature)* Challenge students to predict what would happen to the gas particles inside the cylinder and to the arrow on the pressure gauge if the piston were pushed down. *(The gas particles will be closer together. The arrow on the gauge will point to a higher pressure.)* **learning modality: visual**

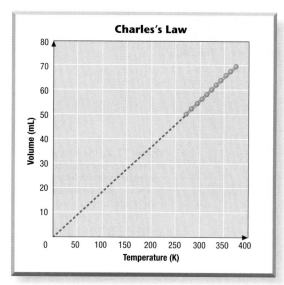

Figure 19 This graph of the data from Figure 17 shows the linear relationship between temperature and volume known as Charles's law. The dotted line predicts how the graph would look if the gas could be cooled to lower temperatures.

or *y*-, axis shows the responding variable, in this case, volume. Each axis is labeled with the name of the variable, the units of measurement, and a range of values.

Look at the graph in Figure 19. It appears as if the line would continue downward if data could be collected for lower temperatures. Such a line would pass through the point (0, 0). When a graph of two variables is a straight line passing through the (0, 0) point, the relationship is linear, and the variables are said to be **directly proportional** to each other. **The graph of Charles's law shows that the volume of a gas is directly proportional to its kelvin temperature under constant pressure.**

☑ *Checkpoint* *On which axis of a graph do you show the responding variable?*

Pressure and Volume

You can perform another experiment to show how pressure and volume are related when temperature is kept constant. Recall that the relationship between pressure and volume is called Boyle's law.

Figure 20 By pushing on the top of the piston, you compress the gas and thereby increase the pressure of the gas inside the cylinder. The data from the experiment are recorded in the table.
Predicting What would happen if you pulled up on the piston?

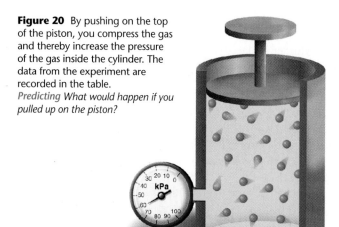

Volume (mL)	Pressure (kPa)
100	60
90	67
80	75
70	86
60	100

Background

History of Science French scientist, mathematician, and philosopher Jacques Charles (1746–1823) began his professional life working as a clerk in the Ministry of Finance in Paris. While there, his interest in electricity led him to invent several devices, including a hydrometer and an aerometer.

In 1783, Charles and another French inventor, Nicholas Robert, were among the first people to go up in a hydrogen-filled balloon. Four years later, Charles developed the principle that describes the directly proportional relationship between the temperature and volume of a gas. He continued to make balloon flights and ascended higher than a kilometer several times. In 1795, Charles was elected a member of France's Academy of Sciences. He later became a professor of physics.

Collecting Data The gas in this experiment is also contained in a cylinder with a movable piston. In this case, however, a pressure gauge indicates the pressure of the gas inside.

The experiment begins with the volume of the gas at 100 mL. The pressure of the gas is 60 kilopascals. Next, the piston is slowly pushed into the cylinder, compressing the gas, or shrinking its volume. The pressure of the gas is recorded after each 10-mL change in volume.

Graphing the Results To observe the relationship of the pressure and volume of a gas, it helps to display the data in another graph. In the pressure-volume experiment, the manipulated variable is volume. Volume is shown on the scale of the horizontal axis from 60 mL to 100 mL. The responding variable is pressure. Pressure is shown on the scale of the vertical axis from 60 kPa to 100 kPa.

As you can see in Figure 21, the points lie on a curve. Notice that the curve slopes downward from left to right. Also notice that the curve is steep close to the vertical axis and becomes less steep close to the horizontal axis. When a graph of two measurements forms this kind of curve, the relationship is nonlinear, and the measurements are said to **vary inversely** with each other. **The graph for Boyle's law shows that the pressure of a gas varies inversely with its volume at constant temperature.** In other words, the pressure of a gas decreases as its volume increases.

Figure 21 This graph of the data from Figure 20 shows the nonlinear relationship between pressure and volume known as Boyle's law. (The broken lines show gaps in the scales.)

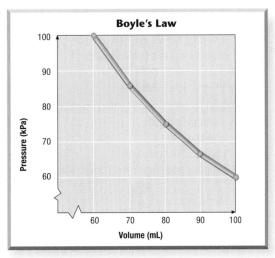

Section 3 Review

1. Describe a graph of Charles's law.
2. Describe a graph of Boyle's law.
3. How can you tell the difference between a graph in which one variable is directly proportional to another and a graph in which two variables vary inversely?
4. **Thinking Critically Interpreting Graphs** Suppose the temperature of the gas in the experiment illustrated in Figure 17 was increased to 400 K (127°C). Use Figure 19 to predict the new volume of the gas.

Science at Home

News Data Look for graphs in your newspaper or in newsmagazines. Point out to members of your family which variable is the manipulated variable and which is the responding variable for each graph. Then compare any line graphs you have found to the graphs in this section. Which of your graphs show two variables that are directly proportional to each other? Do any show variables that vary inversely?

---

3 Assess

Section 3 Review Answers

1. When temperature is the manipulated variable, Charles's law is graphed with temperature on the *x*-axis and volume on the *y*-axis. The graph is a straight line pointing up and to the right.

2. When volume is the manipulated variable, Boyle's law is graphed with volume on the *x*-axis and pressure on the *y*-axis. The graph is a curve pointing down and to the right, steeper near the *y*-axis and less steep near the *x*-axis.

3. Directly proportional—straight line; vary inversely—curve that is steeper near the *y*-axis and more flat near the *x*-axis

4. About 75 mL

Science at Home

Materials *newspapers or magazines* **ACTIVITY**

Before they begin, suggest students define the following terms for their families: manipulated variable, responding variable, directly proportional, and vary inversely.

Program Resources

◆ **Unit 1 Resources** 2-3 Review and Reinforce, p. 53; 2-3 Enrich, p. 54

Media and Technology

🖵 **Transparencies** "Graphs of Charles's Law and Boyle's Law," Transparency 6

Answers to Self-Assessment

Caption Question

Figure 20 If you pull up on the piston, volume will increase and pressure would decrease.

✓ *Checkpoint*

The responding variable is shown on the vertical, or *y*-axis.

Performance Assessment

Skills Check Have students briefly define *directly proportional* and *vary inversely*. Then have students make graphs to illustrate each term.

It's a Gas

Preparing for Inquiry

Key Concept As the pressure applied to a gas is increased, the volume the gas occupies will decrease, and vice versa.

Skills Objectives Students will be able to

♦ measure and record the volume of air in a syringe;

♦ explain the change in volume as a result of increasing pressure;

♦ interpret the data using a graph of the volume as a function of pressure.

Time 20 minutes

Advance Planning Depending on students' experience, you may want to take some time on the day of the lab to give instruction in drawing a best-fit curve through real data points, or else students can connect the points with a series of straight segments.

Alternative Materials

♦ You can use syringes fitted with a Leur-type stopcock or have some means other than clay to seal off the syringes.

♦ *Computer use is optional.*

Guiding Inquiry

Invitation Display a small, hand-held pump, such as a bicycle pump, with the plunger in the "up" position. Ask: **What will happen when the plunger is pushed down?** (*Air will be forced out.*) Then ask: **What would happen if the handle were pushed down when the nozzle of the pump is held closed, so that air cannot get out?** (*The air inside will be under more and more pressure as the plunger is pushed down.*) CAUTION: *Do not actually try this.*

Introducing the Procedure

Have students read through the procedure. Allow students to practice reading the volume of air inside the syringe.

Skills Lab

Drawing Conclusions

You can use a syringe as a model of an air pump. In this lab, you will determine how the pressure exerted on a syringe is related to the volume of the air inside it.

Problem

How does the volume of a gas change as the pressure you exert on it increases?

Materials

strong plastic syringe (with no needle), at least 35 cm^3 capacity
modeling clay
4 books of uniform weight
computer and graphing software (optional)

Procedure

1. Make a data table in your notebook like the one below.
2. Lift the plunger of the syringe as high as it will move without going off scale. The volume in the syringe will be as large as possible.
3. Seal the small opening of the syringe with a piece of clay. The seal must be airtight.

4. Hold the syringe upright with the clay end on the table. With the help of a partner, place a single book on top of the plunger. Balance the book carefully so it does not fall.
5. Read the volume indicated by the plunger and record it in your data table.
6. Predict what will happen as more books are placed on the syringe.
7. Place another book on top of the first book. Read the new volume and record it in your data table.

DATA TABLE			
Adding Books		Removing Books	
Number of Books	Volume (cm^3)	Number of Books	Volume (cm^3)
0		4	
1		3	
2		2	
3		1	
4		0	

Troubleshooting the Experiment

♦ Have one student hold the syringe upright while another uses both hands to balance the books. If students have trouble balancing the books on the syringe, glue the top of each syringe plunger to a wooden block (about 10 cm square and 2–3 cm thick) to provide a larger surface.

♦ Review how to estimate to the nearest 0.5 cm^3. This should give a smoother curve when the graph is drawn.

♦ Students may have trouble sealing their syringes. If students' results are unusual, check whether they have sealed the syringes completely.

8. One by one, place each of the remaining books on top of the plunger. After you add each book, record the volume of the syringe in your data table.

9. Predict what will happen as books are removed from the plunger one by one.

10. Remove the books one at a time. After you remove each book, again record the volume of the syringe in your data table.

Analyze and Conclude

1. Why is this a good model of an air pump? What are the model's limitations?

2. 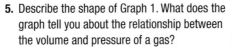 Using a computer or graph paper, make a line graph of the data obtained from Steps 5, 7, and 8. Show volume in cubic centimeters (cm³) on the vertical axis and number of books on the horizontal axis. Title this Graph 1.

3. Make a second line graph of the data obtained from Step 10. Title this Graph 2.

4. Did the results you obtained support your predictions in Steps 6 and 9? Explain.

5. Describe the shape of Graph 1. What does the graph tell you about the relationship between the volume and pressure of a gas?

6. Compare Graph 2 with Graph 1. How can you explain any differences in the two graphs?

7. **Think About It** Did the volume change between the addition of the first and second book? Did it change by the same amount between the addition of the second book and third book? Between the third and fourth book? What is happening to the gas particles in air that could explain this behavior?

Design an Experiment

How could you use ice and warm water to show how the temperature and volume of a gas are related? Design an experiment to test the effect of changing the temperature of a gas. With your teacher's approval, conduct this experiment.

Sample Data Table

Adding Books		Removing Books	
Number of Books	Volume (cm³)	Number of Books	Volume (cm³)
0	63.0	4	49.0
1	63.0	3	49.0
2	60.0	2	52.6
3	53.0	1	56.1
4	49.0	0	61.0

Program Resources

◆ **Unit 1 Resources** Chapter 2 Skills Lab blackline masters, pp. 59–61
◆ **Inquiry Skills Activity Book** Provides teaching and review of all inquiry skills

Media and Technology

 Lab Activity Videotapes
Grade 6, Tape 1

Expected Outcome
As books are added, the volume of the gas in the syringe will decrease. As books are taken away, the volume of the gas will increase.

Analyze and Conclude
1. This model of an air pump is good because it shows that the volume of a gas decreases as the pressure on the gas increases. Limitations of this pump model include the small ranges of pressure and volume.
2. Students' graphs should have correct labels. The volume should decrease as more books are added.
3. Students' graphs should have correct labels. The volume should increase as more books are removed.
4. Answers will depend on students' predictions. In general, predictions from Step 6 will probably be confirmed. Predictions from Step 9 may not be confirmed because the volume may not return to the original volume. As books are removed, the volume of the gas will increase less than it decreased because of friction in the syringe.
5. The graph is curved downward. The graph shows that increasing the pressure by increasing the number of books (greater pressure) decreases the volume of air in the syringe.
6. The graphs should be approximately of the same general shape, but the data points will probably not be the same. Decreasing the number of books (less pressure) increases the volume.
7. Answers will vary depending on students' data. The decrease in volume may become less as more books are added. The particles are being forced closer together as more weight is added. Eventually, there is little room for further compression.

Extending the Inquiry
Design an Experiment Students may suggest placing the sealed syringe in a freezer or in an ice bath, then at room temperature, then in hot water, although the amount of volume change for this temperature range may not be very dramatic.

TEKS: 6.1A; 6.2A, B, C, E; 6.4A; 6.7B

Objectives

After completing the lesson, students will be able to

◆ explain that thermal energy flows from a warmer substance to a cooler substance;

◆ identify examples of changes in state and explain how thermal energy is involved in each example.

1 Engage/Explore

Activating Prior Knowledge

Ask students: **What happens if you leave an ice cube in a glass at room temperature?** *(It melts.)* **Can you change the water back into ice?** *(Yes)* **How?** *(Put the water in the freezer.)*

⬤⬤⬤⬤⬤ DISCOVER ⬤⬤⬤⬤⬤

Skills Focus developing hypotheses

Materials *hand mirrors, soft cloths*

Time 10 minutes

Tips Most students will know that their breath can fog a mirror, but they may not have thought about the effect of distance. Have students begin with the mirror at a distance from their faces in order for them to have a basis for comparison. Remind students that the mirrors are breakable and should be handled with care.

Think It Over Most students will suggest that the mirror becomes fogged as water vapor in their warm breath condenses on the cooler surface of the mirror. Explanations for different results at greater distances may vary. Accept all reasonable explanations. Some students may recognize that when the mirror is at a greater distance, the water vapor disperses through and cools in the air.

DISCOVER ⬤⬤⬤⬤⬤⬤⬤⬤⬤⬤⬤⬤ ACTIVITY

What Happens When You Breathe on a Mirror?

1. Obtain a hand mirror. Clean it with a dry cloth. Describe the mirror's surface.

2. Hold the mirror about 15 cm away from your face. Try to breathe against the mirror's surface.

3. Reduce the distance until breathing on the mirror produces a visible change. Record what you observe.

Think It Over

Developing Hypotheses What did you observe when you breathed on the mirror held close to your mouth? How can you explain that observation? Why did you get different results when the mirror was at greater distances from your face?

GUIDE FOR READING

◆ When thermal energy is transferred, in what direction does it flow?

◆ How does the thermal energy of a substance change when it changes state?

Reading Tip As you read, make an outline that includes the headings and main ideas of the section.

Key Terms thermal energy
• melting • freezing
• vaporization
• evaporation
• boiling
• boiling point
• condensation
• sublimation

Think of what happens to an ice cream cone on a hot summer day. The ice cream quickly starts to drip onto your hand. You're not surprised. You know that ice cream melts if it's not kept cold.

Energy and Changes in State

If you turn on a faucet, the tap water is usually cold unless it comes through a heater. At a warmer temperature, the particles of substance have a higher average energy of motion than at a cooler temperature. The energy that the particles of a substance have is called **thermal energy.** The amount of thermal energy in a substance depends partly on its temperature and the way its particles are arranged.

Thermal energy is transferred from one substance to another as heat. **Thermal energy always flows from a warmer substance to a cooler substance.** When heat flows into a substance, its particles gain energy and move faster. When heat flows from a substance, its particles lose energy and move more slowly. So thermal energy is involved when a substance changes state.

READING STRATEGIES

Reading Tip Suggest that students prepare the main headings of their outlines in advance, leaving space to add information as they read. Help students preview the section and identify the blue-green main headings and purple sub-headings. Suggest that students look for definitions and examples to add to their outlines as they read.

I. Changes in State
  A. Energy and Changes in State
  B. Changes Between Liquid and Solid
    1. Melting
    2. Freezing
  C. Changes Between Liquid and Gas
    1. Vaporization
    2. Boiling Point and Air Pressure
    3. Condensation (outline continues)

Figure 22 A jeweler melts silver before pouring it into a mold. *Predicting What happens to the silver particles as the melted silver cools down?*

You saw that the arrangement and motion of the particles of a substance determine whether the substance is a solid, a liquid, or a gas. The particles of a solid have the least thermal energy. They simply vibrate in a fixed position. When the same substance becomes a liquid, the particles have more thermal energy. They move around freely, although they remain close to one another. The particles of the substance have even more thermal energy as a gas. They are separated from one another and move around in all directions at high speeds. **A substance changes state when its thermal energy increases or decreases by a sufficient amount.**

Changes Between Liquid and Solid

Each specific substance changes states at temperatures that are typical for that substance. But the overall pattern for the way substances change state is the same.

Melting The change in state from a solid to a liquid is called **melting.** In Section 1, you learned that a crystalline solid melts at a specific temperature, called the melting point. The melting point of a substance depends on how strongly its particles attract one another.

Think of an ice cube taken from the freezer. The energy to melt comes from the air in the room. At first, the added thermal energy makes the water molecules vibrate faster, raising their temperature. At 0°C, the water molecules are vibrating so fast that they break free from their positions in ice crystals. For a time, the temperature of the ice stops increasing. Instead, the added energy changes the arrangement of the water molecules from ice crystals into liquid water. This is the process you observe as melting.

✓ *Checkpoint* *What happens to the particles of a solid as it gains more and more thermal energy?*

Answers to Self-Assessment

Caption Question

Figure 22 The silver particles stop moving freely around each other and remain in fixed positions.

✓ *Checkpoint*

The particles vibrate faster, break free of their positions, and move more freely around each other.

2 *Facilitate*

Energy and Changes in State

Including All Students

Students may confuse heat and temperature. Explain that, although these words mean very similar things in everyday life, physicists use them in very specific ways. Temperature is a measure of the average energy of motion of individual particles in a substance. Thermal energy is the total energy of motion of all the particles. Heat is thermal energy moving from a warmer object to a cooler object. Ask students why a gas could have a relatively low temperature but still contain thermal energy. (*The particles still have enough energy of motion to remain in the gaseous state instead of becoming a liquid.*) **learning modality: verbal**

Changes Between Liquid and Solid

Demonstration

Materials *crushed ice or snow, large beaker, thermometer (alcohol), stopwatch or clock, hot plate, goggles, stirring rod*
Time 15 minutes

Place about 5 cm of ice or snow in the beaker, then insert the thermometer and carefully fill the beaker with more ice or snow around the thermometer. Place the beaker on the hot plate and turn on to medium-high heat. Stir the ice water carefully as it melts. Have a volunteer take temperature readings every 2 seconds until all the ice is melted. Continue heating and taking readings until the water reaches room temperature. Turn off the hot plate and remove the beaker to a heat-proof surface. Then ask: **While the ice was melting, did the energy from the hot plate increase the temperature of the water? Explain.** (*No, the energy changed the arrangement of the water molecules from ice crystals to liquid water.*) **learning modality: logical/mathematical**

Changes Between Liquid and Solid, continued

Addressing Naive Conceptions

Students may associate freezing with low temperatures. Ask students to name solids that melt at high temperatures. *(Samples: Plastic, candle wax)* Ask students to explain what happens to melted wax when it cools. *(It solidifies.)* Point out that solidifying is "freezing," even at high temperatures. **learning modality: verbal**

Changes Between Liquid and Gas

Demonstration

Materials *dropper, overhead projector, wax pencil, beaker, water, hot plate*

Time 20 minutes

With the projector on, place a few drops of water inside a small wax circle on the overhead until the circle is almost filled. Observe the water over time. Ask: **What is happening to the water?** *(It is evaporating.)* Next, heat 500 mL of water in a beaker until it boils. Ask: **What is happening to the water?** *(It is boiling.)* Then ask: **How do boiling and evaporation differ?** *(Only surface particles vaporize when water evaporates.)* **learning modality: visual**

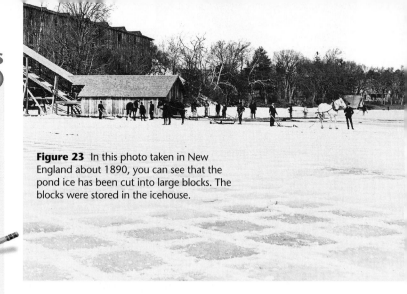

Figure 23 In this photo taken in New England about 1890, you can see that the pond ice has been cut into large blocks. The blocks were stored in the icehouse.

Freezing Now suppose you put the liquid water from the melted ice cube into a freezer. After a while, the water will freeze back into ice. **Freezing** is the change of state from liquid to solid—just the reverse of melting.

When you put liquid water into the freezer, the water loses energy to the cold air in the freezer. At first, the water molecules move more slowly. When the temperature reaches 0°C, the molecules are moving so slowly that they form regular patterns. These patterns are the crystals that form ice. When water freezes, the temperature stays at 0°C until freezing is complete. (This is the same temperature at which ice melts.)

Changes Between Liquid and Gas

Have you ever wondered how clouds form, or why rain falls from clouds? And why do puddles dry up after a rain shower? To answer these questions, you need to look at the ways that water changes between the liquid and gas states.

Vaporization The change from liquid water into water vapor is an example of **vaporization** (vay puhr ih ZAY shuhn). Vaporization occurs when a liquid gains enough energy to become a gas. There are two main types of vaporization.

The first kind, called **evaporation** (ee vap uh RAY shun), takes place only on the surface of a liquid. A drying puddle is an example. The water in the puddle gains energy from the ground, the air, or the sun. The energy enables the molecules on the surface of the puddle to escape into the air. Evaporation also occurs when you sweat. Sweat evaporates as it gains thermal energy from your skin, cooling you down on a hot day or when you exercise.

Figure 24 During evaporation, particles leave the surface of a liquid.

76

Background

Integrating Science The temperature of the water in the Arctic and Antarctic oceans can sometimes fall below freezing. However, certain species of fishes thrive in this environment. Biologists wondered how these fishes, which have large amounts of water in their bodies, could keep from freezing when the water temperature dropped below 0°C. Biologists now know that these fishes contain "antifreeze proteins" that absorb tiny ice crystals that form inside their bodies. This process keeps the ice crystals from growing. Together with the salt in the fishes' body fluids, the antifreeze proteins lower the freezing point of the fishes' blood to below the freezing point of saltwater.

Biologists think the antifreeze proteins evolved in response to the cooling of the Arctic and Antarctic millions of years ago.

Figure 25 During boiling, groups of particles form bubbles of gas at many locations throughout the liquid. These bubbles rise to the surface, where the particles escape. *Applying Concepts What happens to the boiling point of water when the air pressure increases?*

The second kind of vaporization, called **boiling,** takes place inside a liquid as well as at the surface. Each liquid boils at a specific temperature called its **boiling point**. Like the melting point of a solid, the boiling point of a liquid depends on how strongly the particles of the substance are attracted to one another.

Boiling Point and Air Pressure The boiling point of a substance depends on the pressure of the air above a liquid. The lower the air pressure above the liquid, the less energy that molecules in the liquid need to escape into the air. As you go up in elevation, air pressure decreases. At the air pressure in places close to sea level, the boiling point of water is 100°C. In the mountains, however, air pressure is lower, and so is the boiling point of water.

For example, the city of Denver, Colorado, is 1,600 meters above sea level. At this elevation, the boiling point of water is 95°C. When a recipe calls for boiling water, cooks in Denver have to be careful. Food doesn't cook as quickly at 95°C as it does at 100°C.

Condensation The opposite of vaporization is called condensation. **Condensation** occurs when gas particles lose enough thermal energy to become a liquid. Clouds typically form when water vapor in the atmosphere condenses into liquid droplets. When the droplets get heavy enough, they fall to the ground as rain.

You can observe condensation by breathing onto a mirror. When warm water vapor in your breath reaches the cooler surface of the mirror, the water vapor condenses into liquid droplets. The droplets then evaporate into water vapor again.

Remember that when you observe clouds, mist, or steam from boiling water, you are not seeing water vapor, a gas that's impossible to see. What you see in those cases are tiny droplets of liquid water suspended in air.

☑ *Checkpoint How are vaporization and condensation related?*

Using a barometric pressure reading and a handbook of chemistry, have students determine the boiling point of water in your area on a given day. **learning modality: logical/mathematical**

Addressing Naive Conceptions

Materials *drinking glass, water, ice*
Time 20 minutes

Help students correctly infer why drops of water form on the outside of a drinking glass. Fill a drinking glass with ice and water and leave it at room temperature for about 10 minutes. Ask students to observe what forms on the outside of the glass. *(Water droplets or a thin film of water)* Ask: **Where did the water come from?** *(Many students will say from inside the glass.)* Remind students that the water cannot pass through glass. Suggest students apply their knowledge about condensation to make a new inference about how the water appeared. *(Water vapor in the air outside the drinking glass cooled when it came in contact with the ice-cold glass. As it cooled, it condensed and formed droplets of water on the outside of the drinking glass.)* **learning modality: visual**

Answers to Self-Assessment

Caption Question
Figure 25 The boiling point of water increases when the air pressure increases.

☑ *Checkpoint*
They are opposite processes. They occur at the same temperature for any one substance.

Ongoing Assessment

Oral Presentation Have students identify and describe examples of matter changing state between solid and liquid or between liquid and gas.

Changes Between Solid and Gas

Building Inquiry Skills: Applying Concepts

Inform students that frozen water will also undergo sublimation. Ask students if they have ever noticed that the ice in an ice cube tray gets smaller when it is left in the freezer for a long time. Ask why this happens. *(The surface particles of the ice gain enough energy to become a gas and spread out.)* **learning modality: logical/mathematical**

EXPLORING
Changes of State

Have students pause at each lettered point in the graph to examine the drawings that indicate how the water particles behave at that point. *(Drawings show an increase in movement and a decrease in rigid structure as thermal energy increases.)* Ask students to infer why the graph does not show a steady increase in temperature with increasing thermal energy. *(Adding thermal energy does not always increase temperature. All the particles in the material must change state for the temperature to rise.)*
Extend As a class activity or demonstration, find the change in temperature over time as a beaker of ice is heated to a boil, and prepare a graph of the data. Make sure all students wear goggles and exercise care when working with the hot plate and hot water. Refer to the **ELL Handbook** for additional teaching strategies. **learning modality: logical/mathematical**

Cultural Diversity

In English-speaking countries, the states of matter are called *ice*, *water*, and *water vapor*. In Spanish-speaking countries, the words used are *hielo*, *agua*, and *vapor*. In German, the words used are *eis*, *wasser*, and *wasserdampf*. In French, the words are *glace*, *eau*, and *vapeur*. Have students who are non-native English speakers say the words for the solid, liquid, and gas states of water in their native languages.
limited English proficiency

Changes Between Solid and Gas

If you live where the winters are cold, you may have noticed that snow seems to disappear even when the temperature stays well below freezing. This happens because of sublimation. **Sublimation** occurs when the surface particles of a solid gain enough energy to become a gas. Particles do not pass through the liquid state at all. Some solids, such as naphthalene (moth balls), sublime more easily than others, such as table salt.

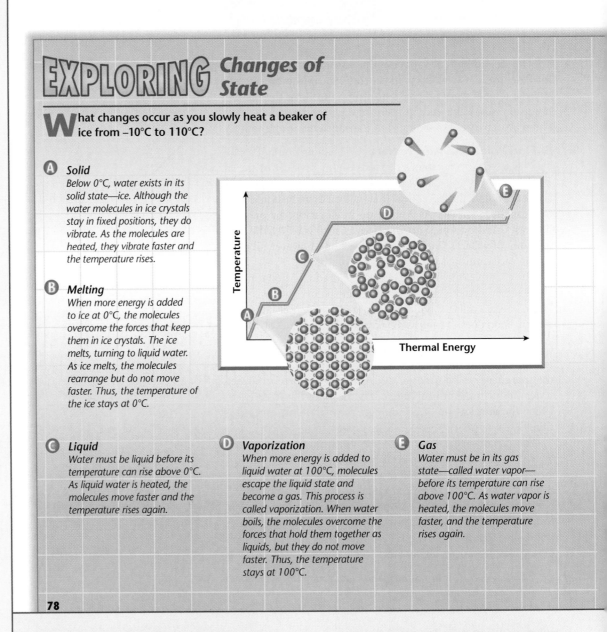

EXPLORING *Changes of State*

What changes occur as you slowly heat a beaker of ice from –10°C to 110°C?

Ⓐ Solid
Below 0°C, water exists in its solid state—ice. Although the water molecules in ice crystals stay in fixed positions, they do vibrate. As the molecules are heated, they vibrate faster and the temperature rises.

Ⓑ Melting
When more energy is added to ice at 0°C, the molecules overcome the forces that keep them in ice crystals. The ice melts, turning to liquid water. As ice melts, the molecules rearrange but do not move faster. Thus, the temperature of the ice stays at 0°C.

Ⓒ Liquid
Water must be liquid before its temperature can rise above 0°C. As liquid water is heated, the molecules move faster and the temperature rises again.

Ⓓ Vaporization
When more energy is added to liquid water at 100°C, molecules escape the liquid state and become a gas. This process is called vaporization. When water boils, the molecules overcome the forces that hold them together as liquids, but they do not move faster. Thus, the temperature stays at 100°C.

Ⓔ Gas
Water must be in its gas state—called water vapor—before its temperature can rise above 100°C. As water vapor is heated, the molecules move faster, and the temperature rises again.

(Graph labels: Temperature, Thermal Energy)

Background

Facts and Figures Understanding the states of matter is important to engineers and other builders. However, those who build out of ice must have a special knowledge of the solid state of water.

A Canadian anthropologist, Diamond Jenness, described the traditional method of building igloos, or snow-and-ice houses, used by the Inuits of Canada and Greenland. Jenness noted that after the key ice block was secured, a lamp was lit inside the snow hut. Heat from the lamp melted the snow on the inside walls. This water hardened quickly when cold outside air was let into the hut. The melted and rehardened snow functioned as a cement to hold the large ice blocks in place. Gradually, heat from the people living and working inside the hut changed the snow dome into a solid dome of ice.

Figure 26 shows a common example of sublimation, the change in dry ice. "Dry ice" is the common name for solid carbon dioxide (CO_2). At ordinary air pressures, carbon dioxide cannot exist as a liquid. So instead of melting, solid carbon dioxide changes directly into a gas. As it changes state, it absorbs thermal energy, so it keeps materials near it cold and dry. For this reason, it's an excellent way to keep temperatures low when a refrigerator is not available. Recall that you cannot see the gas that dry ice forms. The fog around it results when water vapor from the nearby air cools and forms tiny droplets.

Identifying Substances Through Changes of State

Chemists sometimes face the problem of identifying unknown materials. In Chapter 1, you learned that the combination of properties a substance has can be used to identify it. To make such identification possible, chemists have built up a data bank of information about the properties of substances. As a result, comparing melting points and boiling points can be important steps in identifying an unknown material.

Suppose, for example, that chemists are trying to identify three clear, colorless liquids. One is water, another is chloroform (once used to cause sleep during surgery), and a third is ethanol (a type of alcohol). You already know the melting and boiling points of water. Chloroform melts at –64°C and boils at 61°C. Ethanol melts at –117°C and boils at 79°C. You can thus see how testing for these properties would help researchers identify them.

Figure 26 Dry ice is solid carbon dioxide. It changes directly to a gas in the process of sublimation. The energy absorbed in this change of state cools the water vapor in the air, creating fog. *Inferring Describe what happens to the carbon dioxide particles during sublimation.*

Section 4 Review

1. If an object at 50°C is placed in ice water, how will changes in thermal energy affect the temperature of the object?
2. In terms of energy and particle movement, what happens to a liquid as it changes into a gas?
3. What's the main difference between boiling and evaporation?
4. **Thinking Critically Applying Concepts** If you are stranded in a blizzard and are trying to stay warm, why should you melt snow and then drink it instead of just eating snow?

Check Your Progress CHAPTER PROJECT
Use the information you learned in this section to revise your storyboard, if necessary. Then if you are creating a cartoon, draw the cartoon and write the captions. If you are presenting a skit, write a script and stage directions. Rehearse the skit with the members of your group.

Answers to Self-Assessment

Caption Question

Figure 26 Particles go from a solid (in fixed positions and close together) to a gas (moving freely and farther apart in the space available).

Identifying Substances Through Changes of State

Including All Students

Ask: **Which property of ethanol would be easier to determine, melting point or boiling point? Why?** (*Boiling point because alcohol is already a liquid at room temperature, so you can heat the liquid until it boils.*) **learning modality: logical/mathematical**

3 Assess

Section 4 Review Answers

1. The object's temperature will decrease as thermal energy flows from the warmer object to the cooler water.
2. The particles gain energy, move faster, and escape into the air.
3. Evaporation takes place only at the surface of the liquid. Boiling takes place at the surface and inside the liquid.
4. If you eat snow, thermal energy from your body is used to melt the snow and then warm the water to body temperature. If you melt the snow and then drink the water, your body has to use less of its thermal energy.

Check Your Progress CHAPTER PROJECT
Encourage students to compare each frame of their storyboards against the content in this section. A change to one part may require a change to another part. When students are ready, provide materials and time for them to work on their cartoons or skits.

Performance Assessment

Organizing Information Have students make a compare/contrast table to show similarities and differences among vaporization, condensation, and sublimation.

Melting Ice

Preparing for Inquiry

Key Concept When the thermal energy of the particles in a solid increases, the material can change from solid to liquid. Varying the amount of thermal energy available affects the amount of time required for all the solid to melt.

Skills Objectives Students will be able to
- predict which ice cube will melt faster, one in a cup of warm water or one in a cup of room-temperature water;
- measure the temperature changes that take place as the ice cube melts;
- draw conclusions to explain how the addition of thermal energy causes ice to melt.

Time 30 minutes

Advance Planning
- Keep the ice in an insulated container and distribute the pieces when students are ready to use them.
- Heat enough water for all students or have students use warm tap water.
- Set out another volume of water to come to room temperature before the activity begins.
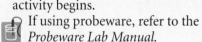 If using probeware, refer to the *Probeware Lab Manual.*

Guiding Inquiry

Troubleshooting the Experiment
- The bulb of the thermometer must be immersed in the water. Make sure students do not use the thermometer to stir the water.
- Allow a sufficient amount of tap water to come to room temperature before the activity begins.

Safety

If students use glass materials, they should wear goggles and use glass items with care. Review the safety guidelines in Appendix A.

Program Resources

- **Unit 1 Resources** Chapter 2 Skills Lab blackline masters, pp. 62–63
- **Probeware Lab Manual** Blackline masters

Media and Technology

Lab Activity Videotapes
Grade 6, Tape 1

MELTING ICE

In this experiment, you will measure temperature as you explore the melting of ice.

Problem

How does the temperature of the surroundings affect the rate at which ice melts?

Materials

thermometer or temperature probes and CBL procedure (optional)
stopwatch or timer
2 plastic cups, about 200 mL each
2 stirring rods, preferably plastic
ice cubes, about 2 cm on each side
warm water, about 40°C to 45°C
water at room temperature, about 20° C

Procedure

1. Read Steps 1–8. Based on your own experience, predict which ice cube will melt faster.
2. Make a data table like the one below.
3. Fill a cup halfway with warm water (about 40°C to 45°C). Fill a second cup to the same depth with water at room temperature.
4. Record the temperature of the water in each cup. If using a temperature probe, see your teacher for instructions.
5. Obtain two same-size ice cubes.
6. Place one piece of ice in each cup. Begin timing with a stopwatch. Gently stir each cup with a stirring rod.
7. Observe both ice cubes carefully. At the moment one of the ice cubes is completely melted, record the time and the temperature of the water in the cup.

8. Wait for the second ice cube to melt. Record its melting time and the water temperature.

Analyze and Conclude

1. Was your prediction in Step 1 supported by the results of the experiment? Explain why or why not.
2. In which cup did the water temperature change the most? Explain this result.
3. When the ice melted, its molecules gained enough energy to overcome the forces holding them together as solid ice. What is the source of that energy?
4. **Think About It** How well could you time the exact moment that each ice cube completely melted? How might errors in measurements affect your conclusions?

Design an Experiment

When a lake freezes in winter, only the top layer turns to ice. Design an experiment to model the melting of a frozen lake during the spring. With your teacher's approval, carry out your experiment. Be prepared to share your results with the class.

DATA TABLE

	Beginning Temperature (°C)	Time to Melt (s)	Final Temperature (°C)
Cup 1			
Cup 2			

Sample Data Table

	Beginning Temperature (°C)	Time to Melt (s)	Final Temperature (°C)
Cup 1	21.5	165	15.9
Cup 2	44.0	70	36.5

Temperature change: Cup 1: 5.6°C; Cup 2: 7.5°C

SECTION 1 States of Matter

Key Ideas

◆ Solids have a definite shape and volume because the particles in a solid are packed tightly together and stay in fixed positions.

◆ Particles in a liquid move freely around one another. A liquid has no definite shape, but it does have a definite volume.

◆ The particles of a gas spread apart to fill all the space available to them. Thus, a gas has neither definite shape nor definite volume.

Key Terms

solid   liquid
crystalline solid   viscosity
melting point   gas
amorphous solid

 SECTION 2 Gas Behavior

Key Ideas

◆ At constant temperature, when the volume of a gas decreases, its pressure increases.

◆ In a rigid container, raising the temperature of a gas increases its pressure.

◆ In a flexible container, raising the temperature of a gas increases its volume.

Key Terms

temperature   Boyle's law
pressure   Charles's law

 SECTION 3 Graphing Gas Behavior

INTEGRATING *MATHEMATICS*

Key Ideas

◆ A graph shows that the volume of a gas and its kelvin temperature are directly proportional at constant pressure.

◆ A graph shows that the volume of a gas at constant temperature varies inversely with its pressure.

Key Terms

graph   vary inversely
directly proportional

SECTION 4 Changes in State

Key Ideas

◆ Thermal energy flows, in the form of heat, from a warmer substance to a cooler substance. The temperature of the warmer substance decreases, and the temperature of the cooler substance increases.

◆ Changes of state can occur when a substance gains or loses thermal energy.

Key Terms

thermal energy   boiling
melting   boiling point
freezing   condensation
vaporization   sublimation
evaporation

Organizing Information

Compare/Contrast Table Copy the compare/contrast table about the states of matter onto a separate sheet of paper. Then complete it and add a title. (For more on compare/contrast tables, see the Skills Handbook.)

State of Matter	Shape	Volume	Example (at room temperature)
a. __?__	Definite	b. __?__	Diamond
Liquid	c. __?__	Definite	d. __?__
Gas	e. __?__	Not definite	f. __?__

Analyze and Conclude

1. Sample: The ice cube in warmer water melted faster because more thermal energy was available.

2. The temperature of the warmer water changed the most because there was a greater difference between it and the ice.

3. The thermal energy of the water

4. Answers will vary. Taking the final temperature too late will increase the time measurement.

Extending the Inquiry

Design an Experiment Sample: The "lake" could be a partially frozen container of water with a layer of ice. One "lake" could be exposed to a lamp (the "sun") while the other is kept in the shade. Check students' plans for safety.

Organizing Information

Compare/Contrast Table
Sample title: States of Matter; **a.** Solid **b.** Definite **c.** Not definite **d.** Sample: Water **e.** Not definite **f.** Sample: Oxygen

Program Resources

◆ **Unit 1 Resources** Chapter 2 Project Scoring Rubric, p. 42
◆ **Performance Assessment** Chapter 2, pp. 8–10
◆ **Chapter and Unit Tests** Chapter 2 Test, pp. 8–11

Media and Technology

 Computer Test Bank
Chapter 2 Test

Reviewing Content

Multiple Choice

1. b 2. c 3. b 4. a 5. d

True or False

6. amorphous 7. true 8. pressure
9. directly 10. higher

Checking Concepts

11. Particles in a solid vibrate back and forth slightly but remain in fixed positions in relation to one another.

12. All liquids flow because their particles are able to move around each other. High-viscosity liquids flow more slowly than low-viscosity liquids.

13. Temperature is a measure of the average speed of the movement of the particles of a substance.

14. The gas particles will spread into the air outside the ball as they move from a space of greater pressure to one of lower pressure.

15. During condensation gas particles lose thermal energy and become a liquid.

16. Water's boiling point is 100°C (at sea level pressure). The water molecules gain enough energy to overcome the forces that hold them together as a liquid, and they move apart, forming water vapor.

17. For a given substance, melting (solid to liquid) and freezing (liquid to solid) are opposite changes at the same temperature. In melting, thermal energy is added. In freezing, thermal energy is removed.

18. Students' stories should demonstrate an understanding of the law they are discussing. If desired, provide resources for students to research the discoveries of their chosen scientist.

Thinking Critically

19. Heating up the table tennis ball would cause the air inside it to expand and push the shell back to its original shape.

20. Diagrams should show the compression of the air mattress (less volume), and so the gas particles are more dense (higher pressure).

Reviewing Content

 Review key concepts online using iText at www.phschool.com

Multiple Choice

Choose the letter of the answer that best completes each statement.

1. A substance whose particles are close together but move is classified as a(n)
   a. crystalline solid.   b. liquid.
   c. gas.   d. amorphous solid.
2. Unlike solids and liquids, a gas will
   a. keep its volume in different containers.
   b. keep its shape in different containers.
   c. expand to fill the space available to it.
   d. decrease in volume when the temperature rises.
3. Boyle's law states that the volume of a gas increases when its
   a. pressure increases.
   b. pressure decreases.
   c. temperature falls.
   d. temperature rises.
4. The vertical axis of a graph shows the
   a. responding variable.
   b. manipulated variable.
   c. constant factors.
   d. same variable as the *x*-axis.
5. When a liquid freezes, its particles
   a. move more rapidly.
   b. escape from its surface more quickly.
   c. vibrate faster.
   d. slow down and form patterns.

True or False

If the statement is true, write true. If it is false, change the underlined word or words to make it a true statement.

6. Rubber and glass become softer and softer over a wide range of temperatures. They are examples of <u>crystalline</u> solids.
7. The energy from the movement of particles is measured by the <u>temperature</u> of a substance.
8. If a gas is contained in a rigid container, raising its temperature will increase its <u>volume</u>.

---

9. Charles's law states that the volume of a gas varies <u>inversely</u> with its temperature.
10. The boiling point of a liquid is <u>lower</u> at sea level than on a mountain.

Checking Concepts

11. Describe the motion of particles in a solid.

12. Compare and contrast liquids with high and low viscosities.

13. How is the temperature of a substance related to the energy of movement of the particles in the substance?

14. What happens to the gas particles when the air in an inflated ball leaks out?

15. What happens during condensation?

16. What happens to water molecules when water is heated from 90°C to 110°C?

17. Compare the processes of melting and freezing.

18. **Writing to Learn** Imagine you are Robert Boyle or Jacques Charles at the time you described the law that came to be known by your name. Tell the story of your experiments and results as you think Boyle or Charles would if either one could talk to the students in your class today. Write down exactly what you would say.

Thinking Critically

19. **Relating Cause and Effect** Explain why placing a dented table tennis ball in boiling water is one way to remove a dent in the ball. Assume it has no holes.

20. **Comparing and Contrasting** Using diagrams, show the gas particles in an air mattress before you lie down on it and while you are lying on it.

21. **Applying Concepts** Describe what happens when an ice cube and solid carbon dioxide are each placed in a warm room. Why do you think the solid carbon dioxide is called "dry ice"?

22. **Inferring** When snow on the ground undergoes sublimation, where does the necessary energy come from?

---

21. The ice cube melts and becomes liquid water and eventually evaporates. The solid carbon dioxide changes directly into a gas. Solid carbon dioxide is called "dry ice" because it doesn't pass through a liquid state before it becomes a gas.

22. The energy comes from thermal energy in the environment.

Applying Skills

23. Graphs should show a straight line pointing up and to the right.

24. The warmer the water, the more the compound dissolves.

25. about 85 g

Applying Skills

At each temperature, the mass of a compound dissolved in 100 mL of water was measured. Use this data to answer Questions 23–25.

Temperature	Mass of Compound Dissolved
(°C)	(g)
0	37
10	47
20	56
30	66
40	75

23. Graphing Graph the data for mass dissolved at each temperature. Label the horizontal axis from 0°C to 60°C and the vertical axis from 0 grams to 100 grams.

24. Interpreting Data What does the graph show about the effect of temperature on the amount of the compound that will dissolve in water?

25. Predicting Assume the amount of the compound dissolved continues to increase as the water is heated. Predict how many grams dissolve at 50°C.

Performance ▼ Assessment
CHAPTER PROJECT

Present Your Project If you prepared a cartoon, read the captions to the class and discuss the illustrations. If you prepared a skit, perform the skit in front of the class. After you finish your presentation, invite the class to ask questions about your project. Be prepared to share the decisions you made in creating your presentation.

Reflect and Record In your journal, describe the strengths and weaknesses of the way you modeled changes of state. How successful was your model? How well did your classmates understand your cartoon or skit? Describe what you learned from observing the projects of your classmates.

Performance ▼ Assessment
CHAPTER PROJECT

Present Your Project Provide enough time for each student or group to make a presentation. Have classmates take notes on the presentations, listing all positive points (accurate, thorough, entertaining, etc.), and recording their questions. Encourage students to share the decisions they made in planning and presenting their models.

Reflect and Record Encourage students to identify concepts or presentations that helped them understand changes of state. Students should compare different groups' depictions of physical changes and identify similarities and differences between different representations.

Test Preparation

Use these questions to prepare for standardized tests.

Read the information below. Then answer Questions 26–29.

A scientist measured the pressure of a sample of a gas at various volumes. The temperature of the gas was kept constant. The data are shown below.

Volume (cm^3)	Pressure (kPa)
15	222
21	159
31	108
50	67

26. At which volume was the pressure the highest?
A 15 cm^3 B 21 cm^3
C 31 cm^3 D 50 cm^3

27. If a measurement were taken when the volume was 25 cm^3, the pressure would be
F about 25 kPa.   G about 70 kPa.
H about 130 kPa.   J about 240 kPa.

28. What would happen to the pressure if the volume were increased to 75 cm^3?
A The pressure will increase.
B The pressure will decrease.
C The pressure will remain the same.
D There is no way to predict the pressure.

29. If you were to construct a graph with volume on the horizontal axis and pressure on the vertical axis, what would your graph look like?
F a straight line slanting up from left to right
G a curve slanting down from left to right
H a straight horizontal line
J a U-shaped curve

Chapter 2 **83**

Test Preparation

26. A **27.** H **28.** B **29.** G

Program Resources

◆ **Inquiry Skills Activity Book** Provides teaching and review of all inquiry skills
◆ **Prentice Hall Assessment System** Provides standardized test practice
◆ **Reading in the Content Area** Provides strategies to improve science reading skills
◆ **Teacher's ELL Handbook** Provides multiple strategies for English language learners

Relating Force and Motion

Sections	Time	Student Edition Activities	Other Activities
CHAPTER PROJECT **Speeds à la Carte** p. 85	Ongoing (2 weeks)	TEKS: 6.1A; 6.2B, C, D, E; 6.4A, B Check Your Progress, pp. 95, 105 Present Your Project, p. 115	**TE** Chapter 3 Project Notes, pp. 84–85
1 Describing, Measuring, and Graphing Motion pp. 86–97 TEKS: 6.6A, B 3.1.1 Explain when an object is in motion and how motion is relative to a reference point. 3.1.2 Calculate an object's speed and velocity using SI units of distance. 3.1.3 Graph motion showing changes in distance as a function of time.	4 periods/ 2 blocks	TEKS: 6.1A; 6.2A, B, C, D, E; 6.4A, B **Discover** How Fast and How Far?, p. 86 **Try This** Sunrise, Sunset, p. 88 **Skills Lab** Inclined to Roll, pp. 96–97	**TE** Building Inquiry Skills: Applying Concepts, p. 87 **TE** Integrating Mathematics, p. 89 **TE** Inquiry Challenge, p. 91 **LM** 3, "Measuring Speed"
2 Force and Acceleration pp. 98–107 TEKS: 6.6A, B 3.2.1 Explain how forces are related to motion. 3.2.2 Describe what happens to the motion of an object as it accelerates. 3.2.3 Calculate the acceleration of an object and graph changing speed and distance of an accelerating object.	4 periods/ 2 blocks	TEKS: 6.1A; 6.2A, B, C, D, E; 6.4A, B **Discover** Will You Hurry Up?, p. 98 **Sharpen your Skills** Predicting, p. 99 **Try This** Over the Edge, p. 101 **Real-World Lab: You and Your Community** Stopping on a Dime, pp. 106–107	**TE** Inquiry Challenge, p. 102 **TE** Integrating Space Science, p. 103
3 **INTEGRATING EARTH SCIENCE** **Water in Motion** pp. 108–112 TEKS: 6.6A, C 3.3.1 Describe how moving water shapes the land. 3.3.2 Trace the path a river takes from its headwaters to its mouth. 3.3.3 Explain how a flood affects the land near a river and how floods can be controlled.	2 periods/ 1 block	TEKS: 6.2B **Discover** What Affects How Water Moves?, p. 108 **Science at Home,** p. 112	**TE** Building Inquiry Skills: Making Models, p. 111
Study Guide/Chapter Assessment pp. 113–115	1 period/ ½ block	**PLM** Provides blackline masters for Probeware labs	**ISAB** Provides teaching and review of all inquiry skills

Key: **CTB** Computer Test Bank
CUT Chapter and Unit Tests
ELL Teacher's ELL Handbook

CHAPTER PLANNING GUIDE

 The Resource Pro® CD-ROM provides flexibility for planning the instruction for any type of schedule.

Program Resources		Assessment Strategies		Media and Technology	
UR UR	Chapter 3 Project Teacher Notes, pp. 62–63 Chapter 3 Project Overview and Worksheets, pp. 64–67	SE TE UR	Performance Assessment: Present Your Project, p. 115 Check Your Progress, pp. 95, 105 Chapter 3 Project Scoring Rubric, p. 68	🌐 🎧	Science Explorer at www.phschool.com Student Edition on Audio CD, English-Spanish, Chapter 3
UR UR UR UR UR	3-1 Section Lesson Plan, p. 69 3-1 Section Summary, p. 70 3-1 Review and Reinforce, p. 71 3-1 Enrich, p. 72 Skills Lab blackline masters, pp. 81–82	SE TE TE	Section 1 Review, p. 95 Ongoing Assessment, pp. 87, 89, 91, 93 Performance Assessment, p. 95	💿 📼 📼 📽	Physical Science Videodisc Unit 3, Side 1, "Travel" Videotape Grade 6, Unit 1, "Travel" Lab Activity Videotapes, Tape 1 Transparency 7, "Exploring Motion Graphs"
UR UR UR UR UR	3-2 Section Lesson Plan, p. 73 3-2 Section Summary, p. 74 3-2 Review and Reinforce, p. 75 3-2 Enrich, p. 76 Real-World Lab blackline masters, pp. 83–85	SE TE TE	Section 2 Review, p. 105 Ongoing Assessment, p. 99, 101, 103 Performance Assessment, p. 105	💿 📼 📼 📽	Physical Science Videodisc Unit 3, Side 1, "Light as a Feather" Videotape Grade 6, Unit 1, "Light as a Feather" Lab Activity Videotapes, Tape 1 Transparency 8, "Graphing Acceleration"
UR UR UR UR	3-3 Section Lesson Plan, p. 77 3-3 Section Summary, p. 78 3-3 Review and Reinforce, p. 79 3-3 Enrich, p. 80	SE TE TE	Section 3 Review, p. 112 Ongoing Assessment, pp. 109, 111 Performance Assessment, p. 112		
ELL GRSW RCA	Provides multiple strategies for English language learners Provides worksheets to promote student comprehension of content Provides strategies to improve science reading skills	SE PA CUT CTB PHAS	Chapter 3 Study Guide/Assessment, pp. 113–115 Chapter 3 Assessment, pp. 11–13 Chapter 3 Test, pp. 12–15 Chapter 3 Test Provides standardized test preparation	📺 Chapter 3 💾	Computer Test Bank, Chapter 3 Test

GRSW Guided Reading and Study Workbook
ISAB Inquiry Skills Activity Book
LM Laboratory Manual

PA Performance Assessment
PHAS Prentice Hall Assessment System
PLM Probeware Lab Manual

RCA Reading in the Content Area
SE Student Edition

TE Teacher's Edition
UR Unit Resources

Student Edition Activities Planner

ACTIVITY	Time (minutes)	Materials *Quantities for one work group*	Skills
Section 1			
Discover, p. 86	15	**Consumable** masking tape **Nonconsumable** meter stick, stopwatch	Inferring
Try This, p. 88	5 min, 6–8 times during 1 day	No special materials are required.	Observing
Skills Lab, pp. 96–97	40	**Consumable** masking tape **Nonconsumable** skateboard, meter stick, protractor, flat board about 1.5 m long, small piece of sturdy cardboard, supports to prop up the board (books, boxes), 2 stopwatches, computer (optional)	Measuring
Section 2			
Discover, p. 98	15	**Consumable** masking tape **Nonconsumable** meter stick, stop watch	Inferring
Sharpen Your Skills, p. 99	15	**Nonconsumable** two spring scales, hooks, wooden block	Predicting
Try This, p. 101	10	**Nonconsumable** coin	Inferring
Real-World Lab, pp. 106–107	40	**Nonconsumable** wooden meter stick, tape measure, 2 stopwatches or watches with second hands	Measuring, Calculating, Inferring
Section 3			
Discover, p. 108	15–20	**Consumable** water **Nonconsumable** rectangular pan, sand and pebbles, small piece of porcelain tile, clump of grassy soil, books to prop up pan, watering can	Predicting
Science at Home, p. 112	15–20	**Consumable** water, paper towel **Nonconsumable** clear plastic jars, one with a cover; soil to fill the covered jar halfway; spoon	Making Models, Observing, Inferring

A list of all materials required for the Student Edition activities can be found on pages T43–T49. You can obtain information about ordering materials by calling 1-800-848-9500 or by accessing the Science Explorer Internet site at **www.phschool.com**.

Texas Essential Knowledge and Skills

(6.1) Scientific processes. The student conducts field and laboratory investigations using safe, environmentally appropriate, and ethical practices. *(Project; Sections 1, 2)*

The student is expected to:

(A) demonstrate safe practices during field and laboratory investigations.

(6.2) Scientific processes. The student uses scientific inquiry methods during field and laboratory investigations. *(Project; Sections 1, 2, 3)*

The student is expected to:

(A) plan and implement investigative procedures including asking questions, formulating testable hypotheses, and selecting and using equipment and technology;

(B) collect data by observing and measuring;

(C) analyze and interpret information to construct reasonable explanations from direct and indirect evidence;

(D) communicate valid conclusions; and

(E) construct graphs, tables, maps, and charts using tools including computers to organize, examine, and evaluate data.

(6.4) Scientific processes. The student knows how to use a variety of tools and methods to conduct science inquiry. *(Project; Sections 1, 2)*

The student is expected to:

(A) collect, analyze, and record information using tools including beakers, petri dishes, meter sticks, graduated cylinders, weather instruments, timing devices, hot plates, test tubes, safety goggles, spring scales, magnets, balances, microscopes, telescopes, thermometers, calculators, field equipment, compasses, computers, and computer probes; and

(B) identify patterns in collected information using percent, average, range, and frequency.

(6.6) Science concepts. The student knows that there is a relationship between force and motion. *(Sections 1, 2, 3)*

The student is expected to:

(A) identify and describe the changes in position, direction of motion, and speed of an object when acted upon by force;

(B) demonstrate that changes in motion can be measured and graphically represented; and

(C) identify forces that shape features of the Earth including uplifting, movement of water, and volcanic activity.

Take It to the Net

 Interactive text at www.phschool.com

Science Explorer comes alive with iText.

■ **Complete student text** is accessible from any computer with Internet access or a CD-ROM drive.

■ **Animations, simulations, and videos** enhance student understanding and retention of concepts.

■ **Self-tests and online study tools** assess student understanding.

■ **Teacher management tools** help you make the most of this valuable resource.

STAY CURRENT with

Find out the latest research and information about mechanics at **www.phschool.com**.

Go to **www.phschool.com**. Select Texas on the navigation bar. Click on the Science icon. Then click on <u>Science Explorer</u> under PH@school.

Speeds à la Carte

TEKS: 6.1A; 6.2B, C, D, E; 6.4A, B

While moving objects are very common in our daily lives, measuring the motion of an object is a very sophisticated notion. In this chapter, students will be introduced to three of the useful ways of measuring and describing motion: speed, velocity, and acceleration. The Chapter Project allows students to develop and practice techniques used to measure motion.

Purpose In this project, students will identify and measure the motion of several different objects.

Skills Focus Students will be able to
- measure distance and time accurately;
- record data in lists or tables;
- apply concepts learned in class to calculate speed;
- communicate their work on display cards.

Project Time Line Students can begin measuring speeds the first week. Some measurements can be completed in a very short period of time, although others, such as the rate at which grass grows, may take longer. Most students should be able to complete all of their measurements within one week. Allow another week for students to prepare display cards for presenting the speeds that they measured. Before beginning the project, see Chapter 3 Project Teacher Notes on pages 62–63 in Unit 1 Resources for more details on carrying out the project. Also, distribute the students' Chapter 3 Project Student Overview and Worksheets and Scoring Rubric on pages 64–68 in Unit 1 Resources.

Suggested Shortcuts Although the project is written to be completed by students individually at home, they could complete parts of the project in groups in the classroom. You may wish to adjust the requirements of each level of success to better match the cooperative capabilities of small groups of students. To ensure that all students have ample opportunities to measure speed, have each student measure at least one speed at home and in class.

3 Relating Force and Motion

WEB ACTIVITY www.phschool.com

SECTION 1 Describing, Measuring, and Graphing Motion
Discover How Fast and How Far?
Skills Lab Inclined to Roll

SECTION 2 Force and Acceleration
Discover Will You Hurry Up?
Real-World Lab Stopping on a Dime

SECTION 3 Water in Motion
Discover What Affects How Water Moves?

Possible Materials
- metric ruler to measure centimeters and millimeters
- device to measure meters such as meter sticks, tape measures, or strings marked in meters
- timing device such as a stop watch or clock

Launching the Project To introduce the project and to stimulate student interest, show students several toys that move in various ways, such as wind up cars or other toys. Some of these should move in straight lines with constant speed, some can move in other ways. Or have one volunteer walk in a straight line, another walk in a circle, while a third walks randomly. Ask: **What are some other examples of motion?** *(Sample: a cloud moving in the sky, an acorn falling from an oak tree, a sprinter running down a track)* **How can we describe different types of motion?** *(Measure distance and time, create a map showing the various positions)*

Allow time for students to read the Chapter Project Overview on pages 64–65 in Unit 1

CHAPTER 3 PROJECT

Speeds à la Carte

Suppose that you have traveled thousands of miles to visit the tropics of South America. Suddenly, vivid reds and blues brighten the green of the rain forest as a group of macaws swoop down and perch above you in a nut tree. They squawk at each other as they crack nuts with their powerful jaws and eat the meat. In a few minutes they spread their wings to take off, and vanish from sight. The macaws cracking nuts, flapping their wings, and flying through the forest are all examples of motion. Your plane flight to South America is another.

In this chapter, you will learn how to describe and measure motion. You will find examples of motion and describe how fast different objects move. You will measure the speeds of various common moving things.

Your Goal To identify several examples of motion and measure how fast each one moves. You will arrange your results from slowest to fastest.

Your project must
◆ include careful distance and time measurements
◆ use your data to calculate the speed of each example
◆ provide display cards that show data, diagrams, and calculations
◆ follow the safety guidelines in Appendix A

Get Started Brainstorm with a group of your classmates several examples of motion. For example, you might consider a feather falling, the water level rising in a bathtub, or the minute hand moving on a clock. Which examples will be easy to measure? Which will be more challenging?

Check Your Progress You'll be working on this project as you study this chapter. To keep your project on track, look for Check Your Progress boxes at the following points.
Section 1 Review, page 95: Create a data table.
Section 2 Review, page 105: Repeat measurements and make calculations.

Present Your Project At the end of the chapter (page 115), you will compare the speeds recorded by the class.

TEKS

In addition to process TEKS, this chapter addresses these concept TEKS as they relate to the chapter's topics.

(6.6) The student knows that there is a relationship between force and motion. The student is expected to:
(A) identify and describe the changes in position, direction of motion, and speed of an object when acted upon by force;
(B) demonstrate that changes in motion can be measured and graphically represented; and
(C) identify forces that shape features of the Earth including uplifting, movement of water, and volcanic activity.

85

Program Resources

◆ **Unit 1 Resources** Chapter 3 Project Teacher Notes, pp. 62–63; Chapter 3 Project Overview and Worksheets, pp. 64–67

Media and Technology

🎧 **Student Edition on Audio CD**
English-Spanish, Chapter 3

www.phschool.com

You will find an Internet activity, chapter self-tests for students, and links to other chapter topics at this site.

Performance Assessment

The Chapter 3 Project Scoring Rubric on page 68 of Unit 1 Resources will help you evaluate how well students complete the Chapter 3 Project. You may wish to share the scoring rubric with your students so they are clear about what will be expected of them. Students will be assessed on
◆ how carefully they measured and how thoroughly they recorded data;
◆ their explanations of how they calculated the speeds;
◆ the clarity of their data and the associated units of measurement in each step of their written displays;
◆ the thoroughness and organization of their display cards.

TEKS: 6.1A; 6.2 A, B, C, D, E; 6.4A, B; 6.6A, B

Objectives

After completing the lesson, students will be able to

◆ explain when an object is in motion and how motion is relative to a reference point;

◆ calculate an object's speed and velocity using SI units of distance;

◆ graph motion showing changes in distance as a function of time.

1 Engage/Explore

Activating Prior Knowledge

Invite students to list various kinds of movement on the board. Ask: **How did you know the object moved?** *(Sample: Because I saw it change position.)* Then ask: **Did the object appear to move slowly or quickly? How could you tell?** *(Sample: It appeared to move slowly because it moved a short distance in a fairly long time.).*

DISCOVER

Skills Focus inferring
Materials *meter stick, stopwatch, masking tape*
Time 15 minutes
Tips Tape a long piece of masking tape to the ground as a starting line. Place another piece of tape 5 m from the first piece for Step 1. Tell students to use a third piece of tape to mark their location after 5 seconds for Step 2. Remind students to walk at a normal pace for the first two measurements. Ask: **How can you change the distance that you travel in 5 seconds?** *(Walk or run faster or slower, take larger or smaller steps.)*
Think It Over The faster you walk, the less time it takes to walk a certain distance. The faster you walk, the farther you will travel in a given time. If you walk a longer distance in a given amount of time, you are walking faster.

SECTION
① Describing, Measuring, and Graphing Motion

DISCOVER ·········· ACTIVITY ····

How Fast and How Far?

1. Find out how long it takes you to walk 5 meters at a normal pace. Record your time.

2. Now find out how far you can walk in 5 seconds if you walk at a normal pace. Record your distance.

3. Repeat Steps 1 and 2, walking slower than your normal pace. Then repeat Steps 1 and 2, walking faster than your normal pace.

Think It Over
Inferring What is the relationship between the distance you walk, the time it takes you to walk, and your walking speed?

GUIDE FOR READING

◆ When is an object in motion?

◆ How can you find the speed and velocity of an object?

Reading Tip Before you read, rewrite the headings in the section as questions. As you read, look for answers.

Key Terms motion
• reference point • meter
• speed • velocity

It's three o'clock and school is over! You hurry out of class to enjoy the bright afternoon. A light breeze is blowing. A few clouds are lazily drifting across the sky, and colorful leaves float down from the trees. Two birds fly playfully over your head. A bunch of frisky squirrels chase one another up a tree. You spend a few minutes with some friends who are kicking a ball around. Then you head home.

Does anything strike you about this afternoon scene? It is filled with all kinds of motion: blowing, drifting, fluttering, flying, and chasing. There are simple motions and complicated motions, motions that are over in a moment, and motions that continue all afternoon.

Gray squirrels ▶

READING STRATEGIES

Reading Tip Discuss with students how they might rewrite each heading as a question. For example, they could write "How do I know when something is in motion?" for *Changing Position— Recognizing Motion.* Have students write down their questions and leave space by each question to add answers as they read.

Study and Comprehension Suggest students write new definitions and formulas on note cards while they are working on the section. Make sure they include the formulas for calculating constant speed and average speed as well as the definition of velocity.

Figure 1 Whether or not an object is in motion depends on the reference point you choose. *Comparing and Contrasting Which people are moving if you compare them to the escalator? Which people are moving if you compare them to Earth?*

How else can you describe all of these examples of motion? There is actually a great deal to understand about how and why all these things move as they do. In this section, you will learn how scientists describe and measure motion.

Changing Position—Recognizing Motion

Deciding if an object is in motion isn't as easy as it sounds. For example, you are probably sitting as you read this paragraph. Are you moving? Other than your eyes blinking and your chest moving up and down, you would probably say that you (and this book) are not moving. An object is in **motion** when its distance from another object is changing. Since the distance between you and the walls of your room is not changing, you conclude that neither you nor the book is moving.

At the same time that you think you are sitting still, you are actually moving about 30 kilometers every second. At that speed, you could travel from New York City to Los Angeles in about 2 minutes! You are moving because you are on planet Earth, which is orbiting the sun. Earth moves about 30 kilometers every second, so you and everything else on Earth are moving at that speed as well.

Whether an object is moving or not depends on your point of view. If you compare the books on a desk to the floor beneath them, they are not moving.

Changing Position— Recognizing Motion

Language Arts Connection

Read aloud an action-filled poem such as "Paul Revere's Ride" by Longfellow. Ask: **What words and phrases does the poet use to describe motion?** (*Sample: raced, crept*) Explain that poets use descriptive language to help readers and listeners understand the poem. **learning modality: verbal**

Building Inquiry Skills: Applying Concepts

Materials *globes, measuring tape*
Time 15 minutes

Have students work in small groups. Ask them to locate their home state on the globe. Then ask them to locate Tokyo, Japan. Have them use the measuring tape to find the distance on the globe between their state and Tokyo. Have a volunteer rotate the globe one-half turn starting from the home state. **Why doesn't our state get closer to or farther away from Japan when the globe turns?** (*Japan is moving around the sun at the same rate as everything else on the globe.*) **cooperative learning**

Using the Visuals: Figure 1

Draw students' attention to the person at the top of the "up" escalator. Ask: **Which people are moving relative to this person?** (*The people on the "down" escalator*) Then ask: **Why isn't this person at the top moving from the point of view of the person a few steps behind him?** (*The distance between them stays the same.*) **learning modality: visual**

Answers to Self-Assessment

Caption Question

Figure 1 The people walking on the escalator are moving with respect to the escalator. All the people are moving with respect to Earth.

Ongoing Assessment

Writing Have students write a paragraph about their trip to school in the morning describing everything they saw that was moving.

Changing Position—Recognizing Motion, continued

TRY THIS

Skills Focus observing
Time 5 minutes, 6 to 8 times during 1 day
Tips Students should pick a place for their observations that they can visit throughout the day, and mark the spot. Have students draw a sketch of their observation area from their reference point, complete with buildings and trees. Direct students to record the position of the sun on their sketches. Remind them to include the time of observation. Ask: **How did the position of the sun at lunch time compare with the position of the sun in the morning and late afternoon?** (*The sun appeared higher in the sky at lunch time than it appeared at other times.*)
Expected Outcome Students should observe that the sun moves across the sky throughout the day. However, they should conclude that they see the sun as moving because they use the things around them as reference points. If they view the same information, but use the sun as a reference point, they can show that Earth is moving.
Extend Using a flashlight and a globe or large ball, have students model the motion of the Earth and the sun. By marking a spot on the ball, students can demonstrate how the sun appears to move from the perspective of someone on Earth. **learning modality: visual**

Including all Students

Students who are still mastering English may have increased difficulty understanding the words in this section that indicate motion. Pair them with native English speakers and have partners find such words, list them, then form sentences using the words.
limited English proficiency

Figure 2 Both the Hubble Space Telescope and the astronaut are actually moving rapidly through space. But compared to the Hubble Space Telescope, the astronaut is not moving, and he can therefore complete necessary repairs.

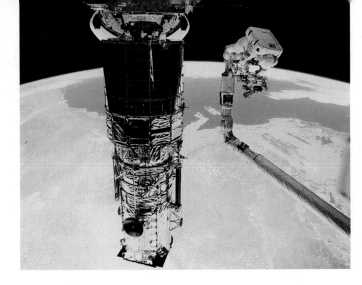

TRY THIS

Sunrise, Sunset

Earth rotates as it moves around the sun. But to you, the sun appears to move.

1. Choose a spot from which you can observe the sky throughout one day.
2. From the same spot, observe the sun at 6 to 8 different times during the day. **CAUTION:** *Be careful not to look directly at the sun.* Describe its position by comparing it with things around you, such as trees and buildings.
3. Draw a diagram of the sun throughout the day.

Observing What reference point(s) did you use to study the sun? Did the sun appear to move when compared with those reference points? Did it really move?

But if you compare them to the sun, the books are moving quite rapidly. Earth and the sun are different reference points. A **reference point** is a place or object used for comparison to determine if something is in motion. **An object is in motion if it changes position relative to a reference point.** You assume that the reference point is stationary, or not moving.

If you have ever been on a slow-moving train, you know that you may not be able to tell the train is moving unless you look out the window. A nearby building is a good reference point, and a glance at it will tell you if you and the train are moving. But it is important to choose your reference point carefully. Have you ever been in a school bus stopped right next to another school bus? Suddenly, you think your bus is moving backward. When you look out the window on the other side, you find that your bus isn't moving at all. Actually, the other bus is moving forward! Your bus seemed to be moving backward because you used the other bus as a reference point. You assumed your reference point was stationary. But in fact, your reference point—the other bus—was really moving.

Describing Distance

INTEGRATING MATHEMATICS To describe motion further, you need to use units of measurement. Whether you realize it or not, you use units, or standard quantities, all the time. You might, for example, measure 2 cups of milk for a recipe, swim 100 yards after school, or buy 3 pounds of fruit at the store. Cups, yards, and pounds are all measurement units.

Scientists all over the world use the same system of measurement units so that they can communicate information clearly.

Background

Integrating Science Throughout recorded time, civilizations have devised methods of measurement. Units of measurement are often based on parts of the human body. For example, the Egyptians called the distance from the fingertips to the elbow a *cubit*. Even the system in use in the United States has some units based on body parts. One example is the *foot*. The standard system of units we use today is a relatively modern innovation. At one time, practically every nation on Earth used a different system of units. This made commerce and trade between nations very difficult. Today, even when different units of measurement are used (such as feet or gallons) they are defined in terms of the standard system of units.

This system of measurement is called the International System of Units, or in French, Système International (SI). SI is a system based on the number ten. This makes calculations with the system relatively easy.

The basic SI unit of length is the **meter** (m). A meter is a little longer than a yard. The Eiffel Tower in Figure 3 is measured in meters. To measure the length of an object smaller than a meter, scientists use the metric unit called the centimeter (cm). The prefix *centi-* means "one hundredth." A centimeter is one hundredth of a meter, so there are 100 centimeters in a meter. The beautiful butterfly in Figure 3 is measured in centimeters. For even smaller lengths, the millimeter (mm) is used. The prefix *milli-* means "one thousandth," so there are 1,000 millimeters in a meter. In the International System, long distances are measured in kilometers (km). The prefix *kilo-* means "one thousand." There are 1,000 meters in a kilometer.

SI units are also used to describe quantities other than length. You can find more information about SI units in the Skills Handbook on page 582 of this textbook.

☑ *Checkpoint* *What unit would you use to describe the width of your thumb?*

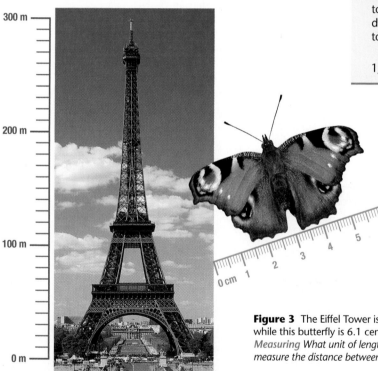

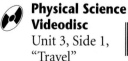

Figure 3 The Eiffel Tower is 300 meters tall, while this butterfly is 6.1 centimeters across. *Measuring What unit of length would you use to measure the distance between Paris and Rome?*

Converting Units

When you convert one metric unit to another, you must move the decimal point.

1. How many millimeters are in 14.5 meters? You are converting from a larger unit to a smaller one, so you multiply. There are 1,000 millimeters in a meter. To multiply by 1,000, move the decimal to the right three places.
14.500 m = 14,500. mm
There are 14,500 mm in 14.5 m.

2. Convert 1,200 centimeters to meters. You are converting from a smaller unit to a larger one, so you divide (move the decimal to the left).
1,200. cm = 12.00 m
1,200 cm equals 12 m.

Describing Distance

 Integrating Mathematics

Materials *meter sticks, classroom items such as a chalkboard, desk, chair, eraser, stapler, sheet of paper*
Time 20 minutes

Challenge students to create a metric measurement inventory of the classroom. Students can measure a variety of 10 or more objects. Have them determine the appropriate unit of measurement for each object and record their findings. Ask: **What was the smallest object you measured? What unit did you use?** (*Sample: paper clip, staple, push pin; millimeter*) **Then ask: What was the largest object you measured? What unit did you use?** (*Sample: chalkboard, bookshelf; meter*) **learning modality: logical/mathematical**

Math TOOLBOX

Time 15 minutes
Tips For Problem 1, show students a meter stick that is divided into millimeters. Ask: **If there are 1,000 mm on 1 meter stick, then how many mm are on 2 meter sticks?** (*2,000*) **On 7.5 meter sticks?** (*7,500*) Then write out the problem 14.5 m × 1,000 mm/m = 14,500 mm. Ask: **Where is the decimal point in the number 14,500? How many places did it move?** (*To the right of the last zero; 3 places to the right*) For Problem 2, ask: **How many centimeters are in 1 meter?** (*100*) Then write out the problem 1,200 cm ÷ 100 cm/m = 12 m. Ask: **If the decimal point for 1,200 centimeters is to the right of the zero, which direction did it move when you converted from centimeters to meters?** (*To the left*) **learning modality: logical/mathematical**

Ongoing Assessment

Skills Check Have students measure the width and length of their index finger in millimeters and convert the answer to centimeters.

Answers to Self-Assessment

Caption Question

Figure 3 The distance between Paris and Rome would be measured in kilometers.

☑ *Checkpoint*

You would measure the width of your thumb in millimeters or centimeters

Social Studies CONNECTION

After students have read the feature, point out that cities are not symmetrical and the "spokes" may be several different widths. City growth is also limited by geographic constraints and legal requirements as well as transportation needs.

In Your Journal Ask students how many kilometers a person could go in one hour along each of the routes. That distance represents the greatest distance people are willing to drive. Students should realize that they would expect to find homes built farther from the center of the city on Highway 1 and Red Rail. Each transportation route should extend away from the city center in a different direction. Have students choose a scale (for example, 1 mm = 1 km) and measure the distance in mm along the transportation route equal to the number of kilometers a person could travel in one hour. Since these distances represent the maximum distance a person is willing to travel, they mark the city boundaries.

 Students can save their maps in their portfolios.

Addressing Naive Conceptions

Some students may think objects that have "speed" must move fast. Direct their attention to a clock. Explain that even though the tip of the hour hand on the clock may move very slowly, it still travels at a measurable speed. Have students measure the circumference of a clock by wrapping a piece of string around the clock and measuring the string with a ruler. Ask: **How long does it take the tip of the hour hand to travel around the clock's face one time?** *(12 hours)* **What is its speed?** *(Answers should be the length of the circumference divided by 12 hours.)* Students can also calculate the speed of the minute and second hands. **learning modality: visual**

Social Studies CONNECTION

Speed affects the shape of cities. Because people want to travel quickly, they live close to major transportation routes—highways and railroads. Thus a city often looks like a hub with spokes coming out of it along the transportation routes.

In Your Journal

People prefer not to travel more than one hour from home to work. The table shows a city's travel routes.

Route	Average Speed
Highway 1	75 km/h
Highway 2	55 km/h
Blue Rail	60 km/h
Red Rail	75 km/h
Main Street	35 km/h

Along which two routes would you expect to find people living farther from the center of the city? Explain why. Draw a map of what you think this city might look like.

Calculating Speed

Scientists use SI units to describe the distance an object travels. A car, for example, might travel 90 kilometers. An ant might travel 2 centimeters. If you know the distance an object travels in a certain amount of time, you know the speed of the object. To be more exact, the **speed** of an object is the distance the object travels in one unit of time. Speed is a rate. A rate tells you the amount of something that occurs or changes in one unit of time.

To calculate the speed of an object, divide the distance the object travels by the amount of time it takes to travel that distance. This relationship can be written as follows.

$$Speed = \frac{Distance}{Time}$$

Speed measurements consist of a unit of distance divided by a unit of time. If you measure distance in meters and time in seconds, you express speed in meters per second (m/s). (The slash is read as "per.") If you measure distance in kilometers and time in hours, you express speed in kilometers per hour (km/h).

If a car travels 90 kilometers in one hour, the car is traveling at a speed of 90 km/h. An ant that moves 2 centimeters in one second is moving at a speed of 2 centimeters per second, or 2 cm/s. The ant is much slower than the car.

Constant Speed A ship traveling across the ocean may move at the same speed for several hours. Or a horse cantering across a field may keep a steady pace for several minutes. If so, the ship and the horse travel at constant speeds. If the speed of an object does not change, the object is traveling at a constant speed. When an object travels at a constant speed, you know that its speed is the same at all times during its motion.

Figure 4 This horse is cantering at a constant speed.

90

Background

History of Science Sundials, invented about 3,500 years ago, measure time by the shadow cast by the sun as it crosses the sky. Water clocks, which measure time by the movement of dripping water, started to be used about 3,500 years ago. By the early eighteenth century, mechanical clocks with cogs and wheels gained or lost only about a second per day. Today, most clocks and watches are powered by a vibrating quartz crystal and are extremely accurate.

Figure 5 The cyclists do not travel at a constant speed throughout this cross-country race. *Comparing and Contrasting How does average speed differ from constant speed?*

If you know the distance an object travels in a given amount of time, you can use the formula for speed to calculate the object's constant speed. Suppose, for example, that the horse in Figure 4 is moving at a constant speed. Find the horse's speed if it canters 21 meters in 3 seconds. Divide the distance traveled, 21 meters, by the time, 3 seconds, to find the horse's speed.

$$Speed = \frac{21 \ m}{3 \ s} = 7 \ m/s$$

The horse's speed is 7 meters per second, or 7 m/s.

Average Speed Most objects do not move at constant speeds for very long. The cyclists in Figure 5, for example, change their speeds many times during the race. They might glide along on level ground, move more slowly as they climb steep inclines, and dash down hills. Occasionally, they stop to fix a tire.

Unlike the horse described earlier, you cannot use any one speed to describe the motion of the cyclists at every point during the race. You can, however, find the average speed of a cyclist throughout the entire race. To find the average speed, divide the total distance traveled by the total time.

Suppose a cyclist travels 32 kilometers during the first two hours of riding, and 13 kilometers during the next hour. The average speed of the cyclist during the trip is the total distance divided by the total time.

$$Total \ distance \ = 32 \ km \ + 13 \ km$$

$$Total \ time = 2 \ h + 1 \ h$$

$$Average \ speed = \frac{45 \ km}{3 \ h} = 15 \ km/h$$

The average speed of the cyclist is 15 kilometers per hour.

☑ *Checkpoint How do you calculate average speed?*

Building Inquiry Skills: Calculating

Ask students what information they need to know to determine the speed of an object. *(The distance it moved and the amount of time it took to move that distance)* Then have them calculate the speed of the following objects:
♦ a baseball that moves 11 m in 1 s *(11 m ÷ 1 s = 11 m/s)*
♦ a car that travels 70 km in 1.75 h *(70 km ÷ 1.75 h = 40 km/h)*
learning modality: logical/ mathematical

Inquiry Challenge

Materials *two or three wind-up toys per group, stopwatches, metric rulers, masking tape*

ACTIVITY

Time 40 minutes

Tips Have students bring toys from home. Challenge students to discover which wind-up toy reaches the highest speed. Students can work in small groups. Have students mark off a "test track" on the floor with masking tape, then measure how long it takes for each toy to travel the length of the track. Suggest students perform at least three trials for each toy and calculate an average speed from the results. To determine if the toy is changing speed during the run, students can compare the average speed of a certain toy measured over two or three different distances. Ask students to describe any changes in each toy's speed during each trial. *(The toys may slow down as they move down the track)* Ask: **For each trial, are you measuring constant speed or average speed?** *(average speed)* After students complete their trials, have a final race with each group choosing one toy that they think will go fastest over a distance chosen by you. **cooperative learning**

Ongoing Assessment

Skills Check Have students find the speed of an asteroid that travels 4,500 km in 60 s. *(4,500 km ÷ 60 s = 75 km/s)*

Describing Velocity

Real-Life Learning

Obtain a set of hurricane-tracking charts from your local weather service. Have students follow weather reports to track the daily progress of any hurricanes. Have students calculate the average speed of a hurricane based on the data they gather. If hurricane charts are unavailable, charts showing the movement of high- or low-pressure systems can be substituted. Ask: **How is this type of information useful to weather forecasters?** *(It helps them predict how long it will take for a hurricane to reach a region so they can warn people who live there.)* **learning modality: visual**

Cultural Diversity

The United States has built an elaborate system of highways for public and freight transportation, while the rail system is primarily used for transportation of heavy freight. Other countries, such as France and Japan, have constructed sophisticated high speed rail systems for public transportation. In small groups, allow students to discuss the relative advantages and disadvantages of primarily using automobiles for public transportation (as opposed to high-speed rail). Have students relate the contrasting systems of public transportation to the availability of natural resources, such as petroleum. **cooperative learning**

Demonstration

Have a student use a compass to determine which direction is North. Have a second student use a stopwatch or watch with a second hand to time a third student who will walk northward for 5 seconds. Have a fourth student measure the distance walked, and have the class calculate the velocity. *(Sample: 6m/5s = 1.2 m/s north)* Have other students repeat the procedure with different times and directions. **learning modality: kinesthetic**

SCIENCE & History

Describing Velocity

Knowing the speed at which something travels does not tell you everything about its motion. For example, if a weather forecaster announces that a severe storm is traveling at 25 km/h, would you prepare for the storm? Storms usually travel from west to east. If you live to the west of the storm and the storm is traveling to the east, you need not worry. But if you live to the east of the storm, take cover.

It is important to know not only the speed of the storm, but also its direction. **When you know both the speed and direction of an object's motion, you know the velocity of the object.**

The Speed of Transportation

The speed with which people can travel from one place to another has increased over the years.

1885

Benz Tricycle Car Introduced

This odd-looking vehicle was the first internal combustion (gasoline-powered) automobile sold to the public. Although it is an ancestor of the modern automobile, its top speed was only about 15 km/h—not much faster than a horse-drawn carriage.

1800   **1850**

1818

National Road Constructed

The speed of transportation has been limited largely by the quality of roadways. The U.S. government paid for the construction of a highway named the Cumberland Road. It ran from Cumberland, Maryland, to Wheeling, in present-day West Virginia. Travel by horse and carriage on the roadway was at a speed of about 11 km/h.

1869

Transcontinental Railroad

After more than six and a half years of work, railroad tracks from each side of the country met in Utah, just north of Great Salt Lake. Passengers could now travel across the United States by steam-powered trains. A cross-country trip took about a week at an average speed of 30 km/h.

92

Background

Facts and Figures The fastest animals are:
- on land, the cheetah (96 km/h)
- in the water, the sailfish (109 km/h)
- in the air, the peregrine falcon (198 km/h)

Speed in a given direction is called **velocity**. If you know the velocity at which an object is moving, you know two different things about the object's motion—its speed and its direction. A weather forecaster may give the speed of the storm as 25 km/h, but you don't know its velocity unless you know that the storm is moving 25 km/h eastward.

Air traffic controllers must keep very close track of the velocities of all of the aircraft under their control. These velocities change more often than the velocities of storm systems. An error in determining a velocity, either in speed or in direction, could lead to a collision.

In Your Journal

The distance between Lufkin, Texas, and Lubbock, Texas, is about 786 kilometers. How many hours would it take to travel this distance for each of the vehicles in the time line if they each traveled at the speed shown? Record your results on a bar graph.

1908
Ford Model T Mass-Produced

Between 1908 and 1927, over 15 million of these automobiles were sold. The Model T had a top speed of 65 km/h.

1956
Inauguration of the Interstate Highway System

The passage of the Federal Aid Highway Act established the Highway Trust Fund. This act allowed the construction of the Interstate and Defense Highways. Nonstop transcontinental auto travel became possible. Speed limits in many parts of the system were more than 100 km/h.

1900   **1950**   **2000**

1936

Pioneer Zephyr Introduced

The first diesel passenger train in the United States was the *Pioneer Zephyr*. The *Zephyr* set a long-distance record, traveling from Chicago to Denver at an average speed of 125 km/h for more than 1,633 km.

1983
TGV in Motion

First introduced in 1983, this French high-speed train now has a top speed of 300 km/h. On its route from Paris to Lyon, it averages 152.6 km/h.

Chapter 3 **93**

SCIENCE & *History*

Review each item along the timeline with students. Ask: **How do you think improvements in transportation affected the lives of people living at that time?** (*Sample: They could go farther to find a job, get supplies, or visit relatives.*) Then ask: **What do you think are some negative effects of widespread rapid transportation?** (*Sample: increased pollution, damage to the environment, accidents at high speeds may be deadlier*) Refer to the **ELL Handbook** for additional teaching strategies.

In Your Journal Allow students to use calculators to calculate how long the journeys would take. (*Horse and carriage (1818), 71.4 hours; steam-powered train (1869), 26.2 hours; Benz Tricycle car (1885), 52.4 hours; Ford Model T car (1908), 12.1 hours; diesel-powered train (1936), 6.29 hours; Interstate highway speed limit (1956), 7.86 hours; French high-speed train (1983), 5.15 hours; These times assume that travel averaged the speed given on the time line.*) Students' graphs should reflect the data given above. Check to make sure that the data are plotted accurately and that the axes are labeled with the appropriate information. **learning modality: logical/mathematical**

EXPLORING
Motion Graphs

Draw students' attention to the first graph. They should recognize that the jogger travels 170 m each minute. To show that speed is constant, show that the average speed between any two points is 170 m/min. Have students copy the graph and extend the line to predict how long she would have to jog to travel 2,550 m. *(15 min)* As students examine the second graph, ask: **What happened during the sixth through eighth minutes?** *(The jogger stopped.)* Then ask students: **What effect did the stop have on the jogger's average speed?** *(Average speed was lowered: 1,190 m ÷ 10 min = 119 m/min.)* Ask: **What was the difference in the jogger's average speed between the first and second day?** *(51 m/min)* Compare the slope of the first and third graphs. *(The slope of the first graph is greater.)* Ask: **How fast would the jogger be traveling if the graph was flat?** *(0 m/min)*

Extend Take students to a running track. Pair students. Ask each pair to create motion graphs based on their own actual motion. For example, one student jogs, then walks, and rests, (1 min for each). The partner records what the other student is doing and the distance he or she travels. Then partners reverse roles. They then work together to graph their data. Pairs share their graphs with the class and ask the class to describe the student's motion. Refer to the **ELL Handbook** for additional teaching strategies. **learning modality: logical/mathematical**

EXPLORING *Motion Graphs*

Motion graphs provide an opportunity to analyze changes in distance and time.

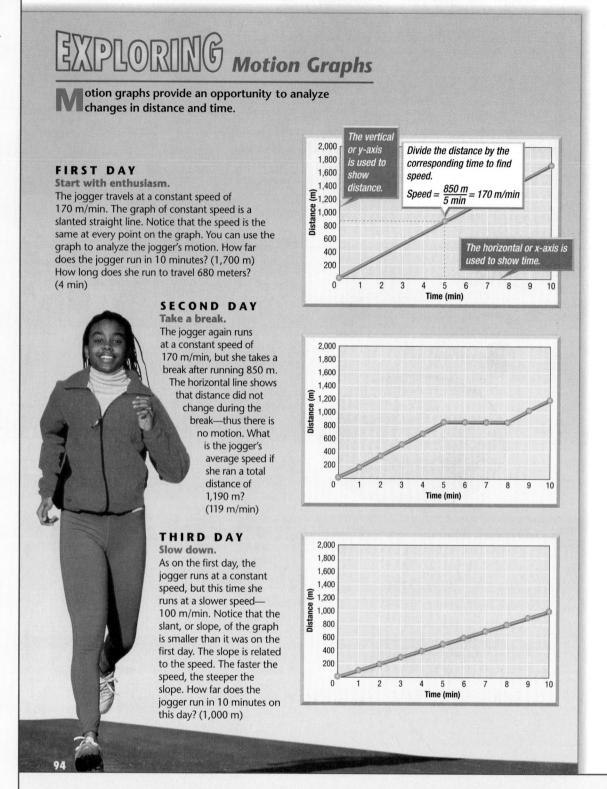

FIRST DAY

Start with enthusiasm.
The jogger travels at a constant speed of 170 m/min. The graph of constant speed is a slanted straight line. Notice that the speed is the same at every point on the graph. You can use the graph to analyze the jogger's motion. How far does the jogger run in 10 minutes? (1,700 m) How long does she run to travel 680 meters? (4 min)

The vertical or y-axis is used to show distance.

Divide the distance by the corresponding time to find speed.

$$Speed = \frac{850 \text{ m}}{5 \text{ min}} = 170 \text{ m/min}$$

The horizontal or x-axis is used to show time.

SECOND DAY

Take a break.
The jogger again runs at a constant speed of 170 m/min, but she takes a break after running 850 m. The horizontal line shows that distance did not change during the break—thus there is no motion. What is the jogger's average speed if she ran a total distance of 1,190 m? (119 m/min)

THIRD DAY

Slow down.
As on the first day, the jogger runs at a constant speed, but this time she runs at a slower speed—100 m/min. Notice that the slant, or slope, of the graph is smaller than it was on the first day. The slope is related to the speed. The faster the speed, the steeper the slope. How far does the jogger run in 10 minutes on this day? (1,000 m)

94

Background

History of Science The *x-y* coordinates that are used for many mathematical and scientific purposes, including graphs of motion, are called *Cartesian Coordinates.* They are named after René Descartes, a French mathematician and philosopher. In 1637, Descartes published a collection of essays called *Discourse on Method.* In one of the essays, *Geometry,* Descartes introduced analytic geometry, a system of representing geometric figures and concepts with algebraic symbols. Although this was a major advance in mathematics, Descartes is better known today for his philosophical works, including the famous statement, "I think, therefore I am."

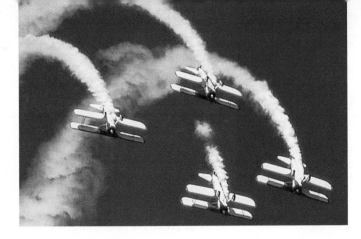

Figure 6 During a complicated maneuver, an airplane's direction changes continuously, along with its speed. Stunt pilots make spectacular use of their control over the velocity of their aircraft.

Graphing Motion

 INTEGRATING MATHEMATICS You can show the motion of an object on a line graph in which you plot distance against time. Time is shown on the horizontal, or *x*-axis. It is represented by the first coordinate of the point—*x*. Distance is shown on the vertical, or *y*-axis. It is represented by the second coordinate of the point—*y*. A point (*x, y*) on the graph represents the location of an object at a particular time. To see examples of how graphs represent motion, read about the jogger in *Exploring Motion Graphs* on page 94.

Section 1 Review

1. Why do you need a reference point to know if an object is moving?
2. What is the difference between an object's speed and an object's velocity?
3. A bamboo plant grows 15 centimeters in 4 hours. At what average speed does the plant grow?
4. **Thinking Critically** **Problem Solving** The distance traveled by two crawling babies is shown in the table. Graph the information, and calculate each baby's speed.

Time (s)	Baby Sarah Distance (m)	Baby Scott Distance (m)
0	0	0
1	0.5	0.4
2	1	0.8
3	1.5	1.2
4	2	1.6

 CHAPTER PROJECT

Check Your Progress

To measure each object's speed, you will need to know how far it moves in a certain amount of time. Create a data table to record your measurements and to show the speeds you calculate. Be sure to choose the best units for each speed measurement. To measure fast speeds, you may choose to measure distance in meters and time in seconds. For slower speeds you may choose to measure distance in centimeters or millimeters, and time in minutes or hours.

Program Resources

◆ **Unit 1 Resources** 3-1 Review and Reinforce, p. 71; 3-1 Enrich, p. 72

Media and Technology

Transparencies "Exploring Motion Graphs," Transparency 7

 Integrating Mathematics

In making motion graphs, students may have trouble deciding which data goes on which axis. Ask: **Does time depend on the distance traveled?** *(No)* **Does distance covered depend on the time?** *(Yes)* Thus, time is considered to be the independent variable, and is shown on the *x*-axis. Ask: **If the jogger runs at a constant speed, what determines how far she can run?** *(The length of time during which she runs.)* **learning modality: logical/mathematical**

3 Assess

Section 1 Review Answers

1. Motion involves a change in position relative to some reference point.
2. Speed describes the rate at which an object moves. Velocity is speed in a given direction.
3. The plant grows at an average speed of 15 cm/4 h, or 3.75 cm/h.
4. Baby Sarah moves at 0.5 m/s. Baby Scott moves at 0.4 m/s.

CHAPTER PROJECT

Check Your Progress

Show students how to record information in a project log. Show them a sketch of the measurement, a list or table of data collected, and a step-by-step calculation of the object's speed. Assign the Chapter Project Worksheet 1, which will help students make the measurements required for this project.

Performance Assessment

Skills Check Give each student a photocopy of the same map. Ask them to pick two places on the map, A and B. Have them use the scale on the map to measure the direct distance between A and B. Ask: **If it takes 2 hours to get from A to B, what speed are you going?** *(Sample: Washington, DC to San Francisco, CA; speed 2,400 km/h)* **What is your velocity?** *(Answers must include speed and direction. Sample: Washington, DC, to San Francisco, CA; velocity 2,400 km/h west.)*

Inclined to Roll

Preparing for Inquiry

Key Concept After an object rolls down a ramp, it will be going faster if the incline is steeper.

Skills Objectives Students will be able to
- measure speed using time taken to travel a certain distance;
- measure the effect of the incline of the ramp on the speed an object attains at the end of the incline;
- begin to think about acceleration.

Time 40 minutes

Advance Planning If you have not yet taught the skill of measuring, refer to the Skills Handbook. Buy 4 ft × 8 ft sheets of 1/2-in plywood or pegboard and have them cut crosswise into six ramps 16 in. wide. Many hardware stores will cut the sheets for you. Since these ramps would be 4 feet long, the starting line on the ramp would be at 1 m. This lab requires plenty of space and may need to be done in a gym or outdoors.

Alternative Materials If no student in a group has a skateboard, ask other students to bring extras. Students can also use four-wheeled toys. If protractors are unavailable, have students measure the height of the ramp at the starting line. This height can be used instead of angle to measure ramp incline.
Computer use is optional.

Guiding Inquiry

Invitation Have students predict what they think they will find. Ask: **Have you ever ridden a roller coaster or bicycled down a hill? How did the incline of the hill affect your final speed?** (*Faster on a steeper hill*) **How did you judge how fast you were traveling?** (*Samples: Trees went by faster; air rushed by faster*) Emphasize that speed is measured relative to an object.

Introducing the Procedure
- Refer students to the photo illustrating the experimental setup.

Skills Lab
Measuring

Inclined to Roll

In this lab, you will practice the skills of measuring time and distance to find the speed of a moving object.

Problem

How does the steepness of a ramp affect how fast an object moves across the floor?

Materials

skateboard
meter stick
protractor
masking tape
two stopwatches
computer (optional)
flat board, about 1.5 m long
small piece of sturdy cardboard
supports to prop up the board (books, boxes)

Procedure

1. In your notebook or on the computer, make a data table like the sample. Include space for five angles.

2. Lay the board flat on the floor. Using masking tape, mark a starting line in the middle of the board. Mark a finish line on the floor 1.5 m beyond one end of the board.

3. Prop up the other end of the board. Use a protractor to measure the angle that the board makes with the ground. Record the angle.

4. Working in groups of three, have one person hold the skateboard so that its front wheels are even with the starting line. As the holder releases the skateboard, the other two students should start their stopwatches.

5. One timer should stop his or her stopwatch when the front wheels of the skateboard reach the end of the incline.

6. The second timer should stop his or her stopwatch when the front wheels reach the finish line. Record the times to the end of the ramp and the finish line in the columns labeled Time 1 and Time 2.

DATA TABLE

Angle (degrees)	Trial Number	Time 1 (to bottom) (s)	Time 2 (to finish) (s)	Avg Time 1 (s)	Avg Time 2 (s)	Avg Time 2 – Avg Time 1 (s)	Avg Speed (m/s)
	1						
	2						
	3						
	1						
	2						
	3						
	1						
	2						

- Show students how to use the stopwatches. Have students roll the skateboard down the ramp a few times to practice using the stopwatches before they collect data.

Troubleshooting the Experiment
- Make sure students begin with a very small incline.
- Make sure the skateboard rolls smoothly at the transition from the ramp to the ground.

Safety

Tell students to be careful when carrying boards. Tell students not to stand on the skateboards, or roll them at other people. Review the safety guidelines in Appendix A.

7. Repeat Steps 4–6 two more times. If your results for the three times aren't within 0.2 seconds of one another, carry out more trials.

8. Repeat Steps 3–7 four more times, making the ramp gradually steeper each time.

9. For each angle of the incline, complete the following calculations and record them in your data table.
   a. Find the average time the skateboard takes to get to the bottom of the ramp (Time 1).
   b. Find the average time the skateboard takes to get to the finish line (Time 2).
   c. Subtract the average Time 1 from the average Time 2.

Analyze and Conclude

1. How can you find the average speed of the skateboard across the floor for each angle of incline? Determine the average speed for each angle and record it in your data table.

2. Which is your manipulated variable and which is your responding variable in this experiment? Explain why. (For a discussion of manipulated and responding variables, see the Skills Handbook.)

3. On a graph, plot the speed of the skateboard (on the *y*-axis) against the angle of the ramp (on the *x*-axis). Connect the points on your graph.

4. What does the shape of your graph show about the relationship between the speed and the angle of the ramp?

5. **Think About It** Do you think your method of timing was accurate? Did the timers start and stop their stopwatches exactly at the appropriate points? How could the accuracy of the timing be improved?

Design an Experiment

A truck driver transporting new cars needs to roll the cars off the truck. You offer to design a ramp to help with the task. What measurements might you make that would be useful? Design an experiment to test your ideas.

Sample Data Table

Angle (degrees)	Time 1 (to bottom) (s)	Time 2 (to finish) (s)	Avg Time 2 – Avg Time 1 (s)	Avg Speed (m/s)
6	1.47	2.75	1.28	1.17
9	1.31	2.40	1.09	1.38
12	1.06	1.88	0.82	1.83
18	0.87	1.58	0.71	2.11
27	0.71	1.28	0.57	2.63

Program Resources

◆ **Unit 1 Resources** Chapter 3 Skills Lab blackline masters, pp. 81–82

Media and Technology

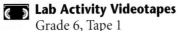 **Lab Activity Videotapes**
Grade 6, Tape 1

Expected Outcome

As the ramp incline increases, the time taken to travel from starting line to bottom of ramp (Average Time 1) will decrease. The time taken to travel from bottom of ramp to finish line will decrease. Thus, average speed will increase as ramp incline increases.

Analyze and Conclude

1. Average speed is distance traveled on floor (distance from bottom of ramp to finish line or 1.5 m) divided by time on floor (Average Time 2 − Average Time 1).
2. The manipulated variable is ramp incline and the responding variable is average speed. The ramp incline is manipulated because that is the variable that is changing in each trial. The average speed will vary, or respond, as the incline changes.
3. Review students' graphs and accept all reasonable graphs.
4. Speed will increase as the incline goes from small (6 degrees) to large (45 or more degrees).
5. Allow students to conclude if their timing methods are accurate. Students could time a particular run. The average of all students could then be used. Alternatively, an electric timing device as used during athletic events such as downhill skiing could be utilized.

Extending the Inquiry

Design An Experiment Students need to know the weight of the cars and the distance between the left and right wheels so that the ramp could be wide enough and strong enough. To measure the angle of the ramp, measure the height of the ramp rather than trying to use a small protractor. To make sure this will work, students can compare the height of their ramp at the start line with the angle measured using a protractor. They can plot height on the *x*-axis and angle on the *y*-axis.

Objectives

After completing the lesson, students will be able to
♦ explain how forces are related to motion;
♦ describe what happens to the motion of an object as it accelerates;
♦ calculate the acceleration of an object and graph changing speed and distance of an accelerating object.

1 Engage/Explore

Activating Prior Knowledge

Ask a volunteer to blow up a balloon and hold the opening firmly shut. Say: **Describe the motion of the balloon right now.** (*The balloon is not moving.*) Then ask: **What could you do to make the balloon move?** (*Release it.*) Now have the volunteer release the balloon. Make sure it is released toward a wall, well away from other students. Ask students to describe when the balloon changed speed or direction as it flew. (*More or less continuously, from the moment of release until it landed*) Tell students in this section they will investigate changing speed and direction.

DISCOVER

Skills Focus inferring
Materials *meter stick, masking tape, stopwatch*
Time 15 minutes
Tips Take students to a large open area or a long hallway where they will not disturb others. When students begin walking, suggest they walk very slowly, and gradually increase their speed until they are moving as fast as they can without running. Caution them not to run.
Think It Over The faster you speed up, the less time it takes to walk the course.

DISCOVER

ACTIVITY

Will You Hurry Up?

1. Measure 10 meters in an area in which you can walk freely. Mark the distance with a piece of masking tape.
2. Walk the 10 meters in such a way that you keep moving faster throughout the entire distance. Have a partner time you.
3. Repeat Step 2, but try to walk the 10 meters in less time than you did before. Try it again, but this time walk it in twice the amount of time as the first. Remember that you must keep speeding up throughout the entire 10 meters.

Think It Over
Inferring How is the change in your speed related to the time you take to walk the 10-meter course?

GUIDE FOR READING

♦ How are forces related to motion?
♦ What happens to the motion of an object as it accelerates?
♦ How is acceleration calculated?

Reading Tip As you read, list the three different types of acceleration. Then give several examples of each.

Key Terms force • net force • unbalanced force • balanced force • friction • acceleration • linear • nonlinear

The pitcher winds up. She throws. The ball speeds to the batter and, *crack*—off the bat it goes. It's going, it's going, gone—a home run!

Before falling beyond the fence, the softball went through several changes in its motion. It started moving in the pitcher's hand, sped up, stopped moving at the bat, changed direction, and eventually slowed down. Most examples of motion involve similar changes. In fact, it is rare for any motion to stay the same for very long. What causes motion to change? A pitcher throwing a ball, a bat hitting a ball, and a catcher stopping a ball all have something in common—they all involve forces.

Forces and Motion

The next time you walk, pay attention to your feet and legs. You will discover that you move as a result of a combination of pushes and pulls. At first, you notice a pulling sensation as the muscles in your leg lift your foot. Then your other foot pushes against the floor, making your body move forward.

◄ The batter exerts a force on the ball with the bat.

READING STRATEGIES

Reading Tip For each kind of acceleration, challenge students to identify at least three examples of objects in motion not in the text. (*Sample: Increasing speed—car starting from stopped position; decreasing speed—jet landing on a runway; changing direction—moon orbiting Earth*) Once students' lists are complete, invite them to share ideas with each other.

Concept Mapping As they complete the section, students can form a concept map using the following terms: *unbalanced force, acceleration, time, speed, direction, distance.*

A push or a pull on an object is called a **force**. When one object pushes or pulls another object, you say that the first object is exerting a force on the second object. **A force can cause an object to start or stop moving or change the way that an object is moving.** Think about some of the forces you exert each day. You exert a force to lift your books, write with a pen, or take out the trash.

Will a force always cause the motion of an object to change? The answer is no. Forces are described by how strong they are as well as the direction in which they act. When more than one force is acting on an object, the forces add together. So if two people push on a car stuck in the snow, the overall force on the car is the sum of their individual forces. Forces can be balanced or unbalanced.

Unbalanced Forces The overall force acting on an object is called the **net force**. When a net force changes an object's motion, the force is said to be an **unbalanced force**. An unbalanced force will result when multiple forces are exerted on an object in the same direction, as in the case of the car in the snow. An unbalanced force may also result when two forces act in different directions on the same object. In this case, the net force is the difference between the two forces. If one force is greater than the other, the net force is in the direction of the greater force. Forces are usually represented by arrows, as shown in Figure 7. In this book, the stronger the force, the wider the arrow. The strength of a force can be measured using a spring scale or a force probe.

Sharpen your Skills

Predicting ACTIVITY

You can use a spring scale to measure forces. First, insert hooks in opposite sides of a wooden block. Attach a spring scale to one of the hooks and pull the spring scale. Observe what happens to the block. Record the reading on the spring's scale. Then, attach a second spring scale to the other hook. Ask a partner to pull on this spring scale with a force greater than the force you used before. At the same time, pull on your spring scale with the same force you used before. Observe what happens to the block.

Try to adjust the forces so that the block does not move.

Figure 7 The man in the photograph exerts a force to push the car. *Applying Concepts When the car moves forward, is the net force balanced or unbalanced?*

Chapter 3 **99**

Program Resources

- ◆ **Unit 1 Resources** 3-2 Lesson Plan, p. 73; 3-2 Section Summary, p. 74
- ◆ **Guided Reading and Study Workbook** 3-2

Answers to Self-Assessment

Caption Question
Figure 7 The net force will be unbalanced.

---

2 Facilitate

Forces and Motion

Addressing Naive Conceptions

Help students understand that all objects, including those at rest, are acted on by forces. Remind them that the force of gravity exerts a pull on all objects. Explain that an object not falling is acted upon by an upward force. **learning modality: verbal**

Sharpen your Skills

Predicting

Materials *two spring scales, hooks, wooden block*
Time 15 minutes
Tips Point out that students are investigating the force needed to move the wooden block in a horizontal direction. They should lay the block flat and then pull on the spring scale to make the block move.
Expected Outcome The reading on the spring scale shows the force applied to the block. When two students pull on opposite ends of the block, the block will move toward the student who is exerting the greater force.
Extend Have students read the sections on the next two pages about contact forces and gravitational forces. Then have them make arrow diagrams showing all the forces on the wooden block (a) when neither student pulls on it, (b) when one students pulls on it, (c) when both students pull on it causing it to move, and (d) when both students pull on it but no motion occurs. **learning modality: tactile/ kinesthetic**

Ongoing Assessment

Oral Presentation Have students give at least two reasons why it is important to know the direction of a force as well as its strength. *(Possible reasons: The direction is needed to find a net force, to predict the direction of motion, to determine whether multiple forces are balanced or unbalanced.)*

99

Forces and Motion, continued

Building Inquiry Skills: Comparing and Contrasting

Discuss why balanced forces are less obvious than unbalanced forces. *(Balanced forces keep things as they are and create no change. Unbalanced forces cause a change in motion.)* Ask: **What happens to a moving object if the forces on it are balanced?** *(The motion of the object does not change.)* **What happens to a moving object if the forces applied to it are unbalanced?** *(The motion changes. It may speed up, slow down or stop, or change direction.)* **learning modality: logical/mathematical**

Types of Forces

Including All Students

Emphasize the cause and effect relationship between forces and motion. Have students describe the type of motion that results from each of the following forces: (1) the forces exerted by two positively charged particles on each other (*the particles move away from each other*), (2) the force of a magnet on a piece of iron (*the piece of iron moves toward the magnet*), (3) the force of friction on a rolling tennis ball (*the ball gradually comes to a stop*). **learning modality: logical/mathematical**

Figure 8 The child exerts a force in one direction, while the wagon exerts a force in the opposite direction. *Relating Cause and Effect If the wagon does not move, what is true about the forces?*

Balanced Forces What happens if two forces acting on an object are equal in strength but acting in opposite directions? Equal forces acting on one object in opposite directions are called **balanced forces.** In this case, the forces cancel out. Balanced forces do not result in a net force. **An unbalanced force will change an object's motion whereas balanced forces will not.** You know this if you have ever played tug-of-war. When the forces pulling on each end of the rope are balanced, the rope does not move. But when one force becomes greater than the other, an unbalanced force results. This force might be great enough to pull one team into the mud.

Types of Forces

There are several kinds of force acting on you and the things around you all the time. You are probably familiar with forces such as friction. Other forces are gravitational force, magnetic force, and electrical force.

Contact Forces Two objects that touch each other are said to be in contact with one another. When two objects are in contact, each object exerts a force on the other that pushes it away. This force is called a contact force. When you push a child on a swing, the contact force of your push makes her move away. When a bulldozer pushes a large pile of dirt, it is using contact force as well. Sometimes a contact force is not obvious. Right now, the chair you are sitting on is exerting a contact force that pushes you up.

Friction Why does a kicked soccer ball eventually stop rolling across the grass? The answer is friction. **Friction** is the force that one substance exerts on another when the two rub against each other. For example, it helps you walk and run. The surfaces of water skis and snowboards are made to reduce friction, so skiers move quickly. Friction slows down moving objects, too. In addition to the soccer ball, it slows automobiles, bicycles, and trains.

Background

Facts and Figures Many measurements in science involve only quantity. Examples include mass, volume, density, and time. For other measurements, a direction is needed as well as a magnitude. Force and velocity are two examples. They have both magnitude and direction.

Whenever a measurement includes both a magnitude and a direction, an arrow called a vector can be used. Usually, the length indicates the magnitude and the angle shows the direction. When two vectors point in the same direction, their net force is found by adding their magnitudes. When the vectors have opposite directions, the net force is found by subtracting. Two vectors that meet at an angle can be combined by drawing a parallelogram. The vectors form adjacent sides of the figure; the diagonal shows the magnitude and direction of the net force.

Gravitational Force If you drop a quarter, it falls to the floor because Earth exerts a force that pulls you and everything near Earth's surface toward Earth's center. This force is known as the gravitational force. The gravitational force acts between all objects in the universe. In fact, the gravitational force is responsible for holding the planets in orbit around the sun. The gravitational force is also responsible for giving you your weight. Weight is a measure of the force of gravity on a mass.

Magnetic Force When you put a magnet on your refrigerator, it doesn't fall down. The reason is that a magnet is a material that attracts certain metals, such as iron, to itself. This attraction is known as the magnetic force. A magnet has two regions, known as poles, where its magnetism is strongest. One pole is called a north pole, and the other is called a south pole. When you arrange magnets so that the north pole of one is near the south pole of the other, the magnets attract one another. If, however, you arrange them so that like poles are near each other, the magnets repel each other. These pushes and pulls are due to the magnetic force.

Electrical Force You have experienced the results of an electrical force if you have ever found your socks stuck to your sweater in the clothes dryer. The electrical force results from the charged parts of the clothing's atoms. When charges are brought near each other, they either exert a pull or a push on each other. Charges that are the same repel each other, and charges that are different attract each other. When objects acquire more of one type of charge than another, they are said to be charged. Like charged particles, charged objects repel or attract one another. A negatively charged shirt attracts a positively charged sock in the clothes dryer, which explains why your clothes stick together.

☑ *Checkpoint* *What kinds of forces are exerted on a leaf that has just fallen from a tree?*

Figure 9 Some forces act on objects without making contact with them. **(A)** This girl is experiencing the force of static electricity. **(B)** A metal needle in a compass is moved by Earth's magnetic forces.

Skills Focus inferring **ACTIVITY**
Materials *coin*
Time 10 minutes
Tips Suggest that students draw the coin in several different positions— completely on the desk, about one-third off the desk, just about to fall off the desk.
Expected Outcome Diagrams should show an downward arrow (gravity) and an upward arrow (the contact force exerted by the desk). When the coin is completely on the desk, the two arrows are the same width. When the coin starts to fall the downward arrow is thicker than the upward arrow showing that the downward force is stronger.
Extend Ask students to explain when the net force on the coin is zero. *(when it is not moving)* Ask: **When the coin starts to fall, is the net force positive or negative?** *(It depends on which sign is assigned to which force arrow. Usually upward forces are positive. If that is the case, the net force will be negative.)*
learning modality: logical/ mathematical

Building Inquiry Skills: Relating Cause and Effect

Draw a diagram to explain to students that a falling object increases its speed until it reaches a constant velocity. Ask: **What force causes the speed to stop increasing?** *(air resistance)* **Why is air resistance a result of the force of friction?** *(It is the result of air rubbing against the falling object.)* **learning modality: visual**

Answers to Self-Assessment

Caption Question
Figure 8 The forces are balanced.

☑ *Checkpoint*
The Earth exerts a gravitational force. The air exerts a contact force causing wind resistance.

Ongoing Assessment

Writing Have students describe an example of each of the following forces they have experienced since they woke up today: contact force, friction, gravitational force, magnetic force, electrical force.

Acceleration

Addressing Naive Conceptions

Students may not realize that acceleration can involve speeding up or slowing down. Ask students which of these statements could be true:

♦ When you step on the gas, the car accelerates.

♦ When you step on the brake, the car accelerates.

Explain that both statements are correct, because acceleration is defined as any change in velocity. Slowing down, or deceleration, is negative acceleration.

learning modality: verbal

Inquiry Challenge

Materials *marble, cardboard tubes, scissors, masking tape, books or blocks*

ACTIVITY

Time 40 minutes

Tips To demonstrate the ways an object can accelerate, invite students to construct tracks for marbles. Organize students in small groups. They can cut the cardboard tubes in half lengthwise and join the sections with masking tape. Tracks must be long enough for the marble to show all forms of acceleration. Tell students the tracks must make the marble speed up, slow down, and change direction. Ask: **How can you arrange the track so that the marble speeds up?** (*Make it so that the marble rolls downward.*) **Slows down?** (*Make it so that it has an upward-sloping section.*) **Changes direction?** (*Make it have a curve.*) **cooperative learning**

Including All Students

Students who are still mastering English may not understand the difference between speed and acceleration. When students say a car is "fast," they usually mean the car accelerates rapidly. Have students use speed and acceleration words in sentences such as: *The runner _____ quickly at the start, but could not keep up her _____ to the finish line.*

limited English proficiency

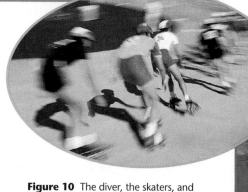

Acceleration

Any type of unbalanced force can change the motion of an object. In other words, an unbalanced force can cause an object to accelerate. **Acceleration** is the rate at which velocity changes. Recall that velocity has two components (speed and direction). Acceleration involves a change in either of these components. **In science, acceleration refers to increasing speed, decreasing speed, or changing direction.**

Increasing Speed Any time an unbalanced force causes the speed of an object to increase, the object experiences acceleration. Can you think of examples of acceleration? A softball accelerates when the pitcher throws it, and again when the batter hits it with the bat. A car that begins to move from a stopped position or speeds up to pass another car is accelerating. The runners in Figure 10 accelerate to sprint down the track. You accelerate as you speed up to catch the bus for school.

Decreasing Speed Just as objects can speed up, they can also slow down. Motion in which speed decreases is also acceleration. This change in speed is sometimes called deceleration. Can you think of examples of deceleration? A ball decelerates as it rolls to a stop. A car decelerates when it comes to a stop at a red light. The diver in Figure 10 decelerates when she enters the water.

Changing Direction A car on a highway may be traveling at constant speed. Thus you may be tempted to conclude that it is not accelerating. Recall, however, that velocity involves *both* speed and direction.

Figure 10 The diver, the skaters, and the runners are all accelerating. *Classifying Can you identify the change in motion in each example?*

Figure 11 The Ferris wheel accelerates as it changes direction. *Making Generalizations* What path does the Ferris wheel follow?

Therefore, an object can be accelerating even if its speed is constant. The car, for example, will be accelerating if it follows a gentle curve in the road or changes lanes. The skaters in Figure 10 accelerate as they round the turns on the track.

Many objects continuously change direction without changing speed. An example of this type of motion is circular motion, or motion along a circular path. The seats on the Ferris wheel in Figure 11 accelerate continuously, because they move in a circle. **INTEGRATING SPACE SCIENCE** The moon also accelerates continuously, because it is always changing direction. Just as Earth revolves around the sun, the moon revolves around Earth. Satellites that orbit Earth continuously accelerate, also.

✓ *Checkpoint* *How is it possible for a car to be accelerating if its speed is a steady 65 km/h?*

Calculating Acceleration

Acceleration describes the rate at which velocity changes. **To determine the acceleration of an object, you must calculate the change in velocity during each unit of time.** This is summarized by the following formula.

$$\text{Acceleration} = \frac{\text{Final velocity} - \text{Initial velocity}}{\text{Time}}$$

If velocity is measured in meters per second, and time is measured in seconds, the unit of acceleration is meters per second per second. This unit is written as m/s^2. This unit may sound peculiar at first. But acceleration is the change in velocity per unit of time, and velocity is the change in distance per unit of time. Therefore, acceleration has two units of time. Suppose velocity is measured in kilometers per hour, and time is measured in hours. Then the unit of acceleration becomes kilometers per hour per hour, or km/h^2.

Answers to Self-Assessment

Caption Questions

Figure 10 The runners are speeding up, the diver is changing direction and slowing down, and the skaters are changing direction.
Figure 11 A circular path

✓ *Checkpoint*

If the car is turning, it would be changing direction and therefore accelerating.

Integrating Space Science

Materials *bicycle, tape, construction paper, scissors* **ACTIVITY**
Time 5 minutes

Make a construction-paper arrow. Tape it to the bicycle wheel so that it points in the direction the wheel will move when spinning. Slowly spin the wheel. Ask: **In what direction is the arrow pointing?** *(In different directions)* Ask: **Does the arrow have acceleration? Explain.** *(Yes, because it changes direction.)* Point out that just like the arrow, the moon, Earth, and satellites accelerate because they constantly change direction. **learning modality: visual**

Calculating Acceleration

Building Inquiry Skills: Calculating

 Content Mastery

Students may have difficulty understanding units of acceleration. Ask them to imagine that they are riding in a car traveling at 30 km/h. Exactly 1 minute later, the speedometer reads 50 km/h. Ask: **What was the change in speed?** *(20 km/h)* Then ask: **What was the change in time?** *(1 min)* Finally, ask: **If you watched the speedometer during that minute, what would you expect to see?** *(The needle moving slowly from 30 km/h to 50 km/h)* Since acceleration is the change in speed over a period of time, the acceleration is written as 20 km/h per min, or 20 km/h/min. **learning modality: logical/ mathematical**

Ongoing Assessment

Drawing Have students make sketches that show three ways an object can accelerate. *(Sketches should show acceleration by speeding up, slowing down, and changing direction.)*

Calculating Acceleration, continued

Using the Visuals: Figure 12

Have students draw a line graph plotting the data for the airplane. Ask students to describe the graph. *(The graph is a straight line sloping up to the right.)* Ask students what this tells them about constant acceleration. *(The speed changes by the same amount each second.)* **learning modality: logical/ mathematical**

Sample Problem

Identify the main parts of the problem for students. Ask: **What is the initial velocity?** *(4 m/s)* **What is the final velocity?** *(22 m/s)* **How long did it take for the roller coaster to get from the top to the bottom of the slope?** *(3 s)* Ask students to complete the calculation. Follow up by asking: **What happens to the velocity each second?** *(It increases by 6 m/s.)* **learning modality: logical/ mathematical**

Practice Problems
1. 10 km/hr/s
2. 1.75 m/s²

Real-Life Learning

Ask students to describe what happens when they ride a bike down a steep hill. *(You move faster and faster.)* Then ask: **Suppose you reach the bottom of a hill traveling 20 km/hr. What additional information do you need to find your acceleration rate?** *(Speed at the top of the hill; time it took to go from the top to the bottom of the hill)* **learning modality: logical/mathematical**

104

Change in Speed Over Time	
Time (s)	Speed (m/s)
0	0
1	8
2	16
3	24
4	32
5	40

Figure 12 The speed of the airplane increases by the same amount each second.

If the object's speed changes by the same amount during each unit of time, the acceleration at any time during its motion is the same. If, however, the acceleration varies, you can describe only the average acceleration.

For an object moving without changing direction, the acceleration of the object is the change in its speed during one unit of time. Consider, for example, a small airplane moving on a runway. The speed of the airplane at the end of each of the first 5 seconds of its motion is shown in Figure 12.

To calculate the acceleration of the airplane, you must first subtract the initial speed (0 m/s) from the final speed (40 m/s). This gives the change in speed, 40 m/s. Then divide the change in speed by the time, 5 seconds. The acceleration is 40 m/s divided by 5 seconds, which is 8 m/s². The acceleration tells you how the speed of the airplane in Figure 12 changes during each second.

Sample Problem

A roller coaster car rapidly picks up speed as it rolls down a slope. As it starts down the slope, its speed is 4 m/s. But 3 seconds later, at the bottom of the slope, its speed is 22 m/s. What is its average acceleration?

Analyze. You know the initial velocity and final velocity of the car, and the length of time during which its velocity changed. You are looking for its acceleration.

Write the formula.
$$Acceleration = \frac{Final\ velocity - Initial\ velocity}{Time}$$

Substitute and solve.
$$Acceleration = \frac{22\ m/s - 4\ m/s}{3\ s}$$

$$Acceleration = \frac{18\ m/s}{3\ s}$$

$$Acceleration = 6\ m/s^2$$

Think about it. The answer is reasonable. If the car's velocity increases by 6 m/s each second, its velocity will be 10 m/s after one second, 16 m/s after two seconds, and 22 m/s after three seconds.

Practice Problem
1. A car advertisement states that a certain car can accelerate from rest to 90 km/h in 9 seconds. Find the car's average acceleration.
2. An eagle accelerates from 15 m/s to 22 m/s in 4 seconds. What is the eagle's average acceleration?

Background

Facts and Figures Warning signs are posted on roadways that have large slopes, or grades. The magnitude of a grade can be stated as a percent. For example, a 6 percent grade has a slope of $\frac{6}{100}$, or 0.06. This means that for every 100 meters, the road rises 6 meters. On the downhill lanes of a steep section of highway, the grade warning is often accompanied by a warning that truck drivers should test the brakes on their vehicles and proceed in a low gear. The uphill lanes of a steep section of highway often have an extra lane, called a climbing lane, for heavy vehicles that have to move up the grade slowly. The grade warnings let a truck driver know to move into the extra lane and allow faster-moving vehicles to pass.

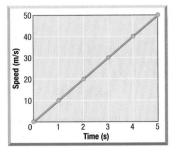

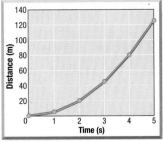

Changes in Speed and Distance Over Time

Time (s)	Speed (m/s)	Distance (m)
0	0	0
1	10	5
2	20	20
3	30	45
4	40	80
5	50	125

Figure 13 These graphs plot the motion of an accelerating object. *Predicting* How would the slant, or slope, of the speed and time graph change if the object were accelerating more rapidly? More slowly? What do you think the graph of a decelerating object would look like?

Notice that after each interval of one second, the speed of the airplane is 8 m/s greater than during the previous interval. So after one second, its speed is 8 m/s. After two seconds, its speed is 8 m/s + 8 m/s, or 16 m/s, and so on. Since the acceleration of the airplane does not change during the 5 seconds, you can use this formula for any time interval during the five seconds. Try it.

Graphing Acceleration

You can use a graph to analyze the motion of an object that is accelerating. Figure 13 shows the data for an object that is accelerating at 10 m/s^2. The graph showing speed versus time is a slanted straight line. The straight line shows that acceleration is constant. For every increase of one second, the speed increases by 10 m/s. Thus the graphed line rises the same amount each second and shows a **linear** relationship. If the object accelerated by a different amount each second, the graph would not be a straight line.

The graph of distance versus time is a curved line and shows a **nonlinear** relationship. This tells you that the distance traveled by the accelerating object varies each second. As the speed increases, the graph curves upward.

Section 2 Review

1. Do all forces cause a change in motion? Explain.
2. What three kinds of change in motion are called acceleration? Give an example of each.
3. What formula is used to calculate acceleration?
4. **Thinking Critically** **Problem Solving** A car is creeping down a deserted highway at 1 m/s. Sometime later, its speed is 25 m/s. This could have happened if the car accelerated at 3 m/s^2 for 8 seconds. Is this the only way the increase in speed could have happened? Explain.

Check Your Progress CHAPTER PROJECT
You can improve the accuracy of your speed estimations by repeating measurements and by using averaged data. Make all your calculations in an organized, step-by-step manner. Prepare display cards that show how you calculated each speed.

Answers to Self-Assessment

Caption Question

Figure 13 If the object were accelerating more rapidly, then the slope of the speed and time line would be greater. If it were accelerating more slowly, then the slope of the line would be smaller. A decelerating object would produce a speed and time graph with a line that falls instead of rises.

Graphing Acceleration

Using the Visuals: Figure 13

Draw student's attention to the line graphs in the figure. Ask: **How is the graph of change in distance over time different from the graph of change in speed over time?** (*The distance-time graph curves upward instead of being a straight line.*) Then ask: **What would happen to the curved graph if the acceleration was less?** (*The graph would curve upward less.*) **learning modality: logical/mathematical**

3 Assess

Section 2 Review Answers

1. No. If the overall force on an object is zero, no change in motion will occur.
2. Increasing speed—a plane taking off; decreasing speed—a car braking; changing direction—a bicycle turning.
3. Acceleration = (Final velocity − Initial velocity)/ Time
4. No. The car could have accelerated at 2 m/s^2 for 12 s, 4 m/s^2 for 6 s, or 6 m/s^2 for 4 s. There are an infinite number of ways for the speed increase to have happened.

Check Your Progress CHAPTER PROJECT
Talk with the whole class about ways to make measurements more accurately. Explain to students why taking several measurements and then calculating the average improves accuracy. Show students ways to organize their calculations to model good problem-solving techniques.

Performance Assessment

Oral Presentation Divide the class into small groups. Have each group write a short scenario involving an object being accelerated, then exchange scenarios with another group and sketch a graph of speed versus time for the scenario. Finally, have each group present its findings to the class.

Stopping on a Dime

Preparing for Inquiry

Key Concept Students will use measurements of reaction times, running speeds, and stopping distances to help them decide where a basketball court should be located.

Skills Objectives Students will be able to
◆ measure reaction time, maximum speed, and stopping distance;
◆ use reaction time, maximum speed, and stopping distance to calculate the total distance a student could travel after crossing an out-of-bounds line;
◆ infer how reaction time, speed, and stopping distance influence total distance

Time 40 minutes

Advance Planning Reserve time and space on the school field or in the gymnasium for Part II of the lab.

Guiding Inquiry

Invitation Have students think about the importance of using measurements and calculations to infer a suitable location of a basketball court. Ask: **When you run out of bounds on a basketball court, what determines how long it takes you to stop?** (*Sample: running speed*)

Introducing the Procedure

◆ Tell students that the distance a basketball player will run past an out-of-bounds line depends on three things. First, on how fast the player is running when he or she goes out of bounds (maximum running speed). Second, on how long it takes the player to realize that he or she is out of bounds (reaction time). Third, on how far a player travels after realizing that he or she needs to stop (stopping distance).
◆ Give students specific instructions concerning where running speed and stopping distance will be measured. Show them where the timer should stand, where the runner will begin,

Stopping on a Dime

The school has decided to put a new basketball court in a small area between two buildings. Safety is an important consideration in the design of the court. You and your friends volunteer to find out experimentally how close the out-of-bounds lines can be to the buildings and still allow players to stop without running into a wall.

Problem

What distance is necessary between the out-of-bounds line and a wall so that a player can stop before hitting the wall?

Skills Focus

measuring, calculating, inferring

Materials

wooden meter stick   tape measure
2 stopwatches or watches with second hands

Procedure

Part I Reaction Time

1. Have your partner suspend a wooden meter stick between your thumb and index finger, as shown. Your thumb and index finger should be about three centimeters apart.
2. Your partner will drop the meter stick without giving you any warning. You will try to grab it with two fingers.
3. Note the level at which you grabbed the meter stick and use the chart shown to determine your reaction time. Record the time in the class data table.
4. Reverse roles with your partner and repeat Steps 1 through 3.

Reaction Time

Distance (cm)	Time (s)	Distance (cm)	Time (s)
15	0.175	25	0.226
16	0.181	26	0.230
17	0.186	27	0.235
18	0.192	28	0.239
19	0.197	29	0.243
20	0.202	30	0.247
21	0.207	31	0.252
22	0.212	32	0.256
23	0.217	33	0.260
24	0.221	34	0.263

and in which direction the runner should run. If possible, go through a sample calculation on the board.

Expected Outcome

A typical reaction time is about 0.2 seconds. A typical running speed is about 5 m/s which produces a stopping distance of about 3 m. Reaction time plus stopping distance means that there should be a safety margin of around 4 m.

Troubleshooting the Experiment

Make sure students do not slow down before reaching the 25-meter mark. Be sure that the person dropping the meter stick does not inadvertently signal the person catching.

Analyze and Conclude

1. Find the student with the lowest time for running the course. Divide the distance (25 m) by this time to get the maximum running speed in meters per second.

CLASS DATA TABLE

Student Name	Reaction Time (s)	Running Time (s)	Stopping Distance (m)

Part II Stopping Distance

5. On the school field or in the gymnasium, mark off a distance of 25 m.
6. Have your partner time how long it takes you to run the course at full speed. **CAUTION:** *Be sure to remove any obstacles from the course.* After you pass the 25-m mark, come to a stop as quickly as possible and remain standing. You must not slow down before the mark.
7. Have your partner measure the distance from the 25-m mark to your final position. This is the distance you need to come to a complete stop. Enter your time and distance into the class data table.
8. Reverse roles with your partner. Enter your partner's time and distance into the class data table.

Analyze and Conclude

1. How can you calculate the average speed of the student who ran the 25-m course the fastest? Find this speed.
2. Multiply the speed of the fastest student (calculated in Question 1) by the slowest reaction time listed in the class data table. Why would you be interested in this product?
3. Add the distance calculated in Question 2 to the longest stopping distance in the class data table. What does this total distance represent?
4. Explain why it is important to use the fastest speed, the slowest reaction time, and the longest stopping distance in your calculations.

5. What other factors should you take into account to get results that apply to a real basketball court?
6. **Apply** Suppose the distance between the out-of-bounds line and the wall in a playground or gymnasium is, according to your calculations, too short for safety. Suggest some strategies that could be used (other than moving the wall) for making that playground safer.

Getting Involved

Visit a local playground and examine it from the viewpoint of safety. Use what you learned about stopping distance as one of your guidelines, but also try to identify other potentially unsafe conditions. Write a letter to the department of parks or to the officials of your town informing them of your findings.

Program Resources

◆ **Unit 1 Resources** Chapter 3 Real-World Lab blackline masters, pp. 83–85

Media and Technology

 Lab Activity Videotapes
Grade 6, Tape 1

Safety

All students should run in the same direction. Students should not be allowed to walk across the area where running speeds are being measured. Review the safety guidelines in Appendix A.

2. The maximum running speed multiplied by the slowest reaction time tells how far the fastest running student would travel out of bounds in meters if he or she had the slowest reaction time before realizing that he or she needed to stop. The distance represents the maximum out of bounds distance possible.
3. Adding the longest stopping distance tells how much farther the student in Question 2 will travel before coming to a complete stop if that student also had the longest measured stopping distance.
4. It's the "worst case scenario." You are calculating the maximum distance it could take a student to stop. In reality, students will either be slower runners or will react faster or will have a shorter stopping distance. Thus all students should be able to stop in a distance that is shorter than you have calculated. To show that this is true, students can calculate how far they would travel given their own measured maximum speed, reaction time, and stopping distance.
5. A player may go out of bounds running sideways, jumping, or stumbling. A player might not immediately realize that he or she is out of bounds. These factors might increase the distance the player traveled.
6. You could add a wide yellow line to let players know when they are approaching the out of bounds. This would alert them to react sooner. You could also place cushions on the wall to reduce the risk of injury in a collision.

Extending the Inquiry

Getting Involved Students should check to make sure that there is enough distance between the out-of-bounds line and any obstructions (trees, walls, parking areas, roads). Students should realize that lines indicating where spectators should sit or stand would prevent a possible collision with a player. Students should note that basketball posts are very close to the court and perhaps should be wrapped in foam. Students should look for cracks in the playing surface.

SECTION 3 Water in Motion

TEKS: 6.2B; 6.6A ,C

Objectives

After completing the lesson, students will be able to

◆ describe how moving water shapes the land;

◆ trace the path a river takes from its headwaters to its mouth;

◆ explain how a flood affects the land near a river and how floods can be controlled.

1 Engage/Explore

Activating Prior Knowledge

Encourage students to describe rivers they have seen. Ask questions such as, **How big is the river? How fast does it flow?** and **What is the land around it like?** List each river's characteristics on the board. Encourage students to keep these characteristics in mind as they read this section.

DISCOVER

Skills Focus predicting
Materials *rectangular pan, sand and pebbles, small piece of porcelain tile, clump of grassy soil, books to prop up pan, watering can, water*
Time 15–20 minutes
Tips Provide a container for disposing of the wet sand, pebbles, and sod.
Expected Outcome Water will flow more quickly on the tile, more slowly on the sand and pebble mixture, and most slowly on the grassy soil. The sand and pebble mixture and soil will absorb some water. The water may erode the sand and pebble mixture to some degree. The sod will show less erosion.
Think It Over Both pouring all the water at once and tilting the pan at a steeper angle will produce a higher flow rate, more erosion of the sand and pebble mixture, and less absorption by the sod.

SECTION 3 Water in Motion

DISCOVER 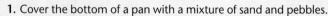 ACTIVITY

What Affects How Water Moves?

1. Cover the bottom of a pan with a mixture of sand and pebbles.

2. Press a small piece of porcelain tile onto the sand mixture to represent pavement. In another area of the pan, press a clump of soil and grass into the sand.

3. Prop up one end of the pan so it slopes gently.

4. Using a watering can, sprinkle "rain" onto the pan's contents.

5. Observe how the water moves when it falls on the sand mixture, on the tile, and on the grass.

6. Wash your hands when you are finished with this activity.

Think It Over

Predicting How would the movement of the water change if you poured the water all at once? If you tilted the pan more steeply?

GUIDE FOR READING

◆ How does moving water shape the land around it?

◆ How does a flood affect the land near a river?

Reading Tip Before you read, use the section headings to make an outline. Leave space to take notes as you read.

Key Terms erosion
• deposition • sediment
• headwaters • flood plain
• meander • oxbow lake
• mouth • delta • flood
• levee

The next time it rains, watch the rainwater flow along the side of a road. Notice how the water picks up leaves and twigs and carries them away. Bits of paper and small pebbles bounce and swirl along in the flow. Even a tiny stream has the power to move objects.

Rivers Shape the Land

Now picture a large river, and think about how its running water can cause erosion. **Erosion** is the process by which fragments of soil and rock are broken off from the ground surface and carried away. Moving water carries these fragments along. Eventually, they are dropped or deposited in a new place. **Deposition** is the process by which soil and rock are dropped in a new location. **The force of moving water shapes many features of Earth's surface.** Rivers, for example, wear away landforms through erosion and build new landforms through deposition. The particles of rock and soil picked up and moved by erosion and deposition are called **sediment.** The river deposits heavier sediment particles first, then lighter ones.

The speed of moving water affects its ability to wear away the land. The faster the water flows, the more force it has. A river traveling at a speed of 1 kilometer per hour can move pebbles along. At 18 kilometers per hour, it can move a boulder the size of an armchair! When a river slows, its force decreases.

READING STRATEGIES

Reading Tip Make sure students understand that "section headings" means the headings in large type above the paragraphs of text in this section, not the titles of the three sections in the entire chapter. Students' outlines should include three main headings: (1) *Rivers Shape the Land*, (2) *Profile of a River*, and (3) *Rivers and Floods*. Suggest that students include two to four key ideas under each main heading.

Study and Comprehension Encourage students to use their completed outlines to write a summary of the lesson and to generate questions to test themselves.

Three factors affect how fast a river flows. One factor is the steepness of its slope. Water flows faster down a mountainside than over a flat plain. A second factor is the volume of water in the river. The more water in a river, the faster the river flows. A third factor is the slope of the channel through which it flows. The river water rubbing against the sides and bottom of the channel creates friction. This friction slows the water's movement. In a shallow narrow channel, almost all the water contacts the sides or bottom, and it moves slowly. In a broad, deep channel, most of the water does not contact the sides, so the river flows faster.

Profile of a River

Follow this rafting trip along a river's entire length to see how the river changes. You can follow the journey in *Exploring a River* on the next page.

The Headwaters Your trip starts near the river's beginning, or source, in the mountains. The many small streams that come together at the source of the river are called the **headwaters.** Your ride through the headwaters is quite bumpy. Your raft bounces through rapids and drops suddenly over a small waterfall. You notice how the fast-flowing water breaks off clumps of soil from the riverbanks and carries them along. This erosion wears away the sides and cuts into the bottom of its channel. The channel gradually widens and deepens.

Downriver As you continue downriver, your ride smoothes out. The land around the river is less steep than it was near the headwaters. Some smaller streams have joined the river, increasing the volume of water. With less water contacting the sides, there is less friction. As a result, although the slope is gentler, the river flows fairly swiftly.

The Flood Plain Next you travel through the middle of a wide valley. The river created this valley over time by eroding the land along its banks. The broad, flat valley through which the river flows is called the **flood plain.**

Figure 14 A hiker carefully avoids the collapsed edge of this dirt road, evidence of moving water's power to erode soil.

Program Resources

◆ **Unit 1 Resources** 3-3 Lesson Plan, p. 77; 3-3 Section Summary, p. 78
◆ **Guided Reading and Study Workbook** 3-3

2 Facilitate

Rivers Shape the Land

Cultural Diversity

Point out that the English language includes many different names for landforms created by erosion and deposition of sediments—*canyon* and *delta*, for example. Ask: **What other names can you think of?** (*Students might suggest* gully, sandbar, mudflat, *and others.*) Emphasize that other languages also include such names, including *arroyo* (Spanish for dry gully), *wadi* (Arabic for river channel), and *billabong* (Native Australian for dead-end channel leading out from a river). Encourage students to suggest other non-English examples from their own cultures or personal reading. Interested volunteers could compile a master list of landform names in English and their corollaries in other languages. **limited English proficiency**

Profile of a River

Including All Students

Call on volunteers to find and read aloud the different definitions of *profile* found in some dictionaries. (*Sample definitions: a side view or outline of an object; a concise description of a person's or thing's most noteworthy characteristics; a table or graph showing the extent to which a person or thing exhibits various tested traits*) Ask: **Which meaning fits the title "Profile of a River"?** (*"A side view or outline" describes the illustration on these pages, while the caption provides "a concise description of a person's or thing's characteristics."*) Suggest that students write a brief profile in their own words of the river described in the text. **learning modality: verbal**

Ongoing Assessment

Writing Have students briefly describe the processes of erosion and deposition in their own words.

Profile of a River, continued

Real-Life Learning

Commercial businesses conduct guided rafting expeditions on many of this country's rivers. Such expeditions teach people much about the ecology of rivers and develop appreciation for our wilderness and its wildlife, but these tours can also cause ecological damage. Suggest that interested students find out more about such rafting expeditions and stage a debate on the pros and cons of wilderness rafting expeditions. **learning modality: verbal**

EXPLORING
a River

To help students focus on the major points presented in this visual essay and make comparisons among the river segments more easily, have them organize the information in a table. This could be done either as a whole-class discussion, with students suggesting the entries for you to write in a table on the board or an overhead transparency, or, preferably, as an individual activity, with each student making his or her own table independently. The terms *Headwaters, Downriver, Flood plain,* and *Mouth* could be written in a horizontal row across the top of the table as the column headings, and terms identifying the types of information presented—such as *Slope, Speed, Volume, Erosion or Deposition?* and *Typical Organisms*—could be written in the far-left vertical column (or vice versa). As students read the text on these two pages and the next page, they can add additional information to the table. If students create their tables independently, provide some follow-up class time for them to share their results and resolve any discrepancies. Refer to the **ELL Handbook** for additional teaching strategies. **learning modality: logical/mathematical**

If students create tables independently, they can save the tables in their portfolios.

EXPLORING a River

A s you follow this river from its headwaters to its mouth, notice how its speed, volume, and shape change. Each part of the river forms different features on Earth's surface.

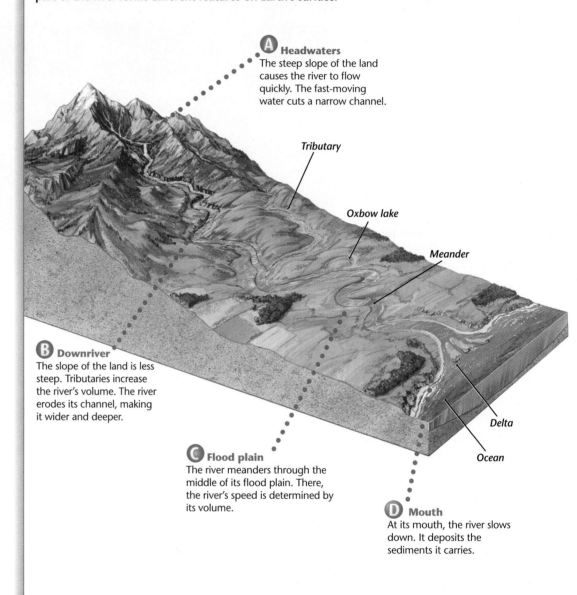

A Headwaters
The steep slope of the land causes the river to flow quickly. The fast-moving water cuts a narrow channel.

Tributary

Oxbow lake

Meander

B Downriver
The slope of the land is less steep. Tributaries increase the river's volume. The river erodes its channel, making it wider and deeper.

C Flood plain
The river meanders through the middle of its flood plain. There, the river's speed is determined by its volume.

Delta

Ocean

D Mouth
At its mouth, the river slows down. It deposits the sediments it carries.

Background

Facts and Figures Another set of terms used to describe a river are the stages of its development: youth, maturity, and old age. A single river may include all three stages.

At the headwaters, where the fast-moving water erodes the underlying land, the river is young. A young river has waterfalls, rapids, a narrow V-shaped valley, and a steep slope.

A mature river erodes its sides more than its bottom, creating a flood plain. A mature river has a gentler slope and a smoother riverbed.

An old river has a flood plain that is much wider than the width of its meanders. An old river may shift course frequently. Oxbow lakes and natural levees are common.

These stages are relative; an "old" river may be more recently formed than some "young" rivers.

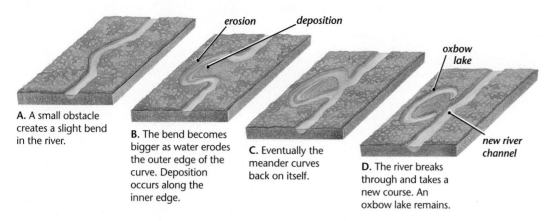

erosion   deposition

A. A small obstacle creates a slight bend in the river.

B. The bend becomes bigger as water erodes the outer edge of the curve. Deposition occurs along the inner edge.

C. Eventually the meander curves back on itself.

D. The river breaks through and takes a new course. An oxbow lake remains.

oxbow lake

new river channel

Figure 15 A river changes its course over time, forming winding meanders. *Predicting The oxbow lake is cut off from the river. What will the oxbow lake look like in the future?*

In places, small obstacles in the river's channel cause the water to flow slightly to one side or the other. This movement creates a bend in the river. As Figure 15 shows, the water erodes the outer edge of the curve, where it flows faster. The river deposits sediments along the inner edge, where it flows slower. This process gradually forms looping curves in the river called **meanders.** Eventually, the river may break through the ends of the meander, carving a new channel. The crescent-shaped, cutoff body of water that remains is called an **oxbow lake.**

The Mouth Your raft trip is nearly over as you approach the river's mouth. The **mouth** is the point where a river flows into another body of water—a larger river, a lake, or an ocean. When the fast-moving waters of a river hit the slower waters of a lake or ocean, the river suddenly slows down. As it slows, the river deposits most of its sediment. These deposits at the river's mouth build up, forming an area called a **delta.** The sediment deposits are rich in nutrients and minerals. As a result, the soil in delta areas is very fertile for farming.

☑ *Checkpoint* *What are some land features shaped by the movement of water?*

Rivers and Floods

A **flood** occurs when the volume of water in a river increases so much that the river overflows its channel. As rain or melting snow adds more water to a river, the river gains in speed and strength. Recall that as the speed of a river increases, so does the amount of force it has. Floods greatly increase a river's ability to erode sediment and change land features. **A flooding river can erode and deposit huge amounts of soil, sand, and gravel. Floods can uproot trees and pluck boulders from the ground.**

Rivers and Floods,
continued

Real-Life Learning

Building levees can sometimes backfire. These walls prevent the natural channel-widening process that rivers undergo as their volume increases. As a result, during a flood, the water has nowhere to go except downstream, making flooding worse for areas farther downstream. **learning modality: logical/ mathematical**

3 Assess

Section 3 Review Answers

1. *Erosion:* Water breaks off pieces of soil and rock and carries them away. *Deposition:* The pieces of soil and rock are carried to a new location, where they build up and form new landforms.
2. A flooding river can uproot trees and boulders, and deposit sediment on the flood plain.
3. A meander is a curve in a river caused by water eroding the outer edge and depositing sediments along the opposite bank.
4. Greater volume and speed of the water increase the river's ability to cause erosion because the river has more force during a flood.

Science at Home

Suggest that students use a variety of types of soil, gravel, pebbles, and sand. Larger, heavier particles settle fastest, and lighter particles take longer. As a river carries sediments, it deposits larger and heavier particles first. The layers of deposits will be similar to those that formed in students' jars.

Performance Assessment

Skills Check Challenge small groups to devise methods for measuring the speed of a local stream or river. Groups could present their ideas in a written report or oral presentation.

Figure 16 A flood can be disastrous for nearby residents, such as the owners of this house. *Making Generalizations Explain how floods can be both harmful and helpful to people.*

As a river overflows onto its flood plain, it slows down, depositing heavier sediment alongside the channel. Sediment deposits actually build a natural defense against floods. These deposits that build up over time into long ridges that parallel the river are called **levees**. These natural levees help keep the river inside its banks. People sometimes build up the natural levees with sandbags or stone and concrete to provide further protection against floods.

Throughout history, people have both feared and welcomed floods. Ancient Egyptians, for instance, called their fertile cropland "the gift of the Nile." Deposition from regular floods left a layer of rich soil on each side of the river, creating a green strip of good land in the middle of the desert. But floods can also wash away bridges and destroy farms, towns, and crops.

Section 3 Review

1. Name and describe the two major processes by which a river moves sediments, thereby shaping the land around it.
2. Describe the effects of a flooding river on the land near the river.
3. What is a meander and how does it form?
4. **Thinking Critically Relating Cause and Effect** During a flood, the volume and speed of the water in a river increases. What effect does this have on a river's ability to cause erosion? Explain.

112

Science at Home

Muddying the Waters With a family member, fill a clear plastic jar half full of dirt and half full of water. Cover the jar tightly. Hold the jar firmly, and shake it. Allow the dirt to settle. Without disturbing the dirt, pour off the water into another jar. Use a spoon to scoop off different layers of dirt onto a paper towel. Observe the dirt layers, and tell your family members how the layers are like those a river deposits.

Program Resources

◆ **Unit 1 Resources** 3-3 Review and Reinforce, p. 79; 3-3 Enrich, p. 80

Answers to Self-Assessment

Caption Question

Figure 16 *Harm:* Injury or death of people and livestock, destruction of buildings and crops, and loss of freshwater supplies, electricity, transportation, and communication *Help:* Deposition of nutrient-rich silt

SECTION 1
Describing, Measuring, and Graphing Motion

Key Ideas
- The motion of an object is determined by its change of position relative to a reference point.
- Speed is the distance an object travels in one unit of time. If an object moves at constant speed, its speed can be determined by dividing the distance it travels by the time taken. If an object's speed varies, then dividing distance by time gives you the object's average speed.
- When you state both the speed of an object and the direction in which it is moving, you are describing the object's velocity.

Key Terms
motion	speed
reference point	velocity
meter	

 SECTION 2
Force and Acceleration

Key Ideas
- A force is a push or pull. Two or more forces acting on an object combine.
- Equal and opposite forces on the same object are called balanced forces. Uneven forces are called unbalanced forces. Unbalanced forces cause objects to accelerate.
- Contact forces, like friction, are exerted by direct contact. Gravitational, electrical, and magnetic forces are exerted without direct contact.
- Acceleration is the rate at which velocity changes. It involves increasing speed, decreasing speed, or changing direction.
- Acceleration can be calculated by dividing the change in velocity by the amount of time it took that change to occur.

Key Terms
force	friction
net force	acceleration
unbalanced force	linear
balanced force	nonlinear

SECTION 3
Water in Motion
*INTEGRATING **EARTH SCIENCE***

Key Ideas
- Moving water, like rivers, can wear away and create landforms through erosion and deposition of sediments.
- Water travels from the headwaters of a river, downriver through flood plains. Sediments collected along the way are deposited in a delta at the mouth of the river.
- Floods occur when a river overflows its channel. Erosion and deposition of sediments are greatly increased by flooding.
- Artificial flood-control levees, like naturally occurring ones, can help harness a river's energy for beneficial purposes.

Key Terms
erosion	flood plain	delta
deposition	meander	flood
sediment	oxbow lake	levee
headwaters	mouth	

Organizing Information

Concept Map Copy the concept map about motion onto a separate sheet of paper. Then complete it and add a title. (For more on concept maps, see the Skills Handbook.)

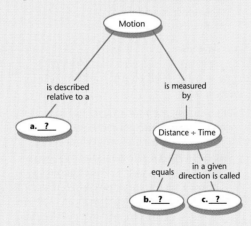

Organizing Information

Concept Map Sample title: *Describing and Measuring Motion*
a. reference point **b.** speed **c.** velocity

Program Resources
- **Unit 1 Resources** Chapter 3 Project Scoring Rubric, p. 68
- **Performance Assessment** Chapter 3, pp. 11–13
- **Chapter and Unit Tests** Chapter 3 Test, pp. 12–15

Media and Technology
Computer Test Bank
Chapter 3 Test

Reviewing Content

Multiple Choice

1. d 2. b 3. b 4. a 5. b

True or False

6. true 7. straight line 8. true 9. speed
10. true

Checking Concepts

11. The warbler has a greater speed, 12 m/s, compared to the hawk's 10 m/s.
12. The insect is accelerating because the direction of its motion is always changing.
13. Erosion occurs less quickly as you travel from the headwaters to the mouth. At the mouth, a river slows down and drops most of its sediment.
14. Over time, sediment deposits build levees parallel to the river. The levees help keep the river inside its banks.
15. This assignment should generate interesting and useful responses. Check that the actual speeds students use are reasonable values for what they are describing.

Thinking Critically

16. Compare the times it takes to travel each block. If they are the same, the car probably stayed at a constant speed. If they are different, then the car accelerated.
17. Since they left at the same time, the first driver had the greater average speed since that driver drove the same distance in less time.
18. The family traveled a total distance of 160 km (80 km/hr × 1 hr + 40 km/hr × 2 hr) in 3 hours. So their average speed is 53.3 km/hr (160 km ÷ 3 hr = 53.3 km/hr). Simply adding the two speeds and dividing by 2 gives an incorrect answer because the family spent more time driving at the slower speed.
19. The levees could help to prevent damaging floods. However, they may also prevent the deposition of rich soil that would be beneficial for agriculture.

CHAPTER 3 ASSESSMENT

Reviewing Content

 Review key concepts online using
iText at www.phschool.com

Multiple Choice

Choose the letter of the best answer.

1. A change in position with respect to a reference point is
   a. acceleration.   b. velocity.
   c. direction.   d. motion.
2. To find the average speed of an object,
   a. add together its different speeds and divide by the number of speeds.
   b. divide the distance it travels by the time taken to travel that distance.
   c. divide the time it takes to travel a distance by the distance traveled.
   d. multiply the acceleration by the time.
3. If you know a car travels 30 km in 20 minutes, you can find its
   a. acceleration.   b. average speed.
   c. direction.   d. graph
4. If you divide the increase in an object's speed by the time taken for that increase, you are determining the object's
   a. acceleration.   b. constant speed.
   c. average speed.   d. velocity.
5. Which of the following features is most typical of the headwaters of a river?
   a. broad, flat valley
   b. waterfalls and rapids
   c. winding meanders
   d. muddy, slow-moving water

True or False

If the statement is true, write true. If it is false, change the underlined word or words to make the statement true.

6. In a moving elevator, you are not moving from the reference point of the <u>elevator</u>.
7. The graph of distance versus time for an object moving at constant speed is a <u>curve</u>.
8. Acceleration is a change in speed or <u>direction</u>.
9. The distance an object travels in one unit of time is called <u>acceleration</u>.
10. Soil and rock are dropped in a new location during <u>deposition</u>.

Checking Concepts

11. Which has a greater speed, a hawk that travels 600 meters in 60 seconds or a tiny warbler that travels 60 meters in 5 seconds? Explain.
12. An insect is on a compact disc that is put into a compact disc player. The disc spins around, and the insect hangs on. Is the insect accelerating? Explain why or why not.
13. How do erosion and deposition change as a river flows from the headwaters to the mouth?
14. How do floods move sediment in such a way that might prevent future floods?
15. **Writing to Learn** Suppose that one day some of the things that usually move very slowly start to go faster, while some things that usually move quickly slow to a snail's pace. Write a description of some events that might occur during such a day. Include a few actual speeds as part of your description.

Thinking Critically

16. **Making Generalizations** Suppose you make two measurements. One is the time that a car takes to travel a city block. The other is the time the car takes to travel the next city block. From these measurements, explain how you decide if the car is moving at a steady speed or if it is accelerating.
17. **Problem Solving** Two drivers start at the same time to make a 100-km trip. Driver 1 takes 2 hours to complete the trip. Driver 2 takes 3 hours, but stops for an hour at the halfway point. Which driver had a greater average speed for the whole trip? Explain.
18. **Applying Concepts** A family takes a car trip. They travel for an hour at 80 km/h and then for 2 hours at 40 km/h. Find the average speed. (*Hint:* Remember to consider the total distance and the total amount of time.)
19. **Inferring** Natural and artificial levees are used for flood control along many rivers. How could levees affect the agricultural regions of a river's flood plain?

Applying Skills

20. Starting line to line B = 2.0 cm; line B to finish line = 5.0 cm
21. 2 cm/s
22. 1.0 cm/s^2

Applying Skills

Use the illustration of the motion of a ladybug to answer Questions 20–22.

A Start   B   C Finish

20. **Measuring** Measure the distance from the starting line to line B, and from line B to the finish line. Measure to the nearest tenth of a centimeter.
21. **Calculating** Starting at rest, the ladybug accelerated to line B and then moved at constant speed until it reached the finish line. If it took 2.5 seconds to move from line B to the finish line, calculate its constant speed during that time.

22. **Interpreting Data** The speed you calculated in Question 21 is also the speed the ladybug had at line B (at the end of its acceleration). If it took 2 seconds to accelerate from the start line to line B, what is its acceleration during that time?

Present Your Project Organize your display cards so that they are easy to follow. Remember to put a title on each card stating the speed that was being measured. Place them in order from the slowest speed to the fastest. Then display your cards to your class. Compare your results with those of other students.

Reflect and Record When you measured the same speed more than once, were the data always the same? Explain. What factors make measuring a speed difficult?

Test Preparation

Use these questions to prepare for standardized tests.

Study the graph. Then answer Questions 23–27.

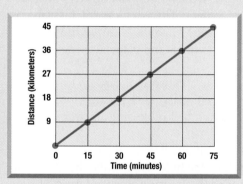

23. What would be the best title for this graph?
    A Train at Rest
    B Train Moving at Constant Acceleration
    C Train Moving at Constant Speed
    D Train Slowing to a Stop

24. During each 15-minute interval, the train travels a distance of
    F 9 kilometers.   G 18 kilometers.
    H 36 kilometers.   J 45 kilometers.
25. According to the graph, how long does it take for the train to travel 27 kilometers?
    A 15 minutes   B 30 minutes
    C 45 minutes   D 1 hour
26. What is the train's speed?
    F 9 km/h   G 18 km/h
    H 36 km/h   J 72 km/h
27. After 75 minutes, the train stops for 5 minutes to pick up passengers. How would the graph look during this period?
    A The line would slant downward.
    B The line would be horizontal.
    C The line would be broken.
    D The line would stop at a point and continue from the same point once the train begins to move again.

Understanding Nature's Designs

Focus on Engineering

This four-page feature explores the process of scientific inquiry by involving students in a high-interest, magazine-like feature about a working scientist, engineer Ioannis Miaoulis. By focusing on Dr. Miaoulis's investigation of engineering principles found in nature, the feature highlights making observations and posing questions as key elements of scientific inquiry.

Students do not need any previous knowledge of forces or mechanics to understand and appreciate this feature.

Scientific Inquiry

◆ Before students read the feature, let them read the title, examine the pictures, and read the captions on their own. Then ask: **What questions came into your mind as you looked at these pictures?** *(Students might suggest questions such as "Why would an engineer study nature?" "How did prairie dogs learn about air currents?" "How do butterfly wings collect heat?" and "Why does a butterfly need heat?")* Point out to students that just as they have questions about what they are seeing, scientists too have questions about what they observe.

UNDERSTANDING NATURE'S DESIGNS

Engineer and Scientist Ioannis Miaoulis
Dr. Miaoulis was born in Greece and grew up there. He then came to the United States to study. He is now a professor of mechanical engineering and Dean of the School of Engineering at Tufts University in Medford, Massachusetts.

Fish in a tank glide under the watchful eye of a video camera. Inside a glass box, spiders spin webs in the wind from a powerful fan. "This is a biomechanics laboratory," says Professor Ioannis Miaoulis (YAHN is my OW lis). "What we study is how animals and plants use energy, motion, and forces."

Miaoulis walks over to a network of earthen tunnels built between two panes of glass. The structure looks like a toy ant farm, but it has a tube for blowing air over the top. Miaoulis explains:

"This is a cross section of a prairie-dog burrow. There are two entrance holes. One hole is flat, while the other one is built up and rounded. Biologists were wondering why. They thought the prairie dogs wanted a good view, but then why not make both holes high and rounded and get a good view from both?"

Background

Engineering is the study of the mathematical and natural sciences and their real-world application. In practice, however, engineering is not a single field. Engineers specialize in various kinds of engineering such as automotive, aerospace, chemical, civil, electronics, industrial, mechanical, textile engineering and many more.

Regardless of which field of engineering a person specializes in, they usually have a basic knowledge of many of the other fields. Real-world engineering involves problems that are complex and involve more than one field of engineering, so a general knowledge is essential.

TALKING WITH IOANNIS MIAOULIS

Miaoulis and his students are learning the likely reason. Wind blowing over a flat surface moves more slowly, because it doesn't have to travel as far as the same breeze going over a rounded surface. "Slow air means high pressure across here" — Miaoulis points to the flat hole. "Fast air going over the rounded hole means low pressure. High pressure here, low pressure there. The holes' shape moves air through the burrow—in the flat hole and out the rounded one. It's prairie-dog air conditioning."

Q *How did you get started in science?*

A I grew up in Athens, Greece. It's a congested and polluted city, but my school was in the woods and I could do things outdoors. I got to love

nature. I dug out anthills to see how they were inside. I found the places where turtles laid their eggs. In the summers, we lived near the ocean and every day I'd go fishing and snorkeling. I got to know each rock underwater. I didn't even know what a scientist was then, but I was observing and thinking through things because I wanted to catch more fish. If the flow of water was in this direction, where would be a good place for the fish to hang out? I was observing flow patterns to see where, how, and why fish build their nests. I still do it, in part to catch them, because I still like fishing. But now I do it to observe them, to figure them out. I was always curious.

A prairie dog uses its paws to feed itself grass from the western prairie.

Air moves through a prairie dog hole that can be more than four meters deep. Side pockets are for nesting and food storage.

How Prairie-Dog Air Conditioning Works

1 Air moves over the flat hole.

2 Air moves faster over the rounded hole. Fast-moving air creates a large pressure drop.

Air flows from an area of high pressure to an area of low pressure. The difference in pressure between the two holes pushes air through the prairie dogs' burrow, creating a breeze.

117

◆ Encourage students to tell what they already know about designs in nature that are also practical. To prompt student thinking, have them brainstorm a list of techniques animals use to camouflage themselves. Alternatively, have students brainstorm a list of ways that animals change their body temperature. For examples, when snakes are losing body heat, they coil in order to reduce their surface area. Point out, however, that the snakes do not understand the physics of temperature loss. Their behavior is instinctual, not learned. Similarly, the prairie dogs have not learned that they should round one burrow hole.

◆ Have a volunteer read the captions on page 117 aloud. Review with students that air moves from higher pressure to lower pressure.

◆ Encourage interested students to think about what kind of apparatus they would want to design to test the amount of breeze underground. The apparatus would be used to experiment with what effect increasing the amount of rounding has on the amount of breeze.

◆ Point out that, although curiosity is a useful characteristic to have, interfering with some animals is not only irresponsible but also illegal. For example, on some beaches where endangered sea turtles lay eggs, signs are posted warning people that disturbing the turtles, the nests, or the eggs will result in fines and imprisonment.

◆ If students seem particularly interested in engineering, share the information in Background on page 116. Also suggest that they consult library books to learn more about the different types of engineering. (See Further Reading, page 119.)

Background

Dr. Miaoulis is a professor of mechanical engineering. Mechanical engineers design, test, build, and operate machinery. Some mechanical engineers specialize in particular types of machines such as pumps or automobile engines. Mechanical engineers also design and build manufactured goods. Often, an engineer must design not only a product, but also the machine that will make

the product. Mechanical engineers who design cars, for example, would also help to design the car assembly process.

Because machinery generates heat, mechanical engineers need to know about heating, ventilation, and energy. Students will be introduced to some of these topics in this book.

- Ask students to name items they have taken apart to see how they worked. Ask students if they ever changed the design of something so that it would work better. Ask students: **What characteristics do you need to be able to take something apart and put it back together again?** *(Student answers will vary. Samples: methodical, careful, organized, tidy)*

- Point out that some people most enjoy studying pure sciences; in other words, studying the laws of science because of their own beauty and logic. Other people enjoy learning how to apply the pure facts of science in practical ways.

- Bring to class a computer chip or a photograph of a chip for students who do not know what they look like. Point out that computer chips do not make any noise. The sound a computer is making when it is turned on is usually the sound of the fan. Most computers have fans to keep the chips from overheating.

- Ask students: **Why did Dr. Miaoulis choose to study butterflies rather than lizards to solve the problem of chips heating unevenly?** *(Butterfly wings are made of thin films. Lizard skin is not.)* **How do we know that butterflies need heat?** *(We see them basking in the sun.)*

Butterfly wings are studied under bright lights to learn how evenly they absorb heat.

A microscopic view of a butterfly wing shows the many thin, overlapping layers that collect heat from the sun.

118

Q *You teach engineering. Is that different from science?*

A Well, I enjoyed doing things with my hands, taking things apart and seeing how they worked, building things and making them work. I found that what I enjoyed about studying was learning science and then doing something with it. And that's engineering. I try to discover something about an animal that nobody ever understood before. Then I'll use that information to design something that will make people's lives easier.

Q *How have you used nature in your engineering designs?*

A Here's an example. I got interested in how heat travels in the chips that make computers work.

> **What we study is how animals and plants use energy, motion, and forces.**

They're made in very thin layers or films, thinner than one-hundredth the thickness of your hair. Sometimes, if chips don't heat evenly, they fall apart when you try to make them. I wondered if any plants or animals had solved that problem—using thin films to control how heat was absorbed or reflected. We looked for animals that bask or lie in the sun, or for animals and insects that depend on the warmth of the sun.

Background

Besides studying butterflies and prairie dog tunnels, Dr. Miaoulis and his students have studied other animals in the Comparative Biomechanics Laboratory. By studying sea anemones in a current, they are learning how the anemone's shape helps it filter food from sea water without being swept away by the current. He has also studied other sea creatures in water currents to see how their shape enables them to survive. Dr. Miaoulis hopes that understanding the design of these creatures will provide solutions to human design problems in the future.

With supervision, interested students can access the web page of Dr. Miaoulis's Comparative Biomechanics Laboratory at Tufts University at **www.tufts.edu/as/tampl/cbl/**.

Why is a maple seed shaped as it is?

A seed tends to detach when the wind is blowing.

Because of its winglike shape, the seed spirals slowly to the ground. So, in the wind, it travels away from the tree.

A seed that falls away from the roots and shade of the parent tree has a better chance to grow.

If you touch a butterfly, you get a dust on your fingers. When I was little I used to catch butterflies and didn't really understand what the dust was. If you slice those "dust" particles, you find that they are made of many layers. These thin films are little solar collectors. Butterflies can change the amount of heat they catch. They just change the angle at which they hold the thin films on their wings up to the sun. Large areas of butterfly wings heat evenly. So we're looking at the layers on butterfly wings to learn how to make computer chips that will transfer heat more evenly.

Q *How do you come up with the questions you ask?*

A It depends. Sometimes it's simply by observing things. If you see a maple seed with wings falling in a fancy way, you might not even think

twice about it. But if you start observing and appreciating nature, you start asking questions about how things work. Why would it help the tree to have a seed that could be blown by the wind? I can combine my love of nature from when I was small with what I've learned of science and engineering.

Maple seeds can fall to the ground any time from May to early fall.

In Your Journal

Do you, too, have "a questioning eye"? Miaoulis carefully observes plants and animals and asks himself questions about them. Quietly observe some animals in your environment (pets, insects, birds) for 15 or 20 minutes. Then write down four "how" or "why" questions about the movement and speed of the animals. For example, why does a frog have a stop-and-start movement?

◆ If possible, bring winged maple seeds to class or ask students who live near maple trees to bring seeds to class. Or have students trace the shape of the seeds on paper. Students cut out paper seeds and drop them to compare how they fall. Ask: **Is the shape of the maple seed wing the only factor, or does the seed wing have other features that affect its fall?** *(Accept all reasonable answers.)* Challenge interested students to continue experimenting with different paper seed wings to find how thickness, texture, and size affect the seed's fall.

In Your Journal Point out to students that they can find insects in places that are neither large nor nature-like. They can find insects in a vacant lot, in a garden bed, or around playing fields in the school yard. Provide follow-up in class by giving students a brief opportunity to share the questions they wrote. Extend the discussion by asking: **Where would you begin looking for answers to your questions? Did you observe something about the animal that you had never been aware of before the exercise?**

READING STRATEGIES

Further Reading

◆ Hooker, Saralinda, Christopher Ragus, and Mario G. Salvadori, *The Art of Construction: Projects and Principles for Beginning Engineers.* Chicago Review Press, 1990.
◆ Neill, William, and Pat Murphy. *By Nature's Design (An Exploratorium Book).* Chronicle Books, 1993.

◆ Willis, Delta. *The Sand Dollar and the Slide Rule: Drawing Blueprints from Nature.* Perseus Press, 1996.
◆ Freedman, David H. "The Butterfly Solution," *Discover Magazine,* Vol. 18, Number 4, April 1997.

CHAPTER 4 Cells: The Building Blocks of Life

Sections	Time	Student Edition Activities	Other Activities	
CHAPTER PROJECT **Mystery Object** p. 121	Ongoing (2 weeks)	TEKS: 6.1A; 6.2B, C, D Check Your Progress, pp. 129, 137, 152 Present Your Project, p. 155	TE	Chapter 4 Project Notes, pp. 120–121
1 What Is Life? pp. 122–130 TEKS: 6.3A, D, E; 6.10A, B; 6.12A, B 4.1.1 List the characteristics that all living things share. 4.1.2 Differentiate between structure and function, and identify how structure complements function. 4.1.3 Explain how scientists used controlled experiments to disprove the idea of spontaneous generation. 4.1.4 Identify what all living things need to survive.	2–3 periods/ 1–1½ blocks	TEKS: 6.1A; 6.2A, B, C, D, E; 6.4A **Discover** Is It Living or Nonliving?, p. 122 **Try This** React!, p. 124 **Sharpen Your Skills** Designing an Experiment, p. 128 **Skills Lab: Designing Experiments** Please Pass the Bread!, p. 130	TE TE TE	Demonstration, p. 123 Building Inquiry Skills: Applying Concepts, p. 124 Integrating Chemistry, p. 128
2 INTEGRATING TECHNOLOGY Discovering Cells pp. 131–137 TEKS: 6.3D, E; 6.10B 4.2.1 Explain how the invention of the microscope contributed to scientists' understanding of living things. 4.2.2 Determine that all organisms are composed of cells and state the three points of the cell theory. 4.2.3 Describe how a light microscope works, including how a lens magnifies an object.	1–2 periods/ ½–1 block	TEKS: 6.1A, B; 6.2B, C; 6.4A **Discover** Is Seeing Believing?, p. 131 **Sharpen Your Skills** Observing, p. 136	TE TE TE TE LM	Building Inquiry Skills: Classifying, p. 132 Social Studies Connection, p. 133 Including All Students, p. 135 Integrating Physics, p. 136 4, "How to Use a Microscope"
3 Looking Inside Cells pp. 138–148 TEKS: 6.10A, B, C; 6.11B 4.3.1 Identify the cell wall, cell membrane, and nucleus, and describe their functions. 4.3.2 Identify other organelles in the cell. 4.3.3 Compare bacterial cells with plant and animal cells. 4.3.4 Identify the levels of organization in organisms, including cells, tissues, organs, organisms, and populations; describe how structure complements function at those levels.	3–4 periods/ 1½–2 blocks	TEKS: 6.1A; 6.2B, C; 6.3C; 6.4A **Discover** How Large Are Cells?, p. 138 **Try This** Gelatin Cell, p. 144 **Science at Home,** p. 147 **Skills Lab: Observing** A Magnified View of Life, p. 148	TE TE TE TE TE	Building Inquiry Skills: Comparing and Contrasting, p. 140 Inquiry Challenge, p. 141 Including All Students, p. 143 Demonstration, pp. 143, 144 Building Inquiry Skills: Observing, p. 145; Classifying, p. 146
4 Introduction to Genetics pp. 149–152 TEKS: 6.11A, B, C 4.4.1 Identify cells as structures containing genetic material, and interpret the role of genes in inheritance. 4.4.2 Differentiate between asexual and sexual reproduction. 4.4.3 Identify some changes in traits that can occur over several generations through natural occurrence and selective breeding.	2 periods/ 1 block	TEKS: 6.2B, C **Discover** Can You Identify the Mother?, p. 149 **Sharpen Your Skills** Observing, p. 151	TE	Including All Students, p. 150
Study Guide/Chapter Assessment pp. 153–155	1 period/ ½ block	PLM Provides blackline masters for Probeware labs	ISAB	Provides teaching and review of all inquiry skills

Key: **CTB** Computer Test Bank
CUT Chapter and Unit Tests
ELL Teacher's ELL Handbook

CHAPTER PLANNING GUIDE

 The Resource Pro® CD-ROM provides flexibility for planning the instruction for any type of schedule.

Program Resources	Assessment Strategies	Media and Technology
UR Chapter 4 Project Teacher Notes, pp. 2–3 **UR** Chapter 4 Project Overview and Worksheets, pp. 4–7	**SE** Performance Assessment: Present Your Project, p. 155 **TE** Check Your Progress, pp. 129, 137, 152 **UR** Chapter 4 Project Scoring Rubric, p. 8	Science Explorer at www.phschool.com Student Edition on Audio CD, English-Spanish, Chapter 3
UR 4-1 Section Lesson Plan, p. 9 **UR** 4-1 Section Summary, p. 10 **UR** 4-1 Review and Reinforce, p. 11 **UR** 4-1 Enrich, p. 12 **UR** Skills Lab blackline masters, pp. 25–27	**SE** Section 1 Review, p. 129 **TE** Ongoing Assessment, pp. 123, 125, 127 **TE** Performance Assessment, p. 129	Life Science Videodisc Unit 1, Side 2, "It's Alive!" Videotape Grade 6, Unit 1, "It's Alive!" Lab Activity Videotapes, Tape 1 Transparencies 9, "Exploring Redi's Experiment"; 10, "Exploring Pasteur's Experiment"
UR 4-2 Section Lesson Plan, p. 13 **UR** 4-2 Section Summary, p. 14 **UR** 4-2 Review and Reinforce, p. 15 **UR** 4-2 Enrich, p. 16	**SE** Section 2 Review, p. 137 **TE** Ongoing Assessment, pp. 133, 135 **TE** Performance Assessment, p. 137	Transparency 11, "The Compound Microscope"
UR 4-3 Section Lesson Plan, p. 17 **UR** 4-3 Section Summary, p. 18 **UR** 4-3 Review and Reinforce, p. 19 **UR** 4-3 Enrich, p. 20 **UR** Skills Lab blackline masters, pp. 28–29	**SE** Section 3 Review, p. 147 **TE** Ongoing Assessment, pp. 139, 141, 143, 145 **TE** Performance Assessment, p. 147	Life Science Videodisc Unit 1, Side 2, "What's in a Cell?"; "Evolution of Cells" Videotape Grade 6, Unit 1, "What's in a Cell?"; "Evolution of Cells" Lab Activity Videotapes, Tape 1 Transparencies 12, "Exploring a Plant Cell"; 13, "Exploring an Animal Cell"; 14, "Levels of Organization in the Body"
UR 4-4 Section Lesson Plan, p. 21 **UR** 4-4 Section Summary, p. 22 **UR** 4-4 Review and Reinforce, p. 23 **UR** 4-4 Enrich, p. 24	**SE** Section 4 Review, p. 152 **TE** Performance Assessment, p. 155	
ELL Provides multiple strategies for English language learners **GRSW** Provides worksheets to promote student comprehension of content **RCA** Provides strategies to improve science reading skills	**SE** Chapter 4 Study Guide/Assessment, pp. 153–155 **PA** Chapter 4 Assessment, pp. 14–16 **CUT** Chapter 4 Test, pp. 20–23 **CTB** Chapter 4 Test **PHAS** Provides standardized test preparation	Chapter 4 Computer Test Bank, Chapter 4 Test

GRSW Guided Reading and Study Workbook
ISAB Inquiry Skills Activity Book
LM Laboratory Manual

PA Performance Assessment
PHAS Prentice Hall Assessment System
PLM Probeware Lab Manual

RCA Reading in the Content Area
SE Student Edition

TE Teacher's Edition
UR Unit Resources

Student Edition Activities Planner

ACTIVITY	Time (minutes)	Materials *Quantities for one work group*	Skills
Section 1			
Discover, p. 122	10	**Nonconsumable** wind-up toys	Forming Operational Definitions
Try This, p. 124	10	**Consumable** lemon slices **Nonconsumable** small mirrors	Classifying
Sharpen your Skills, p. 128	30	**Consumable** thin potato slices, paper towel **Nonconsumable** hair dryers, balance	Predicting
Skills Lab, p. 130	20 first day, 5/day for the next 5 days	**Consumable** paper plates, bread without preservatives, sealable plastic bags, tap water, packing tape **Nonconsumable** plastic dropper, computer (optional)	Controlling Variables
Section 2			
Discover, p. 131	10	**Consumable** black and white newspaper photograph **Nonconsumable** scissors, hand lens, microscope	Observing
Sharpen Your Skills, p. 136	15	**Consumable** pond water **Nonconsumable** prepared slide of cork, microscope, plastic dropper, slide, coverslip	Observing
Section 3			
Discover, p. 138	10	**Nonconsumable** calculator, metric ruler	Inferring
Try This, p. 144	10/10	**Consumable** packet of colorless gelatin, warm water, other miscellaneous materials to represent cell structures **Nonconsumable** rectangular or round pan	Making Models
Science at Home, p. 147	home	No special materials are required.	Comparing and Contrasting
Skills Lab, p. 148	40	**Consumable** water, *Elodea* leaf **Nonconsumable** plastic dropper, microscope slide, microscope, prepared slide of animal cells, colored pencils, forceps, coverslip	Observing, Comparing and Contrasting
Section 4			
Discover, p. 149	5	No special materials are required.	Observing, Comparing and Contrasting
Sharpen Your Skills, p. 151	30	**Nonconsumable** books, encyclopedias, multimedia resources	Observing, Comparing and Contrasting

A list of all materials required for the Student Edition activities can be found on pages T43–T49. You can obtain information about ordering materials by calling 1-800-848-9500 or by accessing the Science Explorer Internet site at **www.phschool.com**.

Texas Essential Knowledge and Skills

(6.1) Scientific processes. The student conducts field and laboratory investigations using safe, environmentally appropriate, and ethical practices. *(Project; Sections 1, 2, 3)*

The student is expected to:

(A) demonstrate safe practices during field and laboratory investigations.

(6.2) Scientific processes. The student uses scientific inquiry methods during field and laboratory investigations. *(Project; Sections 1, 2, 3, 4)*

The student is expected to:

(A) plan and implement investigative procedures including asking questions, formulating testable hypotheses, and selecting and using equipment and technology;

(B) collect data by observing and measuring;

(C) analyze and interpret information to construct reasonable explanations from direct and indirect evidence;

(D) communicate valid conclusions; and

(E) construct graphs, tables, maps, and charts using tools including computers to organize, examine, and evaluate data.

(6.3) Scientific processes. The student uses critical thinking and scientific problem solving to make informed decisions. *(Sections 1, 2, 3)*

The student is expected to:

(A) analyze, review, and critique scientific explanations, including hypotheses and theories, as to their strengths and weaknesses using scientific evidence and information;

(C) represent the natural world using models and identify their limitations;

(D) evaluate the impact of research on scientific thought, society, and the environment; and

(E) connect Grade 6 science concepts with the history of science and contributions of scientists.

(6.4) Scientific processes. The student knows how to use a variety of tools and methods to conduct science inquiry. *(Sections 1, 2, 3)*

The student is expected to:

(A) collect, analyze, and record information using tools including beakers, petri dishes, meter sticks, graduated cylinders, weather instruments, timing devices, hot plates, test tubes, safety goggles, spring scales, magnets, balances, microscopes, telescopes, thermometers, calculators, field equipment, compasses, computers, and computer probes.

(6.10) Science concepts. The student knows the relationship between structure and function in living systems. *(Sections 1, 2, 3)*

The student is expected to:

(A) differentiate between structure and function;

(B) determine that all organisms are composed of cells that carry on functions to sustain life; and

(C) identify how structure complements function at different levels of organization including organs, organ systems, organisms, and populations.

(6.11) Science concepts. The student knows that traits of species can change through generations and that the instructions for traits are contained in the genetic material of the organisms. *(Sections 3, 4)*

The student is expected to:

(A) identify some changes in traits that can occur over several generations through natural occurrence and selective breeding;

(B) identify cells as structures containing genetic material; and

(C) interpret the role of genes in inheritance.

(6.12) Science concepts. The student knows that the responses of organisms are caused by internal or external stimuli. *(Section 1)*

The student is expected to:

(A) identify responses in organisms to internal stimuli such as hunger or thirst;

(B) identify responses in organisms to external stimuli such as the presence or absence of heat or light.

Take It to the Net

 Interactive text at www.phschool.com

Science Explorer comes alive with iText.

- **Complete student text** is accessible from any computer with Internet access or a CD-ROM drive.

- **Animations, simulations, and videos** enhance student understanding and retention of concepts.

- **Self-tests and online study tools** assess student understanding.

- **Teacher management tools** help you make the most of this valuable resource.

STAY CURRENT with **SCIENCE NEWS**®

Find out the latest research and information about cells at **www.phschool.com**.

Go to **www.phschool.com**. Select Texas on the navigation bar. Click on the Science icon. Then click on Science Explorer under PH@school.

Mystery Object

TEKS: 6.1A; 6.2B, C, D

It can be difficult to determine whether some objects are alive or not. This project allows students to observe the characteristics that make living things different from nonliving things.

Purpose In this project, students observe an object to determine whether it is alive. Students also develop strategies for distinguishing between living and nonliving objects.

Skills Focus After completing the Chapter 4 Project, students will be able to
◆ brainstorm about the characteristics of life;
◆ observe characteristics of objects to infer whether they are alive;
◆ carry out tests for signs of life;
◆ communicate their findings about their mystery object to the class.

Project Time Line This project requires about two weeks. Some living things, such as small insects and larvae, will show obvious signs of life at first glance. Other objects, such as seeds, brine-shrimp eggs, or plants, may take a week or so to reveal signs of life. During the first two days, students should observe their objects and record their observations. Allow at least three days for students to carry out their tests for life characteristics. Remind them to include data tables as well as drawings in their project notebooks. Finally, give students time to analyze their data, classify their objects, and plan their presentations.

Possible Materials Provide students with living and nonliving objects, and instructions on their care.
◆ Living "mystery objects" may include: brine shrimp; slime mold; bread mold; insect larvae; goldfish; plants; yeast (add one spoonful of baker's yeast and sugar to 250 mL warm water; observe under microscope); and seeds (soak lentil seeds in water overnight then wrap in wet paper towel; place towel in plastic bag and store in dark; observe daily).
◆ Nonliving "mystery objects" may include: pebbles; vermiculite; lead shot (looks like seeds); artificial plants (look real but do not grow or have a

cellular structure); soluble salts in a saturated solution (crystal gardens appear to grow); hair (cellular structure, but no longer living); and toys with microchips (can have complex responses).
◆ Plastic petri dishes and paper towels are useful for germinating seeds. BTB solution (bromthymol blue) can be used to test for the presence of carbon dioxide in water environments.
◆ Provide equipment such as a microscope, glass slides and cover slips, scissors, plastic dropper, hand lens, and a ruler. Show students how to use a microscope and make thin cross-sections.

Safety

CAUTION: Glass and sharp objects can cause injury. Handle with care.

CHAPTER 4 Cells: The Building Blocks of Life

Both the pink coral fungus and the newt sitting beside it are alive.

WEB ACTIVITY www.phschool.com

120

Mystery Object

Suppose that you visited a location like the one in this scene. Imagine yourself standing perfectly still, all your senses alert to the things around you. You wonder which of the things around you are alive. The newt clearly is, but what about the rest? Is the pink thing alive? Are the other things living or nonliving?

In this chapter, you will learn that it is not always easy to determine whether something is alive. This is because living things share some characteristics with nonliving things. To explore this idea firsthand, you will be given a mystery object to observe. How can you determine if your object is a living thing? What signs of life will you look for?

Your Goal To study an object for several days to determine whether or not it is alive.

To complete this project successfully, you must
- care for your object following your teacher's instructions
- observe your object each day, and record your data
- determine whether your object is alive
- follow the safety guidelines in Appendix A

Get Started With a few classmates, brainstorm a list of characteristics that living things share. Can you think of any nonliving things that share some of these characteristics? Which characteristics on your list can help you conclude whether or not your mystery object is alive?

Check Your Progress You'll be working on this project as you study this chapter. To keep your project on track, look for Check Your Progress boxes at the following points.

Section 1 Review, page 129: Carry out your tests.
Section 2 Review, page 137: Record your observations daily.
Section 4 Review, page 152: Classify the object as living or nonliving.

Present Your Project At the end of the chapter (page 155), you will display your object and present evidence for whether or not it is alive. Be prepared to answer questions from your classmates.

TEKS

In addition to process TEKS, this chapter addresses these concept TEKS as they relate to the chapter's topics.

(6.10) The student knows the relationship between structure and function in living systems. The student is expected to:
(A) Differentiate between structure and function;
(B) determine that all organisms are composed of cells that carry on functions to sustain life; and
(C) identify how structure complements function at different levels of organization including organs, organ systems, organisms, and populations.

(6.11) The student knows that traits of species can change through generations and that the instructions for traits are contained in the genetic material of the organisms. The student is expected to:

(A) identify some changes in traits that can occur over several generations through natural occurrence and selective breeding;
(B) identify cells as structures containing genetic material; and
(C) interpret the role of genes in inheritance.

(6.12) The student knows that the responses of organisms are caused by external and internal stimuli. The student is expected to:
(A) identify responses of organisms to internal stimuli such as hunger or thirst;
(B) identify responses in organisms to external stimuli such as the presence or absence of heat or light.

121

Program Resources

- **Unit 2 Resources** Chapter 4 Project Teacher Notes, pp. 2–3; Chapter 4 Project Overview and Work-sheets, pp. 4–7

Media and Technology

 Student Edition on Audio CD
English-Spanish, Chapter 4

 **WEB ACTIVITY** www.phschool.com

You will find an Internet activity, chapter self-tests for students, and links to other chapter topics at this site.

Launching the Project Bring a few living organisms, such as a plant, a snail, and a fish, into the classroom to show students. Ask: **What characteristics do these objects have in common?** *(They grow; they respond to changes in the environment.)* Talk about the distinguishing characteristics that scientists use to classify the objects as living. Ask: **What tests could you design that would help you observe the characteristics of these living organisms?** *(Measure size over a period of time.)* Discuss how scientists develop and test hypotheses. Allow students to read the description of the project in their text and in the Chapter 4 Project Overview on pages 4–5 in the Unit 2 Resources. Distribute copies of the Chapter 1 Project Worksheets on pages 6–7 for students to review. Tell students that all tests must be approved so that living organisms are not injured.

Performance Assessment

The Chapter 4 Project Scoring Rubric on page 8 will help you evaluate how well students complete the Chapter 4 Project. Students will be assessed on
- the detail of their observations;
- how well they design tests to determine whether their object is alive;
- the accuracy and organization of their testing and documentation, including how well they follow directions for the care of their objects;
- whether they draw appropriate conclusions from their tests and present their results to the class in a clear and organized manner.

By sharing the Chapter 4 Project Scoring Rubric with students at the beginning of the project, you will make it clear to them what they are expected to do.

What Is Life?

TEKS: 6.1A; 6.2A, B, C, D, E; 6.3A, D, E; 6.4A; 6.10A, B; 6.12A, B

Objectives

After completing the lesson, students will be able to

- list the characteristics all living things share;
- differentiate between structure and function, and identify how structure complements function;
- explain how scientists used controlled experiments to disprove the idea of spontaneous generation;
- identify what all living things need to survive.

1 Engage/Explore

Activating Prior Knowledge

Ask students to describe the most unusual living thing they have seen. Ask: **What did it look like? Where did it live? What was so unusual about it?** Write the heading *Living Things* on the board and list the organisms as students identify them. Have students describe whether they thought the organism was a plant, animal, or other form of life such as a mushroom.

DISCOVER

Skills Focus forming operational definitions
Materials *wind-up toys*
Time 10 minutes
Tips Do not wind toys too tightly. Urge students to think of all living things, not just animals, as they make their lists.
Expected Outcome Students could say that because the toy moves it is alive, or because the toy does not eat, grow, or reproduce, it is not alive.
Think It Over Students should conclude that growth is a characteristic shared by all living things, while characteristics such as sleeping or talking are not.

What Is Life?

DISCOVER ···· ACTIVITY

Is It Living or Nonliving?

1. Your teacher will give you and a partner a wind-up toy.
2. With your partner, decide who will find evidence that the toy is alive and who will find evidence that the toy is not alive.
3. Observe the wind-up toy. Record the characteristics of the toy that support your position about whether or not the toy is alive.
4. Share your lists of living and nonliving characteristics with your classmates.

Think It Over
Forming Operational Definitions Based on what you learned from the activity, create a list of characteristics that living things share.

GUIDE FOR READING

- What characteristics do all living things share?
- What are structure and function?
- What do living things need to survive?

Reading Tip As you read, use the headings to make an outline of the characteristics and needs of living things.

Key Terms organism
- cell • structure
- function • stimulus
- external stimulus
- internal stimulus
- response • reproduce
- spontaneous generation
- autotroph • heterotroph
- homeostasis

Looking like the slimy creatures in horror movies, "blobs" appeared in towns near Dallas, Texas, in the summer of 1973. Jellylike masses overran yards and porches all over the towns. People around Dallas were worried until biologists, scientists who study living things, put their minds at ease. The blobs were slime molds—living things usually found on damp, decaying material on a forest floor. The unusually wet weather around Dallas that year provided ideal conditions for the slime molds to grow in people's yards.

The Characteristics of Living Things

If you were asked to name some living things, or **organisms,** you might name yourself, a pet, and maybe some insects or plants. But you would probably not mention a moss growing in a shady spot, the mildew on bathroom tiles, or the slime molds that oozed across the lawns in towns near Dallas. But all of these things are also organisms that share six important characteristics with all other living things. **All living things are made of cells, contain similar chemicals, use energy, grow and develop, respond to their surroundings, and can reproduce.**

Figure 1 Slime molds similar to these grew in yards and porches in towns near Dallas, Texas.

READING STRATEGIES

Reading Tip Remind students that making an outline helps readers organize information so they remember key points and important details. As a guide for students, begin outlining the first main topic on the board. Complete the outline for this heading as a class. Then have students work independently to complete the rest of the outline.

I. The Characteristics of Living Things
  A. Cellular organization
    1. basic unit of structure and function
    2. unicellular or multicellular
  B. The Chemicals of Life
    1. all living cells composed of chemicals
    2. primary chemicals of life: water, carbohydrates, proteins, lipids, and nucleic acids

◄ Animal cells

◄ Plant cells

Figure 2 Like all living things, the butterfly and the leaf are made of cells. Although the cells of different organisms are not identical, they share important characteristics. *Making Generalizations In what ways are cells similar?*

Cellular Organization All organisms are made of cells, which carry on the functions necessary to sustain life. A **cell** is the basic unit of **structure** and **function** in an organism. **An organism's structure is the way it is made. The function of a part of an organism is the job it performs.** An organism's structure includes what its parts are like and how they are put together. In an organism, structure and function are usually closely related. For example, your hand has a thumb that can touch all your other fingers. This structure enables your hand to perform the function of grasping objects.

Organisms may be composed of only one cell or of many cells. Unicellular, or single-celled, organisms include bacteria (bak TEER ee uh), the most numerous organisms on Earth. A bacterial cell carries out all of the functions necessary for the organism to stay alive. Multicellular organisms are composed of many cells. The cells of many multicellular organisms are specialized to do certain tasks. For example, you are made of trillions of cells. Specialized cells in your body, such as muscle and nerve cells, work together to keep you alive. Nerve cells carry messages from your surroundings to your brain. Other nerve cells then carry messages to your muscle cells, making your body move.

The Chemicals of Life The cells of all living things are composed of chemicals. The most abundant chemical in cells is water. Other chemicals called carbohydrates (kahr boh HY draytz) are a cell's main energy source. Two other chemicals, proteins (PROH teenz) and lipids (LIP idz), are the building materials of cells, much like wood and bricks are the building materials of houses. Finally, nucleic (noo KLEE ik) acids are the genetic material—the chemical instructions that direct the cell's activities.

2 Facilitate

The Characteristics of Living Things

Using the Visuals: Figure 2

Content Mastery

Make sure students understand that the images in the circles are magnified many times. Have students describe differences between the structure of the plant and animal cells in the figure. *(Animal cells—rounded, have dark spots in the centers; plant cells—rectangular, have green structures inside them)* Point out that plant and animal cells have more similarities than differences. **learning modality: visual**

Demonstration

Materials *charcoal, piece of chalk, nail, small sack of fertilizer, bottle of carbonated water*
Time 10 minutes

ACTIVITY

Ask if students have heard that all the chemicals in a human body cost only a few dollars. Show the materials, explaining that in simple forms the chemicals would not cost much to buy. Challenge students to identify the chemicals in each item: charcoal *(carbon)*; chalk *(calcium)*; nail *(iron)*; fertilizer *(phosphorus, nitrogen, and potassium)*; carbonated water *(carbon dioxide and water)*. Explain that the human body can convert these nonliving chemicals into complex arrangements of molecules such as carbohydrates, proteins, lipids, and nucleic acids, which help the body function and provide its structure. **learning modality: verbal**

Program Resources

♦ **Unit 2 Resources** 4-1 Lesson Plan, p. 9; 4-1 Section Summary, p. 10
♦ **Guided Reading and Study Workbook** 4-1

Answers to Self-Assessment

Caption Question

Figure 2 Cells are the basic building blocks of animal and plant tissues. They are composed of complex chemicals and can perform tasks necessary to life.

Ongoing Assessment

Skills Check Have each student choose one living thing and explain how he or she knows it is alive.

The Characteristics of Living Things, continued

Skills Focus classifying
Materials *small mirrors, lemon slices*
Time 10 minutes
Tips Ask: **What does a dog do when it sees a big, juicy steak?** (*Sample: wags tail, acts excited, salivates*) Ask: **Which is the stimulus and which is the response?** (*Stimulus is the steak; response is tail wagging, acting excited, salivating.*) Remind students not to taste the lemon slices.
Expected Outcome clapping hands—sudden motion close to eyes/eyes blink; covering eyes, then uncover—change in light intensity/pupil contracts; lemon—smell/mouth puckers
Extend Challenge students to list at least 5 other stimulus / response actions demonstrated by plants or animals. Have them tell whether the stimulus is external or internal. (*Samples: feel pain—yelp or howl; see a predator—run away; feel heat—pull away; light source—plant stem turns toward. The last three samples are external. The first could be external or internal, depending on the source of pain.*)
learning modality: tactile/ kinesthetic

Building Inquiry Skills: Applying Concepts

Materials *crystal "gardens"*

Tips Crystals exhibit growth similar to that of living systems. Inexpensive crystal "gardens" are available from toy stores, novelty shops, and scientific-supply houses. Allow students to construct the gardens and observe crystal growth for a few days. After crystals form, have students list the characteristics of living things, then state whether the crystals have each characteristic. Ask: **Based on your observations, do you think the crystals are alive?** After class discussion, have students write short paragraphs to support their conclusions. **learning modality: logical/mathematical**

Figure 3 Over time, a tiny acorn develops into a giant oak tree. A great deal of energy is needed to produce the trillions of cells that make up the body of an oak tree.
Comparing and Contrasting In what way does the structure of the seedling resemble that of the oak tree? In what ways is it different?

Acorn   *Seedling*   *Oak tree*

React!

In this activity, you will test your responses to three different stimuli.

1. Have a partner clap his or her hands together about six inches in front of your face. Describe how you react.

2. Look at one of your eyes in a mirror. Cover the eye with your hand for a minute. While looking in the mirror, remove your hand. Observe how the size of your pupil changes.

3. Bring a slice of lemon close to your nose and mouth. Describe what happens.

Classifying For each action performed, name the stimulus and the response. Identify whether the stimulus was external or internal.

Energy Use The cells of organisms use energy to do what living things must do, such as grow and repair injured parts. An organism's cells are always hard at work. For example, as you read this paragraph, your eye and brain cells are busy. The cells of your stomach and intestine are digesting food. Your blood cells are moving chemicals around your body. If you've hurt yourself, some of your cells are repairing the damage.

Growth and Development Living things grow and develop. Growth is the process of becoming larger. Development is the process of change that occurs during an organism's life to produce a more complex organism. For example, as multicellular organisms develop, their cells become specialized. To grow and develop, organisms use energy to create new cells.

You may argue that some nonliving things grow and change as they age. For example, a pickup truck rusts as it ages. Icicles grow longer as more water freezes on their tips. But pickup trucks and icicles do not use energy to change and grow. They also don't become more complex over time.

Response to Surroundings If you've ever seen a plant in a sunny window, you may have observed that the plant's stems have bent so that the leaves face the sun. Like a plant bending toward the light, all organisms react to changes in their environment. A change in an organism's surroundings that causes the organism to react is called a **stimulus** (plural *stimuli*). **External stimuli** come from outside the organism. External stimuli include things such as light, sound, and the temperature of the environment. **Internal stimuli** come from within the organism—for example, hunger and thirst.

An organism reacts to a stimulus with a **response**—an action or change in behavior. For example, has someone ever leapt out at you from behind a door? If so, it's likely that you jumped or screamed. Your friend's sudden motion was the external stimulus that caused your startled response. Your response to the internal stimulus of thirst might be to drink a glass of water. Nonliving things, such as rocks, do not react to stimuli as living things do.

Reproduction Another characteristic of organisms is the ability to **reproduce,** or produce offspring that are similar to the parents. Robins lay eggs that develop into young robins that closely resemble their parents. Sunflowers produce seeds that develop into sunflower plants, which in turn make more seeds. Bacteria produce other bacteria exactly like themselves.

☑ *Checkpoint* How do growth and development differ?

Life Comes From Life

Today, people know that all organisms are the result of reproduction by living things. Four hundred years ago, however, people believed that life could sometimes appear from nonliving material. For example, when people saw flies swarming around decaying meat, they concluded that flies could arise from rotting meat. When frogs appeared in muddy puddles after heavy rains, people concluded that frogs could sprout from the mud in ponds. The mistaken idea that living things arise from nonliving sources is called **spontaneous generation.**

It took hundreds of years of experiments to convince people that spontaneous generation does not occur. One scientist who did some of these experiments was an Italian doctor, Francesco Redi. In the mid-1600s, Redi designed a controlled experiment to show that flies do not spontaneously arise from decaying meat. In a controlled experiment, a scientist carries out two tests that are identical in every respect except for one factor. The one factor that the scientist changes is called the variable. The scientist can conclude that any differences in the results of the two tests must be due to the variable.

Figure 4 All organisms respond to changes in their surroundings. This willow ptarmigan's feathers have turned white in response to its snowy surroundings. This Alaskan bird's white plumage will help protect the bird from animals that feed on it.

Building Inquiry Skills: Communicating

To help students better understand the experiments that helped disprove spontaneous generation, tell students they will work in groups to design illustrated posters of Redi and Pasteur's experiments. Divide students into groups. Have them read over the experiments and choose one to illustrate. Suggest they brainstorm how they will present the experiments, perhaps sketching a couple of ideas before they decide on a final model. The illustrations should show all aspects of the experiment, and each of the steps should be labeled or explained. Posters can range from flowcharts to illustrated stories, such as in a comic book format. Tell students to include the scientists' reasoning and conclusions and a title for the poster. Each of the students in the group should work on producing the poster; for example, by drawing or coloring the illustrations or writing captions. They can present their posters as a group to their classmates. Posters can be displayed in the classroom and in the school hall. **learning modality: visual**

Answers to Self-Assessment

Caption Question

Figure 3 The seedling and the tree are both made of cells that contain complex chemicals; use energy, grow and develop; respond to their environment, and are capable of reproduction. Both have stems, roots, and leaves; and are plants. They differ in their size and in their number of cells.

☑ *Checkpoint*

Growth is the process of becoming larger. Development is a process of change that produces a more complex organism.

Ongoing Assessment

Oral Presentation Have students give brief presentations to the class on the topic *How to Design a Controlled Experiment.* Each student should design a different experiment. Encourage students to use visuals in their presentations.

Life Comes From Life, continued

Language Arts Connection

Some students may have problems distinguishing the variable in an experiment. Write the prefix *vari* on the chalkboard and point out that it means "diverse" or "having different aspects or characteristics." Pair students and have them look up words that begin with *vari*, including *variable, variable star, variation,* and *vary*. Suggest that students find synonyms that will help them identify the variable in an experiment. They should discuss the meanings quietly among themselves. Call on students to share their synonyms and definitions with the class. After the class discussion, students should write in their journals what is meant by the variable in an experiment. **limited English proficiency**

The Needs of Living Things

Addressing Naive Conceptions

Students may be confused by the statement that plants make their own food because they are familiar with products marketed as "plant food." Show students the label from a plant-food package. Most of these products contain forms of nitrogen, phosphorus, and potassium. Tell students that these chemicals are not actually food because they are not an energy source, but nutrients that plants need to convert sunlight, water, and carbon dioxide into food. **learning modality: verbal**

Even after Redi's work, many people continued to believe that bacteria could be produced by spontaneous generation. In the mid-1800s, however, the French chemist Louis Pasteur designed some controlled experiments that finally proved spontaneous generation does not happen. The controlled experiments of Francesco Redi and Louis Pasteur helped to convince people that living things do not arise from nonliving material. Look at *Exploring the Experiments of Redi and Pasteur* to learn more about the experiments they performed.

☑ *Checkpoint* In a controlled experiment, what is the term for the one factor that scientists change?

EXPLORING the Experiments of Redi and Pasteur

Redi designed one of the first controlled experiments. By Pasteur's time, controlled experiments were standard procedure. As you explore, identify the variable in each experiment.

FRANCESCO REDI

REDI'S EXPERIMENT

① Redi placed meat in two identical jars. He left one jar uncovered. He covered the other jar with a cloth that let in air.

② After a few days, Redi saw maggots (young flies) on the decaying meat in the open jar. There were no maggots on the meat in the covered jar.

③ Redi reasoned that flies had laid eggs on the meat in the open jar. The eggs hatched into maggots. Because flies could not lay eggs on the meat in the covered jar, there were no maggots there. Therefore, Redi concluded that the decaying meat did not produce maggots.

126

Background

History of Science In 1651, an English physician, William Harvey, published a book describing his studies of reproduction. Harvey speculated that insects, worms, and frogs arise from seeds or eggs. Redi had read Harvey's book, so it may have inspired his experiments.

In 1860, the French Academy of Sciences offered a prize to anyone who could "throw new light" on spontaneous generation, and Pasteur responded. He had shown that

organisms in air caused fermentation in milk and alcohol, and decided to investigate whether the organisms were always in the air or arose by spontaneous generation. Pasteur's conclusion that microorganisms develop from other microorganisms in the air was supported in 1876 by another Englishman, physicist John Tyndall. Tyndall was able to show that pure air did not contribute to the production of organisms as regular air did.

The Needs of Living Things

Imagine yourself biking through a park on a warm spring day. As you ride by a tree, you see a squirrel running up the tree trunk. Although it may seem that squirrels and trees do not have the same basic needs as you, they do. All organisms need four things to stay alive. **Living things must satisfy their basic needs for energy, water, living space, and stable internal conditions.**

Energy You read earlier that organisms need a source of energy to live. They use food as their energy source. Organisms differ in the ways they obtain their energy. Some organisms, such as plants, use the sun's energy along with carbon dioxide, a gas found in Earth's atmosphere, and water to make their own food.

PASTEUR'S EXPERIMENT

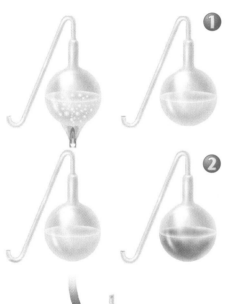

LOUIS PASTEUR

1 In one experiment, Pasteur put clear broth into two flasks with curved necks. The necks would let in oxygen but keep out bacteria from the air. Pasteur boiled the broth in one flask to kill any bacteria in the broth. He did not boil the broth in the other flask.

2 In a few days, the unboiled broth became cloudy, showing that new bacteria were growing. The boiled broth remained clear. Pasteur concluded that bacteria do not spontaneously arise from the broth. New bacteria appeared only when living bacteria were already present.

Later, Pasteur took the curve-necked flask containing the broth that had remained clear and broke its long neck. Bacteria from the air could now enter the flask. In a few days, the broth became cloudy. This evidence confirmed Pasteur's conclusion that new bacteria appear only when they are produced by existing bacteria.

Chapter 4 **127**

After students have read about the experiments of Redi and Pasteur, lead students in a discussion of controlled experiments. Draw a compare/contrast table on the chalkboard. Ask: **In Redi's experiment, what factors were identical in each test?** *(Both had meat in a jar and both were exposed to air.)* Invite a volunteer to fill in the compare/contrast table. Ask: **How did the tests differ?** *(Redi covered one of the jars with a cloth.)* Write the answer in the compare/contrast table. Ask: **What factor is the variable?** *(The cloth covering the jar so that flies could not reach the meat. If necessary, remind students that the cloth still allowed the meat to be exposed to air.)* Challenge students to make either a compare/contrast table or a Venn diagram for Pasteur's experiment. When students have finished, ask: **What is the variable in Pasteur's experiment?** *(Whether or not he boiled the broth in the flask to kill any bacteria in the broth)*

Extend Encourage the class to role-play an encounter between the scientists and people who have a strong belief in spontaneous generation. Have two students act as Redi and Pasteur and explain their arguments in answer to questions posed by the class. Refer to the **ELL Handbook** for additional teaching strategies. **learning modality: verbal**

Portfolio Students can save their Venn diagrams or compare/contrast tables in their portfolios.

Media and Technology

Transparencies "Exploring Redi's Experiment," Transparency 9; "Exploring Pasteur's Experiment," Transparency 10

Answers to Self-Assessment

☑ *Checkpoint*

Variable

Ongoing Assessment

Writing Ask students to explain how we now know that spontaneous generation does not take place.

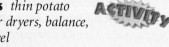

Designing Experiments

Materials *thin potato slices, hair dryers, balance, paper towel* **ACTIVITY**

Time 30 minutes

Before class, slice the potatoes thin *(but not too thin or they will blow away)*. Keep slices in a container of cold water to keep them hydrated. Remind students to thoroughly dry potato slices.

Expected Outcome Students should use the balance to find the mass of the wet potato slice, then use the hairdryer to dry the potato. Students next find the mass of the dry potato slice, then subtract to find the mass of the water lost. Slices should be placed on a paper towel on a tray or other flat surface and turned frequently. Students should calculate the water content to be about 40%.

Extend Have students test other fruits and vegetables such as apples, bell peppers, or carrots. They should predict the moisture content before they begin. **learning modality: tactile/ kinesthetic**

 Integrating Chemistry

Materials *2 small beakers, 60 mL water, 60 mL vegetable oil, salt, sugar, wooden stirrers* **ACTIVITY**

Time 10 minutes

Half the class should try to dissolve 10 g salt in a beaker of water and in a beaker of oil. The other half should try to dissolve 10 g sugar in the water and oil. Remind students not to taste the materials, and make sure they clean up all spills immediately. Encourage students to compare results. *(The water dissolves both salt and sugar. The oil does not dissolve salt.)* Tell students that salt and sugar are both necessary to sustain human life. Ask: **Why is water and not oil the liquid that fills your cells?** *(Oil doesn't dissolve chemicals such as salt.)* **learning modality: tactile/kinesthetic**

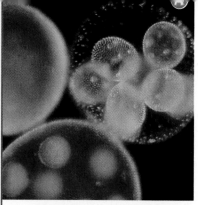

Figure 5 All organisms need a source of energy to live. **(A)** *Volvox* is an autotroph that uses the sun's energy to make its own food. **(B)** This American lobster, a heterotroph, is feeding on a herring. *Applying Concepts How do heterotrophs depend on autotrophs for energy?*

Designing Experiments

Your teacher will give you a slice of potato. Predict what percentage of the potato's mass is water. Then come up with a plan to test your prediction. For materials, you will be given a hair dryer and a balance. Obtain your teacher's approval before carrying out your plan. How does your result compare with your prediction? **ACTIVITY**

Organisms that make their own food are called **autotrophs** (AW tuh trawfs). *Auto-* means "self" and *-troph* means "feeder." Autotrophs use the food they make as an energy source to carry out their life functions.

Organisms that cannot make their own food are called **heterotrophs** (HET uh roh trawfs). *Hetero-* means "other." A heterotroph's energy source is also the sun—but in an indirect way. Heterotrophs either eat autotrophs and obtain the energy in the autotroph's stored food, or they consume other heterotrophs that eat autotrophs. Animals, mushrooms, and slime molds are examples of heterotrophs.

Water All living things need water to survive—in fact, most organisms can live for only a few days without water. Organisms need water to do things such as obtain chemicals from their surroundings, break down food, grow, move substances within their bodies, and reproduce.

INTEGRATING CHEMISTRY One important property of water that is vital to living things is its ability to dissolve more chemicals than any other substance on Earth. In your body, for example, water makes up 92 percent of the liquid part of your blood. The food that your cells need dissolves in the blood and is transported throughout your body. Wastes from cells also dissolve in the blood and are carried away. Your body's cells also provide a watery environment in which chemicals are dissolved. In a sense, you can think of yourself as a person-shaped sack of water in which other substances are dissolved. Fortunately, your body contains some substances that do not dissolve in water, so you hold your shape.

Background

History of Science The concept of homeostasis was developed by a French scientist, Claude Bernard. Bernard was born in 1813, the son of an unsuccessful vineyard owner. Bernard first studied digestion and the breakdown of glycogen. From his experiments, he concluded that the cells of "higher animals" are relatively isolated from the outside environment and are bathed by body fluids. He called these fluids "internal seawater" and spoke of how they had evolved to allow for more complex life forms. Walter Cannon, an American physiologist, first used the term *homeostasis* some 50 years after Bernard's studies.

Living Space All organisms need a place to live—a place to get food and water and find shelter. Because there is a limited amount of living space on Earth, some organisms may compete for space. Plants, for example, occupy a fixed living space. Above the ground, their branches and leaves compete for living space with those of other plants. Below ground, their roots compete for water and minerals. Unlike plants, organisms such as animals move around. They may either share living space with others or compete for living space.

Stable Internal Conditions Because conditions in their surroundings can change significantly, organisms must be able to keep the conditions inside their bodies constant. The maintenance of stable internal conditions despite changes in the surroundings is called **homeostasis** (hoh mee oh STAY sis). You know that when you are healthy your body temperature stays constant despite temperature changes in your surroundings. Your body's regulation of temperature is an example of homeostasis.

Other organisms have different mechanisms for maintaining homeostasis. For example, imagine that you are a barnacle attached to a rock at the edge of the ocean. At high tide, the ocean water covers you. At low tide, however, your watery surroundings disappear, and you are exposed to hours of sun and wind. Without a way to keep water in your cells, you'd die. Fortunately, a barnacle can close up its hard outer plates, trapping droplets of water inside. In this way, the barnacle can keep its body moist until the next high tide.

Figure 6 A tree trunk provides these mushrooms with food, water, and shelter.

Section 1 Review

1. Name six characteristics that you have in common with a tree.
2. What is meant by the terms *structure* and *function?*
3. List the four things that all organisms need.
4. How did Pasteur's experiment show that bacteria do not arise spontaneously in broth?
5. **Thinking Critically Applying Concepts** Critically analyze Redi's experiment. First decide what Redi's hypothesis probably was. Then decide whether the results of the experiment supported that hypothesis. Explain your reasoning.

Check Your Progress ◢ CHAPTER PROJECT
At this point, you should be ready to carry out your tests for signs of life following your teacher's directions. Before you start, examine your mystery object carefully, and record your observations. Also, decide whether you need to revise the list of life characteristics you prepared earlier. *(Hint:* Do not be fooled by the object's appearance— some organisms appear dead during certain stages of their lives.)

Chapter 4 **129**

Answers to Self-Assessment

Caption Question

Figure 5 Heterotrophs cannot produce their own food, so they obtain their energy from the food they eat. They either eat autotrophs and obtain the energy stored in the food made by the autotrophs, or they eat other heterotrophs that eat autotrophs.

---

3 Assess

Section 1 Review Answers

1. Cellular organization, similar chemicals, use energy, grow and develop, respond to surroundings, and can reproduce.
2. An organism's structure is the way that it is made; for example, what its parts are like and how they are put together. The function of a part of an organism is the job that the part performs.
3. A source of energy, water, living space, and stable internal conditions
4. By heating the broth in one flask, Pasteur killed the bacteria in the broth. No bacteria grew in the heated broth until the broth was exposed to bacteria in the air. Unheated broth was the control.
5. Sample: Redi's hypothesis was probably that maggots do not arise spontaneously from decaying meat but develop from eggs laid by flies. The results of his experiment supported that hypothesis. Maggots appeared only in the uncovered jar that allowed flies to reach the meat and lay eggs.

Check Your Progress ◢ CHAPTER PROJECT
Make sure students are caring for their objects according to your instructions. As you review plans, discuss with students any plans that require deviation from the care instructions. Plans should test for different characteristics and predict how students expect a living thing to respond to each test. Work with students to revise any plans that do not meet your approval.

Performance Assessment

Writing Have students invent a living thing that meets all the criteria outlined in this section. Students should describe their creature and may draw a picture of it.

Portfolio Students can save their descriptions and drawings in their portfolios.

129

Please Pass the Bread!

Preparing for Inquiry

Key Concept Bread mold needs water to grow.

Skills Objective Students will be able to
◆ control variables to determine the effects of different factors;
◆ draw conclusions about how various factors affect the growth of bread mold.

Time 20 minutes first day; 5 minutes per day for the next 5 days or so

Advance Planning The day before, obtain bread without preservatives. *Computer use is optional.*

Guiding Inquiry

Troubleshooting the Experiment

Students can draw the bread as a grid. A 5 × 5 grid contains 25 squares, so each represents 4% of the slice. Students can use this drawing to estimate the mold growth.

Expected Outcome

More mold grows on the moistened bread than on the unmoistened bread.

Analyze and Conclude

1. Mold grows faster with moisture, darkness, and warmth.
2. The variable was moisture. Manipulated variables will vary.
3. The mold needed water, food (bread), and a place to grow (a dark, warm space).
4. Controlling variables means keeping all conditions the same except the one that the experimenter purposely changes. Experimenters need to be sure which variable caused a specific change.

Extending the Inquiry

Students' designs will vary but should show that mold spores are in the air.

Safety

Do not open sealed bags. Released mold spores could aggravate allergies, asthma, or other medical problems.

Skills Lab

Designing Experiments

Please Pass the Bread!

In this lab, you will control variables in an investigation into the needs of living things.

Problem

What factors are necessary for bread molds to grow?

Materials

paper plates
plastic dropper
bread without preservatives
sealable plastic bags

tap water
packing tape
computer (optional)

Procedure

1. Predict which factors might affect the growth of bread mold. Record your ideas.
2. To test the effect of moisture on bread mold growth, place two slices of bread of the same size and thickness on separate, clean plates.
3. Add drops of tap water to one bread slice until the whole slice is moist. Keep the other slice dry. Expose both slices to the air for 1 hour.
4. Put each slice into its own bag. Press the outside of each bag to remove the air. Seal the bags. Then use packing tape to seal the bags again. Store the bags in a warm, dark place.
5. Use a paper and pencil or the computer to copy the data table. Use the table to organize, examine, and evaluate your data.
6. Every day for at least 5 days, briefly remove the sealed bags from their storage place. Record whether any mold has grown. Estimate the area of the bread where mold is present. **CAUTION:** *Do not unseal the bags. At the end of the experiment, give the sealed bags to your teacher.*
7. Choose another factor that may affect mold growth, such as temperature or the amount of light. Set up an experiment to test the factor you choose. Remember to keep all conditions the same except for the one you are testing.

Analyze and Conclude

1. What conclusions can you draw from each of your experiments?
2. What was the variable in the first experiment? In the second experiment?
3. What basic needs of living things were demonstrated in this lab? Explain.
4. **Think About It** What is meant by "controlling variables"? Why is it necessary to control variables in an experiment?

Design an Experiment

Suppose that you lived in Redi's time. A friend tells you that molds just suddenly appear on bread. Design an experiment to show that the new mold comes from existing mold. Consult your teacher before performing the experiment.

DATA TABLE	Moistened Bread Slice		Unmoistened Bread Slice	
	Mold Present?	Area with Mold	Mold Present?	Area with Mold
Day 1				
Day 2				

Sample Data Table

	Moistened Bread Slice		Unmoistened Bread Slice	
	Mold Present?	Area with Mold	Mold Present?	Area with Mold
Day 1	No		No	
Day 2	No		No	

Program Resources

◆ **Unit 2 Resources** Chapter 4 Skills Lab blackline masters, pp. 25–27
◆ **Inquiry Skills Activity Book** Provides teaching and review of all inquiry skills

Media and Technology

 Lab Activity Videotapes
Grade 6, Tape 1

SECTION 2 Discovering Cells

DISCOVER  ········· ACTIVITY

Is Seeing Believing?

1. ✂ Cut a black-and-white photograph out of a page in a newspaper. With your eyes alone, closely examine the photo. Record your observations.

2. Examine the same photo with a hand lens. Record your observations.

3. Place the photo on the stage of a microscope. Use the clips to hold the photo in place. Shine a light on the photo. Focus the microscope on part of the photo. (To learn how to use the microscope, see Appendix B.) Record your observations.

4. Think of a way to reuse or recycle the newspapers.

Think It Over

Observing What did you see in the photo with the hand lens and the microscope that you could not see with your eyes alone?

A majestic oak tree shades you on a sunny day at the park. A lumbering rhinoceros wanders over to look at you at the zoo. After a rain storm, mushrooms sprout in the damp woods. An oak tree, a rhinoceros, and a mushroom are all living things. What makes all of these living things alike? If you said that they are made of cells, you are correct.

Cells are the basic units of structure and function in living things. Just as bricks are the building blocks of a house or school, cells are the building blocks of living things. Since you are alive, you are made of cells. Look closely at the skin on your arm.

Figure 7 This building is made up of individual bricks. Similarly, all living things are made up of individual cells.

GUIDE FOR READING

◆ How did the invention of the microscope contribute to scientists' understanding of living things?

◆ What is the cell theory?

◆ How does a microscope lens magnify an object?

Reading Tip As you read, make a flowchart showing how the contributions of several scientists led to the development of the cell theory.

Key Terms microscope
• compound microscope
• cell theory • magnification
• resolution

Chapter 4 **131**

READING STRATEGIES

Reading Tip Students should include in their flowcharts contributions made by Janssen, Hooke, Leeuwenhoek, Schlieden, Schwann, and Virchow. Suggest that students illustrate their flowcharts and share them with the class. Also suggest that they save their flowcharts to use as study guides.

You may want to help students construct their flowcharts by writing the first entry or two on the board.

| **Janssen** |
| made one of first |
| compound microscopes |

↓

| **Hooke** |
| saw compartments in |
| cork and called them cells |

SECTION 2 Discovering Cells

TEKS: 6.1A, B; 6.2B, C; 6.3D, E; 6.4A; 6.10B

Objectives

After completing the lesson, students will be able to

◆ explain how the invention of the microscope contributed to scientists' understanding of living things;

◆ determine that all organisms are composed of cells and state the three points of the cell theory;

◆ describe how a light microscope works, including how a lens magnifies an object.

1 Engage/Explore

Activating Prior Knowledge

Help students appreciate the large number of cells that make up living things like themselves, by asking: **How many individual grains of sand do you think make up a beach?** (*Students probably will say millions or billions.*) Point out that humans and many other living things are composed of billions of tiny components as well. These components, called cells, are too small to be seen without a microscope.

········· DISCOVER ·········

Skills Focus observing
Materials *black and white newspaper photograph, scissors, hand lens, microscope*
Time 10 minutes
Tips Set up several microscopes around the room and, if necessary, review with students how to use them.
Expected Outcome With the hand lens and microscope, students should see the individual dots of ink that make up the newspaper photograph. This will help them appreciate how the hand lens and microscope allow them to see objects too small to be seen with the naked eye.
Think It Over Students may say that with the hand lens and microscope they can see that the black and grey shaded areas in the picture actually are made up of separate tiny dots of ink.

2 Facilitate

First Sightings of Cells

Building Inquiry Skills: Classifying

Materials *a collection of several different small* 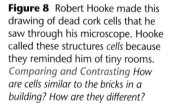 *items that represent living or nonliving things, such as wood, rubber, cotton, silk, wool, hair, coral, bone, leaves, paper, sand, silt, pebbles, rocks, marbles, and plastic*

Time 10 minutes

Give each student several different items, and instruct students to divide the items into two groups, living things and nonliving things. Tell students to classify as living any item that was part of or is made up of once-living things. Have students compare their groupings and resolve any differences. Ask: **In addition to being composed of cells, can you think of other ways that living things differ from nonliving things?** *(Possible answers are that living things take in energy, give off waste, grow and develop, respond to their environment, and reproduce.)* **learning modality: tactile/kinesthetic**

Using the Visuals: Figure 8

Help students appreciate how much Hooke's research contributed to scientific thought—specifically, the understanding of the nature of living things. Call students' attention to the figure, and then point out that Hooke could not photograph what he saw under the microscope because there were no cameras then. Fortunately, Hooke was a gifted artist, and when he published his book, it became a bestseller. Ask: **Why do you think people were so interested in seeing Hooke's drawings?** *(Because they were drawings of things that up until that time had been invisible, so the book opened up a whole new world to people.)* **learning modality: visual**

No matter how hard you look with your eyes alone, you won't be able to see individual skin cells. The reason is that cells are very small. In fact, one square centimeter of your skin's surface contains over 100,000 cells.

First Sightings of Cells

Until the late 1500s there was no way to see cells. No one even knew that cells existed. Around 1590, the invention of the microscope enabled people to look at very small objects. **The invention of the microscope made it possible for people to discover and learn about cells.**

A **microscope** is an instrument that makes small objects look larger. Some microscopes do this by using lenses to focus light. The lenses used in light microscopes are similar to the clear curved pieces of glass used in eyeglasses. A simple microscope contains only one lens. A hand lens is an example of a simple microscope. A light microscope that has more than one lens is called a **compound microscope.**

Robert Hooke One of the first people to observe cells was the English scientist and inventor Robert Hooke. In 1665, Hooke described the structure of a thin slice of cork using a compound microscope he had built himself. Cork, the bark of the cork oak tree, is made up of cells that are no longer alive. To Hooke, the cork looked like tiny rectangular rooms, which he called *cells.* Hooke described his observations this way: "These pores, or cells, were not very deep. . . ." You can see Hooke's drawings of cork cells in Figure 8. What most amazed Hooke was how many cells the cork contained. He calculated that in a cubic inch there were about 1.2 billion cells—a number he described as "most incredible."

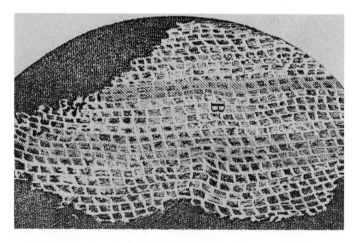

Figure 8 Robert Hooke made this drawing of dead cork cells that he saw through his microscope. Hooke called these structures *cells* because they reminded him of tiny rooms. *Comparing and Contrasting How are cells similar to the bricks in a building? How are they different?*

Background

History of Science Robert Hooke's compound microscope was revolutionary. Hooke also made, improved, or described many other inventions. His work on spring elasticity, for which Hooke's Law is named, led him to invent a spiral spring that led to timepieces. By building the first Gregorian reflecting telescope, Hooke was able to make drawings of Mars that were later used to determine its period of rotation.

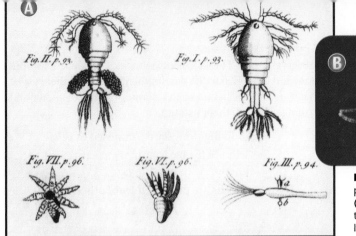

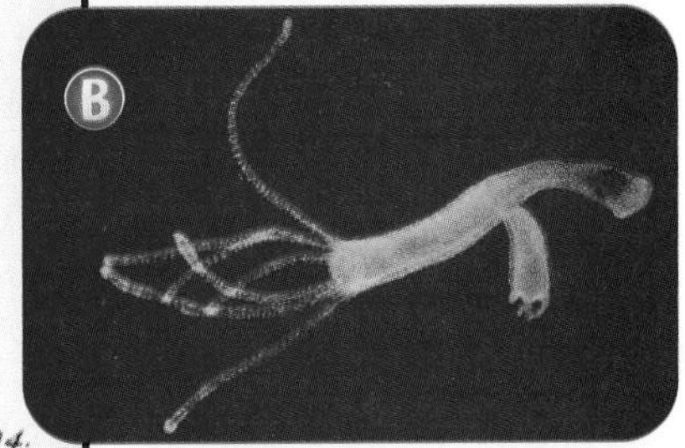

Figure 9 Microscopes allow people to look at very small objects. **(A)** Anton van Leeuwenhoek made these drawings of organisms in the late 1600s after looking through a simple microscope. **(B)** This is a hydra, a tiny water organism, as seen through a modern microscope. Compare this hydra to the one Leeuwenhoek drew, which is labeled Fig. III.

Anton van Leeuwenhoek At about the same time that Robert Hooke made his discovery, Anton van Leeuwenhoek (LAY vun hook) also began to observe tiny objects with microscopes. Leeuwenhoek was a Dutch businessman and amateur scientist who made his own lenses. He then used the lenses to construct simple microscopes.

One of the things Leeuwenhoek looked at was water from a pond. He was surprised to see one-celled organisms, which he called *animalcules* (an uh MAL kyoolz), meaning "little animals."

Leeuwenhoek looked at many other specimens, including scrapings from teeth. Leeuwenhoek was the first person to see the tiny single-celled organisms that are now called bacteria. Leeuwenhoek's many discoveries caught the attention of other researchers. Many other people began to use microscopes to see what secrets they could uncover about cells.

Matthias Schleiden and Theodor Schwann Over the years, scientists have continued to use and improve the microscope. They have discovered that all kinds of living things are made up of cells. In 1838, a German scientist named Matthias Schleiden (SHLY dun) concluded that all plants are made of cells. He based this conclusion on his own research and on the research of others before him. The next year, another German scientist, Theodor Schwann, concluded that all animals are also made up of cells. Thus, stated Schwann, all living things are made up of cells.

Schleiden and Schwann had made an important discovery about living things. However, they didn't understand where cells came from. Until their time, most people thought that living things could come from nonliving matter. In 1855, a German doctor, Rudolf Virchow (FUR koh) proposed that new cells are formed only from existing cells. "All cells come from cells," wrote Virchow.

☑ *Checkpoint* *What did Schleiden and Schwann conclude about cells?*

Building Inquiry Skills: Inferring

Help students infer the nature of the scientific process by asking: **Why do you think it took almost 200 years after cells were discovered for scientists to conclude that all living things consist of cells?** *(Students may say that there were far fewer scientists and microscopes than today, yet scientists had to examine thousands of samples of living things before they could reasonably conclude that all living things are made of cells.)* **learning modality: logical/mathematical**

Using the Visuals: Figure 9

Call students' attention to the figure and ask them to compare and contrast Leeuwenhoek's drawing in Fig. III with the photo of the hydra. Ask: **What are the similarities between the drawing and the photo?** *(They are both of the same organism as seen under a microscope.)* **What are the differences?** *(The drawing shows less detail than the photo.)* Point out that scientists needed the ability to draw accurate sketches before photography was developed in the 19th century. **learning modality: visual**

Social Studies Connection

ACTIVITY

After students read about the achievements of Anton van Leeuwenhoek on page 133, have them do library research to find out about the remarkable era in Dutch history in which Leeuwenhoeck lived. Students can use print and CD-ROM encyclopedias as well as history books and magazine articles. You might assign students, or small groups of students, different research focuses such as commercial and maritime power, optics development, or art in early 17th-century Holland. Have students or groups share their findings with the class by making and presenting a poster, timeline, or oral report. **learning modality: verbal**

Program Resources

- **Unit 2 Resources** 4-2 Lesson Plan, p. 13; 4-2 Section Summary, p. 14
- **Guided Reading and Study Workbook** 4-2

Answers to Self-Assessment

Caption Question

Figure 8 Cells are the building blocks of organisms as bricks are the building blocks of buildings. However, bricks, unlike cells, are not alive.

☑ *Checkpoint*

Schleiden concluded that all plants are made of cells. Schwann concluded that all animals are also made of cells.

Ongoing Assessment

Writing Have students explain how the invention of the microscope led to the discovery of the cell.

Guide students who need more help in organizing and comprehending the technical information in the feature. First point out that, up until 1933, all microscopes operated under the same general principle: They used lenses to focus light on or through an object in order to magnify it enough to be seen by the human eye. Then ask: **How do electron microscopes differ from light microscopes?** (*Instead of using light, electron microscopes use electrons to "see" an object.*) **How does this difference make electron microscopes better?** (*They can magnify objects much more than light microscopes and provide different views of an object.*) **What are TEMs, SEMs, and STMs?** (*Transmission electron microscope, scanning electron microscope, and scanning tunneling microscope, respectively.*) **How are TEMs, SEMs, and STMs the same, and how are they different?** (*All three use electrons instead of light to view objects. A TEM sends electrons through objects, so it is good for seeing the insides of things. A SEM sends electrons over the surfaces of objects, so it can create three-dimensional images of them. A STM records electrons "leaking" from the surface of objects, so it can show individual molecules on the object's surface.*) **Which type of electron microscope has the greatest magnification?** (*STM, which can magnify an object up to 1,000,000 times its actual size*)

In Your Journal To stimulate ideas in visual learners, have students look at the many figures throughout the chapter that contain pictures of objects as seen through a microscope. Advise students to consider the time period they are writing about if they choose one of the earlier microscopes for their advertisement. Point out that, although Hooke's 17th century sketch of cork cells in Figure 8 looks crude compared with the late 20th century electron microscope photo of the single-celled organism in Figure 16, Hooke's images were novel and exciting to the people who lived at that time. Refer to the **ELL Handbook** for additional teaching strategies. **learning modality: verbal**

The Cell Theory

The observations of Hooke, Leeuwenhoek, Schleiden, Schwann, Virchow, and others led to the development of the **cell theory.** The cell theory is an explanation of the relationship between cells and living things. **The cell theory states:**

- ◆ **All living things are composed of cells.**
- ◆ **Cells are the basic unit of structure and function in living things.**
- ◆ **All cells are produced from other cells.**

The Microscope—Improvements Over Time

The discovery of cells would not have been possible without the microscope. Microscopes have been improved in many ways over the last 400 years.

1660

Hooke's Compound Microscope

Robert Hooke improved the compound microscope. The stand at the right holds oil for a flame, which shines light on the specimen under the microscope.

1600   **1750**

1590

First Compound Microscope

Hans Janssen and his son Zacharias, Dutch eyeglass makers, made one of the first compound microscopes. Their microscope was simply a tube with a lens at each end.

1683

Leeuwenhoek's Simple Microscope

Although Leeuwenhoek's simple microscope used only one tiny lens, it could magnify a specimen up to 266 times. Leeuwenhoek was the first person to see many one-celled organisms, including bacteria.

134

Background

Facts and Figures To differentiate among particular cell structures under a microscope, scientists may stain the tissue to be examined. Different stains color different structures inside cells. For example, a stain called hematoxylin colors the cell's nucleus, the area where most nucleic acids in the cell are found.

Before staining the tissue, a scientist shaves off extremely thin slices with a precision cutting instrument called a microtome. The microtome can cut slices so thin that they are less than one cell thick. This allows a clear view of even the tiniest cell structures. When the slices are stained, scientists can differentiate among numerous tiny cell structures.

The cell theory holds true for all living things, no matter how big or small, or how simple or complex. Since cells are common to all living things, they can provide information about all life. And because all cells come from other cells, scientists can study cells to learn about growth, reproduction, and all other functions that living things perform. By learning about cells and how they function, you can learn about all types of living things.

☑ *Checkpoint* Which scientists contributed to the development of the cell theory?

In Your Journal

Choose one of the microscopes. Write an advertisement for it that might appear in a popular science magazine. Be creative. Emphasize the microscope's usefulness or describe the wonders that can be seen with it.

1933
Transmission Electron Microscope (TEM)

The German physicist Ernst Ruska created the first electron microscope. TEMs make images by sending electrons through a very thinly sliced specimen. They can only examine dead specimens, but are very useful for viewing internal cell structures. TEMs can magnify a specimen up to 500,000 times.

1981
Scanning Tunneling Microscope (STM)

A STM measures electrons that leak, or "tunnel," from the surface of a specimen. With a STM, scientists can see individual molecules on the outer layer of a cell. STMs can magnify a specimen up to 1,000,000 times.

1900   **2050**

1886
Modern Compound Light Microscope

German scientists Ernst Abbe and Carl Zeiss made a compound light microscope similar to this one. The horseshoe stand helps keep the microscope steady. The mirror at the bottom focuses light up through the specimen. Modern compound light microscopes can magnify a specimen up to 1,000 times.

1965
Scanning Electron Microscope (SEM)

The first commercial SEM is produced. This microscope sends a beam of electrons over the surface of a specimen, rather than through it. The result is a detailed three-dimensional image of the specimen's surface. SEMs can magnify a specimen up to 150,000 times.

Chapter 4 **135**

Addressing Naive Conceptions

Content Mastery

Students may think the cell theory is not well-established because it is called a theory. Explain that in everyday speech, people often use the word *theory* to mean speculation or conjecture. However, in science a theory is a well-tested concept that consistently explains a wide range of observations and predicts future events. Point out that a theory may be the best explanation to date, but no theory is beyond dispute. Ask: **Do you think the cell theory has been proven conclusively? Explain.** (*No, it is not possible for scientists to examine every single living thing to determine if it is composed of cells, and a single exception would disprove the theory.*) **learning modality: verbal**

Including All Students

Materials *microscope, slide, coverslip*

Time 15 minutes

Let students actually experience the difference that the degree of magnification can make in how objects appear under a microscope. Have students choose a suitable object, such as a strand of human hair, to place on a slide with a coverslip and view under the microscope, first at low and then at high power. For students whose movements are limited, you can use a microprojector to project the images on a screen. Have students draw a simple sketch of what they see under each magnification. Remind them to label their drawings with the magnification. Ask volunteers to share their drawings with the class and have other students try to identify each object from the drawings. **learning modality: visual**

Ongoing Assessment

Oral Presentation Call on students at random to state Leeuwenhoek's contributions to science. (*Leeuwenhoek made microscopes powerful enough to see single-celled organisms, and he was the first person to see bacteria.*)

How a Light Microscope Works

Integrating Physics

Materials *convex lens (hand lens)*
Time 10 minutes

Group students in pairs, and instruct one student to hold a hand lens steady at about 10 cm above a page. Tell the other student to move closer to or farther from the lens until the letters on the page come into focus. At this point, have both students note the relative positions of the eye, lens, and page and compare them with their positions in Figure 10. Ask: **At what position is your eye?** (*At the point where the light rays converge*) By moving their eye farther back from the lens, students can see the difference between magnification and resolution. Ask: **How does the object appear now?** (*Even larger but blurry, or out of focus*) Have students switch positions and repeat the activity.
learning modality: tactile/ kinesthetic

Sharpen your Skills

Observing

Materials *prepared slide of cork, microscope, pond water, plastic dropper, slide, coverslip*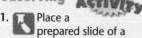
Time 15 minutes
Tips Make sure students have focused the microscope and can see the cells clearly before they start their drawings.
Expected Outcome Students' drawings of cork cells should resemble Hooke's drawing on page 132. Students' drawings of pond water should show various microorganisms. Leeuwenhoek called the organisms he saw "little animals" because they moved as animals move.
Extend Ask: **What do you think a drop of tap water would look like under the microscope?** (*It would contain few if any microorganisms.*) **learning modality: visual**

Sharpen your Skills

Observing

1. Place a prepared slide of a thin slice of cork on the stage of a microscope.
2. Observe the slide under low power. Draw what you see.
3. Put a small, very thin piece of tomato, onion, or lettuce on a slide. Repeat Step 2.
4. Place a few drops of pond water on another slide and cover it with a coverslip. Repeat Step 2.
5. Wash your hands after handling pond water.

Observing How does your drawing in Step 2 compare to Hooke's drawing in Figure 8 on page 132? Based on your observations in Step 4, why did Leeuwenhoek call the organisms he saw "little animals"?

How a Light Microscope Works

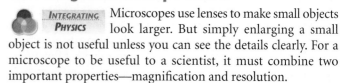

Microscopes use lenses to make small objects look larger. But simply enlarging a small object is not useful unless you can see the details clearly. For a microscope to be useful to a scientist, it must combine two important properties—magnification and resolution.

Magnification The first property, **magnification,** is the ability to make things look larger than they are. **The lens or lenses in a light microscope magnify an object by bending the light that passes through them.** If you examine a hand lens, you will see that the glass lens is curved, not flat. The center of the lens is thicker than the edges. A lens with this curved shape is called a convex lens. Look at Figure 10 to see how light is bent by a convex lens. The light passing through the sides of the lens bends inward. When this light hits the eye, the eye sees the object as larger than it really is.

Because a compound microscope uses more than one lens, it can magnify an object even more. Light passes through a specimen and then through two lenses. Figure 10 also shows the path that light takes through a compound microscope. The first lens near the specimen magnifies the object. Then a second lens near the eye further magnifies the enlarged image. The total magnification of the microscope is equal to the magnifications of the two lenses multiplied together. For example, if the first lens has a magnification of 10 and the second lens has a magnification of 40, then the total magnification of the microscope is 400.

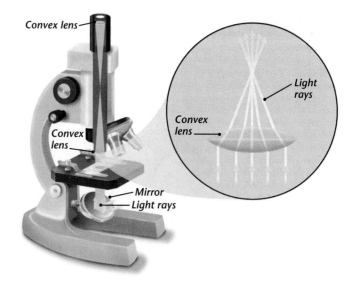

Figure 10 Microscopes use lenses to make objects look larger. A compound microscope has two convex lenses. Each convex lens bends light, making the image larger. *Calculating If one lens had a magnification of 10, and the other lens had a magnification of 50, what would the total magnification be?*

Background

Facts and Figures A light microscope can magnify objects up to 2,000 times their original size, but such high powers of magnification are possible only when the lenses are immersed in oil. A light microscope does not have the power to provide a high-resolution image of a very tiny object. To obtain high levels of resolution while magnifying very small things, such as viruses and the smaller cell structures, an electron microscope is needed. Electron microscopes can magnify objects up to one million times.

Resolution To create a useful image, a microscope must also help you see individual parts clearly. The ability to clearly distinguish the individual parts of an object is called **resolution.** Resolution is another term for the sharpness of an image.

For example, when you use your eyes to look at a photo printed in a newspaper, it looks like a complete picture from one side to the other. That picture, however, is really made up of a collection of small dots. To the unaided eye, two tiny dots close together appear as one. If you put the photo under a microscope, however, you can see the dots. You see the dots not only because they are magnified but also because the microscope improves resolution. Good resolution—being able to see fine detail—is not needed when you are reading the newspaper. But it is just what you need when you study cells.

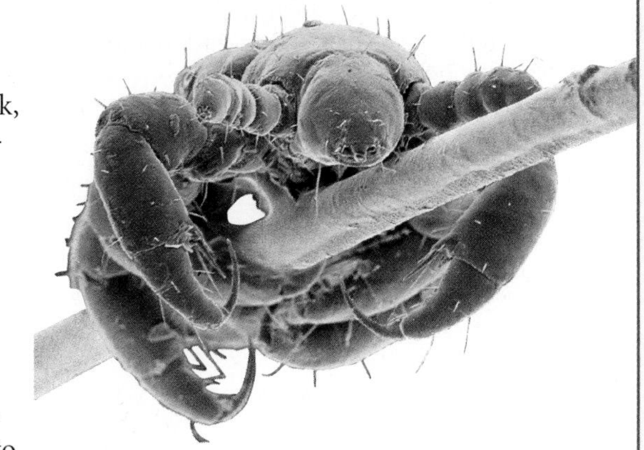

Electron Microscopes

The microscopes used by Hooke, Leeuwenhoek, and other early researchers were all light microscopes. Since the 1930s, scientists have developed a different type of microscope called an electron microscope. Electron microscopes use a beam of electrons instead of light to examine a specimen. Electrons are tiny particles that are smaller than atoms. The resolution of electron microscopes is much higher than the resolution of light microscopes. As the technology of microscopes keeps improving, scientists will continue to learn more about the structure and function of cells.

Figure 11 This head louse, shown clinging to a human hair, was photographed through a scanning electron microscope. It has been magnified to about 80 times its actual size.

Section 2 Review

1. How did the invention of the microscope affect scientists' understanding of living things?
2. Explain the three main ideas of the cell theory.
3. How does a compound microscope use lenses to magnify an object?
4. Explain why both magnification and resolution are important when viewing a small object with a microscope.
5. **Thinking Critically** **Applying Concepts** Why do scientists learn more about cells each time the microscope is improved?

Check Your Progress

CHAPTER PROJECT

Observe your object at least once a day. Record your observations in a data table. Draw accurate diagrams. *(Hint: Measuring provides important information. Take measurements of your object regularly. If you cannot measure it directly, make estimates.)*

Program Resources

◆ **Unit 2 Resources** 4-2 Review and Reinforce, p. 15; 4-2 Enrich, p. 16
◆ **Laboratory Manual** 4, "How to Use a Microscope"

Media and Technology

 Transparencies "The Compound Microscope," Transparency 11

Answers to Self-Assessment

Caption Question

Figure 10 The total magnification would be 10 × 50, or 500.

Electron Microscopes

Including All Students

Urge students who need extra challenges to work together to prepare a presentation on electron microscopes, which may be difficult for some students to understand. The presentation should explain in simple terms how electron microscopes work and why electron microscopes can magnify so greatly. **cooperative learning**

3 Assess

Section 2 Review Answers

1. The invention of the microscope made it possible for people to discover and learn about cells.
2. According to the cell theory, all living things are made of cells, cells are the basic building blocks of life, and they are the only source of new cells.
3. Light passing through the first lens magnifies the object; then light passing through the second lens magnifies the image of the object even more.
4. Both magnification and resolution are important because magnification makes an object larger whereas resolution sharpens the image so you can see details.
5. Each time the microscope is improved, scientists can see structures in cells in greater detail and more clearly.

Check Your Progress

CHAPTER PROJECT

Make sure students spend time making observations of their object. If students seem bored because their object is not doing anything, encourage them to consider whether this inactivity proves that the object is not alive, or whether they should revise their methods of observation. For example, encourage students to explain how they could be sure that the object is not breathing or growing.

Performance Assessment

Skills Check Have students compare and contrast light microscopes and electron microscopes.

SECTION 3 Looking Inside Cells

TEKS: 6.1A; 6.2B, C; 6.3C; 6.4A; 6.10A, B, C; 6.11B

Objectives

After completing the lesson, students will be able to

- identify the cell wall, cell membrane, and nucleus, and describe their functions;
- identify other organelles in the cell;
- compare bacterial cells with plant and animal cells;
- identify the levels of organization in organisms, including cells, tissues, organs, organisms, and populations; describe how structure complements function at those levels.

1 Engage/Explore

Activating Prior Knowledge

Introduce students to the division of labor among structures in cells by relating it to the division of labor in a community. Ask: **How are the various jobs in a town divided up among people?** (*Possible answers might include: shopkeepers supply food, police officers enforce laws, and the mayor and city council members make decisions.*) **Why is it effective to divide the labor in this way?** (*By dividing the labor, people can become specialized at the work they do and do it more effectively.*)

DISCOVER

Skills Focus inferring
Materials *calculator, metric ruler*
Time 10 minutes
Tips Have partners measure each other's height with a metric ruler.
Expected Outcome A student who is 1.5 m tall would be the same height as a stack of 1,500 amebas. The same student would be 150,000 body cells tall.
Think It Over Students should infer that they cannot see body cells without a microscope because they are too small.

DISCOVER

How Large Are Cells?

1. Look at the organism in the photo. The organism is an ameba, a large single-celled organism. This type of ameba is about 1 millimeter (mm) long.

2. Multiply your height in meters by 1,000 to get your height in millimeters. How many amebas would you have to stack end-to-end to equal your height?

3. Many of the cells in your body are about 0.01 mm long—one hundredth the size of an ameba. How many body cells would you have to stack end-to-end to equal your height?

Think It Over

Inferring Look at a metric ruler to see how small 1 mm is. Now imagine a distance one-hundredth as long, or 0.01 mm. Why can't you see your body's cells without the aid of a microscope?

GUIDE FOR READING

- What functions do the cell membrane, nucleus, and other organelles perform?
- What levels of organization do organisms exhibit?

Reading Tip Preview *Exploring Plant and Animal Cells* on pages 142–143. List any unfamiliar terms. As you read, write a definition for each.

Key Terms • organelle
• cell wall • cell membrane
• nucleus • chromosome
• cytoplasm • mitochondria
• endoplasmic reticulum
• ribosome • Golgi body
• chloroplast • vacuole
• lysosome • prokaryote
• eukaryote • tissue • organ
• organ system • population

Imagine you're in California standing next to a giant redwood tree. You have to bend your head way back to see the top of the tree. Some of these trees are over 110 meters tall and more than 10 meters in circumference! How do redwoods grow so large? How do they carry out all the functions necessary to stay alive?

To answer these questions, and to learn many other things about living things, you are about to take an imaginary journey. It will be quite an unusual trip. You will be traveling inside a living redwood tree, visiting its tiny cells. On your trip you will observe some of the structures found in plant cells. You will also learn about some of the differences between plant and animal cells.

◀ A giant redwood tree

138

READING STRATEGIES

Reading Tip Have students list all the unfamiliar boldface terms in *Exploring Plant and Animal Cells.* They will probably include terms such as endoplasmic reticulum and mitochondrion among others. You may want to suggest that they list the words on notecards and write the definition of each word on the other side of the card. They can use the cards to study.

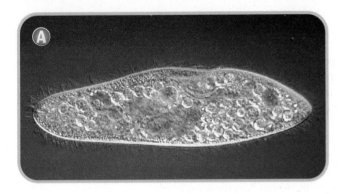

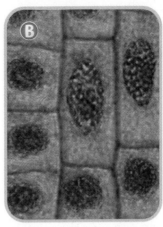

Figure 12 All cells have cell membranes, but not all cells have cell walls. The cell membrane of this single-celled paramecium (A) controls what substances enter and leave the cell. The cell walls of these onion root cells (B) have been stained green so you can see them clearly. Cell walls protect and support plant cells.

As you will discover on your journey, cells themselves contain even smaller structures. These tiny cell structures, called **organelles,** carry out specific functions within the cell. Just as your stomach, lungs, and heart have different functions in your body, each organelle has a different function within the cell. The cell is a system, and the organelles and other cell structures are its parts. You can see the organelles found in plant and animal cells in *Exploring Plant and Animal Cells* on pages 142 and 143. Now it's time to hop aboard your imaginary ship and prepare to enter a typical plant cell.

Cell Wall

Entering a plant's cell is a bit difficult. First you must pass through the cell wall. The **cell wall** is a rigid layer of nonliving material that surrounds the cells of plants and some other organisms. The cell wall is made of a tough, yet flexible, material called cellulose. If you think of a wooden desk, you will have a good idea of what cellulose is. Wood contains a lot of cellulose.

The cells of plants and some other organisms have cell walls. In contrast, the cells of animals and some other organisms lack cell walls. A plant's cell wall functions to protect and support the cell. In woody plants, the cell walls are very rigid. This is why giant redwood trees can stand so tall. Each cell wall in the tree adds strength to the tree. Although the cell wall is stiff, many materials, including water and oxygen, can pass through the cell wall quite easily. So sail on through the cell wall and enter the cell.

☑ *Checkpoint* *What is the function of the cell wall?*

Cell Membrane

After you pass through the cell wall, the next structure you encounter is the **cell membrane.** All cells have cell membranes. In cells with cell walls, the cell membrane is located just inside the cell wall. In other cells, the cell membrane forms the outside boundary that separates the cell from its environment.

Chapter 4 **139**

Answers to Self-Assessment

☑ *Checkpoint*
The function of the cell wall is to help protect and support the cell.

---

2 *Facilitate*

Cell Wall

Building Inquiry Skills: Inferring

Extend the analogy in the text by first naming several different parts of the body, including the brain, skin, and blood vessels, and challenging students to identify their roles in the body. Point out that each cell, like the body as a whole, has structures that perform similar functions. Then ask: **What are the functions of some organelles you would expect to find in the cell?** *(Answers should include an organelle like the brain to control the rest of the cell, an organelle like the skin to enclose and protect the cell, and an organelle like the blood vessels to carry materials from one part of the cell to another.)* **learning modality: logical/mathematical**

Cell Membrane

Including All Students

Help students still mastering English build language skills and improve their understanding of the cell membrane. First, challenge students to find the origin of the word *membrane* in a dictionary. *(Membrane comes from the Latin word,* membrana, *which means "skin.")* Then ask: **Do you think the skin on your body is a good analogy for the cell membrane? Why or why not?** *(Most students probably will say that the skin is a good analogy for the cell membrane, because both the cell membrane and the skin enclose and protect what's inside.)* **limited English proficiency**

Ongoing Assessment

Oral Presentation Call on students at random to identify differences and similarities between cell walls and cell membranes.

Language Arts
CONNECTION

The analogy in the text, in which the cell membrane is compared with a window screen, is an extended analogy, because it is more than just a brief statement of comparison. Referring to the nucleus as the cell's "brain" is a simple analogy.

In Your Journal Examples of simple analogies in this section include referring to the mitochondria as the cell's "powerhouses" and the ribosomes as the cell's "factories." After students have finished writing in their journals, ask: **Why do analogies help you better understand the parts of a cell?** *(Because they compare them with things that are more familiar or easier to understand.)*
learning modality: verbal

Nucleus

Building Inquiry Skills: Comparing and Contrasting

Time 5 minutes

ACTIVITY

Help students avoid confusing the cell membrane and nuclear membrane by having them form two concentric circles in the classroom and asking: **Which circle represents the nuclear membrane? Which circle represents the cell membrane?** *(The inner circle represents the nuclear membrane. The outer circle represents the cell membrane.)* **How is the nuclear membrane like the cell membrane? How is it different?** *(Both are thin films that enclose and protect what is inside the membrane. However, the nuclear membrane encloses and protects just the cell's nucleus, whereas the cell membrane encloses and protects the entire cell.)*
learning modality: tactile/ kinesthetic

Language Arts
CONNECTION

Writers often use analogies to help readers understand unfamiliar ideas. In an analogy, a writer explains something by comparing it to something similar with which the reader is more familiar. For example, the author of this textbook describes the cell membrane by making an analogy to a window screen. This analogy helps the readers understand that the cell membrane is a boundary that separates the cell from the outside environment.

In Your Journal

Identify other analogies used by the author. Then choose two cell parts from this section. Write an analogy for each part that helps explain its structure or function.

As your ship nears the edge of the cell membrane, you notice that there are tiny openings, or pores, in the cell membrane. You steer toward an opening. Suddenly, your ship narrowly misses being struck by a chunk of waste material passing out of the cell. **You have discovered one of the cell membrane's main functions: the cell membrane controls what substances come into and out of a cell.**

Everything the cell needs—from food to oxygen—enters the cell through the cell membrane. Harmful waste products leave the cell through the cell membrane. For a cell to survive, the cell membrane must allow these materials to pass into and out of the cell. In a sense, the cell membrane is like a window screen. The screen keeps insects out of a room. But holes in the screen allow air to enter and leave the room.

Nucleus

As you sail inside the cell, a large, oval structure comes into view. This structure, called the **nucleus** (NOO klee us), acts as the "brain" of the cell. **You can think of the nucleus as the cell's control center, directing all of the cell's activities.**

Nuclear Membrane Notice in Figure 13 that the nucleus is surrounded by a nuclear membrane. Just as the cell membrane protects the cell, the nuclear membrane protects the nucleus. Materials pass in and out of the nucleus through small openings, or pores, in the nuclear membrane. So aim for that pore just ahead and carefully glide into the nucleus.

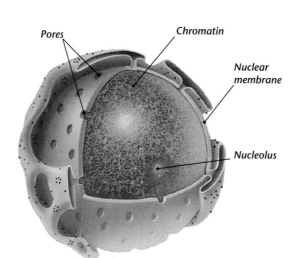

Pores　*Chromatin*　*Nuclear membrane*　*Nucleolus*

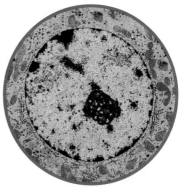

Figure 13 The nucleus is the cell's control center. The chromatin in the nucleus contains instructions for carrying out the cell's activities.

Background

Facts and Figures In both plant and animal cells, mitochondria have a smooth outer membrane and a folded inner membrane with a lot of surface area where chemical reactions take place. Because energy is released during these chemical reactions, mitochondria frequently are called the "powerhouses" of the cell.

Both mitochondria and chloroplasts have a double membrane and the ability to divide. In addition, both contain small amounts of DNA. These three features also characterize some bacteria, leading some biologists to think that mitochondria and chloroplasts are descendants of bacteria that lived as independent organisms long ago.

Chromosomes The nucleus contains thin strands called chromatin. Chromatin contains the genetic material, the instructions that direct the functions of a cell. For example, the instructions in the chromatin ensure that leaf cells grow and divide to form more leaf cells. When cells begin to divide, the chromatin strands coil and condense to form structures called **chromosomes.** When an existing cell divides, a copy of its genetic material is passed on to each new cell. You'll learn more about how cells divide in Chapter 5.

Nucleolus As you prepare to leave the nucleus, you spot a small object nearby. This structure, the nucleolus, is where ribosomes are made. Ribosomes are the organelles where proteins are produced.

☑ *Checkpoint* *Where in the nucleus is genetic material found?*

Organelles in the Cytoplasm

As you leave the nucleus, you find yourself in the **cytoplasm,** the region between the cell membrane and the nucleus. Your ship floats in a clear, thick, gel-like fluid. The fluid in the cytoplasm is constantly moving, so your ship does not need to propel itself. Many cell organelles are found in the cytoplasm. **The organelles in a cell function to produce energy, build and transport needed materials, and store and recycle wastes.**

Mitochondria As you pass into the cytoplasm, you see rod-shaped organelles called **mitochondria** (my tuh KAHN dree uh) (singular *mitochondrion*). Mitochondria are called the "power-houses" of the cell because they produce most of the energy the cell needs to carry out its functions. Muscle cells and other very active cells have large numbers of mitochondria.

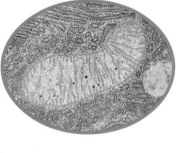

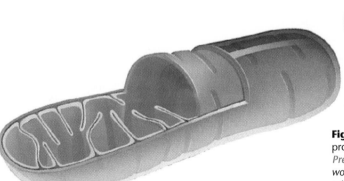

Figure 14 The mitochondria produce most of the cell's energy. *Predicting In what types of cells would you expect to find a lot of mitochondria?*

Answers to Self-Assessment

☑ *Checkpoint*

The genetic material in the nucleus is found in strands called chromatin.

Caption Question

Figure 14 You would expect to find a lot of mitochondria in muscle cells and other very active cells.

Addressing Naive Conceptions

Students may think that different types of cells within an organism must contain different genetic material. Point out that the same genetic material is found in every cell of an organism. Explain that different cells, such as skin and blood cells, look and function so differently because they respond to different genetic instructions. Ask: **Can you think of an analogy to cells containing the same genetic material, yet looking and functioning differently because they are following different genetic instructions?** *(One analogy is the same cookbook being used by different cooks to make different recipes.)* **learning modality: verbal**

Organelles in the Cytoplasm

Inquiry Challenge

Materials *sheets of plain white paper, markers, cans of food, bottles of water, batteries, storage boxes, other miscellaneous items*
Time 15 minutes

ACTIVITY

After students have read about all of the organelles, challenge them to make a human model of a cell that shows how two or more organelles function. One possible way is for one student to represent each type of organelle and the rest of the class to represent the cell and nuclear membranes. Provide students with paper and markers for making signs and with props such as those listed above. Have them demonstrate the functioning of the organelles. *(For example, a sign labeled "protein" might be passed from a student representing a ribosome to a student representing an endoplasmic reticulum, who then carries the "protein" to the students representing the cell membrane, one of whom passes the sign out of the "cell.")* **cooperative learning**

Ongoing Assessment

Drawing Ask students to draw a cell and label the three structures of the nucleus.

Organelles in the Cytoplasm, continued

EXPLORING
Plant and Animal Cells

Call students' attention to the feature, and ask if they have any questions. Point out that some cell structures, including Golgi bodies, ribosomes, and mitochondria, are defined on just one drawing or the other because they are much the same in both plant cells and animal cells. Help students organize the material in the feature by creating a table on the chalkboard titled "Comparison of Plant and Animal Cells." For headings use *Similarities* and *Differences,* and for rows use *Plants* and *Animals.* Encourage students to interpret the diagrams and other information in the feature to help fill in the cells of the table. Stimulate their thinking by asking: **Which organelles are found only in plant cells? Which are found in both plant and animal cells?** (*Except for cell walls and chloroplasts, most organelles are found in both plant and animal cells.*) Complete the table as students volunteer their ideas. When the table is finished, you may want to have students copy it in a notebook and refer to it as they study this section. Refer to the **ELL Handbook** for additional teaching strategies. **learning modality: verbal**

Addressing Naive Conceptions

Emphasize that the drawings of plant and animal cells shown in the feature are generalized representations of cells. In reality, cells can take on many different shapes and sizes. They also can vary in the specific organelles they contain. For comparison, show students drawings of other types of cells, such as leaf and root cells for plants and muscle and bone cells for animals. In each drawing, challenge students to locate the cell membrane and organelles if these are visible. Ask: **Why do you think different cells look so different from each other?** (*Because they play different roles in the organism.*) **learning modality: visual**

142

EXPLORING Plant and Animal Cells

On these pages, you can compare structures found in two kinds of cells: plant cells and animal cells. As you study these cells, remember that they are generalized cells. In living organisms, cells vary somewhat in shape and structure.

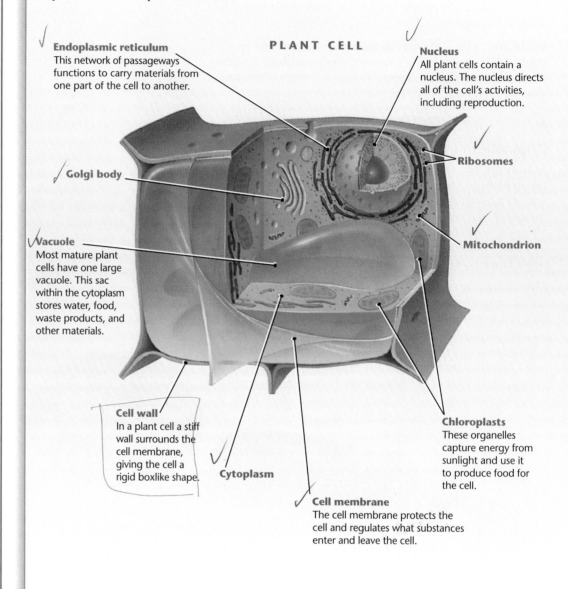

PLANT CELL

Endoplasmic reticulum
This network of passageways functions to carry materials from one part of the cell to another.

Nucleus
All plant cells contain a nucleus. The nucleus directs all of the cell's activities, including reproduction.

Ribosomes

Golgi body

Mitochondrion

Vacuole
Most mature plant cells have one large vacuole. This sac within the cytoplasm stores water, food, waste products, and other materials.

Cell wall
In a plant cell a stiff wall surrounds the cell membrane, giving the cell a rigid boxlike shape.

Cytoplasm

Chloroplasts
These organelles capture energy from sunlight and use it to produce food for the cell.

Cell membrane
The cell membrane protects the cell and regulates what substances enter and leave the cell.

Background

Facts and Figures Many types of organisms are unicellular. Bacteria are single-celled organisms called prokaryotes. Prokaryotic cells do not contain nuclei and most other cell organelles. Many protists, such as paramecia and amebas, are unicellular organisms called eukaryotes. Eukaryotic cells contain nuclei and most cell organelles.

Paramecia have many hairlike projections called cilia that beat rhythmically to propel the paramecia through water. Paramecia also use cilia to obtain food. Amebas move by forming pseudopods, or "false feet"—bulges in their cell membranes into which cytoplasm flows. To feed, amebas surround smaller organisms with their pseudopods, thereby entrapping their prey in vacuoles inside the cytoplasm of their cells.

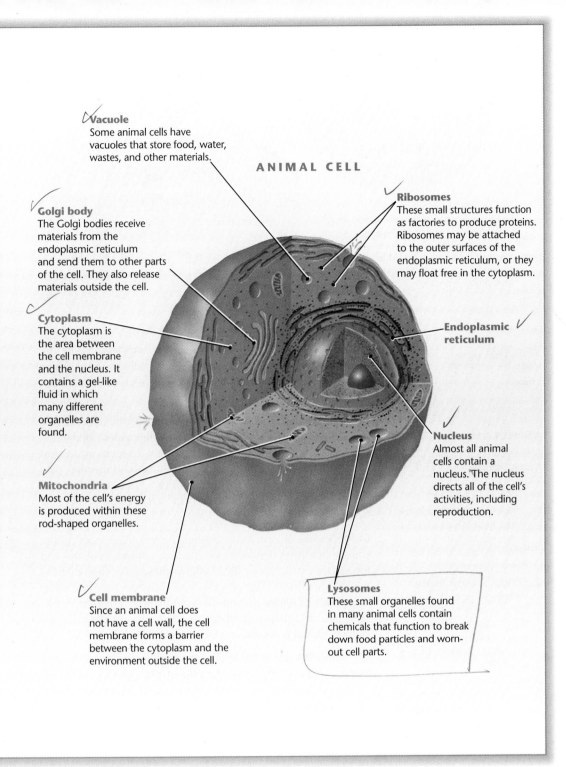

Vacuole
Some animal cells have vacuoles that store food, water, wastes, and other materials.

ANIMAL CELL

Golgi body
The Golgi bodies receive materials from the endoplasmic reticulum and send them to other parts of the cell. They also release materials outside the cell.

Cytoplasm
The cytoplasm is the area between the cell membrane and the nucleus. It contains a gel-like fluid in which many different organelles are found.

Mitochondria
Most of the cell's energy is produced within these rod-shaped organelles.

Cell membrane
Since an animal cell does not have a cell wall, the cell membrane forms a barrier between the cytoplasm and the environment outside the cell.

Ribosomes
These small structures function as factories to produce proteins. Ribosomes may be attached to the outer surfaces of the endoplasmic reticulum, or they may float free in the cytoplasm.

Endoplasmic reticulum

Nucleus
Almost all animal cells contain a nucleus. The nucleus directs all of the cell's activities, including reproduction.

Lysosomes
These small organelles found in many animal cells contain chemicals that function to break down food particles and worn-out cell parts.

Including All Students

Materials *10 index cards*
Time 20 minutes

Students who are not native English speakers and any other students who are having difficulty with the material on the parts of the cell may benefit from creating and using flash cards. On one side of each flash card, students should write the name of a cell structure. On the other side, they should state the structure's function in the cell. When students have finished, check to make sure they have correctly identified each cell structure. For example, ask: **What does the cell membrane do?** (*It protects the cell and controls what enters and leaves it.*) **What does the nucleus do?** (*It directs all the cell's activities*) Then divide students into pairs and challenge them to use their flash cards to quiz each other.
limited English proficiency

Demonstration

Materials *microprojector, prepared slide of plant cells, prepared slide of animal cells*
Time 10 minutes

Help students relate the generalized cells shown in *Exploring Plant and Animal Cells* to actual plant and animal cells. Use a microprojector to project first a prepared slide of plant cells and then a prepared slide of animal cells onto a screen. (If a microprojector is not available, use an opaque projector and photographs of plant and animal cells.) Challenge students to locate the cell wall or cell membrane, nucleus, and other organelles on the projected images. Encourage students to describe how the actual cells vary in shape and structure from the generalized cells in the text.
learning modality: visual

Media and Technology

Transparencies "Exploring a Plant Cell," Transparency 12; "Exploring an Animal Cell," Transparency 13

Ongoing Assessment

Skills Check Have students write two lists, one summarizing the similarities between plant and animal cells, the other summarizing the differences.
 Students can save their lists in their portfolios.

Organelles in the Cytoplasm, continued

 TRY THIS

Skills Focus making **ACTIVITY**
models

Materials *packet of colorless gelatin, warm water, other miscellaneous materials to represent cell structures, rectangular or round pan*

Time 10 minutes one day; 10 minutes later the same day

Tips Advise students to stir the gelatin until it dissolves completely in the warm water. Suggest that they leave the gelatin in the refrigerator for up to an hour until it starts to thicken before they add the "cell structures." Make sure the water is not too hot for students to work safely.

Expected Outcome Students should create a round gelatin mold to represent an animal cell or a rectangular gelatin mold to represent a plant cell. The gelatin should contain objects to represent each of the cell structures described on pages 142 or 143, and there should be a key identifying and describing each of the structures.

Extend Challenge hands-on learners to make a model of an animal cell with gelatin using a resealable plastic bag instead of a pan for a mold. Give students a chance to handle the plastic bag after the gelatin in it solidifies, then ask: **Why is the plastic-bag model a better representation of an animal cell than the pan model?** *(There is no "cell wall," as there is with the pan, to support the cell and make it rigid.)* **learning modality: tactile/kinesthetic**

Demonstration

Materials *wilted houseplant, water* **ACTIVITY**

Time 5 minutes at the beginning of class, 5 minutes at the end of class

Call students' attention to the passage in the text that describes how plants look when their vacuoles are full of water and how they look when their vacuoles do not contain much water. Then show students a wilted coleus or impatiens that is in need of water. Water the plant thoroughly. By the end of class, the plant should no longer be drooping. Ask: **Why is the plant no longer wilted?** *(Its vacuoles have filled up with water.)* **learning modality: visual**

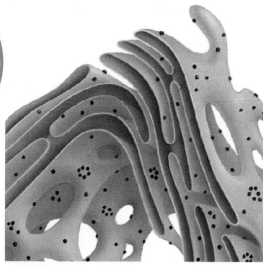

Figure 15 The endoplasmic reticulum is a passageway through which proteins and other materials move within the cell. The spots on the outside of the endoplasmic reticulum are ribosomes, structures that produce proteins.

 **TRY THIS**

Gelatin Cell

Make your  **ACTIVITY**
own model of
a cell.

1. Dissolve a packet of colorless gelatin in warm water. Pour the gelatin into a rectangular pan (for a plant cell) or a round pan (for an animal cell).

2. Choose different materials that resemble each of the cell structures found in the cell you are modeling. Insert these materials into the gelatin before it begins to solidify.

Making Models On a sheet of paper, develop a key that identifies each cell structure in your model. Describe the function of each structure.

Endoplasmic Reticulum As you sail farther into the cytoplasm, you find yourself in a maze of passageways called the **endoplasmic reticulum** (en duh PLAZ mik rih TIK yuh lum) or ER. These passageways carry proteins and other materials from one part of the cell to another.

Ribosomes Attached to the outer surface of the endoplasmic reticulum are small grainlike bodies called **ribosomes.** Other ribosomes are found floating in the cytoplasm. Ribosomes function as factories to produce proteins. The attached ribosomes pass the proteins to the endoplasmic reticulum. From the interior of the endoplasmic reticulum, the proteins will be transported to the Golgi bodies.

Golgi Bodies As you move through the endoplasmic reticulum, you see structures that look like a flattened collection of sacs and tubes. These structures, called **Golgi bodies,** can be thought of as the cell's mailroom. The Golgi bodies receive proteins and other newly formed materials from the endoplasmic reticulum, package them, and distribute them to other parts of the cell. The Golgi bodies also release materials outside the cell.

Chloroplasts Have you noticed the many large green structures floating in the cytoplasm? The cells of plants and some other organisms have these structures. Animal cells do not have them. These organelles, called **chloroplasts,** capture energy from sunlight and use it to produce food for the cell. It is the chloroplasts that give plants their green color. You will learn more about chloroplasts in Chapter 6.

Background

Integrating Science Bacteria are found virtually everywhere, both inside and outside the human body. Some bacteria cause no harm—in fact, we need them to help break down food and eliminate waste. Other bacteria are harmful, and when they enter the body they may make us ill. Common examples of harmful bacteria include *Streptococcus* bacteria, which cause "strep" throat, and *Salmonella* bacteria, which cause food poisoning.

Bacteria are the most abundant life forms on Earth, and they have existed almost as long as the planet itself. In fact, some fossil bacteria have been found that are about 3.5 billion years old.

Vacuoles Steer past the chloroplasts and head for that large, round, water-filled sac floating in the cytoplasm. This sac, called a **vacuole** (VAK yoo ohl), is the storage area of the cell. Most plant cells have one large vacuole. Some animal cells do not have vacuoles; others do.

Vacuoles store food and other materials needed by the cell. Vacuoles can also store waste products. Most of the water in plant cells is stored in vacuoles. When the vacuoles are full of water, they make the cell plump and firm. Without much water in the vacuoles, the plant wilts.

Lysosomes Your journey through the cell is almost over. Before you leave, take another look around you. If you carefully swing your ship around the vacuole, you may be lucky enough to see a lysosome. **Lysosomes** (LY suh sohmz) are small round structures that contain chemicals that break down large food particles into smaller ones. Lysosomes also break down old cell parts and release the substances so they can be used again. In this sense, you can think of the lysosomes as the cell's cleanup crew. Lysosomes are found in both animal cells and plant cells.

Although lysosomes contain powerful chemicals, you need not worry about your ship's safety. The membrane around a lysosome keeps these harsh chemicals from escaping and breaking down the rest of the cell.

Bacterial Cells

The plant and animal cells that you just learned about are very different from the bacterial cell you see in Figure 16. First, bacterial cells are usually smaller than plant or animal cells. A human skin cell, for example, is about 10 times as large as an average bacterial cell.

There are several other ways in which bacterial cells are different from plant and animal cells. **While a bacterial cell does have a cell wall and a cell membrane, it does not contain a nucleus.** Organisms whose cells lack a nucleus are called **prokaryotes** (proh KAR ee ohtz). The bacterial cell's genetic material, which looks like a thick, tangled string, is found in the cytoplasm. Bacterial cells contain ribosomes, but none of the other organelles found in plant or animal cells. Organisms whose cells contain a nucleus and many of the organelles you just read about are called **eukaryotes** (yoo KAR ee ohtz).

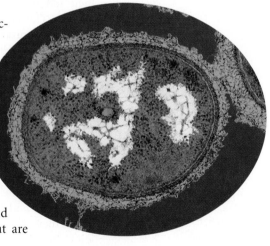

Figure 16 This single-celled organism is a type of bacteria. Bacterial cells lack a nucleus and some other organelles.
Applying Concepts Where is the genetic material in a bacterial cell found?

Media and Technology

 Life Science Videodisc
Unit 1, Side 2,
"What's in a Cell?"

Chapter 5

Life Science Videodisc
Unit 1, Side 2,
"Evolution of Cells"

Chapter 2

Answers to Self-Assessment

Caption Question

Figure 16 The genetic material in a bacterial cell is found in the cytoplasm.

Bacterial Cells

Using the Visuals: Figure 16

Call students' attention to the figure, and then read the following description from the text of a bacterial cell's genetic material: ". . . a thick, tangled string found in the cytoplasm." Ask: **Can you find this bacterium's genetic material?** *(Help students who cannot find the genetic material locate it in the figure.)* **Besides a nucleus, what organelles does this bacterium appear to be lacking?** *(Possible answers include mitochondria, chloroplasts, and endoplasmic reticulum.)* **learning modality: visual**

Building Inquiry Skills: Observing

Materials *soil, water, plastic dropper, microscope slide, coverslip, microscope*
Time 15 minutes

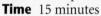

Have students observe bacterial cells under a microscope. Mix soil into water, and let the mixture sit out in an open, shallow container for several days. Then place drops of the water on microscope slides. Invite students to observe the water under high power and sketch any bacterial cells they find. Have them compare their sketches with photos of bacteria from either textbooks or encyclopedias. **learning modality: visual**

Ongoing Assessment

Skills Check Have each student create a table listing at least five organelles in the cell and summarizing their functions.

Portfolio Students can save their tables in their portfolios.

Structure and Function in Cells

Help visual learners relate cell structure to function. First have students compare the nerve cell and the red blood cells shown in the figure with the model animal cell shown on page 143. Then ask: **In what ways do the real cells look different from the model?** (*The nerve cell looks like it has "arms," and the red blood cells look flattened or donut-shaped.*) **How do you think each cell's shape helps it do its job?** (*The "arms" on nerve cells help them reach out and send messages to other cells; the flatness of red blood cells helps them squeeze through tiny blood vessels.*)
learning modality: visual

Levels of Organization

Building Inquiry Skills: Classifying

Have students work in small groups. Assign each group one of the following organs: lung, small intestine, kidney, brain, rib, heart, thyroid gland, biceps, skin, pancreas. Using books in the library, have students find out the name of the organ system to which their assigned organ belongs. Have groups share their findings by making a class chart on the board. Write the heads *Organ* and *Organ System* on the board. Have one student from each group make and complete a row for the organ that his or her group was assigned. **cooperative learning**

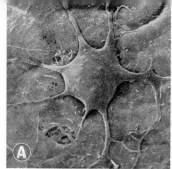
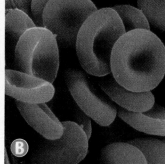

Figure 17 Your body contains a variety of different types of cells. **(A)** Nerve cells have long projections through which messages are sent throughout the body. **(B)** Red blood cells are thin and flexible, which allows them to fit through tiny blood vessels.

Structure and Function in Cells

Unlike bacteria and other single-celled organisms, plants, animals, and other complex organisms contain many cells. Cells in many complex organisms are specialized—that is, different kinds of cells perform different functions. Many plants, for example have root cells that are specialized to absorb water from soil. In animals, one kind of specialized cells—muscle cells—enables movement. Nerve cells are specialized to carry messages that enable the animal to respond to external and internal stimuli.

The structure of specialized cells enables them to perform their functions. For example, red blood cells, such as those shown in Figure 17, carry oxygen throughout the body. Their thin, flexible structure helps them squeeze through tiny blood vessels. Nerve cells have long, threadlike projections that act something like telephone wires. These "wires" carry messages throughout your body.

Levels of Organization

Cells in complex organisms interact with other cells to perform their functions. This can happen because cells are grouped together. **The bodies of many multicellular organisms have four levels of organization—cells, tissues, organs, and organ systems.**

A group of cells that performs a specialized function is called a **tissue.** Your body contains tissues specialized for functions such as absorbing materials, transporting materials, and support. Bone tissue demonstrates how structure relates to function at the tissue level of organization. The cells in bone tissue produce a hard, strong material that supports the body.

The next level of organization is the **organ,** which is a group of tissues that perform a specific function. The stomach, heart, and bones in your body are organs. Like cells and tissues, organs have structures that help them perform their function. Bones, which support the body, are hard and sturdy because of the tissues of which they are composed. In addition, bones come together in joints. Joints give your body flexibility and enable movement.

146

Background

Integrating Science Thanks to chemical technology, many worn-out or damaged organs can be replaced totally or in part by plastics. Plastics can be stronger than steel or lighter than a sheet of paper. Two properties—harmlessness to the human body and unaffected by chemicals in the body—make certain plastics useful in medicine. For example, if a hip, knee, elbow, or shoulder joint breaks because of an accident or wears out from a disease (such as arthritis), it can be replaced with an artificial joint made of plastics. Plastics have also been used to replace parts of the intestines and faulty valves in the heart.

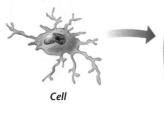

Cell

Tissue

Organ

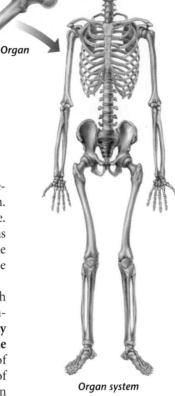

Organ system

Figure 18 An animal's skeletal system has different levels of organization. Bone cells make up tissues, and tissues make up organs such as the thigh bone.
Classifying Is the skull best classified as an organ or as a tissue?

An **organ system,** such as your digestive, circulatory, and skeletal systems, is a group of organs that perform a complex function. The skeletal system functions to support the body and give it shape. In addition, the skeleton protects delicate internal organs such as the brain and lungs. The strength and hardness of bones enable the skeleton to perform the functions of support and protection. The structure and arrangement of bones give the body its shape.

 INTEGRATING ENVIRONMENTAL SCIENCE Every organism interacts with other organisms and the environment in which it lives. **Because of this interaction, many environmental scientists add another level of organization: the population.** A **population** is all the members of one kind of organism in a particular area. So you can think of the levels of organization in living things this way: cells, tissues, organs, organ systems, organisms, and populations.

Section 3 Review

1. What is the function of the cell membrane?
2. Why is the nucleus sometimes called the control center of the cell?
3. Name two plant cell parts that are not found in animal cells. What is the function of each part?
4. Describe the levels of organization that complex organisms exhibit.
5. **Thinking Critically Inferring** How might a cell wall be an advantage to a bacterial cell? (*Hint:* Think of the functions of the cell wall in plant cells.)

Science at Home

Building Blocks Ask family members to help you find five items in your house that are made of smaller things. Make a list of the items and identify as many of their building blocks as you can. Be sure to look at prepared foods, furniture, and books. Discuss with your family how these building blocks come together to make up the larger objects. Do these objects or their building blocks possess any characteristics of living things?

Answers to Self-Assessment

Caption Question

Figure 18 The skull is best classified as an organ.

3 Assess

Section 3 Review Answers

1. It separates a cell from its environment and controls what substances go into and come out of the cell.
2. It holds the genetic material, which contains the instructions for the cell's functions.
3. The cell wall supports and stiffens the cell, and the chloroplasts make food for the cell.
4. Complex organisms exhibit four levels of organization: cells, the building blocks of living things; tissues, groups of cells that perform specialized functions, such as transporting materials; organs, groups of tissues, such as the heart that perform specific functions; and organ systems, groups of organs that perform complex functions such as circulation. A fifth level of organization, the population, is all the members of one kind or organism in an area.
5. A cell wall might help protect a bacterial cell.

Science at Home

Suggest that students look for items made of **ACTIVITY** smaller things in five different areas of their homes or among five different types of things. For example, students could look for items in the kitchen, living room, bedrooms, and bathroom. Or they could look for foods, toys, furniture, or tools.

Performance Assessment

Drawing Have students draw a plant cell, animal cell, and bacterial cell and label their structures.

A Magnified View of Life

Preparing for Inquiry

Key Concept Plant and animals cells have both similarities and differences.

Skills Objectives Students will be able to
◆ observe and draw cells under the microscope;
◆ compare and contrast plant and animal cells.

Time 40 minutes

Advance Planning You can order prepared slides of animal cells from a biological supply company.

Alternative Materials You may wish to have students use prepared slides of plant cells instead of preparing their own slides.

Guiding Inquiry

Troubleshooting the Experiment

◆ Tell students to raise the lenses before going from low to high power so they do not damage the microscope or slide.
◆ Check to be sure students have focused their microscopes correctly.
◆ Remind students to label their diagrams with the magnification.

Expected Outcome

Students should observe individual plant and animal cells under the microscope and draw diagrams that show their similarities and differences.

Analyze and Conclude

1. Both kinds of cells have a cell membrane, nucleus, and such organelles as mitochondria and ribosomes.
2. Plant cells have a cell wall and chloroplasts, whereas animal cells do not.
3. The color is green; it comes from chloroplasts in the plant cells.
4. So you do not forget details

Extending the Inquiry

More to Explore Provide students with slides of animal cells that look very different, such as red blood cells and muscle cells, and check that students can identify differences among them.

A Magnified View of Life

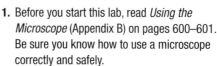

In this lab, you will use your observation skills to compare plant and animal cells.

Problem

How are plant and animal cells alike and different?

Materials

plastic dropper
water
microscope slide
microscope
colored pencils
prepared slide of animal cells

Elodea leaf
forceps
coverslip

Procedure

1. Before you start this lab, read *Using the Microscope* (Appendix B) on pages 600–601. Be sure you know how to use a microscope correctly and safely.

Part 1 Observing Plant Cells

2. Use a plastic dropper to place a drop of water in the center of a slide. **CAUTION:** *Slides and coverslips are fragile. Handle them carefully. Do not touch broken glass.*
3. With forceps, remove a leaf from an *Elodea* plant. Place the leaf in the drop of water on the slide. Make sure that the leaf is flat. If it is folded, straighten it with the forceps.
4. Holding a coverslip by its edges, slowly lower it onto the drop of water and *Elodea* leaf. If any air bubbles form, tap the slide gently to get rid of them.

5. Use a microscope to examine the *Elodea* leaf under low power. Then, carefully switch to high power.
6. Observe the cells of the *Elodea* leaf. Draw and label what you see, including the colors of the cell parts. Record the magnification.
7. Discard the *Elodea* leaf as directed by your teacher. Carefully clean and dry your slide and coverslip. Wash your hands thoroughly.

Part 2 Observing Animal Cells

8. Obtain a prepared slide of animal cells. The cells on the slide have been stained with an artificial color.
9. Observe the animal cells with a microscope under both low and high power. Draw and label the cell parts that you see. Record the magnification.

Analyze and Conclude

1. How are plant and animal cells alike?
2. How are plant and animal cells different?
3. What natural color appeared in the plant cells? What structures give the plant cells this color?
4. **Think About It** Why is it important to record your observations while you are examining a specimen?

More to Explore

Observe other prepared slides of animal cells. Look for ways that animal cells differ from each other. Obtain your teacher's permission before carrying out these observations.

148

Program Resources

◆ **Unit 2 Resources** Chapter 4 Skills Lab blackline masters, pp. 28–29

Media and Technology

Lab Activity Videotapes
Grade 6, Tape 1

Safety

Remind students to handle glass slides and coverslips carefully. Review the safety guidelines in Appendix A.

SECTION 4 Introduction to Genetics

DISCOVER • ACTIVITY

Can You Identify the Mother?

1. Look at the photograph of the girl. Carefully observe the characteristics of her face.

2. Now look at the photographs of each of the three women. Observe their characteristics.

3. One of the women is the girl's mother. Decide which woman is the mother.

Think It Over

Observing What characteristics did you use to make your decision?

Y ou have probably noticed that offspring tend to resemble their parents. Maybe you see that your cousin's hair is the same color as his mother's. If you save seeds from sunflowers in the fall and then plant them the next spring, the flowers that grow look like sunflowers. They don't look like tulips or lilies. The new sunflowers resemble the flowers of the plants that produced the seeds.

Offspring resemble parents because organisms inherit characteristics from their parents. The physical characteristics that an organism can pass on to its offspring are called **traits.** Human traits include such characteristics as eye color and whether hair is straight or curly. Some traits of sunflowers are the color and shape of the petals, the shape of the leaves, and the way leaves are arranged on the stem.

Parents to Offspring

In Section 3, you learned that chromatin in the nucleus of the cell contains genetic material that directs the cell's activities. This genetic material also plays a role in **heredity,** or the process by which traits pass from parents to offspring. **Organisms resemble their parents because they inherit genetic material from their parents. Genetic material is contained in cells.** The scientific study of heredity is called genetics.

GUIDE FOR READING

◆ What determines the characteristics that an organism inherits?

◆ What is selective breeding?

Reading Tip As you read, make an outline of this section. Use the main headings as the main topics for your outline.

Key Terms trait • heredity
• DNA • gene
• asexual reproduction
• sexual reproduction
• sperm • egg
• selective breeding

Chapter 4 **149**

SECTION 4 Introduction to Genetics

Objectives

After completing the lesson, students will be able to
◆ identify cells as structures containing genetic material, and interpret the role of genes in inheritance;
◆ differentiate between asexual and sexual reproduction;
◆ identify some changes in traits that can occur over several generations through natural occurrence and selective breeding.

1 Engage/Explore

Activating Prior Knowledge

Ask students if they have ever noticed that some traits such as freckles, height, and food allergies "run" in families. Then ask students to offer their ideas on how such traits are passed from parents to offspring. Write their ideas on the board and revise these later as students progress through this section.

• • • • • • • • DISCOVER • • • • • • • •

Skills Focus observing
Time 5 minutes
Tips Allow visually challenged students to work with partners who can clearly describe the photographs aloud. Students can remain in pairs, discussing the photographs and formulating answers together.
Expected Outcome The woman on the far right is the girl's mother.
Think It Over Students may mention characteristics such as hair color and shape of face and mouth.

---

2 Facilitate

Parents to Offspring

Using the Visuals: Figure 20

Ask students to compare the puppies to their mother. Then ask students if any of the puppies' characteristics give hints about what the father is like. **learning modality: visual**

The Role of Genes in Inheritance

Using the Visuals: Figure 19

Call students' attention to the figure. Have them compare and contrast the two ducks. Ask: **What characteristics do these ducks share?** (*Sample: The ducks have a similar shape, a bill, are male, have wings and colorful plumage, and can float on the surface of water.*) Ask: **In what ways are the ducks different?** (*Sample: Their plumage and markings are different; their bills differ in shape, color, and size.*) Ask: **Which of the traits that you identified are determined by genes?** (*All the traits are determined by genes.*) **learning modality: visual**

Asexual and Sexual Reproduction

Including All Students

To help students understand the variation that comes from sexual reproduction, draw two dogs on the board (stick figures will do). One dog should have long legs, a straight tail, and pointed ears. The other dog should have short legs, a curled tail, and floppy ears. Ask students to draw one possible offspring of a mating between these two dogs. Make sure that students choose one of the two expressions of each of the three traits (leg length, tail, ears). Call on volunteers to describe or show their drawings. You may wish to tally how often students chose the different combinations of traits. (Eight different combinations of these three traits are possible.) **learning modaltiy: logical/mathematical**

150

Figure 19 The wood duck (top) and the mallard (bottom) are similar in some ways but different in others. Their similarities and differences are determined by genes.

Figure 20 This cell (left) is reproducing asexually, by dividing into two new cells that will be identical to the original cell. In contrast, dogs reproduce sexually. The puppies (right) are not identical to either of their parents.

The Role of Genes in Inheritance

Chromosomes are partly composed of long-chain molecules called deoxyribonucleic acid (dee ahk see ry boh noo KLEE ic), or DNA. **DNA** is the genetic material that carries information about an organism that is passed from parents to offspring.

Some of the DNA in chromosomes consists of genes. A **gene** is a section of DNA that controls a trait that an organism inherits. For example, a gene determines whether or not you have dimples when you smile. The structure of a grasshopper's wing and the shape of a maple leaf are both determined by genes. Genes are like recipes. Just as a recipe contains instructions for preparing food, genes contain instructions for building and running cells. Each chromosome contains a large number of genes.

Asexual and Sexual Reproduction

Genetic material is passed from parents to offspring during reproduction. Some organisms, such as bacteria, usually reproduce asexually. **Asexual reproduction** is a reproductive process that involves only one parent, not two. The offspring of asexual reproduction have genes that are identical to those of the parent organism. A bacterial cell, for example, usually reproduces asexually by dividing into two new cells. The genes in the new cells are exactly like the genes in the parent cell. Therefore, the two new bacterial cells will have the same traits, and these traits will be the same as those of the parent cell.

Many organisms, including most animals and many plants, reproduce sexually. In **sexual reproduction,** new organisms result from the combination of genetic material from two parent organisms. New organisms are usually produced by the joining of sperm and eggs, which are cells that are specialized for reproduction. A **sperm** is the male sex cell, and an **egg** is the female sex cell. Both the sperm and the egg contain genetic material. The traits of the new organism are determined by genetic material from both the male and the female parents.

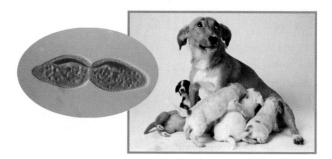

150

Background

History of Science In Section 2, students read about the role of Anton van Leeuwenhoeck in the invention of the microscope and the development of cell theory. Leeuwenhoeck was the first person to observe human sperm under a microscope. In 1677, he hypothesized that sperm contained a miniature child that grew larger inside the mother's body. Not until 1879, after significant improvements had been made in the microscope, did scientists observe the joining of egg and sperm in animals. This observation, first made by German zoologists Herman Fol and Oscar Hertwig, led scientists to formulate a correct hypothesis about the roles of male and female sex cells in reproduction.

Figure 21 Many garden flowers, such as these zinnias, are the result of selective breeding. *Inferring What traits would be desirable in garden flowers?*

Sexual Reproduction and Change

The offspring of sexually reproducing organisms, such as humans, inherit genetic material from both parents. Therefore, while children may resemble their parents, they are not exactly like either their mother or their father. Children usually look even less like their grandparents. And there may be very little resemblance between great-grandchildren and their great-grandparents. Sexually reproducing organisms change from generation to generation. That happens because the genetic material is re-sorted, over and over, each time reproduction occurs.

☑ *Checkpoint* *Why aren't the offspring of sexually reproducing organisms identical to either of their parents?*

Changing Traits by Selective Breeding

Since the beginning of agriculture, farmers have tried to improve the quality of crops and farm animals. **Selective breeding** is a technique used to improve the quality of organisms by selecting, or choosing, certain organisms for reproduction. **In selective breeding, organisms that have certain desired traits are mated to produce offspring with the desired traits of both parents. The desired traits are produced by the combination of genetic material that the offspring inherit from both of their parents.** The process of selective breeding may take many generations to produce organisms with the desired combination of traits. Selective breeding has produced prize-winning racehorses, cotton plants that yield strong fibers, and large, juicy tomatoes.

Santa Gertrudis cattle, which originated on the King Ranch in southeastern Texas, were produced by selective breeding. Around 1910, breeders on the King Ranch began mating Brahman cattle with shorthorn cattle, hoping to produce cattle with the desired traits of both breeds. Shorthorn cattle have tender and tasty beef but do not do well in the hot environment of the King Ranch. In contrast, hardy Brahman cattle thrive in the heat, but the beef they produce is not as good as the shorthorns' beef.

Observing

Use reference materials to learn more about different breeds of cats. Consult books, encyclopedias, and multimedia resources. You can also contact local veterinarians and cat breeders.

Choose cats from two breeds and observe their photographs carefully. Read the text descriptions of each cat's traits. Create a compare/contrast table that compares three traits in these breeds, such as eye color, length of hair, and shape of head and face.

Sexual Reproduction and Change

Building Inquiry Skills: Observing

Show students photographs of family groups. Ask students to identify some traits that can be seen in family members. Have students tell how children are similar and different from the parents. **learning modality: visual**

Changing Traits by Selective Breeding

Sharpen your **Skills**

Observing

Materials *books, encyclopedias, multimedia resources*
Time 30 minutes
Expected Outcome Students can find information by searching an encyclopedia or library catalog using a head such as "modern cat breeds" or the names of specific breeds such as Burmese and Havana brown. You may wish to have students work in pairs, each researching to find information about one cat breed. A sample compare/contrast table appears below.

Trait	Burmese	Havana brown
eye color	gold	green
length of hair	short	short
coat color	sable, blue, champagne, or platinum	brown

Extend Have students extend their tables by comparing and contrasting the same traits in two additional cat breeds. Alternatively, have students repeat the activity, this time comparing and contrasting traits in two dog breeds. **learning modality: visual**

Ongoing Assessment

Writing Have students explain how genes are like recipes or use a different analogy to explain the role of genes in inheritance.

151

Answers to Self-Assessment

Caption Question

Figure 21 Traits such as petal color, flower shape, fragrance, and resistance to pests and disease would be desirable in garden flowers.

☑ *Checkpoint*

Offspring of sexually reproducing organisms inherit genetic material from both parents, so they are not identical to either one.

Changing Traits in Nature

Addressing Naive Conceptions

Students may think that insects develop resistance to chemicals as a result of being exposed to the chemicals. Remind students that the resistance was always there in some individual insects. When the chemicals were applied, they killed off many insects, leaving the resistant ones to breed. Compare the "selection" of the resistant insects by the chemical to the selection of certain animals by a breeder. Ask students if they have heard of drug-resistant bacteria. The use of antibiotics on bacteria can have similar effects to the use of chemicals on insects. If some bacteria are resistant to an antibiotic and survive its use, their offspring will have the same resistance, and will not be killed by more of the same antibiotic. **learning modality: logical/mathematical**

3 Assess

Section 4 Review Answers

1. The traits that an organism inherits from its parents are determined by genes.
2. Selective breeding
3. Asexual reproduction involves only one parent; sexual reproduction involves two parent organisms. Genetic material is inherited in both kinds of reproduction.
4. Sample: No, because some human characteristics, such as being a good friend or a cooperative student, can be determined by a person's environment or by changes in a person's environment.

.... CHAPTER PROJECT

Check Your Progress

Provide students with guidelines to analyze their data and design their displays.

Performance Assessment

Skills Check Have students make a flowchart that shows the steps involved in producing heat-resistant cattle with flavorful, tender beef.

Figure 22 Santa Gertrudis cattle were bred on the King Ranch in Texas.

Eventually, several generations of selective breeding produced heat-resistant cattle with tender, flavorful beef. This new breed of cattle was named Santa Gertrudis. The genes of Santa Gertrudis cattle come from both shorthorn and Brahman cattle. Now, generation after generation, Santa Gertrudis cattle pass the desirable characteristics on to their offspring.

☑ *Checkpoint* *What is selective breeding?*

Changing Traits in Nature

Selective breeding is planned and carried out by farmers and breeders. But the traits of organisms can also change over generations naturally. The changes that occur in organisms often help those organisms survive better in their environments.

Consider, for example, what often happens when chemicals called pesticides are used to kill harmful insects. When a pesticide is first used on a field, it kills almost all the insects in the field. But a few insects survive because they have naturally occurring changes in some genes that help them resist the pesticide. The surviving insects reproduce. When those insects reproduce, some of their offspring inherit genes that enable the offspring to survive the pesticide. This process happens over and over, generation after generation. In each generation, the only insects that survive are those that are resistant to the harmful effects of the pesticide. After many years, most of the insects in the field will be resistant to the pesticide. The pesticide has lost its effectiveness, because it can no longer kill most of the harmful insects.

? Section 4 Review

1. What determines the traits that an organism inherits from its parents?
2. What is the name for the process that produced Santa Gertrudis cattle?
3. What is the difference between asexual reproduction and sexual reproduction?
4. **Thinking Critically** **Inferring** Do you think that all of an organism's characteristics are determined by genes? Explain your answer.

Check Your Progress CHAPTER PROJECT

Now that you have completed your observations, analyze your data. Arrange your data in a chart or diagram. Find another object that is familiar to you and similar to your mystery object. Compare the two objects. Conclude whether your object is alive.

Program Resources

◆ **Unit 2 Resources** 4-4 Review and Reinforce, p. 23; 4-4 Enrich, p. 24

Answers to Self-Assessment

☑ *Checkpoint*

Selective breeding is a technique in which organisms that have desired traits are mated to produce offspring with the desired traits of both parents.

Concept Map Sample Title: Needs of Living Things; **a.** water **b.** living space **c.** autotrophs **d.** heterotrophs **e.** food and water

SECTION 1 — What Is Life?

Key Ideas
◆ All living things are made of cells, contain similar chemicals, use energy, grow and develop, respond to their surroundings, and reproduce.
◆ An organism's structure is the way it is made. The function of a part of an organism is the job it performs.
◆ All living things need energy, water, living space, and stable internal conditions.

Key Terms
organism	external stimulus	spontaneous
cell	internal stimulus	generation
structure	response	autotroph
function	reproduce	heterotroph
stimulus		homeostasis

SECTION 2 — Discovering Cells
INTEGRATING TECHNOLOGY

Key Ideas
◆ The microscope enabled the discovery of cells.
◆ Cells make up all living things, are the basic units of structure and function in living things, and are produced from other cells.

Key Terms
microscope	magnification
compound microscope	resolution
cell theory	

SECTION 3 — Looking Inside Cells

Key Ideas
◆ Levels of organization in complex organisms include cells, tissues, organs, and organ systems.

Key Terms
organelle	endoplasmic	prokaryote
cell wall	reticulum	eukaryote
cell membrane	ribosome	tissue
nucleus	Golgi body	organ
chromosome	chloroplast	organ system
cytoplasm	vacuole	population
mitochondria	lysosome	

SECTION 4 — Introduction to Genetics

Key Ideas
◆ Organisms resemble their parents because they inherit genetic material from their parents. Genetic material is contained in DNA in cells.
◆ In selective breeding, organisms that have certain traits are mated to produce the desired traits in their offspring. The desired traits are produced by the combination of genes that the offspring inherit from both their parents.

Key Terms
trait	sexual reproduction
heredity	sperm
DNA	egg
gene	selective breeding
asexual reproduction	

Organizing Information

Concept Map Copy the concept map about the needs of organisms onto a separate sheet of paper. Then complete it and add a title. (For more on concept maps, see the Skills Handbook.)

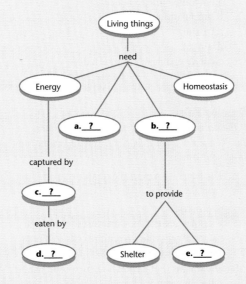

Program Resources

◆ **Unit 2 Resources** Chapter 4 Project Scoring Rubric, p. 4
◆ **Performance Assessment** Chapter 4, pp. 14–16
◆ **Chapter and Unit Tests** Chapter 4 Test, pp. 20–23

Media and Technology

Computer Test Bank
Chapter 4 Test

Reviewing Content
Multiple Choice
1. b 2. a 3. c 4. b 5. d

True or False
6. an organ 7. compound
8. Mitochondria 9. true 10. autotrophs

Checking Concepts
11. Students might point out that plants will bend toward sunlight and that plants grow, develop, and reproduce.
12. The structure of the skeletal system, its strength and hardness of bones, enable this organ system to perform its functions of support and protection.
13. The microscope allowed scientists to observe the cells that make up living things. Over the years, they discovered that all living things are made up of cells.
14. Selective breeding is a technique used to improve the quality of organisms by choosing certain organisms for reproduction. Selected organisms, which have certain desired traits, are mated to produce offspring with the desired traits of both parents.
15. Sample: A plant might respond to light by bending toward it.
16. Students' articles should describe the discoveries of either Robert Hooke or Anton van Leeuwenhoek and relate them to the microscope.

Thinking Critically
17. Although all robots use energy and some respond to their surroundings, they do not use energy to grow and develop. Living things are made out of cells and are able to reproduce themselves.
18. This recipe may have worked because the grains attracted mice into the open pot. To disprove this, you could observe the pot to make sure mice did not enter, or cover the pot so air could enter, but mice could not.
19. The cell theory states that all living things are composed of cells, that cells are the basic unit of structure and function in living things, and that all cells are produced from other cells. A dog is a living thing. Therefore, a dog is composed of cells, cells are the basic unit of structure and function in a dog, and all the dog's cells are produced from other cells.

Reviewing Content
 Review key concepts online using iText at www.phschool.com

Multiple Choice
Choose the letter of the best answer.

1. The idea that life could spring from nonliving matter is called
   a. development.
   b. spontaneous generation.
   c. homeostasis.
   d. evolution.
2. The ability of microscopes to distinguish fine details is called
   a. resolution.
   b. bending.
   c. magnification.
   d. active transport.
3. In plant and animal cells, the control center of the cell is the
   a. chloroplast.
   b. ribosome.
   c. nucleus.
   d. Golgi body.
4. All of one kind of organism in an area make up a(n)
   a. chromosome.
   b. population.
   c. tissue.
   d. organ.
5. Genetic material is contained in
   a. vacuoles   b. cell walls
   c. lysosomes   d. DNA

True or False
If the statement is true, write true. If it is false, change the underlined word or words to make the statement true.

6. The heart is an example of <u>an organ system</u>.
7. Cells were discovered using <u>electron</u> microscopes.
8. <u>Vacuoles</u> are the "powerhouses" of the cell.
9. Bacterial cells differ from the cells of plants and animals in that they lack a <u>nucleus</u>.
10. Organisms that make their own food are called <u>heterotrophs</u>.

Checking Concepts
11. Your friend thinks that plants are not alive because they do not move. How would you respond to your friend?
12. Explain how the structure of the skeletal system is related to its function.
13. What role did the microscope play in the development of the cell theory?
14. What is selective breeding?
15. Give an example of an external stimulus and describe how an organism might respond to this stimulus.
16. **Writing to Learn** Suppose you had been a reporter assigned to cover early scientists' discoveries about cells. Write a brief article for your daily newspaper that explains one scientist's discoveries. Be sure to explain both how the discoveries were made and why they are important.

Thinking Critically
17. **Classifying** How do you know that a robot is not alive?
18. **Relating Cause and Effect** When people believed that spontaneous generation occurred, there was a recipe for making mice: Place a dirty shirt and a few wheat grains in an open pot; wait three weeks. List the reasons why this recipe might have worked. How could you demonstrate that spontaneous generation was not responsible for the appearance of mice?
19. **Applying Concepts** Explain how the cell theory applies to a dog.
20. **Predicting** Could a cell survive without a cell membrane? Give reasons to support your answer.
21. **Comparing and Contrasting** How are plant and animal cells similar? How are they different? To answer these questions, make a list of the different organelles in each cell. Explain how each organelle is vital to the life and function of a plant or animal.

20. A cell could not survive without a cell membrane because it would not have a barrier to control what substances moved into and out of the cell.
21. They both have nuclei. Plant cells have cell walls and chloroplasts and animal cells do not.
Mitichondria—produce energy for plant and animal cells
Edoplasmic reticulum—provides an internal transport system for plant and animal cells

Ribosomes—places where proteins are produced in plant and animal cells
Golgi bodies—package and distribute protein made in plant and animal cells
Chloroplasts—make food in plant cells
Vacuole—storage areas in plant and some animal cells
Lysosomes—contain chemicals that break down food particles

Applying Skills

A student designed an experiment to test how light affects the growth of plants. Refer to the illustrations below to answer Questions 22–25.

22. Controlling Variables Is this a controlled experiment? If not, why not? If so, identify the manipulated variable.

23. Developing Hypotheses What hypothesis might this experiment be testing?

24. Predicting Based on what you know about plants, predict how each plant will have changed after two weeks.

25. Designing Experiments Design a controlled experiment to determine whether the amount of water that a plant receives affects its growth.

Performance ▼ Assessment
CHAPTER PROJECT

Present Your Project Prepare a display presenting your conclusion about your mystery object. Describe the observations that helped you reach your conclusion. Compare your ideas with those of other students. If necessary, defend your work.

Reflect and Record Make a list of the characteristics of life that you observed in your mystery object. Which were hard to study? Explain in your journal why some characteristics were hard to investigate.

Applying Skills

22. Yes; the light is the manipulated variable.

23. Sample hypothesis: If plants do not have enough light, they will die.

24. In two weeks, the plant on the left will be dead, but the plant on the right will be healthy.

25. Sample experiment: Two plants receive the same light, but one receives one-fourth cup of water a day, and the other one-fourth cup every two days.

Performance ▼ Assessment
CHAPTER PROJECT

Present Your Project Students' displays should be well organized and describe how students tested their hypotheses. Have each student give a brief presentation to the class describing how the results of their tests support their conclusions. Encourage students to talk about results that they found surprising.

Reflect and Record Students may have had trouble determining whether their object was alive if it was a fungus, a plant, or an animal such as coral that does not move.

Test Preparation

Use these questions to prepare for standardized tests.

Study the table. Then answer Questions 26–30.

Cell	Nucleus	Cell Wall	Cell Membrane
Cell A	Yes	Yes	Yes
Cell B	Yes	No	Yes
Cell C	No	Yes	Yes

26. Which cell is probably an animal cell?
  A cell A   **B** cell B
  C cell C   **D** none of the above

27. Which cell is probably a plant cell?
  F cell A   **G** cell B
  H cell C   **J** none of the above

28. Which cell is a prokaryote?
  A cell A   **B** cell B
  C cell C   **D** none of the above

29. In Cell B, where would the genetic material be found?
  F in the mitochondria
  G in the vacuoles
  H in the nucleus
  J in the cell membrane

30. Which cell(s) would most likely contain chloroplasts?
  A cell A   **B** cell B
  C cell C   **D** cell B and cell C

Test Preparation

26. B **27.** F **28.** C **29.** H **30.** A

Program Resources

◆ **Inquiry Skills Activity Book** Provides teaching and review of all inquiry skills
◆ **Prentice Hall Assessment System** Provides standardized test practice
◆ **Reading in the Content Area** Provides strategies to improve science reading skills
◆ **Teacher's ELL Handbook** Provides multiple strategies for English language learners

Cell Processes and Energy

Sections	Time	Student Edition Activities	Other Activities	
CHAPTER PROJECT **Egg-speriment with a Cell** p. 157 TEKS: 6.10B	Ongoing (2–3 weeks)	TEKS: 6.1A; 6.2B, C, D, E; 6.3C Check Your Progress, pp. 162, 168, 177 Present Your Project, p. 181	TE	Chapter 5 Project Notes, pp. 156–157
1 The Cell in Its Environment pp. 158–162 TEKS: 6.10A, B 5.1.1 Describe the three methods by which materials move into and out of cells. 5.1.2 Compare passive transport to active transport. 5.1.3 Explain why cells are small.	2–3 periods/ 1–1½ blocks	TEKS: 6.2A, B, C **Discover** How Do Molecules Move?, p. 158 **Try This** Diffusion in Action, p. 160	TE TE TE TE LM	Including All Students, p. 159 Integrating Chemistry, p. 159 Demonstration, p. 160, 162 Inquiry Challenge, p. 161 5, "Cell Membranes and Permeability"
2 🔵 **INTEGRATING CHEMISTRY** **The Cell and Energy** pp. 163–169 TEKS: 6.10B 5.2.1 Describe the process of photosynthesis. 5.2.2 Explain how the sun supplies all organisms with the energy they need. 5.2.3 Describe the events that occur during respiration. 5.2.4 Describe the relationship between photosynthesis and respiration. 5.2.5 Describe alcoholic and lactic-acid fermentation.	2–3 periods/ 1–1½ blocks	TEKS: 6.1A; 6.2B, C, D, E; 6.4A **Discover** Where Does the Energy Come From?, p. 163 **Try This,** Yeast Fest, p. 167 **Real-World Lab: You and Your Environment** Gases in Balance, p. 169	TE TE	Building Inquiry Skills: Making Models, p. 164 Inquiry Challenge, p. 166
3 Cell Division pp. 170–178 TEKS: 6.10B; 6.11B 5.3.1 Identify the events that take place during the three stages of the cell cycle. 5.3.2 Describe the structure of DNA and DNA replication.	2–3 periods/ 1–1½ blocks	TEKS: 6.1A; 6.2A, B, C, D, E; 6.3C; 6.4A **Discover** What Are the Cells Doing?, p. 170 **Try This** Modeling Mitosis, p. 172 **Sharpen Your Skills** Interpreting Data, p. 173 **Skills Lab: Calculating** Multiplying by Dividing, p. 178	TE TE TE TE	Building Inquiry Skills: Calculating, p. 172 Demonstration, p. 173 Inquiry Challenge, pp. 174, 175, 176 Including All Students, p. 175
Study Guide/Chapter Assessment pp. 179–181	1 period/ ½ block	**PLM** Provides blackline masters for Probeware labs	**ISAB**	Provides teaching and review of all inquiry skills

Key: **CTB** Computer Test Bank
CUT Chapter and Unit Tests
ELL Teacher's ELL Handbook

CHAPTER PLANNING GUIDE

 The Resource Pro® CD-ROM provides flexibility for planning the instruction for any type of schedule.

Program Resources	Assessment Strategies	Media and Technology
UR Chapter 5 Project Teacher Notes, pp. 30–31 **UR** Chapter 5 Project Overview and Worksheets, pp. 32–35	**SE** Performance Assessment: Present Your Project, p. 181 **TE** Check Your Progress, pp. 162, 168, 177 **UR** Chapter 5 Project Scoring Rubric, p. 36	Science Explorer at www.phschool.com Student Edition on Audio CD, English-Spanish, Chapter 5
UR 5-1 Section Lesson Plan, p. 37 **UR** 5-1 Section Summary, p. 38 **UR** 5-1 Review and Reinforce, p. 39 **UR** 5-1 Enrich, p. 40	**SE** Section 1 Review, p. 162 **TE** Ongoing Assessment, pp. 159, 161 **TE** Performance Assessment, p. 162	Life Science Videodisc Unit 1, Side 2, "How Does It Get in There?" Videotape Grade 6, Unit 2, "How Does It Get in There?" Transparency 15, "Passive and Active Transport"
UR 5-2 Section Lesson Plan, p. 41 **UR** 5-2 Section Summary, p. 42 **UR** 5-2 Review and Reinforce, p. 43 **UR** 5-2 Enrich, p. 44 **UR** Real-World Lab blackline masters, pp. 49–50	**SE** Section 2 Review, p. 168 **TE** Ongoing Assessment, pp. 165, 167 **TE** Performance Assessment, p. 168	Lab Activity Videotapes, Tape 2 Transparency 16, "Photosynthesis"
UR 5-3 Section Lesson Plan, p. 45 **UR** 5-3 Section Summary, p. 46 **UR** 5-3 Review and Reinforce, p. 47 **UR** 5-3 Enrich, p. 48 **UR** Skills Lab blackline masters, pp. 51–53	**SE** Section 3 Review, p. 177 **TE** Ongoing Assessment, pp. 171, 173, 175 **TE** Performance Assessment, p. 177	Lab Activity Videotapes, Tape 2 Transparencies 17, "Exploring the Cell Cycle"; 18, "DNA Structure"; 19, "DNA Replication"
ELL Provides multiple strategies for English language learners **GRSW** Provides worksheets to promote student comprehension of content **RCA** Provides strategies to improve science reading skills	**SE** Chapter 5 Study Guide/Assessment, pp. 179–181 **PA** Chapter 5 Assessment, pp. 17–19 **CUT** Chapter 5 Test, pp. 24–27 **CTB** Chapter 5 Test **PHAS** Provides standardized test preparation	Chapter 5 Computer Test Bank, Chapter 5 Test

GRSW Guided Reading and Study Workbook
ISAB Inquiry Skills Activity Book
LM Laboratory Manual

PA Performance Assessment
PHAS Prentice Hall Assessment System
PLM Probeware Lab Manual

RCA Reading in the Content Area
SE Student Edition

TE Teacher's Edition
UR Unit Resources

Student Edition Activities Planner

ACTIVITY	Time (minutes)	Materials — Quantities for one work group	Skills
Section 1			
Discover, p. 158	10	**Consumable** air freshener spray	Developing Hypotheses
Try This, p. 160	10	**Consumable** cold water, food coloring **Nonconsumable** small clear plastic cup, plastic dropper	Inferring
Section 2			
Discover, p. 163	5	**Nonconsumable** solar-powered calculator that does not have batteries	Inferring
Try This, p. 167	20	**Consumable** warm water, 5 mL sugar, 1.0 mL dried yeast, 2 straws **Nonconsumable** 2 test tubes with stoppers, test tube rack	Observing
Real-World Lab, p. 169	20/15	**Consumable** 2 *Elodea* plants, bromthymol blue solution, straws **Nonconsumable** marking pens, 100-mL plastic graduated cylinder, 3 250-ml flasks with stoppers, light source	Controlling Variables, Interpreting Data
Section 3			
Discover, p. 170	15	**Consumable** yeast culture, methylene blue stain **Nonconsumable** plastic dropper, microscope slide with coverslip, microscope	Developing Hypotheses
Try This, p. 172	10	**Consumable** construction paper, 3 different colored pipe cleaners	Making Models
Sharpen Your Skills, p. 173	5	No special materials are required.	Interpreting Data
Skills Lab, p. 178	40	**Nonconsumable** microscope, colored pencils, calculator or computer (optional), prepared slides of onion root tip cells undergoing cell division	Observing, Calculating, Interpreting Data

A list of all materials required for the Student Edition activities can be found on pages T43–T49. You can obtain information about ordering materials by calling 1-800-848-9500 or by accessing the Science Explorer Internet site at **www.phschool.com**.

Texas Essential Knowledge and Skills

(6.1) Scientific processes. The student conducts field and laboratory investigations using safe, environmentally appropriate, and ethical practices. *(Project; Sections 2, 3)*
The student is expected to:
(A) demonstrate safe practices during field and laboratory investigations.

(6.2) Scientific processes. The student uses scientific inquiry methods during field and laboratory investigations. *(Project; Sections 1, 2, 3)*
The student is expected to:
(A) plan and implement investigative procedures including asking questions, formulating testable hypotheses, and selecting and using equipment and technology;
(B) collect data by observing and measuring;
(C) analyze and interpret information to construct reasonable explanations from direct and indirect evidence;
(D) communicate valid conclusions; and
(E) construct graphs, tables, maps, and charts using tools including computers to organize, examine, and evaluate data.

(6.3) Scientific processes. The student uses critical thinking and scientific problem solving to make informed decisions. *(Project; Section 3)*
The student is expected to:
(C) represent the natural world using models and identify their limitations.

(6.4) Scientific processes. The student knows how to use a variety of tools and methods to conduct science inquiry. *(Sections 2, 3)*
The student is expected to:
(A) collect, analyze, and record information using tools including beakers, petri dishes, meter sticks, graduated cylinders, weather instruments, timing devices, hot plates, test tubes, safety goggles, spring scales, magnets, balances, microscopes, telescopes, thermometers, calculators, field equipment, compasses, computers, and computer probes.

(6.10) Science concepts. The student knows the relationship between structure and function in living systems. *(Project; Sections 1, 2, 3)*
The student is expected to:
(A) differentiate between structure and function;
(B) determine that all organisms are composed of cells that carry on functions to sustain life.

(6.11) Science concepts. The student knows that traits of species can change through generations and that the instructions for traits are contained in the genetic material of the organisms. *(Section 3)*
The student is expected to:
(B) identify cells as structures containing genetic material.

Take It to the Net

 Interactive text at www.phschool.com

Science Explorer comes alive with iText.

■ **Complete student text** is accessible from any computer with Internet access or a CD-ROM drive.

■ **Animations, simulations, and videos** enhance student understanding and retention of concepts.

■ **Self-tests and online study tools** assess student understanding.

■ **Teacher management tools** help you make the most of this valuable resource.

STAY CURRENT with **SCIENCE NEWS**®

Find out the latest research and information about cells at **www.phschool.com**.

Go to **www.phschool.com**. Select Texas on the navigation bar. Click on the Science icon. Then click on <u>Science Explorer</u> under PH@school.

Egg-speriment With a Cell

TEKS: 6.1A; 6.2B, C, D, E; 6.3C; 6.10B

In the Chapter 5 Project, students will learn about an essential structure found in all cells—the cell membrane. During the course of the project, students will carry out experiments, make observations, and draw conclusions about how the cell membrane functions.

Purpose In the Chapter 5 Project, students will observe how fluids move across the semi-permeable membrane surrounding a raw egg.

Skills Focus After completing the Chapter 5 Project, students will be able to
◆ predict how various liquids will affect an egg;
◆ observe how the liquids affect the egg;
◆ measure and record changes in the egg;
◆ graph data of the egg's circumference;
◆ draw conclusions about what processes occurred during the experiment.

Project Time Line The project will require at least two weeks—longer if students break their eggs and have to start over. On the first day, have students read about the Chapter 5 Project in their text, and ask if they have any questions. Then hand out the Chapter 5 Project Overview and Student Worksheets, pages 32–35 in Unit 2 Resources. You might also wish to give students a copy of the Chapter 5 Project Scoring Rubric, page 36 in Unit 2 Resources, so they know what will be expected of them. Encourage students to read the Overview and do the Worksheets early in the project.

If students will be working in groups, divide the class into groups at this time. Also set aside some class time during the course of the project for group members to work on the project. If students are doing the project individually, allow a few minutes each day for students to share their observations and ask questions. Students might also need class time at the end of the project to prepare their presentations.

For more detailed information on planning and supervising the Chapter 5 Project, see Chapter 5 Project Teacher Notes, pages 30–31 in Unit 2 Resources.

CHAPTER

5 Cell Processes and Energy

The thin shells of these eggs control what substances reach the developing chick inside.

WEB ACTIVITY

www.phschool.com

156

Suggested Shortcuts To speed up the project, you can have each student soak his or her egg in a different liquid, after first soaking the eggs in vinegar for two days. One student should use water, one student water with food coloring, and one student salt water, but the other students could soak their eggs in a liquid of their choice. Then students can pool their results.

You can limit the amount of student involvement in the project by doing it as a class project. First have students brainstorm predictions about what will happen to the egg when it is soaked in the various liquids, and record their predictions on the chalkboard. Then set up the experiment with the egg soaking in a container of vinegar. Every other day change the liquid in which the egg is soaking, according to the directions in the text. Assign a different student to measure and record changes in the size of the egg each day, and give all the students a chance to observe how the egg is changing. Have each student create a data table and graph.

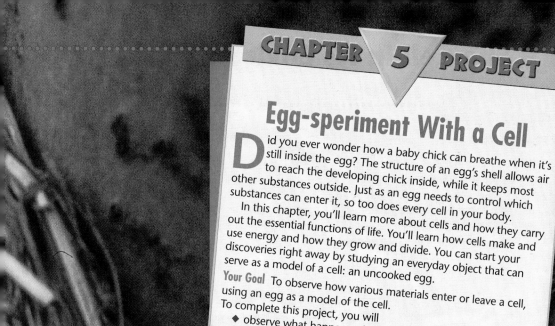

CHAPTER 5 PROJECT

Egg-speriment With a Cell

Did you ever wonder how a baby chick can breathe when it's still inside the egg? The structure of an egg's shell allows air to reach the developing chick inside, while it keeps most other substances outside. Just as an egg needs to control which substances can enter it, so too does every cell in your body.

In this chapter, you'll learn more about cells and how they carry out the essential functions of life. You'll learn how cells make and use energy and how they grow and divide. You can start your discoveries right away by studying an everyday object that can serve as a model of a cell: an uncooked egg.

Your Goal To observe how various materials enter or leave a cell, using an egg as a model of the cell.

To complete this project, you will

- observe what happens when you soak an uncooked egg in vinegar, then in water, food coloring, salt water, and finally in a liquid of your choice
- measure the circumference of the egg every day, and graph your results
- explain the changes that your egg underwent
- follow the safety guidelines in Appendix A

Get Started Predict what might happen when you put an uncooked egg in vinegar for two days. How might other liquids affect an egg? Find a place where you can leave your egg undisturbed. Then begin your egg-speriment!

Check Your Progress You will be working on this project as you study this chapter. To keep your project on track, look for Check Your Progress boxes at the following points.

Section 1 Review, page 162: Make measurements and record data.
Section 2 Review, page 168: Experiment with different liquids.
Section 3 Review, page 177: Graph your data and draw conclusions.

Present Your Project At the end of the chapter (page 181), you will display your egg and share your results.

TEKS

In addition to process TEKS, this chapter addresses these concept TEKS as they relate to the chapter's topics.

(6.10) The student knows the relationship between structure and function in living systems. The student is expected to:
(A) differentiate between structure and function;
(B) determine that all organisms are composed of cells that carry on functions to sustain life.

(6.11) The student knows that traits of species can change through generations and that the instructions for traits are contained in the genetic material of the organisms. The student is expected to:
(B) identify cells as structures containing genetic material.

157

Program Resources

- **Unit 2 Resources** Chapter 5 Project Teacher Notes, pp. 30–31; Chapter 5 Project Overview and Worksheets, pp. 32–35

Media and Technology

 Student Edition on Audio CD English-Spanish, Chapter 5

WEB ACTIVITY www.phschool.com

You will find an Internet activity, chapter self-tests for students, and links to other chapter topics at this site.

Possible Materials Any clean plastic containers can be used to soak the eggs, as long as the containers are large enough for the eggs to be completely covered by liquid. Plastic is better than glass because eggs are less likely to break if they bump against plastic. Containers with tight-fitting lids may help avoid spills and broken eggs, but lids are not necessary.

Students can use either white or brown eggs. Large eggs will show a greater change in size, making it easier for students to observe the results of osmosis. Make sure that none of the eggs is cracked to begin with. Encourage students to use a wide variety of liquids for soaking their eggs, such as corn syrup, milk, orange juice, or shampoo. To measure their egg, students can use a flexible cloth or vinyl tape or a piece of string and a ruler.

Launching the Project Introduce the project by showing students a chicken egg. State that the egg is similar to a single large cell. Point out that in this project, students will study an egg to learn more about how cells function. Ask: **Why do you think you will be using an egg to study the cell instead of an actual cell, such as a human skin cell?** *(Because most cells are too small to be seen without a microscope. Also, unlike most cells mounted on microscope slides, eggs are still alive.)* Say that, although a chicken egg is larger than any of the cells in their own bodies, it has many of the same structures. Explain that the cell membrane is the structure they will focus on in this project.

Performance Assessment

To assess students' performance in this project, use the Chapter 5 Project Scoring Rubric on page 36 of Unit 2 Resources. Students will be assessed on

- how accurately and consistently they make measurements and record their data;
- the neatness and accuracy of their graphs and diagrams;
- how well their conclusions display an understanding of the functions of a cell membrane;
- their participation in a group, if they worked in groups.

Objectives

After completing the lesson, students will be able to
◆ describe the three methods by which materials move into and out of cells;
◆ compare passive transport to active transport;
◆ explain why cells are small.

1 Engage/Explore

Activating Prior Knowledge

Introduce students to the idea of the cell membrane as a gatekeeper by helping them recall how a sieve or colander works. Ask: **Why might you use a sieve or colander?** (*Possible answers might include to strain lumps out of gravy or to drain vegetables or pasta.*) **What do all these things have in common?** (*They involve using a filter to separate large from small particles or solids from liquids.*) Tell students that the cell membrane acts like a filter, too, by allowing some substances, but not others, to pass in and out of the cell.

DISCOVER

Skills Focus developing hypotheses
Materials *air freshener spray*
Time 10 minutes
Tips When spraying the air freshener, spray up or down rather than in the direction of students.
Expected Outcome The spray should diffuse evenly throughout the classroom, reaching students at the same distance from the source at about the same time.
Think It Over The farther each student was from the teacher, the longer it took for the student to smell the air freshener. Students may hypothesize that particles in the spray moved from an area of higher concentration to an area of lower concentration.

158

SECTION
1 The Cell in Its Environment

DISCOVER · ACTIVITY

How Do Molecules Move?

1. With your classmates, stand so that you are evenly spaced throughout the classroom.

2. Your teacher will spray an air freshener into the room. When you first begin to smell the air freshener, raise your hand.

3. Note how long it takes for other students in the classroom to smell the scent.

Think It Over
Developing Hypotheses How was each student's distance from the teacher related to when he or she smelled the air freshener? Develop a hypothesis about why this pattern occurred.

GUIDE FOR READING

◆ How does the structure of the cell membrane relate to its function?

◆ What is the difference between passive transport and active transport?

Reading Tip Before you read, use the headings to make an outline about how materials move into and out of cells. As you read, make notes about each process.

Key Terms diffusion
• selectively permeable
• osmosis • passive transport
• active transport

▼ The *Mir* space station

158

How is a cell like a space station? The walls of a space station protect the astronauts inside from the airless vacuum of space. Food, water, and other supplies must be brought to the space station by shuttles from Earth. In addition, the space station needs to be able to get rid of wastes. The doors of the space station allow the astronauts to bring materials in and move wastes out into the shuttle to be returned to Earth.

Like space stations, cells have structures that protect them from the outside environment. As you learned, all cells are surrounded by a cell membrane that separates the cell from the outside environment. Just like the space station, the cell has to take in needed materials and get rid of wastes. It is the cell membrane that controls what materials move into and out of the cell.

The Cell Membrane as Gatekeeper

The cell membrane has a structure that makes it **selectively permeable,** which means that some substances can pass through it while others cannot. **The selectively permeable structure of the cell membrane enables it to regulate the materials that enter and leave the cell.** You can think of the cell membrane as being like a gatekeeper at an ancient castle. It was the gatekeeper's job to decide when to open the gate to allow people to pass into and out of the castle. The gatekeeper made the castle wall "selectively permeable"—it was permeable to friendly folks but not to enemies.

A cell membrane is usually permeable to substances such as oxygen, water, and carbon dioxide. On the other hand, the cell membrane is usually not permeable to some large molecules and salts. Substances that can move into and out of a cell do so by one of three methods: diffusion, osmosis, or active transport.

READING STRATEGIES

Reading Tip Have students preview the main headings of the section. Remind students to leave space between headings so that they can add details as they read. Write the main headings of the outline on the board, as shown in the right column. After students have read the section, call on volunteers to add details.

I. The Cell Membrane as Gatekeeper
II. Diffusion: Molecules in Motion
   A. What Causes Diffusion
   B. Diffusion in Cells

Study and Comprehension Encourage visual learners to preview the section by looking at the figures and reading the captions. This is also a good way for them to review after reading the section.

Diffusion—Molecules in Motion

The main method by which small molecules move into and out of cells is diffusion. **Diffusion** (dih FYOO zhun) is the process by which molecules tend to move from an area of higher concentration to an area of lower concentration. The concentration of a substance is the amount of the substance in a given volume.

If you did the Discover activity, you observed diffusion in action. The area where the air freshener was sprayed had many molecules of freshener. The molecules gradually moved from this area of higher concentration to the other parts of the classroom, where there were few molecules of freshener, and thus a lower concentration.

What Causes Diffusion? Molecules are always moving. As **INTEGRATING CHEMISTRY** they move, the molecules bump into one another. The more molecules there are in an area, the more collisions there will be. Collisions cause molecules to push away from one another. Over time, the molecules of a substance will continue to spread out. Eventually they will be spread evenly throughout the area.

Diffusion in Cells Have you ever used a microscope to observe one-celled organisms in pond water? These organisms obtain the oxygen they need to survive from the water around them. There are many more molecules of oxygen in the water outside the cell than there are inside the cell. In other words, there is a higher concentration of oxygen molecules in the water than inside the cell. Remember that the structure of the cell membrane is permeable to oxygen molecules. The oxygen molecules diffuse from the area of higher concentration—the pond water—through the cell membrane to the area of lower concentration—the inside of the cell.

Figure 1 Molecules move by diffusion from an area of higher concentration to an area of lower concentration. **(A)** There is a higher concentration of molecules outside the cell than inside. **(B)** The molecules diffuse into the cell. Eventually, there is an equal concentration of molecules inside and outside the cell.
Predicting What would happen if the concentration of the molecules outside the cell was lower than the concentration inside?

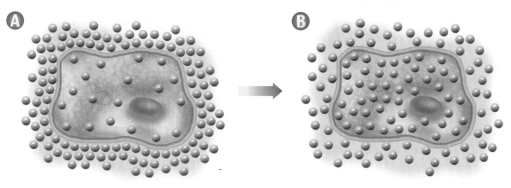

Answers to Self-Assessment

Caption Question

Figure 1 If the concentration of molecules outside the cell was lower than the concentration inside, the molecules would diffuse out of the cell.

2 Facilitate

The Cell Membrane as Gatekeeper

Including All Students

Materials *cheesecloth, spoon, applesauce*
Time 10 minutes

Have students place a small amount of applesauce in the middle of a piece of cheesecloth. Have them pull the edges together and, over a sink, try to squeeze the applesauce through the cloth. Have students examine what remains in the pouch, then ask: **How is the cheesecloth like a cell membrane?** *(It allows some but not all substances to pass through.)*
learning modality: tactile/ kinesthetic

Diffusion—Molecules in Motion

Integrating Chemistry

Materials *tablespoon, cornstarch, two cups, water, resealable plastic bag, plastic dropper, iodine*

Time 15 minutes

To demonstrate diffusion through a selectively permeable membrane, stir a tablespoon of cornstarch into half a cup of water and pour the mixture into a plastic bag. Seal the bag, rinse it off to remove any cornstarch, and place it in a clean cup half full of plain water. Add 20 drops of iodine to the water in the cup. Later, show students the cup and ask. **Why did the water in the bag turn purple?** *(Iodine molecules passed through the plastic into the bag and interacted with the starch.)* **Why didn't the water in the cup turn purple?** *(The starch molecules were too big to pass through the bag.)*
learning modality: visual

Ongoing Assessment

Drawing Have students diagram what happens if the concentration of molecules outside a cell is lower than the concentration inside.

Diffusion—Molecules in Motion, continued

Skills Focus inferring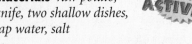
Materials *small clear plastic cup, cold water, plastic dropper, food coloring*
Time 10 minutes
Expected Outcome The large drop of food coloring will diffuse throughout the water in the cup, and the water will have an even shade of color.
Extend Encourage students to predict how changing the parameters of the experiment would affect the outcome. For example, ask: **How do you think the results of the activity would be different if you had used a larger amount of water?** (*Diffusion would have taken longer, and the water would have turned a lighter shade of color.*) **learning modality: logical/mathematical**

Osmosis—The Diffusion of Water Molecules

Demonstration

Materials *raw potato, knife, two shallow dishes, tap water, salt*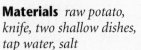

Time 5 minutes; 5 minutes

Use a potato to demonstrate the process of osmosis. At the beginning of class, cut a raw potato in half and hollow out a small depression in the curved side of each half. Place the halves flat-side down in shallow dishes containing a small amount of tap water. Place a pinch of salt in the depression of one of the potato halves, and then set the two halves aside. At the end of class, have students observe what has happened to the two potato halves. (*The depression without salt has become dried out, whereas the depression with salt has filled with water.*) Ask: **Where did the water in the depression come from?** (*The water moved by osmosis from an area of higher concentration in the potato cells to an area of lower concentration in the depression containing salt.*) **learning modality: visual**

Here's how you can observe the effects of diffusion.

1. Fill a small clear plastic cup with cold water. Place the cup on a table and allow it to sit until there is no movement in the water.
2. Use a plastic dropper to add one large drop of food coloring to the water.
3. Observe the water every minute. Note any changes that take place. Continue to observe until you can no longer see any changes.

Inferring What role did diffusion play in the changes you observed?

Osmosis—The Diffusion of Water Molecules

Like oxygen, water passes easily into and out of cells through the cell membrane. The diffusion of water molecules through a selectively permeable membrane is called **osmosis.** Osmosis is important to sustain life because cells cannot function properly without adequate water.

Remember that molecules tend to move from an area of higher concentration to an area of lower concentration. In osmosis, water molecules move by diffusion from an area where they are highly concentrated through the cell membrane to an area where they are less concentrated. This can have important consequences for the cell.

Look at Figure 2 to see the effect of osmosis on cells. In Figure 2A, red blood cells are bathed in a solution in which the concentration of water is the same as it is inside the cells. This is the normal shape of a red blood cell.

Now look at Figure 2B. The red blood cells are floating in water that contains a lot of salt. The concentration of water molecules outside the cells is lower than the concentration of water molecules inside the cells. This is because the salt takes up space in the salt water, so there are fewer water molecules. As a result, water moves out of the cells by osmosis, and the cells shrink.

Finally, consider Figure 2C. The red blood cells are floating in water that contains a very small amount of salt. The water inside the cells contains more salt than the solution they are floating in. Thus, the concentration of water outside the cell is greater than it is inside the cell. The water moves into the cell, causing it to swell.

☑ *Checkpoint* How is osmosis related to diffusion?

Figure 2 Osmosis is the diffusion of water molecules through a selectively permeable membrane.

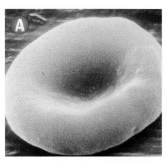 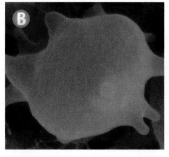 

(A) This is the normal shape of a red blood cell.

(B) This cell has shrunk because water moved out of it by osmosis.

(C) This cell is swollen with water that has moved into it by osmosis.

Background

Integrating Science Did you ever wonder why most fish cannot live in both freshwater and salt water? The answer lies in osmosis, which requires freshwater and saltwater fishes to have very different adaptations.

When fishes live in salt water, the water outside their body is saltier than the water inside their cells. Therefore, fishes lose a lot of water into the water around them by osmosis.

To compensate, they must drink a lot of water, use active transport to get rid of the excess salt, and produce very little urine.

In contrast, when fishes live in freshwater, the water inside their body cells is saltier than the water outside. Therefore, they gain a lot of water by osmosis. To compensate, they usually do not drink, and they produce large amounts of very dilute urine.

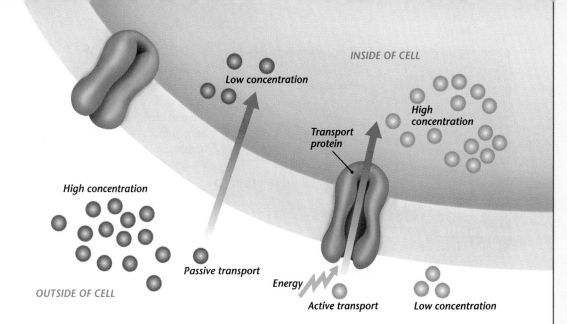

INSIDE OF CELL

Low concentration

High concentration

Transport protein

High concentration

OUTSIDE OF CELL

Passive transport

Energy

Active transport

Low concentration

Active Transport

If you have ever ridden a bicycle down a long hill, you know that it doesn't take any of your energy to go fast. But pedaling back up the hill does take energy. For a cell, moving materials through the cell membrane by diffusion and osmosis is like cycling downhill. These processes do not require the cell to use any energy. The movement of materials through a cell membrane without using energy is called **passive transport.**

What if a cell needs to take in a substance that is in higher concentration inside the cell than outside? The cell would have to move the molecules in the opposite direction than they naturally move by diffusion. Cells can do this, but they have to use energy—just as you would use energy to pedal back up the hill. **Active transport** is the movement of materials through a cell membrane using energy. **The main difference between passive transport and active transport is that active transport requires the cell to use energy while passive transport does not.**

Transport Proteins A cell has several ways of moving materials by active transport. In one method, transport proteins in the cell membrane function to "pick up" molecules outside the cell and carry them in, using energy in the process. Transport proteins also carry molecules out of cells in a similar way. Some substances that are carried into and out of cells in this way include calcium, potassium, and sodium.

Figure 3 Diffusion and osmosis are forms of passive transport. These processes do not require the cell to use any energy. Active transport, on the other hand, requires the use of energy. *Interpreting Diagrams How are passive and active transport related to the concentrations of the molecules inside and outside the cell?*

Inquiry Challenge

Materials *small board, stack of books, toy car*

Time 5 minutes

Challenge pairs of students to model active and passive transport using the materials listed above. *(The most likely way is to make an inclined plane with the board and books, and then to roll the toy car down the ramp to simulate passive transport and push it up the ramp to simulate active transport.)* Ask: **Why do you need to supply energy to move the toy car up the ramp?** *(To overcome the force of gravity)* **Why is energy needed to actively transport some substances into the cell?** *(To move the substances from an area of lower to an area of higher concentration)* **cooperative learning**

Building Inquiry Skills: Relating Cause and Effect

Help students better understand the role of transport proteins in active transport by developing the analogy in the text. Ask: **What plays a similar role in active transport as your muscles play when you pedal a bicycle up a hill?** *(Transport proteins, because they require energy to move something that could not move on its own)* **learning modality: logical/ mathematical**

Answers to Self-Assessment

☑ *Checkpoint*

Osmosis is water diffusion through a selectively permeable membrane.

Caption Question

Figure 3 Passive transport—molecules move from higher to lower concentration. Active transport—molecules move from lower to higher concentration.

Ongoing Assessment

Skills Check Have students draw a Venn diagram that relates active and passive transport. *(Students' diagrams should show that active transport requires energy and passive transport does not. The overlap area should indicate that in both processes, materials move in and out of cells.)*

Why Are Cells Small?

Demonstration

Materials *one-gallon aquarium, cold and room-temperature water, measuring cup, food coloring*

Time 5 minutes

Demonstrate how materials move through cytoplasm by creating a convection current in water. Pour half a cup of very cold colored water into an aquarium filled with room-temperature water. Ask: **How would increasing the size of the tank affect how long it takes the colored water to reach the bottom?** *(It would take longer.)*
learning modality: visual

3 Assess

Section 1 Review Answers

1. The cell membrane has a selectively permeable structure, meaning that it can regulate the materials that enter and leave the cell. In diffusion, molecules move from an area of higher to an area of lower concentration. In osmosis, water molecules move by diffusion. In active transport, molecules are helped across cell membranes by transport proteins.
2. Both passive and active transport refer to the movement of substances across cell membranes. Active transport requires energy; passive transport does not.
3. Substances can travel faster through the cytoplasm of small cells.
4. The cell will shrink as it loses water.

Check Your Progress
CHAPTER PROJECT

Make sure students have started soaking their eggs in vinegar and are measuring and recording their curcumferences every day. Check that they always measure the eggs in the same way.

Performance Assessment

Skills Check Have students make a concept map that includes the terms *diffusion, osmosis, passive transport,* and *active transport*.

162

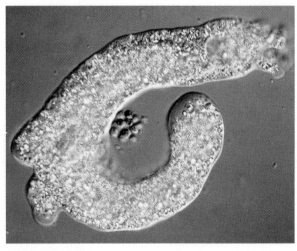

Figure 4 A cell can move some materials into itself by engulfing them. This single-celled ameba is engulfing a smaller single-celled organism. *Applying Concepts How does this process differ from passive transport?*

Transport by Engulfing You can see another method of active transport in Figure 4. First the cell membrane surrounds, or engulfs, a particle. Once the particle is engulfed, the cell membrane pinches off and forms a vacuole within the cell. The cell must use energy in this process.

Why Are Cells Small?

As you know, most cells are so small that you cannot see them without a microscope. Have you ever wondered why cells are so small? One reason is related to how materials move into and out of cells.

As a cell's size increases, more of its cytoplasm is located farther from the cell membrane. Once a molecule enters a cell, it is carried to its destination by a stream of moving cytoplasm, somewhat like the way currents of water in the ocean move a raft. But in a very large cell, the streams of cytoplasm must travel farther to bring materials to all parts of the cell. It would take much longer for a molecule to reach the center of a very large cell than it would in a small cell. Likewise, it would take a long time for wastes to be removed. If a cell grew too large, it could not function well enough to survive. When a cell reaches a certain size, it divides into two new cells. You will learn more about cell division later in this chapter.

Section 1 Review

1. Describe the structure of the cell membrane. Then explain three methods by which substances can move into and out of cells.
2. How are passive transport and active transport similar? How do they differ?
3. Why is small size an advantage to a cell?
4. **Thinking Critically** **Predicting** A single-celled organism is transferred from a tank of fresh water into a tank of salt water. How will the cell change? Explain.

162

Check Your Progress
CHAPTER PROJECT

By now you should have started your "egg-speriment" by soaking an uncooked egg in vinegar. Leave your egg in the vinegar for at least two days. Each day, rinse your egg in water and measure its circumference. Record all of your observations. (*Hint:* Handle the egg gently. If your egg breaks, don't give up or throw away your data. Simply start again with another egg and keep investigating.)

Program Resources

◆ **Unit 2 Resources** 5-1 Review and Reinforce, p. 39; 5-1 Enrich, p. 40

Answers to Self-Assessment

Caption Question

Figure 4 Engulfing requires energy while passive transport does not.

SECTION 2 The Cell and Energy

DISCOVER

Where Does the Energy Come From?

1. Obtain a solar-powered calculator that does not use batteries. Place the calculator in direct light.
2. Cover the solar cells with your finger. Note how your action affects the number display.
3. Uncover the solar cells. What happens to the number display?
4. Now cover all but one of the solar cells. How does that affect the number display?

Think It Over

Inferring From your observations, what can you infer about the energy that powers the calculator?

It's a beautiful summer afternoon—a perfect day for spending time in the park. Dogs play together under a nearby tree. Blue jays swoop down from the tree's branches, hunting for food. "Let's go for a bike ride," suggests your cousin. "Great idea," you say, and you ride off down the path.

Dogs playing, birds flying, people biking—all of these activities require energy. Where do you think this energy comes from? Believe it or not, the energy comes from the sun. In fact, the sun is the source of almost all the energy used by living things on Earth.

What Is Photosynthesis?

All living things need energy. Their cells need energy to carry out functions that sustain life such as transporting substances into and out of cells. You and other heterotrophs eat food to supply your cells with energy. But plants and some other organisms are autotrophs that use the sun's energy to make their own food.

The process by which a cell of an autotroph captures the energy in sunlight and uses it to make food is called **photosynthesis** (foh toh SIN thuh sis). Chloroplasts contain chemicals that absorb light. One of these is **chlorophyll,** which gives chloroplasts their green color. Chlorophyll and other light-absorbing chemicals capture light energy and use it to power photosynthesis. In plants, it occurs in their cells' chloroplasts.

> **GUIDE FOR READING**
>
> ◆ What happens during the process of photosynthesis?
> ◆ What events occur during respiration?
> ◆ How are photosynthesis and respiration related?
>
> *Reading Tip* Before you read, write definitions of *photosynthesis* and *respiration*. After reading this section, revise your definitions.
>
> *Key Terms* photosynthesis • chlorophyll • respiration • fermentation

Figure 5 Photosynthesis occurs inside chloroplasts in the cells of plants and some other organisms. *Applying Concepts What is the source of energy in photosynthesis?*

Chapter 5 **163**

SECTION 2 The Cell and Energy

TEKS: 6.1A; 6.2B, C, D, E; 6.4A; 6.10B

Objectives

After completing the lesson, students will be able to

◆ describe the process of photosynthesis;
◆ explain how the sun supplies all organisms with the energy they need;
◆ describe the events that occur during respiration;
◆ describe the relationship between photosynthesis and respiration;
◆ describe alcoholic and lactic-acid fermentation.

1 Engage/Explore

Activating Prior Knowledge

Ask students: **How many of you have houseplants in your home?** *(Most will probably say they do.)* **Where are houseplants usually placed?** *(Near a window or where they will receive light)* **What happens if a houseplant doesn't get enough light?** *(They get spindly, turn yellow, and may die.)* **Why do plants need light?** *(Some students may know that plants use light energy to make food. Accept all responses without comment at this time.)*

DISCOVER

Skills Focus inferring
Materials *solar-powered calculator that does not use batteries*
Time 5 minutes
Tips If necessary, show students where the solar cells are located on the calculator.
Expected Outcome When all the solar cells are covered, the number display should go blank. When all but one of the solar cells are covered, the number display should flicker and fade.
Think It Over Students should infer that energy to power the calculator comes from sunlight.

2 Facilitate

What Is Photosynthesis?

Using the Visuals: Figure 5

Explain that the inset photo is a microscopic view of chloroplasts. Ask: **What makes chloroplasts green?** *(Chlorophyll)* **What is the role of chlorophyll in photosynthesis?** *(It captures light energy used in the second stage of photosynthesis.)* **learning modality: visual**

The Events of Photosynthesis

Including All Students

Explain that chemical equations balance by having the same number of each type of atom on both sides of the equation. The subscript numerals show the number of atoms in each molecule. The numerals in front show how many molecules of that compound are involved in the reaction. Challenge students to count the number of each type of atom on both sides of the equation. **learning modality: logical/mathematical**

Building Inquiry Skills: Making Models

Materials *bingo chips, buttons, cereal or pasta pieces, or other small objects in three different colors or shapes*
Time 10 minutes

Divide the class into pairs, and provide each pair with enough small objects to represent the carbon, oxygen, and hydrogen atoms on one side of the photosynthesis equation. Have one member of each pair arrange the objects to represent the left side of the equation. Then have the other member of the pair rearrange the same objects to represent the right side of the equation. Ask: **What part of the photosynthesis equation is not represented?** *(The energy required to make the reaction occur)* **learning modality: tactile/kinesthetic**

The Events of Photosynthesis

Photosynthesis is a complex process that results in chemical change. Recall from Chapter 1 that, during a chemical change, substances may combine to form new substances. **During photosynthesis, cells capture energy from sunlight and use it to change carbon dioxide gas and water into oxygen and sugars, such as glucose.** Some of the sun's energy is stored as chemical energy in the sugar molecules made during photosynthesis.

The events of photosynthesis can be summed up by the following chemical equation:

$$6\,CO_2 + 6\,H_2O \xrightarrow{\text{light energy}} C_6H_{12}O_6 + 6\,O_2$$

carbon dioxide   water   glucose   oxygen

Notice that the raw materials—6 molecules of carbon dioxide and 6 molecules of water—are on the left side of the equation. The products—1 molecule of glucose and 6 molecules of oxygen—are on the right side of the equation. An arrow, which is read as "yields," connects the raw materials to the products. Light energy, which is necessary for the chemical reaction to occur, appears above the arrow.

☑ *Checkpoint* What two substances are produced during the process of photosynthesis?

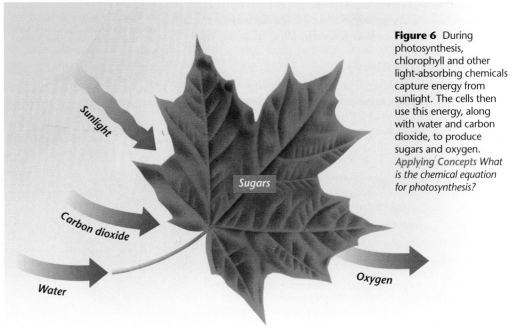

Figure 6 During photosynthesis, chlorophyll and other light-absorbing chemicals capture energy from sunlight. The cells then use this energy, along with water and carbon dioxide, to produce sugars and oxygen. *Applying Concepts What is the chemical equation for photosynthesis?*

164

Background

History of Science The discovery of photosynthesis usually is attributed to the Dutch physician Jan Ingenhousz. In 1779, Ingenhousz demonstrated that plants need sunlight to replenish air. That is, plants produce oxygen in the presence of sunlight.

Figure 7 Both the caterpillar and the western bluebird obtain their energy indirectly from the sun.

Storing and Releasing the Energy in Food

What happens to the products of photosynthesis? Plant cells use some of the glucose for food. Their cells break down the glucose molecules to release the chemical energy the molecules contain. This energy is then used to carry out the plant's functions. Other glucose molecules are converted to cellulose, a chemical that plays an important role in the structure of the cell walls of plants. When heterotrophs, such as the ones in Figure 7, eat food from plants or animals that have eaten plants, they take in the plant's stored food.

The other product of photosynthesis is oxygen. Most of the oxygen passes out of the plant and into the atmosphere. Today, Earth's atmosphere is about 21 percent oxygen. Autotrophs have produced almost all of this oxygen through photosynthesis. The oxygen in Earth's atmosphere is important because most living things need oxygen to survive. Why? Most living things use oxygen in the cells of their bodies to release the energy in food.

To understand how cells store and use energy, think about how you might save money. You would probably put it in a savings account at a bank. When you wanted to buy an item, you would withdraw some money. Cells store and use energy in a similar way. For example, during photosynthesis, plants capture energy from sunlight and "save" it in the form of substances such as sugars. When their cells need energy, plants "withdraw" it by breaking down the sugars and releasing energy from their sugars. Similarly, when you eat, you add to your body's energy savings account. When your cells need energy, they make a withdrawal and break down the food to release its energy. Read on to discover how your cells break down food.

Using the Visuals: Figure 7

Point out that not all the energy converted to food by autotrophs is available to the heterotrophs that depend on them. In fact, only about 10 percent of the energy at a given level in a food chain is available to organisms at the next level of the food chain. Ask: **Why are there fewer caterpillars than the plants they eat, and fewer birds than caterpillars?** *(Because there is less and less energy available to support life as you move up the food chain)* **learning modality: visual**

Building Inquiry Skills: Inferring

Ask students: **When do you think plants would need to "withdraw" the energy stored in their cells as complex carbohydrates?** *(During the winter when plants have lost their leaves and cannot photosynthesize)* **learning modality: logical/mathematical**

Media and Technology

 Transparencies "Photosynthesis," Transparency 16

Answers to Self-Assessment

Caption Question

Figure 6 $6CO_2 + 6H_2O \xrightarrow{\text{light energy}} C_6H_{12}O_6 + 6O_2$

✓ *Checkpoint*

Oxygen and glucose

Ongoing Assessment

Writing Have students explain how life on Earth depends on the sun.

165

What Is Respiration?

Figure 8 All organisms need energy to live. **(A)** Although these mushrooms don't move, they still need a continuous supply of energy to grow and reproduce. **(B)** This leopard frog uses the energy stored in carbohydrates to leap great distances. *Applying Concepts What is the name of the process by which cells obtain the energy they need?*

What Is Respiration?

After you eat a meal, your body converts some of the food into the sugar glucose. When cells need energy, they obtain that energy from glucose in a process called **respiration. During respiration, cells break down simple food molecules such as glucose and release the energy they contain.** Because living things need an ongoing supply of energy, the cells of all living things carry out respiration continuously.

The term *respiration* might be confusing. You have probably used it to mean breathing, which is the moving of air in and out of your lungs. To avoid confusion, the respiration process that occurs in cells can be called cellular respiration. However, the double use of the term *respiration* points out an important connection. Breathing brings oxygen into your lungs, and most cells need oxygen for cellular respiration.

Cellular respiration occurs in the mitochondria of an organism's cells. The overall process of cellular respiration is summarized in the following equation:

$$C_6H_{12}O_6 \; + \; 6\,O_2 \; \longrightarrow \; 6\,CO_2 \; + \; 6\,H_2O \; + \; energy$$
glucose   oxygen   carbon dioxide   water

Notice that the raw materials for cellular respiration are glucose and oxygen. Plants and other organisms that undergo photosynthesis make their own glucose. The glucose in the cells of animals and other organisms comes from the food they consume. The oxygen comes from the air or water surrounding the organism.

☑ *Checkpoint* What substance is broken down during respiration?

166

Background

Facts and Figures Respiration is often compared to combustion because both processes involve the breakdown of molecules in the presence of oxygen to produce energy and carbon dioxide. However, respiration is a much slower, more controlled process than combustion. If respiration is like carrying a bundle down five flights of stairs, combustion is like dropping it from a fifth-story window.

History of Science The discovery of the nature of cellular respiration is attributed jointly to the French chemist Antoine Laurent Lavoisier and the French physicist, mathematician, and astronomer Pierre Laplace. In 1780 they published the results of their experiments showing that animal respiration is a form of combustion.

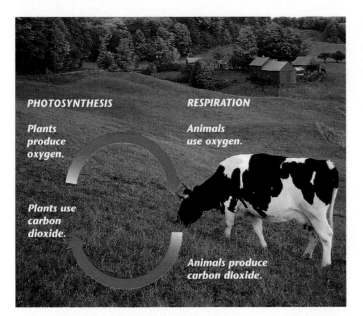

PHOTOSYNTHESIS

RESPIRATION

Plants produce oxygen.

Animals use oxygen.

Plants use carbon dioxide.

Animals produce carbon dioxide.

Figure 9 Photosynthesis and respiration can be thought of as opposite processes. All organisms, including plants, undergo respiration.
Interpreting Photographs How do these two processes keep the levels of oxygen and carbon dioxide in the atmosphere fairly constant?

Comparing Photosynthesis and Respiration

Do you notice anything familiar about the equation for respiration? You are right if you said it is the opposite of the equation for photosynthesis. During photosynthesis, carbon dioxide and water are used to produce sugars and oxygen. During respiration, sugars and oxygen are used to produce carbon dioxide and water. **Photosynthesis and respiration can be thought of as opposite processes.** Together, they form a cycle that keeps the levels of oxygen and carbon dioxide fairly constant in Earth's atmosphere. Living things use both gases over and over again.

Fermentation

Some cells are able to obtain energy from food without using oxygen. For example, some single-celled organisms live where there is no oxygen, such as in the mud of lakes or swamps. These organisms obtain their energy through **fermentation,** an energy-releasing process that does not require oxygen. The amount of energy released from each sugar molecule during fermentation, however, is much lower than the amount released during respiration.

Alcoholic Fermentation One type of fermentation occurs in yeast and some other single-celled organisms. This process is sometimes called alcoholic fermentation because alcohol is one of the products made when these organisms break down sugars. The other products are carbon dioxide and a small amount of energy.

Yeast Feast

  ACTIVITY

1. Fill two test tubes half full of warm water. Add 5 milliliters of sugar to one of the test tubes.
2. Add 0.5 milliliter of yeast (unicellular organisms) to each tube. Stir the contents of each tube. Put a stopper in each tube.
3. Observe any changes that occur in the test tubes over the next 10 to 15 minutes.

Inferring Describe what occurred in each test tube. Use your knowledge to explain any energy-related processes you observed.

Fermentation, continued

Health Connection

Tell students that researchers have hypothesized that eating a high-carbohydrate diet before a long race slows the buildup of lactic acid in the muscles and helps prevent muscle soreness and fatigue. Challenge students to design an experiment to test this hypothesis. Call on volunteers to describe their experimental designs. *(The most likely design compares muscle soreness and fatigue in two groups of runners, one group that has been eating a high-carbohydrate diet and one that has been eating a low-carbohydrate diet.)* **learning modality: logical/mathematical**

3 Assess

Section 2 Review Answers

1. Raw materials: carbon dioxide, water, products: oxygen, sugars
2. Cells break down simple food molecules and release the energy that the molecules contain.
3. They can be thought of as opposite processes: During photosynthesis, carbon dioxide and water are used to produce sugar and oxygen. During respiration, sugar and oxygen are used to produce carbon dioxide and water.
4. oxygen
5. Yes; plant cells carry out respiration to produce energy for cell functions from molecules such as glucose.

Check Your Progress
CHAPTER PROJECT

Make sure students are not having problems with the project. Call on volunteers to describe the changes they have noticed in their egg. *(After two days in vinegar, the shell should have dissolved and the egg should have increased in size and become rubbery in texture.)*

Performance Assessment

Writing Have students describe the similarities and differences between alcoholic and lactic-acid fermentation.

The products of alcoholic fermentation are important to bakers and brewers. The carbon dioxide produced by yeast causes dough to rise, and it creates the air pockets you see in bread. Carbon dioxide is also the source of bubbles in alcoholic drinks such as beer and sparkling wine.

Lactic-Acid Fermentation Another type of fermentation takes place at times in your body, and you've probably felt its effects. Think of a time when you've run as fast as you could for as long as you could. Your leg muscles were pushing hard against the pavement, and you were breathing quickly. Eventually, however, your legs became tired and you couldn't run any more.

No matter how hard you breathed, your muscle cells used up the oxygen faster than it could be replaced. Because your cells lacked oxygen, they used the process of fermentation to produce energy. One by-product of this type of fermentation is a substance known as lactic acid. When lactic acid builds up, your muscles feel weak, tired, and sore.

Figure 10 When an athlete's muscles run out of oxygen, lactic-acid fermentation occurs. The athlete's muscles feel tired and sore. *Inferring Which muscles in this runner were producing the most lactic acid?*

Section 2 Review

1. What are the raw materials needed for photosynthesis? What are the products?
2. What happens during respiration?
3. Explain the relationship between photosynthesis and respiration.
4. What raw material used in respiration is *not* needed for fermentation to occur?
5. **Thinking Critically** **Applying Concepts** Do plant cells need to carry out respiration? Explain.

Check Your Progress
CHAPTER PROJECT

At this point, you should soak your egg for one or two days in water, then in water with food coloring, then in salt water, and finally in another liquid of your choice. Continue to rinse your egg and measure and record its circumference every day. Your egg should be going through some amazing changes in appearance.

Program Resources

◆ **Unit 2 Resources** 5-2 Review and Reinforce, p. 43; 5-2 Enrich, p. 44
◆ **Unit 2 Resources** Chapter 5 Real-World Lab blackline masters, pp. 49–50

Answers to Self-Assessment

Caption Question

Figure 10 Cells in the runner's leg muscles were producing the most lactic acid.

Gases in Balance

Problem

How are photosynthesis and respiration related?

Skills Focus

controlling variables, interpreting data

Materials

marking pens   straws
2 *Elodea* plants   light source
plastic graduated cylinder, 100-mL
bromthymol blue solution
3 flasks with stoppers, 250-mL

Procedure

1. Bromthymol blue can be used to test for carbon dioxide. To see how this dye works, pour 100 mL of bromthymol blue solution into a flask. Record its color. **CAUTION:** *Bromthymol blue can stain skin and clothing. Avoid spilling or splashing it on yourself.*

2. Provide a supply of carbon dioxide by gently blowing into the solution through a straw until the dye changes color. Record the new color. **CAUTION:** *Do not suck any of the solution through the straw.*

3. Copy the data table into your notebook. Add 100 mL of bromthymol blue to the other flasks. Then blow through clean straws into each solution until the color changes.

4. Now you will test to see what gas is used by a plant in the presence of light. Obtain two *Elodea* plants of about the same size.

5. Place one plant into the first flask. Label the flask "L" for light. Place the other plant in the second flask. Label the flask "D" for darkness. Label the third flask "C" for control. Put stoppers in all three flasks.

	DATA TABLE	
	Color of Solution	
Flask	Day 1	Day 2
L (light)		
D (dark)		
C (control)		

6. Record the colors of the three solutions under Day 1 in your data table.

7. Place the flasks labeled L and C in a lighted location as directed by your teacher. Place the flask labeled D in a dark location as directed by your teacher. Wash your hands thoroughly when you have finished.

8. On Day 2, examine the flasks and record the colors of the solutions in your data table. Follow your teacher's instructions for disposing of all materials.

Analyze and Conclude

1. Explain why the color of each solution did or did not change from Day 1 to Day 2.

2. Why was it important to include the flask labeled C as part of this experiment?

3. Predict what would happen if you blew into the flask labeled L after you completed Step 8. Explain your prediction.

4. **Apply** How does this lab show that photosynthesis and respiration are opposite processes?

More to Explore

Suppose you were to put an *Elodea* plant and a small fish in a stoppered flask. Predict what would happen to the levels of oxygen and carbon dioxide in the flask. Explain your prediction.

Sample Data Table

Flask	Color of Solution	
	Day 1	Day 2
L (light)	yellow	blue
D (dark)	yellow	yellow
C (control)	yellow	yellow

Media and Technology

Lab Activity Videotapes
Grade 6, Tape 2

Safety

Stress to students that they should not inhale the bromthymol blue solution through the straw. Review the safety guidelines in Appendix A.

You and Your Environment

Gases in Balance

Preparing for Inquiry

Key Concept Photosynthesis and respiration are opposite processes.
Skills Objectives Students will be able to
◆ control other variables while investigating whether photosynthesis requires light;
◆ interpret data on color to detect carbon dioxide in solutions.
Time 20 minutes on Day 1; 15 minutes on Day 2
Advance Planning Purchase *Elodea* plants at an aquarium supply store.

Guiding Inquiry

Troubleshooting the Experiment
◆ Make sure students realize that the solution will turn blue again if the carbon dioxide is used up.

Expected Outcome
The solution in flask L should change from yellow to blue; the solution in flasks D and C should remain yellow.

Analyze and Conclude
1. The solution in flask L changed because photosynthesis used up the carbon dioxide. The solution in flask D remained the same because the plant had no light for photosynthesis. The solution in flask C remained the same because there was no plant to undergo photosynthesis.
2. Flask C was needed to rule out the possibility that the solution in flask L changed color just because it was placed in the light.
3. The solution would turn yellow again because it would contain carbon dioxide.
4. The lab showed that carbon dioxide is given off in respiration and used in photosynthesis. These two processes form a cycle that keeps levels of oxygen and carbon dioxide constant.

Extending the Inquiry

More to Explore The levels would reach a stable balance as the plant and fish recycled the two gases.

Cell Division

TEKS: 6.1A; 6.2A, B, C, D, E; 6.3C; 6.4A; 6.10B; 6.11B

Objectives

After completing the lesson, students will be able to

- identify the events that take place during the three stages of the cell cycle;
- describe the structure of DNA and DNA replication.

1 Engage/Explore

Activating Prior Knowledge

Introduce students to the cell cycle by relating it to the human life cycle. Ask: **What are the stages that people go through during their lives, starting with infancy and ending with old age?** *(Students are likely to name or describe the additional stages of childhood, adolescence, and adulthood.)* Point out that cells, like people, undergo a life cycle, called the cell cycle. During the stages of the cell cycle, cells grow and mature. Just as the human life cycle starts again with reproduction, the cell cycle starts over again when the cell divides.

⋯⋯⋯ DISCOVER ⋯⋯⋯

Skills Focus developing hypotheses
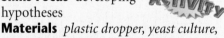
Materials *plastic dropper, yeast culture, stained microscope slide, coverslip, microscope*
Time 15 minutes
Tips You can prepare a yeast culture by stirring dry yeast and sugar into warm water. Stain slides ahead of time by adding a drop of methylene blue to each slide and letting it dry. You could also use prepared slides of yeast cells.
Expected Outcome Students should observe and sketch yeast cells, some of which are in the process of budding to form daughter cells.
Think It Over Students may say that the "double cells" are dividing. The most likely hypothesis is that yeast cells split in two when they reproduce.

170

DISCOVER ⋯⋯⋯⋯⋯⋯⋯⋯⋯⋯ ACTIVITY

What Are the Cells Doing?

1. 🖐 Use a plastic dropper to transfer some yeast cells from a yeast culture to a microscope slide. Your teacher has prepared the slide by drying methylene blue stain onto it. Add a cover-slip and place the slide under a microscope.

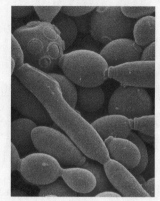

2. Examine the cells on the slide. Use low power first, then high power. Look for what appears to be two cells attached to each other. One cell may be larger than the other. Draw what you see.

Think It Over

Developing Hypotheses What process do you think the "double cells" are undergoing? Develop a hypothesis that might explain what you see.

GUIDE FOR READING

- What events take place during the three stages of the cell cycle?
- What is the role of DNA replication?

Reading Tip Before you read, use the headings to outline the process of cell division. As you read, draw pictures to help you understand the process.

Key Terms cell cycle
- interphase • replication
- mitosis • chromatid
- cytokinesis

In the early autumn, many local fairs run pumpkin contests. Proud growers enter their largest pumpkins, hoping to win a prize. If you've never seen these prize-winning pumpkins, you would be amazed. Some have masses close to 400 kilograms and can be as big as a doghouse. What's even more amazing is that these giant pumpkins began as small flowers on pumpkin plants. How did the pumpkins grow so big?

A pumpkin grows in size by increasing both the size and the number of its cells. A single cell divides, forming two cells. Then two cells divide, forming four, and so on. This process of cell division does not occur only in pumpkins, though. In fact, many cells in your body are undergoing cell division as you read this page.

READING STRATEGIES

Reading Tip Suggest that students preview the section and list the headings, leaving space to add details. After students read the material under a heading, they should stop and write descriptions and make sketches of a cell undergoing division.

Study and Comprehension After students read this section, encourage them to create a concept map using the boldfaced terms. Call on students to name the stage of the cell cycle and the phases of mitosis to make sure they are not confusing the two.

The Cell Cycle

Think about the cells you learned about in Chapter 4. Each cell contains many different structures, including a cell membrane, a nucleus, mitochondria, and ribosomes. To divide into two equal parts, the cell would need to either duplicate the structures or divide them equally between the two new cells. Both cells would then contain everything they need in order to function.

The regular sequence of growth and division that cells undergo is known as the **cell cycle.** You can see details of the cell cycle in *Exploring the Cell Cycle* on pages 174 and 175. Notice that the cell cycle is divided into three main stages. As you read about each stage, follow the events that occur as one "parent" cell divides to form two identical "daughter" cells.

Stage 1: Interphase

The first stage of the cell cycle is called **interphase.** Interphase is the period before cell division occurs. Even though it is not dividing, the cell is quite active during this stage. **During interphase, the cell grows to its mature size, makes a copy of its DNA, and prepares to divide into two cells.**

Growth During the first part of interphase, the cell doubles in size and produces all the structures needed to carry out its functions. For example, the cell enlarges its endoplasmic reticulum, makes new ribosomes, and produces enzymes. Both mitochondria and chloroplasts make copies of themselves. The cell's structure matures, and it grows to its full size.

DNA Replication After a cell has grown to its mature size, the next part of interphase begins. The cell makes a copy of the DNA in its nucleus in a process called **replication.** Recall that DNA is a nucleic acid found in the chromatin in a cell's nucleus. DNA is the genetic material that holds all the information that the cell needs to carry out its functions. The replication of a cell's DNA is very important, since each daughter cell must have a complete set of DNA to survive. At the end of DNA replication, the cell contains two identical sets of DNA. One set will be distributed to each daughter cell. You will learn the details of DNA replication later in this section.

Figure 11 The cells that make up this young monkey are the same size as those that make up its mother. However, the adult has many more cells in its body. *Applying Concepts What is the name of the regular sequence of growth and division that a cell undergoes?*

Program Resources

◆ **Unit 2 Resources** 5-3 Lesson Plan, p. 45; 5-3 Section Summary, p. 46
◆ **Guided Reading and Study Workbook** 5-3

Answers to Self-Assessment

Caption Question

Figure 11 This process is called the cell cycle.

---

2 Facilitate

The Cell Cycle

Including All Students

Guide students who need more help in organizing the information in this section. Point out that the focus of the section is cell division, but cell division is just part of the cell cycle. Ask: **What are the three stages of the cell cycle?** (*interphase, mitosis, and cytokinesis*) As students identify the three stages, list them on the chalkboard under the heading "Cell Cycle." Point out that the stages of mitosis and cytokinesis, are relatively short, whereas interphase is by far the longest stage. **limited English proficiency**

Stage 1: Interphase

Building Inquiry Skills: Inferring

Help students appreciate the role of DNA replication by having them infer what would happen if cell division occurred without DNA replication occurring first during interphase. Ask: **How would this affect the daughter cells?** (*Each daughter cell would have just half the DNA of the parent cell. With only half the DNA, the daughter cells would be unable to direct all cell activities and the cells probably would not survive.*) **learning modality: logical/mathematical**

Language Arts Connection

Tell students that interphase in the cell cycle is like childhood and adolescence in the human life cycle. Ask: **Do you think this is a good analogy? Why or why not?** (*Students may say it is a good analogy because during interphase, like childhood and adolescence, the cell grows and matures.*) **learning modality: verbal**

Ongoing Assessment

Writing Have students write a paragraph explaining the significance of replication in cell division.

Stage 2: Mitosis

Skills Focus making models

Materials *construction paper, different colored pipe cleaners*

Time 10 minutes

Expected Outcome Students should place three pairs of pipe cleaners, which represent three chromosomes, on the construction paper, which represents the cell. In prophase, both pipe cleaners in each pair should be joined at the center, and all the paired pipe cleaners should be clustered together. In metaphase, the paired pipe cleaners should be lined up across the center. In anaphase, the pipe cleaners in each pair should be separated and moved part way toward opposite ends. In telophase, the separated pipe cleaners should be located at opposite ends. Students may say that their model helped them see mitosis as a continuous process.

Extend Ask: **How could you use your model to show the next stage of the cell cycle?** (*Cytokinesis could be modeled by cutting the paper into two equal pieces and placing half the pipe cleaners on each piece.*) **learning modality: tactile/ kinesthetic**

Building Inquiry Skills: Calculating

Materials *calculator*

Time 5 minutes

Help students appreciate how quickly cell division can lead to a large number of cells. Challenge students to calculate how many cells there would be after a cell divides once, twice, three times, and so on, up to ten times. Then ask: **With each division that occurs, how does the number of cells change?** (*The number doubles.*) **learning modality: logical/mathematical**

Figure 12 During mitosis, the chromatin condenses to form rodlike chromosomes. Each chromosome consists of two identical strands, or chromatids. *Interpreting Diagrams What is the name of the structure that holds the chromatids together?*

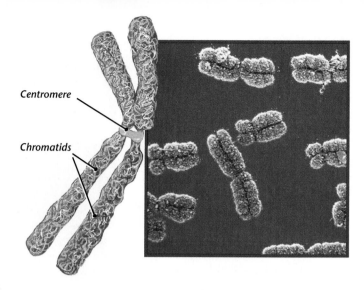

Centromere

Chromatids

Modeling Mitosis

Refer to *Exploring the Cell Cycle* as you carry out this activity.

1. Construct a model of a cell that has three chromosomes. Use a piece of construction paper to represent the cell. Use different-colored pipe cleaners to represent the chromosomes. Make sure that the chromosomes look like double rods.

2. Position the chromosomes in the cell where they would be during prophase.

3. Repeat Step 2 for metaphase, anaphase, and telophase.

Making Models How did the model help you understand the events of mitosis? In what ways was the model unlike the actual process of mitosis?

Preparation for Division Once the cell's DNA has replicated, preparation for cell division begins. The cell produces structures that it will use to divide during the rest of the cell cycle. At the end of interphase, the cell is ready to divide.

Stage 2: Mitosis

Once interphase is complete, the second stage of the cell cycle begins. **Mitosis** (my TOH sis) is the stage during which the cell's nucleus divides into two new nuclei. **During mitosis, one copy of the DNA is distributed into each of the two daughter cells.**

Scientists divide mitosis into four parts, or phases: prophase, metaphase, anaphase, and telophase. During prophase, the threadlike chromatin in the cell's nucleus begins to condense and coil, like fishing line wrapping around a ball. Under a light microscope, the condensed chromatin looks like tiny rods, as you can see in Figure 12. Since the cell's DNA has replicated, each rod has doubled. Each is an exact copy of the other. Scientists call each doubled rod of condensed chromatin a chromosome. Each identical rod, or strand, of the chromosome is called a **chromatid.** The two strands are held together by a structure called a centromere.

As the cell progresses through metaphase, anaphase, and telophase, the chromatids separate from each other and move to opposite ends of the cell. Then two nuclei form around the chromatids at the two ends of the cell. You can follow this process in *Exploring the Cell Cycle.*

☑ *Checkpoint During which stage of mitosis does the chromatin condense to form rodlike structures?*

Background

Integrating Science The cells in our body divide at varying rates as we grow older, causing the body not only to grow in size, but also to change in shape. During early life, cells in the head divide rapidly so that by birth, the head is very large relative to the body. During early childhood, the cells in the arms and legs divide rapidly, causing the young child's limbs to grow long relative to the trunk. At puberty, the child's body undergoes another spurt in growth and development. Sex hormones influence cells of the bones and muscles to divide rapidly, and within a few years the child reaches adult body size and proportions. The hormones also stimulate rapid growth and development of the sex organs and the secondary sex characteristics, such as breasts and body hair.

Stage 3: Cytokinesis

After mitosis, the final stage of the cell cycle, called **cytokinesis** (sy toh kih NEE sis), completes the process of cell division. **During cytokinesis, the cytoplasm divides, distributing the organelles into each of the two new cells.** Cytokinesis usually starts at about the same time as telophase.

During cytokinesis in animal cells, the cell membrane squeezes together around the middle of the cell. The cytoplasm pinches into two cells with about half of the organelles in each daughter cell.

Cytokinesis is somewhat different in plant cells. A plant cell's rigid cell wall cannot squeeze together in the same way that a cell membrane can. Instead, a structure called a cell plate forms across the middle of the cell. The cell plate gradually develops into new cell membranes between the two daughter cells. New cell walls then form around the cell membranes.

There are many variations of the basic pattern of cytokinesis. For example, yeast cells divide, though not equally. A small daughter cell, or bud, pinches off of the parent cell. The bud then grows into a full-sized yeast cell.

Cytokinesis marks the end of the cell cycle. Two new cells have formed. Each daughter cell has the same number of chromosomes as the original parent cell. At the end of cytokinesis, each cell enters interphase, and the cycle begins again.

☑ *Checkpoint* *When in the cell cycle does cytokinesis begin?*

Length of the Cell Cycle

How long does it take for a cell to go through one cell cycle? The answer depends on the type of cell. In a young sea urchin, for example, one cell cycle takes about 2 hours. In contrast, a human liver cell completes one cell cycle in about 22 hours, as shown in Figure 13. The length of each stage in the cell cycle also varies greatly from cell to cell. Some cells, such as human brain cells, never divide—they remain in the first part of interphase for as long as they live.

Sharpen your Skills

Interpreting Data

Use the circle graph shown in Figure 13 to answer the following questions.

1. How long is the cell cycle shown in the graph?
2. Which stage of the cell cycle would you expect more of the cells to be in at any given time—interphase, mitosis, or cytokinesis? Explain.

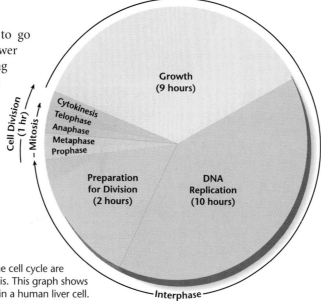

Figure 13 The main stages of the cell cycle are interphase, mitosis, and cytokinesis. This graph shows the average length of each stage in a human liver cell.

Cell Division (1 hr) — Mitosis
Cytokinesis
Telophase
Anaphase
Metaphase
Prophase

Growth (9 hours)

Preparation for Division (2 hours)

DNA Replication (10 hours)

Interphase

Answers to Self-Assessment

☑ *Checkpoint*
The chromatin condenses into rodlike structures during prophase of mitosis.

☑ *Checkpoint*
Cytokinesis is the final stage, beginning at about the same time as telophase.

Caption Question

Figure 12 The centromere holds the chromatids together.

Stage 3: Cytokinesis

Demonstration

Materials *balloon, water*
Time 5 minutes

ACTIVITY

Model an animal cell to show how the cell membrane and cytoplasm change during cytokinesis. Fill a balloon about three-quarters full with water, and then tie the end of the balloon. The balloon represents the cell membrane and the water, the cytoplasm. Ask: **How could this model show what happens to the cell membrane and cytoplasm during cytokinesis?** *(Squeeze the balloon in the middle so that it forms two separate "daughter cells.")* **learning modality: visual**

Length of the Cell Cycle

Sharpen your Skills

Interpreting Data

Time 5 minutes
Tips Make sure students realize that cell division includes *both* mitosis and cytokinesis and takes an hour.

ACTIVITY

Expected Outcome The cell cycle in the graph is 22 hours long. More cells would be in interphase at any given time because it is the longest stage, lasting 21 hours.

Extend Ask: **Which part of interphase would you expect more cells to be in at any given time?** *(DNA replication)* **learning modality: logical/ mathematical**

Using the Visuals: Figure 13

Use the graph to emphasize the relative lengths of the stages of the cell cycle. Ask: **If each stage of the cell cycle took place in half the time, would the lines on the graph change? Why or why not?** *(They would not change, because each stage of the cycle would still make up the same percentage of the total cycle.)* **learning modality: logical/mathematical**

Ongoing Assessment

Oral Presentation Call on students at random to state what happens during interphase and mitosis.

EXPLORING

the Cell Cycle

After students have examined the feature, ask: **How are the photographs related to the drawings?** (*The photographs show actual cells at each stage of the cell cycle as they appear under a microscope, whereas the drawings are simplified sketches of the stages.*) Challenge students to find the genetic material in each illustration. Point out that, in prophase, each pair of chromatids consists of the original DNA of the parent cell plus a copy of the DNA, which was made during interphase. To help students appreciate the continuous nature of the cell cycle, tell them that cytokinesis and the last phase of mitosis, telophase, actually overlap in time. Ask: **Why is a circular diagram like this a better way to represent the cell cycle than a straight-line flowchart?** (*Because after the last stage of the cell cycle, the cycle starts over again*) Refer to the **ELL Handbook** for additional teaching strategies. **learning modality: visual**

Inquiry Challenge

Materials *poster board, colored markers, index cards, dice, small objects such as different colored erasers for game tokens*

ACTIVITY

Time 20 minutes

Divide the class into groups, and provide each group with the materials listed above. Challenge each group to create a board game that models the cell cycle. To get from "start" to "finish" on the game board, players must advance through each stage of the cell cycle by correctly answering questions about that stage. For example, to advance from prophase to metaphase, they might be required to answer: **How does the position of the chromosomes in metaphase differ from their position in prophase?** (*In prophase, the chromosomes are clustered in a group in the nucleus; in metaphase, the chromosomes are lined up across the center of the cell.*) When groups have finished creating their games, have them exchange and play the games. **cooperative learning**

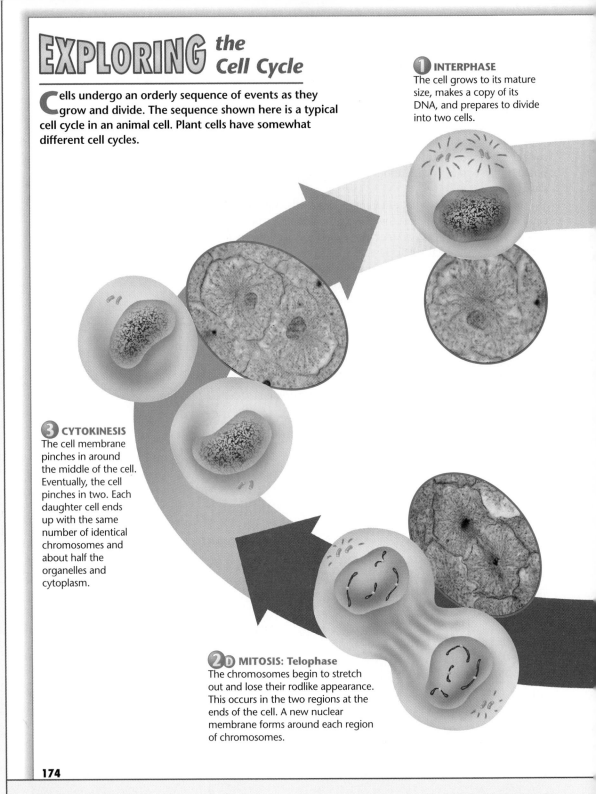

EXPLORING the Cell Cycle

Cells undergo an orderly sequence of events as they grow and divide. The sequence shown here is a typical cell cycle in an animal cell. Plant cells have somewhat different cell cycles.

1 INTERPHASE
The cell grows to its mature size, makes a copy of its DNA, and prepares to divide into two cells.

3 CYTOKINESIS
The cell membrane pinches in around the middle of the cell. Eventually, the cell pinches in two. Each daughter cell ends up with the same number of identical chromosomes and about half the organelles and cytoplasm.

2 D MITOSIS: Telophase
The chromosomes begin to stretch out and lose their rodlike appearance. This occurs in the two regions at the ends of the cell. A new nuclear membrane forms around each region of chromosomes.

174

Background

History of Science With the development of dyes for staining microscope specimens in the 1800s, scientists could see organelles in the nucleus and learn the details of mitosis. Some of the dyes stained the granular material in the nucleus, so it was given the name *chromatin,* from the Greek word *chroma,* meaning "color." With the dye, chromatin could be seen condensing into rodlike structures during cell division. These rodlike structures were called chromosomes, or "colored bodies" (the Greek word *soma* means "body.") By the late 1800s, German zoologist Theodor Boveri was able to show that, following mitosis, both daughter cells contain an exact copy of the chromosomes of the parent cell.

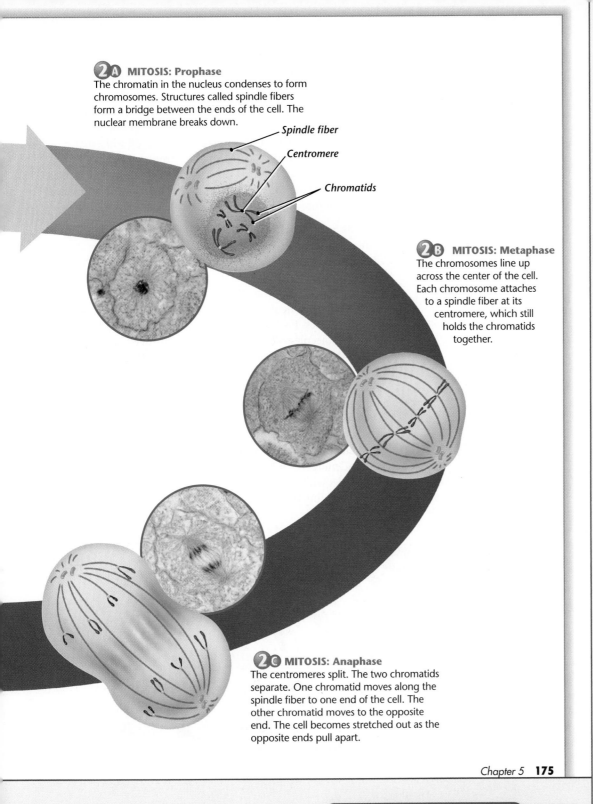

2A MITOSIS: Prophase
The chromatin in the nucleus condenses to form chromosomes. Structures called spindle fibers form a bridge between the ends of the cell. The nuclear membrane breaks down.

Spindle fiber

Centromere

Chromatids

2B MITOSIS: Metaphase
The chromosomes line up across the center of the cell. Each chromosome attaches to a spindle fiber at its centromere, which still holds the chromatids together.

2C MITOSIS: Anaphase
The centromeres split. The two chromatids separate. One chromatid moves along the spindle fiber to one end of the cell. The other chromatid moves to the opposite end. The cell becomes stretched out as the opposite ends pull apart.

Media and Technology

Transparencies "Exploring the Cell Cycle," Transparency 17

Including All Students

Materials index cards
Time 20 minutes

Urge students who are still mastering English to create flash cards for the stages of the cell cycle and the phases of mitosis. Suggest that they write the name of each stage or phase on one side of an index card, and describe it in their own words on the other side. After students have finished making their flash cards, check to see that they have included all the stages of the cell cycle and all the phases of mitosis. Also make sure that students have correctly described each stage or phase. For example, ask: **What occurs during metaphase?** *(The chromosomes form a line across the middle of the cell, and each chromosome is joined to a spindle fiber.)* Encourage pairs of students to quiz each other using their flash cards.
limited English proficiency

Inquiry Challenge

Materials *construction paper, colored markers, tape or safety pins*
Time 15 minutes

Challenge the class to make a human model of the nucleus to show how mitosis occurs. *(One possible model is for a few pairs of students, representing paired chromatids, to stand face to face and join hands, while the other students, representing the nuclear membrane, join hands in a circle around them.)* Provide students with the materials listed above so they can make and wear signs that show which part of the nucleus they represent. After the class has formed the model, challenge students to move in ways that demonstrate the major events of mitosis. Ask: **How could you model the chromatin inside the nucleus during the other stages of the cell cycle?** *(To model cytokinesis and interphase, the formerly paired students might stand at random inside the "nuclears" and not hold hands.)*
learning modality: tactile/ kinesthetic

Ongoing Assessment

Writing Have students write a list, in chronological order, of the major events that occur during mitosis.

DNA Replication

Inquiry Challenge

Materials *toothpicks, white and colored miniature marshmallows*

Time 15 minutes

Challenge hands-on learners to make a three-dimensional model of a DNA molecule using the materials listed above. *(The most likely way is to use toothpicks to join together white marshmallows, representing sugar and phosphate molecules, and colored marshmallows, representing nitrogen bases.)* Suggest to students that they make keys for their models that show which part of the DNA molecule the different components represent. Then ask: **How does your model show that adenine only pairs with thymine and guanine only pairs with cytosine?** *(In their models, students should have joined colored marshmallows representing different bases in the correct pairings.)* **learning modality: tactile/ kinesthetic**

Building Inquiry Skills: Inferring

Encourage students to infer what would happen if an error in DNA replication occurred. Ask: **What do you think would be the outcome if one or more of the nitrogen bases were assembled in the wrong order in a new DNA molecule?** *(Answers may vary. Students may say that the new DNA molecule might not be able to properly direct cell functions. They also might say that any future copies of the new DNA molecule would contain bases in the wrong order, so the error would spread if the cells survived and divided.)* **learning modality: logical/mathematical**

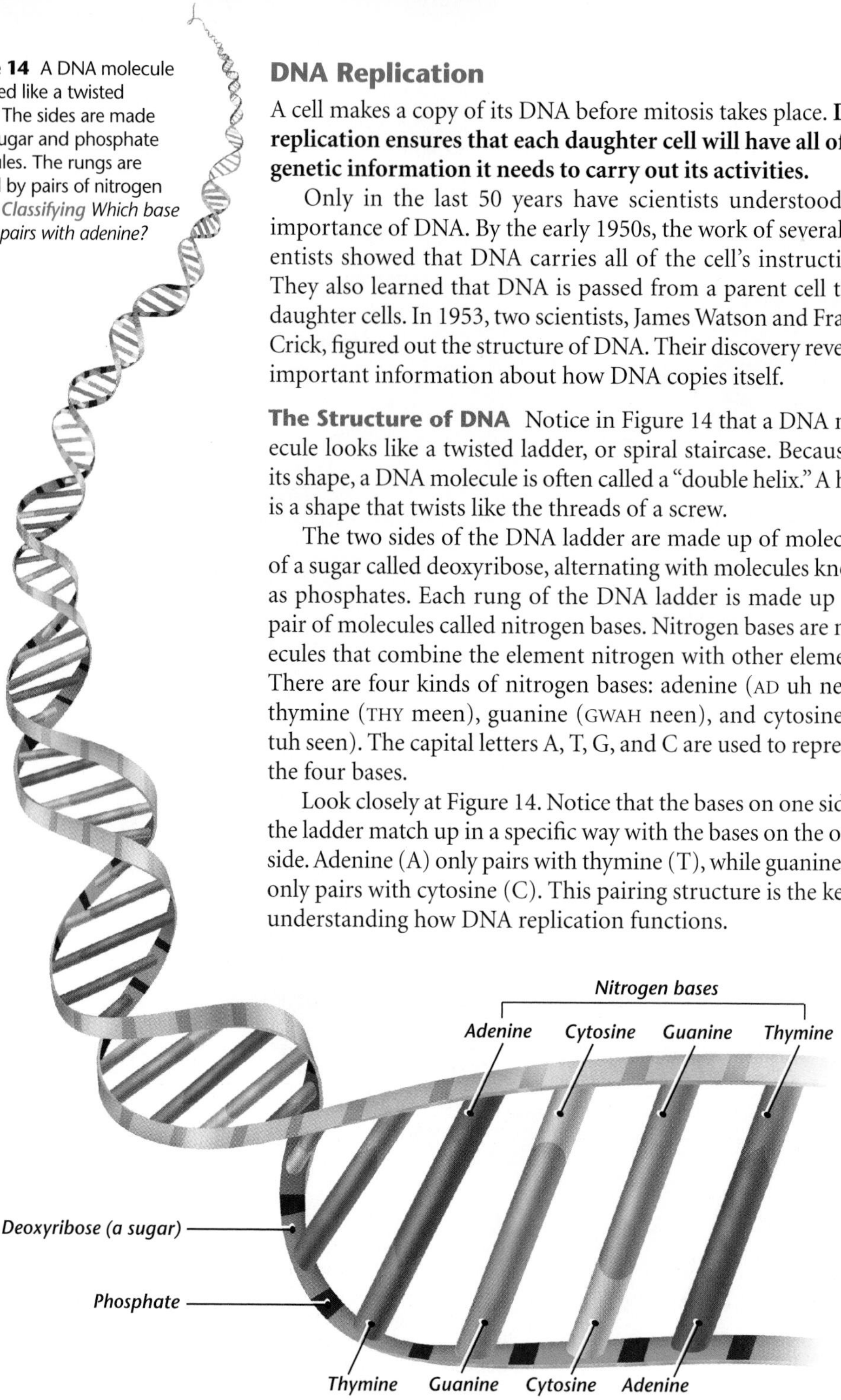

Figure 14 A DNA molecule is shaped like a twisted ladder. The sides are made up of sugar and phosphate molecules. The rungs are formed by pairs of nitrogen bases. *Classifying Which base always pairs with adenine?*

DNA Replication

A cell makes a copy of its DNA before mitosis takes place. **DNA replication ensures that each daughter cell will have all of the genetic information it needs to carry out its activities.**

Only in the last 50 years have scientists understood the importance of DNA. By the early 1950s, the work of several scientists showed that DNA carries all of the cell's instructions. They also learned that DNA is passed from a parent cell to its daughter cells. In 1953, two scientists, James Watson and Francis Crick, figured out the structure of DNA. Their discovery revealed important information about how DNA copies itself.

The Structure of DNA Notice in Figure 14 that a DNA molecule looks like a twisted ladder, or spiral staircase. Because of its shape, a DNA molecule is often called a "double helix." A helix is a shape that twists like the threads of a screw.

The two sides of the DNA ladder are made up of molecules of a sugar called deoxyribose, alternating with molecules known as phosphates. Each rung of the DNA ladder is made up of a pair of molecules called nitrogen bases. Nitrogen bases are molecules that combine the element nitrogen with other elements. There are four kinds of nitrogen bases: adenine (AD uh neen), thymine (THY meen), guanine (GWAH neen), and cytosine (SY tuh seen). The capital letters A, T, G, and C are used to represent the four bases.

Look closely at Figure 14. Notice that the bases on one side of the ladder match up in a specific way with the bases on the other side. Adenine (A) only pairs with thymine (T), while guanine (G) only pairs with cytosine (C). This pairing structure is the key to understanding how DNA replication functions.

Nitrogen bases

Adenine   Cytosine   Guanine   Thymine

Deoxyribose (a sugar)

Phosphate

Thymine   Guanine   Cytosine   Adenine

Background

History of Science In 1953, Watson and Crick described the structure of the DNA molecule. To determine DNA's structure, they used English chemist Rosalind Franklin's X-ray photographs showing the helical appearance of DNA along with much other data. Franklin died in 1956, before Watson and Crick were awarded the Nobel Prize for their work on DNA's structure.

Facts and Figures When DNA replicates, the process requires more than 20 different enzymes to separate the strands of parent DNA and join the nucleotides in the correct sequence in the DNA copies. Although mistakes sometimes happen during this process, they are rare, occurring, on average, once in every one billion replications of any given base pair in a DNA molecule.

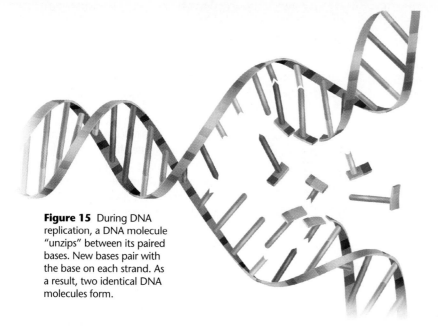

Figure 15 During DNA replication, a DNA molecule "unzips" between its paired bases. New bases pair with the base on each strand. As a result, two identical DNA molecules form.

The Replication Process DNA replication begins when the two sides of the DNA molecule unwind and separate, like a zipper unzipping. As you can see in Figure 15, the molecule separates between the paired nitrogen bases on each rung. Next, nitrogen bases that are floating in the nucleus pair up with the bases on each half of the DNA molecule. Remember that the pairing of bases follows definite rules: A always pairs with T, while G always pairs with C. Once the new bases are attached, two new DNA molecules are formed. The order of the bases in each new DNA molecule will exactly match the order in the original DNA molecule.

Section 3 Review

1. What are the three main stages of the cell cycle? Briefly describe the events that occur at each stage.
2. Why must the DNA in a cell replicate before the cell divides?
3. How does cytokinesis differ in plant and animal cells?
4. **Thinking Critically** **Predicting** Suppose that during anaphase, the centromeres did not split, and the chromatids did not separate. Predict the results.

Check Your Progress   CHAPTER PROJECT
Begin to think about why the egg changed as it did at each stage of the project. Consider how each of the different substances affected your egg. (*Hint:* Water plays a crucial role in the activities of a cell. How has water been involved in your investigation?) Organize your results into a report and make a graph of your egg's changing circumference. You may want to include diagrams to explain the processes that took place.

Chapter 5 **177**

Answers to Self-Assessment

Caption Question

Figure 14 Thymine always pairs with adenine.

---

3 Assess

Section 3 Review Answers

1. The stages are interphase, mitosis, and cytokinesis. In interphase, the cell grows and DNA replicates; in mitosis, the nucleus divides and a copy of DNA goes to each daughter cell; in cytokinesis, the cytoplasm divides into two new cells.
2. The DNA must replicate so that each daughter cell will have all the genetic information it needs.
3. In plant cells, new cell membranes develop across the middle of the cell and separate the cytoplasm of the daughter cells. In animal cells, the cell membrane squeezes together around the middle of the cell and pinches the cytoplasm into the daughter cells.
4. Both chromatids of a chromosome would go to the same pole, so neither daughter cell would get the correct number of chromosomes. Probably neither cell would survive.

Check Your Progress   CHAPTER PROJECT
Have students graph their egg's diameter on one axis and the date it was measured on the other. They also should indicate on their graphs what liquid the egg was soaking in each day.

Performance Assessment

Writing Have students explain why the pairing of nitrogen bases is the key to understanding DNA replication.

Multiplying by Dividing

Preparing for Inquiry

Key Concept Mitosis occurs quickly, and cells spend most of their time in interphase.

Skills Objectives Students will be able to
- observe cells in different stages of the cell cycle;
- calculate the amount of time cells spend in each stage of the cell cycle;
- interpret data to compare how long cells spend in mitosis with the total time of the cell cycle.

Time 40 minutes

Advance Planning Prepared slides can be purchased from a biological supply company.

Alternative Materials Slides of other rapidly dividing cells undergoing division may be used if nuclear structures show up clearly. *Computer use is optional.*

Guiding Inquiry

Troubleshooting the Experiment
- Urge students to review the photographs in *Exploring the Cell Cycle* on pages 174–175.

Expected Outcome

Students should observe and sketch cells undergoing interphase and the four phases of mitosis. Most of the cells they count should be in the interphase stage of the cell cycle, but errors in counting and differences in samples may give varying results.

Analyze and Conclude

1. The most likely answer is interphase.
2. Answers will vary depending on students' data. Answers for the sample data are: interphase, 641 minutes; prophase, 50 minutes; metaphase, 14 minutes; anaphase, 7 minutes; telophase, 7 minutes.
3. Based on the sample data, the amount of time spent in mitosis is 11 percent. Students' answers will vary depending on their data.

Skills Lab

Calculating

Multiplying by Dividing

Problem

How long do the stages of the cell cycle take?

Materials

microscope
colored pencils
calculator or computer (optional)
prepared slides of onion root tip cells undergoing cell division

Procedure

1. Place the slide on the stage of a microscope. Use low power to locate a cell in interphase. Then switch to high power, and make a labeled drawing of the cell. **CAUTION:** *Slides and coverslips break easily. Do not allow the objective to touch the slide.*

2. Repeat Step 1 to find cells in prophase, metaphase, anaphase, and telophase. Then use pencil and paper or the computer to copy the data table.

3. Return to low power. Find an area with many cells dividing. Switch to the magnification that lets you see about 50 cells (for example, 100×).

DATA TABLE			
Stage of Cell Cycle	First Sample	Second Sample	Total Number
Interphase			
Mitosis: Prophase			
Metaphase			
Anaphase			
Telophase			
Total number of cells counted			

4. Examine the cells row by row, and count the cells that are in interphase. Record that number in the data table under *First Sample*.

5. Examine the cells row-by-row four more times to count the cells in prophase, metaphase, anaphase, and telophase. Record the results.

6. Move to a new area on the slide. Repeat Steps 3–5 and record your counts in the column labeled *Second Sample*.

7. Fill in the column labeled *Total Number* by adding the numbers across each row.

8. Add the totals for the five stages to find the total number of cells counted.

Analyze and Conclude

1. Which stage of the cell cycle did you observe most often?

2. The cell cycle for onion root tips takes about 720 minutes (12 hours). Use your data and the formula below to find the number of minutes each stage takes. Do your calculations with a pencil and paper, a calculator, or a computer.

$$\text{Time for each stage} = \frac{\text{Number of cells at each stage}}{\text{Total number of cells counted}} \times 720 \text{ min}$$

3. **Think About It** Compare the amount of time spent in mitosis with the total time for the whole cell cycle.

More to Explore

Examine prepared slides of animal cells undergoing cell division. Use drawings and descriptions to compare plant and animal mitosis.

Safety

Remind students to handle slides and coverslips carefully. Review the safety guidelines in Appendix A.

Program Resources

- **Unit 2 Resources** Chapter 5 Skills Lab blackline masters, pp. 51–53

Sample Data Table

Stage of Cell Cycle	First Sample	Second Sample	Total Number
Interphase	43	46	89
Mitosis: Prophase	3	4	7
Metaphase	1	1	2
Anaphase	1	0	1
Telophase	0	1	1

CHAPTER 5 STUDY GUIDE

 SECTION 1

The Cell in Its Environment

Key Ideas

◆ The cell membrane is selectively permeable. This structure enables it to perform the function of regulating the materials that enter and leave the cell.

◆ Substances move into and out of a cell by one of three methods: diffusion, osmosis, or active transport.

◆ The main method by which substances move into and out of cells is diffusion. Diffusion is the process by which molecules tend to move from an area of higher concentration to an area of lower concentration.

◆ Water molecules pass into and out of a cell through osmosis, which is the diffusion of water molecules through a selectively permeable membrane.

◆ Active transport requires the cell to use energy, while passive transport does not.

Key Terms

selectively permeable
diffusion
osmosis
passive transport
active transport

 SECTION 2

The Cell and Energy

INTEGRATING CHEMISTRY

Key Ideas

◆ During photosynthesis, cells capture energy from sunlight and use it to change carbon dioxide gas and water into oxygen and sugars, such as glucose.

◆ During respiration, cells break down simple food molecules such as glucose and release the energy they contain.

◆ Photosynthesis and respiration can be thought of as opposite processes.

Key Terms

photosynthesis
chlorophyll

respiration
fermentation

SECTION 3

Cell Division

Key Ideas

◆ The cell cycle is the regular sequence of growth and division that cells undergo.

◆ During interphase, the cell grows to its mature size, makes a copy of its DNA, and prepares to divide into two cells.

◆ Mitosis is the stage during which the cell's nucleus divides into two new nuclei. During mitosis, one copy of the DNA is distributed to each of the two daughter cells.

◆ During cytokinesis, the cytoplasm divides, distributing the organelles into each of the two new cells.

◆ DNA replication, which occurs before mitosis, ensures that each daughter cell will have all of the genetic information it needs to carry out its activities.

Key Terms

cell cycle
interphase
replication

mitosis
chromatid
cytokinesis

Organizing Information

Cycle Diagram Copy the cycle diagram about the cell cycle onto a separate sheet of paper. Then complete it and add a title. (For more on cycle diagrams, see the Skills Handbook.)

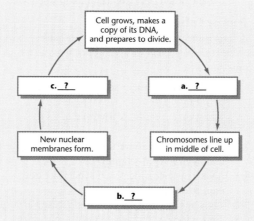

Chapter 5 **179**

Extending the Inquiry

More to Explore Interphase and mitosis are very similar in plant and animal cells, except that the centrioles appear during prophase in animal cells. Challenge students to predict whether animal or plant cells spend longer in mitosis. Then have them design an experiment to test their prediction.

Organizing Information

Cycle Diagram a. Chromatin condenses to form chromosomes, spindle fibers form, and the nuclear membrane breaks down. **b.** The chromatids separate and move to opposite ends of the cell. **c.** The cell membrane pinches in around the middle of the cell, and the cell divides. Sample title: The Cell Cycle

Program Resources

◆ **Unit 2 Resources** Chapter 5 Project Scoring Rubric, p. 36
◆ **Performance Assessment** Chapter 5, pp. 17–19
◆ **Chapter and Unit Tests** Chapter 5 Test, pp. 24–27

Media and Technology

Lab Activity Videotapes
Grade 6, Tape 2

Computer Test Bank
Chapter 5 Test

Reviewing Content
Multiple Choice
1. a 2. b 3. a 4. c 5. c

True or False
6. true 7. active transport 8. true
9. fermentation 10. interphase

Checking Concepts

11. The selectively permeable structure of the cell membrane enables it to fulfill its function of regulating the materials that enter and leave the cell.

12. Diffusion is the process by which molecules tend to move from an area of higher concentration to an area of lower concentration. Diffusion helps the cell take in the substances it needs and get rid of those it does not need.

13. During photosynthesis, energy from sunlight is changed into chemical energy, which is used to convert carbon dioxide and water into oxygen and sugars, including glucose.

14. Heterotrophs get energy by eating plants or other organisms that eat plants. Plants get energy from the sun.

15. Organisms need to carry out respiration in order to provide energy for cell processes.

16. During the cell cycle, the parent cell divides into two identical cells. These daughter cells contain the same DNA and the same organelles. During mitosis each of the chromosome pairs is split, with half of each pair going to each new daughter cell. Organelles and cytoplasm are divided between the two daughter cells during telophase and cytokinesis.

17. Students' paragraphs should include the following points: Respiration and photosynthesis are opposite processes. The raw materials of respiration are the same as the products of photosynthesis. The raw materials of photosynthesis are the same as the products of respiration. Photosynthesis uses carbon dioxide from the atmosphere and produces oxygen. Respiration uses oxygen from the atmosphere and produces carbon dioxide.

Reviewing Content

 Review key concepts online using iText at www.phschool.com

Multiple Choice
Choose the letter of the best answer.

1. The process by which water moves across a cell membrane is called
   a. osmosis.
   b. active transport.
   c. diffusion.
   d. resolution.

2. The movement of materials through a cell membrane without using energy is called
   a. active transport.
   b. passive transport.
   c. selective permeability.
   d. metaphase.

3. What process is responsible for producing most of Earth's oxygen?
   a. photosynthesis
   b. replication
   c. mutation
   d. reproduction

4. The process in which a cell makes an exact copy of its DNA is called
   a. fermentation.
   b. respiration.
   c. replication.
   d. reproduction.

5. Chromatids are held together by a
   a. spindle.   b. chloroplast.
   c. centromere.   d. cell membrane.

True or False
If the statement is true, write true. If it is false, change the underlined word or words to make the statement true.

6. The <u>cell membrane</u> is selectively permeable.

7. Transport proteins are involved in <u>passive transport</u>.

8. The process of respiration takes place mainly in the <u>mitochondria</u>.

9. An energy-releasing process that does not require oxygen is <u>replication</u>.

10. The stage of the cell cycle when DNA replication occurs is <u>telophase</u>.

Checking Concepts

11. Explain how the selectively permeable structure of the cell membrane relates to one of the functions of the cell membrane.

12. What is diffusion? What role does diffusion play in the cell?

13. Briefly explain what happens to energy from the sun during photosynthesis.

14. Explain how heterotrophs depend on the sun for energy.

15. Why do organisms need to carry out the process of respiration?

16. How do the events of the cell cycle ensure that the daughter cells will be identical to the parent cell?

17. **Writing to Learn** Write a paragraph comparing and contrasting photosynthesis and respiration. Be sure to discuss how the two processes maintain the oxygen and carbon dioxide balance in the atmosphere.

Thinking Critically

18. **Comparing and Contrasting** Compare and contrast the processes of alcoholic fermentation and lactic acid fermentation. Explain how the two processes are alike and different.

19. **Predicting** Suppose a volcano spewed so much ash into the air that it blocked most of the sunlight that usually strikes Earth. How might this affect the ability of animals to obtain the energy they need to live?

20. **Applying Concepts** Explain the relationship between the processes of breathing and respiration.

21. **Inferring** Suppose one strand of a DNA molecule contained the following bases: A C G T C T G. What would the bases on the other strand be?

22. **Problem Solving** Explain why it is important that the cell cycle results in daughter cells that are identical to the parent cell.

Thinking Critically

18. Both alcoholic fermentation and lactic fermentation are processes through which cells obtain energy from food without using oxygen. The products of these processes and the kinds of cells that undergo them are different. Alcoholic fermentation produces alcohol, carbon dioxide, and a small amount of energy. It occurs in single-celled organisms such as yeast. Lactic fermentation also produces energy, but it also yields the by-product lactic acid. It occurs in the muscle cells of multi-celled organisms such as humans.

19. Answers may vary. *Sample answer:* The ash from the volcano would block the sun and prevent plants from using its energy to make food. Plants would die out, and the animals and other organisms that get their energy from plants would die out as well.

20. Breathing brings oxygen into the body for respiration. Respiration uses the oxygen to break down food and provide energy for the body's needs.

21. T G C A G A C

Applying Skills

Use the table below to answer Questions 23–25.

Percentages of Nitrogen Bases In the DNA of Various Organisms

Nitrogen Base	Human	Wheat	*E. coli* bacterium
Adenine	30%	27%	24%
Guanine	20%	23%	26%
Thymine	30%	27%	24%
Cytosine	20%	23%	26%

23. Graphing For each organism, draw a bar graph to show the percentages of each nitrogen base in its DNA.

24. Interpreting Data What is the relationship between the amounts of adenine and thymine in the DNA of each organism? Between the amounts of guanine and cytosine?

25. Inferring Based on your answer to Question 24, what can you infer about the structure of DNA in these three organisms?

Performance CHAPTER PROJECT **Assessment**

Present Your Project Bring in your egg, your graph, and any diagrams you made. As a class or in groups, discuss your results and conclusions. Then, as a group, try to agree on answers to these questions: What happened to the eggshell? What process took place at each stage of the experiment?

Reflect and Record In your notebook, describe what you learned from doing this "egg-speriment." Which part of the project was the most surprising? Why? When did you begin to understand what was happening to the egg? If you did the project again, what would you do differently? Why?

Test Preparation

Use these questions to prepare for standardized tests.

Study the equations. Then answer Questions 26–28.

Photosynthesis

$$6\,CO_2 + 6\,H_2O \xrightarrow{\text{light energy}} C_6H_{12}O_6 + 6\,O_2$$

Respiration

$$C_6H_{12}O_6 + 6\,O_2 \rightarrow 6\,CO_2 + 6\,H_2O + \text{energy}$$

26. What products are produced during photosynthesis?
   A carbon dioxide and water
   B light energy and carbon dioxide
   C carbon dioxide and sugar
   D sugar and oxygen

27. What raw materials are needed for respiration to occur?
   F energy and water
   G carbon dioxide, water, and energy
   H sugar and oxygen
   J sugar and carbon dioxide

28. Why are the words "light energy" written above the arrow in the photosynthesis equation?
   A Light energy is necessary for the reaction to occur.
   B Light energy is produced during the reaction.
   C Oxygen can exist only in the presence of light.
   D Sugar can exist only in the presence of light.

Program Resources

♦ **Inquiry Skills Activity Book** Provides teaching and review of all inquiry skills
♦ **Prentice Hall Assessment System** Provides standardized test practice
♦ **Reading in the Content Area** Provides strategies to improve science reading skills
♦ **Teacher's ELL Handbook** Provides multiple strategies for English language learners

---

22. The daughter cells need the same genetic material that the parent cell had in order to live.

Applying Skills

23. The bars in the graph should correspond to the percentages in the table. There should be four bars for each organism.

24. The percents of adenine and thymine are equal. The percents of guanine and cytosine also are equal.

25. In all of the organisms, adenine is paired with thymine and guanine is paired with cytosine.

Performance CHAPTER PROJECT **Assessment**

Present Your Project Have students display their eggs and share their graphs showing how the size of their egg changed and what it was soaking in each day. If students made diagrams showing how water moved into or out of the cell by osmosis, have them share these as well. Guide the class discussion so that students come to the conclusion that the eggshell dissolved in the vinegar, and that the egg increased and decreased in size because of osmosis.

Reflect and Record Students may say that this "egg-speriment" helped them understand the process of osmosis and how important the cell membrane is to the cell. The most surprising part may have been how the texture of the egg changed. Most students probably began to understand what was happening to the egg when they read about osmosis in Section 1. If they did the project over, students may say they would test a greater variety of liquids.

Test Preparation

26. D **27.** H **28.** A

From Bacteria to Plants

Sections	Time	Student Edition Activities	Other Activities
CHAPTER PROJECT **Cycle of a Lifetime** p. 183 TEKS: 6.10C	Ongoing (4-5 weeks)	TEKS: 6.2B Check Your Progress, pp. 189, 203, 211 Present Your Project, p. 215	**TE** Chapter 6 Project Notes, pp. 182–183
1 Classifying Living Things pp. 184–189 TEKS: 6.10B; 6.11B 6.1.1 Explain why scientists organize living things into groups. 6.1.2 Describe the classification system of Linnaeus. 6.1.3 Identify the characteristics biologists use today to classify organisms. 6.1.4 Name the seven levels of classification used by scientists. 6.1.5 List the six kingdoms into which all organisms are classified.	2–3 periods/ 1–1½ blocks	TEKS: 6.2C **Discover** Can You Organize a Junk Drawer?, p. 184	**TE** Inquiry Challenge, p. 185 **TE** Including All Students, p. 186 **TE** Building Inquiry Skills: Making Models, p. 187 **TE** Real-Life Learning, p. 188 **TE** Building Inquiry Skills: Classifying, p. 189
2 Bacteria pp. 190–195 TEKS: 6.10A, B, C; 6.11B 6.2.1 Describe ways in which bacteria cells are different from all other organisms' cells. 6.2.2 Tell how bacteria eat, reproduce, and survive. 6.2.3 List the ways in which bacteria affect people's lives.	2–3 periods/ 1–1½ blocks	TEKS: 6.1A, B; 6.2A, B, C, D, E; 6.3B, C; 6.4A **Discover** How Fast Do Bacteria Multiply?, p. 190 **Try This** Bacteria for Breakfast, p. 192 **Science at Home** , p. 193 **Real-World Lab: You, the Consumer** Do Disinfectants Work? pp. 194-195	
3 Protists and Fungi pp. 196–203 TEKS: 6.10A, B, C; 6.12B 6.3.1 Describe the characteristics of animal-like, plantlike, and fungus-like protists. 6.3.2 Describe the characteristics of fungi.	2–3 periods/ 1–1½ blocks	TEKS: 6.1A, B; 6.2B, C; 6.4A **Discover** What Lives in a Drop of Water?, p. 196 **Try This** Feeding Paramecia, p. 200	**TE** Inquiry Challenge, pp. 197, 199, 201 **TE** Building Inquiry Skills: Observing, pp. 201, 202 **LM** 6, "Comparing Protists"
4 The Plant Kingdom pp. 204–212 TEKS: 6.10A, B, C; 6.11B; 6.12A, B 6.4.1 Identify the characteristics that all plants share. 6.4.2 Describe the structure of a seed. 6.4.3 Describe how plants reproduce. 6.4.4 Explain how plants respond to stimuli.	3–4 periods/ 1½–2 blocks	TEKS: 6.1A; 6.2A, B, C, D; 6.4A, B **Discover** What Do Leaves Reveal about Plants?, p. 204 **Try This** What Stomata?, p. 205 **Try This** The In-Seed Story, p. 208 **Skills Lab: Developing Hypotheses** Which Way Is Up?, p. 212	**TE** Using the Visuals, p. 205 **TE** Building Inquiry Skills: Observing, pp. 206, 207, 208 **TE** Demonstration, p. 210
Study Guide/Chapter Assessment pp. 213–215	1 period/ ½ block	**PLM** Provides blackline masters for Probeware labs	**ISAB** Provides teaching and review of all inquiry skills

Key: **CTB** Computer Test Bank
CUT Chapter and Unit Tests
ELL Teacher's ELL Handbook

CHAPTER PLANNING GUIDE

 The Resource Pro® CD-ROM provides flexibility for planning the instruction for any type of schedule.

Program Resources	Assessment Strategies	Media and Technology
UR Chapter 6 Project Teacher Notes, pp. 54–55 UR Chapter 6 Project Overview and Worksheets, pp. 56–59	SE Performance Assessment: Present Your Project, p. 215 TE Check Your Progress, pp. 189, 203, 211 UR Chapter 6 Project Scoring Rubric, p. 60	🌐 Science Explorer at www.phschool.com 🎧 Student Edition on Audio CD, English-Spanish, Chapter 6
UR 6-1 Lesson Plan, p. 61 UR 6-1 Section Summary, p. 62 UR 6-1 Review and Reinforce, p. 63 UR 6-1 Enrich, p. 64	SE Section 1 Review, p. 189 TE Ongoing Assessment, pp. 185, 187 TE Performance Assessment, p. 189	💿 Life Science Videodisc Unit 2, Side 1, "*Pantera leo?*" 📼 Videotape Grade 6, Unit 2, "*Pantera leo?*" ▦ Transparency 20, "Seven Levels of Classification"
UR 6-2 Lesson Plan, p. 65 UR 6-2 Section Summary, p. 66 UR 6-2 Review and Reinforce, p. 67 UR 6-2 Enrich, p. 68 UR Real-World Lab blackline masters, pp. 77–79	SE Section 2 Review, p. 193 TE Ongoing Assessment, p. 191 TE Performance Assessment, p. 193	💿 Life Science Videodisc Unit 2, Side 1, "Positive Bacteria" 📼 Videotape Grade 6, Unit 2, "Positive Bacteria" 📼 Lab Activity Videotapes, Tape 2 ▦ Transparency 21, "The Structure of a Bacterial Cell"
UR 6-3 Lesson Plan, p. 69 UR 6-3 Section Summary, p. 70 UR 6-3 Review and Reinforce, p. 71 UR 6-3 Enrich, p. 72	SE Section 3 Review, p. 203 TE Ongoing Assessment, pp. 197, 199, 201 TE Performance Assessment, p. 203	💿 Life Science Videodisc Unit 2, Side 1, "Fungi and Algae" 📼 Videotape Grade 6, Unit 2, "Fungi and Algae" ▦ Transparencies 22, "Exploring Protozoans— Ameba"; 23 "Exploring Protozoans— Paramecium"; 24 "The Structure of a Euglena"; 25, "The Structure of a Mushroom"
UR 6-4 Lesson Plan, p. 73 UR 6-4 Section Summary, p. 74 UR 6-4 Review and Reinforce, p. 75 UR 6-4 Enrich, p. 76 UR Skills Lab blackline masters, pp. 80–81	SE Section 4 Review, p. 211 TE Ongoing Assessment, pp. 205, 207, 209 TE Performance Assessment, p. 211	▦ Transparencies 26, "The Structure of a Leaf"; 27 "The Structure of Seeds"; 28 "The Structure of a Flower" 📼 Lab Activity Videotapes, Tape 2
ELL Provides multiple strategies for English language learners GRSW Provides worksheets to promote student comprehension of content RCA Provides strategies to improve science reading skills	SE Chapter 6 Study Guide/Assessment, pp. 213–215 PA Chapter 6 Assessment, pp. 20–22 CUT Chapter 6 Test, pp. 28–31 CTB Chapter 6 Test PHAS Provides standardized test preparation	💻 Chapter 6 💾 Computer Test Bank, Chapter 6 Test

GRSW Guided Reading and Study Workbook
ISAB Inquiry Skills Activity Book
LM Laboratory Manual

PA Performance Assessment
PHAS Prentice Hall Assessment System
PLM Probeware Lab Manual

RCA Reading in the Content Area
SE Student Edition

TE Teacher's Edition
UR Unit Resources

Student Edition Activities Planner

ACTIVITY	Time (minutes)	Materials — Quantities for one work group	Skills
Section 1			
Discover, p. 184	15	**Nonconsumable** items such as scotch tape, pencils, rubber bands, stamps, markers, erasers, rulers, envelopes, paper clips, paper	Classifying
Section 2			
Discover, p. 190	20	**Consumable** paper cups; dried lima, kidney, or navy beans	Inferring
Try This, p. 192	20	**Consumable** unpasteurized yogurt, methylene blue **Nonconsumable** plastic dropper, glass slide, cover slip, microscope, lab apron	Observing
Science at Home, p. 193	home	**Consumable** labels from food products with bacteria	Observing
Real-World Lab, pp. 194–195	30 first day; 15 each of next 3 days	**Consumable** 2 household disinfectants, sterile nutrient agar, transparent tape, 3 sealable plastic bags **Nonconsumable** clock, 2 plastic droppers, wax pencil, computer (optional)	Observing, Inferring, Drawing Conclusions
Section 3			
Discover, p. 196	25	**Consumable** pond water **Nonconsumable** plastic dropper, microscope slide, cover slip, microscope	Observing
Try This, p. 200	15	**Consumable** paramecium culture, *Chlorella* culture, cotton fibers **Nonconsumable** plastic dropper, microscope slide, microscope	Inferring
Section 4			
Discover, p. 204	10	**Consumable** leaf from a jade plant or a plant with thick, fleshy leaves; leaf from a temperate-climate plant, such as a maple, oak, or common garden plant **Nonconsumable** hand lens	Inferring
Try This, p. 205	15	**Consumable** lettuce, water **Nonconsumable** slide, coverslip, microscope	Observing
Try This, p. 208	10	**Consumable** dried kidney, lima, or black beans; dried yellow or green peas; shelled peanuts **Nonconsumable** hand lens	Observing
Skills Lab, p. 212	30, plus a few min. a day for a week	**Consumable** 4 corn seeds, paper towels, water, masking tape, clay **Nonconsumable** marking pencil, plastic petri dish, scissors	Developing Hypotheses, Designing Experiments

A list of all materials required for the Student Edition activities can be found on pages T43–T49. You can obtain information about ordering materials by calling 1-800-848-9500 or by accessing the Science Explorer Internet site at **www.phschool.com.**

Texas Essential Knowledge and Skills

(6.1) Scientific processes. The student conducts field and laboratory investigations using safe, environmentally appropriate, and ethical practices. *(Sections 2, 3, 4)*
The student is expected to:
(A) demonstrate safe practices during field and laboratory investigations; and
(B) make wise choices in the use and conservation of resources and the disposal or recycling of materials.

(6.2) Scientific processes. The student uses scientific inquiry methods during field and laboratory investigations. *(Project; Sections 1, 2, 3, 4)*
The student is expected to:
(A) plan and implement investigative procedures including asking questions, formulating testable hypotheses, and selecting and using equipment and technology;
(B) collect data by observing and measuring;
(C) analyze and interpret information to construct reasonable explanations from direct and indirect evidence;
(D) communicate valid conclusions; and
(E) construct graphs, tables, maps, and charts using tools including computers to organize, examine, and evaluate data.

(6.3) Scientific processes. The student uses critical thinking and scientific problem solving to make informed decisions. *(Section 2)*
The student is expected to:
(B) draw inferences based on data related to promotional materials for products and services;
(C) represent the natural world using models and identify their limitations.

(6.4) Scientific processes. The student knows how to use a variety of tools and methods to conduct science inquiry. *(Sections 2, 3, 4)*
The student is expected to:
(A) collect, analyze, and record information using tools including beakers, petri dishes, meter sticks, graduated cylinders, weather instruments, timing devices, hot plates, test tubes, safety goggles, spring scales, magnets, balances, microscopes, telescopes, thermometers, calculators, field equipment, compasses, computers, and computer probes; and
(B) identify patterns in collected information using percent, average, range, and frequency.

(6.10) Science concepts. The student knows the relationship between structure and function in living systems. *(Project; Sections 1, 2, 3, 4)*
The student is expected to:
(A) differentiate between structure and function;
(B) determine that all organisms are composed of cells that carry on functions to sustain life; and
(C) identify how structure complements function at different levels of organization including organs, organ systems, organisms, and populations.

(6.11) Science concepts. The student knows that traits of species can change through generations and that the instructions for traits are contained in the genetic material of the organisms. *(Sections 1, 2, 4)*
The student is expected to:
(B) identify cells as structures containing genetic material.

(6.12) Science concepts. The student knows that the responses of organisms are caused by internal or external stimuli. *(Sections 3, 4)*
The student is expected to:
(A) identify responses in organisms to internal stimuli such as hunger or thirst;
(B) identify responses in organisms to external stimuli such as the presence or absence of heat or light.

Take It to the Net

 Interactive text at www.phschool.com

Science Explorer comes alive with iText.

- **Complete student text** is accessible from any computer with Internet access or a CD-ROM drive.

- **Animations, simulations, and videos** enhance student understanding and retention of concepts.

- **Self-tests and online study tools** assess student understanding.

- **Teacher management tools** help you make the most of this valuable resource.

STAY CURRENT with

Find out the latest research and information about bacteria, protists, fungi, and plants at **www.phschool.com**.

Go to **www.phschool.com**. Select Texas on the navigation bar. Click on the Science icon. Then click on Science Explorer under PH@school.

Cycle of a Lifetime

TEKS: 6.2B; 6.10C

Although most students are aware that plants grow from seeds, they may never have observed each stage in the life of a seed plant. This project will allow students to observe a plant's growing cycle.

Purpose In this project, students will grow plants from seeds and make detailed observations of the plant's life cycle from germination through growth, flowering, and pollination.

Skills Focus After completing the Chapter 6 Project, students will be able to
♦ pose questions about how plants grow and reproduce;
♦ observe different parts of the seed plant life cycle;
♦ communicate their findings about seed plants to their classmates.

Project Time Line This project will take 4–5 weeks to complete. Students should plant their seeds as soon as possible; germination will take several days. During this time, students should discuss the life cycle of plants and what they expect to observe. They should set up their data tables and prepare to take measurements. Around week three, the plants should have flowers that are ready for pollination. Students should be able to collect new seeds by the fourth week. At this time they should prepare their displays and work on their class presentations. Before beginning the project, see Chapter 6 Project Teacher Notes on pages 54–55 in Unit 2 Resources for more details on carrying out the project. Also, distribute to students the Chapter 6 Project Overview, Worksheets, and Scoring Rubric on pages 56–60 in Unit 2 Resources.

Possible Materials Students will need basic gardening supplies: fast-growing seeds (seeds that flower in about 28 days, such as seeds from fast-growing plants from biological suppliers or from tomatoes, peas, etc.), potting trays, potting soil, water, and cotton swabs for transferring pollen.

CHAPTER
6 **From Bacteria to Plants**

WEB ACTIVITY
www.phschool.com

1 **Classifying Living Things**
Discover Can You Organize a Junk Drawer?

2 **Bacteria**
Discover How Fast Do Bacteria Multiply?
Real-World Lab Do Disinfectants Work?

3 **Protists and Fungi**
Discover What Lives in a Drop of Water?

4 **The Plant Kingdom**
Discover What Do Leaves Reveal About Plants?
Skills Lab Which Way Is Up?

182

Launching the Project To introduce the project and to stimulate student interest, ask: **How do we get more plants?** (*Discussion should lead to the answer "seeds."*) Then ask: **How do we get seeds?** This should lead to a discussion of seed production.

Allow time for students to read the description of the project in their text and the Chapter Project Overview on pages 56–57 in Unit 2 Resources. Then encourage discussions on the life cycle of seed plants. Make sure students

know how to care for the plant so that it will grow well and provide useful information for their observations. Answer any initial questions students may have, and distribute copies of the Chapter 6 Project Worksheets on pages 58–59 in Unit 2 Resources.

You may want to have students work in small groups as a cooperative learning task. To ensure that every student will have ample opportunity to care for the plants, each group should consist of no more than three students.

CHAPTER 6 PROJECT

Cycle of a Lifetime

In a shady valley, tiny mosses cover the banks of a stream. Overhead, tall trees stretch their branches to the light. Can organisms that seem so different have anything in common? In this chapter, you'll find out. And in this chapter's project, you'll learn how some of these organisms reproduce. You'll grow some seeds, then care for the plants until they, in turn, produce their own seeds.

Your Goal To care for and observe a plant throughout its life cycle.

To complete this project successfully you must
- grow a plant from a seed
- observe and describe key parts of your plant's life cycle, such as seed germination and pollination
- harvest and plant the seeds that your growing plant produces
- follow the safety guidelines in Appendix A

Get Started Observe the seeds that your teacher gives you. In a small group, discuss what conditions the seeds might need to grow. What should you look for after you plant the seeds? What kinds of measurements could you make? Will it help to make drawings? When you are ready, plant your seeds.

Check Your Progress You'll be working on this project as you study this chapter. To keep your project on track, look for Check Your Progress boxes at the following points.
Section 1 Review, page 189: Observe the developing seedlings.
Section 3 Review, page 203: Pollinate your flowers.
Section 4 Review, page 211: Collect the seeds from your plant and plant some of them.

Present Your Project At the end of the chapter (page 215), you'll present an exhibit showing the plant's life cycle.

Mosses carpet the rocks along this stream in Pennsylvania's Pocono Mountains.

TEKS

In addition to process TEKS, this chapter addresses these concept TEKS as they relate to the chapter's topics.

(6.10) The student knows the relationship between structure and function in living systems. The student is expected to:
(A) differentiate between structure and function;
(B) determine that all organisms are composed of cells that carry on functions to sustain life; and
(C) identify how structure complements function at different levels of organization including organs, organ systems, organisms, and populations.

(6.11) The student knows that traits of species can change through generations and that the instructions for traits are contained in the genetic material of the organisms. The student is expected to:
(B) identify cells as structures containing genetic material.

(6.12) The student knows that the responses of organisms are caused by internal or external stimuli. The student is expected to:
(A) identify responses in organisms to internal stimuli such as hunger or thirst;
(B) identify responses in organisms to external stimuli such as the presence or absence of heat or light.

183

Program Resources

- **Unit 2 Resources** Chapter 6 Project Teacher Notes, pp. 54–55; Chapter 6 Project Overview and Worksheets, pp. 56–59

Media and Technology

🎧 **Student Edition on Audio CD**
English-Spanish, Chapter 6

www.phschool.com

You will find an Internet activity, chapter self-tests for students, and links to other chapter topics at this site.

Performance Assessment

The Chapter 6 Project Scoring Rubric on page 60 of Unit 2 Resources will help you evaluate how well students complete the Chapter 6 Project. Students will be assessed on
- how well and consistently they care for their plants;
- the completeness of their observation entries, including measurements of stem, leaves, and flowers;
- how well they apply chapter concepts to their observations;
- the thoroughness and organization of their presentations.

By sharing the Chapter 6 Project Scoring Rubric with students at the beginning of the project, you will make it clear to them what they are expected to do.

TEKS: 6.2C; 6.10B; 6.11B

Objectives

After completing the lesson, students will be able to

◆ explain why scientists organize living things into groups;

◆ describe the classification system of Linnaeus;

◆ identify the characteristics biologists use today to classify organisms;

◆ name the seven levels of classification used by scientists;

◆ list the six kingdoms into which all organisms are classified.

1 Engage/Explore

Activating Prior Knowledge

Ask students: **How do libraries organize their books?** *(First by whether they are fiction or nonfiction, then by subject matter, then in alphabetical order by author's last name, first name, and finally title)* Discuss with students how difficult it would be to find a book in the library without some sort of organizing system.

• • • • DISCOVER • • • •

Skills Focus classifying

Materials *items such as scotch tape, pencils, rubber bands, stamps, markers, erasers, rulers, envelopes, paper clips, paper*

Time 15 minutes

Tips Avoid using sharp objects. Stress that items in a set must share at least one common trait.

Expected Outcome A variety of classification systems may be proposed. For example, students may group by function (items you write with) or by shape (round).

Think It Over Each grouping system will have strengths and weaknesses. Criteria for usefulness will vary. Possibilities include systems that emphasize similar functions or systems that allow objects to be found quickly.

SECTION 1 Classifying Living Things

DISCOVER • ACTIVITY

Can You Organize a Junk Drawer?

1. Your teacher will give you some items that you might find in the junk drawer of a desk. Your job is to organize the items.

2. Examine the objects and decide on three groups into which you can sort them.

3. Place each object into one of the groups based on how the item's features match the characteristics of the group.

4. Compare your grouping system with those of your classmates.

Think It Over

Classifying Explain which grouping system seemed most useful.

GUIDE FOR READING

◆ What characteristics do scientists consider when they classify an organism?

◆ What are the six kingdoms into which all organisms are grouped?

Reading Tip Before you read, look at the list of the boldfaced vocabulary terms. As you read, write the meaning of each term in your own words.

Key Terms classification
• taxonomy
• binomial nomenclature
• genus • species

Suppose you had only ten minutes to run into a supermarket to get what you need—milk and tomatoes. In most supermarkets this would be easy. First, you'd go to the dairy aisle for the milk. Then you'd go to the produce aisle and find the tomatoes.

Now imagine shopping for these items in a market where the shelves are not organized. To find what you need, you'd have to search through shelves in which apples, boxes of cereal, cans of tuna, and many more items were all mixed together. You could be there for a long time!

Why Do Scientists Classify Organisms?

Just as shopping can be a problem in a disorganized store, learning about organisms could also be a problem without organization. Scientists have identified at least 1.7 million kinds of organisms on Earth. This number includes all forms of life, from bacteria to plants and animals. It is important for biologists to have these living things organized into groups. **Classification** is the process of grouping things based on their shared traits. Biologists use classification to organize living things into groups so that the organisms are easier to study.

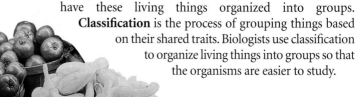

◄ Vegetables organized by type

184

READING STRATEGIES

Reading Tip Have students write the vocabulary words on the fronts of index cards and their definitions on the backs. Students can work in pairs to quiz each other and practice pronouncing the words. Sample definition: Classification—a system of grouping things according to their similarities.

Study and Comprehension Before students read the section, have them write the main section headings in their notebooks, leaving enough space between headings to write at least three sentences. As students read each section, they should summarize it before reading the next section. Remind students to identify the main idea and restate it in their own words.

The scientific study of how living things are classified is called **taxonomy** (tak SAHN uh mee). Living things that are classified together have similar characteristics. Taxonomy is useful because after an organism is classified, a scientist knows a lot about the organism's structures and its relationships to other organisms. For example, crows are classified as birds. This classification lets you know that crows, like all birds, have wings, feathers, and beaks. In addition, you know that a crow shares more characteristics with other birds than it does with other kinds of animals, such as fishes or insects.

☑ *Checkpoint* *What is classification?*

The Classification System of Linnaeus

Modern taxonomy has its roots in a classification system developed in the 1750s by a Swedish scientist named Carolus Linnaeus. Linnaeus observed many organisms. He placed organisms in groups based on their observable features.

Linnaeus also used his observations to devise a naming system for organisms. In Linnaeus's naming system, called **binomial nomenclature** (by NOH mee ul NOH men clay chur), each organism is given a two-part name.

The first part of an organism's scientific name is its genus. A **genus** (JEE nus) (plural *genera*) is a classification grouping that contains similar, closely related organisms. For example, pumas, ocelots, and house cats are all classified in the genus *Felis*. Organisms that are classified in the genus *Felis* share features such as sharp, retractable claws and behaviors such as hunting.

The second part of an organism's scientific name identifies its species. A **species** (SPEE sheez) is a group of similar organisms that can mate and produce fertile offspring. A species name sets one species in a genus apart from the other species in the genus. The species name often describes a distinctive feature of an organism, such as where it lives or its color. For example, the species name of a housecat is *Felis domesticus*. The Latin word *domesticus* means "of the house" in Latin.

Figure 1 These animals belong to the genus *Felis*. **(A)** The species of the puma is *Felis concolor*. **(B)** The ocelot belongs to the species *Felis pardalis*. **(C)** The species name of the house cat is *Felis domesticus*. *Classifying List one characteristic that distinguishes* Felis pardalis *from the other two species.*

---

2 Facilitate

Why Do Scientists Classify Organisms?

Inquiry Challenge

Materials *igneous, metamorphic, and sedimentary rocks; three labeled boxes*
Time 20 minutes

ACTIVITY

Display a specimen of each of the three rock types. Pass out additional rocks to small groups of students so that every group has one of each kind to examine and classify. Have groups classify their rocks. **limited English proficiency**

The Classification System of Linnaeus

Building Inquiry Skills: Applying Concepts

Content Mastery

Write these scientific names on the board: *Perognathus californicus, Perognathus nelsoni, Perognathus spinatus*. Tell students that these are the names of three different North American pocket mice. Challenge students to see how much information they can infer about these animals just from their names. *(They are from the same genus. Students may also infer that* nelsoni *was discovered by someone named Nelson, or* californicus *is found in California.)*
learning modality: logical/mathematical

Program Resources

◆ **Unit 2 Resources** 6-1 Lesson Plan, p. 61; 6-1 Section Summary, p. 62
◆ **Guided Reading and Study Workbook** 6-1

Answers to Self-Assessment

Caption Question

Figure 1 spots

☑ *Checkpoint*

The process of grouping things based on shared traits

Ongoing Assessment

Writing Have students describe the difference between classification and taxonomy.

Language Arts
CONNECTION

Ask students to consider the term *binomial nomenclature*. *Bi* translates as "two" or "twice" while *nomen* means "name." Ask: **How does English provide hints about the meanings of Latin terms?** (*Sample: In the term "Viola missouriensis," English helps identify Missouri as a location of the plant.*)

In Your Journal Provide biology textbooks, dictionaries, and encyclopedias. (*Musca domestica: housefly; Hirudo medicinalis: medicinal leech. Students may recognize the words* domestic *or* medicine.)
learning modality: verbal

Classification Today

Building Inquiry Skills: Comparing and Contrasting

Display pictures of the bones in a bat's wing, a whale's flipper, and a human's arm and hand. Draw students' attention to the long upper bone (humerus) of the human arm and ask them to compare the bones in similar locations in the other animals. Ask: **How does this bone compare to the bone in the same location in the bat? The whale?** (*Bat: wider at the shoulder and narrower at the elbow; whale: proportionately much shorter and heavier*) This questioning strategy may be applied to the lower arm bones (radius and ulna), the wrist bones (carpels), hand (metacarpals) and fingers (phalanges).
learning modality: visual

Including All Students

Content Mastery

ACTIVITY

Give students index cards and ask them to visually depict the levels of where they live as if they were using a classification system. (*Visual representations might include a series of concentric circles to show the increasingly specific levels of country, state, county, city, street, and house number.*)
learning modality: visual

Language Arts
CONNECTION

You don't have to understand Latin to know that you should avoid an organism named *Ursus horribilis. Ursus horribilis* is commonly known as a grizzly bear. The Latin word *ursus* means "bear" and *horribilis* means "horrible or feared."

A species name describes an organism like an adjective describes the noun it modifies. Some names describe a specific trait; others tell who discovered the organism. Other names tell you where the organism lives. Guess where you'd find the plant *Viola missouriensis.*

In Your Journal

Look up the meanings of these species names: *Musca domestica, Hirudo medicinalis,* and *Cornus florida.* Then find some English words derived from the Latin terms.

Classification Today

Like Linnaeus, biologists today classify organisms on the basis of observable characteristics. **When biologists classify an organism, they look at its structure. They also look at the way it develops, or changes, during its life. Biologists also examine the organism's DNA.** As you learned in Chapter 4, DNA is a molecule in cells that determines an organism's inherited characteristics. The more similar two organisms are in their DNA and other characteristics, the more closely they are probably related.

The Seven Levels of Classification Today's classification system uses several levels to classify organisms. Organisms are grouped into seven major levels by shared characteristics. The more characteristics that organisms have in common, the more classification levels they share.

The broadest level of classification is a kingdom. Within each kingdom, there are more specific levels called phyla (FY luh) (singular *phylum*). Within each phylum are levels called classes. Each class is divided into orders. Each order contains families, and each family contains at least one genus. Finally, within a genus, there are species.

To help you understand a classification system made up of several levels, imagine a room filled with everybody in your state. First, the people who live in your *town* raise their hands. Next, those people who live in your *neighborhood* raise their hands. Then those who live on your *street* raise their hands. Finally, those people who live in your *house* raise their hands. Each time, fewer people raise their hands. But you would be in all of the groups.

In the classification system just described, the most general level is the state. The most specific level is the house. Similarly, in the classification of organisms, the most general level is the kingdom. The most specific level is the species.

Classifying an Owl Take a close look at Figure 2 to see how the levels of classification apply to the great horned owl, a member of the animal kingdom. Look at the top row of the figure. As you can see, a wide variety of organisms also belong to the animal kingdom. Now, look at the other levels. Notice that as you move down the levels, there are fewer kinds of organisms in each group. More importantly, the organisms in each level share more characteristics. For example, the class Aves includes all birds, while the order Strigiformes includes only owls. Different species of owl have more in common with each other than with other birds.

☑ *Checkpoint* **List the seven major levels of classification from the broadest to the most specific.**

Background

Facts and Figures The name *horned owl* can refer to any owl in the genus *Bubo*, but usually relates to the great horned owl (*Bubo virginianis*) of the Americas. The great horned owl ranges from the Arctic to the Strait of Magellan at the tip of South America. It is adapted to deserts and forests, and migrates only when food is scarce.

Great horned owls can be more than 60 cm long and weigh as much as 2 kilos. The female can have a wingspan of 200 cm. These owls are often called "tigers of the sky," because they are so large and aggressive. They have been known to evict eagles from their nests. Although great horned owls prefer prey like rabbits, they are one of the few predators that prey on skunks.

Kingdom Animalia

Phylum Chordata

Class Aves

Order Strigiformes

Family Strigidae

Genus *Bubo*

Species *Bubo virginianus*

Figure 2 Scientists use seven levels to classify organisms such as the great horned owl. Notice that, as you move down the levels, the number of organisms decreases. The organisms at lower levels share more characteristics.
Interpreting Diagrams How many levels do a robin and the great horned owl share?

Building Inquiry Skills: Making Models

Materials *posterboard or other heavyweight paper, pen, ruler, colored pencils, glue, scissors, nature magazines, dictionaries*
Time 50 minutes

Direct students to create model classification charts for their pets similar to the one shown in Figure 2 for the owl. Provide students with lists of the class, order, and family of several common pets, and encourage them to find the genus and species. Some students might like to attach pictures of their pets at the species level. **learning modality: visual**

Media and Technology

 Life Science Videodisc
Unit 2, Side 1, "*Panthera leo?*"

Chapter 1

 Transparencies "Seven Levels of Classification," Transparency 20

Answers to Self-Assessment

Caption Question

Figure 2 The robin and the great horned owl share three levels: kingdom, phylum, and class.

 Checkpoint

kingdom, phylum, class, order, family, genus, species

Ongoing Assessment

Skills Check Ask students to tell you which classification level will always have the greatest number of organisms and which level will always have the smallest number and why. (*Kingdom, species; because kingdom contains all organisms in that category and species is a specific organism*)

Six Kingdoms

Language Arts Connection

Ask: **Why do you think archaebacteria have that name?** (*The name means "ancient bacteria," and these bacteria are like the earliest life forms.*) **learning modality: verbal**

Real-Life Learning

Materials *plastic bucket with dilute suspension of blue tempera and water, soap, paper towels, plastic dropcloth*

Time 30 minutes

Direct students to dip their hands in the bucket of diluted tempera and let them air-dry. Then students should close their eyes and wash their hands without looking. Students should see if they have removed all the "bacteria." Ask: **What can you infer about washing your hands from this experiment?** (*If blue stain remains on their hands, they have not removed all the bacteria.*) **learning modality: tactile/ kinesthetic**

Real-Life Learning

Encourage students to contact local organic gardening centers to find out more about the role of fungi in the decay process in a compost pile. **learning modality: verbal**

Figure 3 Heat-loving archaebacteria thrive in this hot spring in Yellowstone National Park.

Figure 4 Both *Staphylococcus aureus* (**A**) and *Escherichia coli* (**B**) are eubacteria. *Staphylococcus aureus* bacteria make up about 30 percent of the bacteria on your skin. *Escherichia coli* bacteria are found in your digestive tract.

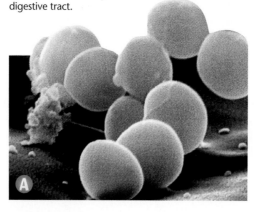

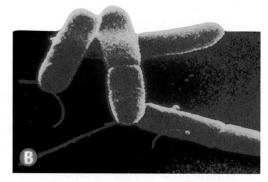

Six Kingdoms

Today, scientists classify all organisms into six kingdoms. **The six kingdoms of organisms are archaebacteria, eubacteria, protists, fungi, plants, and animals.** An organism is classified into a particular kingdom based on specific characteristics. They include the type of cells found in the organism, whether the organism is unicellular or multicellular, and how the organism obtains food. While the organisms within a kingdom vary greatly, members of a kingdom share those characteristics.

Archaebacteria In 1983, scientists took a water sample from a spot deep in the Pacific Ocean where hot gases and molten rock boiled into the ocean from Earth's interior. To their surprise, they discovered unicellular organisms in the water sample. Today, scientists classify these tiny organisms in a kingdom called archaebacteria (ahr kee bak TEER ee uh).

Archaebacteria are prokaryotes. Recall that prokaryotes are organisms whose cells lack a nucleus. Archaebacteria can be either autotrophic or heterotrophic.

Eubacteria What do the bacteria that produce yogurt have in common with the bacteria that give you strep throat? They both belong to the kingdom known as eubacteria (yoo bac TEER ee uh). Like archaebacteria, eubacteria are unicellular prokaryotes. And like archaebacteria, some eubacteria are autotrophs while others are heterotrophs. Eubacteria are classified in their own kingdom, however, because their chemical makeup is different from that of archaebacteria.

Background

History of Science The terms *prokaryotic* and *eukaryotic* were first used by Eduoard Chatton, a French marine biologist. In 1937, he published an article in which he suggested the use of *procariotique* for organisms that were then classified as bacteria and blue-green algae. He derived this term from the Greek prefix *pro-*, which means "before," and *karyon*, which means "kernel," or "nucleus."

Prokaryotes are organisms that are similar to more primitive life forms that existed before the development of the nucleus. Chatton suggested the use of *eucariotique* for organisms whose cells contain a nucleus. The Greek prefix *eu-* means "true." So eukaryotes are organisms whose cells contain a true nucleus, as opposed to genetic material in the cytoplasm.

Protists Protists are sometimes called the "odds and ends" kingdom because the members of this kingdom are so different from one another. Some protists are unicellular and some are multicellular. Some are heterotrophs and some are autotrophs. However, all protists are eukaryotes, which are organisms whose cells contain nuclei.

Fungi Fungi include organisms such as yeasts, mushrooms, and molds. Like protists, fungi are eukaryotes. Most fungi are many-celled organisms, but a few, such as yeasts, are unicellular. Fungi are found almost everywhere on land, but only a few live in water. All fungi are heterotrophs. Most fungi feed on dead or decaying organisms.

Plants Dandelions on a lawn, mosses in a forest, and tomatoes in a garden are some familiar kinds of plants. All plants are multicellular eukaryotes. In addition, plants are autotrophs. Some plants produce flowers, while other plants do not.

Animals A dog, a flea on the dog's ear, and a rabbit the dog chases are all animals. Animals are multicellular eukaryotes that are heterotrophs. At some point in their lives, most animals can move from one place to another. You will learn more about animals in Chapter 7.

Figure 5 The animal you see peeking out of this cuplike fungus is a poison arrow frog. These organisms live in the forests of Central America. *Interpreting Photographs Which organisms in the photograph are heterotrophs?*

Section 1 Review

1. What is taxonomy? What characteristics do taxonomists use to classify organisms?
2. List the six kingdoms into which all organisms are classified.
3. Explain how organisms are named.
4. **Thinking Critically Classifying** In a rain forest, you see an unfamiliar green organism. As you watch, an ant walks onto one of its cuplike leaves. The leaf closes and traps the ant. Do you have enough information to classify this organism into a kingdom? Why or why not?

> **Check Your Progress** CHAPTER PROJECT
>
> If your seeds haven't germinated yet, they soon will. For the next few days keep a close watch on your young plants to see how they grow. How do they change in height? How do the leaves appear and grow? (*Hint:* Consider using drawings or photographs as part of your record keeping.)

Program Resources

◆ **Unit 2 Resources** 6-1 Review and Reinforce, p. 63; 6-1 Enrich, p. 64

Answers to Self-Assessment

Caption Questions

Figure 5 Both the frog and the fungus are heterotrophs.

---

3 Assess

Section 1 Review Answers

1. Taxonomy is the scientific study of how living things are classified. Taxonomists use an organism's structure, development over the life cycle, and DNA to classify it.
2. Archaebacteria, eubacteria, protists, fungi, plants, animals
3. Organisms are named using binomial nomenclature. The first part of the name is the genus; the second, the species.
4. Some kingdoms can be eliminated, but there is not enough information to make a definite identification. The organism is multicellular, so it is not an archaebacteria or a eubacteria. It is green, so it may be an autotroph, but because it is trapping food, it may be a heterotroph. So it might be a plant or an animal or a multicellular protist.

> **Check Your Progress** CHAPTER PROJECT
>
> By now, seeds should have germinated. If some seeds have not germinated, allow students to start over or to observe seeds that have germinated. Make sure students make detailed diagrams, drawings, or photographs of their observations.

Performance Assessment

Drawing Invite students to sketch a member of each kingdom and describe the characteristics that place the organism in that kingdom.

SECTION 2 Bacteria

TEKS: 6.1A, B; 6.2A, B, C, D, E; 6.3B, C; 6.4A; 6.10A, B, C; 6.11B

Objectives

After completing the lesson, students will be able to

◆ describe ways in which bacteria cells are different from all other organisms' cells;

◆ tell how bacteria eat, reproduce, and survive;

◆ list ways in which bacteria affect people's lives.

1 Engage/Explore

Activating Prior Knowledge

Display samples of yogurt and Swiss cheese. Ask students what these foods have in common, then record their responses on the board. Tell students that these products are both produced with the help of certain kinds of bacteria. Ask: **What other foods can you think of that might be prepared with the aid of bacteria?** *(Sample: Buttermilk, sauerkraut, sour cream)*

DISCOVER

Materials *paper cups; dried lima, kidney, or navy beans*

Time 20 minutes

Tips Remind students to calculate the elapsed time based on the fact that it takes 20 minutes for bacteria to divide.

Expected Outcome Cup 1–1 bean; Cup 2–2 beans; Cup 3–4 beans; Cup 4–8 beans; Cup 5–16 beans; Cup 6–32 beans; Cup 7–64 beans; Cup 8–128 beans. There are 128 cells in the eighth generation. Two hours and twenty minutes have passed since there was only 1 bacterium.

Think It Over Students will probably infer that the numbers increase rapidly because each bacterium can double every 20 minutes.

DISCOVER ··········· ACTIVITY

How Fast Do Bacteria Multiply?

1. Your teacher will give you some beans and paper cups. Number the cups 1 through 8. Each bean will represent a bacterial cell.

2. Put one bean into cup 1 to represent the first generation of bacteria. Approximately every 20 minutes, a bacterial cell reproduces by dividing into two cells. Put two beans into cup 2 to represent the second generation of bacteria.

3. Calculate how many bacterial cells there would be in the third generation if each cell in cup 2 divided into two cells. Place the correct number of beans in cup 3.

4. Repeat Step 3 for each of the remaining cups. All the cups should now contain beans. How many cells would be in the eighth generation? How much time would have elapsed since the first generation?

Think It Over
Inferring Based on this activity, explain why the number of bacteria can increase rapidly in a short time.

GUIDE FOR READING

◆ How are the cells of bacteria different from those of all other organisms?

◆ Why are bacteria important to you?

Reading Tip Before you read, write a paragraph stating what you know about bacteria. As you read, add information to your paragraph.

Key Terms flagellum • binary fission • conjugation • endospore • decomposer

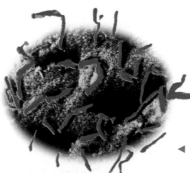

Y ou may not know it, but seconds after your birth, tiny organisms invaded your body. Today millions of these unicellular organisms coat your skin. They swarm inside your nose, throat, and mouth. In fact, there are more of these organisms living in your mouth than there are people living on Earth. They are found nearly everywhere—in soil, rocks, volcanoes, Arctic ice, and all living things. These organisms are bacteria.

The Bacterial Cell

As you read in Chapter 4, the cells of bacteria differ from the cells of other organisms in important ways. **Bacteria are prokaryotes. The genetic material in their cells is not contained in a nucleus.** In addition to lacking a nucleus, the cells of prokaryotes lack many other structures, such as mitochondria, that are found in the cells of eukaryotes.

Cell Shape The cells of bacteria have three basic shapes: spherical, rodlike, or spiral. The shape of a bacterial cell helps scientists identify the bacterium. The chemical makeup of the bacterium's outermost structure, its rigid cell wall, determines the cell's shape.

◀ Bacteria on the surface of a human tooth

READING STRATEGIES

Reading Tip Suggest that students leave a line of space between each line when they write their paragraphs. That way, there will be space to revise the paragraph and add information to it.

Study and Comprehension As students read, remind them of these strategies for breaking down information:

◆ Read the title, headings, subheadings, and captions to get an overview.

◆ Read one section of text at a time, line by line. Reread parts you did not understand fully.

◆ Jot down unfamiliar words. Try to determine the meanings or look them up.

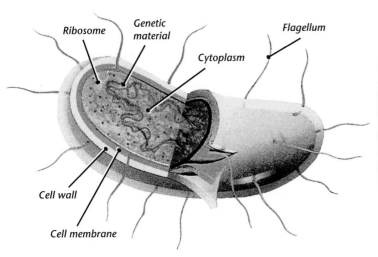

Ribosome
Genetic material
Cytoplasm
Flagellum
Cell wall
Cell membrane

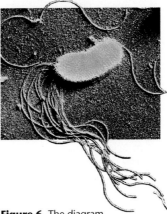

Figure 6 The diagram shows the structures found in a typical bacterial cell. *Interpreting Photographs Which structures can you locate in the photograph of the bacterium? What roles do these structures play?*

Cell Structures and Functions Inside the cell wall is the cell membrane, which controls the movement of materials into and out of the cell. In the gel-like material of the cytoplasm are ribosomes, the sites where proteins are made. The genetic material, which looks like a thick, tangled string, is also located in the cytoplasm. If the genetic material were untangled, it would be circular.

You can see the cell wall, ribosomes, and genetic material of a bacterial cell in Figure 6. You also see **flagella** (fluh JEL uh) (singular *flagellum*), which extend from the cell membrane and pass out through the cell wall. A bacterial cell may have one or many flagella. The long, whiplike structure of a flagellum enables it to perform its function of moving the bacterial cell from one place to another. A flagellum moves the cell by spinning in place like a propeller.

✓ *Checkpoint* *List four structures found in bacterial cells.*

Energy Needs

Like all organisms, bacteria must obtain food. Some bacteria are autotrophs that capture and use the sun's energy to make their own food, much as plants do. Other bacteria, such as those that live deep in the ocean, are autotrophs that use the energy from chemical substances in their environment to make their food. Still other bacteria are heterotrophs that consume autotrophs or other heterotrophs as food.

Bacteria use their food to supply the energy they need. Most bacteria use oxygen to break down food and release its energy. However, some bacteria do not need oxygen for respiration. In fact, they die if oxygen is present in their surroundings.

Chapter 6 **191**

Program Resources

◆ **Unit 2 Resources** 6-2 Lesson Plan, p. 65; 6-2 Section Summary, p. 66
◆ **Guided Reading and Study Workbook** 6-2

Media and Technology

 Transparencies "The Structure of a Bacterial Cell," Transparency 21

Answers to Self-Assessment

Caption Question

Figure 6 Flagellum—helps the bacterium move. Cell wall—protects bacterium.

✓ *Checkpoint*

Accept any four: cell wall, cell membrane, ribosomes, genetic material, flagella

2 Facilitate

The Bacterial Cell

Building Inquiry Skills: Comparing and Contrasting

Content Mastery

Write the terms *prokaryote* and *eukaryote* on the board. Challenge students to explain the differences and similarities between the two types of cells. *(Both have genetic material and reproduce by cell division. Prokaryotes do not have a nucleus or other cell structures.)*
learning modality: verbal

Energy Needs

Building Inquiry Skills: Designing Experiments

Tell students you are going to work with them to design an experiment to test conditions that are favorable for bacterial growth, using dried beans, water, and three beakers. Discuss the needs of living things and lead students to develop a plan to test the need for food and water. *(Plans will vary. Students may suggest setting out three beakers—one with dry beans, one with water, and one with beans in water.)* Tell students that, after a few days, a mixture of beans and water will become cloudy due to the growth of bacteria, while the dry beans and plain water will be unchanged. CAUTION: Because of the risk of growing pathogenic or anaerobic bacteria (with the accompanying foul odors), students should not do the experiment. **learning modality: logical/mathematical**

Ongoing Assessment

Writing Have students explain the function of each of these structures: cell wall, cell membrane, ribosome, flagellum.

191

Reproduction

Using the Visuals: Figure 7

As students study the forms of bacterial reproduction ask: **What main difference can you see between conjugation and binary fission?** *(Binary fission—only one cell is involved; conjugation—two cells are involved.)* Then ask: **How does conjugation result in the production of new bacteria?** *(After conjugation, the original cells have new combinations of genetic material.)* **learning modality: visual**

Survival Needs

Building Inquiry Skills: Inferring

Ask students why the ability to form endospores is important to a species of bacteria. *(Endospores allow bacteria to survive long periods of poor environmental conditions in order to reproduce when conditions improve.)* **learning modality: logical/mathematical**

Bacteria and the Living World

Skills Focus observing **ACTIVITY**
Materials *unpasteurized yogurt, plastic dropper, methylene blue, glass slide, cover slip, microscope, lab apron*
Time 20 minutes
Tips Students will need to use the highest powers of the microscope. As they observe the bacteria, have students classify them by their shape: spherical, rod, or spiral. Caution them to avoid getting methylene blue on their skin or clothing.
Observing The bacteria appear as dark-blue capsule-shaped dots against a cloudy, pale blue background. Students will be unable to see them unless they are using high-powered microscopes.
Extend Challenge students to observe yogurt that contains added *Lactobacillus acidophilus* (the contents will be listed on the label) and to draw what they observe.
learning modality: visual

192

Bacteria for Breakfast

In this activity, you will observe helpful bacteria in a common food. **ACTIVITY**

1. Put on your apron. Add water to plain yogurt to make a thin mixture.
2. With a plastic dropper, place a drop of the mixture on a glass slide.
3. Use another plastic dropper to add one drop of methylene blue dye to the slide. **CAUTION:** *This dye can stain your skin.*
4. Put a coverslip on the slide.
5. Observe the slide under both the low and high power lenses of a microscope.
6. Dispose of the materials as your teacher instructs.

Observing Draw a diagram of what you see under high power. Label any cell structures that you see.

192

Reproduction

In Figure 7A you see bacteria reproducing by **binary fission**, a process in which one cell divides to form two identical cells. Binary fission is a form of asexual reproduction. In binary fission, the cell first duplicates its genetic material. Then it divides into two cells that contain the same genetic material.

Some bacteria, such as those in Figure 7B, sometimes undergo a form of sexual reproduction called conjugation. During **conjugation** (kahn juh GAY shun), one cell transfers some of its genetic material into another cell through a thread-like bridge between the cells. After the transfer, the cells separate. These bacteria can then reproduce by binary fission. Conjugation results in bacteria that differ genetically from their parents.

☑ *Checkpoint* **What is conjugation?**

Survival Needs

Sometimes conditions in the environment become unfavorable for the growth of bacteria. For example, food sources can disappear or wastes can build up. Some bacteria respond to an unfavorable environment by forming endospores that survive these conditions. An **endospore** is a small, thick-walled, resting cell that forms inside a bacterial cell. For the most part, it contains the cell's genetic material. Endospores can survive for many years because they resist freezing, heating, and drying. When conditions are suitable, they can open and grow again.

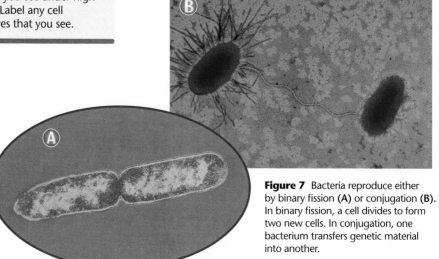

Figure 7 Bacteria reproduce either by binary fission (**A**) or conjugation (**B**). In binary fission, a cell divides to form two new cells. In conjugation, one bacterium transfers genetic material into another.

Background

Integrating Science The tomb of the Egyptian pharaoh Tutankhamen was discovered by the archaeologist Howard Carter in 1922. In the seven years following the discovery, eleven people, including Lord Carnarvon (who had paid for the excavation), died. The story of a curse was made up by security guards to keep away looters. Others have speculated that bacterial endospores sealed up in the tomb were responsible for the deaths. This seems unlikely, however because there are few similarities between the deaths of the individuals. However, it is possible for some bacterial spores to survive for a long time. *Bacillus anthracis*, the bacteria that causes anthrax, can live in the soil for many decades or longer. Archaeologists who excavate in areas where anthrax is known to have occurred must take precautions.

Figure 8 Scientists use bacteria such as these *Ochrobactrum anthropi* to help clean up oil spills. *Applying Concepts* How do bacteria clean up spilled oil?

Bacteria and the Living World

When you think about bacteria, you might think first of strep throat or ear infections. The bacteria that cause these diseases are eubacteria. **Although some bacteria do cause diseases, most bacteria interact with you and other organisms in harmless or positive ways.**

Bacteria play positive roles in fuel and food production as well as in environmental recycling and cleanup. For example, archaebacteria that died millions of years ago produced methane gas. Today, this methane gas is the major component in about 20 percent of Earth's deposits of natural gas, a fuel that heats many homes. Some eubacteria that grow in milk produce dairy products such as buttermilk, yogurt, and cheeses.

Some bacteria living in Earth's soil are **decomposers,** organisms that break down large molecules in dead organisms into smaller molecules. Decomposers recycle Earth's matter by returning basic chemicals to the environment for other organisms to reuse. Other recycling bacteria live in the roots of plants such as peanuts and soybeans. They use the nitrogen in air to form compounds the plants need to grow. Finally, some bacteria help clean up oil spills on land and water. These bacteria convert the dangerous chemicals in oil into harmless substances.

Section 2 Review

1. How is a bacterial cell different from the cells of other kinds of organisms?
2. List four ways in which bacteria are important to you.
3. Describe three ways that bacteria may obtain food.
4. **Thinking Critically Comparing and Contrasting** How are binary fission and conjugation alike? How do they differ?

Science at Home

Helpful Bacteria With a family member, look around your kitchen for foods that are made using bacteria. Read the labels on the foods to see if the role of bacteria in the food's production is mentioned. Discuss with your family member the helpful roles that bacteria play in people's lives.

Program Resources

◆ **Unit 2 Resources** 6-2 Review and Reinforce, p. 67; 6-2 Enrich, p. 68

Media and Technology

 Life Science Videodisc Unit 2, Side 1, "Positive Bacteria"

Chapter 4

Answers to Self-Assessment

Caption Question

Figure 8 By converting the chemicals in oil to harmless substances

✓ *Checkpoint*

Conjugation is a form of sexual reproduction involving the transfer of some genetic material from one cell to another.

Real-Life Learning

Ask: **Have you ever been told to eat yogurt after having taken a prescription for antibiotics?** (*Some students may have had this experience.*) Tell students that antibiotics get rid of bacteria that make you sick but may also kill helpful bacteria in the intestines. Yogurt contains bacteria, so eating yogurt replaces the helpful bacteria. **learning modality: visual**

3 Assess

Section 2 Review Answers

1. Bacterial cells are prokaryotic; the cells of other organisms are eukaryotic.
2. Sample answer (any four): produce methane gas, produce dairy products, decompose dead organisms, recycle matter, clean up oil spills.
3. Bacteria obtain food by using the sun's energy or chemical energy to make their own food, or they consume other organisms.
4. Binary fission and conjugation are both forms of reproduction that produce offspring. They differ in that the offspring of binary fission have genetic material identical to that of the parent cell, and the offspring of conjugation differ genetically from their parents.

Science at Home

Provide students with a list of key words to look for on product labels to help them identify bacteria in products—for example, *live* or *active cultures, enzymes.* Encourage students to share their findings from home with classmates.

Performance Assessment

Writing Have students write a paragraph describing bacteria that are helpful to humans.

Do Disinfectants Work?

Preparing for Inquiry

Key Concept The growth of bacteria can be controlled through the use of disinfectants.

Skills Objective Students will be able to

◆ observe bacterial growth on petri dishes;

◆ infer how well a disinfectant controls bacterial growth;

◆ draw conclusions regarding the best way to use disinfectants.

Time 30 minutes first day, 15 minutes for each of the next three days

Advance Planning Instead of having students inoculate the agar plates with bacteria from their fingers, you may want them to use cultures of nonpathogenic bacteria, which can be obtained from biological supply companies. Bring to class disinfectants, such as pine-scented cleaners or bleach, that contain different active ingredients. Dilute disinfectants at least tenfold to reduce the possibility of injury to students. Make sure the room is well ventilated. Review the use of the eyewash apparatus in case disinfectant is accidentally splashed into the eye of a student. Because disinfectants may stain clothes, students may want to bring an old shirt or apron to wear over their clothes during the lab. After opening a package of agar plates, use all the plates right away or dispose of leftover plates, because they will not remain sterile. *Computer use is optional.*

Guiding Inquiry

Invitation

Ask students why some cleaning products contain disinfectants. Students should discuss the fact that bacteria are present everywhere around them. Controlling bacteria using disinfectants helps prevent disease transmission and food spoilage. Students should be able to explain how they will test the ability of a disinfectant to control bacteria in this lab.

Do Disinfectants Work?

When your family goes shopping, you may buy disinfectants that kill microorganisms such as bacteria. You will compare the effects of two disinfectants.

Problem

How well do disinfectants control the growth of bacteria?

Skills Focus

observing, inferring, drawing conclusions

Materials

clock
2 plastic droppers
2 household disinfectants
3 plastic petri dishes with sterile nutrient agar
3 sealable plastic bags
computer (optional)
wax pencil
transparent tape

Procedure

1. With a computer or a pencil and paper, make a data chart to organize your observations.

2. Work with a partner. Obtain 3 petri dishes containing sterile agar. Without opening them, use a wax pencil to label the bottoms "A," "B," and "C." Write your initials beside each letter.

3. Wash your hands thoroughly with soap, then run a fingertip across the surface of your worktable. Your partner should hold open the cover of petri dish A while you run that fingertip gently across the agar in a zig-zag motion. Close the dish immediately.

4. Repeat Step 3 for dishes B and C.

5. Use a plastic dropper to transfer 2 drops of one disinfectant to the center of petri dish A. Open the cover just long enough to add the disinfectant to the dish. Close the cover immediately. Record the name of the disinfectant in your data chart. **CAUTION:** *Do not inhale vapors from the disinfectant.*

6. Repeat Step 5 for dish B but add 2 drops of the second disinfectant. **CAUTION:** *Do not mix any disinfectants together.*

7. Do not add any disinfectant to dish C.

8. Tape down the covers of all 3 petri dishes so that they will remain tightly closed. Then carefully slide each petri dish into a plastic bag. Seal the bags and tape them closed. Allow the 3 dishes to sit upright on your work surface for at least 5 minutes. **CAUTION:** *Do not open the bags or petri dishes again.* Wash your hands with soap and water.

9. As directed by your teacher, store the petri dishes in a warm, dark place where they can remain for at least 3 days. Remove them only to make a brief examination each day.

DATA CHART

Petri Dish	Disinfectant	Day 1	Day 2	Day 3
A				
B				
C				

Introducing the Procedure

◆ Pour out enough of each disinfectant into small containers so that students can fill their droppers without inserting them into the bottle of disinfectant. Caution students not to mix samples.

Program Resources

◆ **Unit 2 Resources** Chapter 6 Real-World Lab blackline masters, pp. 77–79

Media and Technology

Lab Activity Videotapes
Grade 6, Tape 2

10. After one day, observe the contents of each dish without removing the bags or covers. Estimate the percentage of the agar surface that shows any changes. Record your observations. Return the dishes to their storage place when you have finished observing. Wash your hands with soap.

11. Repeat Step 10 after the second day and again after the third day.

12. After you and your partner have made your last observations, return the petri dishes to your teacher unopened.

Analyze and Conclude

1. Use the information in your data chart to examine and evaluate your observations. How did the appearance of dish C change during the lab?

2. How did the appearance of dishes A and B compare with dish C? Explain any similarities or differences.

3. How did the appearance of dishes A and B compare with each other? How can you account for any differences?

4. Why was it important to set aside one petri dish that did not contain any disinfectant?

5. **Apply** Based on the results of this lab, what recommendation would you make to your family about the use of disinfectants? Where in the house do you think these products would be needed most?

Design an Experiment

Go to a store and look at soap products that claim to be "antibacterial" soaps. How do their ingredients differ from other soaps? How do their prices compare? Design an experiment to test how well these products control the growth of bacteria. Get your teacher's approval before performing the experiment.

Safety

Dilute the bleach at least tenfold to reduce the chances of injury to students. Caution students to use care when working with the disinfectants. Keep an eyewash apparatus on hand in case disinfectant is accidentally splashed into a student's eye. Tell students to inform you immediately if a spill occurs.

Review the safety guidelines in Appendix A. Autoclave the petri dishes before disposing of them. Do not open the petri dishes. Be sure to check your district's and state's guidelines for the proper disposal of bacterial cultures.

◆ Explain that students will store petri dishes upside down so that any condensed water will collect on the inside cover of the dish instead of dropping into the agar.

Troubleshooting the Experiment

Stress the safety procedures associated with any lab dealing with bacteria. Emphasize that students must not unseal the plastic bags or open the petri dishes after the initial procedures.

Expected Outcome

Several colonies of bacteria should grow on the control dish C. Dishes A and B should have fewer colonies, smaller colonies, or both.

Analyze and Conclude

1. Answers will vary, but students should report numerous bacterial colonies growing on the agar surface.

2. Dishes A and B should have fewer colonies, smaller colonies, or both.

3. Answers will vary depending on the disinfectants used. Any differences between A and B may be due to the relative effectiveness of the two disinfectants. They could also be due to other factors such as the distribution of different kinds of bacteria picked up off the work surface.

4. The dish without disinfectant, dish C, was the control. It shows how bacteria grew when no disinfectant was applied.

5. Students may mention using disinfectants to clean locations and implements associated with food preparation, bathroom facilities, children's rooms, and in cases of family illness.

Extending the Inquiry

Design an Experiment Encourage students to compare the labels of antibacterial soaps with the labels of disinfectants to look for any common ingredients. Students' plans should include clear and safe procedures and should clearly identify the control and the variables to be tested. Check your school's policy and students' plans before allowing them to perform their experiment.

TEKS: 6.1A, B; 6.2B, C; 6.4A; 6.10A, B, C; 6.12B

Objectives

After completing the lesson, students will be able to
◆ describe the characteristics of animal-like, plantlike, and fungus-like protists;
◆ describe the characteristics of fungi.

1 Engage/Explore

Activating Prior Knowledge

Before class, place several drops of vegetable oil in a small dish of water. Add a few drops of green food coloring to the water. To begin, place the dish on an overhead projector. Ask students: **How can you tell whether the blobs you see are alive?** (*Sample: Check for reaction to stimuli, taking in food, breathing, movement*)

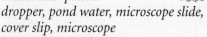
DISCOVER

Skills Focus observing
Materials *plastic dropper, pond water, microscope slide, cover slip, microscope*
Time 25 minutes
Tips Have students predict what they might observe in the water. Suggest students use their high-power objective lenses if they have them.
Expected Outcome Both algae and protozoans should be visible. Green algae have a greenish tint, but most organisms appear colorless. Organisms with flagella could be either protozoans or algae.
Think It Over Students will probably associate movement with life.

SECTION
3 Protists and Fungi

DISCOVER •••••••••••••••••••••••••••••••• **ACTIVITY**

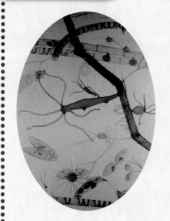

What Lives in a Drop of Water?

1. Use a plastic dropper to place a drop of pond water on a microscope slide.
2. Put the slide under your microscope's low-power lens. Focus on the objects you see.
3. Find at least three different objects that you think might be organisms. Observe them for a few minutes.
4. Draw the three organisms in your notebook. Below each sketch, describe the movements or behaviors of the organism. Work with your teacher to devise a plan for disposing of the materials. Wash your hands thoroughly when you have finished.

Think It Over
Observing What characteristics did you observe that made you think that each organism was alive?

GUIDE FOR READING

◆ What are the characteristics of animal-like, plantlike, and fungus-like protists?

◆ What characteristics do fungi share?

Reading Tip Before you read, preview the headings. Record them in outline form, leaving space for writing notes as you read.

Key Terms protozoan
• pseudopod • cilia • parasite
• host • algae • spore
• hyphae • budding

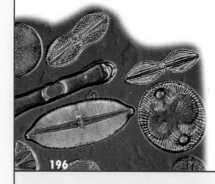

Look at the objects in Figure 9. What do they look like? Jewels? Crystal ornaments? You might be surprised to learn that these beautiful structures are the walls of unicellular protists called diatoms. Believe it or not, diatoms provide food for many organisms that live in the ocean.

The Protist Kingdom

Diatoms are only one type of organism classified in the protist kingdom. The protist kingdom is sometimes referred to as the "junk drawer" kingdom. A "junk drawer" is filled with odds and ends, such as pencils, ticket stubs, and postcards. The protist kingdom is filled with organisms that don't fit easily into other kingdoms. However, these organisms do share some characteristics. They are all eukaryotes, or organisms that have cells with nuclei. In addition, almost all protists live in moist areas.

Despite these common characteristics, the word that best describes the protist kingdom is *diversity*. For example, many protists are unicellular organisms. But some protists are multicellular. In fact, the protists known as giant kelps can be over 100 meters long. Protists also vary in how they obtain food.

Figure 9 These delicate-looking diatoms are classified in the protist kingdom.

196

Some protists are heterotrophs, some are autotrophs, and others are both. Some protists cannot move, while others zoom around in their surroundings.

Because protists vary greatly, scientists have proposed different ways of grouping these organisms. One useful way of grouping protists is to divide them into three categories: animal-like protists, plantlike protists, and fungus-like protists.

☑ *Checkpoint* *What characteristics do all protists share?*

Animal-like Protists

What image pops into your head when you think of an animal? A tiger chasing prey? A snake slithering onto a rock? Most people associate animals with movement. **Like animals, animal-like protists have structures that enable them to move around. And these organisms, like animals, are heterotrophs.** Unlike animals, however, animal-like protists, which are also called **protozoans** (proh tuh ZOH unz), are unicellular.

When an organism moves, it is usually responding to a stimulus. Protozoans move in response to a variety of external stimuli. For example, protozoans move toward food, such as bacteria. Protozoans may move away from harmful chemicals. Some protozoans respond to the stimulus of light by moving toward it. Others move away from light.

Protozoans With Pseudopods One group of protozoans uses structures called pseudopods (SOO doh pahdz) to move and obtain food. **Pseudopods** are temporary bulges of the cell membrane. The cytoplasm flows into the bulge and the rest of the organism follows. Amebas are protozoans that form pseudopods. Amebas use pseudopods to respond to external stimuli. Amebas move away from bright light and toward food.

Figure 10 The protist kingdom includes animal-like, plantlike, and fungus-like organisms. **(A)** These shells contained unicellular, animal-like protists called foraminifera. **(B)** This red alga is a multicellular, plantlike protist that lives on ocean floors. **(C)** This yellow slime mold is a fungus-like protist.
Comparing and Contrasting In what way are animal-like protists similar to animals? How do they differ?

The Protist Kingdom

Building Inquiry Skills: Forming Operational Definitions

Display pictures of protists such as slime molds, paramecia, euglenoids, diatoms, and algae in stations around the room. Have small groups list the characteristics they observe. Ask students if it is possible to create an operational definition of a protist. Have students consider this as they read the rest of the section.
learning modality: visual

Animal-like Protists

Inquiry Challenge

Materials *plastic dropper, ameba culture, microscope slide, cover slip, microscope*
Time 20 minutes
Tips Challenge students to identify the pseudopod action of an ameba they observe. Have them place a drop of the ameba culture on a slide, carefully add a cover slip, and then observe the organisms under low and high power. Ask: **Can you tell when the ameba is using its pseudopods to eat and when it is using them to move?** (*Students may say that when the ameba is eating, it wraps two pseudopods around the food; when it is moving, it puts out a pseudopod and flows into it.*) Students can sketch what they observe and label the parts of the ameba. Observations should include the organism's shape, size, and motion.
learning modality: visual

Answers to Self-Assessment

Caption Question

Figure 10 Animal-like protists are like animals in that they are heterotrophs, moving from place to place to obtain food. They are different in that they are unicellular.

☑ *Checkpoint*

All protists are eukaryotes and live in moist surroundings.

Ongoing Assessment

Writing Have students explain why protists are thought of as the "junk drawer" kingdom by describing characteristics, categories, and examples of protists.

EXPLORING
Protozoans

Ask students: **What do these protists have in common?** (*They eat the same things, they both have nuclei, cytoplasm, food vacuoles, and contractile vacuoles.*) Ask: **What is different about them?** (*Amebas live in soil and water, paramecia only in water; paramecia move with cilia, amebas move with pseudopods; paramecia ingest food into an oral groove, amebas surround food with pseudopods; amebas have one nucleus, paramecia have two.*) As students list the similarities and differences, include them in a Venn diagram on the board. Then draw students' attention to the number and shapes of the contractile vacuoles in the two protists. Remind students that amebas live in soil or water, and paramecia live only in the water. Then ask: **What characteristics of the ameba do you think make it suited to living in either soil or water?** (*Sample: They can take any shape and flow easily through different substances. The contractile vacuole allows excess water to be expelled.*) **What characteristics of the paramecium do you think make it suited to living only in water?** (*Sample: The cilia act like tiny oars to move the paramecium through the water and sweep food into the oral groove. The cilia would not be as effective in a solid environment such as soil. Their rigid shape may make it difficult to move through compacted soil. The two contractile vacuoles remove excess water from the cell.*) Refer to the **ELL Handbook** for additional teaching strategies. **learning modality: logical/mathematical**

Protozoans With Cilia Members of a second group of protozoans have structures called cilia that they use to move and obtain food. **Cilia** (SIL ee uh) are hairlike projections from cells that move with a wavelike pattern. Cilia move an organism by acting something like tiny oars. Their movement also sweeps food into the organism. One type of protozoan with cilia is a paramecium. Look at *Exploring Protozoans* to compare the structures of an ameba and a paramecium and to learn about the functions of each structure. Notice that the cell of a paramecium has a greater variety of structures than that of an ameba.

Protozoans With Flagella Members of a third group of protozoans use flagella to move. These organisms often live inside the bodies of other organisms. For example, protozoans with flagella

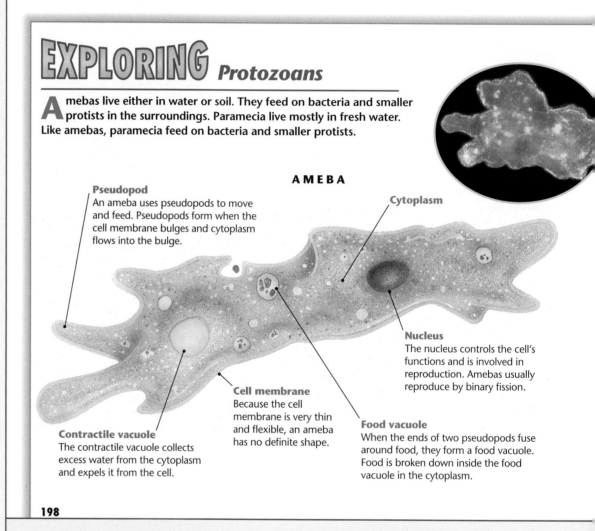

EXPLORING Protozoans

Amebas live either in water or soil. They feed on bacteria and smaller protists in the surroundings. Paramecia live mostly in fresh water. Like amebas, paramecia feed on bacteria and smaller protists.

AMEBA

Pseudopod
An ameba uses pseudopods to move and feed. Pseudopods form when the cell membrane bulges and cytoplasm flows into the bulge.

Cytoplasm

Nucleus
The nucleus controls the cell's functions and is involved in reproduction. Amebas usually reproduce by binary fission.

Cell membrane
Because the cell membrane is very thin and flexible, an ameba has no definite shape.

Food vacuole
When the ends of two pseudopods fuse around food, they form a food vacuole. Food is broken down inside the food vacuole in the cytoplasm.

Contractile vacuole
The contractile vacuole collects excess water from the cytoplasm and expels it from the cell.

198

Background

Facts and Figures Free-living protists encounter changes in temperature, water acidity, food supply, moisture, and light. Many survive during these changes by entering a dormant stage—forming cysts with tough walls that act as protective coverings. During encystment, protozoans that have flagella and cilia lose them, and the contractile vacuole and food vacuoles

disappear. Many protozoans can form cysts, and biologists believe this ability formed early in their history.

Some parasitic protozoans, such as the one that causes amebic dysentery, also form cysts. The cysts are excreted and survive in the soil or water, and humans who come into contact with the cysts can be infected.

live in the intestines of termites. These protozoans digest the wood that the termites eat, producing sugars for themselves and for the termites.

Other Protozoans A fourth group of protozoans, called sporozoans, are characterized more by the way they live than by the way they move. Sporozoans are **parasites,** organisms that live on or in another organism, the **host,** and harm that organism. Sporozoans feed on the cells and body fluids of their hosts. Some sporozoans use flagella to move, and others depend on hosts for transport. One sporozoan even slides from place to place on a layer of slime that it produces. A sporozoan called *Plasmodium* causes the disease malaria in people.

☑ *Checkpoint* *What is the function of a pseudopod?*

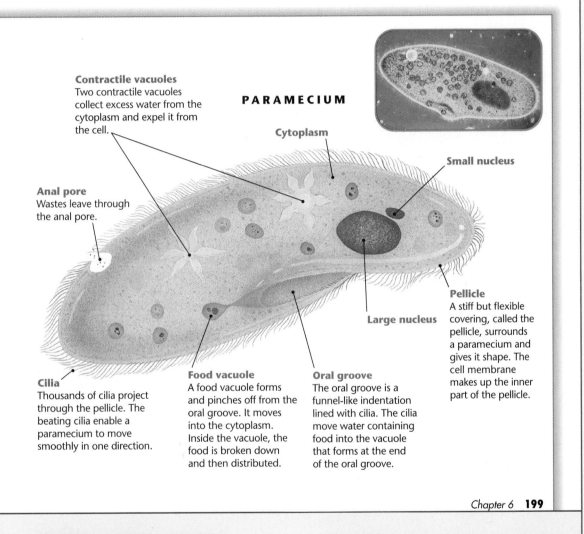

PARAMECIUM

Contractile vacuoles
Two contractile vacuoles collect excess water from the cytoplasm and expel it from the cell.

Cytoplasm

Small nucleus

Anal pore
Wastes leave through the anal pore.

Pellicle
A stiff but flexible covering, called the pellicle, surrounds a paramecium and gives it shape. The cell membrane makes up the inner part of the pellicle.

Large nucleus

Cilia
Thousands of cilia project through the pellicle. The beating cilia enable a paramecium to move smoothly in one direction.

Food vacuole
A food vacuole forms and pinches off from the oral groove. It moves into the cytoplasm. Inside the vacuole, the food is broken down and then distributed.

Oral groove
The oral groove is a funnel-like indentation lined with cilia. The cilia move water containing food into the vacuole that forms at the end of the oral groove.

Materials *microscope, slide and cover slip, water, plastic dropper, paramecium culture, ice*
Time 30 minutes

Challenge students to form hypotheses about how water temperature affects the activity level of a paramecium, then design experiments using the materials above to test their hypotheses. *(Sample design: materials— two or more paramecium cultures, plastic dropper, microscope, slides, cover slips; procedure— put the paramecia in water of varying temperatures, then examine them under the microscope; results— paramecia are active at room temperature and slow down at about 2°C.)* After you review their designs, have students carry out their experiments and report their findings to the class. **learning modality: logical/mathematical**

ACTIVITY

Media and Technology

 Transparencies "Exploring Protozoans—Ameba," Transparency 22; "Exploring Protozoans—Paramecium," Transparency 23

Answers to Self-Assessment

☑ *Checkpoint*
Pseudopods are used to move and obtain food (respond to external stimuli).

Ongoing Assessment

Oral Presentation Have students compare and contrast the characteristics of an ameba and a paramecium.

Plantlike Protists

Using the Visuals: Figure 11

Content Mastery

Ask students: **How many cells does a Euglena have?** *(one)* Point out that the structures such as flagella, the eyespot, and the chloroplast are all part of the same cell. Some students may be confused that a unicellular organism has so many parts. Explain that cells are the smallest structures capable of performing all the functions required for life. Ask: **Is the cell shown in the figure specialized to do certain tasks?** *(No, it performs all the functions necessary to maintain the Euglena's life.)* **learning modality: visual**

TRY THIS

Skills Focus inferring
Materials *plastic dropper, paramecium culture, Chlorella culture, microscope slide, cotton fibers, microscope*
Time 15 minutes
Tips Another way to slow down the paramecia is to add one drop of a 2–3% solution of clear gelatin to the drop of culture on the slide. Make sure students wash their hands immediately after the activity.
Inferring Students should see green food vacuoles form inside the paramecia. Students should conclude that paramecia are heterotrophs because they ingest the *Chlorella*. *Chlorella* behave like autotrophs because they do not seem to be ingesting food and are green like plants.
Extend Have students predict how long it will take the paramecia to ingest all the *Chlorella*, then check their slides at regular intervals to test their predictions. Have students turn off the lights on the microscopes when they are not making observations to avoid overheating the paramecia. **learning modality: visual**

Figure 11 Euglenas are unicellular algae that live in fresh water. In sunlight, euglenas make their own food. Without sunlight, they obtain food from their environment.

Eyespot
Contractile vacuole
Chloroplast (used in food production)
Flagellum
Nucleus
Pellicle

TRY THIS

Feeding Paramecia

In this activity you will feed *Chlorella*, a plantlike protist, to paramecia.

1. Use a plastic dropper to place one drop of paramecium culture on a microscope slide. Add some cotton fibers to slow down the paramecia.

2. Use the microscope's low-power objective to find some paramecia.

3. Add one drop of *Chlorella* to the paramecium culture on your slide.

4. Switch to high power and locate a paramecium. Observe what happens. Then wash your hands.

Inferring What evidence do you have that paramecia are heterotrophs? That *Chlorella* are autotrophs?

Plantlike Protists

If you've ever seen seaweed at a beach, then you are familiar with a type of plantlike protist. Plantlike protists, which are commonly called **algae** (AL jee), are even more varied than animal-like protists. **The one characteristic that all algae share is that, like plants, they are autotrophs.**

Some algae live in the soil, others live on the barks of trees, and still others live in fresh water or salt water. Algae that live in ponds, lakes, and oceans are an important food source for other organisms in the water. In addition, most of the oxygen in Earth's atmosphere is made by these algae.

Algae range greatly in size. Some algae, such as diatoms and euglenas, are unicellular. Recall from Chapter 4 that a unicellular organism carries out all the functions necessary for life. Unlike other algae, euglenas like the ones shown in Figure 11 can be heterotrophs under certain conditions. Euglenas are green and use flagella to move. In contrast, some diatoms move on slime that oozes out of slits in their cell walls.

Other algae are groups of unicellular organisms that live together in colonies. Unlike true multicellular organisms, an algae colony contains few or no cells that are specialized to perform specific functions. Like unicellular organisms, most cells in a colony carry out all the life processes.

Still other algae, such as seaweeds, are multicellular organisms. Multicellular algae contain cells that are specialized to perform specific tasks. For example, giant kelps, which are a kind of seaweed, have many plantlike tissues and organs. Holdfasts anchor the alga to rocks. Stalks support the leaflike blades. Brown algae also have gas-filled sacs called bladders that allow the algae to float upright in the water.

Background

Facts and Figures Algae are used commonly in the United States only as a food additive. Worldwide, though, many people consume large amounts of algae as a food source. In fact, the algae harvested every year are worth billions of dollars.

The most widely farmed alga is *Porphyra*, a red alga. It is grown directly on nets for convenient harvesting. Before it is eaten, it is washed, chopped, and formed into layers to dry. Other algae, like *Palmaria palmata* and *Laminaria*, are harvested by hand.

The green algae *Monostroma* and *Ulva*, also known as sea lettuce, are eaten in salads, soups, and other dishes. *Chlorella*, another green alga, is known for its high protein content (53–65%), and has been considered an efficient source of nutrition for astronauts on long space journeys.

Fungus-like Protists

A third group of protists are the fungus-like protists. **Fungus-like protists are heterotrophs, have cell walls, and use spores to reproduce.** A **spore** is a tiny cell that is able to grow into a new organism. All fungus-like protists are able to move at some point in their lives. In Figure 12, you can see a type of fungus-like protist called a water mold.

☑ *Checkpoint* What is a spore?

The Fungi Kingdom

Like the fungus-like protists, fungi use spores to reproduce. The cricket-killing fungus in Figure 13 began as a spore that fell on a living cricket. Tiny threads from the spore began to grow into the cricket's body. The threads released chemicals that dissolved the cricket's tissue. Then some threads thickened, forming the stalks with knobs at their ends that grew out of the cricket's body. When the knobs break open, they will release thousands of spores, which the wind may carry to new victims.

Although you may not have heard of a cricket-killing fungus before, you are probably familiar with other kinds of fungi. For example, the molds that grow on stale bread or decaying fruit are all fungi. The mushrooms that sprout in forests or yards are fungi. Unicellular yeasts that make bread rise are also fungi.

Most fungi share three important characteristics: They are eukaryotes, use spores to reproduce, and are heterotrophs that feed in a similar way. In addition, fungi need moist, warm places in which to grow. They thrive on moist foods, damp tree bark, lawns coated with dew, damp forest floors, and even wet bathroom tiles.

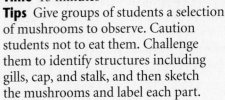

Figure 12 The threadlike water mold is a protozoan parasite that grows on fish. The water mold eventually kills the fish. *Applying Concepts What is a parasite?*

Figure 13 A bush cricket has been attacked by a killer fungus.

Media and Technology

 Life Science Videodisc
Unit 2, Side 1,
"Fungi and Algae"

Chapter 5

 Transparencies "The Structure of a Euglena," Transparency 24

Answers to Self-Assessment

Caption Question

Figure 12 An organism that feeds on its host, harming it.

☑ *Checkpoint*

A spore is a cell that can grow into a new organism.

Fungus-like Protists

Inquiry Challenge

Materials *compound microscope, slime mold culture, plastic petri dish with cover, oatmeal*

Time 15 minutes for setup, 10 minutes for observation after 24 hours

Tips Pair students. Give each pair a covered petri dish containing slime mold culture to observe under the microscope. Partners can take turns observing and sketching what they see. Ask students to predict how slime molds will react when oatmeal is placed in the dish. They can test their predictions by uncovering the dish, putting a few flakes about 1 mm from a branch of the slime mold, and putting the cover back on. Allow students to place the dish in a cool, dark place. After 24 hours, the slime mold should increase in size, spread across, then engulf the oatmeal flakes. Ask: **What did you observe that suggests the slime mold is alive?** (*It moved toward the oatmeal and engulfed it.*) Caution students to wash their hands thoroughly after the activity. Review the safety guidelines in Appendix A. Dispose of the petri dishes and all other materials according to the proper procedures. Check your district's and state's guidelines for the proper disposal of fungal cultures. **learning modality: visual**

The Fungi Kingdom

Building Inquiry Skills: Observing

Content Mastery

Materials *mushrooms from the grocery store, hand lens*

Time 15 minutes

Tips Give groups of students a selection of mushrooms to observe. Caution students not to eat them. Challenge them to identify structures including gills, cap, and stalk, and then sketch the mushrooms and label each part. **learning modality: visual**

Ongoing Assessment

Writing Ask students to describe the characteristics of plantlike or fungus-like protists.

Cell Structure of Fungi

Using the Visuals: Figure 14

As students study the figure, ask: **How "do the above-ground hyphae of the mushroom differ from those underground?** *(The hyphae above ground are more tightly packed than the hyphae under the surface.)* **learning modality: visual**

How Do Fungi Obtain Food?

Using the Visuals: Figure 14

Have students note the way hyphae grow from the surface and spread out in the ground. Ask: **Why do the hyphae grow deeper and deeper into the ground?** *(As they consume the food in one part of the ground, they grow into another part to get more food.)* **learning modality: visual**

Reproduction in Fungi

Building Inquiry Skills: Observing

Materials *mushroom spores, eyedropper, water, microscope, slide, and cover slip*

ACTIVITY

Tips Two days previous, make a spore print by placing a mushroom cap gill-side down on a piece of white paper. Have students use the eyedropper to place a drop of water on the spore print. Then, they can draw up the water with the dropper, place a drop on a microscope slide, and cover it with a cover slip. Allow them to observe the spores under a microscope. Encourage students to sketch their observations and include the color and shape of the spores. Ask: **What is the function of these spores?** *(Spores are the reproductive cells that will produce new mushrooms.)* **learning modality: tactile/ kinesthetic**

Cell Structure of Fungi

Yeasts are unicellular fungi, but other fungi are multicellular. The cells of multicellular fungi are arranged in structures called hyphae. **Hyphae** (HY fee) (singular *hypha*) are branching, thread-like tubes that make up the bodies of multicellular fungi.

The appearance of a fungus depends on how its hyphae are arranged. In some fungi, such as fuzzy-looking molds, the hyphae are loosely tangled. In other fungi, hyphae are packed tightly together. For example, the stalks and caps of the mushrooms in Figure 14 are made of hyphae packed so tightly that they appear solid. Underground, however, the hyphae of these mushrooms form a loose, threadlike maze.

How Do Fungi Obtain Food?

Some fungi feed on the remains of dead organisms. Other fungi are parasites that break down the chemicals in living organisms. For example, athlete's foot is a disease caused by a fungus that feeds on chemicals in a person's skin.

Fungi absorb food through hyphae that grow into the food source. First, the fungus grows hyphae into a food source. Then digestive chemicals ooze from the hyphae into the food. The chemicals break down the food into small molecules that the hyphae can absorb. Imagine yourself sinking your fingers into a chocolate cake and dripping digestive chemicals out of your fingertips. Then imagine your fingers absorbing the digested particles of the cake. That's how a fungus feeds.

Hyphae are a good example of how structure is related to function in organisms. The long, threadlike structure of a fungus's hyphae provide a large surface area for absorbing food. The larger the surface area, the greater the amount of food that can be absorbed.

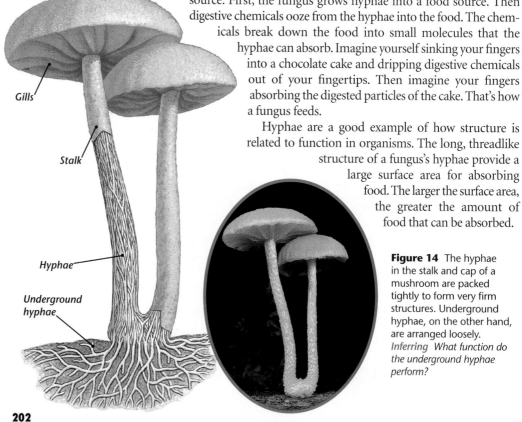

Cap

Gills

Stalk

Hyphae

Underground hyphae

Figure 14 The hyphae in the stalk and cap of a mushroom are packed tightly to form very firm structures. Underground hyphae, on the other hand, are arranged loosely. *Inferring What function do the underground hyphae perform?*

202

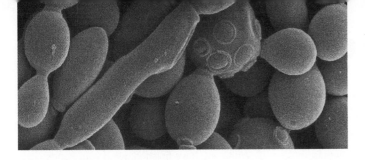

Reproduction in Fungi

Like it or not, fungi are everywhere. The way they reproduce guarantees that they survive and spread. Fungi usually reproduce by means of spores that are lightweight and have protective coverings. They travel easily through air or water to new sites.

Asexual Reproduction Most fungi reproduce both asexually and sexually. When there is adequate moisture and food, most fungi reproduce asexually by growing spore-producing reproductive hyphae. Fungi produce thousands of spores. However, only a few of them fall where conditions are right for them to grow into new organisms.

Unicellular yeast cells undergo a form of asexual reproduction called **budding.** In budding, no spores are produced. Instead, a small yeast cell grows from the body of a large parent cell in a way that might remind you of a bud forming on a tree branch. The new cell then breaks away and lives on its own.

Sexual Reproduction When growing conditions become unfavorable, fungi may reproduce sexually. In sexual reproduction, the hyphae of two fungi grow together. Then a new spore-producing structure grows from the joined hyphae. These spores develop into fungi that have a combination of the genetic material of both parents.

Section 3 Review

1. List the characteristics of animal-like protists, plantlike protists, and fungus-like protists.
2. List three characteristics that fungi share.
3. Explain how the threadlike structure of a fungus's hyphae enables the fungus to obtain a large amount of food.
4. How do fungi reproduce?
5. **Thinking Critically Classifying** Explain why mushrooms are classified as fungi rather than plants.

CHAPTER PROJECT

Check Your Progress
Your plants should now have, or will soon have, flowers. Make a diagram of the flower's structure. When the flowers open, you'll have to pollinate them. This work is usually done by insects or birds. After pollination, watch how the flower changes. (*Hint:* Pollination is explained on pages 209–210. Discuss with your teacher and classmates how to pollinate the flowers.)

Program Resources

◆ **Unit 2 Resources** 6-3 Review and Reinforce, p. 71; 6-3 Enrich, p. 72
◆ **Laboratory Manual** 6, "Comparing Protists"

Media and Technology

Transparencies "The Structure of a Mushroom," Transparency 25

Answers to Self-Assessment

Caption Question
Figure 14 The underground hyphae absorb food from the soil.

3 Assess

Section 3 Review Answers

1. Animal-like protists: unicellular, heterotrophic. Plantlike protists: uni- or multicellular, autotrophic. Fungus-like protists: heterotrophic, have cell walls, and reproduce using spores.
2. Fungi are eukaryotic, use spores to reproduce, and are heterotrophs that feed in a similar way.
3. The hyphae grow into the food sources and spread out, creating a large surface area for absorbing food.
4. Fungi reproduce asexually by growing spore-producing reproductive hyphae or by budding. Fungi may also reproduce sexually when the hyphae of two fungi grow together and form a new spore-producing structure.
5. Mushrooms are classified as fungi because they are heterotrophic. Plants are autotrophic.

CHAPTER PROJECT

Check Your Progress
Check the growth of the plants. If you observe that some of the plants are not thriving, discuss their care with students. When the plants flower, help students pollinate them. The two best methods are to use the bee parts that come in a seed-growing kit, or to tap the flower gently and collect the pollen on a piece of paper. The pollen can then be placed on the stigma. A third method is to use cotton swabs, but this may not be as successful. Discuss with students how these methods compare to the ways plants are pollinated in nature.

Performance Assessment

Oral Presentation Have small groups make presentations on the structure of fungi, how they obtain food, and their reproduction. Presentations should include labeled sketches.

SECTION 4 The Plant Kingdom

TEKS: 6.1A; 6.2A, B, C, D; 6.4A, B; 6.10A, B, C; 6.11B; 6.12A, B

Objectives

After completing the lesson, students will be able to

- identify the characteristics that all plants share;
- describe the structure of a seed;
- describe how plants reproduce;
- explain how plants respond to stimuli.

1 Engage/Explore

Activating Prior Knowledge

Show students a potted plant and ask them to name two ways that it is different from an animal. *(Sample: It does not walk around; it has leaves.)*

DISCOVER ··· ACTIVITY

Skills Focus inferring
Materials *hand lens, leaf from a jade plant or another plant with thick, fleshy leaves; leaf of a temperate-climate plant, such as a maple, oak, or common garden plant*
Time 10 minutes
Tips Select leaves that display adaptations easily associated with protection from bright sun and dry weather. Both leaves should be green in color.
Expected Outcome Students should observe a difference in leaf thickness, texture, and size.
Think It Over Students should infer that the plant with the small, thick, fleshy leaf lives in the desert, and that the plant with the larger, thinner, more delicate leaf lives in an area of average rainfall. Students will probably say that the thick leaf looks like it has water in it.

SECTION 4 The Plant Kingdom

DISCOVER ············· ACTIVITY

What Do Leaves Reveal About Plants?

1. Your teacher will give you two leaves from plants that grow in two very different environments: a desert and an area with average rainfall.

2. Carefully observe the color, size, shape, and texture of the leaves. Touch the surfaces of each leaf. Examine each leaf with a hand lens. Record your observations in your notebook.

3. When you have finished, wash your hands thoroughly with soap and water.

Think It Over
Inferring Use your observations to determine which plant lives in the desert and which does not. Give at least one reason to support your inference.

GUIDE FOR READING

- What are the characteristics of plants?
- What is the structure of a seed?
- How do plants respond to their surroundings?

Reading Tip Before you read, write at least three characteristics of plants that you already know. As you read, add to your list.

Key Terms vascular tissue
- stomata • fertilization
- zygote • embryo
- seed • cotyledon
- pollen • ovule
- flower • stamen
- pistil • fruit
- tropism
- hormone

Imagine a forest where a thick mat of fungi, mosses, and ferns carpets the floor. Because there is no bare soil, seedlings start their lives on fallen logs. Ferns hang like curtains from the limbs of giant hemlock trees. Douglas fir trees grow taller than 20-story buildings. Other plants with strange names—vanilla leaf, self-heal, and licorice fern—also grow in the forest.

Such a forest exists on the western slopes of the Olympic Mountains in the state of Washington. Native Americans named the forest Hoh, which means "fast white water," after a river there. In parts of the forest, over 300 centimeters of rain fall each year. Many plants thrive in this moist environment.

The Hoh rain forest ▶

READING STRATEGIES

Reading Tip After students have made their lists, ask if they have already studied any of these characteristics. Suggest that they attempt to describe characteristics they've seen before and modify their descriptions as they read.

Study and Comprehension Instruct students to use the headings in the section to create an outline that shows main points and key details. Start an outline, such as the one shown below, to guide students.
I. What is a Plant?
   A. a eukaryote that contains many cells

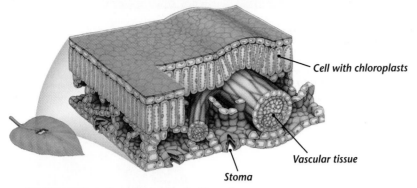

Cell with chloroplasts

Vascular tissue

Stoma

Figure 16 The structure of a leaf helps the plant to perform photosynthesis. *Inferring What kind of substance does vascular tissue carry away from a leaf to cells throughout the plant?*

What Is a Plant?

Members of the plant kingdom share important characteristics. **Plants are multicellular eukaryotes that produce their food through photosynthesis. In addition, many plants have vascular tissue, leaves, roots, and stems.**

Vascular Tissue Most plants have vascular tissue to transport needed materials to their cells. **Vascular tissue** is an internal system of tubelike structures that carry water, minerals, and food. Materials move quickly through vascular tissue. In addition, vascular tissue supports the bodies of plants, enabling them to grow large. Plants with vascular tissue are called vascular plants.

Nonvascular plants, such as mosses, do not have vascular tissue. Nonvascular plants can only pass materials from one cell to the next. Therefore, materials do not travel very far or very quickly. Also, nonvascular plants lack the support that vascular tissue provides. Without vascular tissue, these plants cannot grow very wide or tall. *Exploring Plant Groups* on the next two pages shows examples of nonvascular and vascular plants.

Leaves In vascular plants, leaves are organs that carry out photosynthesis. Nonvascular plants, on the other hand, have leaflike structures where photosynthesis occurs. The structure of a leaf is ideal for photosynthesis. For example, photosynthesis takes place in chloroplasts. Notice in Figure 16 that the cells with the most chloroplasts are near the leaf's upper surface, where they are exposed to the sun. Vascular tissue carries the water needed for photosynthesis to the leaf. Plants also need carbon dioxide for photosynthesis. Carbon dioxide enters a leaf through tiny pores called **stomata** (STOH muh tuh) (singular *stoma*), which control the movement of gases into and out of the leaf. When stomata are open, carbon dioxide enters the leaf while oxygen and water vapor move out.

What Stomata?

In this activity, you will use a microscope to observe stomata in leaf tissue.

1. Carefully break a lettuce leaf so that a thin, transparent layer on the underside separates from the rest of the leaf.
2. Cut a small section of this transparent layer and put it on a slide. Add one or two drops of water and add a coverslip.
3. Find and observe some stomata under low power and then high power.
4. Count the number of stomata that you see under high power. Compare that number to the number observed by other students.

Observing A range is the lowest number and highest number of items in a sample. What was the lowest number of stomata counted? The highest number?

2 Facilitate

What Is a Plant?

Including All Students

Give students who need extra help time to review terms such as *eukaryote*, *photosynthesis*, and *chloroplast*. Suggest students create a glossary of words that includes the phonetic English pronunciation and the definition in English. **limited English proficiency**

Using the Visuals: Figure 16

Obtain prepared slides of **ACTIVITY** leaf cross sections and allow students to observe the slides with a microscope. Students should refer to Figure 16 and compare what they see in the prepared cross sections with the cells shown in the drawing.

TRY THIS

Skills Focus observing
Materials *lettuce, water, slide and coverslip, microscope*
Time 15 minutes
Tips To save time, you can set up the microscope yourself and invite students to observe the stomata. Be sure to use a layer from the underside of the leaf, where the stomata are located.
Expected Outcome Students should be able to see tiny pores in the leaf surface.
Extend Ask: **How do stomata control the amount of gas that passes into and out of the leaf?** *(By opening and closing.)*
learning modality: visual

Answers to Self-Assessment

Caption Question
Figure 16 Food produced by photosynthesis

Ongoing Assessment

Writing Have students list the major characteristics of plants.

EXPLORING

Plant Groups

After students have examined the visual essay, ask them the following questions:

◆ **Upon what characteristics does the division of the plant kingdom into major groups depend?** *(whether the plants have vascular tissue or not, and whether they reproduce by spores or seeds)*

◆ **Why is a club moss not a true moss?** *(Club moss has vascular tissue, and true mosses do not.)*

◆ **What is the main difference between gymnosperms and angiosperms?** *(Gymnosperms have seeds without a protective covering, and angiosperms have seeds enclosed in fruit.)*

Extend Invite students to explore the diversity of plants in your area. Take students on a walk around the school and have them record descriptions of ten different plants that they see. Each description should include the place where they found the plant, the plant's estimated size, any distinguishing characteristics, and a sketch or photograph of the plant. Make sure students classify each plant into one of the groups shown in the visual essay. Refer to the **ELL Handbook** for additional teaching strategies. **learning modality: visual**

Building Inquiry Skills: Observing

Materials *hand lens, peat* 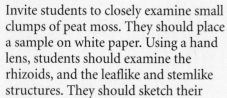 *moss, white paper*
Time 10 minutes

Invite students to closely examine small clumps of peat moss. They should place a sample on white paper. Using a hand lens, students should examine the rhizoids, and the leaflike and stemlike structures. They should sketch their samples and label the parts.

Portfolio Students can save their sketches in their portfolios. **limited English proficiency**

EXPLORING Plant Groups

Plants can be classified according to the presence or absence of vascular tissue and how they reproduce.

NONVASCULAR PLANTS

Plants in this group lack vascular tissue and use spores for reproduction. These plants do not have true roots, stems or leaves. Nonvascular plants are low-growing plants that live in moist areas.

▲ **Mosses**
This is a closeup view of a moss. The spores with which the moss reproduces are produced in a capsule at the top of the stalklike structures.

Liverworts ▲
Liverworts, such as the one shown here, are nonvascular plants. They are named for the shape of the plant's body, which looks somewhat like a human liver.

VASCULAR PLANTS: SEEDLESS

In addition to vascular tissue, these plants have roots, stems, and leaves. These plants reproduce by means of spores and must live in moist areas.

▲ **Club mosses**
Because club mosses have vascular tissue, they are not really mosses. This club moss looks something like a small pine tree.

▲ **Ferns**
Ferns like this one have underground roots and stems. The fern's leaves are called fronds.

Background

Integrating Science Peat moss, which can be used as a fuel, stores chemical energy from decaying plants and animals. This energy can be harnessed to provide fuel for people to use.

Before peat can be used as fuel, it must be cut into blocks and dried. The peat can also be compressed into bricks and made into high-quality charcoal. Peat burns easily and can produce about two-thirds as much heat as the same amount of bituminous coal.

Between 286 and 360 million years ago, layers of rock and sand from the oceans repeatedly covered many thick peat beds. These layers increased the heat and pressure on the peat and caused it to harden into lignite, a low-grade form of coal. Even greater pressure, such as that exerted by the forces of mountain building, further transformed the lignite into hard, bituminous coal.

VASCULAR PLANTS: SEEDS

These plants have vascular tissues and produce seeds. Seed plants have roots, stems, and leaves. There are two kinds of seed plants: gymnosperms and angiosperms. The seeds of gymnosperms are "naked"; that is, they do not develop within any protective covering. Angiosperms are flowering plants. They produce seeds in structures that develop into fruits.

◀ **Gymnosperms**
Gymnosperms include conifers, such as this ponderosa pine. Conifers produce seeds in cones. Most conifers are evergreens that keep their needles year-round.

▲ **Angiosperms**
Grasses and apple trees are both angiosperms. Like all angiosperms, grasses produce seeds that are enclosed in fruits. Apple trees produce flowers in the spring. The seeds develop inside apples, which are fruits.

Cultural Diversity

Every culture relies on plants, especially angiosperms, as a resource for food, construction materials, medicines, clothing, and decoration. Date palms are very important in North Africa and the Middle East, where the dates are used for food and the leaves and stalks are woven into baskets, furniture, rugs, and rope. Mangrove trees are used for their wood and sweet fruit, as well as for an astringent tanning solution produced by the bark. Assign students a country or region to investigate. Students should prepare a display showing the kinds of plants that grow in that region and how the plants are used by native populations. Some areas to assign include the Philippine Islands, the Amazon River basin, Kenya, Puerto Rico, and Thailand. **learning modality: verbal**

Building Inquiry Skills: Observing

Materials *female pine cones, nuts, apple or other fruits*
Time 10 minutes
Have students examine the materials provided. Encourage students to shake the pine cones to see if any seeds fall out. Unless the pine cones are old and have lost their seeds, shaking should cause seeds to fall out. Ask students to shake the nuts and fruits. Seeds will not fall out of these. Ask: **How would you classify the plant that bore a pine cone?** *(gymnosperm)* **Why?** *(The seeds are not enclosed in the pine cone, but are on the scales.)* **What do nuts and fruit have in common?** *(They are both protective coverings for seeds.)* **learning modality: tactile/kinesthetic**

Ongoing Assessment

Oral Presentation Ask students to describe a plant they know and classify it according to whether it has vascular tissue and how it reproduces.

What Is a Plant?, continued

Building Inquiry Skills: Observing

Materials *hand lens, celery leaf stalk, dissecting knife*
Time 20 minutes

Explain to students that they will analyze the transport and support systems in a celery leaf stalk. Give each student a celery leaf stalk to examine. Students should cut the base of the stalk cleanly with a knife. CAUTION: *Knives are sharp and should be handled with care.* Students can then look at different parts of the stalk using a hand lens. Allow them to pull off strands of the stalk or cut the stalk lengthwise to make observations. Ask: **What is the function of the long fibers in a celery stalk?** (*The stalk is made up of long, narrow tubes or fibers that are bundled together. These carry materials and provide support.*)
learning modality: visual

Reproduction

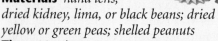

Skills Focus observing
Materials *hand lens; dried kidney, lima, or black beans; dried yellow or green peas; shelled peanuts*
Time 10 minutes
Tips Soak the beans in water for 2 hours before the activity. Soak the peas for 24 hours. Remove peanuts from their shells 3 or 4 days before the activity, and store them in a moist place so the cotyledons will open.
Expected Outcome Students should notice that each of these seeds is composed of two sections that can be easily separated. After they separate the seed, students should see the tiny leaves and root (and possibly the miniature stem) of the embryo plant.
Observing Students' sketches should include the seed coat, which protects the embryo and food from drying out; the cotyledons, which contain stored food; and the embryo, which will develop into a mature plant.
Extend Challenge students to repeat the activity with other kinds of seeds.
learning modality: visual

208

The In-Seed Story

1. Your teacher will give you a hand lens and two different seeds that have been soaked in water.

2. Carefully observe the outside of each seed. Draw what you see.

3. Gently remove the coverings of the seeds. Then carefully separate the parts of each seed. Use a hand lens to examine the inside of each seed. Draw what you see.

Observing Based on your observations and the diagrams below, label the parts of each seed. Then describe the function of each part next to its label.

Roots and Stems Vascular plants have roots and stems. Roots are organs that anchor plants in the ground and absorb water and nutrients from soil. Stems carry substances back and forth between the roots and leaves. They also support plants and hold up leaves to the sun. Nonvascular plants do not have true roots or stems. However, they have structures that are similar to roots and stems and perform the same functions.

✓ *Checkpoint* What is the function of roots?

Reproduction

The life cycles of plants have two stages, or generations. In one stage, the plant produces spores, the tiny cells that can grow into new organisms. A spore develops into the plant's other stage, in which the plant undergoes sexual reproduction that involves fertilization. **Fertilization** occurs when a sperm cell unites with an egg cell. Sperm cells and egg cells contain genetic information. The fertilized egg is called a **zygote.** A young organism that develops from a zygote is called an **embryo.**

Seeds In seed plants, including gymnosperms and angiosperms, an embryo develops inside a seed. A **seed** is a structure that contains a young plant inside a protective covering. **A seed has three important parts—an embryo, stored food, and a seed coat.** The embryo has the beginnings of roots, stems, and leaves. The embryo uses food stored in the seed until it can make its own food. In some plants, food is stored inside one or two seed leaves, or **cotyledons** (kaht uh LEED unz). The outer covering of a seed is called the seed coat. The seed coat protects the embryo and its food and keeps them from drying out.

Figure 17 The structures of three different seeds are shown in this diagram.

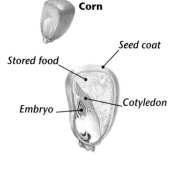
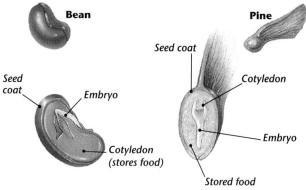

208

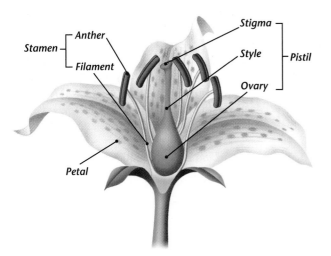

Stamen — Anther, Filament
Stigma, Style — Pistil
Ovary
Petal

Figure 18 Like most flowers, this lily contains both male and female reproductive structures. *Interpreting Photographs What structures in the diagram can you find in the photograph?*

After seeds have formed, they are usually scattered, or dispersed, sometimes far from where they were produced. Seeds are dispersed in several ways. Wind carries some seeds from one place to another. Animals may eat seeds, and then deposit them elsewhere in wastes. Seeds may stick to an animal's fur and hitch a ride to a new place. When seeds land in a suitable area, they can germinate, or begin to grow. To develop into a new plant, a seed needs light, water, and nutrients.

Cones Gymnosperms usually have reproductive structures called cones. Most gymnosperms have two types of cones: male cones and female cones. Male cones produce tiny grains of pollen. **Pollen** contains the microscopic cells that will later become sperm cells. Female cones produce ovules. An **ovule** (OH vyool) is a structure that contains an egg cell. During reproduction, pollen from a male cone reaches a female cone. Fertilization occurs when a sperm cell and an egg cell join together in an ovule on the female cone. After fertilization occurs, the zygote develops into the embryo part of the seed.

Flowers Most of the plants that you see around you are angiosperms. In these plants, the seeds are produced in **flowers,** which are the reproductive organs of some kinds of seed plants. Look at Figure 18 to see the parts of a typical flower. Within the petals are the flower's male and female reproductive organs. **Stamens** (STAY munz) are the male reproductive parts. Pollen is produced in the knobby structure, or anther, at the top of the stamen. Each of the female parts, or **pistils,** has a hollow organ called an ovary. In the ovary are the ovules that contain egg cells.

Chapter 6 **209**

Answers to Self-Assessment

Caption Question

Figure 18 Petals, stamens (anther and filament), pistil

☑ *Checkpoint*

Roots anchor plants and absorb water and minerals from the ground.

209

Reproduction, continued

Addressing Naive Conceptions

Some students may think that pollination and fertilization are the same process. Point out that pollination is necessary for fertilization, but they are not the same. In fact, there is a time delay after pollination occurs before fertilization occurs. Ask students to explain the two processes. *(In pollination, pollen is dusted onto the flower's stigma. In fertilization, an egg and a sperm unite.)* **learning modality: verbal**

Plant Responses and Growth

Demonstration

Materials *small potted plant, such as a bean plant; materials to support the pot*
Time 10 minutes, with observations one week later

Students who are mastering English will benefit from this dramatic presentation. Place the plant on a ledge near a window or light. Ask: **In what direction is the plant growing? Why?** *(The stem is growing upward, toward the light and away from the pull of gravity.)* Support the pot on its side so the stem is parallel to the floor. Ask students to predict what the plant will look like in a week. After one week, the plant's new growth should be pointing up, with a bend between the old and new growth. Ask the students to explain what happened in terms of the plant's tropisms. *(The plant's positive phototropism and negative gravitropism caused it to grow upward.)* Refer to the **ELL Handbook** for additional teaching strategies. **limited English proficiency**

Language Arts Connection

Students may be familiar with the word *perennial* from phrases such as "the perennial favorite." Ask students to think of other phrases using *annual, biennial, perennial,* or similar words. Have students compose sentences using these words. **cooperative learning**

Figure 19 The face of this sunflower turns on its stalk throughout the day so that it always faces the sun.
Making Generalizations How does a positive phototropism help a plant survive?

A flower is pollinated when a grain of pollen falls on the top of a pistil, called the stigma. Because the stigma is sticky, pollen adheres to it. In time, the sperm cell fertilizes the egg cell in the ovule. The zygote develops into the embryo part of the seed. As the seed develops, the ovary changes into a **fruit,** which is a ripened ovary and other structures that enclose one or more seeds. Apples and cherries are fruits. So are many foods you usually call vegetables, such as tomatoes and squash.

Plant Responses and Growth

As you learned in Chapter 4, all living things respond to stimuli in their surroundings. Animals usually respond to stimuli by moving. **Unlike animals, plants commonly respond to stimuli by growing either toward or away from a stimulus.**

Tropisms A plant's growth response toward or away from a stimulus is called a **tropism** (TROH pihz uhm). If a plant grows toward the stimulus, it shows a positive tropism. If a plant grows away from a stimulus, it shows a negative tropism.

Plants respond to three important external stimuli: touch, light, and gravity. For example, the stems of many vines, such as grapes and morning glories, respond positively to touch. They coil around any object they touch. All plants grow toward light, which is a positive tropism. The parts of plants respond differently to gravity. Roots grow downward, which is a positive tropism. However, stems grow upward, which is a negative tropism to gravity.

Hormones Plants are able to respond to touch, light, and gravity because they produce hormones. A **hormone** is a chemical produced inside an organism that affects the organism's body processes, such as growth and development. Hormones act as internal stimuli that cause an organism's cells, tissues, and organs to respond in specific ways. In addition to tropisms, plant hormones also control the formation of flowers, stems, and leaves, the shedding of leaves, and the development and ripening of fruit.

Background

Integrating Science Many of the adaptations that attract pollinators to flowers—such as fragrance and color—also attract humans. For example, the flowers of many plants, such as jasmine, rose, and lavender, are used to create strong and attractive scents.

The art of making perfume requires knowledge of both chemistry and botany. For the best perfume, the flowers must be gathered at exactly the right time in the plant's life cycle. Isolating floral compounds often requires a large number of flowers. It takes approximately 113 kg of rose petals to make one ounce of attar of rose.

In addition to flowers, other parts of angiosperms are often valued for their scents. The seeds of the musk mallow tree of India are used for perfume.

Figure 20 A flowering plant is classified as an annual, biennial, or perennial depending on the length of its life cycle. **(A)** These morning glories are annuals. **(B)** This foxglove, *Digitalis purpurea*, is a biennial. **(C)** This peony, a perennial, will bloom year after year.

Life Spans of Flowering Plants If you've ever planted a garden, you know that many flowering plants grow, flower, and die in one year. Flowering plants that live for only one growing season are called annuals. Marigolds, petunias, and pansies are all annuals. Wheat, tomatoes, and cucumbers are also annuals.

Flowering plants that live for two years are called biennials (by EN ee ulz). In the first year, biennials grow roots, very short stems, and leaves. During their second year, they grow new stems and leaves, produce flowers and seeds, and then die. Parsley, celery, and most kinds of foxglove are biennials.

Flowering plants that live any longer than two years are called perennials. Some perennials, such as peonies and asparagus, have leaves and above-ground stems that die each winter. These perennials produce new leaves and stems each spring. Most perennials, however, have woody stems that do not die each winter. Bristlecone pines, oak trees, and honeysuckle are examples of woody-stemmed perennials.

Section 4 Review

1. List the characteristics that all plants share.
2. What is the function of a seed coat?
3. How do plants respond to stimuli?
4. Describe the functions of roots, stems, and leaves.
5. **Thinking Critically** **Classifying** Is the grass that grows in most lawns an annual, biennial, or perennial? Explain.

Check Your Progress
CHAPTER PROJECT
Your plants should be near the end of their growth cycle. Continue to observe them. Harvest the seeds carefully, observe them, and compare them with the original seeds. If you have time, plant a few of these new seeds to begin the life cycle again.

Answers to Self-Assessment

Caption Question

Figure 19 Positive phototropism keeps a plant facing toward light so that it gets enough energy to make its food.

---

3 Assess

Section 4 Review Answers

1. All plants are multicellular eukaryotes that produce their food through photosynthesis.
2. The seed coat protects the embryo and its food and keeps them from drying out.
3. Plants usually respond to stimuli by growing toward or away from them.
4. Roots anchor plants in the ground and absorb water and minerals. Stems carry substances back and forth between the roots and the leaves. They also support plants and hold their leaves up to the sun. Leaves carry out photosynthesis.
5. Grass is a perennial because it grows year after year without replanting.

Check Your Progress
CHAPTER PROJECT
Help students collect seeds. Collect data from each student or group and find the average number of seeds produced per plant. If time permits, have students plant these seeds to begin the life cycle again. Emphasize that this second cycle should be similar to the one they just observed. Check students' data tables for completeness and make sure their diagrams are labeled appropriately.

Performance Assessment

Drawing Have students draw a seed and label the embryo, stored food, and seed coat. Then have students describe the labeled parts.

 Students can save their drawings and descriptions in their portfolios.

Developing Hypotheses

Which Way Is Up?

Preparing for Inquiry

Key Concept When the new root emerges from a germinating seed, it always grows downward; the new stem always grows upward.

Skills Objective Students will be able to
◆ develop hypotheses to explain how the growth of a seed is affected by gravity.

Time 30 minutes, plus a few minutes each day for a week

Advance Planning Make sure there are enough corn seeds for you to give four seeds to each student or group. Soak the seeds in water for 24 hours before the lab.

Alternative Materials Other seeds that can be used include lima beans, sunflowers, squash, oats, and cucumbers. If you use glass petri dishes, remind students to follow all the safety procedures associated with the use of glass.

Guiding Inquiry

Invitation Ask students to imagine what plants would be like if gravity did not influence the growth of plants. (*The plant might sometimes grow up, other times grow in other directions.*)

Introducing the Procedure

Make sure students understand that the seeds must be kept in exactly the same position throughout the experiment. Show two sample petri dishes, one in which the positions of the seeds can shift and one that is properly packed.

Analyze and Conclude

1. Roots grew from the pointed tip of the seed, while the stem grew from the rounded part. The roots always grew downward, and the stems always grew upward, bending if necessary.
2. Students should be able to explain any inconsistencies between their hypotheses and the evidence.
3. Plants usually grow toward light. Light was excluded so the direction of growth was affected only by gravity. The dark also simulates the underground environment in which seeds usually germinate.

4. Answers will vary. Students should realize that the results show that the direction of growth is influenced by gravity, not the direction in which the seeds are planted.

Extending the Inquiry

Design an Experiment Students may want to place their petri dish so that it is exposed to light on only one side to observe any differences in the growth of the four plants. Remind them to take gravity into account.

Skills Lab

Developing Hypotheses

Which Way Is Up?

In this lab, you will develop and test a hypothesis about how seedlings respond to gravity.

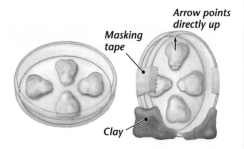

Arrow points directly up

Masking tape

Clay

Problem

How is the growth of a seed affected by gravity?

Materials

4 corn seeds	plastic petri dish
paper towels	scissors
water	masking tape
marking pencil	clay

Procedure

1. Read over the entire procedure. Then, with your group, develop a hypothesis about the direction in which the seedlings will grow in response to gravity.
2. Arrange four seeds that have been soaked in water for 24 hours in a petri dish. The pointed ends of the seeds should face the center of the dish, as shown in the illustration.
3. Place a circle cut from a paper towel over the seeds. Moisten one or more paper towels with water so that they are wet but not dripping. Pack them in the dish to hold the seeds firmly in place. Cover the dish, and seal it with tape.
4. Lay the dish upside-down so the seeds show. Use a marking pencil to draw a small, outward-facing arrow over one of the seeds, as shown in the illustration. Turn the dish over and write your name and the date on it.
5. Use clay to stand up the petri dish so that the arrow points upward. Put the petri dish in a dark place.

6. Once a day for a week, remove the petri dish and check it. Do not open the dish. Observe and sketch the seeds. Note the seeds' direction of growth. Then return the dish, making sure that the arrow points upward.

Analyze and Conclude

1. What new structures emerged as the seeds developed? How did the direction of growth compare from seed to seed?
2. Did your results confirm your hypothesis? If not, describe any differences between your hypothesis and your results.
3. Why was it necessary to grow these seeds in the dark?
4. **Think About It** What evidence or ideas did you consider when you wrote your hypothesis? Did any of your ideas change as a result of this experiment? Explain.

Design an Experiment

How will your seedlings respond if you now allow them to grow in the light? Design an experiment to find out. Obtain your teacher's approval before carrying out your experiment.

Program Resources

◆ **Unit 2 Resources** Chapter 6 Skills Lab blackline masters, pp. 80–81
◆ **Inquiry Skills Activity Book** Provides teaching and review of all inquiry skills

Media and Technology

 Lab Activity Videotapes
Grade 6, Tape 2

SECTION **1** **Classifying Living Things**

Key Ideas

◆ Biologists classify an organism by its structure, development, and DNA.
◆ The six kingdoms of organisms are archaebacteria, eubacteria, protists, fungi, plants, and animals.

Key Terms

classification   genus
taxonomy   species
binomial nomenclature

 SECTION **2** **Bacteria**

Key Ideas

◆ Bacteria are prokaryotes. The genetic material in their cells is not contained in a nucleus.
◆ Although some bacteria cause disease, most bacteria are harmless or beneficial.

Key Terms

flagellum   endospore
binary fission   decomposer
conjugation

SECTION **3** **Protists and Fungi**

Key Ideas

◆ Animal-like protists are heterotrophs that have structures that enable them to move.
◆ Like plants, all algae are autotrophs.
◆ Fungus-like protists are heterotrophs, have cell walls, and use spores to reproduce.
◆ Fungi are eukaryotes, use spores to reproduce, and are heterotrophs that absorb their food.
◆ Most fungi reproduce both asexually and sexually.

Key Terms

protozoan   parasite   spore
pseudopod   host   hyphae
cilia   algae   budding

 SECTION **4** **The Plant Kingdom**

Key Ideas

◆ Plants are multicellular eukaryotes that produce food through photosynthesis. Most plants have vascular tissue, leaves, roots, and stems.
◆ A seed has three main parts—an embryo, stored food, and a seed coat.
◆ Plants respond to external stimuli by growing either away from or toward the stimulus.

Key Terms

vascular tissue   seed   stamen
stomata   cotyledon   pistil
fertilization   pollen   fruit
zygote   ovule   tropism
embryo   flower   hormone

Organizing Information

Concept Map Copy the concept map about seed plants onto a separate piece of paper. Then complete the map. (For more on concept maps, see the Skills Handbook.)

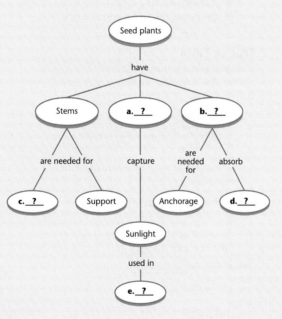

Organizing Information

Concept Map **a.** Leaves **b.** Roots **c.** Transportation **d.** Water and Nutrients **e.** Photosynthesis

Program Resources

◆ **Unit 2 Resources** Chapter 6 Project Scoring Rubric, p. 60
◆ **Performance Assessment** Chapter 6, pp. 20–22
◆ **Chapter and Unit Tests** Chapter 6 Test, pp. 28–31

Media and Technology

 Computer Test Bank
Chapter 6 Test

Reviewing Content

Multiple Choice

1. c 2. a 3. a 4. b 5. b

True or False

6. True 7. True 8. prokaryote 9. True
10. True

Checking Concepts

11. The scientific name of an organism tells you its genus and species.
12. Cell wall: protects bacterial cell and determines its shape. Cell membrane: controls movement of substances into and out of the cell. Ribosomes: make proteins. Genetic material: controls cell processes. Flagella: move the cell.
13. Binary fission: one bacterial cell divides to form two identical cells. Conjugation: one cell transfers some of its genetic material into another. The cells separate, and then they can divide.
14. Animal-like protists can move toward food and capture it. Plantlike protists, usually called algae, are autotrophs and make their own food. Fungus-like protists are heterotrophs.
15. The major difference is that fungi are heterotrophs and plants are autotrophs.
16. Vascular tissue is important because it transports water, minerals, and food throughout the plant. It also supports the plant. Example: rose.
17. A plant hormone is a chemical produced by the plant that affects its body processes, such as growth and development. Plant hormones control (*any three*): tropisms; the formation of flowers, stems, and leaves; the shedding of leaves; and the development and ripening of fruit.
18. Sample: I begin to grow hyphae. These hyphae burrow into the rotting apple, providing me with water and food. Soon I'm a full-grown fungus.

Thinking Critically

19. *Entameba histolytica* and *Entameba coli* are most closely related. They are members of the same genus.
20. To discourage the growth of mildew in a basement, a homeowner must make the basement dry. To do this, he or she can waterproof the foundation and/or install a dehumidifier to reduce the moisture.

Reviewing Content

 Review key concepts online using
iText at www.phschool.com

Multiple Choice

Choose the letter of the best answer.

1. The science of placing organisms into groups based on shared characteristics is called
   a. development.   b. biology.
   c. taxonomy.   d. DNA.
2. A genus is divided into
   a. species.   b. phyla.
   c. families. d. classes.
3. Most bacteria are surrounded by a protective structure called the
   a. cell wall.   b. cilia.
   c. protein coat.   d. flagellum.
4. Fungus-like protists are
   a. autotrophs.
   b. heterotrophs.
   c. unable to move.
   d. prokaryotes.
5. Plants produce their food through
   a. chemical breakdown by structures called hyphae.
   b. photosynthesis.
   c. the production of gymnosperms.
   d. vascular tissue.

True or False

If the statement is true, write true. If it is false, change the underlined word or words to make the statement true.

6. <u>Linnaeus</u> devised a system of naming organisms that is called binomial nomenclature.
7. Most <u>archaebacteria</u> live in extreme conditions.
8. In a(n) <u>eukaryote,</u> genetic material is not contained in the nucleus.
9. Most fungi are made up of threadlike structures called <u>hyphae</u>.
10. Plants are <u>autotrophs</u>.

Checking Concepts

11. What does the scientific name of an organism tell you about that organism?
12. What are the parts of a bacterial cell? Explain the function of each.
13. Describe two ways in which bacteria reproduce.
14. Compare how animal-like, fungus-like, and plantlike protists obtain food.
15. What is the major difference between fungi and plants?
16. In what two ways is vascular tissue important to a plant? Give an example of a plant that has vascular tissue.
17. What is a plant hormone? Give three examples of the functions hormones have in the life of the plant.
18. Writing to Learn Imagine that you are a spore just released from a fungus growing on a decaying apple. The apple has been lying on the ground in a neglected orchard. Write a description about what happens to you next.

Thinking Critically

19. Classifying Which two of the following organisms are most closely related: *Entameba histolytica, Esherichia coli, Entameba coli*? Explain your answer.
20. Problem Solving Mildew is a fungus that grows on materials such as paper, leather, and wood. What are some actions that homeowners could take to discourage the growth of mildew in their basement? Explain why these actions might help solve the problem.
21. Applying Concepts Explain why people who grow houseplants on windowsills should turn the plants every week or so.
22. Comparing and Contrasting How are archaebacteria and eubacteria the same? How are they different?

---

21. The plant responds toward the light by bending toward it. In order to prevent lopsided growth, the plant should be turned periodically.
22. Archaebacteria and eubacteria are both unicellular prokaryotes; they are either autotrophic or heterotrophic. They differ in their chemical makeup.

Applying Skills

23. It is always higher
24. One possible answer is that there might have been a heavy rainfall for a few days. Accept all reasonable answers.
25. Growing plants in soil covered with mulch seems more reasonable because plants need moisture to grow and soil that is mulched holds more moisture than soil that is not mulched.

Applying Skills

Some gardeners spread mulch—material such as wood chips, peat moss, or straw—on the soil around plants. The graph compares the moisture retained by soil with and without mulch. Use the graph to answer Questions 23–25.

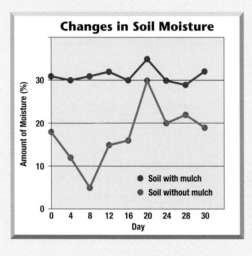

Changes in Soil Moisture

- Soil with mulch
- Soil without mulch

23. **Comparing and Contrasting** How does the amount of moisture in soil covered with mulch differ from the amount of moisture in the uncovered soil?

24. **Inferring** The amount of moisture in both soils increased greatly between days 16 and 20. Explain why this might have happened.

25. **Drawing Conclusions** If you were a gardener, would you grow your plants in soil covered with mulch or in soil that was uncovered? Explain.

Performance CHAPTER PROJECT Assessment

Present Your Project Design a poster that shows the results of your investigation. Do you think that the later generations of plants will go through a similar life cycle? Why or why not?

Reflect and Record What new information did you learn about seed plants by doing this project? If you could do another investigation using these plants, what would you do? Why?

Performance CHAPTER PROJECT Assessment

Present Your Project Encourage students to use a cycle diagram to describe their observations during the life span of the plant in this project. Remind students to include what will happen after the new seeds are germinated. Find a space for students to display their exhibits.

Reflect and Record Discuss the project with students. Make sure they understand the cyclic nature of plant life. Students may suggest using their plants to investigate tropisms or hydroponics. If there is time, allow students to try their new experiments after you approve their plans.

Test Preparation

26. D 27. G 28. D

Test Preparation

Use these questions to prepare for standardized tests.

Use the information to answer Questions 26–28. When bracken ferns grow, their underground stems grow outward and produce new plants. As the map below shows, the new ferns spread into nearby open areas. The bands of color indicate the areas where bracken ferns grew over a four-year period.

Patches of Fern Growth in an Open Field

26. During which year did the ferns grow most slowly?
   - **A** 1996
   - **B** 1997
   - **C** 1998
   - **D** 1999

27. In how many areas in the field were bracken ferns growing in 1997?
   - **F** one
   - **G** two
   - **H** three
   - **J** four

28. The underground stems of bracken ferns do not grow far before producing new plants. What is the most likely explanation for how bracken ferns began to grow in the middle of the field in 1998?
   - **A** It rained less than usual.
   - **B** The temperatures were higher than normal.
   - **C** The whole field was fertilized.
   - **D** Spores blew into a moist part of the field.

Program Resources

- ◆ **Inquiry Skills Activity Book** Provides teaching and review of all inquiry skills
- ◆ **Prentice Hall Assessment System** Provides standardized test practice
- ◆ **Reading in the Content Area** Provides strategies to improve science reading skills
- ◆ **Teacher's ELL Handbook** Provides multiple strategies for English language learners

Animals

Sections	Time	Student Edition Activities		Other Activities
CHAPTER PROJECT **Animal Adaptations** p. 217 TEKS: 6.10A, C	Ongoing (3–4 weeks)	TEKS: 6.2C; 6.3C **Check Your Progress**, pp. 220, 236, 245 **Present Your Project**, p. 259	TE	Chapter 7 Project Notes, pp. 216–217
1 **What Is an Animal?** pp. 218–220 TEKS: 6.10A, B, C; 6.12A, B 7.1.1 Describe four major characteristics of animals. 7.1.2 Explain how animals reproduce. 7.1.3 Describe the relationship between animal body structures and functions. 7.1.4 Differentiate between a vertebrate and an invertebrate.	2 periods/ 1 block	TEKS: 6.2B, C **Discover** Is It an Animal?, p. 218		
2 **INTEGRATING MATHEMATICS** **Symmetry** pp. 221–222 TEKS: 6.10A, B, C 7.2.1 Distinguish between bilateral and radial symmetry, and describe how animals exhibit these kinds of symmetry.	1 period/ $\frac{1}{2}$ block	TEKS: 6.2B **Discover** How Many Ways Can You Fold It?, p. 221 **Science at Home** p. 222		
3 **Sponges, Cnidarians, Worms, and Mollusks** pp. 223–229 TEKS: 6.10A, B, C; 6.12B 7.3.1 Relate structure and function in sponges and cnidarians. 7.3.2 Identify the three main groups of worms. 7.3.3 Describe the structure of a mollusk.	4–5 periods/ 2–2$\frac{1}{2}$ blocks	TEKS: 6.1A; 6.2A, B, C, D; 6.4A **Discover** How do Natural and Synthetic Sponges Compare?, p. 223 **Try This** Hydra Doing?, p. 224 **Science at Home** p. 228 **Skills Lab:** Developing Hypotheses, Earthworm Responses, p. 229	TE TE TE TE	Building Inquiry Skills: Observing, pp. 224, 226 Inquiry Challenge, p. 225 Including All Students, p. 226 Exploring a Snail, p. 227
4 **Arthropods and Echinoderms** pp. 230–236 TEKS: 6.10A, C; 6.12A, B 7.4.1 Describe the structures characteristic of arthropods. 7.4.2 Describe the structures that characterize insects. 7.4.3 Identify the characteristics of echinoderms.	3–4 periods/ 1$\frac{1}{2}$–2 blocks	TEKS: 6.2A, B, C; 6.3C **Discover** Will It Bend and Move?, p. 230 **Sharpen your Skills** Designing Experiments, p. 234	TE TE TE TE LM	Including All Students, p. 231 Building Inquiry Skills: Interpreting Diagrams, p. 232 Using the Visual, p. 235 Inquiry Challenge, p. 235 7, "Characteristics of Sea Stars"
5 **Fishes, Amphibians, and Reptiles** pp. 237–246 TEKS: 6.3D; 6.10A, C; 6.12B 7.5.1 Explain the function of a vertebrate's skeletal system. 7.5.2 Describe characteristics of fishes, amphibians, reptiles.	4–5 periods/ 2–2$\frac{1}{2}$ blocks	TEKS: 6.1A; 6.2B, C, D; 6.4A **Discover** How Is an Umbrella Like a Skeleton?, p. 237 **Sharpen your Skills** Communicating, p. 238 **Sharpen your Skills** Drawing Conclusions, p. 243	TE TE	Building Inquiry Skills: Observing, p. 240; Inferring, p. 244 Including All Students, p. 241
6 **Birds and Mammals** pp. 247–256 TEKS: 6.10A, C; 6.12A, B 7.6.1 Identify the common characteristics of birds. 7.6.2 Describe the characteristics that mammals share.	2–3 periods/ 1–1$\frac{1}{2}$ blocks	TEKS: 6.1A; 6.2A, B, C, D, E; 6.3D; 6.4A **Discover** What Are Feathers Like?, p. 247 **Try This** Eggs-animation, p. 250 **Sharpen your Skills** Inferring, p. 253 **Science at Home** p. 255 **Real World Lab:** You, the Consumer, p. 256	TE TE TE TE	Including All Students, pp. 248, 252 Inquiry Challenge, p. 249 Building Inquiry Skills: Observing, pp. 250, 254 Integrating Environmental Science, p. 251
Study Guide/Chapter Assessment pp. 257–259	1 period/ $\frac{1}{2}$ block	**PLM** Provides blackline masters for Probeware labs	**ISAB**	Provides teaching and review of all inquiry skills

Key: **CTB** Computer Test Bank
CUT Chapter and Unit Tests
ELL Teacher's ELL Handbook

CHAPTER PLANNING GUIDE

 The Resource Pro® CD-ROM provides flexibility for planning the instruction for any type of schedule.

Program Resources	Assessment Strategies	Media and Technology
UR Chapter 7 Project Teacher Notes, pp. 82–83 UR Chapter 7 Project Overview and Worksheets, pp. 84–87	SE Performance Assessment: Present Your Project, p. 259 TE Check Your Progress, pp. 220, 236, 245 UR Chapter 7 Project Scoring Rubric, p. 88	Science Explorer at www.phschool.com Student Edition on Audio CD, English-Spanish, Chapter 7
UR 7-1 Section Lesson Plan, p. 89 UR 7-1 Section Summary, p. 90 UR 7-1 Review and Reinforce, p. 91 UR 7-1 Enrich, p. 92	SE Section 1 Review, p. 220 TE Performance Assessment, p. 220	Life Science Videodisc Unit 3, Side 1, "Through Their Eyes" Videotape Grade 6, Unit 2, "Through Their Eyes"
UR 7-2 Section Lesson Plan, p. 93 UR 7-2 Section Summary, p. 94 UR 7-2 Review and Reinforce, p. 95 UR 7-2 Enrich, p. 96	SE Section 2 Review, p. 222 TE Performance Assessment, p. 222	
UR 7-3 Section Lesson Plan, p. 97 UR 7-3 Section Summary, p. 98 UR 7-3 Review and Reinforce, p. 99 UR 7-3 Enrich, p. 100 UR Skills Lab blackline masters, pp. 113–115	SE Section 3 Review, p. 228 TE Ongoing Assessment, pp. 225, 227 TE Performance Assessment, p. 228	Life Science Videodisc Unit 3, Side 1, "Spineless" Videotape Grade 6, Unit 2, "Spineless" Lab Activity Videotapes, Tape 2 Transparencies 29, "Structure of an Earthworm"; 30, "Exploring a Snail"
UR 7-4 Section Lesson Plan, p. 101 UR 7-4 Section Summary, p. 102 UR 7-4 Review and Reinforce, p. 103 UR 7-4 Enrich, p. 104	SE Section 4 Review, p. 236 TE Ongoing Assessment, pp. 231, 233, 235 TE Performance Assessment, p. 236	Life Science Videodisc Unit 3, Side 1, "Insect Success Stories" Videotape Unit 2, "Insect Success Stories" Transparencies 31, "Structure of a Grasshopper"; 32, "Exploring Insect Metamorphosis"
UR 7-5 Section Lesson Plan, p. 105 UR 7-5 Section Summary, p. 106 UR 7-5 Review and Reinforce, p. 107 UR 7-5 Enrich, p. 108	SE Section 5 Review, p. 245 TE Ongoing Assessment, pp. 239, 241, 243 TE Performance Assessment, p. 245	Life Science Videodisc Unit 3, Side 1, "Backbones"; "Travelin' Along" Videotape "Backbones"; "Travelin' Along" Transparencies 33, "Exploring a Bony Fish"; 34, "Frog Metamorphosis"; 35, "A Reptile Egg"
UR 7-6 Section Lesson Plan, p. 109 UR 7-6 Section Summary, p. 110 UR 7-6 Review and Reinforce, p. 111 UR 7-6 Enrich, p. 112 UR Real World Lab blackline masters, pp. 116–117	SE Section 6 Review, p. 255 TE Ongoing Assessment, pp. 249, 251, 253 TE Performance Assessment, p. 255	Life Science Videodisc Unit 3, Side 1, "How Does Everything Fit?" Videotape Unit 2, "How Does Everything Fit?" Lab Activity Videotapes, Tape 2 Transparencies 36, "Exploring a Bird"; 37, "Circulation in Fishes, Amphibians, and Birds"
ELL Provides multiple strategies for English language learners GRSW Provides worksheets to promote student comprehension of content RCA Provides strategies to improve science reading skills	SE Chapter 7 Study Guide/Assessment, pp. 257–259 PA Assessment Chapter 7, pp. 23–25 CUT Chapter 7 Test, pp. 32–35 CTB Chapter 7 Test PHAS Provides standardized test preparation	Chapter 7 Computer Test Bank, Chapter 7 Test

GRSW Guided Reading and Study Workbook
ISAB Inquiry Skills Activity Book
LM Laboratory Manual

PA Performance Assessment
PHAS Prentice Hall Assessment System
PLM Probeware Lab Manual

RCA Reading in the Content Area
SE Student Edition

TE Teacher's Edition
UR Unit Resources

Student Edition Activities Planner

ACTIVITY	Time (minutes)	Materials _Quantities for one work group_	Skills
Section 1			
Discover, p. 218	15 min	**Nonconsumable** organisms that students can safely observe, such as earthworms, minnows, pill bugs, crickets, potted plants, ferns, and sponges	**Forming Operational Definitions**
Section 2			
Discover, p. 221	10 min	**Consumable** tracing paper **Nonconsumable** scissors, pen or pencil, circular object	Classifying
Section 3			
Discover, p. 223	20 min	**Nonconsumable** natural sponges, synthetic sponges, scissors, hand lens or microscope	Observing
Try This, p. 224	25 min	**Consumable** live hydra **Nonconsumable** small glass bowl or petri dish, hand lens or microscope, toothpicks	Observing
Skills Lab, p. 229	30 min	**Consumable** water, paper towels, 2 earthworms **Nonconsumable** plastic dropper, clock or watch, storage container, cardboard, flashlight, tray	**Developing Hypotheses, Designing an Experiment**
Section 4			
Discover, p. 230	15	**Consumable** sheets of heavy cardboard, about 30 × 45 cm, tape	Inferring
Sharpen Your Skills, p. 234	20	No special materials are required.	**Designing Experiments**
Section 5			
Discover, p. 237	15 min	**Nonconsumable** umbrella	Inferring
Sharpen your Skills, p. 238	50 min	**Consumable** preserved fish, disposable gloves **Nonconsumable** goggles, dissecting tray, blunt probe, hand lens	Communicating
Sharpen your Skills, p. 243	15 min	No special materials are required.	**Drawing Conclusions**
Section 6			
Discover, p. 247	15 min	**Nonconsumable** feathers, hand lens	Observing
Try This, p. 250	20 min	**Consumable** uncooked egg, water **Nonconsumable** bowl, hand lens	Observing
Sharpen your Skills, p. 253	15 min	**Nonconsumable** photos of a variety of mammals, such as horses, bats, rabbits, whales, and seals	Inferring
Real World Lab, p. 256	35 min	**Consumable** hot tap water, room temperature tap water **Nonconsumable** 1 L beaker, clock or watch, a pair of wool socks, three 250-mL container with lids	**Controlling Variables, Interpreting Data**

A list of all materials required for the Student Edition activities can be found on pages T43–T49. You can obtain information about ordering materials by calling 1-800-848-9500 or by accessing the Science Explorer Internet site at **www.phschool.com**.

Texas Essential Knowledge and Skills

(6.1) Scientific processes. The student conducts field and laboratory investigations using safe, environmentally appropriate, and ethical practices. *(Sections 3, 5, 6)*
The student is expected to:
(A) demonstrate safe practices during field and laboratory investigations.

(6.2) Scientific processes. The student uses scientific inquiry methods during field and laboratory investigations. *(Project; Sections 1, 2, 3, 4, 5, 6)*
The student is expected to:
(A) plan and implement investigative procedures including asking questions, formulating testable hypotheses, and selecting and using equipment and technology;
(B) collect data by observing and measuring;
(C) analyze and interpret information to construct reasonable explanations from direct and indirect evidence;
(D) communicate valid conclusions; and
(E) construct graphs, tables, maps, and charts using tools including computers to organize, examine, and evaluate data.

(6.3) Scientific processes. The student uses critical thinking and scientific problem solving to make informed decisions. *(Project; Sections 4, 5, 6)*
The student is expected to:
(C) represent the natural world using models and identify their limitations;
(D) evaluate the impact of research on scientific thought, society, and the environment.

(6.4) Scientific processes. The student knows how to use a variety of tools and methods to conduct science inquiry. *(Sections 3, 5, 6)*
The student is expected to:
(A) collect, analyze, and record information using tools including beakers, petri dishes, meter sticks, graduated cylinders, weather instruments, timing devices, hot plates, test tubes, safety goggles, spring scales, magnets, balances, microscopes, telescopes, thermometers, calculators, field equipment, compasses, computers, and computer probes.

(6.10) Science concepts. The student knows the relationship between structure and function in living systems. *(Project; Sections 1, 2, 3, 4, 5, 6)*
The student is expected to:
(A) differentiate between structure and function;
(B) determine that all organisms are composed of cells that carry on functions to sustain life; and
(C) identify how structure complements function at different levels of organization including organs, organ systems, organisms, and populations.

(6.12) Science concepts. The student knows that the responses of organisms are caused by internal or external stimuli. *(Sections 1, 3, 4, 5, 6)*
The student is expected to:
(A) identify responses in organisms to internal stimuli such as hunger or thirst;
(B) identify responses in organisms to external stimuli such as the presence or absence of heat or light.

Take It to the Net

 Interactive text at www.phschool.com

Science Explorer comes alive with iText.

- **Complete student text** is accessible from any computer with Internet access or a CD-ROM drive.

- **Animations, simulations, and videos** enhance student understanding and retention of concepts.

- **Self-tests and online study tools** assess student understanding.

- **Teacher management tools** help you make the most of this valuable resource.

STAY CURRENT with **SCIENCE NEWS**®

Find out the latest research and information about invertebrates and vertebrates at **www.phschool.com**.

Go to **www.phschool.com**. Select Texas on the navigation bar. Click on the Science icon. Then click on <u>Science Explorer</u> under PH@school.

Animal Adaptations

TEKS: 6.2C; 6.3C; 6.10A, C

Adaptations have evolved over time in species because the adaptations allow individual organisms to be more successful at acquiring food, escaping predators, or reproducing. In this project, students will select one adaptation to model in two animals: a vertebrate and an invertebrate.

Purpose In this project, students will investigate and model how adaptations enable animals to survive in their environments.

Skills Focus Students will be able to
◆ make models of adaptations that perform similar functions in two different kinds of organisms;
◆ compare and contrast the adaptations of the two organisms;
◆ communicate to their classmates their findings about the adaptations they model.

Project Time Line Before beginning the project, see Chapter 7 Project Teacher Notes on pages 82–83 in Unit 2 Resources for more details on carrying out the project. Distribute to students Chapter 7 Project Overview, Worksheets, and Scoring Rubric on pages 84–88 in Unit 2 Resources. This project should progress in several stages and will take 3–4 weeks to complete. During the first week, students get together with a partner or in small groups and skim the chapter and any other sources of relevant information such as books and magazines. By the beginning of the second week, students should have selected an adaptation to model. As students complete each chapter section, they should begin to construct a model of one type of organism they studied in the section. To save time and keep students on track, have them work on their projects at home as well as in the classroom. Students should be given about one week to build the model for each organism and then a few days to prepare their class presentation.

Possible Materials Provide a wide variety of materials from which students

This three-horned chameleon has just invited a cricket to lunch.

WEB ACTIVITY
www.phschool.com

216

can choose. Have students bring extra materials that they might have at home for others in the class to use. Some possibilities:
◆ For model building, include toothpicks, pipe cleaners, Styrofoam, cardboard, construction paper, chicken wire, balsa wood, balloons, modeling clay, papier mâché, glue, tape, scissors, paints, markers, and so on.
◆ For information about organisms, students can consult nature magazines and refererence books.

Launching the Project Allow time for students to read the description of the project in their texts and the Chapter 7 Project Overview on pages 84–85 in Unit 2 Resources. To begin the project, allow students to work with others and think about various adaptations. Suggest that they skim the chapter, books, and magazines to help them think about the ways vertebrates and invertebrates are different. Students can discuss the characteristics that allow vertebrates and invertebrates to move, feed, and protect

CHAPTER 7 PROJECT

Animal Adaptations

The chameleon sits still on a twig, as if frozen. Suddenly, the chameleon's long tongue shoots out and captures an unsuspecting cricket, pulling the insect into its mouth. Watch any animal for a few minutes and you will see many ways in which the animal's structure enables it to function in its environment. How does the animal capture food, escape from predators, or obtain oxygen? To help answer these questions, you will create models of two different animals—an invertebrate and a vertebrate—and show how each is adapted to the environment in which it lives.

Your Goal To construct three-dimensional models of an invertebrate and a vertebrate that show how the structure of each is adapted to carry out an essential life function in its environment.

To complete the project successfully, you must
◆ select one important structural characteristic to show
◆ build a three-dimensional model of each animal, showing how the structural characteristic carries out its function
◆ include a poster that explains how each animal's structure is suited to its environment
◆ follow the safety guidelines in Appendix A

Get Started Pair up with a classmate and share what you already know about animals. Discuss the following questions: Where do these organisms live? How do they move around? How do they protect themselves? Begin thinking about the characteristics that you would like to model.

Check Your Progress You'll be working on this project as you study this chapter. To keep your project on track, look for Check Your Progress boxes at the following points:

Section 1 Review, page 220: Select two animals to model.
Section 4 Review, page 236: Assemble materials and begin construction.
Section 5 Review, page 245: Finish the models. Begin your poster.

Present Your Project At the end of the chapter (page 259), you will display your models and poster.

TEKS

In addition to process TEKS, this chapter addresses these concept TEKS as they relate to the chapter's topics.

(6.10) The student knows the relationship between structure and function in living systems. The student is expected to:
(A) differentiate between structure and function;
(B) determine that all organisms are composed of cells that carry on functions to sustain life; and
(C) identify how structure complements function at different levels of organization including organs, organ systems, organisms, and populations.

(6.12) The student knows that the responses of organisms are caused by external and internal stimuli. The student is expected to:
(A) identify responses in organisms to internal stimuli such as hunger or thirst;
(B) identify responses in organisms to external stimuli such as the presence or absence of heat or light.

217

---

themselves. Suggest that students choose adaptations that are quite different from those of other students. To make sure everyone is on track and understands the project, you may wish to hold a class discussion after this brainstorming period. Before they construct their models, students should sketch the design and think about the materials they will need to complete the model. Where appropriate, suggest that students model only a part of the organisms. For example, if they are modeling feeding behaviors, they could model the mouths. Pass out copies of the Chapter 7 Project Worksheets on pages 86–87 in Unit 2 Resources for students to review.

You could have students work in small groups as a cooperative learning task. To ensure that every student will have ample opportunity to participate in model planning and building, each group should consist of three to four students.

Program Resources

◆ **Unit 2 Resources** Chapter 7 Project Teacher Notes, pp. 82–83; Chapter 7 Project Overview and Worksheets, pp. 84–85

Media and Technology

 Student Edition on Audio CD
English-Spanish, Chapter 7

WEB ACTIVITY www.phschool.com

You will find an Internet activity, chapter self-tests for students, and links to other chapter topics at this site.

Performance Assessment

The Chapter 7 Project Scoring Rubric on page 88 of Unit 2 Resources will help you evaluate how well students complete the Chapter 7 Project. You may wish to share the scoring rubric with your students so they are clear about what is expected of them. Students will be assessed on
◆ the thoroughness of their research into the adaptation that they model, and the appropriateness and accuracy of their sketches;
◆ the size, proportion, and accuracy of their models;
◆ the clarity and thoroughness of their posters;
◆ the thoroughness and organization of their presentations.

SECTION 1 What Is an Animal?

TEKS: 6.2B, C; 6.10A, B, C; 6.12A, B

Objectives

After completing the lesson, students will be able to
◆ describe four major characteristics of animals;
◆ explain how animals reproduce;
◆ describe the relationship between animal body structures and functions;
◆ differentiate between a vertebrate and an invertebrate.

1 Engage/Explore

Activating Prior Knowledge

Ask: **What does an animal look like? How is it different from a flower or a tree?** Have students brainstorm ideas. Have students sketch an animal on a piece of paper and list three things that make it an animal. (*Sample answer: An animal must eat other living things.*) Lead students to realize that there is tremendous diversity among animals.

 DISCOVER

Skills Focus forming operational definitions
Materials *organisms that students can safely observe such as earthworms, minnows, pill bugs, crickets, potted plants, ferns, and sponges*
Time 15 minutes
Tips Make sure students record whether or not each specimen is an animal while looking at that specimen. Ask students to give at least one reason for their choice. Invite them to discuss their decisions in small groups. Remind students to treat all living things with care.
Expected Outcome Students should recognize animals such as earthworms and minnows. They may not recognize sponges as animals.
Think It Over Students may note behavioral characteristics such as eating and movement or physical features such as mouths, hair, legs, fins, or wings.

SECTION 1 What Is an Animal?

DISCOVER · ACTIVITY

Is It an Animal?

1. Carefully examine each of the organisms that your teacher gives you.
2. Decide which ones are animals. Think about the reasons for your decision. Wash your hands after handling each of the organisms.

Think It Over
Forming Operational Definitions What characteristics did you use to decide whether each organism was an animal?

GUIDE FOR READING

◆ What characteristics do all animals have in common?
◆ How are structure and function related in an animal's body?

Reading Tip Before you begin to read, write your own definition of *animal*. Add to it or change it as you read.

Key Terms adaptation • herbivore • carnivore • predator • prey • omnivore • invertebrate • vertebrate

A hairy, brown tarantula lurks silently in its burrow under the ground. A beetle walks above the burrow, unaware of the danger. Suddenly the huge spider jumps out of its burrow, grabs the beetle, and injects venom into the beetle's body. Soon the beetle will be the tarantula's dinner.

Characteristics of Animals

Both the fast-moving tarantula and the unlucky beetle are animals. All species of animals are similar in some important ways. **Animals are many-celled organisms whose cells are specialized to carry on functions that sustain life. All animals are heterotrophs. In addition, most animals reproduce sexually and can move from place to place.**

Like all living things, animals must obtain everything they need, such as food, water, and oxygen, from their environment. To survive, animals also need to avoid danger. To reproduce, they must find mates. In accomplishing these tasks, animals respond to both external and internal stimuli. For example, when an animal senses danger in its environment, it responds by moving away. When the animal experiences the internal stimulus of thirst or hunger, it responds by drinking water or eating food.

◀ Tarantula

218

READING STRATEGIES

Reading Tip When defining the term *animal*, students may find it helpful to list some characteristics they have noticed in animals. Remind students to modify their definitions as they read. Suggest that they note the material under *Characteristics of Animals* to help them add to their definitions.

Study and Comprehension Have students outline the main ideas of the section. Outlines should include the characteristics of animals (multicellular, heterotroph, sexual reproduction, movement); how animals reproduce; structure and function in animals; and classification of animals.

218

Figure 1 Animals have different methods of obtaining food. **(A)** A carpet snake uses its body to strangle a lizard for a meal. **(B)** A macaw uses its curved beak to feed on fruits and seeds.

How Animals Reproduce

Animals typically reproduce sexually. A male sperm cell and a female egg cell unite, producing a new individual. Some animals can also reproduce asexually. A tiny animal called a hydra, for example, reproduces asexually by forming buds that eventually break off to form new hydras.

Structure and Function in Animals

Animals' bodies and behaviors are adapted to their environments. An **adaptation** is a characteristic that helps an organism survive in its environment and reproduce. **Many animal body structures are adaptations that enable the animal to perform specific functions.** A box turtle, for example, has a strong, tough shell that helps the animal protect itself. The light-producing structures of fireflies function to attract mates.

Adaptations for Getting Food Every animal is a heterotroph—it must obtain food by eating other organisms. Some animals, **herbivores,** eat only plants. Grasshoppers, termites, cows, horses, and pandas are herbivores. Animals such as wolves and spiders that only eat other animals are **carnivores.** Many carnivores are **predators** that hunt and kill other animals, their **prey.** An animal that eats both plants and animals is an **omnivore.** Grizzly bears are omnivores. They eat berries and roots, as well as insects, fish, and other small animals.

Animals have adaptations for obtaining the kinds of food they eat. Wolves, for example, run down their prey. A wolf's adaptations include sharp claws, speed, and excellent hearing and eyesight. The mouths of insects are adapted for highly specific ways of getting food. For example, a bee has a bristly tongue that laps nectar from flowers, and a mosquito has sharp mouthparts for jabbing skin and sucking the blood that it feeds on.

✓ *Checkpoint* *What is the term for an animal that eats only plants?*

Media and Technology

Life Science Videodisc
Unit 3, Side 1,
"Through Their Eyes"
Chapter 1

Program Resources

◆ **Unit 2 Resources** 7-1 Lesson Plan, p. 89; 7-1 Section Summary, p. 90
◆ **Guided Reading and Study Workbook** 7-1

Answers to Self-Assessment

 Checkpoint

An herbivore is an animal that eats only plants.

---

 2 Facilitate

Characteristics of Animals

Using the Visuals: Figure 1

Draw students' attention to Figure 1. Then ask: **Does this figure show animals? How can you tell?** Elicit information on what characteristics students used to form their answer. **learning modality: visual**

How Animals Reproduce

Building Inquiry Skills: Comparing and Contrasting

Ask students for one similarity and one difference between sexual and asexual reproduction. *(Similarity: offspring result; difference: sexual reproduction—two parents needed; asexual—one parent needed.)* **learning modality: logical/mathematical**

Structure and Function in Animals

Including All Students

For the benefit of students who are learning English, contrast the meanings, spellings, and pronunciations of *predator* and *prey.* Point out that both words derive from the Latin word *praedari,* meaning "to plunder." **limited English proficiency**

Ongoing Assessment

Skills Check Have students make a compare/contrast chart to compare the processes of sexual reproduction and asexual reproduction.

219

Classification of Animals

Using the Visuals: Figure 2

Ask students to classify the sea turtle and gannet as vertebrates or invertebrates and to support their classifications. *(Both are vertebrates because they have backbones.)* **learning modality: visual**

3 Assess

Section 1 Review Answers

1. Multicellular; obtain food by eating other organisms (heterotrophic)
2. The strong, tough shell of a box turtle protects its body.
3. An invertebrate, such as a jellyfish, does not have a backbone. A vertebrate, such as a frog, has a backbone.
4. Responding to external stimuli helps animals survive by finding food and escaping danger.

Check Your Progress   CHAPTER PROJECT

Review and approve students' adaptation and animal choices. Make sure that the adaptations they have chosen can be easily modeled for the vertebrate and for the invertebrate. Help students locate reference sources.

Performance Assessment

Oral Presentation Provide students with magazines or books containing photographs of animals. Ask each student to choose a photograph of an animal. Have students present their photographs to the class and describe at least two characteristics a scientist would use to classify the organism as an animal. Then show students a plant or a photograph of a plant. Ask them to explain why that organism is *not* an animal.

Figure 2 Animals move in different ways. A green sea turtle (left) swims, while a gannet (right) flies. *Applying Concepts How is the turtle's leg structure adapted for moving in water?*

How Animals Move At some point in their lives, most animals can move freely. Many animal movements are related to obtaining food, reproducing, or escaping danger. Animals have various structures that function in movement. For example, earthworms have muscles for burrowing through the soil. Birds and insects have wings for flying. Long hind legs and powerful leg muscles enable frogs to leap.

Classification of Animals

Remember that biologists classify living things into six kingdoms, and that one of these is the animal kingdom. Within the animal kingdom there are about 35 phyla, or large groups.

One important characteristic used to classify animals is the presence or absence of a backbone. An animal that does not have a backbone is called an **invertebrate.** Jellyfishes, worms, snails, crabs, spiders, and insects are all invertebrates. Most animal species—about 95 percent—are invertebrates. In contrast, a **vertebrate** is an animal that has a backbone. Fishes, amphibians, reptiles, birds, and mammals are all vertebrates.

Section 1 Review

1. Describe two characteristics of all animals.
2. In what way is the structure of a box turtle's body adapted to function in protecting the turtle?
3. Define *invertebrate* and *vertebrate*. Give an example of each.
4. **Thinking Critically Applying Concepts** Why is it important for animals to be able to respond to stimuli in their external environment?

Check Your Progress   CHAPTER PROJECT

By now you should be narrowing your choices for the two animals to model. Remember that you need to choose one invertebrate and one vertebrate. (*Hint:* Skim Sections 3 through 6 in this chapter for ideas for animals that you might model.)

Program Resources

◆ **Unit 2 Resources** 7-1 Review and Reinforce, p. 91; 7-1 Enrich, p. 92

Answers to Self-Assessment

Caption Question

Figure 2 The broad, flat leg allows the turtle to push water aside, propelling itself forward.

SECTION 2 Symmetry

DISCOVER

How Many Ways Can You Fold It?

1. Trace the triangle at left onto a sheet of paper and cut it out. Then draw a circle by tracing the rim of a glass or other round object. Cut out the circle.

2. Fold the triangle so that one half matches the other. Do the same with the circle.

3. See how many different ways you can fold each figure so that the two halves are identical.

Think It Over

Classifying Can you think of animals whose body shape could be folded in the same number of ways as the triangle? As the circle?

As they flit gracefully and delicately over a meadow, brightly colored butterflies are a beautiful sight on a sunny afternoon. As you can see in Figure 3, a large copper butterfly's body has two halves, and each half looks almost like a reflection of the other. A balanced arrangement, called symmetry, is characteristic of all complex animals. **Two kinds of symmetry—bilateral and radial—are found in animals.** The butterfly has bilateral symmetry. An object has **bilateral symmetry,** or line symmetry, if you could draw a line that would divide it into halves that are mirror images.

Unlike a butterfly, a sea anemone is circular if you look at it from the top. Any line drawn through its center will divide the sea anemone into two symmetrical halves. The sea anemone exhibits **radial symmetry**—it has many lines of symmetry that all go through a central point. You can see this in Figure 4 on the next page.

☑ *Checkpoint* How is radial symmetry different from bilateral symmetry?

GUIDE FOR READING

◆ What types of symmetry do complex animals exhibit?

Reading Tip Before you read, preview Figures 3 and 4. Write a few sentences comparing and contrasting the organisms in the illustrations.

Key Terms bilateral symmetry • radial symmetry

Figure 3 If you could draw a line through this butterfly's body, it would divide the animal into two mirror-image halves.
Applying Concepts What is this balanced arrangement called?

SECTION 2 Symmetry

TEKS: 6.2B; 6.10A, B, C

Objective

After completing the lesson, students will be able to

◆ distinguish between bilateral and radial symmetry, and describe how animals exhibit these kinds of symmetry.

1 Engage/Explore

Activating Prior Knowledge

Bring to class a selection of bilaterally symmetrical and asymmetrical shapes, pictures, or objects such as leaves, shells, keys, gloves, and scissors. Show students each object, then sort the objects into two groups—symmetrical and asymmetrical.

DISCOVER

Skills Focus classifying
Materials *tracing paper, scissors, pen or pencil, circular object*
Time 10 minutes
Tips Suggest that students first determine how many ways the triangle can be folded before they attempt to fold the circle.
Expected Outcome The triangle can be folded one way into identical halves, and that the circle could be folded in an infinite number of ways.
Think It Over Triangle: butterflies, tigers, and dogs. Circle: sea urchin and jellyfish.

2 Facilitate

Animals with Radial Symmetry

Building Inquiry Skills: Applying Concepts

Have students identify objects that have radial symmetry. (*Plate, wheel, pie, starfish*)

221

READING STRATEGIES

Reading Tip Comparisons will probably focus on the overall structures of the animals: the butterfly has a distinct front end, and its body consists of two similar halves, while the sea anemone is round and does not have a front end. Have students update their comparisons as they read and learn new content.

Answers to Self-Assessment

Caption Question
Figure 3 bilateral symmetry

☑ *Checkpoint*
A radially symmetrical shape has many lines of symmetry. A bilaterally symmetrical shape has one line of symmetry.

Animals with Bilateral Symmetry

3 Assess

Section 2 Review Answers

1. Bilateral or radial symmetry. An object has bilateral symmetry if one line can be drawn that divides it into two symmetrical halves. It has radial symmetry if any line drawn through the center divides it into two symmetrical halves.
2. Animals with radial symmetry live in water, do not move fast or at all, and have food brought to them.
3. Students' drawings should show a bilaterally symmetrical animal with the line of symmetry marked.
4. Sense organs at the front allow predators to sense prey in front of them. They move quickly and efficiently.

Science at Home

Ask students to list the advantages of having a distinct front end. Suggest students show their lists to a family member when explaining bilateral symmetry.

Performance Assessment

Drawing Have each student sketch two familiar objects or living things in the classroom. One should be bilaterally symmetrical, the other radially symmetrical. Ask students to mark the line of bilateral symmetry on the first sketch and the center point on the second sketch.

 Students can save their sketches in their portfolios.

Animals With Radial Symmetry

Animals such as sea anemones, corals, and jellyfish have radial symmetry. The external body parts of these animals are equally spaced around a central point, like spokes on a bicycle wheel. Because of the circular arrangement of their parts, radially symmetrical animals do not have distinct front or back ends.

Animals with radial symmetry have several characteristics in common. All of them live in water. Most of them do not move very fast—either they stay in one spot, are moved along by water currents, or creep along the bottom. Few radially symmetrical animals are able to go out in search of prey. Instead, their watery environment carries food to them.

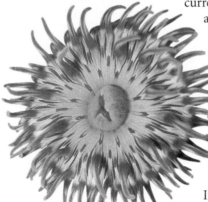

Figure 4 Sea anemones have radial symmetry. A radially symmetrical object has many lines of symmetry that all go through a central point.

Animals With Bilateral Symmetry

Most animals you are familiar with, such as fishes, worms, and insects, have bilateral symmetry. For example, a fish has only one line of symmetry that divides it into mirror images. Each half of a fish has one eye, one nostril, half of a mouth, and one of each of the fish's pairs of fins. Your body also has bilateral symmetry.

In general, bilaterally symmetrical animals are larger and more complex than those with radial symmetry. Animals with bilateral symmetry have a front end that goes first as the animal moves along. Their bilaterally symmetrical structure enables them to move more quickly and efficiently than most animals with radial symmetry. This is partly because bilaterally symmetrical animals have sense organs in their front ends that function to pick up information about what is in front of them. Swift movement and sense organs help bilaterally symmetrical animals get food and avoid enemies.

Section 2 Review

1. What two types of symmetry do complex animals exhibit? Describe each type.
2. What are the characteristics of radially symmetrical animals?
3. Draw a view of a bilaterally symmetrical animal that shows its symmetry. Draw the line of symmetry.
4. **Thinking Critically Relating Cause and Effect** How does a bilaterally symmetrical structure help a predator catch prey?

222

Science at Home

Front-End Advantages With a family member, observe as many different animals as possible in your yard or at a park. Look in lots of different places, such as in the grass, under rocks, and in the air. Explain to your family member the advantage to an animal of having a distinct front end. What is this type of body arrangement called?

SECTION 3 Sponges, Cnidarians, Worms, and Mollusks

DISCOVER •••••••••••••••••••••• ACTIVITY

How Do Natural and Synthetic Sponges Compare?

1. Examine a natural sponge, and then use a hand lens or a microscope to take a closer look at its surface. Look carefully at the holes in the sponge. Draw what you see through the lens.

2. ✂ Cut out a small piece of sponge and examine it with a hand lens. Draw what you see.

3. Repeat Steps 1 and 2 with a synthetic kitchen sponge.

Think It Over

Observing What are three ways a natural and synthetic sponge are similar? What are three ways they are different?

Sponges don't look or act like most animals you know. In fact, they are so different that for a long time, people thought that sponges were plants. Like plants, adult sponges stay in one place. But unlike most plants, sponges take food into their bodies, which qualifies them for membership in the animal kingdom.

Characteristics of Sponges

You might use a brightly colored synthetic sponge to mop up a spill. That sponge is filled with holes, and so are the animals called sponges. **The body of a sponge is something like a bag that is pierced all over with openings called pores. The pores are important in functions such as reproducing and obtaining food and oxygen.** Most sponges have irregular shapes without symmetry. While some of their cells do specialized jobs, sponges lack the tissues and organs that most other animals have.

A sponge obtains everything it needs, including food and oxygen, from water that enters its body through its pores. Water flows from the pores into a central cavity. There, the sponge's cells take in oxygen from the water. Food particles in the water, including tiny organisms such as bacteria and protists, are trapped by cells that line the sponge's central cavity. Water then leaves the sponge through one large opening. Water that leaves the sponge carries waste materials away.

Pink sponges on a
Caribbean coral reef ▶

GUIDE FOR READING

◆ How are structure and function related in sponges and cnidarians?

◆ What are the three main groups of worms?

◆ What is the structure of a mollusk like?

Reading Tip As you read, create a compare/contrast table about sponges, cnidarians, worms, and mollusks. Indicate whether each kind of animal has specialized tissues and organs.

Key Terms cnidarian • anus • mollusk • gills • radula

READING STRATEGIES

Reading Tip Suggest that students set up their compare/contrast tables before they read. A sample table is shown. Encourage students to read their completed charts as a way to review the section.

Characteristic	Sponges	Cnidarians	Worms	Mollusks
Body plan	Asymmetrical	Radial symmetry	Bilateral symmetry	Bilateral symmetry
Feeding methods				
Specialized tissues				
Organs				

SECTION 3 Sponges, Cnidarians, Worms, and Mollusks

TEKS: 6.1A; 6.2A, B, C, D; 6.4A; 6.10A, B, C; 6.12B

Objectives

After completing the lesson, students will be able to

◆ relate structure and function in sponges and cnidarians;

◆ identify the three main groups of worms;

◆ describe the structure of a mollusk.

1 Engage/Explore

Activating Prior Knowledge

Bring in a basin of water and a sponge. Ask students to tell you ways sponges are used around the house. (*Mopping floors, wiping up spills, washing dishes*) Ask: **What feature of sponges makes them useful?** (*They soak up liquids.*) Inform students that natural sponges were once live animals, and that divers have harvested sponges for thousands of years.

••••••••• DISCOVER ••••••••

Skills Focus observing ACTIVITY
Materials *natural sponges, synthetic kitchen sponges, scissors, hand lens or microscope*
Time 20 minutes
Tips Natural sponges can often be found in cosmetic departments or can be ordered from a biological supply house. Direct students' attention to the pores on the surfaces of the sponges. Tell them that pores in a natural sponge are the openings of pathways through the sponge. Openings on a synthetic sponge are not connected by regular pathways. Students can draw diagrams to compare and contrast features of natural and synthetic sponges.
Expected Outcome Students will observe similarities and differences between natural and artificial sponges.
Think It Over Both have pores, hold liquid, and are soft. They are different in material, color, texture, and shape.

2 Facilitate

Characteristics of Sponges

Building Inquiry Skills: Observing

Materials *large plastic beaker, water, plastic dropper, food coloring, clock or watch*
Time 20 minutes
Place students in groups and invite them to investigate how oxygen in the water diffuses into a sponge's cells. First have them fill a beaker three-quarters full of water and allow the water to stand for 2 minutes. Then put eight drops of food coloring into the water. Ask students to describe what the food coloring looks like as it enters the water. *(The food coloring is dark and concentrated at the point it enters the beaker.)* Have students observe the water every 2 minutes over a 10-minute period. Ask: **What happened to the food coloring?** *(The food coloring spread evenly throughout the water.)* Tell students the way the food coloring spreads throughout the water is diffusion, and is similar to the way oxygen in water diffuses into a sponge's cells. **learning modality: visual**

Cnidarians

Skills Focus observing
Materials *live hydra, small glass bowl or petri dish, hand lens or microscope, toothpicks*
Time 25 minutes
Tips You can order hydras from a biological supply house. Guide students to observe characteristics of a cnidarian.
Expected Outcome The hydras will respond by wrapping their tentacles around the toothpick.
Observing It moves from place to place in a somersaulting fashion.
Extend Ask if anyone sees a hydra with a bulb or bud developing on its stalk. If so, explain that the hydra is reproducing asexually. **learning modality: visual**

Hydra Doing?
In this activity, you will observe hydras in action.

1. Put a drop of water that contains hydras in a small unbreakable bowl or petri dish. Allow it to sit for about 15 minutes.
2. Use a hand lens to examine the hydras as they swim. Then gently touch the tentacles of a hydra with the end of a toothpick. Watch what happens.
3. Return the hydras to your teacher, and wash your hands.

Observing Describe a hydra's method of movement.

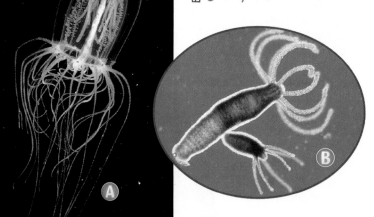

A

B

A sponge the size of a teacup is able to remove food from about 5,000 liters of water per day. That's enough water to fill a truckload of two-liter soft-drink bottles!

Cnidarians

Jellyfishes, sea anemones, hydras, and corals are cnidarians. **Cnidarians** (nih DAIR ee uhnz) are soft-bodied, radially symmetrical invertebrates that have long, wavy tentacles arranged around an opening called a mouth. The tentacles are covered with stinging cells. **Cnidarians are carnivores that use stinging cells to capture their prey and to defend themselves.** Cnidarians reproduce both sexually and asexually.

Cnidarians have two different body plans. A polyp, such as the hydra in Figure 5, is shaped something like a vase and has its mouth opening at the top. A bowl-shaped medusa, such as a jellyfish, has its mouth opening at the bottom.

Structure and Function in Digestion A cnidarian captures its prey by using its stinging cells to inject venom, a poisonous substance that paralyzes fish and other prey. The tentacles then pull the prey into the cnidarian's mouth. From there the food passes into a body cavity where it is digested. Because cnidarians have a digestive system with only one opening, undigested food is expelled through the mouth.

Specialized Tissues Unlike sponges, cnidarians have specialized tissues. For example, muscle-like tissues enable cnidarians to move. Jellyfishes swim through the water, and hydras turn slow somersaults. These movements are directed by nerve cells that are spread out like a spider web, or net. This nerve net helps the cnidarian respond quickly to the external stimuli of danger or the presence of food.

☑ *Checkpoint* *How does a cnidarian obtain and digest food?*

Figure 5 All cnidarians live in watery environments. **(A)** Jellyfishes are cnidarians that live in the ocean. **(B)** Hydras live in freshwater ponds and lakes, where they reproduce by budding.

Program Resources

◆ **Unit 2 Resources** 7-3 Lesson Plan, p. 97; 7-3 Section Summary, p. 98
◆ **Guided Reading and Study Workbook** 7-3

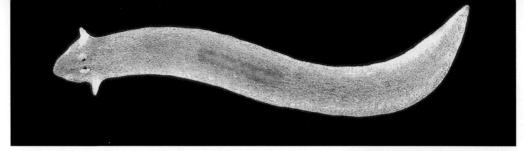

Figure 6 Planarians are flatworms that live in ponds, streams, and oceans. The eyespots on the planarian's head can distinguish between light and dark.
Inferring How is having a distinct front end an advantage to a planarian?

Worms

You might think that all worms are small, slimy, and wiggly. But many worms do not fit that description. Some worms are almost three meters long and are as thick as your arm. Others look like glowing, furry blobs.

Structure of Worms All worms are invertebrates with bilateral symmetry. They all have long, narrow bodies without legs. In addition, all worms have tissues, organs, and organ systems. Unlike sponges or cnidarians, worms have head and tail ends.

Function of a Brain Some kinds of worms have a brain, which is an organ made of nerve tissue located in the head end. A worm's brain and sense organs, such as organs sensitive to light and touch, are part of its nervous system. An animal's nervous system receives stimuli from outside and inside the body. It also directs the way in which the body responds to stimuli.

A worm's nervous system functions to detect and respond quickly to external stimuli such as food, predators, and light. Worms respond to the stimulus of food by moving toward it and eating it. Worms withdraw from predators, and many worms also avoid light.

Flatworms

Biologists classify worms into several phyla. **Three major worm phyla are flatworms, roundworms, and segmented worms. Flatworms have flat bodies, which distinguishes them from roundworms and segmented worms.** A planarian, which is one kind of flatworm, is shown in Figure 6. Planarians feed on smaller animals and decaying material. Planarians rely mainly on smell to locate food.

Roundworms

The next time you walk along a beach, consider that about a million tiny roundworms live in each square meter of damp sand. Roundworms have cylindrical bodies. **Unlike cnidarians or flatworms, roundworms have a digestive system that is like a tube, open at both ends.** Food enters at the animal's mouth.

Worms

Inquiry Challenge

Materials *planarians, small flashlights, transparent containers, bottled water, dark paper or foil*

Time 30 minutes

Tips This activity may also be done as a demonstration. It will work better in a partially darkened room. Divide the class into groups and distribute a petri dish (or other small transparent container) to each group. Place a planarian in each dish and cover it with a few drops of water. Have students predict how the planarians will react to light and record their prediction. Have students cover half the container with paper or foil and then shine the flashlight on the container. Students should observe that the planarians move out of the light.
cooperative grouping

 Students can save their observation notes in their portfolios.

Flatworms

Including All Students

Content Mastery

Point out that the terms *flatworm, roundworm,* and *segmented worm* all describe major visible characteristics of the groups—all flatworms have flat bodies, and so forth. If students know the meanings of the words *flat, round,* and *segmented,* they will also know the major distinguishing characteristics of each group. **limited English proficiency**

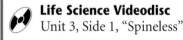
Answers to Self-Assessment

Caption Question

Figure 6 Having a distinct head end is an advantage because the planarian can pick up information about what is in front of it and move forward.

✓ *Checkpoint*

A cnidarian injects venom into its prey. Then it uses its tentacles to pull the food into its mouth. Digestion occurs in the body cavity.

Ongoing Assessment

Writing Ask students describe the function of an animal's nervous system *(Receives stimuli from outside the body; directs the body to respond to stimuli.)*

Roundworms

Including All Students

Some students may need extra help to understand the difference between digestive systems with one or two openings. Show students two cardboard tubes, one open at both ends, the other sealed at one end. Ask: **What animal's digestive system could the sealed tube represent?** *(planarian, cnidarian)* **What animal's digestive system could the open tube represent?** *(roundworm, human, dog)* Show students marbles or small pebbles and tell them these items represent food. Fill the sealed tube with "food." Then pass "food" through the open tube. Lead students to understand that one advantage of a digestive system with two openings is that the animal can continue to eat while food eaten earlier passes through its digestive tract. **learning modality: kinesthetic**

Building Inquiry Skills: Observing

Materials *earthworm, transparent container, construction paper, soil*

Tips Have students observe earthworms in a container of soil. Use soil that is loose and moist. Mist the soil if it starts to dry out. Keep the container out of direct sunlight. Have students wrap the jar walls with dark construction paper. That way the worms, which naturally avoid the light, may burrow along the outside wall of the jar. Have students note the earthworm's location in the soil. Ask: **When the segments at the front end of the worm contract, do the segments at the back end contract at the same time?** *(No, segments contract independently.)* **learning modality: visual**

Figure 7 If you were to look at roundworms such as these under a microscope, you would see their bodies thrashing from side to side.

Wastes exit through an opening, the **anus,** at the far end of the tube. Food travels in one direction through the roundworm's digestive system, as it does in most complex animals.

A one-way digestive system is something like an assembly line, with a different part of the digestive process happening at each place along the line. First food is broken down into small molecules. Then the small food molecules are absorbed into the animal's body. Finally wastes are eliminated.

☑ *Checkpoint* *What is a roundworm's digestive system like?*

Segmented Worms

When you look at an earthworm, you notice that its body seems to consist of a series of rings separated by grooves, something like a vacuum-cleaner hose. **Earthworms and other segmented worms have bodies made up of many linked sections called segments.** In Figure 8, you can see an earthworm's segments, as well as its internal organs. Like roundworms, earthworms have a one-way digestive system with two openings.

The circulatory system of an earthworm consists of blood that is pumped through blood vessels. An earthworm's circulatory system carries needed materials to cells and carries waste products away. Segmented worms have a closed circulatory system. In a closed circulatory system, like your own, blood moves only within a connected network of tubes called blood vessels. In contrast, some animals, such as insects, have an open circulatory system in which blood leaves the blood vessels and sloshes around inside the body. A closed circulatory system can move blood around an animal's body much more quickly than an open circulatory system can.

Figure 8 An earthworm's body is divided into over 100 segments. Some organs are repeated in most segments; others exist in only a few. *Interpreting Diagrams* What is an earthworm's circulatory system like?

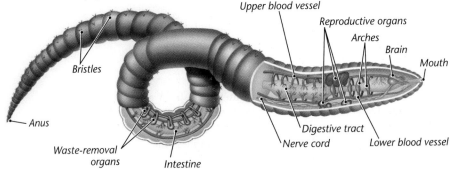

Upper blood vessel

Reproductive organs

Arches

Brain

Mouth

Bristles

Anus

Waste-removal organs

Intestine

Nerve cord

Digestive tract

Lower blood vessel

226

EXPLORING a Snail

Like other gastropods, a snail has a head with sense organs, and it has a wide, muscular foot. The snails shown here live in a pond.

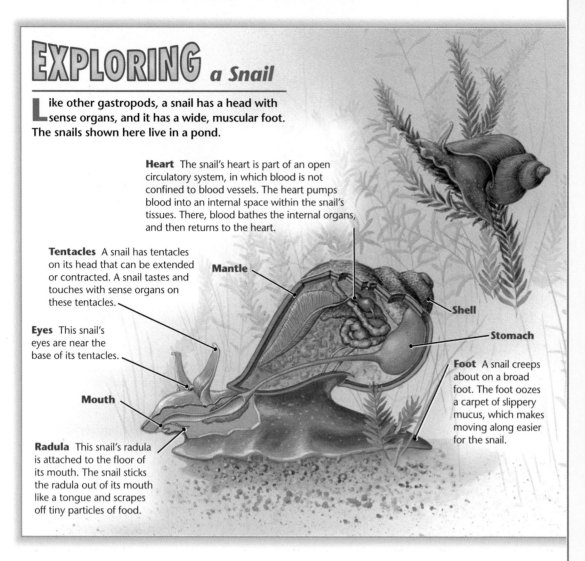

Heart The snail's heart is part of an open circulatory system, in which blood is not confined to blood vessels. The heart pumps blood into an internal space within the snail's tissues. There, blood bathes the internal organs, and then returns to the heart.

Tentacles A snail has tentacles on its head that can be extended or contracted. A snail tastes and touches with sense organs on these tentacles.

Eyes This snail's eyes are near the base of its tentacles.

Mouth

Radula This snail's radula is attached to the floor of its mouth. The snail sticks the radula out of its mouth like a tongue and scrapes off tiny particles of food.

Mantle

Shell

Stomach

Foot A snail creeps about on a broad foot. The foot oozes a carpet of slippery mucus, which makes moving along easier for the snail.

What Are Mollusks?

Snails, clams, and octopuses all belong to the **mollusk** phylum. **Mollusks are invertebrates with soft, unsegmented bodies that are often protected by hard outer shells. In addition, mollusks have a thin layer of tissue called a mantle, which covers their internal organs.** The mantle also produces the mollusk's shell. Most mollusks move with a muscular organ called a foot. You can see the foot of one kind of mollusk in *Exploring a Snail*. The feet of different kinds of mollusks have different structures for various functions, such as crawling, digging, or catching prey.

Answers to Self-Assessment

Caption Question

Figure 8 An earthworm has a closed circulatory system; blood moves only within a network of blood vessels.

☑ *Checkpoint*

A roundworm has a one-way digestive system. Food enters through the mouth, and waste exits through the anus.

What Are Mollusks?

Building Inquiry Skills: Classifying

Have students list the characteristics mollusks and segmented worms have in common and those that are unique to each organism. Then ask: **Based on this information, do you think mollusks and segmented worms are closely related? Why?** *(Answers will vary. Be sure students support their answer.)* **learning modality: logical/mathematical**

Cultural Diversity

Regions with such diverse cultures as Japan, France, and Brazil possess unique methods of flavoring and cooking mollusks, such as oysters, clams, squid, and mussels. Have students research ethnic cookbooks and find out how mollusks are prepared and eaten in different cultures. Students should bring a copy of a recipe to class. If possible, have students prepare the recipes at home and describe the experience of cooking and eating the mollusk dish. **learning modality: tactile/ kinesthetic**

EXPLORING a Snail

Materials *live snails in an aquarium, hand lens*
Time 20 minutes
Tips Reinforce the information presented in the visual essay by allowing students to observe live snails in an aquarium. Ask students to examine the snail in the visual essay and compare to the snails in the aquarium. Caution them not to touch the snails or tap on the sides of the aquarium. Have students look for the parts of the snail that are labeled in the visual essay. *(Students should be able to see the tentacles, mouth, foot, and shell. They may be able to see the eyes.)* **learning modality: visual**

Ongoing Assessment

Writing Have students create a checklist of characteristics that identify an animal as a mollusk.

3 Assess

Section 3 Review Answers

1. A sponge obtains food from the water that enters its pores. Food particles are trapped by cells that line the sponge's central cavity. A cnidarian uses its stinging cells to poison its prey. The tentacles then pull the prey into the cnidarian's mouth, where it passes into a body cavity.

2. Flatworms have flat bodies; roundworms have cylindrical bodies; and segmented worms have bodies made up of many linked sections.

3. Mollusks are invertebrates with soft unsegmented bodies covered by a thin layer of tissue called a mantle. They often have a protective outer shell.

4. The function of gills to is remove oxygen from water. In mollusks, cilia cover the gills, and their beating motion makes water flow over the gills. The gills have a rich supply of blood vessels that take in oxygen from the water.

Science at Home

Ask students which animals they expect to find (*Snails, oysters, clams, squid, canned clams, smoked oysters*). If possible, suggest students visit a seafood store with a large variety of seafood.

ACTIVITY

Performance Assessment

Writing Ask students to write four diary entries, the first from the viewpoint of a sponge, the second from the viewpoint of a cnidarian, the third from the viewpoint of a worm, and the fourth from the viewpoint of a mollusk. Entries should include what and how the animals eat, and a description of the animals' physical features.

 Students can save their diary entries in their portfolios.

228

Figure 9 The octopus (below) and the nudibranch (right) belong to different groups of mollusks. *Applying Concepts What are the major structural characteristics of mollusks?*

Most water-dwelling mollusks have **gills,** organs that remove oxygen from water. The gills are attached to the mantle and have a rich supply of blood vessels. Within these thin-walled blood vessels, oxygen from the surrounding water moves into the blood, while carbon dioxide diffuses out. The gills of most mollusks are covered with tiny hairlike structures called cilia. The beating movement of these cilia makes water flow over the gills.

Many mollusks have a **radula** (RAJ oo luh), which is a flexible ribbon of tiny teeth. Acting like sandpaper, the tiny teeth scrape food from a surface such as a leaf. A radula may have as many as 250,000 teeth.

The shells of mollusks are strong shields that help protect the animals from predators. Some snails withdraw into their shells when conditions are dry and then come out when conditions are moist again. When they are sealed up in this way, snails can survive incredibly long times. In one museum the shells of two land snails, presumed to be dead, were glued to a piece of cardboard. Four years later, when someone put the cardboard in water, one of the snails crawled away!

 Section 3 Review

1. Contrast the ways in which sponges and cnidarians obtain food.
2. List the three major phyla of worms and describe the shapes of the worms' bodies.
3. Describe the bodies of mollusks.
4. **Thinking Critically** **Applying Concepts** What is the function of gills? How does the structure of a mollusk's gills enable them to perform this function?

228

Science at Home

Edible Mollusks Visit a supermarket with a family member. Identify any mollusks that are being sold as food. Be sure to look in places other than the fish counter, such as the canned-foods section. Discuss the parts of the mollusks that are used for food and the parts that are not edible.

Answers to Self-Assessment

Caption Question

Figure 9 Soft, unsegmented bodies; mantle

Program Resources

◆ **Unit 2 Resources** 7-3 Review and Reinforce, p. 99; 7-3 Enrich, p. 100
◆ **Unit 2 Resources** Chapter 7 Skills Lab blackline masters, pp. 113–115

Media and Technology

 Lab Activity Videotapes Grade 6, Tape 2

Earthworm Responses

In this lab, you will make hypotheses about how earthworms respond to the stimuli of moisture and light.

Wet paper towel — *Earthworms* — *Dry paper towel*

Tray

Problem

Do earthworms prefer dry or moist conditions? Do they prefer light or dark conditions?

Materials

plastic dropper	water	cardboard
clock or watch	paper towels	flashlight
2 earthworms	storage container	tray

Procedure

1. Which environment do you think earthworms prefer—dry or moist? Record your hypothesis in your notebook.
2. Use the dropper to sprinkle water on the worms. Keep the worms moist at all times.
3. Fold a dry paper towel and place it on the bottom of one side of your tray. Fold a moistened paper towel and place it on the other side.
4. Moisten your hands. Then place the earthworms in the center of the tray. Make sure that half of each earthworm's body rests on the moist paper towel and half rests on the dry towel. Handle the worms gently.
5. Cover the tray with the piece of cardboard. After five minutes, remove the cardboard and observe whether the worms are on the moist or dry surface. Record your observations.
6. Repeat Steps 4 and 5.
7. Return the earthworms to their storage container. Moisten the earthworms with water.
8. Which do you think earthworms prefer—strong light or darkness? Record your hypothesis in your notebook.
9. Cover the whole surface of the tray with a moistened paper towel.
10. Place the earthworms in the center of the tray. Cover half of the tray with cardboard. Shine a flashlight onto the other half.
11. After five minutes, note the locations of the worms. Record your observations.
12. Repeat Steps 10 and 11.
13. Moisten the earthworms and put them in the location designated by your teacher. Wash your hands after handling the worms.

Analyze and Conclude

1. Which environment did the worms prefer—moist or dry? Bright or dark? Did the worms' behavior support your hypotheses?
2. Explain how the worms' responses to the external stimuli of moisture and light help them survive.
3. **Think About It** What knowledge or experiences helped you make your hypotheses at the start of the experiments?

Design an Experiment

Do earthworms prefer a smooth or rough surface? Write your hypothesis. Then design an experiment to answer the question. Check with your teacher before carrying out your experiment.

Safety

- Handle the earthworms gently.
- Keep the earthworms from drying out by misting them frequently with cool water in a spray bottle.
- Do not leave the earthworms unattended. Return them to their container when you are finished with them.
- Wash your hands after the experiment.
- Review the safety guidelines in Appendix A.

3. A typical response might suggest that earthworms are usually found in dark, moist places.

Extending the Inquiry

Design an Experiment Sample hypothesis: if earthworms can move to either a rough or smooth surface, they will move to the rough surface. To test this hypothesis, students might suggest using a rough surface such as sandpaper on one side of a tray and a smooth surface such as ceramic tile on the other. Remind students that their experiments must only test one factor at a time.

Earthworm Responses

Preparing for Inquiry

Key Concept A hypothesis is a prediction about the outcome of an experiment.
Skills Objective Students will be able to
◆ develop hypotheses.
Time 30 minutes
Advance Planning You can get worms from a biological supply company, a bait shop, or loose garden soil. Keep earthworms moist at all times.
Alternative Materials Cake pans can be used for trays.

Guiding Inquiry

Invitation Ask: **Think about the places you are likely to see an earthworm. Would these places likely be dry or moist?** *(moist)* **Light or dark?** *(dark)*

Introducing the Procedure
◆ Give students time to read through the procedure and ask questions to clarify any steps they do not understand.
◆ Suggest that students conduct a trial before they actually collect data.

Troubleshooting the Experiment
◆ Be sure worms are handled gently. Rough handling can harm the worms and prevent them from moving.
◆ Have students check to make sure their dry paper towel remains dry. If a dry paper towel becomes damp, have the student replace it with a dry towel.

Expected Outcome
◆ The worms generally prefer the moist towel and move toward it.
◆ Worms usually prefer a dark environment and move toward it.

Analyze and Conclude
1. Moist; dark; if students predicted these results, their hypotheses were supported.
2. Sample: Earthworms live in dark, moist soil. They will dry out without water. Light usually means an earthworm is in the sun where it could dry out.

TEKS: 6.2A, B, C; 6.3C; 6.10A, C; 6.12A, B

Objectives

After completing this lesson, students will be able to

♦ describe the structures characteristic of arthropods;

♦ describe the structures that characterize insects;

♦ identify the characteristics of echinoderms.

1 Engage/Explore

Activating Prior Knowledge

Ask students whether they have ever seen spiders, scorpions, insects, crabs, sea stars, or sand dollars. Ask volunteers to describe these animals. Use leading questions to prompt students to mention the external shells or spiny skins of these animals. Tell students that the features they described are characteristics of arthropods and echinoderms, which they will learn about in this section.

DISCOVER

Skills Focus inferring
Materials *sheets of heavy cardboard, about 30 × 45 cm; tape*
Time 15 minutes
Tips Use cardboard that is flexible enough to roll into a tube and tape that is strong enough to stay attached when students attempt to bend their elbows. Students whose partners already have an arm wrapped in cardboard will need assistance when putting on their own tubes.
Expected Outcome Students will find that restricting their joints makes it impossible for them to bend their elbows.
Think It Over Joints in skeletons allow movement.

DISCOVER •••••••••••••••••••••••••• ACTIVITY

Will It Bend and Move?

1. Have a partner roll a piece of cardboard around your arm to form a tube that covers your elbow. Your partner should put three pieces of tape around the tube to hold it closed—one at each end and one in the middle.

2. With the tube in place, try to write your name on a piece of paper. Then try to scratch your head.

3. Keep the tube on your arm for 10 minutes. Observe how the tube affects your ability to do things.

Think It Over

Inferring Insects and many other animals have rigid skeletons on the outside of their bodies. Why do their skeletons need joints?

GUIDE FOR READING

♦ What structures characterize arthropods?

♦ What combination of structures characterizes insects?

♦ What are typical echinoderm characteristics?

Reading Tip Before you read, rewrite the headings in this section as questions. Write answers to the questions as you read.

Key Terms arthropod
• exoskeleton • insect • thorax
• abdomen • metamorphosis
• larva • pupa • nymph
• crustacean • arachnid
• echinoderm • endoskeleton

Every September, thousands of visitors pass through central Texas. These visitors are monarch butterflies, flying southward toward their winter home in Mexico. Some fly thousands of kilometers before they reach their destination. The monarch butterflies that make this long journey have never been to Mexico before. But somehow they find their way to the same trees where their ancestors spent the previous winter.

The Arthropod Phylum

Monarch butterflies, which are insects, belong to the **arthropod** phylum. **An arthropod is a bilaterally symmetrical invertebrate with a structure that includes an external skeleton, a segmented body, and jointed attachments called appendages.** Wings, mouthparts, and legs are all appendages. In addition, arthropods have open circulatory systems—the blood leaves the blood vessels and bathes the internal organs.

A Skeleton on the Outside If you were an arthropod, you would be completely covered by a waterproof shell. This tough **exoskeleton,** or outer skeleton, functions to protect the animal and help prevent evaporation of water. As an arthropod grows larger, its skeleton cannot expand. Arthropods solve this problem by occasionally shedding their exoskeletons and growing new ones that are larger. The process of shedding an outgrown exoskeleton is called molting.

READING STRATEGIES

Reading Tip Pair students after they have read the sections and rewritten the headings. Have them try to answer each other's questions without referring to the section. Then have students compare answers and check them with the text. Sample question: What are the important characteristics of the arthropod phylum? What are insects like?

Vocabulary Point out that both *pod* in arthropod and *pede* in centipede come from roots meaning "foot." *Podos* is a Greek root, *ped* is Latin. Challenge students to think of more words containing these roots. (*Sample: tripod, pedal, pedestal*)

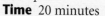

Figure 10 Some arthropods, like the Sally lightfoot crab at left, have a hard exoskeleton. Others, like the Promethea moth caterpillar below, have a leathery exoskeleton. *Making Generalizations What role does an exoskeleton play?*

Segmented Bodies Arthropods' bodies are segmented, something like an earthworm's. The segmented body plan is easiest to see in centipedes and millipedes, which have bodies made up of many identical-looking segments. You can also see segments on the tails of shrimp and lobsters.

In some groups of arthropods, several body segments are joined into distinct sections, with each section specialized to perform specific functions. Figure 11 shows the number of body sections and other physical characteristics that are typical of the three largest groups of arthropods.

Appendages Just as your fingers are jointed appendages attached to your palms, many arthropods have jointed appendages, such as legs, attached to their bodies. The jointed structure of appendages gives the animal flexibility and enables it to move. Some arthropod appendages are highly specialized. For example, many arthropods, including lobsters, crayfish, and insects, have antennae (singular *antenna*). An antenna is an appendage on the head that contains sense organs. A crayfish's antennae have organs for smelling, tasting, touching, and keeping balance. The balance-sensing structures enable a crayfish to respond to internal stimuli that indicate the position of the crayfish's body.

Figure 11 Arthropod groups differ in the numbers of body sections, legs, and antennae, and in where the animals are found.

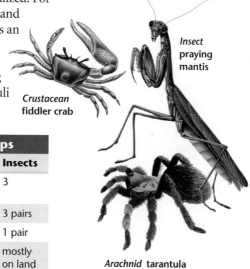

Crustacean **fiddler crab**

Insect **praying mantis**

Arachnid **tarantula**

Comparisons of the Largest Arthropod Groups

Characteristic	Crustaceans	Arachnids	Insects
Number of body sections	2 or 3	2	3
Number of legs	5 or more pairs	4 pairs	3 pairs
Number of antennae	2 pairs	none	1 pair
Where found?	in water or damp places	mostly on land	mostly on land

Program Resources

◆ **Unit 2 Resources** 7-4 Lesson Plan, p. 101; 7-4 Section Summary, p. 102
◆ **Guided Reading and Study Workbook** 7-4

Media and Technology

 Transparencies "Structure of a Grasshopper," Transparency 31

Answers to Self-Assessment

Caption Question

Figure 10 An exoskeleton prevents water loss and provides protection.

2 Facilitate

The Arthropod Phylum

Including All Students

Materials *fresh or frozen whole crab leg; whole shrimp with head.*
ACTIVITY
Time 20 minutes
Tips Some students may need extra help to identify the features of an arthropod's exoskeleton. Allow them to handle and examine the two specimens. Help students see that both exoskeletons are jointed. Make sure students wash their hands after handling the specimens.
Extend Have students compare the exoskeleton of the shrimp to that of the crab. Ask students: **Which of the two animals has the more flexible exoskeleton?** *(Shrimp)* **The stronger exoskeleton?** *(Crab)* **learning modality: tactile/kinesthetic**

Including All Students

To help students remember the meaning of *exoskeleton*, point out that *external* and *exoskeleton* both begin with *ex.* Explain that the prefixes *ex-* and *exo-* may mean "outside." Have students think of other words that begin with these prefixes. *(Exit, expedition)* **limited English proficiency**

Using the Visuals: Figure 11

Divide the class into groups. Assign each group two of the arthropod groups in the table—for example, crustaceans and insects. Students in each group should then work together to create Venn diagrams comparing and contrasting the two arthropod groups. In addition to using the information in Figure 11, encourage students to look ahead to the parts of this section that describe those groups. **cooperative learning**

Ongoing Assessment

Writing Have students describe three characteristics of arthropods. *(Invertebrates; have jointed appendages, exoskeletons, segmented bodies, open circulatory systems)*

231

Insects

Building Inquiry Skills: Interpreting Diagrams

Obtain intact dead grasshoppers from a pet or bait shop. Have students review each external feature from Figure 12 and work together to identify that feature on their specimens. Students should wash hands after finishing. **cooperative learning**

Addressing Naive Conceptions

Students may think spiders are insects. Ask: **How can you identify an animal as an insect by looking at its body?** (*If it is an insect, it has three body sections.*) Show students pictures of spiders and have them try to identify the head, thorax, and abdomen. Ask: **Are these animals insects?** (*No*) **How do you know?** (*They have only two body sections.*) **learning modality: visual**

Building Inquiry Skills: Comparing and Contrasting

Content Mastery

Have students make Venn diagrams to compare and contrast gradual and complete metamorphosis. **learning modality: logical/mathematical**

Real-Life Learning

Have students work in groups to list examples of insect feeding behavior—and its results—that they might notice around their homes. (*Examples: insect pests on house plants; fruit flies on fruit; termites; moths on wool clothing; fleas on pets; weevils in flour; ants in food left out*) **cooperative learning**

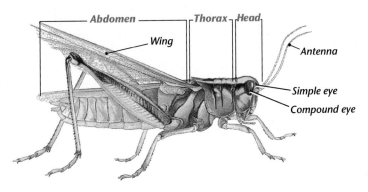

Figure 12 A grasshopper's body, like that of every insect, consists of three sections.
Interpreting Diagrams To which section are a grasshopper's legs attached?

Labels: Abdomen, Thorax, Head, Wing, Antenna, Simple eye, Compound eye

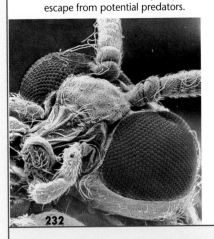

Figure 13 Most insects, like this black fly, have compound eyes with many lenses. Because compound eyes are very effective at seeing movement, insects can quickly escape from potential predators.

232

Insects

Scientists have identified about 875,000 different species of arthropods, and there are probably many more that have not yet been discovered. The major groups of arthropods are insects, crustaceans, arachnids, centipedes, and millipedes. The largest arthropod group is the insects.

Characteristics of Insects A butterfly is an **insect,** as are dragonflies, cockroaches, and bees. **Insects are arthropods with three body sections, six legs, one pair of antennae, and usually one or two pairs of wings.** Sense organs, such as the eyes and antennae, are located on an insect's head. The three body regions are the head, thorax, and abdomen. An insect's **thorax,** or midsection, is the section to which wings and legs are attached. The **abdomen** contains many of the insect's internal organs. You can see all three body sections on the grasshopper in Figure 12.

From Egg to Adult Insects begin life as tiny, hard-shelled, fertilized eggs. After they hatch, insects develop into adults through **metamorphosis** (met uh MAWR fuh sis), a process in which an animal's body undergoes dramatic changes in form. As you can see in *Exploring Insect Metamorphosis*, each insect species undergoes one of two different types of metamorphosis. Complete metamorphosis has four dramatically different stages—egg, larva, pupa, and adult. A **larva** is an immature form of an animal that looks very different from an adult. Insect larvae usually look something like worms. After a time, a larva becomes a **pupa** (plural *pupae*). During the pupal stage, the insect is enclosed in a protective covering and gradually changes into the adult form.

In gradual metamorphosis, there is no distinctly different larval stage. An egg hatches into a stage called a **nymph,** which often resembles the adult insect. A nymph may molt several times before becoming an adult.

☑ *Checkpoint* List the stages of complete metamorphosis.

Background

History of Science Entomology, or the study of insects, was extremely popular in Europe during the 1800s. The French scientist Jean Henri Fabre (1823–1915) became renowned for his study of the structure and behavior of insects. Fabre studied social insects such as bees and wasps as well as other insects, observing them in their natural environments. One of his discoveries involved the predation of stinging wasps. Fabre found that wasps target their stingers for their prey's nerve centers so that the prey becomes paralyzed and cannot move. This allows the wasp to save the prey for later. The work of Henri Fabre greatly enhanced understanding and appreciation of these insects.

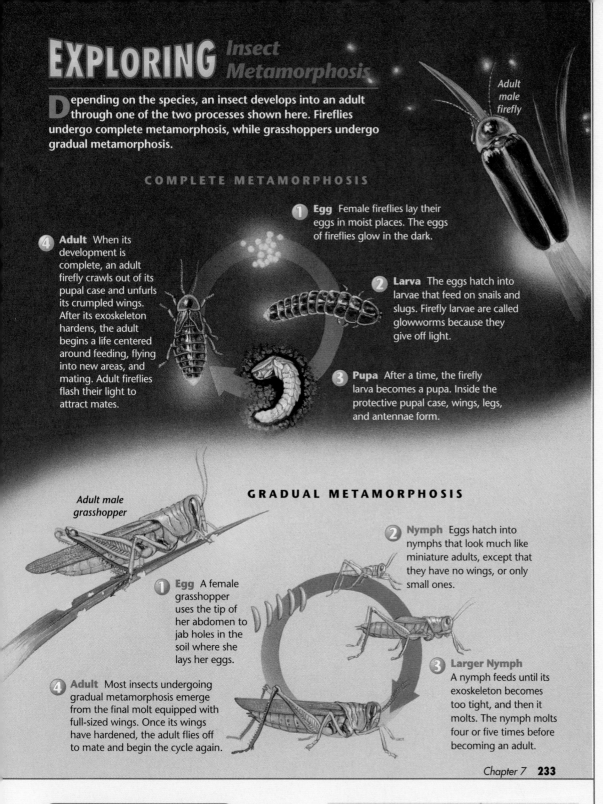

EXPLORING Insect Metamorphosis

Depending on the species, an insect develops into an adult through one of the two processes shown here. Fireflies undergo complete metamorphosis, while grasshoppers undergo gradual metamorphosis.

Adult male firefly

COMPLETE METAMORPHOSIS

1 Egg Female fireflies lay their eggs in moist places. The eggs of fireflies glow in the dark.

2 Larva The eggs hatch into larvae that feed on snails and slugs. Firefly larvae are called glowworms because they give off light.

3 Pupa After a time, the firefly larva becomes a pupa. Inside the protective pupal case, wings, legs, and antennae form.

4 Adult When its development is complete, an adult firefly crawls out of its pupal case and unfurls its crumpled wings. After its exoskeleton hardens, the adult begins a life centered around feeding, flying into new areas, and mating. Adult fireflies flash their light to attract mates.

GRADUAL METAMORPHOSIS

Adult male grasshopper

1 Egg A female grasshopper uses the tip of her abdomen to jab holes in the soil where she lays her eggs.

2 Nymph Eggs hatch into nymphs that look much like miniature adults, except that they have no wings, or only small ones.

3 Larger Nymph A nymph feeds until its exoskeleton becomes too tight, and then it molts. The nymph molts four or five times before becoming an adult.

4 Adult Most insects undergoing gradual metamorphosis emerge from the final molt equipped with full-sized wings. Once its wings have hardened, the adult flies off to mate and begin the cycle again.

EXPLORING

Insect Metamorphosis

Point out that the visual essay contrasts the metamorphoses of a firefly and a grasshopper. The insects are similar in that they lay eggs. However, once the eggs hatch, the insects develop quite differently. Ask: **How is a firefly's metamorphosis different from a grasshopper's?** (*A firefly goes through four distinct stages, whereas a grasshopper changes its form gradually.*) **When does the grasshopper acquire wings?** (*After the final molt*) **What do adults do that larvae and nymphs do not?** (*Reproduce*) **Extend** Allow interested students to cultivate mealworms and describe the kind of metamorphosis the mealworm undergoes. (*Complete*) Challenge them to compare the different stages of mealworm development with the different stages of firefly development. Refer to the **ELL Handbook** for additional teaching strategies. **learning modality: visual**

Media and Technology

 Transparencies "Exploring Insect Metamorphosis," Transparency 32

 Life Science Videodisc Unit 3, Side 1, "Insect Success Stories"

 Chapter 5

Answers to Self-Assessment

Caption Question

Figure 12 The grasshopper's legs are attached to its thorax.

✓ *Checkpoint*

The stages of complete metamorphosis are egg, larva, pupa, adult.

Ongoing Assessment

Oral Presentation Have students list stages of gradual and complete metamorphosis. (*Gradual metamorphosis—egg, nymph, adult; complete metamorphosis— egg, larva, pupa, adult*)

Crustaceans

Sharpen your *Skills*

Designing Experiments

Time 20 minutes

Tips Remind students that their hypotheses should be statements of what type of environment they think pill bugs will prefer. Their experimental design should include both dry and moist environments and a procedure for determining the pill bugs' preference. To save time, you might choose one experiment to be performed. The pill bugs will prefer the moist environment.

Extend Have students find out more about pill bugs or other crustaceans and the structures that help them function in their environments. **learning modality: logical/mathematical**

Arachnids

Addressing Naive Conceptions

Clear up some misconceptions about spiders by asking students to decide if the following statements are true or false.

◆ **All spiders catch their prey in webs.** *(False. Some spiders use webs, but others chase or trap their prey.)*

◆ **Spiders' bites are extremely dangerous to people.** *(False. Spiders rarely bite people, and most spider bites are uncomfortable but not dangerous.)*

learning modality: verbal

Sharpen your Skills

Designing Experiments

Pill bugs are crustaceans that roll up in a ball when they are disturbed. Make a hypothesis about whether pill bugs prefer a moist environment or a dry environment. Then design an experiment to test your hypothesis. Your experiment should not harm the pill bugs in any way. (*Hint:* Study the procedure for the Skills Lab *Earthworm Responses* on page 229.) Write your planned procedure and show it to your teacher. Obtain your teacher's approval before performing the experiment.

Crustaceans

If you've ever eaten shrimp cocktail or crab cakes, you've dined on crustaceans. A **crustacean** is an arthropod that has two or three body sections and usually has three pairs of appendages that are structured for chewing. In addition, crustaceans always have five or more pairs of legs. Crabs, barnacles, shrimp, and lobsters are all crustaceans. Nearly every kind of watery environment, from the ocean depths to freshwater lakes to puddles, is home to crustaceans.

Arachnids

Spiders, mites, and ticks are the arachnids that people most often encounter. To qualify as an **arachnid** (uh RAK nid), an arthropod must have only two body sections. The first section is a combined head and chest. The hind section, the abdomen, contains the arachnid's reproductive organs and part of its digestive tract. Arachnids have eight legs, but no antennae. They breathe either with organs called book lungs or with a network of tiny tubes that lead to openings on the exoskeleton.

Spiders are the most familiar and most fascinating kind of arachnid. All spiders are predators, and most of them eat insects. Some spiders, such as tarantulas and wolf spiders, run after their prey, while others, such as golden garden spiders, spin webs and wait for their prey to become entangled in them. Spiders have hollow fangs, organs whose function is injecting venom into prey. Spider venom turns the tissues of the prey into mush. Later the spider uses its fangs like drinking straws to suck up the mush.

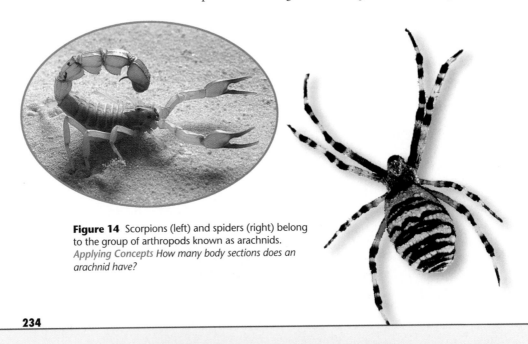

Figure 14 Scorpions (left) and spiders (right) belong to the group of arthropods known as arachnids. *Applying Concepts How many body sections does an arachnid have?*

Background

Facts and Figures Horseshoe crabs are not crabs or crustaceans. They are actually more closely related to arachnids because they have feeding pincers like scorpions and lack antennae. Because its basic body design has remained almost unchanged for millions of years, the horseshoe crab is often called a "living fossil." Their fossil relatives are recognized as far back as 505 million years ago, and forms similar to modern-day horseshoe crabs as far back as 208 million years ago.

Horseshoe crabs have been used in eye research because of their large eyes and large optic nerve (the nerve that sends signals from the eye to the brain). In addition, a substance in the crabs' blood, which kills invading bacteria, is now used to test drugs to make sure they are bacteria-free before they are given to people.

Figure 15 Millipedes (left) and centipedes (right) are arthropods with many body segments.

Centipedes and Millipedes

Centipedes and millipedes have highly segmented bodies, as you can see in Figure 15. Centipedes have one pair of legs attached to each segment, and some centipedes have over 100 segments. In fact, the word *centipede* means "hundred feet." Centipedes are swift predators with sharp jaws. They inject venom into the smaller animals that they catch for food.

Millipedes, which may have more than 80 segments, have two pairs of legs on each segment—more legs than any other arthropod. Though *millipede* means "thousand feet," they don't have quite that many. Most millipedes are herbivores that graze on partly decayed leaves. When they are disturbed, millipedes can curl up into an armored ball and squirt an awful-smelling liquid at a potential predator.

☑ *Checkpoint* How are millipedes different from centipedes?

The Echinoderm Phylum

They look like stars, pincushions, coins, and cucumbers—are these creatures really animals? Sea stars, sea urchins, sand dollars, and sea cucumbers are echinoderms. An **echinoderm** (ee KY noh durm) is a radially symmetrical invertebrate that lives on the ocean floor. *Echinoderm* means "spiny skinned." This name is appropriate because the skin of most of these animals is supported by a spiny internal skeleton, or **endoskeleton,** made of plates.

Adult echinoderms have a unique kind of radial symmetry in which body parts, usually in multiples of five, are arranged like spokes on a wheel. If you count the legs on a sea star or the body sections of a sea urchin, you will almost always get five or a multiple of five.

Centipedes and Millipedes

Using the Visuals: Figure 15

To help students compare the millipede to one of the arachnids in Figure 14, have them draw each organism. Instruct them to label characteristics specific to millipedes and arachnids. *(millipedes—two pairs of legs on each segment; arachnids—4 pairs of legs on front section)* **learning modality: visual**

The Echinoderm Phylum

Inquiry Challenge

Materials *surgical gloves*
Time 20 minutes
Challenge students to see how a water vascular system works by allowing them to make their own simple tube system. First, ask students to suggest ways they could model a water vascular system using the surgical gloves. When students have finished making suggestions, propose this model. Students can fill surgical gloves with water without stretching the gloves. Then they can tie off the openings with rubber bands, and squeeze the gloves in various ways to make different fingers stand up or droop down. Inform students that the muscles surrounding the tubes in an echinoderm's water vascular system squeeze to move water through the tubes and create suction in the tube feet. Ask students: **In this activity, what models the action of these muscles?** *(Hands squeezing the fingers of the glove)* Collect gloves and rubber bands at the end of the activity. **learning modality: tactile/kinesthetic**

Answers to Self-Assessment

Caption Question

Figure 14 Two body sections.

☑ *Checkpoint*

Centipedes have one pair of legs per segment; millipedes have two. Centipedes are carnivores and millipedes are herbivores.

Ongoing Assessment

Writing Have students describe one distinguishing characteristic of each of the following groups: crustaceans, arachnids, centipedes, and millipedes. *(Crustaceans—five or more pairs of legs; arachnids—two body sections; centipedes—one pair of legs per body segment; millipedes—two pairs of legs per body segment)*

The Echinoderm Phylum, continued

Including All Students

In this section, students encounter terms that are difficult to pronounce and understand. Guide students whose native language is not English in the pronunciation of words such as *vascular* and *echinoderm*. Allow them to practice saying the words with a partner until they master the pronunciation. **limited English proficiency**

3 Assess

Section 4 Review Answers

1. All arthropods are bilaterally symmetrical; are invertebrates; have an external skeleton; have a segmented body; and have jointed appendages.
2. Insects have three body segments, six legs, one pair of antennae, and usually one or two pairs of wings.
3. All echinoderms have five-part radial symmetry, an endoskeleton, and a water vascular system.
4. The tube feet, which are part of the water vascular system, act like suction cups, allowing the echinoderm to grip objects.
5. Complete metamorphosis consists of dramatically different stages: egg, larva, pupa, and adult. Gradual metamorphosis does not have a distinct larval stage. The egg hatches into a nymph, which may molt several times before becoming an adult.

```
........................   CHAPTER
                            PROJECT
```
Check Your Progress

Check that students have chosen appropriate animal structures to model. Have students show you their sketches before they begin to assemble their models.

Performance Assessment

Drawing Have students sketch an insect and label three major characteristics that classify it as an insect. (*Three body sections, one pair of antennae, and wings*)

Figure 16 The blue-and-red sea cucumber (**A**), sea star (**B**), and sand dollar (**C**) are all echinoderms. *Observing What type of symmetry do these organisms exhibit?*

In addition to five-part radial symmetry and an endoskeleton, echinoderms also have an internal fluid system called a water vascular system. The water vascular system functions in movement and food-gathering. The water vascular system consists of fluid-filled canals within the echinoderm's body. Portions of the canals can contract, squeezing water into organs called tube feet, which are external parts of the water vascular system.

If you turn a sea star upside down, you will see rows of moving tube feet. The ends of tube feet are sticky. When these organs are filled with water, they function like suction cups. The stickiness and suction enable the tube feet to grip the surface beneath the echinoderm. Because of this ability to grip surfaces, echinoderms can move across underwater rocks and the sea floor. They also use their tube feet to capture prey, such as clams, by sticking to them. The echinoderms then eat the soft parts of the prey.

 Section 4 Review

1. Identify four structural characteristics that all arthropods share.
2. Describe the basic body structure of an insect.
3. What characteristics are shared by all echinoderms?
4. How does the structure of an echinoderm's water vascular system function in gripping objects?
5. **Thinking Critically Comparing and Contrasting** Describe the stages in complete metamorphosis and gradual metamorphosis. Explain how the two processes are both similar and different.

236

```
                            CHAPTER
                            PROJECT
```
Check Your Progress

You should assemble the materials you need and begin to construct your models. Reference books, software, and magazine articles can give you information about the structures of the animals you have chosen. (*Hint:* Make a sketch of each model before you begin to put the parts together.)

Program Resources

◆ **Unit 2 Resources** 7-4 Review and Reinforce, p. 103; 7-4 Enrich, p. 104
◆ **Laboratory Manual** 7, "Characteristics of Sea Stars"

Answers to Self-Assessment

Caption Question

Figure 16 These organisms exhibit five-part radial symmetry.

SECTION 5 Fishes, Amphibians, and Reptiles

GUIDE FOR READING

◆ What is the function of a vertebrate's skeletal system?

◆ What are the main characteristics of fishes, amphibians, and reptiles?

Reading Tip As you read, write brief summaries of the information under each heading.

Key Terms vertebra
• ectotherm • endotherm
• cartilage • atrium • ventricle
• kidney

Yellow mud turtle ▼

On a sunny day, a small yellow mud turtle crawls slowly but steadily out of a pond. The pond and its bank are the turtle's fast-food restaurant. The turtle finds a fat, juicy worm to eat. After feeding, the yellow mud turtle settles down on the pond bank to warm itself in the sun. As the turtle moves and feeds, and even as it lies still in the sun, its body is supported by its bony skeleton.

Vertebrates

Turtles are reptiles, and reptiles are vertebrates. Other vertebrates include fishes, amphibians, birds, and mammals. Vertebrates are animals with a backbone. The backbone is formed by many similar bones, called **vertebrae** (singular *vertebra*) that are lined up in a row like beads on a string. Joints between the vertebrae give the backbone flexibility. You are able to bend over and tie your sneakers partly because your backbone is flexible.

A vertebrate's backbone is part of an endoskeleton, or internal skeleton. The endoskeleton is made up of organs called bones. The endoskeleton supports and protects the body, helps give it shape, and gives muscles a place to attach. The muscles are part of the muscular system, which is the body system responsible for movement.

Chapter 7 **237**

SECTION 5 Fishes, Amphibians, and Reptiles

TEKS: 6.1A 6.2B, C, D; 6.3D; 6.4A; 6.10A, C; 6.12B

Objectives

After completing this lesson, students will be able to
◆ explain the function of a vertebrate's skeletal system;
◆ describe the characteristics of fishes, amphibians, and reptiles.

1 Engage/Explore

Activating Prior Knowledge

Ask students to recall what they learned about vertebrates and invertebrates in Section 1. Then ask a volunteer to list on the board all the kinds of vertebrates and invertebrates the students see in a single day. Once the lists are completed, have them compare and contrast several obvious ways vertebrates and invertebrates are similar and ways they are different.

DISCOVER

Skills Focus inferring
Materials *umbrella*
Time 15 minutes

Tips To avoid injuries, make sure students are standing in an open area away from others when they open the umbrella.
Expected Outcome Students should understand that, without its ribs, an umbrella loses its support and cannot function.
Think It Over The umbrella's ribs provide support to the umbrella and give it shape, just as bones support and give shape to the human body. The ribs of an umbrella are different from human bones in that they are near the surface, rather than deep within the body and covered by soft tissue. **learning modality: tactile/kinesthetic**

Vertebrates

Using the Visuals: Figure 17

Students may not understand the text explanation of the relationship between the backbone and the endoskeleton. Instruct students to place a finger at the base of the angelfish's tail and trace along the vertebrae until they come to its head. **limited English proficiency**

Regulating Body Temperature

Addressing Naive Conceptions

Students may think that "coldblooded" animals are always cold. In fact, the body temperature of an ectotherm can be greater than that of the typical endotherm. The body temperature of an ectotherm reflects the temperature of its environment. **learning modality: verbal**

Characteristics of Fishes

Sharpen your *Skills*

Skills Focus
communicating
Materials *preserved fish, goggles, dissecting tray, blunt probe, hand lens, disposable gloves*
Time 50 minutes
Tips Provide gloves to all students. Help students see the connection between the mouth and gill slits by letting them pass the end of the probe into the fish's mouth and out through the gill openings. Students should wash their hands after handling the fish.
Extend Have students closely examine the feathery structure of the gills. Ask: **How is the structure of the gills related to their functions?** (*The feathery structure provides more surface area for absorbing oxygen.*) **learning modality: tactile/kinesthetic**

Figure 17 An angelfish is supported by its bony skeleton. Also observe how the skeleton gives shape to the fish's body. *Comparing and Contrasting How is a vertebrate's endoskeleton different from an arthropod's exoskeleton?*

Sharpen your **Skills**

Communicating

Put on your goggles. Observe a preserved fish. Note its size, shape, and the number and locations of its fins. Lift the gill cover and observe the gill with a hand lens. Make a diagram of your observations, and include a written description. Wash your hands.

Ask a classmate to check your work to make sure it clearly communicates what you observed. Then make any necessary improvements.

In addition to the backbone, the vertebrate's skeletal system includes the skull and ribs. The hard skull protects the brain and sense organs. The ribs attach to the vertebrae and protect the heart, lungs, and other internal organs. Many vertebrates also have arm and leg bones adapted for a variety of movements, such as running and flying. When a vertebrate runs, flies, or even breathes, the muscular and skeletal systems work together. Because these two organ systems interact so closely, together they are sometimes called the musculoskeletal system.

☑ *Checkpoint* *What is a function of a skull?*

Regulating Body Temperature

When the yellow mud turtle basks in the sun, it has a higher body temperature than when it is swimming in the cool pond. Most fishes, amphibians, and reptiles are **ectotherms,** which are animals that have a body temperature that is close to the temperature of their environment. In contrast, birds and mammals are endotherms. **Endotherms** have a stable body temperature that is typically much warmer than their environment. Because endotherms can keep their body temperatures stable, they can live in a greater variety of environments than ectotherms can.

Characteristics of Fishes

Fishes make up the largest group of vertebrates—nearly half of all vertebrate species are fishes. **A fish is an ectothermic vertebrate that lives in the water and has fins, which are structures used for moving. Most fishes obtain oxygen through gills and have scales.** Scales are thin, overlapping plates that cover the skin.

Obtaining Oxygen A fish's gills are a good example of how structure relates to function. The gills, which look like tiny red feathers, contain many blood vessels that have a large combined surface area. This large surface area enables the gills to absorb a large

---

Background

Facts and Figures All animals, whether they are ectotherms or endotherms, need to maintain their body temperatures within a relatively narrow range. One reason is that an animal's enzymes function only within a narrow temperature range. Enzymes are proteins that speed up chemical reactions within cells. For example, enzymes help break food molecules into simpler sub-

stances, releasing energy in the process. Without enzymes, these reactions could take hours or even days; with enzymes they take place in seconds. However, because enzymes are delicate chemicals, a substantial change in body temperature slows down or destroys them. If an animal's body temperature is too high or too low, enzyme activity stops, and the body will not function the way it should.

amount of oxygen. As water flows over the gills, oxygen moves from the water into the fish's blood, while carbon dioxide, a waste product, moves out of the blood and into the water.

The Circulatory System From the gills, blood travels throughout the fish's body, supplying the body cells with oxygen. In a fish's circulatory system, blood travels in one loop. The heart pumps blood to the gills. From the gills, blood travels to the rest of the body and then back to the heart. Trace this path in Figure 18. In this book, oxygen-rich blood is red in color and oxygen-poor blood is blue in color.

Kinds of Fishes

Biologists classify fishes into three major groups: jawless fishes, cartilaginous fishes, and bony fishes. Mouth structure and type of skeleton distinguish these types of fishes from one another.

Jawless Fishes Hagfish and lampreys are the only kinds of jawless fishes. Unlike other fishes, jawless fishes have no scales. Their skeletons are made of cartilage. Like bone, **cartilage** is a strong tissue that supports the body, but it is flexible and softer than bone. (Your ears are supported by cartilage.) Jawless fishes have mouth structures that scrape, suck, and stab their food.

Cartilaginous Fishes Sharks, rays, and skates are cartilaginous (cahrt uhl AJ uh nuhs) fishes. As the group's name suggests, the skeletons of these fishes are made of cartilage, just like the skeletons of jawless fishes. However, unlike lampreys and hagfishes, cartilaginous fishes have jaws and pairs of fins. Also, pointed, toothlike scales cover their bodies, giving them a texture that is rougher than sandpaper.

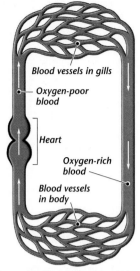

Figure 18 Trace the path of blood through a fish's one-loop circulatory system.

Blood vessels in gills
Oxygen-poor blood
Heart
Oxygen-rich blood
Blood vessels in body

Figure 19 This sand tiger shark (left) has many sharp teeth. Lampreys (right) are jawless fish that also have sharp teeth. *Applying Concepts How are the structures of these fishes' teeth related to their functions?*

Chapter 7 **239**

Addressing Naive Conceptions

Some students may not realize that gases such as oxygen and carbon dioxide can dissolve in liquids like water. To reinforce this concept, use the example of a carbonated beverage. Ask: **What happens when you pop the top on a soft drink?** *(Bubbles form.)* **Where does the gas in the bubbles come from?** *(It was dissolved in the liquid.)* Also, some students may look at Figure 18 and think that some blood is blue. Tell students that blood is red in color. Some blood is bright red (oxygen-rich) and some is dark red (oxygen-poor). In this book, blood that is oxygen-rich is red in color and blood that is oxygen-poor is blue in color. **learning modality: verbal**

Kinds of Fishes

Using the Visuals: Figure 19

Direct students to locate the mouth of the jawless fish in the figure. Have them describe the mouth. Ask them whether the lamprey's mouth looks like the mouths of fishes they are familiar with. *(Students will probably say no.)* Invite students to infer how the lamprey's specialized mouth helps it feed. Inform students that the lamprey feeds by attaching to a living fish, boring a hole in the fish's side, and eating the fluids that leak out. Its teeth help the lamprey stay attached to its host. **learning modality: verbal**

Answers to Self-Assessment

Caption Questions

Figure 17 The endoskeleton is inside the animal's body and includes a backbone made of vertebrae. The exoskeleton is outside the animal's body and does not include a backbone.

Figure 19 Sharks' teeth are sharp, enabling them to capture prey. Lampreys' teeth are sharp and pointed, enabling them to stab their food.

✓ *Checkpoint*
Skulls protect the brain and sense organs.

Ongoing Assessment

Writing Have students compare and contrast endotherms and ectotherms and give examples of each.

Kinds of Fishes, continued

EXPLORING
a Bony Fish

Direct students to explain the function of each structure shown in the visual. Then ask them to think of how the structures described in the visual accomplish that function. For example, ask: **How does the tail fin help the perch move through the water?** *(The tail fin provides a large surface to push against the water, propelling the fish.)* Choose pairs of students, and have them describe how they think each structure works. Refer to the **ELL Handbook** for additional teaching strategies. **learning modality: visual**

Building Inquiry Skills: Observing

ACTIVITY

Locate an aquarium or fishpond where students can conduct a scientific study of the behavior of fishes. Students should spend at least 10 minutes (more if possible) observing and recording interesting behavior. Suggest that students choose one species of fish to observe. Give them these questions to direct their observations:

◆ Is this a bony fish, a jawless fish, or a cartilaginous fish?
◆ How does the fish interact with its surroundings?
◆ What does it eat?
◆ How does it find food?
◆ How does it react to stimuli, such as sound?
◆ How does it interact with other fishes?
◆ What habitat does it seem to prefer?
Students will probably not be able to answer all the questions within the allotted time, but they may be able to devise strategies for answering them. **learning modality: visual**

Bony Fishes Most familiar kinds of fishes, such as trout, tuna, and goldfish, have skeletons made of hard bone. Bony fishes make up about 95 percent of all fish species. Some live in the lightless depths of the ocean, while others thrive in light-filled waters, such as those in coral reefs or shallow ponds.

The body of a bony fish is covered with scales, and a pocket on each side of the head holds the fish's gills. Each gill pocket is covered by a flexible flap that opens to release water. Most bony fishes have an organ called a swim bladder, an internal gas-filled sac that helps the fish stabilize its body at different depths. To learn more about the functions of the major structures of bony fishes, look closely at the perch in *Exploring a Bony Fish*.

☑ *Checkpoint* **What is cartilage?**

EXPLORING *a Bony Fish*

In a quiet, shady area near the bank of a stream or pond, you might find some yellow perch swimming along. These freshwater fish, which like slow-moving water, travel in groups called schools.

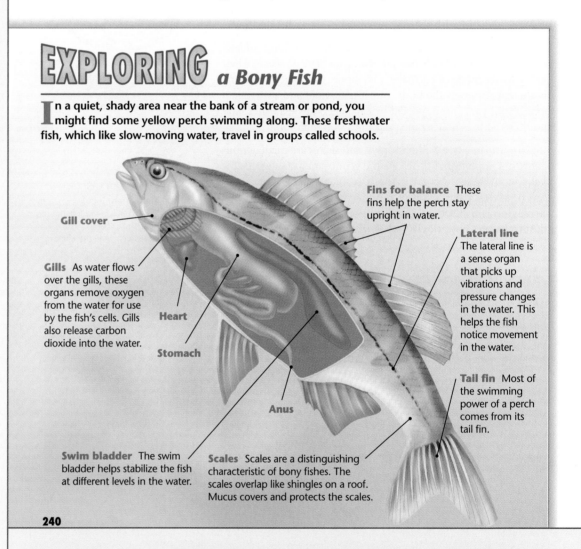

Gill cover

Gills As water flows over the gills, these organs remove oxygen from the water for use by the fish's cells. Gills also release carbon dioxide into the water.

Heart

Stomach

Anus

Fins for balance These fins help the perch stay upright in water.

Lateral line The lateral line is a sense organ that picks up vibrations and pressure changes in the water. This helps the fish notice movement in the water.

Tail fin Most of the swimming power of a perch comes from its tail fin.

Swim bladder The swim bladder helps stabilize the fish at different levels in the water.

Scales Scales are a distinguishing characteristic of bony fishes. The scales overlap like shingles on a roof. Mucus covers and protects the scales.

240

Amphibians

Frogs, toads, and salamanders are amphibians. **An amphibian is an ectothermic vertebrate that spends its early life in water and its adult life on land, returning to water to reproduce.**

Respiratory and Circulatory Systems The circulatory system of a tadpole—the larval form of a frog or toad—has a single loop structure, like that of a fish. In contrast, the circulatory system of many adult amphibians has a two-loop structure. As you read about the pattern of blood circulation, trace the path of blood through the amphibian's circulatory system shown in Figure 21. In the first loop, blood flows from the heart to the lungs and skin, where it picks up oxygen. Lungs and skin are organs in the respiratory system, the organ system that moves oxygen from the outside environment into the body. The respiratory system also removes waste carbon dioxide from the body.

From the lungs and skin, oxygen-rich blood returns to the heart. In the second loop, the blood flows to the rest of the body, delivering oxygen-rich blood to the cells. The respiratory and circulatory systems function together to deliver oxygen to the body's cells. Oxygen enters the body through the respiratory system, and blood carries the oxygen to the cells.

The hearts of most amphibians have three inner spaces, or chambers. The two upper chambers of the heart, called **atria** (singular *atrium*), receive blood. One atrium receives oxygen-rich blood from the lungs, and the other receives oxygen-poor blood from the rest of the body. From the atria, blood moves into the lower chamber, the **ventricle,** which pumps blood out to the lungs and body. In the ventricle, there is some mixing of oxygen-rich and oxygen-poor blood.

Metamorphosis Most amphibians lay their eggs in water. Amphibian eggs are coated with clear jelly that keeps moisture in and helps protect against infection. An embryo, or tiny living organism, develops inside each egg. Amphibian eggs hatch into larvae that swim and have gills for obtaining oxygen. Most amphibians undergo metamorphosis, and as they become adults, they lose their gills and acquire lungs.

Figure 21 An adult amphibian's circulatory system has two loops. One loop runs from the heart to the lungs and back, and the second runs from the heart to the body and back. *Interpreting Diagrams Where does the blood pick up oxygen?*

Blood vessels in lungs

Oxygen-poor blood

Right atrium

Left atrium

Ventricle

Oxygen-rich blood

Blood vessels in body

Media and Technology

 Transparencies "Exploring a Bony Fish," Transparency 33

 Life Science Videodisc
Unit 3, Side 1,
"Backbones"

Chapter 3

Answers to Self-Assessment

Caption Question

Figure 21 The blood picks up oxygen is the lungs and skin.

✓ *Checkpoint*

Cartilage is a strong, flexible tissue that supports the body.

Amphibians

Including All Students

Materials *25 red balloons*
Time 5 minutes

This activity helps students to understand oxygen uptake in an adult amphibian's circulatory system. Position students at five stations representing parts of the circulatory system—lungs, body, right atrium, left atrium, and ventricle. Place 25 red balloons, representing oxygen, at the lungs station. Slowly clap your hands to indicate heartbeats. At each heartbeat, students change stations in the direction of blood flow. For example, students at the body station will move to the right atrium. Students at the ventricle move to the lungs or back to the body. Students at the lungs will pick up a balloon, and students at the body must drop off a balloon if they are holding one. A student holding a balloon represents oxygen-rich blood. A student without a balloon represents oxygen-poor blood. Continue for 3 or 4 minutes. Ask: **Where in an adult amphibian's circulatory system is oxygen acquired?** (*The lungs and skin*) **Where is oxygen released?** (*In the body*) **Where does mixing of oxygen-rich and oxygen-poor blood occur?** (*In the ventricle*) **learning modality: tactile/kinesthetic**

Ongoing Assessment

Writing Have students write a brief paragraph in which they compare and contrast the characteristics and habitats of amphibians and fishes. (*Compare—Amphibians and fishes both have internal skeletons, a backbone, and a closed circulatory system. Both typically lay their eggs in water. Contrast—Most adult amphibians have lungs, whereas most fishes have gills. Amphibians have a two-loop circulatory system; fish have one loop.*)

 Students can save their paragraphs in their portfolios.

Amphibians, continued

Using the Visuals: Figure 22

The stages of frog metamorphosis are shown from right to left. This could possibly be confusing to students who are accustomed to reading from left to right. Have students trace the stages of development from right to left, stating at least one change at each stage. For example, they might trace from stage four to five and say "tail disappears."
learning modality: visual

Building Inquiry Skills: Inferring

Once students are familiar with amphibian metamorphosis, ask: **Why is water essential for amphibian development?** *(Amphibians' eggs are laid and hatch in water. Their larvae live in water.)* Then ask: **How does acquiring lungs change the life of amphibians?** *(They are able to leave the water, breathe air, and live on land.)* **learning modality: verbal**

Kinds of Amphibians

Addressing Naive Conceptions

Ask students if they have heard that someone who touches a toad will get warts. Explain that this belief is merely a superstition—touching a toad's skin will not cause warts. Ask: **Can you think of any reasons why this superstition came about?** *(Toads' skin is bumpy and looks "warty." People assumed that toads' "warts" were contagious. Though toads don't cause warts, their secretions can irritate skin, sometimes severely.)* **learning modality: logical/ mathematical**

242

Figure 22 shows the process in which a frog tadpole undergoes metamorphosis. During metamorphosis, amphibians develop strong skeletons and muscular limbs. This body structure enables movement on land. Because it is not supported by water, a land animal needs a strong skeletal system to support its body against the pull of gravity.

☑ *Checkpoint* *Compare the functions of the atria and ventricle.*

Kinds of Amphibians

Frogs and toads are amphibians that are adapted for hopping and leaping. This movement requires powerful hind-leg muscles and a skeleton that can absorb the shock of landing. The feet of frogs and toads have other structural adaptations, too. The webbed feet and long toes of bullfrogs help the frogs dart through the water. Tree frogs have toe pads with adhesive suckers that function as secure holds when the frogs leap from twig to twig.

Salamanders are amphibians that keep their tails as adults. Their bodies are long and usually slender. The legs of salamanders are not adapted for jumping. Salamanders creep around and ambush the small invertebrates that they eat.

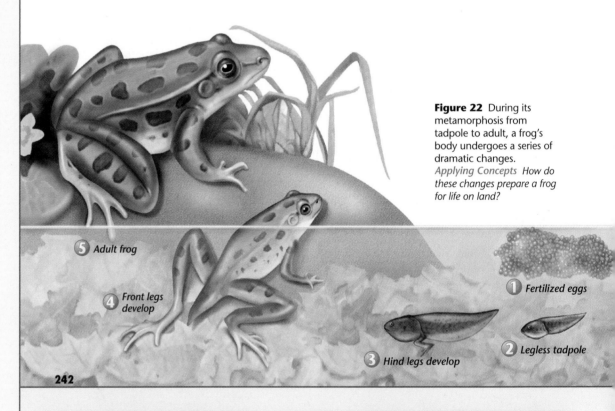

Figure 22 During its metamorphosis from tadpole to adult, a frog's body undergoes a series of dramatic changes. *Applying Concepts How do these changes prepare a frog for life on land?*

⑤ *Adult frog*

④ *Front legs develop*

③ *Hind legs develop*

② *Legless tadpole*

① *Fertilized eggs*

242

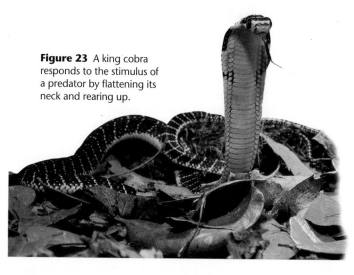

Figure 23 A king cobra responds to the stimulus of a predator by flattening its neck and rearing up.

Reptiles

The king cobra of Southeast Asia, which can grow to more than 4 meters, is the world's longest venomous snake. When it encounters a predator, a king cobra flattens its neck and rears up. Its ropelike body sways back and forth, and its tongue flicks in and out. The king cobra and other snakes are reptiles. Like other reptiles, king cobras lay their eggs on land rather than in water.

A reptile is an ectothermic vertebrate that has lungs and scaly skin. Unlike amphibians, reptiles can spend their entire lives on dry land. Reptiles usually get their oxygen only from the air. Most reptiles breathe entirely with lungs. Like adult amphibians, most reptiles have a two-loop circulatory system and a heart with three chambers.

Entire Life on Land You can think of a land animal as a pocket of water held within a bag of skin. To thrive on land, an animal must have adaptations that keep the water within the "bag" from evaporating in the dry air. Unlike amphibians, which have thin, moist skin, reptiles have dry, tough, scale-covered skin that functions both to protect the reptile and to keep water inside its body.

Another adaptation that helps keep water inside a reptile's body is its **kidneys**, which are organs of the excretory system. An animal's excretory system collects wastes that are produced by cells and removes them from the body. The kidneys filter wastes from the blood. The wastes are then excreted in a watery fluid called urine. As the kidneys of a reptile produce urine, they concentrate it, removing most of the water. Therefore, reptiles lose very little water in urine.

Sharpen your Skills

Drawing Conclusions

Scientists incubated, or raised, eggs of one alligator species at four different temperatures. When the alligators hatched, the scientists counted the numbers of males and females. The table below shows the results.

Incubation Temperature	Number of Females	Number of Males
29.4°C	80	0
30.6°C	19	13
31.7°C	13	38
32.8°C	0	106

Use the data to answer these questions.
1. What effect does incubation temperature have on the sex of the alligators?
2. Suppose a scientist incubated 50 eggs at 31°C. About how many of the alligators that hatched would be males? Explain.

Reptiles

Sharpen your Skills

Drawing Conclusions

Skills Focus drawing conclusions
Time 15 minutes
Tips So that students can answer Question 1 accurately, make sure they understand that the answer is based on the proportion of males to females in the groups of eggs, not the absolute number. To help students answer Question 2, explain that the incubation temperature is the temperature at which the eggs were kept after they were laid—not the temperature at which the female was kept before she laid them.
Expected Outcome The warmer the incubation temperature, the greater the proportion of males; About half, or 25, would be males, because 31°C is between 30.6°C, at which there were more females than males, and 31.7°C, at which there were more males than females. Accept any answer close to that.
Extend Ask students to think of an experiment that could test whether incubation temperature affects the percentage of eggs that hatch. Do not allow students to perform their experiments. *(Sample experiment: Incubate three groups of 100 eggs at three different temperatures and then count the number of alligators that hatch.)*
learning modality: logical/ mathematical

Media and Technology

 Transparencies "Frog Metamorphosis," Transparency 34

Answers to Self-Assessment

Caption Question

Figure 22 These changes prepare a frog to breathe air and move about on land.

 Checkpoint

The atria receive blood from the lungs and body. The ventricle pumps blood to the lungs and body.

Ongoing Assessment

Drawing Direct students to draw a diagram of the reptile circulatory system that indicates the two-loop circulatory system of a reptile, the chambers of a reptile's heart, and the locations of oxygen-rich and oxygen-poor blood in the reptile's circulatory system. *(Students' drawings should be similar to Figure 21, page 241.)*

Portfolio Students can save their diagrams in their portfolios.

Kinds of Reptiles

An Egg With a Shell The reptile egg is one of the most important adaptations that enable reptiles to live their entire lives on land. Unlike an amphibian's egg, a reptile's egg has a shell and membranes, as you can see in Figure 24. One membrane holds the yolk, which provides food for the embryo. Another membrane holds the liquid that surrounds the embryo. Together, the shell, membranes, and liquid protect the embryo and help keep it from drying out. Because their eggs conserve water, reptiles—unlike amphibians—can lay their eggs on dry land.

☑ *Checkpoint* *List two functions of a reptile's skin.*

Kinds of Reptiles

About 7,000 kinds of reptiles are alive today. Most of these reptiles are either lizards or snakes. Other major groups of reptiles include turtles as well as alligators and crocodiles.

Lizards Lizards have four legs, usually with claws on the toes. Many lizards have long tails, slender bodies, movable eyelids, and external ears. A few lizards, such as the iguana, are herbivores that eat leaves. Most lizards, however, are carnivores. Chameleons, which are found in Africa and India, have a sticky tongue. When a chameleon sees an insect, its tongue shoots out rapidly in response to the stimulus. That tongue extends as long as the chameleon's head and body put together!

Snakes Unlike lizards, snakes have no legs. If you've ever seen a snake slither across the ground, you know that when it moves, its long, thin body bends into curves. Snakes, which are carnivores, have adaptations that help them eat large prey. For example, a snake's jawbones can spread widely apart. In addition, the bones of a snake's skull can move to let the snake swallow an animal much larger in diameter than itself.

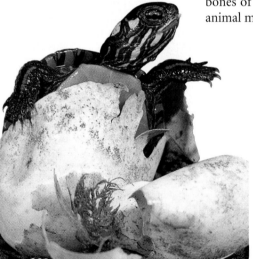

Figure 24 The diagram shows the structure of the egg from which this turtle is hatching. One membrane holds the liquid that surrounds the embryo. The liquid keeps the embryo moist and keeps it from getting crushed. A second membrane holds the yolk, which provides the embryo with food.

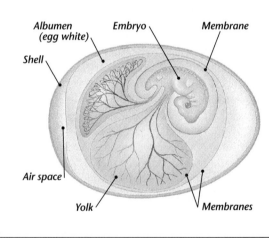

Albumen (egg white) — Embryo — Membrane — Shell — Air space — Yolk — Membranes

Figure 25 The chameleon (left) and the alligator (right) belong to different groups of reptiles.
Applying Concepts *To what group of reptiles does the chameleon belong?*

Turtles A turtle is a reptile whose body is covered by a protective shell, which is made from the turtle's ribs and backbone. The bony plates of the shell are covered by large scales. Some turtle shells can cover the whole body—a box turtle can draw its head, legs, and tail inside its shell for protection. Turtles like the snapping turtle have much smaller shells. Soft-shelled turtles, as their name suggests, have shells that are as soft as pancakes. Soft-shelled turtles lie in stream beds, concealed from predators, with only their nostrils and eyes above the sand.

Alligators and Crocodiles If you walk along a lake in Brazos Bend State Park, you just might see an alligator swimming silently in the water. Most of the alligator's body lies beneath the surface, but you can see its large, bulging eyes. Alligators and crocodiles are carnivores that hunt mostly at night. They have several structural adaptations that function to help them capture prey. For example, they use their strong, muscular tails to swim rapidly through the water after prey. Their jaws are also equipped with many large, sharp, pointed teeth. Their jaw muscles are extremely strong, helping the animals bite their prey.

Section 5 Review

1. What are three functions of a vertebrate's endoskeleton?
2. Describe the major characteristics of fishes, amphibians, and reptiles.
3. The Greek roots of the word *amphibian* mean "double life." Explain how "double life" applies to an amphibian's life cycle.
4. Describe three adaptations that enable reptiles to live on land.
5. **Thinking Critically** **Applying Concepts** Explain how the structure of a snake's jawbones and skull enable the snake to feed.

Check Your Progress CHAPTER PROJECT
Complete the models and begin working on the poster. (*Hint:* Before you finish the models, ask a friend to help you check to make sure that your models demonstrate the structure-function relationships that you chose to model.)

Section 5 Review Answers

1. A vertebrate's endoskeleton supports and protects its body, helps give it shape, and gives muscles a place to attach.
2. Fishes: water-dwelling ectothermic vertebrates with fins, gills, and scales. Amphibians: ectothermic vertebrate that spends its early life in water and adult life on land, returning to water to reproduce. Reptiles: ectothermic vertebrate with lungs and scaly skin; can spend whole life on dry land.
3. The early stages of an amphibian's life occur in the water; the adult stages on land. Thus amphibians can be said to have a double life.
4. Reptiles can live on land because they have dry, tough skin that keeps water in; kidneys that conserve water; and eggs that have a shell that keeps the embryo from drying out.
5. A snake's jawbones can spread wide apart, allowing it to eat large prey. Its skull bones can move to enable the snake to swallow an animal much larger than itself.

Check Your Progress CHAPTER PROJECT
In addition to having students check each other's models, you may wish to review their models before they begin on their posters.

Media and Technology

 Transparencies "A Reptile Egg," Transparency 35

 Life Science Videodisc Unit 3, Side 1, "Travelin' Along"

Chapter 8

Program Resources

◆ **Unit 2 Resources** 7-5 Review and Reinforce, p. 107; Enrich, p. 108

Answers to Self-Assessment

Caption Question

Figure 25 Lizards.

☑ *Checkpoint*

Skin protects the body and keeps in water.

Performance Assessment

Skills Check Have students compare the circulatory systems of fishes, amphibians, and reptiles. Column heads could be: Number of Loops, Where Blood Picks up Oxygen, Structure of Heart.

Animals and Medical Research

Purpose

To discuss the issue of using animals in medical research

Role-Play

Time 90 minutes

◆ Stimulate discussion with a role-playing scenario. A family member has a life-threatening illness. Scientists have developed a treatment for the illness, but it must be tested on animals before it can be approved for human use. Should the research be done? Choose volunteers to play the roles of family members, doctors, members of the Food and Drug Administration, and people against using animals in medical research.

◆ Guide students in their understanding of the practical and moral obligations of each character. Remind them that doctors have a responsibility to protect the health and well-being of their patients. The FDA was established to protect the safety of all Americans.

◆ To help students make a decision, they can think about the following issues:

1. What is the potential benefit of the proposed research? How great are the potential benefits to humanity?

2. How many animals will be tested? Research can be categorized as using a few animals (fewer than 20), or many animals (more than 20).

3. Will the animals be killed? How much pain will they experience? What animals will be involved?

◆ Prior to the role-playing exercise, invite students to interview community members involved in this issue. Students might contact universities or hospitals to speak with medical researchers or local veterinarians and humane society representatives. Suggest they prepare a list of questions before they call. Encourage students to share their findings with classmates and incorporate the results in the role-playing and You Decide writing activity.

Animals and Medical Research

In laboratories around the world, scientists search for cures for cancer, AIDS, and other diseases. Scientists use millions of animals each year in research—mostly to test drugs and surgical procedures. Finding treatments could save millions of human lives. However, these experiments can hurt and even kill animals.

The Issues

Why Is Animal Testing Done? If you have ever used an antibiotic or other medicine, animal testing has helped you. The United States Food and Drug Administration requires that new medicines be tested on research animals before they can be used by humans. Through testing, researchers can learn whether a drug works and what doses are safe. Because of animal research, many serious diseases can now be treated or prevented. New treatments for AIDS, cancer, and Alzheimer's disease are also likely to depend on animal testing.

Which Animals Are Used for Testing? Most often mice, rats, and other small mammals are used. These animals reproduce rapidly, so scientists can study many generations in a year. Since apes and monkeys are similar to humans in many ways, they are often used to test new treatments for serious diseases. In other cases, researchers use animals that naturally get diseases common to humans. Cocker spaniels, for example, often develop glaucoma, an eye disease that can cause blindness. Surgeons may test new surgical treatments for the disease on cocker spaniels.

What Happens to Research Animals? In a typical laboratory experiment, a group of animals will first be infected with a disease. Then they will be given a drug to see if it can fight off the disease. In many cases, the animals suffer, and some die. Some people are concerned that laboratory animals do not receive proper care.

What Are the Alternatives? Other testing methods do exist. For example, in some cases, scientists can use computer models to test drugs or surgical treatments. Another testing method is to mix drugs with animal cells grown in petri dishes. Unfortunately, neither computer models nor cell experiments are as useful as tests on living animals.

You Decide

1. Identify the Problem

In a sentence, describe the controversy over using animals in medical research.

2. Analyze the Options

Review the different positions. Is animal testing acceptable? Is it acceptable for some animals but not for others? Is animal research never acceptable? List the benefits and drawbacks of each option.

3. Find a Solution

Suppose you are a scientist who has found a possible cure for a type of cancer. The drug needs to be tested on research animals first, but you know that testing could harm the animals. What would you do? Support your opinion with sound reasons.

You Decide

◆ Students' responses to Identify the Problem and Analyze the Options should be based on the concepts and issues presented in the text. In response to Find a Solution, students may discuss issues raised in the role-playing.

◆ Make sure students understand that there are no "correct" opinions or solutions. As with many complex social issues, no single solution satisfies everyone. Provide examples of other difficult social issues as models.

Background

Reference Against Animal Research
Peter Singer. *Animal Liberation.* New York. Random House. 1990.

Reference Supporting Animal Research
Julian Groves. *Hearts and Minds: The Controversy over Laboratory Animals.* Philadelphia. Temple University Press. 1997.

SECTION
6 Birds and Mammals

TEKS: 6.1A; 6.2A, B, C, D, E; 6.3D; 6.4A; 6.10A, C; 6.12A, B

DISCOVER .... ACTIVITY

What Are Feathers Like?

1.  Examine a feather. Observe its overall shape and structure. Use a hand lens to examine the many hairlike barbs that project out from the feather's central shaft.

2. With your fingertip, gently stroke the feather from bottom to top. Observe whether the barbs stick together or separate.

3. Gently separate two barbs in the middle of the feather. Rub the separated edges with your fingertip.

4. Use a hand lens to examine the feather, including the edges of the two separated barbs. Draw a diagram of what you observe.

5. Now rejoin the two separated barbs by gently pulling outward from the shaft. Then wash your hands.

Think It Over
Observing Once barbs have been separated, is it easy to rejoin them? How might this be an advantage to the bird?

O n a clear spring morning, as the sun is beginning to rise, a male painted bunting flies from a low thicket to the high branch of a bush. He perches on the branch and sings his clear, musical song. With his brilliant red, blue, and green coloring, the male painted bunting is one of the most beautiful birds in North America. If you ever see one of these colorful birds, you won't soon forget it.

What Is a Bird?

Birds all share certain characteristics. **A bird is an endothermic vertebrate that has feathers and a four-chambered heart, and lays eggs.** Like reptiles, birds have scales on their feet. Most birds can fly.

Feathers are a major structural adaptation that enable birds to fly. Birds have different types of feathers. A contour feather is one of the large feathers that give shape to a bird's body. When a bird flies, these feathers help it balance and steer. In addition to contour feathers, birds have short, soft, fluffy down feathers next to the skin. Down feathers function to trap heat and keep the bird warm. In effect, down feathers cover a bird in lightweight long underwear.

◀ Painted bunting

Chapter 7 **247**

GUIDE FOR READING

◆ What characteristics do birds have in common?

◆ What characteristics do all mammals share?

Reading Tip As you read this section, make a compare/contrast table in which you compare birds and mammals on their body coverings, pattern of blood circulation, and method of reproduction.

Key Terms diaphragm
• mammary glands
• monotreme • marsupial
• gestation period
• placental mammal
• placenta

Objectives

After completing the lesson, students will be able to
◆ identify the common characteristics of birds;
◆ describe the characteristics that mammals share.

1 Engage/Explore

Activating Prior Knowledge

Ask students who have birds or mammals as pets to describe their pets' physical characteristics and behavior. Students can use their descriptions as a basis for making generalizations about the characteristics of birds and mammals. If any of their generalizations are incorrect, make sure that students correct them after they have read the chapter.

.... DISCOVER ....

Skills Focus observing **ACTIVITY**
Materials *feathers, hand lens*
Time 15 minutes
Tips Try to have a variety of contour feathers. Good sources are wooded areas, beaches, pet stores, bird sanctuaries, or biological supply houses. Fresh feathers should be frozen for 72 hours to kill organisms. Point out the shaft and barbs of a feather.
Expected Outcome Feathers have a central shaft with a vane made up of flexible barbs that link together but can be pulled apart.
Think It Over The barbs rejoin easily; this helps birds smooth their feathers quickly to fly.

READING STRATEGIES

Reading Tip Suggest that students set up their compare/contrast tables before they read. Students can fill in each box as they find the relevant information. Encourage students to read their completed charts as a way to review the section.

Program Resources

◆ **Unit 2 Resources** 7-6 Lesson Plan, p. 109; 7-6 Section Summary, p. 110
◆ **Guided Reading and Study Workbook** 7-6

2 Facilitate

What Is a Bird?

Including All Students

To help students under-stand the characteristics of birds, pair students who are still mastering English with students who are proficient in English. Have each pair list the following terms: *endothermic, vertebrate, feathers, four-chambered heart,* and *egg-laying.* Challenge student pairs to write brief definitions of each term and to list three or four animals that share these characteristics. *(Sample: Vertebrates have backbones and include lizards, giraffes, and fish.)* **limited English proficiency**

Eating Like a Bird

Building Inquiry Skills: Making Models

Materials *saltine cracker, plastic jar, several small pebbles*

Time 10 minutes

Tell students that birds eat small stones, which help the gizzard to grind food. In this activity, students can model the action of stones in a bird's gizzard. Direct students to place a saltine cracker in a plastic jar along with several small pebbles. Have them put the lid on the jar and shake it for 30 seconds. Ask: **What happened to the cracker?** *(It broke into smaller pieces.)* **How is the jar like a gizzard?** *(Both grind food using stones.)* **How are they different?** *(The gizzard is a muscular wall that squeezes as it grinds the food. The jar is a hard container that has to be shaken to grind the food.)*

learning modality: tactile/ kinesthetic

Figure 26 The roseate spoonbill catches small animals by sweeping its long, flattened bill back and forth under water. *Applying Concepts How is the structure of this bird's bill related to its function?*

Flight involves the muscular and skeletal systems. Large, powerful chest muscles attach to wing bones in the skeletal system. The chest muscles make the wing bones move. Many of a bird's bones are nearly hollow, making the bird's body extremely lightweight.

Eating Like a Bird

A bird's digestive system is also important in flight, because the digestive system delivers food to body cells. Like all animals, birds use the food they eat for energy. It takes an enormous amount of energy to power the muscles used in flight.

Birds respond to the internal stimulus of hunger by eating a huge amount of food. Each day an average bird eats food equal to about a quarter of its body weight. When people say, "You're eating like a bird," they usually mean that you're eating very little. But if you were actually eating as a bird does, you would be eating huge meals. You might eat 100 hamburger patties in one day!

Birds have no teeth. To capture, grip, and handle food, birds use their bills and claws. Each species of bird has a bill structured to help it feed. For example, the pointy, curved bill of a hawk acts like a meat hook. A hawk holds its prey with its claws and uses its sharp bill to pull off bits of flesh.

Each organ in a bird's digestive system is structured to process food. Many birds have a crop for storing food after swallowing it. Find the crop in *Exploring a Bird*. The crop is connected to the stomach, which begins to break food down. The gizzard squeezes and grinds the partially digested food.

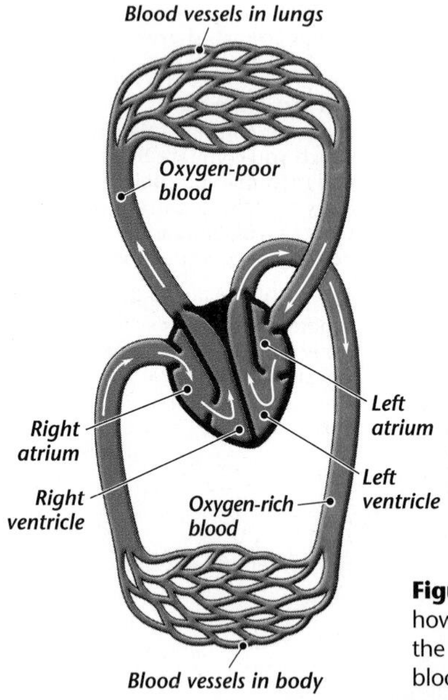

Delivering Oxygen to Cells

Cells must receive plenty of oxygen to release the energy contained in food. The cells of flying birds need large amounts of energy to power flight. Therefore, birds need a highly efficient way to get oxygen into their lungs and to their cells. Birds have a system of air sacs that connect to their lungs. The air sacs enable birds to obtain much more oxygen from each breath of air than other animals can.

Recall from Section 5 that both the circulatory system and the respiratory system are involved in transporting oxygen to cells. Unlike amphibians and most reptiles, whose hearts have three chambers, birds have hearts with four chambers—two atria and two ventricles. Figure 27 shows the path of blood through a bird's two-loop circulatory system.

Blood vessels in lungs

Oxygen-poor blood

Right atrium

Right ventricle

Oxygen-rich blood

Left atrium

Left ventricle

Blood vessels in body

Figure 27 Birds have hearts with four chambers. Notice how the left side of the heart is completely separate from the right side. This separation prevents oxygen-rich blood from mixing with oxygen-poor blood.

248

Background

Facts and Figures Birds can have unusual ways of obtaining food. Hummingbirds sip nectar while hovering in midair. Woodpecker finches use a broken piece of cactus spine to pry grubs and insects out of tree bark. African secretary birds stamp snakes with their feet before eating them. Owls use a keen sense of hearing to listen for prey. In the dark, an owl can accurately locate a mouse rustling in the leaves and grass. Some vultures can smell a potential meal from a great distance.

The right side of a bird's heart pumps blood to the lungs, where the blood picks up oxygen. Oxygen-rich blood then returns to the left side of the heart, which pumps it to the rest of the body. The advantage of a four-chambered heart is that there is no mixing of oxygen-rich and oxygen-poor blood. Therefore, blood that arrives in the body's tissues has plenty of oxygen.

☑ *Checkpoint* *How does the structure of a bird's heart provide an efficient way of delivering oxygen to cells?*

EXPLORING a Bird

If you are strolling through a grassy field or meadow in spring, you might hear the beautiful song of a meadowlark. Notice how a meadowlark's body is adapted for flight and for a high level of activity.

Air sacs A bird's lungs are connected to a series of air sacs. Air sacs help provide the bird's body with the rich supply of oxygen it needs.

Bill A meadowlark uses its bill to catch insects and pick up seeds.

Contour feathers Contour feathers give a bird its shape. Without its contour feathers, a bird cannot fly.

Crop

Heart Like all birds, meadowlarks have a four-chambered heart that keeps oxygen-rich blood separate from oxygen-poor blood. Thus the blood arriving at the tissues carries the most oxygen possible.

Gizzard The muscular gizzard churns food and grinds it to a paste.

Chapter 7 **249**

Answers to Self-Assessment

Caption Question

Figure 26 The broad, flat shape of the bill helps the spoonbill catch fish when the bill is dragged underwater.

☑ *Checkpoint*

A four-chambered heart prevents oxygen-rich blood from mixing with oxygen-poor blood, ensuring that cells get plenty of oxygen.

Delivering Oxygen to Cells

Inquiry Challenge

Have students find their pulse rates and count how many times they breathe in 1 minute. Then have able students run in place for 1 minute. (CAUTION: *Students with medical problems that preclude running should be excused from the activity.*) Have students find their new pulse and breathing rates. Ask them to form hypotheses about what happens to a bird's heart and breathing rate when it flies. **learning modality: tactile/kinesthetic**

EXPLORING
a Bird

Ask students to find the structures in the visual essay that help the bird fly. Most will select the feathers and wings. Point out other structures. Ask: **How do the air sacs and heart work as a bird flies?** (*The air sacs provide the oxygen. The heart pumps oxygen-rich blood to the body.*) Have students find the structures that are parts of the bird's digestive system. Ask: **How does the crop benefit the bird?** (*It allows the bird to store food.*) Have students trace the path through the digestive system. (*From the bill to the crop, to the stomach, to the gizzard, to the intestines*)

Extend Meadowlarks live in grassy environments and move mostly by flying. Have students examine photos of birds that are adapted for other forms of movement, such as ocean birds that dive and swim. Students can compare the bills, feathers, and body shapes of these birds. Refer to the **ELL Handbook** for additional teaching strategies. **learning modality: visual**

Ongoing Assessment

Skills Check Have students make a flowchart of the passage of food through a bird's digestive system.

 Students can save their flowcharts in their portfolios.

Quick Response to Stimuli

Building Inquiry Skills: Observing

Materials *binoculars*
Time 30 minutes

Take students outdoors to observe the way birds rely on their nervous systems. Students can use binoculars to observe and record specific activities, such as taking off, pecking, preening, or calling. They should also identify the senses that the bird probably used to perform the behavior. **learning modality: visual**

Reproducing and Caring for Young

Demonstration

Materials *3 uncooked chicken eggs, a heavy book, clay, cotton balls*
Time 10 minutes

Place the eggs in clay supports, small ends up, in a triangular pattern. Pad between the eggs with cotton. Ask students to predict what will happen when you place a book on the eggs. Demonstrate this. Then ask: **How do strong eggs benefit birds?** *(They will not break if they roll or when a bird sits on them.)* **learning modality: visual**

TRY THIS

Skills Focus observing
Materials *uncooked egg, bowl, hand lens, water*
Time 20 minutes
Tips Uncooked eggs can carry bacteria. Tell students not to put eggs in their mouths. Use only a little water in Step 3.
Answers There is an air pocket between the shell and the membrane. The water stays in the shell. The yolk provides food.
Observing Diagrams should identify the white spot, shell, yolk, egg white, and membrane.
Extend Have students gently roll an uncooked egg on a hard surface, and infer how the shape of an egg protects the embryo. *(The egg rolls in a circle, so it is less likely to roll out of the nest.)*
learning modality: visual

Figure 28 Owls are predators that hunt mostly at night. Sharp vision and keen hearing help owls find prey in the darkness.
Relating Cause and Effect What organs enable birds to respond quickly to stimuli?

TRY THIS

Eggs-amination

Like reptile eggs, bird eggs protect the developing embryo, provide food for it, and keep it from drying out.

1. Look at the surface of a chicken egg with a hand lens. Then gently crack the egg into a bowl. Do not break the yolk.

2. Note the membrane attached to the inside of the shell. Then look at the blunt end of the egg. What do you see?

3. Fill one part of the eggshell with water. What do you observe?

4. Find the egg yolk. What is its function?

5. Look for a small white spot on the yolk. This marks the spot where the embryo would have developed if the egg had been fertilized.

6. Wash your hands with soap.

Observing Draw a labeled diagram of the egg that names each structure and describes its function.

Quick Response to Stimuli

In order to fly, birds must be able to respond to stimuli very quickly. To appreciate why, imagine how quickly you would have to respond if you were a sparrow trying to land safely on a tree branch. You approach the tree headfirst, diving into a maze of tree branches. You have only an instant to find a place where you can land safely, without crashing into the other branches. A bird can respond quickly because of its well-developed brain and sense organs, including its eyes and ears. A flying vulture, for example, can spot food on the ground from a height of more than one and one-half kilometers.

Reproducing and Caring for Young

Bird eggs are similar to reptile eggs, except that the shells of bird eggs are harder. In most bird species, the female lays the eggs in a nest that has been prepared by one or both parents. Bird eggs will only develop at a temperature close to the body temperature of the parent bird. A parent bird usually incubates the eggs by sitting on them to keep them warm. When it is ready to hatch, a chick pecks its way out of the eggshell. Most parent birds feed and protect their young at least until they are able to fly.

☑ *Checkpoint* How do bird eggs differ from reptile eggs?

Why Birds Are Important

 INTEGRATING ENVIRONMENTAL SCIENCE Birds play an important role in the environment. Nectar-eating birds, like hummingbirds, carry pollen from one flower to another, thus enabling some flowers to reproduce. Seed-eating birds, like painted buntings, and fruit-eating birds carry the seeds of plants to new places. This happens when the birds eat the fruits or seeds of a plant, fly to a new location, and then eliminate some of the seeds in digestive wastes. In addition, birds are some of the chief predators of pest animals. Hawks and owls eat many rats and mice, and many birds feed on insect pests.

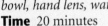

Background

Facts and Figures The incubation period for bird eggs depends on the species of bird. Warblers, which are small birds, incubate their eggs for just 10 days. Albatrosses, which are large birds, incubate their eggs for about 10 weeks. The award for the most energy-efficient brooding strategy, however, has to go to the cowbird. Cowbirds do not incubate their eggs at all, but instead lay their eggs in the nests of other birds. Even though the cowbird egg is larger than the other birds' eggs, the unknowing foster parents incubate the egg of the intruder anyway. When the cowbird egg hatches, the cowbird chick is usually much larger than the other chicks. The cowbird chick eventually becomes so large that it pushes the smaller rival chicks out of the nest or takes their food. The foster parents raise the lone cowbird chick, never realizing that it is not their own.

What Is a Mammal?

Mammals are a diverse group of vertebrates that include dogs, cats, buffaloes, kangaroos, and spiny anteaters. Tiny mice are mammals, and so are huge elephants. Mammals share many characteristics. **All mammals are endothermic vertebrates with a four-chambered heart and skin covered with fur or hair. The young of most mammals are born alive, and every young mammal is fed with milk produced in its mother's body.** In addition, mammals have teeth of different shapes that are adapted to their diets. Like birds, mammals have a circulatory system with two loops. In one loop, blood picks up oxygen from the lungs. In the second loop, blood delivers oxygen to the body cells.

Fur and Hair

All mammals have fur or hair at some point in their lives. Like a bird's down feathers, thick fur provides lightweight insulation that prevents body heat from escaping. Fur and hair help mammals maintain a stable body temperature in cold weather. Mammals also have a layer of fat beneath their skins. Fat, like fur and feathers, is an insulating material that keeps heat in the body.

The amount of hair that covers the skin of a mammal varies a great deal from group to group. Some mammals, such as whales and manatees, have only a few bristles. Others, including dogs and weasels, have thick fur. In general, animals that live in cold regions have thicker coats of fur than animals that live in warm environments.

Figure 29 The amount of fur or hair covering a mammal's body varies greatly. Armadillos (left) live in hot regions and have little hair. Gray wolves (right) live in cooler regions and have thick fur coats during the cold winter months. *Applying Concepts What function does fur perform?*

Why Birds Are Important

Integrating Environmental Science

Emphasize the important roles birds play in pollinating plants and eliminating pests. Encourage students to care for birds in their own neighborhood. As trees are cut down, nesting habitats are lost. A birdhouse gives birds a place to nest. Have students research a particular bird and then design and build a birdhouse for birds that live in their neighborhood. **learning modality: verbal**

What Is a Mammal?

Cultural Diversity

Nearly all cultures use domesticated mammals. The yak in Tibet, the ox in Western Europe, and the llama in South America transport loads and help farmers plow fields. Tell students mammals also provide milk and meat, rich sources of protein. In some cultures, such as that of the Masai people in East Africa, the cow is so highly valued that it is used as currency. **learning modality: verbal**

Fur and Hair

Building Inquiry Skills: Comparing and Contrasting

Provide pictures of different mammals, including some with a lot of hair and some with very little. Include pictures of the animals' heads and faces. Ask students: **Are there some kinds of hair that all these mammals have?** (*Most mammals have whiskers around the eyes, lips, and muzzle.*) **learning modality: visual**

Ongoing Assessment

Writing Invite students to speculate about how the fur or hair of a mammal living in the Arctic tundra might differ from the fur or hair of a mammal living in the Amazon rain forest. (*The fur or hair of the mammal living in the tundra will probably be thicker than the fur or hair of the animal living in the rain forest.*)

Structure and Function of Teeth

Including All Students

Students who are mastering English may need extra help to remember the names for the types of teeth. Obtain models or preserved jaws of a herbivore and a carnivore, such as a cow and a cat. Label the four types of teeth and have students say the names as they touch the teeth. Have students use the structure of the teeth to determine which animal is a carnivore and which is a herbivore. If you use preserved jawbones, have students wash their hands after this activity. **limited English proficiency**

Breathing

Building Inquiry Skills: Observing

Have students place a hand flat on their abdomens about 6 cm above the navel. Ask students to describe the movement of their rib cages when they take a deep breath and then let it out. (*The ribs expand when they take a deep breath and contract when they let it out.*) **learning modality: tactile/kinesthetic**

Nervous System and Senses

Inquiry Challenge

Materials *orange peel, cloves, vanilla extract, small containers, blindfold*
Time 30 minutes

Have groups of students design a simple experiment to answer a question about the senses using these materials. (*Sample: Can humans find their way using only their sense of smell?*) Groups should write plans for your approval before they perform the experiment. Have students predict the outcome, perform the experiment, and draw a conclusion. **cooperative learning**

Figure 30 Lions have sharp, pointed teeth. Note the especially long canine teeth. *Inferring What kind of diet do lions eat?*

Structure and Function of Teeth

The structure of mammals' teeth enables mammals to chew their food, breaking it into small bits that make digestion easier. Unlike reptiles and fishes, whose teeth usually all have the same shape, most mammals have teeth with four different shapes. Incisors are flat-edged teeth used to bite off and cut parts of food. Canines are sharply pointed teeth that stab food and tear into it. Premolars and molars grind and shred food into tiny bits.

The size, shape, and hardness of a mammal's teeth reflect its diet. For example, the canines of carnivores are especially large and sharp. Large carnivores, such as lions and tigers, use their canines to hold prey while killing it. Herbivores, such as deer, have molars with broad, flat surfaces that can mash plants.

Breathing

Like reptiles and birds, all mammals breathe with lungs—even mammals such as whales that live in the ocean. Mammals breathe in and out because of the combined action of rib muscles and a large muscle called the **diaphragm**. The diaphragm is located at the bottom of the chest. The lungs are organs with a huge, moist surface area. Because of the large surface area, a lot of oxygen can move from the air into the bloodstream.

☑ *Checkpoint* *How do mammals take air into their bodies?*

Nervous System and Senses

The brains of mammals enable them to learn, remember, and respond to stimuli in complex ways. Squirrels, for example, feed on nuts. To do this, they must crack the nutshell to get to the nut meat inside. Squirrels learn to use different methods to crack different kinds of nuts, depending on where the weak points in each kind of shell are located.

The senses of mammals are highly developed and adapted for the ways that individual species live. Tarsiers, which are active at night, have huge eyes that enable them to see in the dark. Monkeys, gorillas, and chimpanzees are able to see objects in color. This ability is extremely useful because these mammals are most active during the day when colors are visible.

252

Background

Facts and Figures The fossil record of mammal teeth is fairly easy for paleontologists to trace. The earliest form of a mammal molar was shaped like a triangle. Opossum molars still have this shape. As mammals diversified, they ate different types of food. For example, the anteater is a mammal that has become specialized to eat insects such as ants. The anteater's elongated skull and tongue allow it to remove insects from underground nests. Its lower jaw has become smaller and it has fewer teeth.

Figure 31 Young mammals usually require much parental care. On a rocky slope in Alaska, this Dall's sheep keeps a close watch on her lamb.

Reproduction

Although a few kinds of mammals lay shelled eggs, the young of most mammals develop within their mothers' bodies and are never enclosed in an eggshell. All mammals, even those that lay eggs, feed their young with milk produced in the mother's **mammary glands.**

Young mammals are usually quite helpless for a long time after being born. Many are born without a coat of insulating fur. Their eyes are often sealed and may not open for weeks. For example, black bear cubs are surprisingly tiny when they are born. The blind, nearly hairless cubs have a mass of only 240 to 330 grams—about as small as a grapefruit. The mass of an adult black bear, in contrast, ranges from about 120 to 150 kilograms—about 500 times as large as a newborn cub!

Young mammals generally stay with their mother or both parents for an extended time. For example, black bear cubs follow their mother for about a year after their birth. During that time, they learn how to be bears. They learn things that are important to their survival, such as which mushrooms and berries are good to eat and how to find the good-tasting grubs in a rotten log.

Figure 32 Mammals, like these springboks, have large brains. A springbok's brain processes complex stimuli from the external environment. This enables the springbok to respond quickly.

Sharpen your Skills

Inferring

Mammals move in a variety of ways—running, flying, swimming, climbing. Obtain photos of a variety of mammals, such as horses, bats, rabbits, whales, and seals. Observe the limbs of each animal. Infer how the structure of the animal's limbs functions to enable the mammal to move in a specific way.

Chapter 7 **253**

Figure 33 The duck-billed platypus (left) is a monotreme. The opossums (right) are marsupials. *Comparing and Contrasting How are monotremes different from marsupials?*

Monotremes

Biologists classify mammals into three groups: monotremes, marsupials, and placental mammals. Mammals are classified into one of these groups on the basis of how their young develop. Mammals that lay eggs are called **monotremes.** Spiny anteaters and duck-billed platypuses, which are found only in Australia and New Guinea, are the only monotremes alive today. Like all mammals, monotremes feed their young with milk.

Spiny anteaters look like pincushions with long noses. As their name implies, spiny anteaters eat ants, which they dig up with their powerful claws. The duck-billed platypus has webbed feet and a bill, but it also has fur. Platypuses live in water. The female lays her eggs in an underground nest.

Marsupials

Koalas, kangaroos, wallabies, and opossums are some of the better-known marsupials. **Marsupials** are mammals whose young are born alive, but at an early stage of development. They usually continue to develop in a pouch on their mother's body. Marsupials are found mostly in South America, Australia, and New Guinea. Marsupials have a very short **gestation period,** the length of time between fertilization and birth. Opossums, which are the only marsupials found in North America, have a gestation period of only about 13 days.

Newborn marsupials are tiny—the newborns of one opossum species are only about 10 millimeters long! They crawl along the wet fur of their mother's belly until they reach her pouch. Once inside, they find one of her nipples and attach to it. They remain in the pouch at least until they have grown enough to peer out of the pouch opening.

☑ *Checkpoint* *What do the young of marsupials do immediately after they are born?*

Placental Mammals

Unlike a monotreme or a marsupial, a **placental mammal** develops inside its mother's body until its body systems can function independently. The name of this group comes from the **placenta,** an organ in pregnant female mammals through which materials pass between the mother and the developing embryo. Food and oxygen pass from the mother to her young through the placenta. Wastes pass from the young through the placenta to the mother, where they are eliminated by her body. The umbilical cord connects the young to the placenta. Most mammals are placental mammals.

Placental mammals are classified into groups on the basis of characteristics such as how they eat and how their bodies are adapted for moving. For example, whales, dolphins, and porpoises form one group of mammals that have adaptations for swimming. The mammals in the carnivore group, which includes cats, dogs, otters, and seals, are all predators that have enlarged canine teeth. Rabbits and hares are leaping mammals. They have long hind legs specialized for spectacular jumps.

Primates, which include monkeys, apes, and humans, all have large brains and eyes that face forward. In addition, the forelimbs of many primates have adaptations for grasping. Many primates have opposable thumbs—thumbs that can touch the other four fingers.

Placental mammals vary in the length of their gestation periods. Generally, the larger the placental mammal, the longer its gestation period. For example, African elephants are the largest land-dwelling placental mammals. The gestation period for an elephant averages about 21 months. A house mouse, on the other hand, gives birth after a gestation period of only about 21 days.

Figure 34 Jack rabbits have legs adapted for jumping. Streamlined bodies and flippers enable dolphins to move swiftly through water.

Section 6 Review

1. What are the characteristics of birds?
2. List five characteristics that all mammals share.
3. Describe the structure and function of down feathers and contour feathers.
4. Explain the difference in the development of the young of monotremes, marsupials, and placental mammals.
5. **Thinking Critically Making Generalizations** What characteristics enable birds and mammals to live in colder environments than reptiles can?

Science at Home

Mammals' Milk With a family member, examine the nutrition facts listed on a container of whole milk. What types of nutrients does whole milk contain? Discuss why milk is an ideal source of food for young, growing mammals.

Chapter 7 **255**

Program Resources

◆ **Unit 2 Resources** 7-6 Review and Reinforce, p. 111; 7-6 Enrich, p. 112

---

3 Assess

Section 6 Review Answers

1. Birds are endothermic vertebrates; have feathers and a four-chambered heart; and lay eggs.
2. All mammals are endothermic vertebrates, have four-chambered hearts, have skin with fur or hair, and produce milk.
3. Contour feathers are large and help shape the bird's body. They are used to balance and steer during flight. Down feathers are small and fluffy. They trap heat and keep the bird warm.
4. Monotremes hatch from eggs. Marsupials are born at an early stage of development and remain in their mother's pouch for a while. Placental mammals develop inside the mother and are born when their body systems can function independently.
5. Mammals and birds are endothermic and have fur, hair, or feathers to keep them warm.

Science at Home

Show students the nutrition facts listed on a milk label so they will know what to look for.

ACTIVITY

Answers to Self-Assessment

Caption Question

Figure 33 Marsupials give birth to live young. Monotremes lay eggs.

✓ *Checkpoint*

The young of marsupials crawl into their mother's pouch, find one of her nipples, and attach to it.

Performance Assessment

Drawing Invite students to sketch a bird and a mammal. They should then list those of its characteristics that are unique to birds and mammals. *(Answers will vary depending on the animals chosen and the detail achieved in students' sketches.)*

You, the Consumer

Keeping Warm

Preparing for Inquiry

Key Concept Wool is an insulator that helps an animal or object stay warm.

Skills Objective Students will be able to
◆ control variables and determine whether dry and wet wool have different insulating properties.

Time 35 minutes

Advance Planning Make sure groups use identical containers, such as plastic yogurt cups. *Computer use is optional.*

Guiding Inquiry

Invitation Discuss different uses of insulation.

Introducing the Procedure
Students will compare temperature changes to find whether wet or dry wool insulates better.

Troubleshooting the Experiment
Supply a large container of hot water so that all "hot water" used will be the same temperature, around 40–45°C.

Expected Outcome
The containers should cool in this order: no sock, wet sock, dry sock.

Analyze and Conclude
1. Students should graph data with time on the *x*-axis, temperature on the *y*-axis.
2. The temperature changed most in the uncovered container, then the wet, then the dry. Wool keeps animals warm even when it is wet.
3. Sample: Yes. Wet gloves will keep you warmer than no gloves.

Extending Inquiry

Design an Experiment Remind students to use materials of the same thickness.

You, the Consumer

KEEPING WARM

Any time you wear wool, you are using a mammalian adaptation to keep warm. Suppose a manufacturer were to claim that its wool socks keep your feet warm whether the socks are wet or dry. In this investigation, you will test that claim.

Problem

Do wool products provide insulation from the cold? How well does wool insulate when it is wet?

Skills Focus

controlling variables, interpreting data

Materials

tap water, hot
beaker, 1 L
clock or watch
a pair of wool socks
tap water, room temperature
3 containers, 250 mL, with lids

scissors
3 thermometers
graph paper
computer (optional)

Procedure

1. Put one container into a dry woolen sock. Soak a second sock with water at room temperature, wring it out so it's not dripping, and then slide the second container into the wet sock. Both containers should stand upright. Leave the third container uncovered.

2. Use your computer or a pencil and paper to create a data table. List the containers in the first column. Provide four more columns in which to record the water temperatures during the experiment.

3. Use scissors to carefully cut a small "X" in the center of each lid. Make the X just large enough for a thermometer to pass through.

4. Fill a beaker with about 800 mL of hot tap water. Then pour hot water nearly to the top of each of the three containers. **CAUTION:** *Avoid spilling hot water on yourself or others.*

5. Place a lid on each of the containers, and insert a thermometer into the water through the hole in each lid. Gather the socks around the thermometers above the first two containers so that the containers are completely covered.

6. Immediately measure the temperature of the water in each container, and record it in your data table. Take temperature readings every 5 minutes for at least 15 minutes.

Analyze and Conclude

1. Graph your results using a different color to represent each container. Graph time in minutes on the horizontal axis and temperature on the vertical axis.

2. Compare the temperature changes in the three containers. Relate your findings to the insulation characteristics of mammal skin coverings.

3. **Apply** Suppose an ad for wool gloves claims that the gloves keep you warm even if they get wet. Do your findings support this claim? Why or why not?

Design an Experiment

Design an experiment to compare how wool's insulating properties compare with those of other natural materials (such as cotton) or manufactured materials (such as acrylic). Obtain your teacher's approval before conducting your experiment.

Sample Data Table

Container	Temp. 0 min (°C)	Temp. 5 min (°C)	Temp. 10 min (°C)	Temp. 15 min (°C)
No Sock	45	36	29	25
Wet Sock	47	44	39	36
Dry Sock	46	44	41	38

Safety

Students should walk slowly when carrying glass containers or hot water to avoid breakage or spills. Students should be cautious when putting holes in lids with scissors. When handling glass thermometers, students should not force thermometers through the holes in lids. They can make a larger hole if the thermometer does not fit. Review the safety guidelines in Appendix A.

1 What Is an Animal?

Key Ideas
◆ Animals are many-celled heterotrophs that move, with structures for specific functions.

Key Terms

adaptation   predator   invertebrate
herbivore   prey   vertebrate
carnivore   omnivore

2 Symmetry

INTEGRATING **MATHEMATICS**

Key Idea
◆ The bodies of most animals have symmetry.

Key Terms
bilateral symmetry   radial symmetry

3 Sponges, Cnidarians, Worms and Mollusks

Key Ideas
◆ A sponge is pierced all over with pores.
◆ Cnidarians use stinging cells to capture prey.
◆ Three major phyla of worms are flatworms, roundworms, and segmented worms.
◆ Mollusks have soft bodies, mantles, and are often protected by shells.

Key Terms
cnidarian   anus   mollusk   gills   radula

4 Arthropods and Echinoderms

Key Ideas
◆ An arthropod has an external skeleton, segmented body, and jointed appendages.
◆ Insects have three body sections and six legs.
◆ Echinoderms have five-part radial symmetry, an endoskeleton, and a water vascular system.

Key Terms

arthropod   metamorphosis   crustacean
exoskeleton   larva   arachnid
thorax   pupa   echinoderm
abdomen   nymph   endoskeleton

5 Fishes, Amphibians, and Reptiles

Key Ideas
◆ A vertebrate's endoskeleton supports, protects, and gives shape to the body.
◆ A fish is an ectothermic vertebrate with fins. Most fishes have gills and scales.
◆ An amphibian spends its early life in water and its adult life on land.
◆ A reptile has lungs and scaly skin.

Key Terms

vertebra   cartilage   ventricle
ectotherm   atrium   kidney
endotherm

6 Birds and Mammals

Key Ideas
◆ A bird is an egg-laying endothermic vertebrate that has feathers and a four-chambered heart.
◆ A mammal has a four-chambered heart and fur or hair. Young mammals are fed with milk.

Key Terms

diaphragm   gestation period
mammary glands   placental mammal
monotreme   placenta
marsupial

Organizing Information

Compare/Contrast Table Copy the table comparing fish groups onto a separate sheet of paper. Then complete the table and add a title.

Kind of Fish	Kind of Skeleton	Jaws?	Scales?	Example
Jawless Fishes	a. ?	no	b. ?	c. ?
d. ?	e. ?	f. ?	toothlike scales	shark
Bony Fishes	bone	g. ?	h. ?	i. ?

Organizing Information

Compare/Contrast Table Sample Title: The Characteristics of Different Fish Groups; **a.** cartilage **b.** none **c.** lamprey or hagfish **d.** cartilaginous fishes **e.** cartilage **f.** yes **g.** yes **h.** yes **i.** Sample: trout, tuna, or goldfish

Program Resources

◆ **Unit 2 Resources** Chapter 7 Project Scoring Rubric, p. 88
◆ **Performance Assessment** Chapter 7, pp. 23–25
◆ **Chapter and Unit Tests** Chapter 7 Test, pp. 32–35
◆ **Unit 2 Resources** Real-World Lab blackline masters, pp. 116–117

Media and Technology

 Computer Test Bank
Chapter 7 Test

 Lab Activity Videotapes
Grade 6, Tape 2

Reviewing Content
Multiple Choice
1. b 2. b 3. d 4. c 5. c

True or False
6. true 7. bilateral 8. a closed 9. true
10. down

Checking Concepts

11. Earthworms have muscles for burrowing in the soil; birds and insects have wings for flying; frogs have long hind legs and powerful leg muscles so they can jump.

12. Invertebrates do not have backbones; for example, jellyfish and beetles. Vertebrates have a backbone; for example, fish and birds.

13. A sponge gets oxygen from the water that flows into its central cavity.

14. A flatworm has a digestive system closed at one end; a roundworm has a digestive system open at both ends.

15. Many worms move away from or avoid light.

16. A snail's radula is attached to the floor of its mouth. It sticks out the radula to scrape tiny particles of food off a surface.

17. Frogs have powerful legs for leaping; salamanders creep along the ground. As adults, frogs have no tails and salamanders do.

18. A reptile's egg has protective membranes and a shell. This structure keeps the embryo safe and keeps water in the shell, allowing reptiles to lay eggs on land.

19. Birds have contour feathers that help it balance and steer. Their bones are nearly hollow, making their bodies light. They have powerful chest muscles to move their wings.

20. In pregnant placental mammals, the placenta passes materials from mother to young and wastes from young to mother.

21. Sample: A cnidarian's nerve net senses the stimulus of food—a fish. It responds by moving toward the fish and using its stinging cells to inject venom and paralyze its prey. Then the tentacles pull the fish into the cnidarian's mouth.

Reviewing Content

 Review key concepts online using iText at www.phschool.com

Multiple Choice
Choose the letter of the best answer.

1. Organisms that eat both plants and animals are called
   a. autotrophs. b. omnivores.
   c. herbivores. d. carnivores.
2. An animal with many lines of symmetry
   a. is bilaterally symmetrical.
   b. is radially symmetrical.
   c. has no symmetry.
   d. has line symmetry.
3. Which of these is true of the legs of arthropods?
   a. They always number six.
   b. They are always attached to the abdomen.
   c. They are rigid.
   d. They are jointed.
4. Adult frogs must return to the water to
   a. catch flies.
   b. obtain their food.
   c. reproduce.
   d. moisten their gills.
5. Kangaroos, koalas, and opossums are all
   a. monotremes.
   b. cephalopods.
   c. marsupials.
   d. placental mammals.

True or False
If the statement is true, write true. If it is false, change the underlined word or words to make the statement true.

6. <u>All</u> animals are made up of many cells.
7. Fish have <u>radial</u> symmetry.
8. An earthworm has <u>an open</u> circulatory system.
9. Reptiles and amphibians are <u>ectotherms.</u>
10. Fur and <u>contour</u> feathers have similar functions.

Checking Concepts

11. Describe three structural adaptations that enable animals to move in specific ways.

12. How is an invertebrate different from a vertebrate? Identify two invertebrates and two vertebrates.

13. How does a sponge obtain oxygen?

14. Contrast a roundworm's digestive system to that of a planarian.

15. How do many worms respond to the stimulus of light?

16. Explain how a snail uses its radula.

17. How are salamanders different from frogs?

18. Describe the structure of a reptile's egg. Explain how the structure enables reptiles to lay eggs on land.

19. How is the structure of a bird's body adapted for flight?

20. What is the function of a placenta?

21. **Writing to Learn** Write a description of a cnidarian catching a fish. Explain the function of the cnidarian's nerve net and tentacles in this process. In your description, use the words *stimulus* and *response*.

Thinking Critically

22. **Applying Concepts** Which capital letters of the alphabet have bilateral symmetry? Radial symmetry?

23. **Inferring** Most echinoderms live in water that is churned by strong waves. How might the structure and function of an echinoderm's tube feet be an advantage in such an environment?

24. **Comparing and Contrasting** Contrast the circulatory systems of fishes, amphibians, and birds.

25. **Relating Cause and Effect** If a bird loses too many contour feathers, it cannot fly. Why do you think that this is the case?

26. **Comparing and Contrasting** Why do you think some scientists might consider monotremes to be a link between reptiles and mammals?

Thinking Critically

22. Bilateral symmetry: A, B, C, D, E, H, I, K, M, T, U, V, W, Y. Radial symmetry: O and X.

23. The tube feet of an echinoderm act as suction cups, allowing it to grip underwater rocks or the sea floor as water churns around it, so the animal is not dashed about and harmed by the moving water.

24. A fish has a one-loop circulatory system. An adult amphibian has a two-loop circulatory system with a three-chambered heart. A bird has a two-loop circulatory system with a four-chambered heart.

25. Without contour feathers to help it balance and steer, a bird loses its ability to fly.

26. Unlike other mammals and like reptiles, monotremes' young hatch from eggs.

Applying Skills

The data table below shows the approximate gestation period of several mammals and the approximate length of time that those mammals care for their young after birth. Use the information in the table to answer Questions 27–29.

Mammal	Gestation Period	Time Spent Caring for Young After Birth
Deer mouse	0.75 month	1 month
Chimpanzee	8 months	24 months
Harp seal	11 months	0.75 month
Elephant	21 months	24 months
Bobcat	2 months	8 months

27. **Graphing** Decide which kind of graph would be best for showing the data in the table. Then construct two graphs—one for gestation period and the other for time.

28. **Interpreting Data** Which mammals in the table care for their young for the longest time? The shortest time?

29. **Drawing Conclusions** What seems to be the general relationship between the size of the mammal and the length of time for which it cares for its young? Which animal is the exception to this pattern?

Performance CHAPTER PROJECT Assessment

Present Your Project Display your models in a creative way—for example, show the models in action and show details of the animals' environments. Also display your poster.

Reflect and Record In your journal, list all the adaptations you learned from your classmates' presentations. How did constructing a three-dimensional model help you understand the characteristics of these animals? What were the limitations of the models you constructed?

Test Preparation

Use these questions to prepare for standardized tests.

Study the graph. Then answer Questions 30–33.

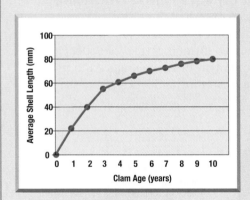

30. What is the best title for this graph?
   A Clamshell Growth over Time
   B The Ages of a Clam
   C The Maximum Size of Clams
   D The Life Span of Clams

31. In some states, the minimum harvesting size for clams is 40 millimeters. Approximately how long does it take new clams to reach this size?
   F 1 year   G 2 years
   H 3 years   J 4 years

32. Based on the graph, which generalization about clam growth is correct?
   A Clam growth is most rapid during years 5 through 10.
   B Clam growth is most rapid during years 0 through 5.
   C Clam growth is equally rapid each year.
   D Clam growth is very slow.

33. How many millimeters larger was the average clam at age 2 compared to age 1?
   F 8 millimeters
   G 15 millimeters
   H 18 millimeters
   J 25 millimeters

Applying Skills

27. Two bar graphs, one showing gestation period, and the other showing length of time young are cared for.
28. Longest: chimpanzee and elephant. Shortest: harp seal.
29. The larger the mammal, the longer it cares for its young. The exception is the harp seal.

Performance CHAPTER PROJECT Assessment

Present Your Project Have students give oral presentations explaining their models and the relationship between structure and function in the animals they chose.
Reflect and Record In assessing their work, students should explain how making the models helped them understand particular animal structures. They should say which parts of their work were most and least successful, and why. They should also discuss the limitations of their models. For example, many models will not show the animals' structures entirely accurately or the models may lack detail.

Test Preparation

30. A 31. G 32. B 33. H

Program Resources

- **Inquiry Skills Activity Book** Provides teaching and review of all inquiry skills
- **Prentice Hall Assessment System** Provides standardized test practice
- **Reading in the Content Area** Provides strategies to improve science reading skills
- **Teacher's ELL Handbook** Provides multiple strategies for English language learners

Unlocking the Secrets of Cells

Focus on Molecular Biology

This four-page feature presents an interview with a working scientist, molecular biologist Lydia Villa-Komaroff. Using Dr. Villa-Komaroff's work in developing a technique to produce human insulin, this interview focuses on scientific problem solving as a key element of scientific inquiry.

Cell structure and function and basic genetics were introduced in Chapter 4 and Chapter 5. However, students need not have any previous knowledge of the content of these chapters to understand and appreciate this feature.

Scientific Inquiry

Before students read the interview, encourage them to read the title and the captions and examine the pictures. Then ask: **What is the focus of this scientist's work?** *(To use genetic engineering to produce human proteins, such as insulin)* **What is diabetes?** *(Some students may know that diabetes is a disorder in which the body cannot control levels of sugar in the blood.)* Explain that the bodies of people with diabetes do not produce enough insulin.

UNLOCKING THE
Secrets of Cells

It takes courage and dedication to follow your dreams. Lydia Villa-Komaroff learned that early in her career. She comes from a family of courageous Mexican American women. Her mother and both grandmothers were strong role models for her. Their support, as well as her father's, encouraged her to pursue a career in science. As a molecular biologist, Dr. Villa-Komaroff studies the role of proteins in the growth and development of living things.

In 1976, Lydia was part of a team conducting genetic engineering, a technique by which scientists transfer genes from one organism into another. Today, scientists use this technique to produce medicines, to treat diseases, and to improve crops. In the 1970s, genetic engineering was a new idea. It was feared by many people who thought it might have harmful results. In fact, the city where Lydia worked banned genetic engineering.

To continue her research, Lydia was forced to move her lab to another state. She spent a year away from many of her colleagues and friends. "It was a frustrating and lonely time," she recalls.

Lydia Villa-Komaroff is Vice President for Research at Northwestern University in Chicago, Illinois. She earned her Ph.D. in cell biology at the Massachusetts Institute of Technology. An avid skier and photographer, Lydia also loves to read, particularly mysteries and biographies.

260

Background

Biology is the study of living things. It is a very broad area of study, and most biologists specialize in a certain field. Molecular biologists, like Lydia Villa-Komaroff, study the molecules that direct cellular processes in organisms. Molecular biology developed from the study of genetics and incorporates principles of biochemistry and physics as they apply to biology. Research in molecular biology has begun to explain why certain genes are expressed in some cells, but not in others. Molecular biologists often manipulate DNA or RNA to help them understand the functions of particular proteins. Knowledge about how genes are regulated and how their proteins function has direct applications to medicine and agriculture.

But her hard work paid off. The ban was lifted, and soon after, Lydia helped discover a method for making insulin. Insulin is used to treat people who suffer from diabetes. Discovering a way to make insulin launched a new industry—biotechnology. It marked a personal triumph for Lydia. "Scientifically, that was the most exciting time of my life," she says. "There were any number of reasons to think we couldn't make insulin. But we planned it, we tried it, and no experiment before or since has worked so smoothly."

Many secrets of the human cell remain to be unlocked. Lydia hopes to provide some of the keys.

Talking With Dr. Lydia Villa-Komaroff

Q *How did you become interested in science?*

A My Mexican grandmother was very interested in natural history—plants in particular. She had books we used to look at with beautiful color pictures of plants. What really sparked my interest was just following her around, learning about the plants in our garden, and going out collecting wild spinach with her.

Q *What made you choose a career in biology?*

A I had an incredibly exciting developmental biology course in college. One time we camped out in the lab for 36 hours so we could watch frogs develop. Normally you study that in pictures in textbooks. But we were seeing it happen in real life. It was very exciting.

Q *What does a molecular biologist do?*

A We study development at the most basic level: what goes on within a cell. Think of the cell as a house, with many different parts—the foundation, the walls, the roof, and lots of bricks and wood and wiring. I'm interested in finding out how that structure gets built.

Dr. Villa-Komaroff explains her work to a group of students.

261

◆ Help students sort the information about cells and relate it to the house analogy by listing on the board the terms used in the interview. You might wish to diagram both a house and a cell and label them with the terms. Also record each molecule's role in the cell. *(DNA: blueprints, hereditary information that determines the traits of an organism; RNA: copy of blueprints that goes to the construction site; proteins: bricks and mortar and hammers and drills, make up cell structure and read DNA and RNA to build other proteins)*

◆ Have students study the diagram that illustrates Dr. Villa-Komaroff's technique to produce insulin. Relate the house-building analogy to this diagram by pointing out the parts of the cell that are used to make human insulin. The human insulin gene, the bacterial chromosome, and the plasmid are all DNA. Dr. Villa-Komaroff used certain proteins as "saws" to cut the human insulin gene out of human DNA. She used other proteins as "bolts" to connect the human insulin gene to the plasmid. Once the bacteria took up the plasmid, the bacteria's machinery made the human insulin as if it were its own protein.

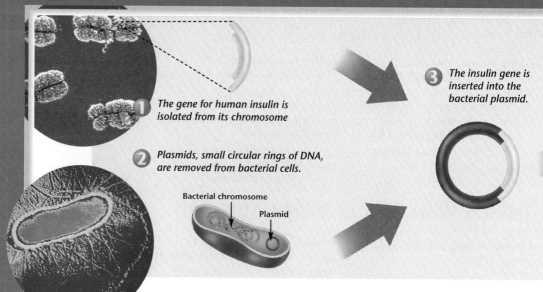

1 The gene for human insulin is isolated from its chromosome

2 Plasmids, small circular rings of DNA, are removed from bacterial cells.

Bacterial chromosome

Plasmid

3 The insulin gene is inserted into the bacterial plasmid.

Dr. Villa-Komaroff pioneered the use of genetic engineering to produce human proteins, such as insulin.

Q *Is there a plan or blueprint for building a cell?*

A All the instructions are in the DNA. That is the material in the nucleus of a cell that carries the hereditary information that determines traits, such as your skin and hair color. The machinery, which is made up of proteins, comes in and reads bits of that information, which are called genes. Then DNA is copied into RNA, a message that travels out to the part of the cell where all the building activity goes on. Other proteins read it and start to produce the materials that the cell needs to work.

Q *Are proteins the tools or the structure of a cell?*

A Actually, they're both. Proteins are the building blocks of cells, like the bricks and mortar in a house. But they're also the machinery that builds cells, like hammers and drills. Proteins make up the cell, and build the cell.

Q *What other information does DNA contain?*

A It contains coding instructions to make sure the right information gets used at the right time. If you were building a house, you couldn't put up the roof before you had walls. In building a human, a certain amount of the head needs to be in place, for example, before you can make eyes. So it's very important for a cell to know what information to use, and when to use it.

Q *How do cells know when to start and stop building?*

A It's still not clear how that process is coordinated. There are certain genes that we understand very well. We know what signals they send the cell to say it's time to become a heart or a liver. But how does the cell know when to use that information, and when to stop? Those are some of the big questions that we're trying to answer.

Background

Plasmids are small, circular molecules of DNA found in some bacterial cells. They are separate from the chromosomal DNA of bacteria, and they carry genes that are not essential to the basic functions of the bacterial cell. Plasmids require the bacterial chromosome's machinery for replication and for making their proteins. Plasmids commonly carry genes for resistance to specific antibiotics. Bacterial cells that contain these plasmids are resistant to those antibiotics.

4 Plasmids with the insulin gene are taken up by the bacterial cells. The gene directs the cell to produce insulin.

5 The insulin is collected and used to treat people with diabetes.

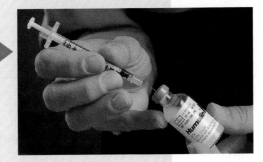

Q *What was the significance of the technique you developed to produce insulin?*

A People with diabetes used to be treated with pig insulin. But pig insulin is in short supply and therefore expensive. The work we did showed how to make a lot of insulin very cheaply, by growing it in bacteria. And it's human insulin.

Q *How did you trick the cell into making insulin?*

A We were able to isolate the gene with instructions for making insulin. We then inserted it into bacteria. Basically, we tricked the bacteria into thinking the gene was one of its own pieces of DNA. The bacteria then made insulin.

Q *Why didn't you give up when your research was banned?*

A We were doing very important work. To quit would have been to admit that the ban was right. We knew that others were doing the same research. You can't win a race if you quit.

Q *Were you ever discouraged?*

A There were times when I was discouraged, but I think that is true of anyone doing something where there is no guarantee of success. I think I've always approached a project with the idea that I have to give it my best shot.

Q *What advice would you give a person planning a science career?*

A You can't be entirely sure what you'll be able to do. The world is changing too fast. The important thing is to find something you like, and learn it very well. If you follow what you like, it may be different in 10 years, but it will be a logical extension of your own interests.

In Your Journal

As a young scientist, Lydia continued her research in genetic engineering in spite of obstacles that blocked her work. What does her action tell you about her as a person? Describe some character traits that you think would help a scientist to be successful. Why would those traits be important?

◆ Discuss Dr. Villa-Komaroff's success in her work. Ask: **What can you learn from Dr. Villa-Komaroff's success?** *(Accept all answers, encouraging students to explain their answers. If necessary, focus students on Villa-Komaroff's character traits.)* Help students realize that they can also be successful in whatever they choose to do in their lives by following the example of Dr. Villa-Komaroff.

In Your Journal Students should identify Dr. Villa-Komaroff as being persistent and confident about the importance of her work. Students might use these same character traits to describe a successful scientist. Successful scientists are also creative thinkers, good problem solvers, good communicators, focused on details, careful observers, cooperative, and hard workers. Students should also describe how these character traits would help a scientist in his or her work. In the process, they should identify the different aspects or duties of a scientist. You might allow class time to discuss these character traits. Invite students to describe the traits they wrote about in their journals. Help students realize that these character traits are useful in many other careers in addition to careers in the sciences.

CHAPTER 8

Ecosystems

Sections	Time	Student Edition Activities ACTIVITY		Other Activities
CHAPTER PROJECT ▼ **What's a Crowd?** p. 265 TEKS: 6.1A; 6.2A, B, C, D, E	Ongoing (2–3 weeks)	Check Your Progress, pp. 271, 286 Present Your Project, p. 289	**TE**	Chapter 8 Project Notes, pp. 264–265
1 Components of an Ecosystem pp. 266–272 TEKS: 6.10C; 6.12C 8.1.1 Identify the needs that are met by an organism's habitat. 8.1.2 Identify the components of an ecosystem to which organisms respond, including biotic and abiotic parts of an ecosystem. 8.1.3 Describe the levels of organization within an ecosystem. 8.1.4 Define ecology and state what ecologists do.	2 periods/ 1 block	TEKS: 6.1A; 6.2B, C, D, E; 6.4A **Discover** What's in the Scene?, p. 266 **Try This** With or Without Salt?, p. 268 **Skills Lab: Making Models** A World in a Bottle, p. 272	**TE** **TE**	Building Inquiry Skills; Observing, p. 269 Using the Visuals: p. 270
2 ⊚ *INTEGRATING MATHEMATICS* **Studying Populations** pp. 273–279 TEKS: 6.8C; 6.12C 8.2.1 Describe how ecologists determine the size of a population. 8.2.2 Explain what causes populations to change in size. 8.2.3 Identify factors that limit population growth.	3 periods/ 1½ block	TEKS: 6.2A, B, C, D, E; 6.3C; 6.4A, B **Discover** What's the Bean Population?, p. 273 **Sharpen Your Skills** Calculating, p. 274 **Try This** Elbow Room, p. 277 **Science at Home,** p. 278 **Real-World Lab: Careers in Science** Counting Turtles, p. 279	**TE** **TE** **LM**	Inquiry Challenge, p. 274 Building Inquiry Skills: Calculating, pp. 275, 276 8, "Weather and Whooping Cranes"
3 Energy in an Ecosystem pp. 280–286 TEKS: 6.8B, C 8.3.1 Explain how energy flows in living systems. 8.3.2 List some cycles in nature in which matter and energy interact. 8.3.3 Describe what happens when biomass decays.	2 periods/ 1 blocks	TEKS: 6.2B, C; 6.4A **Discover** What's Eating What?, p. 280 **Sharpen Your Skills** Communicating, p. 282	**TE**	Including All Students, p. 285
Study Guide/Chapter Assessment pp. 287–289	1 period/ ½ block	**PLM** Provides blackline masters for Probeware labs	**ISAB** Provides teaching and review of all inquiry skills	

Key: **CTB** Computer Test Bank
CUT Chapter and Unit Tests
ELL Teacher's ELL Handbook

CHAPTER PLANNING GUIDE

 The Resource Pro® CD-ROM provides flexibility for planning the instruction for any type of schedule.

Program Resources	Assessment Strategies	Media and Technology
UR Chapter 8 Project Teacher Notes, pp. 2–3 UR Chapter 8 Project Overview and Worksheets, pp. 4–7	SE Performance Assessment: Chapter 8 Present Your Project, p. 289 TE Check Your Progress, pp. 271, 286 UR Chapter 8 Project Scoring Rubric, p. 8	Science Explorer at www.phschool.com Student Edition on Audio CD, English-Spanish, Chapter 8
UR 8-1 Lesson Plan, p. 9 UR 8-1 Section Summary, p. 10 UR 8-1 Review and Reinforce, p. 11 UR 8-1 Enrich, p. 12 UR Skills Lab blackline masters, pp. 21–22	SE Section 1 Review, p. 271 TE Ongoing Assessment, pp. 267, 269 TE Performance Assessment, p. 271	Earth Science Videodisc Unit 6, Side 2, "Touch the Earth Gently" Videotape Grade 6, Unit 3, "Touch the Earth Gently" Lab Activity Videotapes, Tape 3 Transparency 38, "Levels of Organization in an Ecosystem"
UR 8-2 Lesson Plan, p. 13 UR 8-2 Section Summary, p. 14 UR 8-2 Review and Reinforce, p. 15 UR 8-2 Enrich, p. 16 UR Real-World Lab blackline masters, pp. 23–25	SE Section 2 Review, p. 278 TE Ongoing Assessment, pp. 275, 277 TE Performance Assessment, p. 278	Lab Activity Videotapes, Tape 3
UR 8-3 Lesson Plan, p. 17 UR 8-3 Section Summary, p. 18 UR 8-3 Review and Reinforce, p. 19 UR 8-3 Enrich, p. 20	SE Section 3 Review, p. 286 TE Ongoing Assessment, pp. 281, 283, 285 TE Performance Assessment, p. 286	Life Science Videodisc Unit 6, Side 2, "The Wonder of Ngorongoro"; "Cycles in Nature" Videotape Grade 6, Unit 3, "The Wonder of Ngorongoro"; "Cycles in Nature" Transparencies 39, "Exploring a food Chain"; 40, "A Food Web"; 41, "The Nitrogen Cycle"
ELL Provides multiple strategies for English language learners GRSW Provides worksheets to promote student comprehension of content RCA Provides strategies to improve science reading skills	SE Chapter 8 Study Guide/Assessment, pp. 287–289 PA Chapter 8 Assessment, pp. 26–28 CUT Chapter 8 Test, pp. 40–43 CTB Chapter 8 Test PHAS Provides standardized test preparation	Chapter 8 Computer Test Bank, Chapter 8 Test

GRSW Guided Reading and Study Workbook
ISAB Inquiry Skills Activity Book
LM Laboratory Manual

PA Performance Assessment
PHAS Prentice Hall Assessment System
PLM Probeware Lab Manual

RCA Reading in the Content Area
SE Student Edition

TE Teacher's Edition
UR Unit Resources

Student Edition Activities Planner

ACTIVITY	Time (minutes)	Materials — Quantities for one work group	Skills
Section 1			
Discover, p. 266	10–15	**Consumable** old magazines, paste or glue, sheet of white paper **Nonconsumable** scissors, three pencils of different colors	Inferring
Try This, p. 268	10–15; 5/day for 3 days	**Consumable** 2 L spring water, 25 g noniodized salt, 4 paper squares, brine shrimp eggs **Nonconsumable** 4 600-mL beakers, pen, stirrers, hand lens (optional)	Drawing Conclusions
Skills Lab, p. 272	40; 5/day for 3 days	**Consumable** gravel, soil, charcoal, moss plants, 2 vascular plants **Nonconsumable** pre-cut, clear plastic bottle; spray bottle; rubber band; plastic wrap	Making Models
Section 2			
Discover, p. 273	5–10	**Nonconsumable** 2 large plastic jars, ruler, small beaker, timer, dried beans	Forming Operational Definitions
Sharpen Your Skills, p. 274	5	No special materials are required.	Calculating
Try This, p. 277	10–15	**Consumable** masking tape **Nonconsumable** meter stick, small jigsaw puzzle, watch or clock	Making Models
Science at Home, p. 278	home	**Nonconsumable** dictionary or other book	Calculating
Real-World Lab, p. 279	40	**Consumable** model paper turtle population, graph paper **Nonconsumable** calculator, computer and spreadsheet program (optional)	Calculating, Graphing, Predicting
Section 3			
Discover, p. 280	30	**Consumable** paper **Nonconsumable** field guides, binoculars, hand lenses	Inferring
Sharpen Your Skills, p. 282	60	**Nonconsumable** CD-ROM or print encyclopedias or other reference materials	Communicating

A list of all materials required for the Student Edition activities can be found on pages T43–T49. You can obtain information about ordering materials by calling 1-800-848-9500 or by accessing the Science Explorer Internet site at **www.phschool.com**.

Texas Essential Knowledge and Skills

(6.1) Scientific processes. The student conducts field and laboratory investigations using safe, environmentally appropriate, and ethical practices. *(Section 1)*

The student is expected to:

(A) demonstrate safe practices during field and laboratory investigations.

(6.2) Scientific processes. The student uses scientific inquiry methods during field and laboratory investigations. *(Sections 1, 2, 3)*

The student is expected to:

(A) plan and implement investigative procedures including asking questions, formulating testable hypotheses, and selecting and using equipment and technology;

(B) collect data by observing and measuring;

(C) analyze and interpret information to construct reasonable explanations from direct and indirect evidence;

(D) communicate valid conclusions; and

(E) construct graphs, tables, maps, and charts using tools including computers to organize, examine, and evaluate data.

(6.3) Scientific processes. The student uses critical thinking and scientific problem solving to make informed decisions. *(Section 2)*

The student is expected to:

(C) represent the natural world using models and identify their limitations.

(6.4) Scientific processes. The student knows how to use a variety of tools and methods to conduct science inquiry. *(Sections 1, 2, 3)*

The student is expected to:

(A) collect, analyze, and record information using tools including beakers, petri dishes, meter sticks, graduated cylinders, weather instruments, timing devices, hot plates, test tubes, safety goggles, spring scales, magnets, balances, microscopes, telescopes, thermometers, calculators, field equipment, compasses, computers, and computer probes; and

(B) identify patterns in collected information using percent, average, range, and frequency.

(6.8) Science concepts. The student knows that complex interactions occur between matter and energy. *(Sections 2, 3)*

The student is expected to:

(B) explain and illustrate the interactions between matter and energy in the water cycle and in the decay of biomass such as in a compost bin; and

(C) describe energy flow in living systems including food chains and food webs.

(6.10) Science concepts. The student knows the relationship between structure and function in living systems. *(Section 1)*

The student is expected to:

(C) identify how structure complements function at different levels of organization including organs, organ systems, organisms, and populations.

(6.12) Science concepts. The student knows that the responses of organisms are caused by internal or external stimuli. *(Sections 1, 2)*

The student is expected to:

(C) identify components of an ecosystem to which organisms may respond.

Take It to the Net

 Interactive text at www.phschool.com

Science Explorer comes alive with iText.

- **Complete student text** is accessible from any computer with Internet access or a CD-ROM drive.

- **Animations, simulations, and videos** enhance student understanding and retention of concepts.

- **Self-tests and online study tools** assess student understanding.

- **Teacher management tools** help you make the most of this valuable resource.

STAY CURRENT with **SCIENCE NEWS**®

Find out the latest research and information about ecology at **www.phschool.com**.

Go to **www.phschool.com**. Select Texas on the navigation bar. Click on the Science icon. Then click on Science Explorer under PH@school.

What's a Crowd?

TEKS: 6.1A; 6.2A, B, C, D, E

Limiting factors affect the distribution, health, and size of populations. In this project, students will design their own experiments to test the effect of one limiting factor—crowding—on sample populations of plants.

Purpose This project will give students an opportunity to observe the effect of crowding on plant growth and enhance understanding of the procedures involved in scientific experimentation. To complete the project successfully, students must develop a testable hypothesis about crowding and plant growth; design an experiment that involves identifying and controlling variables, measuring plant growth, and recording data; infer the effects of the limiting factor; and communicate results to the rest of the class.

Skills Focus After completing the Chapter 8 Project, students will be able to

◆ design an experiment to test the effect of crowding on plant growth;

◆ identify and control variables;

◆ measure plant growth, record data, and analyze results;

◆ communicate experimental procedures and results in a written report and graph.

Project Time Line The project requires two to three weeks to complete. During the first phase, groups plan an experiment and submit the plan for your review, culminating with planting the seeds before the conclusion of Section 1. While students study sections 2 and 3, each group conducts its experiment and records data. At the conclusion of Section 3, groups prepare written reports and presentations.

Possible Materials

◆ Wisconsin Fast Plants™ (*Brassica rapa*), a strain of radishlike plants specifically developed for their short life cycle, are the preferred choice for this project. They germinate within 24 hours, develop leaves within one week and flowers in about two weeks, and can be grown easily in a small space. Fast Plant seeds are available from biological supply houses.

CHAPTER **8** Ecosystems

WEB ACTIVITY www.phschool.com

SECTION 1 **Components of an Ecosystem**
Discover What's in the Scene?
Skills Lab A World in a Bottle

SECTION 2 **Studying Populations**
Discover What's the Bean Population?
Real-World Lab Counting Turtles

SECTION 3 **Energy in an Ecosystem**
Discover What's Eating What?

264

◆ Alternatively, students could use radish seeds.

◆ Each group will need several identical planting containers. Possibilities include large margarine tubs, or half-gallon milk cartons with one of the larger sides removed.

◆ Provide potting soil, trowels or large spoons, watering cans or spray bottles, and rulers.

◆ Set aside a location in the classroom where the plant containers will receive direct sunlight or strong indirect light for several hours each day. If sunlight is limited, set up lamps on tables.

Launching the Project To introduce the project, have students examine the photograph and read the first paragraph on page 265. Then ask: **What do sunflowers need to grow well?** *(Students may mention sunlight, water, and soil or the nutrients in soil.)* **Do you think every sunflower seed in this field grew into a mature plant? Why or why not?** *(Students should realize that due to overcrowding, some sprouting plants probably died.)*

Have students read the project description on page 265. Distribute Chapter 8 Project Overview on pages 4–5 in Unit 3 Resources,

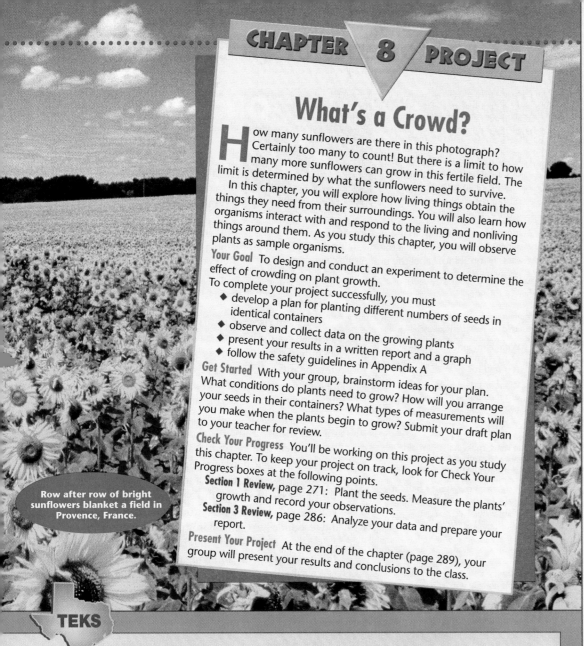

CHAPTER 8 PROJECT

What's a Crowd?

How many sunflowers are there in this photograph? Certainly too many to count! But there is a limit to how many more sunflowers can grow in this fertile field. The limit is determined by what the sunflowers need to survive.

In this chapter, you will explore how living things obtain the things they need from their surroundings. You will also learn how organisms interact with and respond to the living and nonliving things around them. As you study this chapter, you will observe plants as sample organisms.

Your Goal To design and conduct an experiment to determine the effect of crowding on plant growth.

To complete your project successfully, you must

◆ develop a plan for planting different numbers of seeds in identical containers
◆ observe and collect data on the growing plants
◆ present your results in a written report and a graph
◆ follow the safety guidelines in Appendix A

Get Started With your group, brainstorm ideas for your plan. What conditions do plants need to grow? How will you arrange your seeds in their containers? What types of measurements will you make when the plants begin to grow? Submit your draft plan to your teacher for review.

Check Your Progress You'll be working on this project as you study this chapter. To keep your project on track, look for Check Your Progress boxes at the following points.

Section 1 Review, page 271: Plant the seeds. Measure the plants' growth and record your observations.
Section 3 Review, page 286: Analyze your data and prepare your report.

Present Your Project At the end of the chapter (page 289), your group will present your results and conclusions to the class.

Row after row of bright sunflowers blanket a field in Provence, France.

TEKS

In addition to process TEKS, this chapter addresses these concept TEKS as they relate to the chapter's topics.

(6.8) The student knows that complex interactions occur between matter and energy. The student is expected to:
(B) explain and illustrate the interactions between matter and energy in the water cycle and in the decay of biomass such as in a compost bin; and
(C) describe energy flow in living systems including food chains and food webs.

(6.10) The student knows the relationship between structure and function in living systems. The student is expected to:
(C) identify how structure complements function at different levels of organization including organs, organ systems, organisms, and populations.

(6.12) The student knows that the responses of organisms are caused by internal or external stimuli. The student is expected to:
(C) identify components of an ecosystem to which organisms may respond.

265

Program Resources

◆ **Unit 3 Resources** Chapter 8 Project Teacher Notes, pp. 2–3; Chapter 8 Project Overview and Worksheets, pp. 4–7

Media and Technology

Student Edition on Audio CD
English-Spanish, Chapter 8

 **WEB ACTIVITY** www.phschool.com

You will find an Internet activity, chapter self-tests for students, and links to other chapter topics at this site.

---

and let students review the project's procedures. Encourage questions and comments.

Divide the class into groups of two to four students each. Give each student a copy of Chapter 8 Project Worksheet 1 on page 6 in Unit 3 Resources. Allow time for the groups to meet and begin brainstorming ideas. Tell students to use the worksheet to take notes as they brainstorm. Also explain that when their group decides on a final experiment, they should prepare a written plan based on the worksheet steps. Emphasize that you will review the plans before groups begin their experiments.

Tell students that each group's members may divide the project responsibilities among themselves in any way they wish. However, emphasize that *every* group member should be involved in all stages and be prepared to answer questions about the experiment.

In Check Your Progress at the conclusion of Section 3, distribute Chapter 8 Project Worksheet 2 on page 7 in Unit 3 Resources. This worksheet is designed to help students prepare their written reports and graphs.

Performance Assessment

The Chapter 8 Project Scoring Rubric on page 8 in Unit 3 Resources will help you evaluate how well students complete the Chapter 8 Project. Students will be assessed on

◆ their ability to design an experiment to test the effect of crowding on plant growth;
◆ how carefully they have identified and controlled variables in the experiment, made observations and recorded data;
◆ how well they have communicated their procedures, results, and conclusion to the rest of the class;
◆ their participation in their groups.
You may want to share the scoring rubric with students so they are clear about what will be expected of them.

TEKS: 6.1A; 6.2B, C, D, E; 6.4A; 6.10C; 6.12C

Objectives

After completing the lesson, students will be able to

♦ identify the needs that are met by an organism's habitat;

♦ identify the components of an ecosystem to which organisms respond, including biotic and abiotic parts of an ecosystem;

♦ describe the levels of organization within an ecosystem;

♦ define ecology and state what ecologists do.

1 Engage/Explore

Activating Prior Knowledge

Ask: **What is an ecosystem?** (*Students may say it is a particular type of place with different kinds of plants, animals, and other living things living in it. Accept all responses without comment at this time.*) **What kinds of ecosystems do you know of?** (*Students may mention a swamp, desert, seashore, forest, and so forth.*)

··· DISCOVER ···

Skills Focus inferring
Materials *old magazines, scissors, paste or glue, sheet of white paper, three pencils of different colors*
Time 10–15 minutes
Tips Encourage students to look for pictures with close-enough views to allow them to distinguish various living and nonliving things. Also emphasize that the scenes do not have to be "beautiful" so long as each shows a variety of living and nonliving things.
Expected Outcome The specific living things shown will vary. Students should identify water, soil, sunlight, and air among the nonliving things.
Think It Over Students should indicate that living things need water, air, and sunlight and that plants also need soil.

SECTION 1
Components of an Ecosystem

DISCOVER ········· ············ ACTIVITY

What's in the Scene?

1. Choose a magazine picture of a nature scene. Paste the picture onto a sheet of paper, leaving space all around the picture.

2. Identify all the things in the picture that are alive. Use a colored pencil to draw a line from each living thing. Label the organism if you know its name.

3. Use a different colored pencil to draw a line from each nonliving thing and label it.

Think It Over

Inferring How do the organisms in the picture depend on the nonliving things? Using a third color, draw lines connecting organisms to the nonliving things they need.

GUIDE FOR READING

♦ What components of an ecosystem do organisms respond to?

♦ What are the levels of organization within an ecosystem?

Reading Tip Write the section headings in your notebook. As you read, make a list of main ideas and supporting details under each heading.

Key Terms ecosystem • habitat • biotic factor • abiotic factor • population • society • community • ecology

---

A s the sun rises on a warm summer morning, the Texas town is already bustling with activity. Some residents are building homes underground, where it is dark and cool. Other inhabitants are collecting seeds for breakfast. Some younger residents are at play, chasing each other through the grass.

Suddenly, an adult spots a threatening shadow approaching—an enemy has appeared in the sky! The adult cries out, warning the others. Within moments, the town's residents disappear quickly into their underground homes. The town is silent and still, except for a single hawk circling overhead.

Have you guessed what kind of town this is? It is a prairie dog town on the Texas plains. As these prairie dogs dug their burrows, searched for food, and hid from the hawk, they interacted with and responded to their environment, or surroundings. The prairie dogs interacted with living things, such as the grass and the hawk, and with nonliving things, such as the soil. All the living and nonliving things that interact in a particular area make up an **ecosystem.**

◀ Black-tailed prairie dogs

266

READING STRATEGIES

Reading Tip Students should list the main headings *Habitats, Biotic Factors, Abiotic Factors, Structure and Function in Populations, Communities,* and *What Is Ecology?* The subheadings *Water, Sunlight, Oxygen, Temperature,* and *Soil* on pages 268–269 can be listed below the main heading *Abiotic Factors.* Students should also place the boldface terms (with their definitions) and the boldface sentences under the appropriate headings. If any students had difficulty identifying main ideas and supporting details or differentiating between them, work with those students individually or in small groups to provide guidance.

A prairie is just one of the many different ecosystems found on Earth. Other ecosystems in which living things make their homes include mountain streams, deep oceans, swamps, and dense forests.

Habitats

A prairie dog is one type of organism, or living thing. Organisms live in a specific place within an ecosystem. An organism obtains food, water, shelter, and other things it needs to live, grow, and reproduce from its surroundings. The place where an organism lives and that provides the things the organism needs is called its **habitat.**

A single ecosystem may contain many habitats. For example, in a forest ecosystem, mushrooms grow in the damp soil, bears live on the forest floor, termites live in fallen tree trunks, and woodpeckers build nests in the trunks.

Organisms live in different habitats because they have different requirements for survival. A prairie dog obtains the food and shelter it needs from its habitat. It could not survive in a tropical rain forest or on the rocky ocean shore. Likewise, the prairie would not meet the needs of a gorilla, a penguin, or a hermit crab.

Biotic Factors

An organism interacts with and responds to both the living and nonliving things in its environment. The living parts of an ecosystem are called **biotic factors** (by AHT ik). Biotic factors in the prairie dogs' ecosystem include the grass and plants that provide seeds and berries. The hawks, ferrets, badgers, and eagles that hunt the prairie dogs are also biotic factors. In addition, worms, fungi, and bacteria are biotic factors that live in the soil underneath the prairie grass. These organisms keep the soil rich in nutrients as they break down the remains of other living things.

☑ *Checkpoint* *Name a biotic factor in your environment.*

Figure 1 A stream tumbles over mossy rocks in a lush Tennessee forest. This ecosystem contains many different habitats.
Comparing and Contrasting How is the mushrooms' habitat in the forest different from the woodpecker's habitat?

267

Program Resources

◆ **Unit 3 Resources** 8-1 Lesson Plan, p. 9; 8-1 Section Summary, p. 10
◆ **Guided Reading and Study Workbook** 8-1

Answers to Self-Assessment

Caption Question

Figure 1 Mushrooms grow in damp soil on the forest floor, whereas the woodpecker builds nests in tree trunks.

☑ *Checkpoint*

Students may name living organisms such as other people, trees, dogs, or birds.

2 Facilitate

Habitats

Addressing Naive Conceptions *Content Mastery*

Students may not have a clear understanding of the difference between the terms *ecosystem* and *habitat*, since both refer to places where organisms live. Emphasize that the *type* of place where an organism lives—a prairie or a forest, for example—is an ecosystem. The specific *part* of the ecosystem that meets the organism's needs and in which it lives is its habitat. To clarify this difference, first have students name the four specific habitats identified in the text as being part of a forest ecosystem. Create a concept map on the board with *Forest* in one circle and the four habitats in circles below it. Invite students to identify another ecosystem and several habitats within it, and let them come to the board to create another concept map. Continue with other ecosystems and habitats. **learning modality: visual**

Biotic Factors

Including All Students

Invite students who need extra help to identify examples of biotic factors found in the forest ecosystem described on this page. *(In the forest ecosystem, biotic factors include mushrooms, bears, termites, trees, and flickers.)* **learning modality: verbal**

Ongoing Assessment

Skills Check Have each student choose one ecosystem and create a concept map about it. The ecosystem should be identified in the top circle and at least three specific habitats in circles below it.

Portfolio Students can save their concept maps in their portfolios.

Abiotic Factors

Including All Students

Write *abiotic* on the board and underline the prefix *a-*. Ask: **What does *a-* at the beginning of the word mean?** (*"Not" or "opposite of"; if students do not know, have them compare the terms* biotic *and* abiotic *and infer the meaning of* a-.) Emphasize that the English language uses several different prefixes to change the meanings of words. Ask: **What are some other prefixes in English that mean "not"?** (*ab-, un-, non-, dis-*) List the prefixes on the board as students identify them, and ask students to give examples of words with those prefixes, such as *unhappy, nontoxic,* and *disagree.* **limited English proficiency**

Skills Focus drawing conclusions

Materials *4 600-mL beakers, masking tape, pen, 2 L spring water, 25 g noniodized salt, stirrers, brine shrimp eggs, 4 paper squares large enough to cover cups, hand lens (optional)*

Time 10–15 minutes for initial setup, 5 minutes per day for follow-up observations

Tips Let the spring water sit overnight to reach room temperature. Put a small sample of brine shrimp eggs in a paper cup for each group. You may add $\frac{1}{2}$ teaspoon of dry yeast to each beaker to feed the shrimp when they hatch. NOTE: Newly hatched brine shrimp are very tiny and orange in color.

Expected Outcome Eggs will not hatch in beaker A. Eggs will likely hatch best in beaker B, less well in beaker C, and not well or not at all in beaker D. The brine shrimp's habitat must contain salt, but cannot be too salty.

Extend Have each group prepare a larger jar with the saltwater solution that they think is best for brine shrimp, add $\frac{1}{4}$ teaspoon of eggs, and set the covered jar aside. Encourage students to examine the jar every day or two to observe changes in the population's size.

learning modality: tactile/ kinesthetic

Figure 2 This eastern banjo frog is burrowing in the sand to stay cool in the hot Australian desert. *Interpreting Photographs With which abiotic factors is the frog interacting in this scene?*

With or Without Salt?

In this activity you will explore salt as an abiotic factor.

1. Label four 600-mL beakers A, B, C, and D. Fill each with 500 mL of room-temperature spring water.

2. Set beaker A aside. It will contain fresh water. To beaker B, add 2.5 grams of noniodized salt. Add 7.5 grams of salt to beaker C and 15 grams of salt to beaker D. Stir beakers B, C, and D.

3. Add about $\frac{1}{4}$ of a spoonful of brine shrimp eggs to each beaker.

4. Cover each beaker with a square of paper. Keep them away from direct light or heat. Wash your hands.

5. Observe the beakers daily for three days.

Drawing Conclusions In which beakers did the eggs hatch? What can you conclude about the amount of salt in the shrimps' natural habitat?

268

Abiotic Factors

The nonliving parts of an ecosystem are called **abiotic factors** (ay by AHT ik). The abiotic factors to which organisms respond include water, sunlight, oxygen, temperature, and soil.

Water All living things need water to carry out their life processes. Water is particularly important to plants and algae. These organisms use water, along with sunlight and carbon dioxide, to make food in the process called photosynthesis. Other living things eat the plants and algae to obtain energy.

Sunlight Because sunlight is necessary for photosynthesis, it is an important abiotic factor for plants, algae, and other living things. In places that do not receive sunlight, such as dark caves, plants cannot grow. Without plants or algae to provide a source of food, few other organisms can live.

Oxygen Most living things require oxygen to carry out their life processes. Organisms that live on land obtain oxygen from the air, which is about 20 percent oxygen. Fish and other water organisms obtain dissolved oxygen from the water around them.

Temperature The temperatures that are typical of an area determine the types of organisms that can live there. For example, if you took a trip to a warm tropical island, you would see palm trees, bright hibiscus flowers, and tiny lizards. These organisms could not survive on the frozen plains of Siberia.

Some animals respond to very hot or very cold temperatures by altering their environment. For example, prairie dogs line their dens with grass. The grass keeps the prairie dogs warm during the cold and windy winters.

Soil Soil is a mixture of rock fragments, nutrients, air, water, and the decaying remains of living things. Soil in different areas consists of varying amounts of these materials. The type of soil in an area influences the kinds of plants that can grow there.

268

Background

Integrating Science Students may already know that plants and algae require carbon dioxide to carry on photosynthesis. Chlorophyll, the green pigment in plants and some algae, absorbs energy in sunlight. The organism uses this energy to combine carbon dioxide (CO_2) and water (H_2O) in a reaction that produces sugars, including glucose ($C_6H_{12}O_2$), with water and oxygen (O_2) as byproducts. The sugars provide energy for sustaining the organism's life processes. Other organisms can obtain and use this energy by eating plants or algae. Cellular respiration breaks down glucose into carbon dioxide and water, releasing energy.

Many animals, such as prairie dogs, use the soil itself as a home. Billions of microscopic organisms such as bacteria also live in the soil. These tiny organisms play an important role in the ecosystem by breaking down the remains of other living things.

☑ *Checkpoint* *How do biotic factors differ from abiotic factors?*

Structure and Function in Populations

In 1900, travelers saw a prairie dog town in Texas covering an area twice the size of the city of Dallas. The sprawling town contained more than 400 million prairie dogs! These prairie dogs were all members of one species. All the members of one species in a particular area are referred to as a **population.** The 400 million prairie dogs in the Texas town are one example of a population. All the daisies in a field make up a population. In contrast, all the trees in a forest do not make up a population, because they do not all belong to the same species. The area in which a population lives can be as small as a single blade of grass or as large as the whole planet.

In the populations of many species, such as daisies in a field or frogs in a pond, individual members do not interact much except for reproducing and competing with one another for resources. In contrast, the populations of other species are structured: that is, members of the population relate to one another in specific ways. Prairie dogs, for example, live together in colonies. Members of the colony cooperate with one another in functions such as warning about danger. If a prairie dog senses danger, it gives a warning call, and the members of the colony quickly scramble into their burrows. A different call tells the prairie dogs when it is safe to come out. Cooperation helps the members of the population survive.

Some animal populations form highly structured groups called societies. A **society** is a closely related population of animals that work together for the benefit of the whole group. Every member of a honeybee hive, for example, has a specific function. The queen bee lays eggs from which new bees hatch. All the other females, called worker bees, perform such tasks as making honey and defending the hive. Male bees, called drones, function in reproduction by mating with the queen bee.

Figure 3 This milkweed plant is home to a small population of ladybird beetles.

Chapter 8 **269**

Answers to Self-Assessment

Caption Question

Figure 2 Soil (sand), oxygen (air), sunlight, temperature

☑ *Checkpoint*
Biotic factors are living; abiotic factors are nonliving.

Communities

Challenge students to think of a way to show an ecosystem's levels of organization in a diagram. Have each student create a diagram for an ecosystem of his or her own choice. Let students share their diagrams in a class discussion. *(Possible diagram: Concentric circles with the individual organism in the center circle, a population in the second circle, a community with that population and other species in the third circle, and the entire ecosystem with abiotic factors in the outer circle.)* **learning modality: visual**

What Is Ecology?

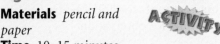

Challenge students to think of other words that end in *-ology. (biology, geology)* Then have them use a dictionary to learn what the first root word in each means. (Bio- *means life,* geo- *means earth.)*

In Your Journal Students' answers may vary slightly depending on the dictionaries they used.
Habitat: from Latin *habitare,* "to inhabit, live in"; *inhabit, habitation, habitual*
Biotic: from Greek *bios,* "life"; *biology, biography, biome*
Community: from Latin *communis,* "common"; *communicate, communication, communal*
Population: from Latin *populus,* "people"; *popular, popularity, populous*
learning modality: verbal

Organism	Population

Language Arts CONNECTION

The word *ecology* comes from two Greek root words: *oikos,* which means "house or place to live," and *logos,* which means "study." Put together, these root words create a term for studying organisms in the place where they live. Many science terms are derived from Greek and Latin root words.

In Your Journal

Use a dictionary to find root words for the following terms from this section: *habitat, biotic, community,* and *population.* For each root word, list its meaning, original language, and other English words containing the root.

Communities

Of course, most ecosystems contain more than one type of organism. The prairie, for instance, includes prairie dogs, hawks, grasses, badgers, and snakes, along with many other organisms. All the different populations that live together in an area make up a **community.**

Figure 4 shows the levels of organization in the prairie ecosystem. **The smallest unit of organization is a single organism, which belongs to a population of other members of its species. The population belongs to a community of different species. The community and abiotic factors together form an ecosystem.**

To be considered a community, the different populations must live close enough together to interact. One way the populations in a community may interact is by using the same resources, such as food and shelter. For example, the tunnels dug by the prairie dogs also serve as homes for burrowing owls and black-footed ferrets. The prairie dogs share the grass with other animals. Meanwhile, prairie dogs themselves serve as food for many species.

What Is Ecology?

Because the populations in the prairie ecosystem interact with one another, any changes in a community affect all the different populations that live there. The study of how living things interact with one another and with their environment is called **ecology.** Ecologists, scientists who study ecology, look at how all the biotic and abiotic factors in an ecosystem are related.

Background

Integrating Science All of Earth's communities are part of a higher level of organization, the *biosphere.* The organisms that make up the biosphere interact with each other. But they also interact in various ways with Earth's other "spheres": the atmosphere (the gases that envelop Earth); the hydrosphere (Earth's water); and the lithosphere (Earth's rocky outer covering and soils). While ecologists study the relationships among the organisms of the biosphere, they also consider the biosphere in relation to the other spheres of the physical environment.

Community

Ecosystem

Figure 4 The smallest level of ecological organization is an individual organism. The largest is the entire ecosystem.

As part of their work, ecologists study how organisms respond to changes in their environment. Living things constantly interact with their surroundings, responding to changes in the conditions around them. Some responses are very quick. For example, when a hawk sees a prairie dog, the hawk responds immediately by swooping down and trying to catch the prairie dog. The prairie dog responds to the hawk by giving a warning bark—and running for cover. Other responses to change in the environment occur more slowly. For example, after a fire on the prairie, it takes some time for the grass to reach its former height and for all the animals to return to the area.

Section 1 Review

1. What are biotic factors? What are abiotic factors?
2. List the following levels of organization in order from the smallest level to the largest: population, organism, ecosystem, community.
3. Why do ecologists study both biotic and abiotic factors in an ecosystem?
4. What is the structure of a honeybee society? What functions do the different members perform?
5. **Thinking Critically** **Applying Concepts** Would all the insects in a forest be considered a population? Why or why not?

Check Your Progress
CHAPTER PROJECT

After your teacher has reviewed your plan, prepare the containers and plant the seeds. Design a data table to record the information you will use to compare the growth in the different containers. When the plants begin to grow, examine them daily and record your observations. Be sure to continue caring for your plants according to your plan. (Hint: Use a metric ruler to measure your growing plants. Besides size, look for differences in leaf color and the number of buds among the plants.)

Section 1 Review Answers

1. Biotic factors are the living parts of an ecosystem; abiotic factors are the nonliving parts of an ecosystem.
2. Organism, population, community, ecosystem
3. Accept all reasonable answers. *Sample answer:* The biotic and abiotic factors in an ecosystem are all related to one another.
4. The structure is the hive. The queen bee lays eggs; all other female honeybees perform tasks such as making honey and defending the hive; male bees function in reproduction by mating with the queen.
5. No; the insects would be of many different species. Only organisms of the same species form a population.

Check Your Progress
CHAPTER PROJECT

Evaluate each group's plan to make sure students have identified and will control the major variables that will affect plant growth in the containers. These include the size of the containers, the amount of soil in each, how densely and how deep the seeds will be planted, the amount and frequency of watering, and the location in which the containers will be placed. Also review students' data tables to make sure they will be recording all relevant data, including plant heights and other observations such as the number and color of leaves and the number of buds on the developing plants.

Media and Technology

 Transparencies "Levels of Organization in an Ecosystem," Transparency 38

Program Resources

◆ **Unit 3 Resources** 8-1 Review and Reinforce, p. 11; 8-1 Enrich, p. 12

Performance Assessment

Skills Check Have each student choose any organism and draw a concept map to identify several biotic and abiotic factors in the organism's habitat.

 Students can save their concept maps in their portfolios.

271

A World in a Bottle

Preparing for Inquiry

Key Concept Organisms can survive in a closed ecosystem so long as their biotic and abiotic needs are met.

Skills Objectives Students will be able to
◆ build a model of a terrestrial ecosystem;
◆ predict whether the habitat will meet the organisms' needs;
◆ make inferences about how the model ecosystem operates.

Time 30 minutes for set-up; 10 minutes per day for observation and notetaking

Advance Planning Collect materials. Cut off the tops of clear plastic 2-liter soda bottles to make 18-cm-tall containers. Obtain small, short vascular plants and mosses from moist, shaded areas.

Guiding Inquiry

Troubleshooting the Experiment
◆ Use vascular plants that require similar amounts of light and moisture.
◆ If fogging is a problem, students can remove the cover until the sides clear. This opens the system, but it shows that reproducing an ecosystem is difficult.

Expected Outcome
The plants should thrive and grow.

Analyze and Conclude
1. Plants, charcoal, soil, gravel, water, light, bottle
2. Yes, light (an abiotic factor)
3. Students' diagrams should show the plants using light, water, and carbon dioxide to make food and oxygen, and using oxygen and producing carbon dioxide to respire. They should also show transpiration.
4. The plant-eating insect would survive for a while. Eventually, the insect may run out of food if it eats plants faster than they can reproduce.
5. The model shows that organisms interact with nonliving things in their environment. It differs in that it is closed, not as complex, and contains fewer organisms and no animals.

A World in a Bottle

In this lab, you will study the interactions between biotic and abiotic factors in a model ecosystem.

Problem

How do organisms survive in a closed ecosystem?

Materials

pre-cut, clear plastic
    bottle
gravel
soil
moss plants
plastic spoon   rubber band
charcoal   2 vascular plants
spray bottle   plastic wrap

Procedure

1. In this lab, you will place plants in moist soil in a bottle that is then sealed. This setup is called a terrarium. Predict whether the plants can survive in this habitat.

2. Spread about 2.5 cm of gravel on the bottom of a pre-cut bottle. Then sprinkle a spoonful or two of charcoal over the gravel.

3. Use the spoon to layer about 8 cm of soil over the gravel and charcoal. As you add the soil, tap it down gently.

4. Scoop out two holes in the soil. Remove the vascular plants from their pots. Gently place their roots in the holes. Then pack the loose soil firmly around the plants' stems.

5. Fill the spray bottle with water. Spray the soil until you see water collecting in the gravel.

6. Cover the soil with the moss plants, including the areas around the stems of the vascular plants. Lightly spray the mosses with water.

7. Tightly cover your terrarium with plastic wrap. Secure the cover with a rubber band. Place the terrarium in bright, indirect light.

8. Observe the terrarium daily for two weeks. Record your observations in your notebook. If its sides fog, move the terrarium to an area with a different amount of light. You may have to move it a few times before the fog disappears. Write down any changes you make in your terrarium's location.

Analyze and Conclude

1. What are the components of the ecosystem in the bottle?
2. Were any biotic or abiotic factors able to enter the terrarium? If so, which ones?
3. Draw a diagram of the interactions between the terrarium's biotic and abiotic factors.
4. Suppose a plant-eating insect were added to the terrarium. Predict whether it would be able to survive. Explain your prediction.
5. **Think About It** Explain how your terrarium models an ecosystem. How does your model differ from an actual ecosystem on Earth?

More to Explore

Make a plan to model a freshwater ecosystem. How would this model be different from the land ecosystem? Obtain your teacher's approval before carrying out your plan.

Extending the Inquiry

More to Explore Review students' plans for feasibility in the classroom and for proper handling of living organisms.

Safety

Make sure students handle the bottle carefully to avoid hurting their fingers on the pre-cut top. Review the safety guidelines in Appendix A.

Program Resources

◆ **Unit 3 Resources** Chapter 8 Skills Lab blackline masters, pp. 21–22

Media and Technology

Lab Activity Videotapes
Grade 6, Tape 3

SECTION 2 Studying Populations

DISCOVER ...... ACTIVITY ....

What's the Bean Population?

1. Fill a plastic jar with dried beans. This is your model population.

2. Your goal is to determine the number of beans in the jar, but you will not have time to count every bean. You may use any of the following to help you determine the size of the bean population: a ruler, a small beaker, another large jar. Set a timer for two minutes when you are ready to begin.

3. After two minutes, record your answer. Then count the actual number of beans. How close was your answer?

Think It Over
Forming Operational Definitions In this activity, you came up with an estimate of the size of the bean population. Write a definition of the term *estimate* based on what you did.

How would you like to change jobs for the day? Instead of being a student, today you are an ecologist. You are working on a project to study the bald eagle population in your area. One question you might ask is how the population size has changed over time. Is the number of bald eagles higher, lower, or the same as it was 50 years ago? To answer this question, you must first determine the present size of the bald eagle population.

Population Density

Ecologists may describe the size of a population as **population density**—the number of individuals in a specific area. Population density can be written as an equation:

$$\text{Population density} = \frac{\text{Number of individuals}}{\text{Unit area}}$$

For instance, suppose you counted 50 monarch butterflies in a garden measuring 10 square meters. The population density would be 50 butterflies per 10 square meters, or 5 butterflies per square meter.

GUIDE FOR READING

◆ How do ecologists determine the size of a population?

◆ What causes populations to change in size?

◆ What factors limit population growth?

Reading Tip Before you read, predict some factors that might cause a population to increase or decrease.

Key Terms population density
• estimate • birth rate
• death rate • immigration
• emigration • limiting factor
• carrying capacity

Bald eagles in Alaska ▶

273

273

2 Facilitate

Population Density

Including All Students
For students who need extra help, provide additional examples so they can practice the calculations—for example, 144 dandelion plants in a lawn 12 m long by 6 m wide (2 plants per square meter). You may want to let students use calculators to solve the problems. Also invite students to make up problems for the class to solve. **learning modality: logical/mathematical**

Determining Population Size

Sharpen your *Skills*

Calculating
Time 5 minutes
Expected Outcome The total population is 100,000 oysters (100 m × 50 m = 5000 square meters × 20 oysters per square meter).
Extend Ask: **Why is your answer only an estimate of the total population?** *(Maybe not every square meter has exactly 20 oysters.)* **learning modality: logical/mathematical**

Inquiry Challenge
Materials *500 wooden toothpicks*
Time 10–15 minutes

Scatter 500 toothpicks over a rectangular area large enough to provide a 1-square-meter section for each student, or use a floor with 1-square-foot tiles, allowing one tile per student. Tell students the total area, but not how many toothpicks you used. Let each student count the number of toothpicks in his or her section (the sample) and then calculate the total "population" of toothpicks. In a follow-up discussion, ask: **Why did different students get different estimates?** *(Different sections—samples—contained different numbers of toothpicks.)* **learning modality: logical/mathematical**

Figure 5 These cone-shaped structures are nests built by cliff swallows in Dinosaur National Monument, Utah. Counting the nests is one way to estimate the cliff swallow population.

Sharpen your *Skills*

Calculating
A bed of oysters measures 100 meters long and 50 meters wide. In a one-square-meter area you count 20 oysters. Estimate the population of oysters in the bed. *(Hint: Drawing a diagram may help you set up your calculation.)*

Determining Population Size

In your work as an ecologist, how can you determine the size of the population you are studying? **Some methods of determining the size of a population are direct and indirect observations, sampling, and mark-and-recapture studies.**

Direct Observation The most obvious way to determine the size of a population is to count, one by one, all of its members. You could count all the bald eagles that live along a river, all the red maple trees in a forest, or all the elephants in a valley in Kenya.

Indirect Observation The members of a population may be small or hard to find. It may then be easier to observe their tracks or other signs rather than the organisms themselves. Look at the mud nests built by cliff swallows in Figure 5. Each nest has one entrance hole. By counting the entrance holes, you can determine the number of swallow families nesting in this area. Suppose that the average number of swallows per nest is four: two parents and two offspring. If there are 120 nests in an area, you can find the number of swallows by multiplying 120 by 4, or 480 swallows.

Sampling In most cases, it is not possible to count every member of a population. The population may be very large, or it may be spread over a wide area. It may be hard to find every individual or to remember which ones have already been counted. Instead, ecologists usually make an estimate. An **estimate** is an approximation of a number, based on reasonable assumptions.

One type of estimating involves counting the number of organisms in a small area (a sample), and then multiplying to find the number in a larger area. To get an accurate estimate, the sample should have the same population density as the larger area. For example, suppose you count 8 red maples in a 10 meter-by-10 meter area of the forest. If the entire forest were 100 times that size, you would multiply your count by 100 to estimate the total population, or 800 red maples.

Mark-and-Recapture Studies Another estimating method is a technique called "mark and recapture." This technique gets its name because some animals are captured and marked, and then released into the environment. Then another group of animals is captured.

Facts and Figures For a species to survive, there must be enough males and females present in a range to mate and reproduce successfully. If the population density and size fall below a critical minimum level, the population declines and may become extinct. This very nearly occurred with the California condor, a scavenger that requires a large range in which to feed.

Development has greatly reduced the California condor's wilderness habitat. In the late 1980s, there were no condors living in the wild. A program to reintroduce zoo-bred condors into the wild began in 1992. Two colonies, one in California and one in Arizona, appear to be succeeding.

The number of marked animals in this second group indicates the population size. For example, if half the animals in the second group are marked, the first sample represented about half the total population.

Here's an example showing how mark and recapture works. First, deer mice in a field are caught in a trap that does not harm the mice. Ecologists count the mice and mark each mouse with a dot of hair dye before releasing it again. Two weeks later, the researchers return and capture mice again. They count how many mice have marks, showing that they were captured the first time, and how many are unmarked. Using a mathematical formula, the scientists can estimate the total population of mice in the field. You can try this technique for yourself in the Real-World Lab at the end of this section.

☑ *Checkpoint* *When is sampling used to estimate a population?*

Changes in Population Size

By returning to a location often and using one of the methods described here, ecologists can monitor the size of a population over time. **Populations can change in size when new members enter the population or when members leave the population.**

Births and Deaths The major way in which new individuals are added to a population is through the birth of offspring. The **birth rate** of a population is the number of births in a population in a certain amount of time. For example, suppose a population of 1,000 snow geese produces 1,400 goslings in a year. The birth rate in this population would be 1,400 goslings per year.

Similarly, the major way that individuals leave a population is by dying. The **death rate** is the number of deaths in a population in a certain amount of time. Suppose that in the same population, 500 geese die in a year. The death rate would be 500 geese per year.

Figure 6 This young hawk is part of a mark-and-recapture study in a Virginia marsh. *Inferring What is the purpose of the silver band on the hawk's leg?*

Figure 7 The birth of new individuals can increase the size of a population. This cheetah mother added five offspring to the population in her area.

Chapter 8 **275**

Changes in Population Size, continued

Building Inquiry Skills: Calculating

Continuing with the example on the previous page, ask: **Suppose 1,600 snow geese died in the same year that 1,400 were born. What would the growth rate be for that year?** *(1,400 − 1,600 = a growth rate of −200 geese per year)* **What does a negative growth rate mean?** *(The population is declining.)* **What might account for a death rate that is higher than the birth rate?** *(Disease; not enough food; eggs, young geese, or adults being eaten by other animals; poisons in the environment; and so on)* **learning modality: logical/mathematical**

Using the Visuals: Figure 8

Review the population changes described in the caption and shown on the graph. Then ask: **Why is it helpful to show population changes in a graph?** *(The lines make the changes easier to see and understand than reading a list of numbers.)* **learning modality: visual**

Math TOOLBOX

If students have difficulty comparing a fraction and a decimal, suggest that they convert the fraction to a decimal.

1. 5 > −6
2. 0.4 < $\frac{3}{5}$
   0.4 < 0.6
3. −2 −(−8) > 7−1.5
   6 > 5.5

learning modality: logical/ mathematical

Math TOOLBOX

Inequalities

The population statement is an example of an inequality. An inequality is a mathematical statement that compares two expressions. Two signs that represent inequalities are:

    < (is less than)
    > (is greater than)

For example, an inequality comparing the fraction $\frac{1}{2}$ to the decimal 0.75 would be written:

$$\frac{1}{2} < 0.75$$

Write an inequality comparing each pair of expressions below.

1. 5 **?** −6
2. 0.4 **?** $\frac{3}{5}$
3. −2 − (−8) **?** 7 − 1.5

The Population Statement When the birth rate in a population is greater than the death rate, the population will generally increase in size. This statement can be written as a mathematical statement using the "is greater than" sign:

If birth rate > death rate, population size increases.

For example, in the snow goose population, the birth rate of 1,400 goslings per year was greater than the death rate of 500 geese per year, and the population would increase in size.

However, if the death rate in a population is greater than the birth rate, the population size will generally decrease. This can also be written as a mathematical statement:

If death rate > birth rate, population size decreases.

Immigration and Emigration The size of a population also can change when individuals move into or out of the population, just as the population of your town changes when families move into town or move away. **Immigration** (im ih GRAY shun) means moving into a population. **Emigration** (em ih GRAY shun) means leaving a population. Emigration can occur when part of a population gets cut off from the rest of the population. For instance, if food is scarce, some members of an antelope herd may wander off in search of better grassland. If they become permanently separated from the original herd, they will no longer be part of that population.

Graphing Population Changes You can see an example of changes in a population of rabbits in Figure 8. The vertical axis shows the numbers of rabbits in the population, while the horizontal axis shows time. The graph shows the size of the population over a 10-year period.

☑ *Checkpoint* *Name two ways individuals can join a population.*

Figure 8 From Year 0 to Year 4, more rabbits were added to the population than were lost, so the population increased. From Year 4 to Year 8, more rabbits left the population than joined it, so the population decreased. From Year 8 to Year 10, the rates of rabbits leaving and joining the population were about equal, so the population remained steady.
Interpreting Graphs In what year did the rabbit population reach its highest point? What was the size of the population in that year?

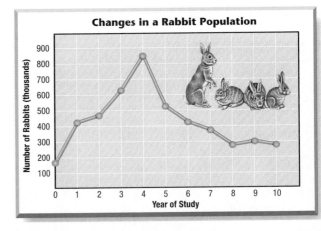

Changes in a Rabbit Population

Background

Facts and Figures When the size of a population grows beyond the carrying capacity of its habitat, a *population crash* may occur. Food shortages, insufficient space for successful reproduction, disease, and other limiting factors result in a death rate much higher than the birth rate, and the population declines sharply.

One example of such a crash occurred with the moose population on Isle Royale before wolves arrived in 1949. Moose came to Isle Royale around 1900 by walking across the frozen lake in winter. Over the next 35 years, the moose population increased to about 3,000. This exhausted their food supply, leading to starvation for 90 percent of the moose. The population increased again until 1948, then declined sharply once more because of lack of food.

Figure 9 **Figure 9** These gannets seem to have heard the saying "Birds of a feather flock together." When there are more birds than the space can support, the population will have exceeded the carrying capacity of the shore.

Limiting Factors

When conditions are good, a population will generally increase. But a population does not keep growing forever. Eventually, some factor in its environment causes the population to stop growing. A **limiting factor** is an environmental factor that prevents a population from increasing. **Some limiting factors for populations are food, space, and weather conditions.**

Food Organisms require food to survive. In an area where food is scarce, this becomes a limiting factor. Suppose a giraffe needs to eat 10 kilograms of leaves each day to survive. The trees in an area can provide 100 kilograms of leaves a day while remaining healthy. Five giraffes could live easily in this area, since they would only require a total of 50 kilograms of food. But 15 giraffes could not all survive—there would not be enough food for all of them. No matter how much shelter, water, and other resources there might be, the population will not grow much higher than 10 giraffes. The largest population that an environment can support is called its **carrying capacity.** The carrying capacity of this environment is 10 giraffes.

Space The birds in Figure 9 are rarely seen on land. These birds, called gannets, spend most of their lives flying over the ocean. They only land on this rocky shore to nest. But as you can see, the shore is very crowded. If a pair of gannets does not have room to build a nest, that pair will not be able to produce any offspring.

Elbow Room

Using masking tape, mark off several one-meter squares on the floor of your classroom. Your teacher will form groups of 2, 4, and 6 students. Each group's task is to put together a small jigsaw puzzle in one of the squares. All the group members must keep their feet within the square. Time how long it takes your group to finish the puzzle.

Making Models How long did it take each group to complete the task? How does this activity show that space can be a limiting factor? What is the carrying capacity of puzzle-solvers in a square meter?

Chapter 8 **277**

3 Assess

1. Direct observation, indirect observation, sampling, mark and recapture
2. If the birth rate is higher than the death rate, the population increases. If the birth rate is lower than the death rate, the population decreases. If the rates are the same, the population stays the same size.
3. Food, space, weather; *food:* The population cannot grow beyond the number that can be supported by the amount of food available (carrying capacity); *space:* If organisms are crowded, some will not be able to reproduce or even survive; *weather:* Severe weather conditions can kill many members of the population.
4. The population may be very large or spread over a wide area, or individual members may be hard to find, or it may be difficult to determine which members have already been counted.
5. 13,500 grasshoppers; the sampling method

Science at Home

Tips Let students try the activity in class before they present it to their family members. Possible methods include: (1) Count the number of words in one line, then multiply by the number of lines on the page. (2) Count the number of words in each of three or four lines, calculate the average number of words per line, and multiply by the number of lines on the page. The second method should produce a more accurate estimate.

Performance Assessment

Oral Presentation Call on various students to identify a factor that affects the size of a population (birth/death rates and immigration/emigration numbers as well as limiting factors).

278

Figure 10 A snowstorm can limit the size of the orange crop.

Those gannets will not contribute to an increase in the gannet population. This means that space for nesting is a limiting factor for these gannets. If the shore were bigger, more gannets would be able to nest there, and the population would increase.

Space is often a limiting factor for plants. The amount of space in which a plant grows can determine how much sunlight, water, and other necessities the plant can obtain. For example, many pine seedlings sprout each year in a forest. But as the trees get bigger, those young trees that are too close together do not have room to spread their roots underground. Other tree branches block out the sunlight that the pine seedlings need to carry on photosynthesis. Some of the seedlings die, limiting the size of the pine population.

Weather Weather conditions such as temperature and amount of rainfall can also limit population growth. Many insect species breed in the warm spring weather. As winter begins, the first frost kills many of the insects. This sudden rise in the death rate causes the insect population to decrease.

A single severe weather event can dramatically change the size of a population by killing many organisms. For instance, a flood or hurricane can wash away nests and burrows just as it damages the homes of humans. An ice storm can limit the populations of crops planted in the early spring.

Section 2 Review

1. List four ways of determining population size.
2. How is birth rate related to population size?
3. List three limiting factors for populations. Choose one and explain how this factor can limit population growth.
4. Explain why it is often necessary for ecologists to estimate the size of a population.
5. **Thinking Critically Problem Solving** A field measures 50 meters by 90 meters. In one square meter, you count 3 grasshoppers. Estimate the total population of grasshoppers in the field. What method did you use to make your estimate?

278

Science at Home

Word Estimates Choose a page of a dictionary or other book that has a lot of type on it. Challenge your family members to estimate the number of words on the page. Have each person explain the method he or she used. Now count the actual number of words on the page. Whose estimate was closest?

Program Resources

◆ **Unit 3 Resources** 8-2 Review and Reinforce, p. 15; 8-2 Enrich, p. 16
◆ **Laboratory Manual** 8, "Weather and Whooping Cranes"

Careers in Science

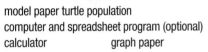 Counting Turtles

For three years, the mark-and-recapture method has been used to monitor the turtle population in a pond. In this lab, you will model this method to complete the study.

Problem

How can the mark-and-recapture method help ecologists monitor the size of a population?

Skills Focus

calculating, graphing, predicting

Materials 💻

model paper turtle population
computer and spreadsheet program (optional)
calculator   graph paper

Procedure

1. 💻 The data table shows the results from the first three years of the study. Copy it into your notebook or spreadsheet, leaving spaces for your data as shown.
2. Your teacher will give you a box representing the pond. Fifteen of the turtles have been marked, as shown in the data table for Year 4.
3. Capture a member of the population by randomly selecting one turtle. Set it aside.
4. Repeat Step 3 nine times. Record the total number of turtles you captured.

5. Examine each turtle to see whether it has a mark. Count the number of recaptured (marked) turtles. Record this number in your data table.

Analyze and Conclude

1. Use the equation below to estimate the turtle population for each year. The first year is done for you as a sample. If your answer is a decimal, round it to the nearest whole number so that your estimate is in "whole turtles." Record the population for each year in the last column of the data table.

$$\text{Total population} = \frac{\text{Number marked} \times \text{Total number captured}}{\text{Number recaptured (with marks)}}$$

Sample (Year 1):
$$\frac{32 \times 28}{15} = 59.7 \text{ or } 60 \text{ turtles}$$

2. Graph the estimated total populations for the four years. Mark years on the horizontal axis. Mark population size on the vertical axis.
3. Describe how the turtle population has changed over the four years of the study. Suggest three possible causes for the changes.
4. **Apply** Use your graph to predict the turtle population in Year 5. Explain your prediction.

Getting Involved

Find out whether any wildlife populations in your area are being monitored by national, state, or local agencies. Make a poster or write an article for the school paper about the population and the method being used to study it.

DATA TABLE

Year	Number Marked	Total Number Captured	Number Recaptured (with Marks)	Estimated Total Population
1	32	28	15	
2	25	21	11	
3	23	19	11	
4	15			

Graph for Question 2

Population Size (vertical axis: 0, 20, 40, 60)
Years (horizontal axis: 1, 2, 3, 4)

Program Resources

◆ **Unit 3 Resources** Chapter 8 Real-World Lab blackline masters, pp. 23–25

Media and Technology

 Lab Activity Videotapes
Grade 6, Tape 3

Careers in Science

Counting Turtles

Preparing for Inquiry

Key Concept The mark-and-recapture method can be used to estimate the size of a population over time.

Skills Objectives Students will be able to
◆ calculate to estimate a population using the mark-and-recapture method;
◆ graph population estimates;
◆ predict the future population.

Time 40 minutes

Advance Planning Prepare a model turtle population for each group. Use 30 small squares cut from paper or index cards to represent turtles. Mark a dot on one side of 15 turtles. Spread all 30 turtles in a box, marked sides down. *Computer use is optional.*

Guiding Inquiry

Troubleshooting the Experiment
In Step 2, clarify that the 15 marked turtles refers to the bottom box in the second column of the table.

Expected Outcome
The number of marked turtles recaptured and students' estimates will vary.

Analyze and Conclude
1. The estimated total populations for Years 1–3 are 60, 48, and 40. The total number captured for Year 4 is 10. In Year 4, if 0 are recaptured, total population cannot be determined; if 1, 150; if 2, 75; if 3, 50; if 4, 38; if 5, 30; if 6, 25; if 7, 21; if 8, 19; if 9, 17; and if 10, 15.
2. See sample graph. Year 4 will vary.
3. The turtle population has declined. Possible causes include limited food, overcrowding, disease, predation, and use of chemicals in the pond.
4. Most students will probably predict a continuing decline in the population.

Extending the Inquiry

Getting Involved
To find information, students can contact their state wildlife authorities.

SECTION
3 Energy in an Ecosystem

SECTION
3 Energy in an Ecosystem

TEKS: 6.2B, C; 6.4A; 6.8B, C

Objectives

After completing the lesson, students will be able to

◆ explain how energy flows in living systems;

◆ list some cycles in nature in which matter and energy interact;

◆ describe what happens when biomass decays.

1 Engage/Explore

Activating Prior Knowledge

Help students recall what they learned previously by asking: **What are some things you have learned about ecosystems in this chapter?** *(Major concepts include habitat, biotic and abiotic factors, structure and function in populations, levels of organization, methods of determining population size, the causes of changes in population size, and limiting factors.)*

DISCOVER

Skills Focus inferring
Time 30 minutes
ACTIVITY
Tips Before leaving the classroom, explain how to use the binoculars, hand lens, and so on. Once outside, guide a volunteer to demonstrate the use of field equipment. Instruct students to follow safety guidelines as described in Appendix A.
Expected Outcome As a class, students may identify a variety of organisms such as ferns, trees, squirrels, snakes, spiders, frogs, birds, and so on. Students should classify all plants that they identify as organisms that make their own food and all other organisms as those that depend on others for food.
Think It Over Answers will vary depending on the ecosystem that the class visits and the organisms that students identify in that ecosystem. Sample: bird—seeds, insects; snake—mice, frogs; frog—flies, spiders.

DISCOVER
ACTIVITY

What's Eating What?

1. With a teacher, visit an ecosystem, such as a park. Bring field equipment such as field guides, binoculars, and a hand lens.

2. Observe your surroundings. Your teacher will tell you how to use the field equipment.

3. Identify as many different organisms as possible, and list them on a sheet of paper.

4. Divide the organisms on the list into two categories: those that make their own food and those that depend on other organisms for food.

Think It Over
Inferring Choose three organisms that do not make their own food. Think of two possible food sources for each organism.

GUIDE FOR READING

◆ How does energy flow in living systems?

◆ What are some cycles in nature in which matter and energy interact?

◆ What happens when biomass decays?

Reading Tip Before you read, rewrite each section heading as a "what" or "how" question. Then write answers to each question as you read.

Key Terms producers
• consumer • decomposer
• food chain • food web
• nitrogen fixation • biomass

It's a warm spring afternoon, a perfect day for a barbecue. Your family and friends are gathered to have a good time. People are talking, playing baseball, and laughing. You're slicing tomatoes for a salad while your cousin pours lemonade. The smell of the chicken sizzling on the grill makes your mouth water. The sun shines brightly on the whole scene.

This barbecue is all about energy. It takes energy to play frisbee and slice tomatoes, and even to talk and laugh. You get the energy to do these things from the food you eat. But where does the energy in the salad and barbecued chicken come from? As you will see, it all starts with that bright sunlight.

An Ecosystem's Energy Source

Since the people at the barbecue must eat food to obtain energy, all of them are heterotrophs. Remember from Chapter 4 that a heterotroph is an organism that cannot make its own food. Animals and fungi are two kinds of heterotrophs. Other organisms, such as plants, can make their own food. As you know, such organisms are called autotrophs.

280

READING STRATEGIES

Reading Tip Begin by rewriting the first section heading as a class. *(What is an ecosystem's energy source?)* You may wish to provide index cards and have students write their questions on one side and their answers on the other side. Let students apply the reading tip without any further assistance. Additional responses might include such questions as *What is dependent on autotrophs?* and *What is the relationship between sunlight and food energy?*

Depending on Autotrophs Heterotrophs are dependent on autotrophs for food, either directly or indirectly. At the barbecue, for example, when you eat potato salad, you are obtaining energy from an autotroph, because the potatoes were produced by potato plants. But even when you eat a hamburger, you are obtaining energy originally produced by autotrophs. Beef cattle—the source of hamburgers—are heterotrophs. But the main source of cattle's food is grass. All plants including grasses are autotrophs.

Sunlight and Food Energy Energy enters most ecosystems from sunlight. That is because most autotrophs make their food through photosynthesis. As you read in Chapter 5, photosynthesis is the process by which plants, algae, and certain microorganisms convert the energy in sunlight to energy stored in plants. In the presence of sunlight, the plant produces molecules in which energy is stored.

By breaking down energy-containing molecules, the plant can use this stored energy to grow and carry out other life processes. When animals and other heterotrophs eat plants, they too can use the energy stored in plants during photosynthesis.

☑ *Checkpoint* **What is the ultimate source of energy for most ecosystems?**

Energy Roles in Ecosystems

Ecologists classify organisms by their role in the flow of energy through ecosystems. The terms ecologists use to describe energy roles are *producer*, *consumer*, and *decomposer*. Because autotrophs produce food and store energy, they are called **producers.** Flowers, grass, seaweed, and cacti are familiar producers.

Heterotrophs that obtain food and energy by eating other organisms are called **consumers.** Consumers include herbivores, carnivores, and omnivores. Herbivores, as you learned in Chapter 7, eat only plants. Cattle, which eat grass, are herbivores. Consumers that eat only animals are called carnivores. Cougars, which eat other animals such as chickens and rabbits, are carnivores. Omnivores, such as bears and most humans, eat both plants and animals.

Figure 11 Plants, which are autotrophs, use the energy in sunlight to make molecules in which energy is stored.
Applying Concepts How do animals use the energy stored in plants?

Program Resources

◆ **Unit 3 Resources** 8-3 Lesson Plan, p. 17; 8-3 Section Summary, p. 18
◆ **Guided Reading and Study Workbook** 8-3

Answers to Self-Assessment

Caption Question

Figure 11 Animals use the energy stored in plants to obtain energy for their own life processes and growth.

☑ *Checkpoint*
The sun

2 *Facilitate*

An Ecosystem's Energy Source

Using the Visuals: Figure 11

Focus students' attention on Figure 11 and the second paragraph, under the heading Sunlight and Food Energy. Ask: **What happens during photosynthesis?** *(The plant converts the energy in sunlight to energy stored in molecules in the plant.)* **In which part of the plant shown in Figure 11 is photosynthesis taking place?** *(The leaves.)* **learning modality: verbal**

Energy Roles in Ecosystems

Addressing Naive Conceptions

Many students might think that all ecosystems are dependent on the sun's energy. Ask: **Do you know of any ecosystems in which producers do not depend on sunlight?** Students may be aware of the ecosystem that exists around deep-ocean hydrothermal vents known as "black smokers." If so, ask them to describe this ecosystem. *(Bacteria use chemicals spewed out of the vents to make their own food; the bacteria in turn are food for other organisms such as shrimp and giant clams.)* **learning modality: verbal**

Ongoing Assessment

Writing Have each student choose one food—sliced tomatoes, barbecued chicken, hamburgers, or potato salad—and write a paragraph identifying the source of the energy that they obtain when they eat that food.

Energy Flow in Food Chains and Food Webs

Figure 12 Plants such as the yucca (**A**) are producers that make their own food. Consumers such as these javelina (**B**) obtain energy by eating other organisms. Mold (**C**) is a decomposer that breaks down wastes and dead organisms.

Some heterotrophs, called **decomposers,** obtain energy by breaking down wastes and the remains of dead organisms. The decomposers break down large molecules in dead organisms into small chemicals, such as minerals, water, and other simple molecules. The decomposers use some of these molecules in their own bodies. The other small molecules are returned to the environment. Mold and some bacteria are decomposers.

☑ *Checkpoint* **What are the three major energy roles organisms play in an ecosystem?**

Energy Flow in Food Chains and Food Webs

Energy enters an ecosystem when producers convert the sun's energy into stored food energy. When a consumer eats a producer, some of this stored food energy is transferred to the consumer. This consumer may be eaten by another consumer, and so on. Each time an organism eats another, some energy is transferred to the feeding organism. Finally, a decomposer breaks down the remains of organisms. Some energy is transferred to the decomposer, and the rest is released, often as heat.

Ecologists use a diagram called a **food chain** to show the flow of energy from organism to organism. **In general, energy flows from producers to consumers to decomposers in an ecosystem.** Follow the energy through the ecosystem shown in *Exploring a Food Chain.*

282

EXPLORING a Food Chain

This food chain is an example of the feeding relationships that might occur in one part of a Texas brush country ecosystem. A food chain always begins with a producer.

4 Bobcat
Third-level consumer
The bobcat is also a carnivore. When a bobcat eats a second-level consumer such as the weasel, the bobcat is called a third-level consumer.

1 Prickly pear cactus
Producer
The cactus converts the sun's energy into the matter that makes up its thick leaves and flowers.

2 Woodrat
First-level consumer
This small rodent obtains energy by eating other organisms, such as the prickly pear cactus. Consumers that eat producers are called first-level consumers.

3 Weasel
Second-level consumer
The weasel is a carnivore and feeds on other consumers. When the weasel eats a first-level consumer such as the woodrat, the weasel is considered a second-level consumer.

Chapter 8 **283**

Media and Technology

 Transparencies "Exploring a Food Chain," Transparency 39; "A Food Web," Transparency 40

 Life Science Videodisc
Unit 6, Side 2, "The Wonder of Ngorongoro"

 Chapter 1

Answers to Self-Assessment

☑ *Checkpoint*
Producer, consumer, and decomposer

EXPLORING

A Food Chain

Ask students: **In what direction do the arrows in a food-chain diagram point?** *(From the organism being eaten to the organism doing the eating.)* **What producer is shown in this food chain?** *(A cactus.)* **If the bobcat ate a woodrat, what consumer level would the bobcat be then?** *(A second-level consumer.)* Challenge students to list organisms in the area where they live and describe feeding relationships. Then have students draw food chains to show these relationships. Refer to the **ELL Handbook** for additional teaching strategies. **learning modality: visual**

Ongoing Assessment

Drawing Have each student draw a food chain of his or her own choice and label each organism to show *(1)* its energy role and *(2)* the level of each consumer.

Energy Flow in Food Chains and Food Webs, continued

Using the Visuals: Figure 13

Help students to identify the producers and consumers shown in Figure 13. **What are the producers in this food web?** *(prickly pear cactus and mesquite)* **What are the first-level consumers?** *(woodrat and desert cottontail)* **What are the second-level consumers?** *(weasel)* **What are the third-level consumers?** *(bobcat and hawk)* **learning modality: visual**

Including All Students

To help students who are having difficulty understanding the concept of a food web, ask them to look back at the food chain on page 283. Then have students trace that food chain in the web shown in Figure 13. Ask students to find other food chains within this food web. **learning modality: visual**

Cycles in Ecosystems

Real-Life Learning

Ask **What is a cycle?** *(A series of things that repeat over and over again)* **What are some examples of cycles?** *(Seasons of the year, days of the week, life cycles of plants and animals, and so forth)* **learning modality: verbal**

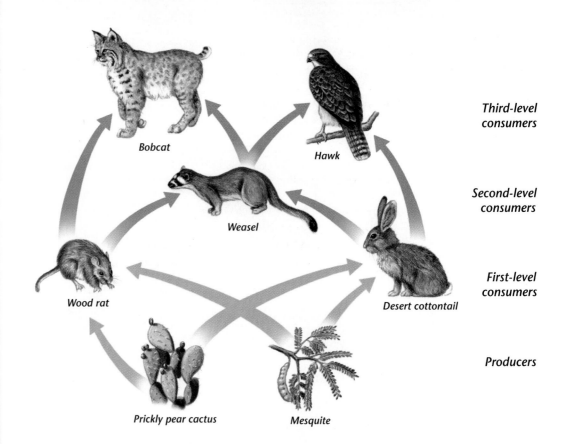

Third-level consumers

Second-level consumers

First-level consumers

Producers

Bobcat

Hawk

Weasel

Wood rat

Desert cottontail

Prickly pear cactus

Mesquite

Figure 13 In an ecosystem, many food chains overlap to form a food web, such as the one shown here.

Many food chains exist in each ecosystem. Some of these food chains overlap. For example, a producer such as a prickly pear is food for other consumers besides a wood rat. A wood rat feeds on other producers besides a prickly pear. And a hawk feeds on many different animals. A diagram called a **food web** shows how many food chains are connected. Figure 13 shows one food web.

☑ *Checkpoint* *What is a food chain?*

Cycles in Ecosystems

As you have read, organisms use energy as it moves through an ecosystem from producer to consumer to decomposer. Certain matter that organisms need, such as water, carbon, and nitrogen, cycles through the ecosystem as well. When a consumer eats a producer, for example, more than just a transfer of energy occurs. A transfer of matter, such as carbon molecules, also occurs. **Some cycles in which matter and energy interact in an ecosystem are the water cycle, the carbon and oxygen cycles, and the nitrogen cycle.** You will read about the water cycle in Chapter 12.

Background

Facts and Figures The sizes of populations in a food web normally vary slightly over time. For example, good growing conditions could cause an increase in populations of producers, leading to an increase in populations of first-level consumers. As the increased first-level consumer populations feed, they may reduce the populations of producers.

Sometimes changes in the size of one population can result in drastic changes in other populations. In the food web shown on this page, a disease might suddenly reduce the size of the rabbit population. This change would reduce the amount of food available to hawks, decreasing the hawk population. Another possible outcome would be that the hawks would eat more weasels, decreasing the weasel population, and also reducing the amount of food available to the bobcat population.

The Carbon and Oxygen Cycles The recycling of carbon and oxygen is linked to the flow of energy in an ecosystem. As you read about the carbon and oxygen cycles, follow the diagram in Figure 14. Carbon dioxide in the air contains the element carbon. Producers take in carbon dioxide gas during photosynthesis. They use the carbon from the carbon dioxide to produce other carbon-containing molecules such as the sugars and starches that are stored in their bodies. A consumer such as a horse then eats plants. It obtains energy from these molecules by breaking them down into simpler molecules. Recall that this process is called respiration. Carbon dioxide gas is released as a waste product of respiration.

Meanwhile, oxygen is also cycling through the ecosystem. Producers release oxygen as a result of photosynthesis. Most organisms take in oxygen and use it during respiration.

The Nitrogen Cycle Although air is about 78 percent nitrogen gas, most organisms cannot use nitrogen. Nitrogen gas, which is called "free" nitrogen, is not combined with other elements. Most organisms can only use nitrogen that is combined with other elements.

The process of combining free nitrogen with other elements is called **nitrogen fixation.** Bacteria that live in swellings called nodules on the roots of some plants perform much nitrogen fixation. These bacteria combine nitrogen with other elements, forming fixed nitrogen, or nitrogen-containing compounds. Consumers use this fixed nitrogen to build proteins and other substances. Nitrogen is also fixed in other ways, such as through the action of lightning on free nitrogen.

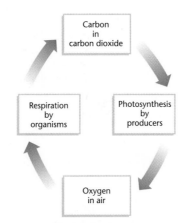

Figure 14 Carbon dioxide is used during photosynthesis. Photosynthesis, in turn, produces oxygen, which is used in respiration. Respiration produces carbon dioxide, and the cycle begins again.

Figure 15 In the nitrogen cycle, nitrogen moves from the air to the soil, into living things, and back into the air.
Interpreting Diagrams How do consumers obtain nitrogen?

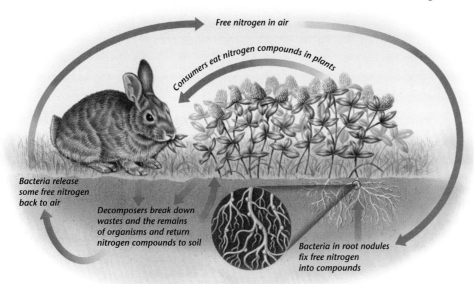

Free nitrogen in air

Consumers eat nitrogen compounds in plants

Bacteria release some free nitrogen back to air

Decomposers break down wastes and the remains of organisms and return nitrogen compounds to soil

Bacteria in root nodules fix free nitrogen into compounds

Chapter 8 **285**

Including All Students

Materials *white and blue index cards, tape*
Time 10–15 minutes

Have students role-play the materials and organisms shown in Figure 15. Assign the following roles: air, clover plants, rabbits, nitrogen-fixing bacteria in nodules on the clover's roots, decomposers in the soil, and bacteria in the soil. Give the "air" students white index cards representing free nitrogen. Give the "nodule bacteria" students blue index cards and tape. The air students hand white cards to the nodule bacteria students, who attach, or "fix," each white card to one of their blue cards and then hand the cards to the "clover plants." Some clover plants should hand their cards to "rabbits." Other clover plants and some rabbits should hand their cards to "decomposers," who in turn hand the cards to "soil bacteria." The soil bacteria detach the blue cards from the white cards and hand the white cards back to the air students, completing the cycle. **learning modality: tactile/ kinesthetic**

Media and Technology

 Transparencies "The Nitrogen Cycle," Transparency 41

 Life Science Videodisc Unit 6, Side 2, "Cycles in Nature"

 Chapter 3

Answers to Self-Assessment

Caption Question

Figure 15 By eating nitrogen compounds in plants

 *Checkpoint*

A food chain is a diagram that shows the flow of energy from organism to organism in an ecosystem.

Ongoing Assessment

Drawing Have each student draw and label a simple diagram of the nitrogen cycle without referring to Figure 15. Students can save their drawings in their portfolios.

The Decay of Biomass

Real-Life Learning

Ask students if they have ever seen a compost pile. Ask students to describe how a compost pile changes over time. (*As materials decay, they cease to be recognizable objects. The volume of the pile decreases as materials decay.*)

3 Assess

Section 3 Review Answers

1. In most ecosystems, energy flows from producers to consumers to decomposers.
2. The water cycle, carbon and oxygen cycles, and nitrogen cycle
3. As the biomass in a compost pile decays, matter in the form of small molecules is produced and energy is released.
4. Plants take in carbon dioxide from the air and release oxygen into the air.
5. Both consumers and decomposers are heterotrophs. Consumers obtain energy by eating other organisms. Decomposers obtain energy by breaking down wastes and the remains of dead organisms.

Check Your Progress
CHAPTER PROJECT

Distribute Chapter 8 Project Worksheet 2, which is designed to help students prepare their written reports and graphs. All groups should graph the data they collected on plant height; some groups may want to create additional graphs for the numbers of leaves and buds. (See Chapter 8 Project Teacher Notes, Unit 3 Resources page 3, for information on graphing possibilities.)

Performance Assessment

Skills Check Have students explain various phrases that you point out in each cycle diagram in this section. See Figures 14 and 15 on page 285.

Figure 16 As the matter in a compost pile decays, both small molecules and energy are produced. *Relating Cause and Effect Why is compost beneficial to plants?*

The Decay of Biomass

If you walk in a forest, you can see many living things. And whether or not you are aware of it, the forest also contains the remains of organisms that have died. The total amount of living matter, and the remains of dead organisms, in an area is the area's **biomass.**

Biomass is matter that contains energy stored in its chemical compounds. When living things die, bacteria and other decomposers break down the material in the biomass. In this decay process, the decomposers break large molecules into smaller ones. **The decay of biomass produces matter in the form of small molecules. This chemical breakdown also releases the energy stored in the chemical compounds in the biomass.** The energy is released in the form of heat.

Gardeners who keep compost piles take advantage of the decay of biomass. You may have seen gardeners add things such as corn husks, rotten vegetables, and grass clippings to a compost pile. The biomass in a compost pile is broken down by decomposers in the pile. Compost makes good fertilizer because producers, such as garden plants, can absorb and use the small molecules produced by the decay of biomass. The chemical breakdown of compost also releases energy. This is why you can often feel heat rising from a compost pile.

Section 3 Review

1. Describe how energy flows through most ecosystems.
2. Name three cycles in which matter and energy interact in ecosystems.
3. Explain what happens to matter and energy as compost decays.
4. What is the role of plants in the carbon and oxygen cycles?
5. **Thinking Critically** Comparing and Contrasting Compare and contrast consumers and decomposers.

Check Your Progress
CHAPTER PROJECT

By now you should be making your final observations of your plants and planning your report. How can you present your data in a graph? Think about what you should put on each axis of your graph. (*Hint:* Draft the written portion of your report early enough to look it over and make any necessary changes.)

Program Resources

◆ **Unit 3 Resources** 8-3 Review and Reinforce, p. 19; 8-3 Enrich, p. 20

Answers to Self-Assessment

Caption Question

Figure 16 Compost is beneficial to plants because compost contains small molecules, produced by the decay of biomass, that plants can absorb and use.

Components of Ecosystems

Key Ideas

◆ All the living and nonliving things that interact in an area make up an ecosystem.

◆ An organism's habitat provides food, water, shelter, and other things the organism needs to live, grow, and reproduce.

◆ Organisms in an ecosystem respond to both biotic and abiotic factors. Abiotic factors found in many environments include water, sunlight, oxygen, temperature, and soil.

◆ A population consists of a single species. The different populations living together in one area make up a community. The community plus abiotic factors form an ecosystem.

◆ Ecologists study how biotic and abiotic factors interact within an ecosystem.

Key Terms

ecosystem	population
habitat	society
biotic factor	community
abiotic factor	ecology

 Studying Populations

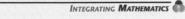 INTEGRATING **MATHEMATICS**

Key Ideas

◆ Ecologists can estimate population size by direct and indirect observations, sampling, and mark-and-recapture studies.

◆ A population changes in size as a result of changes in the birth rate or death rate, or when organisms move into or out of the population.

◆ Population size is controlled by limiting factors such as food, space, and weather conditions.

Key Terms

population density	immigration
estimate	emigration
birth rate	limiting factor
death rate	carrying capacity

 Energy in an Ecosystem

Key Ideas

◆ Energy enters most ecosystems from sunlight.

◆ The terms *producer*, *consumer* and *decomposer* describe the energy roles of organisms in an ecosystem.

◆ In general, energy flows from producers to consumers to decomposers in an ecosystem.

◆ Some cycles in which matter and energy interact are the water cycle, the carbon and oxygen cycles, and the nitrogen cycle.

Key Terms

producer	food web
consumer	nitrogen fixation
decomposer	biomass
food chain	

Organizing Information

Concept Map Copy the flow chart about energy in ecosystems onto a sheet of paper. Complete it and add a title. (For more on flow charts, see the Skills Handbook.)

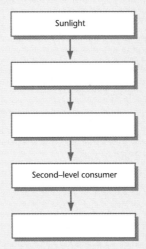

Organizing Information

Concept Map Sample title: Energy flow in Ecosystems

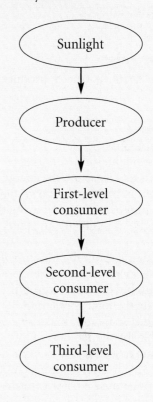

Program Resources

◆ **Unit 3 Resources** Chapter 8 Project Scoring Rubric, p. 8

◆ **Performance Assessment** Chapter 8, pp. 26–28

◆ **Chapter and Unit Tests** Chapter 8 Test, pp. 40–43

Media and Technology

 Computer Test Bank
Chapter 8 Test

Reviewing Content
Multiple Choice
1. a 2. b 3. c 4. b 5. c

True or False
6. biotic 7. true 8. true 9. producers
10. true

Checking Concepts
11. Sample answer: *Biotic:* trees, birds *Abiotic:* sunlight, soil
12. Plants and algae use the energy of sunlight in making their own food through photosynthesis. All living things feed directly or indirectly on plants and algae.
13. Ecologists count the number of organisms in a small area, then multiply by the number of units in the entire area to estimate the total population.
14. Limited space may make it impossible for all members of the population to find places to make nests.
15. Nitrogen fixation is important to organisms because most organisms can use only nitrogen that is combined with other elements. Nitrogen fixation occurs as bacteria that live in nodules on the roots of some plants combine nitrogen with other elements, forming fixed nitrogen or nitrogen-containing compounds.
16. Decomposers are important because they recycle organic matter in ecosystems. Decomposers return simple compounds, including nitrogen compounds, to soil.
17. This carbon dioxide is recycled as producers take it in during photosynthesis.
18. Students should explain that compost makes good fertilizer. Producers—such as garden plants—can absorb and use the small molecules produced by the decay of biomass in a compost pile.

Thinking Critically
19. It is usually not possible to study the entire population of the species because it is too spread out. In addition, because the organism's interaction with other organisms and the environment is specific to that environment, studying a population produces more accurate results than studying an entire species.

Reviewing Content
 Review key concepts online using iText at www.phschool.com

Multiple Choice
Choose the letter of the best answer.

1. Which of the following is *not* an example of a population?
   a. the pets in your neighborhood
   b. the people in a city
   c. the rainbow trout in a stream
   d. the ants in an anthill
2. A prairie dog, a hawk, and a badger all are members of the same
   a. habitat.   b. community.
   c. species.   d. population.
3. All of the following are examples of limiting factors for populations *except*
   a. space   b. food
   c. time   d. weather
4. Energy enters an ecosystem from
   a. decomposers.   b. sunlight.
   c. consumers.   d. producers.
5. An omnivore is a kind of
   a. herbivore.   b. carnivore.
   c. consumer.   d. producer.

True or False
If the statement is true, write true. If it is false, change the underlined word or words to make the statement true.

6. Grass is an example of a(n) <u>abiotic</u> factor in a habitat.
7. A rise in birth rate while the death rate remains steady will cause a population to <u>increase</u> in size.
8. A population in an ecosystem belongs to a <u>community</u> consisting of different species.
9. The <u>consumers</u> in an ecosystem produce food and stored energy.
10. A <u>food chain</u> shows how energy flows from organism to organism in an ecosystem.

Checking Concepts
11. Name two biotic and two abiotic factors you might find in a forest ecosystem.
12. Explain how sunlight is used by plants and algae. How is this process important to other living things in an ecosystem?
13. Describe how ecologists use the technique of sampling to estimate population size.
14. Give an example showing how space can be a limiting factor for a population.
15. Explain why nitrogen fixation is important to organisms. How does it occur?
16. Explain why decomposers are important in an ecosystem.
17. Organisms produce carbon dioxide in the process of respiration. Explain how this carbon dioxide is recycled in an ecosystem.
18. **Writing to Learn** Write a brochure for home gardeners that explains how a compost pile can improve their garden.

Thinking Critically
19. **Making Generalizations** Explain why ecologists usually study a specific population of organisms rather than studying the entire species.
20. **Applying Concepts** Name a biotic factor that you might find in a prairie ecosystem. Describe how a prairie dog might respond to that biotic factor.
21. **Problem Solving** In a summer job working for an ecologist, you have been assigned to estimate the population of grasshoppers in a field. Propose a method to get an estimate and explain how you would carry it out.
22. **Comparing and Contrasting** Explain how a food chain and a food web are similar and how they are different.
23. **Relating Cause and Effect** Nitrogen-fixing bacteria grow in nodules on the roots of clover plants. Farmers sometimes plant clover instead of a crop for one growing season. Explain why this makes the soil more fertile.

20. Sample: Hawk. A prairie dog might run from the hawk.
21. Answers may include indirect observation (counting egg clusters), sampling (counting the number in a small area, then multiplying by the number of units in the entire area), or mark and recapture.
22. Both a food chain and a food web are diagrams that show the flow of energy from organism to organism in an ecosystem. A food web is larger and more complex than a food chain. It shows how the food chains in an ecosystem are connected.
23. Planting clover enriches the field by returning nitrogen-containing molecules to the soil.

Applying Skills

Ecologists monitoring a deer population collected data during a 30-year study. Use the data to answer Questions 24–27.

Year	0	5	10	15	20	25	30
Population (thousands)	15	30	65	100	40	25	10

24. Graphing Make a line graph using the data in the table. Plot years on the horizontal axis and population on the vertical axis.

25. Interpreting Data In which year did the deer population reach its highest point? Its lowest point?

26. Communicating Write a few sentences describing how the deer population changed during the study.

♠ **27. Developing Hypotheses** In Year 16 of the study, this region experienced a very severe winter. How might this have affected the deer population?

Performance ▼ CHAPTER PROJECT Assessment

Present Your Project Review your report and graph to be sure that they clearly state your conclusion about the effects of crowding on plant growth. With your group, decide how you will present your results. Do a practice run-through to make sure all group members feel comfortable with their part.

Reflect and Record Compare your group's results with those of your classmates. Suggest possible explanations for any differences. How could you have improved your plan for your experiment?

Test Preparation

Use these questions to prepare for standardized tests.

Study the graph. Then answer Questions 28–31.

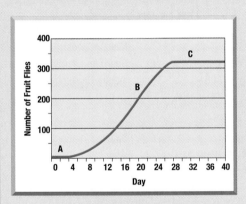

28. What is the best title for this graph?
A Fruit Fly Population Density
B Abiotic Factors and Fruit Flies
C Fruit Fly Population Growth
D Fruit Fly Death Rate

29. At what point on the graph is the population of fruit flies increasing?
F Point A   G Point B
H Point C   J none of the above

30. Which of the following statements may be true of the fruit fly population at Point C?
A The death rate is approximately equal to the birth rate.
B A limiting factor in the environment is preventing the population from increasing.
C There may not be enough food or space to support a larger population.
D All of the above statements may be true.

31. Based on the graph, what is the carrying capacity of the environment in which the fruit flies live?
F approximately 320 fruit flies
G approximately 220 fruit flies
H approximately 410 fruit flies
J approximately 160 fruit flies

Program Resources

- **Inquiry Skills Activity Book** Provides teaching and review of all inquiry skills
- **Prentice Hall Assessment System** Provides standardized test practice
- **Reading in the Content Area** Provides strategies to improve science reading skills
- **Teacher's ELL Handbook** Provides multiple strategies for English language learners

---

Applying Skills

24.

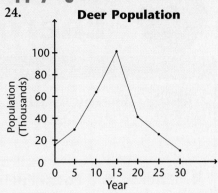

Deer Population

25. *Highest:* Year 15; *lowest:* Year 30

26. *Example:* Beginning with 15,000 deer at the beginning of the study, the population increased steadily through Year 15. From Year 15 through the end of the study, the deer population declined steadily, reaching the population's lowest point, 10,000 deer, in Year 30.

27. The severe winter may have killed weak or injured deer. Food shortages during this winter also may have weakened deer or caused them to starve.

Performance ▼ CHAPTER PROJECT Assessment

Present Your Project Review each group's written report, and let groups present their results to the rest of the class in a poster, display, or oral report. As indicated in the Scoring Rubric, base your evaluation of each group's report on both the written report and the class presentation.

Reflect and Record After all groups have made their class presentations, allow time for students to compare their results and discuss the factors that may have accounted for any differences.

Test Preparation

28. C **29.** G **30.** D **31.** F

Energy Resources

Sections	Time	Student Edition Activities	Other Activities	
CHAPTER PROJECT **Energy Audit** p. 291 TEKS: 6.9	Ongoing (2–3 weeks)	TEKS: 6.2A, B, D **Check Your Progress,** pp. 298, 306, 311 **Present Your Project,** p. 319	**TE**	Chapter 9 Project Notes, pp. 290–291
1 Energy and Fossil Fuels pp. 292–298 TEKS: 6.9A, B, C 9.1.1 Explain how fuels provide energy. 9.1.2 List the three major fossil fuels. 9.1.3 Explain why fossil fuels are considered nonrenewable resources.	3 periods/ 1½ blocks	TEKS: 6.2B, E; 6.4A **Discover** What's in a Piece of Coal?, p. 292 **Sharpen Your Skills** Graphing, p. 295	**TE** **TE** **TE**	Inquiry Challenge, pp. 294, 295 Building Inquiry Skills: Observing, p. 296 Building Inquiry Skills: Calculating, p. 297
2 Renewable Sources of Energy pp. 299–306 TEKS: 6.9A, B, C 9.2.1 Explain how the sun provides energy and describe ways to collect this energy. 9.2.2 Identify and describe various sources of renewable energy.	2 periods/ 1 block	TEKS: 6.2A, B, C, D; 6.3D; 6.4A **Discover** Can You Capture Solar Energy?, p. 299 **Real-World Lab: How It Works** Cooking With Sunshine, p. 305	**TE** **TE** **TE** **LM**	Inquiry Challenge, p. 300 Real-Life Learning, p. 301 Demonstration, p. 303 9, "Solar Heating"
3 **INTEGRATING CHEMISTRY** **Nuclear Energy** pp. 307–311 TEKS: 6.9A, C 9.3.1 Describe nuclear fission and nuclear fusion reactions. 9.3.2 Explain how a nuclear power plant produces electricity.	3 periods/ 1½ blocks	TEKS: 6.2B, C, D, E; 6.3C; 6.4A **Discover** Why Do They Fall?, p. 307 **Try This** Shoot the Nucleus, p. 308 **Sharpen Your Skills** Calculating, p. 308	**TE** **TE** **TE**	Building Inquiry Skills: Making Models, p. 308 Real-Life Learning, p. 310 Inquiry Challenge, p. 310
4 Energy Conservation pp. 312–316 TEKS: 6.9A 9.4.1 List two ways to ensure that there will be enough energy for the future. 9.4.2 Identify things that individuals can do to conserve energy.	2–3 periods/ 1–1½ blocks	TEKS: 6.1A; 6.2B, C; 6.3E; 6.4A **Skills Lab: Designing Experiments** Keeping Comfortable, p. 312 (Probeware version available) **Discover** Which Bulb Is More Efficient?, p. 313 **Science at Home,** p. 316	**TE** **TE**	Building Inquiry Skills: Calculating, p. 314 Building Inquiry Skills: Observing, p. 315
Study Guide/Chapter Assessment pp. 317–319	1 period/ ½ block	**PLM** Provides blackline masters for Probeware labs	**ISAB**	Provides teaching and review of all inquiry skills

Key: **CTB** Computer Test Bank
CUT Chapter and Unit Tests
ELL Teacher's ELL Handbook

290a

CHAPTER PLANNING GUIDE

 The Resource Pro® CD-ROM provides flexibility for planning the instruction for any type of schedule.

Program Resources	Assessment Strategies	Media and Technology
UR Chapter 9 Project Teacher Notes, pp. 26–27 **UR** Chapter 9 Project Overview and Worksheet, pp. 28–31	**SE** Performance Assessment: Present Your Project, p. 319 **TE** Check Your Progress, pp. 298, 306, 311 **UR** Chapter 9 Project Scoring Rubric, p. 32	Science Explorer at www.phschool.com Student Edition on Audio CD, English-Spanish, Chapter 9
UR 9-1 Section Lesson Plan, p. 33 **UR** 9-1 Section Summary, p. 34 **UR** 9-1 Review and Reinforce, p. 35 **UR** 9-1 Enrich, p. 36	**SE** Section 1 Review, p. 298 **TE** Ongoing Assessment, pp. 293, 295, 297 **TE** Performance Assessment, p. 298	Earth Science Videodisc Unit 6, Side 2, "Our Passion for Driving"; "Power for the People" Videotape Grade 6, Unit 3, "Our Passion for Driving"; "Power for the People" Transparency 42, "An Electric Power Plant"
UR 9-2 Section Lesson Plan, p. 37 **UR** 9-2 Section Summary, p. 38 **UR** 9-2 Review and Reinforce, p. 39 **UR** 9-2 Enrich, p. 40 **UR** Real-World Lab blackline masters, pp. 49–50	**SE** Section 2 Review, p. 304 **TE** Ongoing Assessment, pp. 301, 303 **TE** Performance Assessment, p. 304	Physical Science Videodisc Unit 4, Side 2, "Wired to the Sun" Videotape Grade 6, Unit 3, "Wired to the Sun" Lab Activity Videotapes, Tape 3 Transparencies 43, "Exploring a Solar House"; 44, "Exploring a Hydroelectric Power Plant"
UR 9-3 Section Lesson Plan, p. 41 **UR** 9-3 Section Summary, p. 42 **UR** 9-3 Review and Reinforce, p. 43 **UR** 9-3 Enrich, p. 44	**SE** Section 3 Review, p. 311 **TE** Ongoing Assessment, p. 309 **TE** Performance Assessment, p. 311	Transparencies 45, "Nuclear Fission"; 46, "A Nuclear Power Plant"; 47, "Nuclear Fusion"
UR 9-4 Section Lesson Plan, p. 45 **UR** 9-4 Section Summary, p. 46 **UR** 9-4 Review and Reinforce, p. 47 **UR** 9-4 Enrich, p. 48 **UR** Skills Lab blackline masters, pp. 51–53	**SE** Section 4 Review, p. 316 **TE** Ongoing Assessment, p. 315 **TE** Performance Assessment, p. 316	Lab Activity Videotapes, Tape 3
ELL Provides multiple strategies for English language learners **GRSW** Provides worksheets to promote student comprehension of content **RCA** Provides strategies to improve science reading skills	**SE** Chapter 9 Study Guide/Assessment, pp. 317–319 **PA** Chapter 9 Assessment, pp. 29–31 **CUT** Chapter 9 Test, pp. 44–47 **CTB** Chapter 9 Test **PHAS** Provides standardized test preparation	Chapter 9 Computer Test Bank, Chapter 9 Test

GRSW Guided Reading and Study Workbook
ISAB Inquiry Skills Activity Book
LM Laboratory Manual

PA Performance Assessment
PHAS Prentice Hall Assessment System
PLM Probeware Lab Manual

RCA Reading in the Content Area
SE Student Edition

TE Teacher's Edition
UR Unit Resources

Student Edition Activities Planner

ACTIVITY	Time (minutes)	Materials — Quantities for one work group	Skills
Section 1			
Discover, p. 292	10	**Nonconsumable** lignite coal, hand lens	Observing
Sharpen Your Skills, p. 295	15	**Nonconsumable** drawing compass, protractor, calculator or computer (optional)	Graphing
Section 2			
Discover, p. 299	10; 5	**Consumable** 500 mL water **Nonconsumable** 2 sealable clear plastic bags, 2 thermometers	Developing Hypotheses
Real-World Lab, p. 305	40	**Consumable** glue, tape, marshmallows, 3 sheets aluminum foil, 3 sheets oaktag paper **Nonconsumable** scissors, 3 thermometers, 3 dowels or pencils, clock or watch	Predicting, Designing Experiments, Forming Operational Definitions
Section 3			
Discover, p. 307	10	**Nonconsumable** 15 dominoes	Inferring
Try This, p. 308	10	**Nonconsumable** 12 marbles	Making Models
Sharpen Your Skills, p. 309	5	**Nonconsumable** calculator (optional)	Calculating
Section 4			
Skills Lab, p. 312	40	**Consumable** ice water, hot water **Nonconsumable** thermometers or temperature probes, beakers, watch or clock, containers and lids made of paper, plastic foam, plastic, glass, and metal	Measuring, Designing Experiments
Discover, p. 313	20	**Nonconsumable** 60-watt incandescent light bulb and 15-watt compact fluorescent light bulb in packages, lamp, thermometer, clock or watch	Inferring
Science at Home, p. 316	home	No special materials are required.	Observing

A list of all materials required for the Student Edition activities can be found on pages T43–T49. You can obtain information about ordering materials by calling 1-800-848-9500 or by accessing the Science Explorer Internet site at **www.phschool.com**.

Texas Essential Knowledge and Skills

(6.1) Scientific processes. The student conducts field and laboratory investigations using safe, environmentally appropriate, and ethical practices. *(Section 4)*

The student is expected to:

(A) demonstrate safe practices during field and laboratory investigations.

(6.2) Scientific processes. The student uses scientific inquiry methods during field and laboratory investigations. *(Project; Sections 1, 2, 3, 4)*

The student is expected to:

(A) plan and implement investigative procedures including asking questions, formulating testable hypotheses, and selecting and using equipment and technology;

(B) collect data by observing and measuring;

(C) analyze and interpret information to construct reasonable explanations from direct and indirect evidence;

(D) communicate valid conclusions; and

(E) construct graphs, tables, maps, and charts using tools including computers to organize, examine, and evaluate data.

(6.3) Scientific processes. The student uses critical thinking and scientific problem solving to make informed decisions. *(Sections 2, 3, 4)*

The student is expected to:

(C) represent the natural world using models and identify their limitations;

(D) evaluate the impact of research on scientific thought, society, and the environment; and

(E) connect Grade 6 science concepts with the history of science and contributions of scientists.

(6.4) Scientific processes. The student knows how to use a variety of tools and methods to conduct science inquiry. *(Sections 1, 2, 3, 4)*

The student is expected to:

(A) collect, analyze, and record information using tools including beakers, petri dishes, meter sticks, graduated cylinders, weather instruments, timing devices, hot plates, test tubes, safety goggles, spring scales, magnets, balances, microscopes, telescopes, thermometers, calculators, field equipment, compasses, computers, and computer probes.

(6.9) Science concepts. The student knows that obtaining, transforming, and distributing energy affects the environment. *(Project; Sections 1, 2, 3, 4)*

The student is expected to:

(A) identify energy transformations occurring during the production of energy for human use such as electrical energy to heat energy or heat energy to electrical energy;

(B) compare methods used for transforming energy in devices such as water heaters, cooling systems, or hydroelectric and wind power plants; and

(C) research and describe energy types from their source to their use and determine if the type is renewable, nonrenewable, or inexhaustible.

Take It to the Net

 Interactive text at www.phschool.com

Science Explorer comes alive with iText.

■ **Complete student text** is accessible from any computer with Internet access or a CD-ROM drive.

■ **Animations, simulations, and videos** enhance student understanding and retention of concepts.

■ **Self-tests and online study tools** assess student understanding.

■ **Teacher management tools** help you make the most of this valuable resource.

STAY CURRENT with **SCIENCE NEWS®**

Find out the latest research and information about energy and energy resources at **www.phschool.com**.

Go to **www.phschool.com**. Select Texas on the navigation bar. Click on the Science icon. Then click on <u>Science Explorer</u> under PH@school.

Energy Audit

TEKS: 6.2A, B, D; 6.9

Chapter 9 covers the sources and uses of energy and ways to conserve energy. The Chapter 9 Project is designed to provide real-life application of chapter concepts.

Purpose The Chapter 9 Project will give students an opportunity to examine energy uses in their school and suggest ways to reduce the school's energy consumption. Each student group will choose one area of the school to study, identify the types of energy used in that area, and determine the amount of each type of energy used. As students collect and record data, they will consider ways to reduce each type of energy use. Each group will prepare a written report that describes their findings and their ideas for reducing energy uses. The class as a whole will then prepare a proposal for conserving energy throughout the school.

Skills Focus After completing the Chapter 9 Project, students will be able to
- create a data table for recording the types and amounts of energy uses in the area selected for study;
- make observations and record data;
- interpret data and draw conclusions as the basis for recommending ways to reduce energy use;
- communicate findings and recommendations in a written report.

Project Time Line The Chapter 9 Project requires two to three weeks to complete, depending on how long a period of time you want to have students collect and evaluate numerical data, including the school's utility bills and readings of electric meters and fuel gauges. Most observations can be made during a class period. For purposes of comparison, making observations of the same area on different days and at different times of day should help students detect average and unusual uses, such as increased use of heating fuel during a cold spell.

Possible Materials
No special materials are required. Students will find calculators helpful.

CHAPTER 9 Energy Resources

PANK o AMERICA

Electricity makes downtown Los Angeles sparkle at dusk.

WEB ACTIVITY
www.phschool.com

290

Advance Preparation
- Discuss with your school principal what students will be doing in this project, and obtain approval for students to enter areas that are usually off-limits to them, such as the utility room, or the cafeteria's kitchen. If necessary, arrange to have the school custodian or another adult accompany students to these areas.
- Obtain copies of the school's utility and fuel bills for students' use in determining the amounts of energy used.

Launching the Project Invite students to read the Chapter 9 Project description on page 291. Lead students in brainstorming a list of areas in the school that they could study.

Take the class on a tour of the school building and grounds. Encourage students to keep track of the different energy uses they observe—electricity for lighting, fuel oil or natural gas for heating, electricity or natural gas for cooking, gasoline for the school buses, and the like.

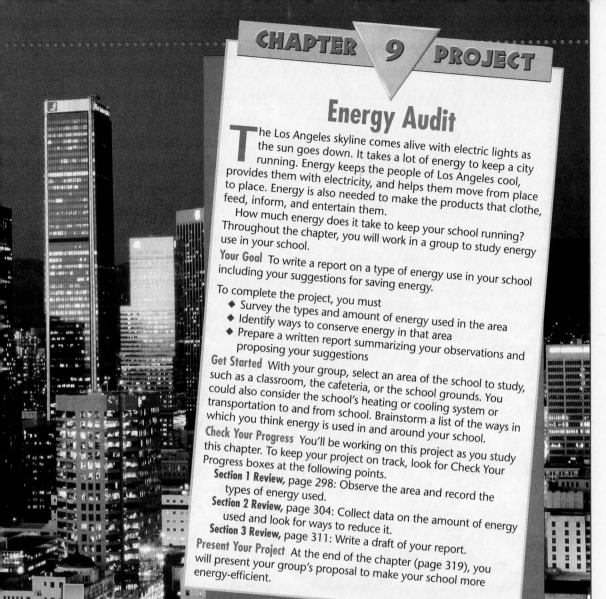

Energy Audit

The Los Angeles skyline comes alive with electric lights as the sun goes down. It takes a lot of energy to keep a city running. Energy keeps the people of Los Angeles cool, provides them with electricity, and helps them move from place to place. Energy is also needed to make the products that clothe, feed, inform, and entertain them.

How much energy does it take to keep your school running? Throughout the chapter, you will work in a group to study energy use in your school.

Your Goal To write a report on a type of energy use in your school including your suggestions for saving energy.

To complete the project, you must
- Survey the types and amount of energy used in the area
- Identify ways to conserve energy in that area
- Prepare a written report summarizing your observations and proposing your suggestions

Get Started With your group, select an area of the school to study, such as a classroom, the cafeteria, or the school grounds. You could also consider the school's heating or cooling system or transportation to and from school. Brainstorm a list of the ways in which you think energy is used in and around your school.

Check Your Progress You'll be working on this project as you study this chapter. To keep your project on track, look for Check Your Progress boxes at the following points.

Section 1 Review, page 298: Observe the area and record the types of energy used.

Section 2 Review, page 304: Collect data on the amount of energy used and look for ways to reduce it.

Section 3 Review, page 311: Write a draft of your report.

Present Your Project At the end of the chapter (page 319), you will present your group's proposal to make your school more energy-efficient.

 TEKS

In addition to process TEKS, this chapter addresses these concept TEKS as they relate to the chapter's topics.

(6.9) The student knows that obtaining, transforming, and distributing energy affects the environment. The student is expected to:

(A) identify energy transformations occurring during the production of energy for human use such as electrical energy to heat energy or heat energy to electrical energy;

(B) compare methods used for transforming energy in devices such as water heaters, cooling systems, or hydroelectric and wind power plants; and

(C) research and describe energy types from their source to their use and determine if the type is renewable, nonrenewable, or inexhaustible.

291

Program Resources

- **Unit 3 Resources** Chapter 9 Project Teacher Notes, pp. 26–27; Chapter 9 Project Overview and Worksheet, pp. 28–31

Media and Technology

Student Edition on Audio CD
English-Spanish, Chapter 9

 **WEB ACTIVITY** www.phschool.com

You will find an Internet activity, chapter self-tests for students, and links to other chapter topics at this site.

Distribute Chapter 9 Project Overview on pages 28–29 of Unit 3 Resources, and have students review the project rules and procedures. Also distribute Chapter 9 Project Worksheet on pages 30–31 of Unit 3 Resources. This worksheet provides instructions on how to read electric and gas meters and provides equivalents for converting different energy units (kilowatt-hours, gallons, and so forth) into the common unit of BTUs.

Divide the class into groups of three or four, and let the groups meet briefly to choose areas to study. Monitor the groups' choices to avoid duplication. As an alternative, you could assign an area to each group.

Tell students that each group's members may divide the project responsibilities among themselves in any way they wish. However, emphasize that *every* group member should take part in identifying the types and amounts of energy uses in the area the group has chosen, recording and analyzing data, and developing the written report, and should be prepared to answer questions about the project.

Additional information on guiding the project is provided in Chapter 9 Project Teacher Notes on pages 26–27 of Unit 3 Resources.

Performance Assessment

The Chapter 9 Project Scoring Rubric on page 28 in Unit 3 Resources will help you evaluate how well students complete the Chapter 9 Project. You may want to share the scoring rubric with students so they are clear about what will be expected of them. Students will be assessed on
- their ability to identify and evaluate all the types of energy used in the area studied;
- their ability to make recommendations for reducing those energy uses and to communicate their findings and recommendations to others;
- their participation in their group.

Objectives

After completing the lesson, students will be able to

◆ explain how fuels provide energy;

◆ list the three major fossils fuels;

◆ explain why fossil fuels are considered nonrenewable resources.

1 Engage/Explore

Activating Prior Knowledge

Ask students: **What is energy?** (*Answers will vary depending on students' prior science learning. Responses may include "strength," "power," "something that makes something else happen," and the like. If necessary, point out that the scientific definition of energy is "the capacity to do work."*)

DISCOVER

Skills Focus observing
Materials *lignite coal, hand lens*

Time 10 minutes
Tips Lignite—the second stage of coal formation after peat—is the only form of coal that may contain recognizable plant remains.
Expected Outcome Students may or may not find fossils of plant remains in the coal samples. If fossils are present, they will be more noticeable with a hand lens.
Think It Over The lignite's texture, layering, and fossils (if present) can be seen more clearly with a hand lens. If fossils are visible, students should be able to infer that coal is made of plant remains.

SECTION

1 Energy and Fossil Fuels

DISCOVER .... ACTIVITY

What's in a Piece of Coal?

1. Observe a chunk of coal. Record your observations in as much detail as possible, including color, texture, and shape.

2. Now use a hand lens to observe the coal more closely.

3. Examine your coal for fossils, imprints of plant or animal remains.

Think It Over

Observing What did you notice when you used the hand lens compared to your first observations? What do you think coal is made of?

GUIDE FOR READING

◆ How do fuels provide energy?

◆ Why are fossil fuels considered nonrenewable resources?

Reading Tip As you read, make a table comparing coal, oil, and natural gas. Describe each fuel and note how it is obtained and used.

Key Terms
• energy transformation • fuel
• combustion • fossil fuel
• hydrocarbon
• nonrenewable resource
• petroleum • refinery
• petrochemical
• reserves

Try to imagine what would happen if the electricity suddenly went off. The lights would go out, plunging your school into darkness. Traffic signals would stop working, causing traffic jams. Computers, microwave ovens, clocks, and radios—nothing would work! Such an event would remind you of the importance of one form of energy—electrical energy, or electricity.

Recall from Chapter 1 that energy is the ability to do work or cause change. Energy exists in several different forms: mechanical, thermal, chemical, electrical, electromagnetic, and nuclear. All the different forms of energy help to meet people's energy needs.

Energy Transformation

Energy can be changed from one form to another. To see how, rub your hands together quickly for several seconds. Did you feel them become warmer? When you moved your hands, they had mechanical energy, the energy of motion. The friction of your hands rubbing together changed some of the mechanical energy to thermal energy, which you felt as heat.

A change from one form of energy to another is called an **energy transformation**, or an energy conversion. Any form of energy can be transformed into any other form.

You encounter energy transformations frequently. A toaster, for example, transforms electrical energy to thermal energy. In an electric motor, electrical energy is transformed to mechanical energy that can be used to run a machine.

◄ Electric power lines stretch against the evening sky.

READING STRATEGIES

Reading Tip Help students set up their tables before they begin to read. Students' tables should consist of columns for coal, oil, and natural gas. The rows should consist of: description, method of obtaining fuel, and use. Encourage students to leave space for additional rows. Students may wish to add further rows to compare advantages and disadvantages or other criteria.

Caption Writing Distribute photocopies of Figure 1. Have each student number the steps shown in the diagram based on the caption description, then write an accompanying key that briefly explains what happens in each numbered step.

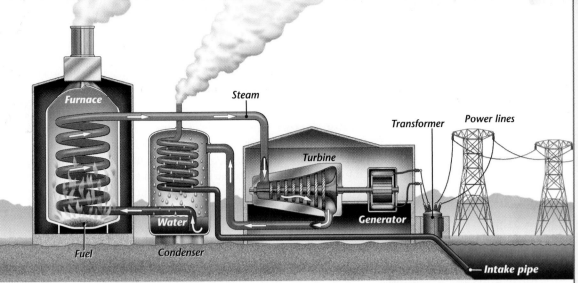

Steam
Transformer
Power lines
Furnace
Turbine
Generator
Water
Fuel
Condenser
Intake pipe

Fuels and Energy

 INTEGRATING PHYSICS How did you travel to school today? Whether you traveled in a car or a bus, walked, or rode your bike, your trip involved transformations of energy. A substance called a **fuel** was the source of that energy. **A fuel is a substance that provides a form of energy—such as heat, light, electricity, or motion—as the result of a chemical change.**

Combustion Fuels contain stored chemical energy, which can be released by burning. The process of burning a fuel is called **combustion.** For example, the fuel used by most cars is gasoline. When gasoline is burned in a car engine, it undergoes a chemical change. The gasoline combines with oxygen, producing carbon dioxide and water. The combustion of gasoline also converts some of the stored chemical energy into thermal energy. This thermal energy is converted to mechanical energy that moves the car.

Production of Electricity The energy stored in fuels can be used to generate electricty. In most power plants, the thermal energy produced by burning fuel is used to boil water, making steam. The mechanical energy of the steam turns the blades of a turbine. The shaft of the turbine is connected to a generator. The generator consists of powerful magnets surrounded by coils of copper wire. As the shaft rotates, the magnets turn inside the wire coil, producing an electric current. The electric current flows through power lines to homes and industries.

✓ *Checkpoint* *What are three energy transformations that might occur in a power plant?*

Figure 1 Electric power plants generate electricity by converting energy from one form to another. In the furnace, fuel is burned, releasing thermal energy. This energy is used to boil water and make steam. The mechanical energy of the moving steam turns the blades of a turbine. The turbine turns the shaft of the generator, producing an electric current.

Program Resources

◆ **Unit 3 Resources** 9-1 Lesson Plan, p. 33; 9-1 Section Summary, p. 34
◆ **Guided Reading and Study Workbook** 9-1

Media and Technology

Transparencies "An Electric Power Plant," Transparency 42

Answers to Self-Assessment

✓ *Checkpoint*

When fuel is burned, chemical energy is converted to thermal energy (heat). Some of the thermal energy is converted to the mechanical energy of moving steam. In a power plant, the mechanical energy is then converted to electrical energy.

---

2 Facilitate

Energy Transformations

 Integrating Physics *Content Mastery*

After students have read about energy conversion and rubbed their hands together, give some other examples of energy conversions and challenge students to infer the energy changes that are occurring. Some examples include a toaster *(Electrical energy is changed to heat energy.)*, light bulb *(Electrical energy is changed to light and heat energy.)*, power saw *(Electrical energy is changed to mechanical and heat energy.)*, and candle *(Chemical energy is changed to light and heat energy.)*. **learning modality: logical/mathematical**

Fuels and Energy

Real-Life Learning

Invite a local auto mechanic or students who are particularly interested in automobiles to bring in and explain diagrams showing how an internal combustion engine works. Suggest that students who need an additional challenge create posters based on the diagrams. Ask: **Besides cars, trucks, buses, and other automobiles, what other devices contain an internal combustion engine?** *(Gasoline-powered lawnmowers, snowblowers, chainsaws, portable generators, and the like)* **learning modality: visual**

Ongoing Assessment

Oral Presentation Call on students at random to identify the energy conversions shown in Figure 1 in the order in which they occur.

Energy Transformations in the Home

Inquiry Challenge

Materials: pencil and paper

Time: 20 minutes

Challenge students to find and name different energy transformations within the school building. (Students may find mechanical, electrical, thermal, chemical, solar, and radiant energies in use.) Ask: **Which form of energy transformation is the most common in this building?** (Sample answer: *Electrical to mechanical energy transformations are most common.*) **Which machine or system required the most number of energy transformations?** (Sample answer: *A coin-operated beverage machine: mechanical to electrical (coin is inserted to start machine), electrical to thermal (electricity is used to keep the beverage hot or cold), and electrical to mechanical (the beverage is dispensed).*) **learning modality: logical/mathematical**

Using the Visuals: Figure 2

Allow students to examine the diagram, then ask: **What energy transformations are being used to cool the food in the refrigerator?** (*Electrical energy to mechanical energy, mechanical energy to thermal energy.*) **Where does the transformation from electrical energy to mechanical energy occur?** (*This transformation occurs at the compressor when it is started.*) **Where does the transformation from mechanical energy to thermal energy occur?** (*This transformation happens when the compressor compresses the gas, causing it to heat up.*) Have students read and answer the caption question. Refer the the **ELL Handbook** for additional teaching strategies. **learning modality: visual**

294

Energy Transformations in the Home

Energy transformations continue even after electrical energy has been produced at a power plant. Household appliances and other devices powered by electricity all transform energy in various ways to perform useful work.

Water Heaters One example of energy transformation in the home is a water heater. Electric water heaters contain a heating element that transforms electrical energy into thermal energy, causing the water to become hotter. In some water heaters, natural gas provides the energy source. Burning this fuel changes stored chemical energy into thermal energy and heats the water.

Cooling Systems Energy transformation can also be used to keep food and buildings cool inside. Does that surprise you? After all, heat naturally flows from a warm object to a cold object—not the other way around. So how are food and buildings kept cool?

Figure 2 This diagram shows the basic parts of a refrigerator.
Interpreting Diagrams How are energy transformations used to cool food?

Heat

MILK

Heat into room

Compressor

Refrigerant

A refrigerator is a device that keeps food cold. It uses an outside energy source to transfer thermal energy from a cool area to a warm area. In your refrigerator, that energy is provided by an electric motor. Perhaps you have felt this energy in the warm air blowing out at the bottom of a refrigerator.

The electric motor in a refrigerator runs a compressor that contains a refrigerant substance. The compressor squeezes together the refrigerant particles in the gas state. This causes the refrigerant's pressure and temperature to rise. As the warmed gas travels through the coils on the outside of the refrigerator, it loses thermal energy to the outside air. As the gas loses thermal energy, it becomes a liquid. The liquid then passes through a valve, which changes the pressure and causes the liquid to evaporate. As it evaporates, it cools. The cold gas is then pumped through tubes inside the walls of the refrigerator. There the gas absorbs thermal energy from inside the refrigerator. The gas then returns to the compressor, and the whole cycle begins again.

An air conditioner operates in the same way. But it cools the air inside a building and transfers thermal energy to the air outdoors.

294

What Are Fossil Fuels?

Most of the energy used today comes from organisms that lived hundreds of millions of years ago. As these plants, animals, and other organisms died, their remains piled up. Layers of sand, rock, and mud buried the dead organisms. Over time, heat and pressure changed the material into other substances. **Fossil fuels** are the energy-rich substances formed from the remains of once-living organisms. The three fossil fuels are oil, natural gas, and coal.

Fossil fuels are made of hydrocarbons. **Hydrocarbons** are energy-rich chemical compounds that contain carbon and hydrogen atoms. During combustion, the carbon and hydrogen combine with oxygen in the air to form carbon dioxide and water. This process releases energy in the forms of heat and light.

Fossil fuels have more hydrocarbons per kilogram than most other fuels. For this reason, they are excellent sources of energy. Combustion of one kilogram of coal, for example, provides twice as much heat as burning one kilogram of wood. Oil and natural gas provide three times the energy of wood.

Because fossil fuels take hundreds of millions of years to form, they are considered nonrenewable resources. Earth's **nonrenewable resources** are natural resources that are not replaced as they are used. For example, Earth's known oil reserves took 500 million years to form. One fourth of this oil has already been used. If fossil fuels continue to be used more rapidly than they are formed, they could eventually run out. Of course, as fossil fuels become more scarce and expensive, people are likely to switch to other sources of energy.

Figure 3 Coal, a fossil fuel, provides the energy for this historic steam engine.

Graphing

Use the data in the table below to make a circle graph showing the uses of energy in the United States. (To review circle graphs, see the Skills Handbook.) You can use the computer to make your graph.

End Use of Energy	Percent of Total Energy
Transportation	26.5
Industry	38.1
Homes and businesses	35.4

Answers to Self-Assessment

Caption Question

Figure 2 As the compressed gas evaporates, it cools and absorbs thermal energy from inside the refrigerator, cooling the food inside as well.

What are Fossil Fuels?

Sharpen your Skills

Graphing

Materials *drawing compass, protractor, calculator or computer (optional)*
Time 15 minutes
Tips To determine the number of degrees for each use, students should first divide each percentage by 100. Then they should multiply each of those numbers by 360° and round off so the three sections total 360°. *Computer use is optional.*
Expected Outcome *Transportation 96°; Industry 137°; Homes and businesses 127°*

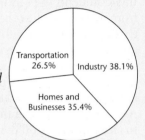

Extend Let students brainstorm specific types of energy uses included in each "end use" category—for example, oil for heating, electricity for refrigeration and lighting, gasoline for automobiles, and so on. **learning modality: logical/ mathematical**

Inquiry Challenge

Materials *clay, soil, sand, pebbles, leaves, colored paper, books or heavy weights*
Time 20 minutes

Challenge students to devise a model showing how fossil fuels form over time. *(Models might include trapping materials such as leaves or pieces of colored paper in layers of soft material such as clay or soil, and then compressing the materials under heavy weights.)* Ask: **What happens to buried materials to turn them into fossil fuels?** *(Over time, heat and pressure change the materials into hydrocarbons.)* **learning modality: kinesthetic**

Ongoing Assessment

Skills Check Have each student create a cycle diagram showing how a refrigerator transfers energy. Students can save their diagrams in their portfolios.

Oil

Figure 4 These workers are preparing to drill an oil well.

Oil

Oil is a thick, black, liquid fossil fuel. It formed from the remains of small animals, algae, and protists that lived in oceans and shallow inland seas hundreds of millions of years ago. **Petroleum** is another name for oil, from the Latin words *petra* (rock) and *oleum* (oil). Most oil deposits are located underground in tiny holes in sandstone or limestone. The oil fills the holes somewhat like water trapped in the holes of a sponge.

Petroleum accounts for more than one third of the energy produced in the world. Fuel for most cars, airplanes, trains, and ships comes from petroleum. Many homes are heated by oil.

The United States consumes about one third of all the oil produced in the world. But only three percent of the world's supply is located in this country. The difference must be purchased from countries with large oil supplies.

Petroleum is a relatively cheap and plentiful energy source. But producing and using petroleum does affect the environment. For example, oil may be spilled into the ocean when an oil tanker runs aground. The spilled oil harms organisms such as fish and birds. Gasoline spilled on land may seep into groundwater, polluting the water supply. Another environmental effect of oil is that burning it contributes to air pollution.

Locating Oil Deposits   Because it is usually located deep below the surface, finding oil is difficult. **INTEGRATING TECHNOLOGY** Scientists can use sound waves to test an area for oil without drilling. This technique relies on the fact that sound waves bounce off objects and return as echoes. Scientists send pulses of sound down into the rocks below ground. Then they measure how long it takes the echoes to return. The amount of time depends on whether the sound waves must travel through solid rock or liquid oils. This information can indicate the most likely places to find oil. However, only about one out of every six wells drilled produces a usable amount of oil.

Refining Oil When oil is first pumped out of the ground, it is called crude oil. Crude oil can be a runny or a thick liquid. In order to be made into useful products, crude oil must undergo a process called refining. A factory where crude oil is separated into fuels and other products by heating is called a **refinery.**

In addition to gasoline and heating oil, many products you use every day are made from refined crude oil. **Petrochemicals** are compounds that are made from oil. Petrochemicals are used in plastics, paints, medicines, and cosmetics.

Oil refineries can affect the environment. Chemicals produced in the refining process may escape into the air or water, causing pollution.

☑ *Checkpoint* *How is petroleum used?*

Natural Gas

Another fossil fuel is natural gas, a mixture of methane and other gases. Natural gas forms from the same organisms as petroleum. Because it is less dense than oil, natural gas often rises above an oil deposit, forming a pocket of gas in the rock.

Pipelines transport the gas from its source to the places where it is used. Natural gas can also be compressed into a liquid and stored in tanks.

Natural gas has several advantages. It produces large amounts of energy, but lower levels of many air pollutants than coal or oil. It is also easy to transport once the network of pipelines is built. One disadvantage of natural gas is that a gas leak can cause a violent explosion and fire.

Gas companies help to prevent dangerous explosions from leaks. If you use natural gas in your home, you probably are familiar with the "gas" smell that alerts you whenever there is unburned gas in the air. You may be surprised to learn that natural gas actually has no odor at all. What causes the strong smell? The gas companies add a chemical with a distinct smell to the gas before it is piped to homes and businesses so that any leaks will be noticed.

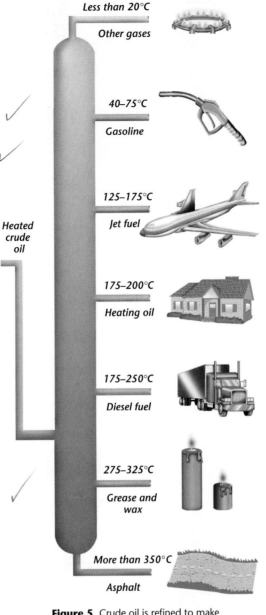

Less than 20°C
Other gases

40–75°C
Gasoline

125–175°C
Jet fuel

Heated crude oil

175–200°C
Heating oil

175–250°C
Diesel fuel

275–325°C
Grease and wax

More than 350°C
Asphalt

Figure 5 Crude oil is refined to make many different products. In the refining process, heat causes the different molecules in crude oil to separate. Different substances vaporize at specific temperatures.

Natural Gas

Building Inquiry Skills: Calculating

Materials *calculator*
Time 5 minutes

Tell students that if all the gas pipelines in the United States were connected, they would reach to the moon and back—twice! Have students use the moon's average distance from Earth *(384,392 km)* to calculate the total length of U.S. gas pipelines. *(384,392 × 4 = 1,537,568 km)* They can extend this activity by comparing this distance to another reference, such as the width of their state. **learning modality: logical/mathematical**

Real-Life Learning

Companies that supply natural gas usually publish materials to teach customers about safety issues when dealing with gas appliances and gas lines. Some companies also can provide a representative to speak to your class about gas safety. Contact your local gas company to request materials and, if available, a speaker. **learning modality: verbal**

Using the Visuals: Figure 5

Help students recognize the pattern of temperatures in the diagram. Students may find it confusing to see the lowest temperature at the top, rather than the bottom of the diagram. Point out that crude oil is a mixture. Different components boil out of the mixture at different temperatures.

Media and Technology

Earth Science Videodisc
Unit 6, Side 2, "Power for the People"
Chapter 2

Answers to Self-Assessment

☑ *Checkpoint*
Petroleum is refined to make fuels and other products, including plastics.

Ongoing Assessment

Oral Presentation Call on students to describe how oil and natural gas formed and how they are found.

Coal

3 Assess

Section 1 Review Answers

1. Thermal energy is transformed to mechanical energy, which is then transformed to electrical energy.
2. Fuels contain stored chemical energy. Burning converts the chemical energy into other forms of energy.
3. *Coal* is a solid fossil fuel formed from decaying plant matter that was changed by heat and pressure. *Oil* is a thick, black liquid fossil fuel formed from the remains of small animals, algae, and protists. *Natural gas* is a mixture of methane and other gases formed from the same organisms as oil.
4. Because fossil fuels take hundreds of millions of years to form, they can be used up faster than they can be replaced.
5. *Advantages:* produces lower levels of many air pollutants; is easy to transport. *Disadvantage:* is highly flammable, so a leak can cause an explosion and fire.
6. *Sample answers:* Coal is more plentiful in the U.S. than oil, and in less demand. Natural gas is difficult to store. Coal would be the best fuel for the power plant.

Figure 6 A miner obtains hard coal from a shaft deep underground.

Coal

Coal is a solid fossil fuel formed from plant remains. People have burned coal to produce heat for thousands of years. Today, coal provides 23 percent of the energy used in the United States. The major use of coal is to fuel electric power plants.

Coal Mining Before it can be used to produce energy, **INTEGRATING TECHNOLOGY** coal has to be removed from the ground, or mined. Some coal is located very deep underground or is mixed with other materials, making it too difficult to obtain. **Reserves** are known deposits of coal (and other fossil fuels) that can be obtained using current technology.

Coal as an Energy Source Coal is the most plentiful fossil fuel in the United States. It is fairly easy to transport, and provides a lot of energy when burned. But coal also has some disadvantages. Coal mining can increase erosion. Runoff from mines can cause water pollution. Finally, burning most types of coal results in more air pollution than burning other fossil fuels. However, new technologies are helping to reduce emissions from burning coal.

In addition, coal mining can be a dangerous job. Thousands of miners have been killed or injured in accidents in the mines. Many more suffer from "black lung," a disease caused by years of breathing coal dust. Fortunately, the mining industry has been working hard to improve conditions. New safety procedures and better equipment, including robots and drills that produce less coal dust, have made coal mining safer.

Section 1 Review

1. Describe the role of energy transformation in the production of electricity.
2. Explain how fuels provide energy.
3. Name and briefly describe the three fossil fuels.
4. Explain why fossil fuels are classified as nonrenewable resources.
5. List two advantages and one disadvantage of natural gas as an energy source.
6. **Thinking Critically Comparing and Contrasting** Compare and contrast the advantages of coal, oil, and natural gas as fuel sources for an electrical power plant. Which would make the best fuel for the power plant?

Check Your Progress
CHAPTER PROJECT

With your team, observe your selected area of the school. Determine which types of energy use take place in this area: heating, cooling, lighting, mechanical devices, electronic equipment, or moving vehicles. Record the specific types and amounts of energy use in a data table. To find the amounts, you will need to collect data from electric meters or fuel gauges. (*Hint:* Observe your area at several different times of the day, since the pattern of energy use may vary.)

Check Your Progress
CHAPTER PROJECT

Point out that the school's meters and gauges show the amount of fuel used for the entire building. To estimate the amount used in each area, students can count the number of rooms in the school and divide the total amount of fuel used by the number of rooms.

SECTION 2 Renewable Sources of Energy

SECTION 2 Renewable Sources of Energy

TEKS: 6.2A, B, C, D; 6.3D; 6.4A; 6.9A, B, C

DISCOVER

Can You Capture Solar Energy?

1. Pour 250 milliliters of water into each of two sealable, clear plastic bags.

2. Measure and record the water temperature in each bag. Seal the bags.

3. Put one bag in a dark or shady place. Put the other bag in a place where it will receive direct sunlight.

4. Predict what the temperature of the water in each bag will be after 30 minutes.

5. Measure and record the ending temperatures.

Think It Over

Developing Hypotheses How did the water temperature in each bag change? What could account for these results?

As the sun rises over the rim of the canyon where your family is camping, you feel its warmth on your face. A breeze stirs, carrying with it the smell of the campfire. Maybe you'll take a morning dip in the warm water of a nearby hot spring.

Even in this remote canyon, there are energy resources all around you. The sun warms the air, the wind blows, and heat from inside Earth warms the waters of the spring. These sources of energy are all **renewable resources**—that is, they are constantly being supplied. Renewable resources, such as sunlight, wind, and trees, are naturally replaced in a short period of time. These resources help meet people's energy needs.

Energy From the Sun

The warmth you feel on a sunny day is **solar energy,** energy from the sun. **The sun constantly gives off energy in the form of light and heat.** In one day, Earth receives enough solar energy to meet the energy needs of the entire world for 40 years. **Solar energy is the source, directly or indirectly, of most renewable energy resources.** Solar energy does not cause pollution. Because solar energy will not run out for several billion years, you could also think of it as an inexhaustible resource. An **inexhaustible resource** is a resource that exists in such large supply that it can be considered almost limitless.

So why hasn't solar energy replaced fossil fuels? One reason is that solar energy is available only when the sun is shining. A backup energy source must be available on cloudy days and at night.

GUIDE FOR READING

◆ How does the sun provide energy?

◆ What are some renewable sources of energy?

Reading Tip Before you read, preview the headings in this section. Predict some sources of energy that are renewable.

Key Terms
• renewable resource
• solar energy
• inexhaustible resource
• hydroelectric power
• biomass fuel
• geothermal energy

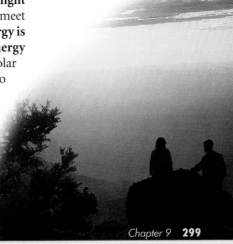

READING STRATEGIES

Reading Tip Based on the headings, students should predict that the sun, wind, flowing water, biomass, and hydrogen are renewable energy sources.

Study and Comprehension Have each student set up a table for taking notes on the advantages and disadvantages of each type of renewable energy source as they read this section.

Program Resources

◆ **Unit 3 Resources** 9-2 Lesson Plan, p. 37; 9-2 Section Summary, p. 38
◆ **Guided Reading and Study Workbook** 9-2

Objectives

After completing the lesson, students will be able to

◆ explain how the sun provides energy and describe ways to collect this energy;

◆ identify and describe various sources of renewable energy.

1 Engage/Explore

Activating Prior Knowledge

Ask: **Besides coal, oil, and natural gas, what other sources of energy do you know of?** (*Answers will depend on students' prior learning. They may mention the renewable resources covered in this section and "atomic" [nuclear] energy, covered in the next section.*)

DISCOVER

Skills Focus developing hypotheses

Materials *500 mL water, 2 sealable clear plastic bags, 2 thermometers*

Time 10 minutes for setup; 5 minutes for follow-up

Tips Provide room-temperature water for Step 1. If your classroom does not have a sunny window, arrange to place bags in another location where there is direct sunlight.

Expected Outcome Specific temperatures will vary.

Think It Over The water temperature stayed the same in the dark/shaded bag, while the water temperature increased in the bag placed in sunlight. The water in that bag absorbed heat energy from the sun.

Energy From the Sun

Inquiry Challenge

Materials *small squares of fabric in different colors, or small jars of different colored paints*
Time 25 minutes

Challenge students to design an experiment to find what color absorbs more heat from the sun and would thus be the best color to paint solar panels. (Students may place pieces of fabric in different solid colors on snow during a sunny day and measure the amount of snow melted beneath the pieces. Alternatively, students can set out small jars of different colors of paint, then measure the relative temperatures of each color.) **learning modality: visual**

Solar Technologies

 Integrating Technology

Materials *several examples of solar cells and small solar-powered motors (available from home-electronics stores)*

Let students examine the solar cells and motors. Encourage them to use the cells and motors to make simple devices that will operate when placed in sunlight— for example, a solar-powered toy boat or car. Ask: **What energy conversions are taking place?** (*Solar energy to electrical energy to mechanical energy*) **learning modality: tactile/kinesthetic**

Figure 7 Aimed at the sun, these mirrors provide power to an electric plant in New South Wales, Australia. *Inferring How does the shape of these mirrors make them more effective?*

Another problem is that although Earth receives a lot of energy from the sun, this energy is spread out. To obtain enough power, the energy must be collected from a huge area.

Solar Technologies

 INTEGRATING TECHNOLOGY Improving technologies to capture and use solar energy will help meet future energy needs. Some current solar technologies are described below.

Solar Plants One way to capture the sun's energy involves using giant mirrors. In a solar plant, rows of mirrors focus the sun's rays to heat a tank of water. The water boils, making steam that can be used to generate electricity.

Solar Cells Solar energy can be converted directly into electricity in a solar cell. A solar cell consists of a "sandwich" of very thin layers of the element silicon and other materials. The upper and lower parts of the sandwich have a negative and a positive terminal, like a battery. When light hits the cell, electrons move across the layers, producing an electric current.

The amount of electricity produced by solar cells depends on the area of the cell and the amount of light available. Solar cells are used to power calculators, lights, telephones, and other small devices. However, it would take more than 5,000 solar cells the size of your palm to produce enough electricity for a typical American home. Building solar cells on a large scale is very expensive. As a result, solar cells are used mostly in areas where fossil fuels are difficult to transport.

✓ *Checkpoint* *What are solar cells made of, and how do they work?*

Background

Integrating Science The solar cells described in the student text are made of crystalline silicon and are also known as photovoltaic (PV) cells. Although suitable for use in calculators and watches, these cells are not very efficient at converting solar energy to electricity and are expensive to produce. A new kind of solar cell made from a thin film of semiconductor material may prove to be more efficient and less expensive.

Media and Technology

 Transparencies "Exploring a Solar House," Transparency 43

 Physical Science Videodisc Unit 4, Side 2, "Wired to the Sun"

 Chapter 7

Solar Heating Systems Solar energy can be used to heat buildings. As shown in *Exploring a Solar House*, there are two types of solar heating systems: passive and active.

A passive solar system converts sunlight into thermal energy without using pumps or fans. If you have ever stepped into a car on a sunny day, you have experienced passive solar heating. Solar energy passes through the car's windows as light. The sun's rays heat the seats and other parts of the car, which then transfer heat to the air. The heated air is trapped inside, so the car gets warmer. The same principle can be used to heat a home.

An active solar system captures the sun's energy, then uses fans and pumps to distribute the heat. Light strikes the black metal surface of a solar collector. There, it is converted to thermal energy. Water is pumped through pipes in the solar collector to absorb the thermal energy. The heated water flows to a storage tank. Pumps and fans distribute the heat throughout the building.

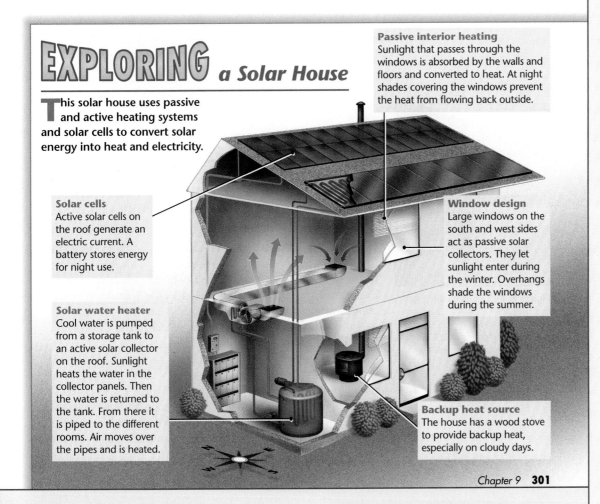

EXPLORING a Solar House

This solar house uses passive and active heating systems and solar cells to convert solar energy into heat and electricity.

Solar cells
Active solar cells on the roof generate an electric current. A battery stores energy for night use.

Solar water heater
Cool water is pumped from a storage tank to an active solar collector on the roof. Sunlight heats the water in the collector panels. Then the water is returned to the tank. From there it is piped to the different rooms. Air moves over the pipes and is heated.

Passive interior heating
Sunlight that passes through the windows is absorbed by the walls and floors and converted to heat. At night shades covering the windows prevent the heat from flowing back outside.

Window design
Large windows on the south and west sides act as passive solar collectors. They let sunlight enter during the winter. Overhangs shade the windows during the summer.

Backup heat source
The house has a wood stove to provide backup heat, especially on cloudy days.

Chapter 9 **301**

After students have reviewed the figure, ask: **Which of these solar systems do you have in your own home?** (*Most students will probably identify the two passive systems, passive interior heating and window design.*) If any students say that their homes are equipped with active solar systems, invite those students to describe the devices and their operation to the rest of the class. Refer to the **ELL Handbook** for additional teaching strategies. **learning modality: verbal**

Real-Life Learning

Materials *2 thermometers, large glass jar*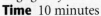
Time 10 minutes

Give students an opportunity to directly observe passive solar heating. On a sunny day, take the class outdoors to a place that receives direct sunlight, but away from pavement. Have students read the two thermometers and note the temperatures. Then put one thermometer in an upside-down glass jar and the other thermometer in open air. Have students compare the temperatures after several minutes. Ask: **Why is the temperature higher inside the glass jar?** (*The glass allows light to pass into the jar but traps heat inside the jar.*) **learning modality: logical/mathematical**

Program Resources

◆ **Laboratory Manual** 9, "Solar Heating"

Answers to Self-Assessment

Caption Question

Figure 7 The curved shape concentrates the sun's rays by reflecting them toward the center of the dish.

☑ *Checkpoint*

They are made of layers of silicon and other materials. When light hits the cell, electrons move across the layers, producing an electric current.

Ongoing Assessment

Oral Presentation Call on students at random to each describe one example of technology that captures solar energy for use by people.

Other Sources of Renewable Energy

Exploring a Hydroelectric Power Plant

Allow students to examine the diagram, then ask: **What energy transformations are taking place in the power plant?** *(Potential energy is transformed to kinetic energy; kinetic energy is transformed to mechanical energy; mechanical energy is transformed to electrical energy.)* Be sure students understand the terms **potential energy** *(energy that is a function of position or condition)* and **kinetic energy** *(energy from motion)*.

Students may be interested to research some famous hydroelectric dams such as Grand Coulee, Oak Creek, or John Day dams. Refer to the **ELL Handbook** for additional teaching strategies. **learning modality: visual**

Building Inquiry Skills: Predicting

Ask students: **Would burning wood or plant wastes in an open fire be a good way to make use of biomass fuels? Why, or why not?** *(No; open burning allows heat to escape and releases pollutants into the atmosphere.)* **How do you think biomass materials must be burned in order to be efficient and nonpolluting fuels?** *(In some sort of closed incinerator that captures harmful waste products and captures all or most of the heat)* **What else would have to be part of the equipment to generate electricity with the heat of the burning fuel?** *(Water to make steam to drive a turbine)* **learning modality: logical/mathematical**

Including All Students

For students who need help with language skills, write the two words on the board, draw boxes around *gas* in *gasoline* and *ohol* in *alcohol,* draw a plus sign between the two boxes, and ask: **What word do these two parts make when you put them together?** *(gasohol)* **limited English proficiency**

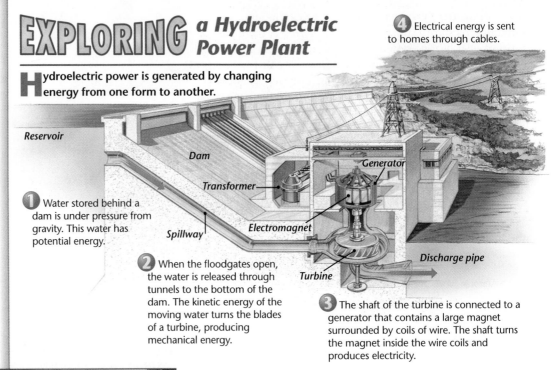

EXPLORING a Hydroelectric Power Plant

Hydroelectric power is generated by changing energy from one form to another.

Reservoir

Dam

Transformer

Spillway

Generator

Electromagnet

Turbine

Discharge pipe

1 Water stored behind a dam is under pressure from gravity. This water has potential energy.

2 When the floodgates open, the water is released through tunnels to the bottom of the dam. The kinetic energy of the moving water turns the blades of a turbine, producing mechanical energy.

3 The shaft of the turbine is connected to a generator that contains a large magnet surrounded by coils of wire. The shaft turns the magnet inside the wire coils and produces electricity.

4 Electrical energy is sent to homes through cables.

Figure 8 This photograph shows the Theodore Roosevelt Dam in Arizona. *Interpreting Photographs What natural feature of the river made this a good location to build a dam?*

Other Sources of Renewable Energy

The sun is one source of renewable energy. **Other renewable energy sources include water, biomass materials, wind, Earth's interior, and hydrogen.**

Flowing Water As water flows over the land into lakes and oceans, it provides another source of energy. Flowing water can turn a turbine and generate electricity in the same way as steam or wind can. A dam across a river blocks the flow of water, creating an artificial lake called a reservoir. Water flows through tunnels at the bottom of the dam. As the water moves through the tunnels, it turns turbines connected to a generator.

Hydroelectric power is electricity produced by flowing water. This type of power is the most widely used source of renewable energy in the world today. Hydroelectric power is inexpensive and does not create air pollution. But hydroelectric power does have drawbacks. In the United States, for example, most suitable rivers have already been dammed. And dams can have negative effects on the environment.

Background

Facts and Figures Besides reducing our dependence on fossil fuels, using biomass fuels helps reduce our waste-disposal problems. In one case in California, the Mesquite Lake Resource Recovery Project, an electric power plant burns cow manure to produce enough electricity for thousands of homes. The manure would otherwise pose a disposal problem because of its high salt content and the presence of seeds that make it undesirable for use as fertilizer.

Some problems are associated with the use of biomass materials. Growing the crops often used as biomass fuels takes up land that could be used for growing other crops. And removing all the stalks, leaves, and roots from a field for use as biomass fuel means that these crop wastes will not decay and enrich the soil. Unprotected soil is also more susceptible to erosion.

Biomass Fuels Wood is one of a group of renewable fuels, called **biomass fuels,** which are fuels made from things that were once alive. Other biomass fuels include crop wastes such as stalks and leaves, food wastes, and even manure. Burning breaks down complex molecules in these fuels, releasing energy.

Biomass materials also can be converted into other fuels. For example, corn, sugar cane, and other crops can be used to make alcohol. Adding the alcohol to gasoline forms a mixture called gasohol. Gasohol can be used as fuel for cars and trucks. The methane produced in some landfills is used for heating buildings. When bacteria decompose waste materials, they convert the waste into methane gas.

Biomass fuels are not widely used. Producing alcohol and methane in large quantities can be expensive. And although wood is renewable, it takes time for new trees to grow. But in the future, biomass fuels may play a larger role in meeting energy needs.

☑ *Checkpoint* *What are the advantages and disadvantages of biomass fuels?*

Geothermal Energy In certain regions, such as Iceland and New Zealand, magma heats underground water to the boiling point. The hot water and steam are valuable sources of **geothermal energy.** In Reykjavik, Iceland, 90 percent of homes are heated by water warmed underground in this way. Geothermal energy can also be used to generate electricity.

Geothermal energy is an unlimited source of cheap energy. Unfortunately, there are only a few places where magma comes close to Earth's surface. Elsewhere, very expensive, deep wells must be drilled to tap this energy. Although it can be costly, geothermal energy is likely to play a part in meeting energy needs in the future.

Wind Wind can be used to turn a turbine and generate electricity. Wind power plants or "wind farms" consist of many windmills. Together, the windmills generate large amounts of electric power.

Although wind now provides less than 1 percent of the world's electricity, it is the fastest-growing energy source. Wind energy is free and does not cause pollution.

Wind energy is not ideal for all locations. Wind turbines require winds that blow fairly steadily. But as fossil fuels become more scarce and expensive, wind generators will probably become more important. Portions of Texas have a high potential for utilizing wind energy.

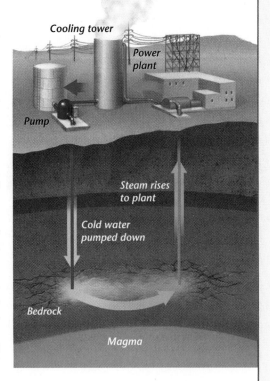

Figure 9 A geothermal power plant uses heat from Earth's interior as an energy source. Cold water is piped deep into the ground, where it is heated by magma. The resulting steam can be used for heat or to generate electricity.

Cooling tower

Power plant

Pump

Steam rises to plant

Cold water pumped down

Bedrock

Magma

Have students work in pairs to create cycle diagrams of the process shown in the figure. Ask: **What do you think the cooling tower is used for?** (*After the steam has been used to turn turbines in the power plant, it is cooled to turn it into liquid water.*) **learning modality: visual**

Including All Students

Support students who need more help in comprehending the term *geothermal.* Write the term *geothermal* on the board and draw a vertical line between the two word parts. Invite volunteers to look up the meaning of each part in a dictionary and read the meanings aloud (*geo,* "Earth"; *thermal,* "heat"). Ask: **What does "geothermal" mean?** (*Earth-heat, or heat inside Earth*) **limited English proficiency**

Hydrogen Power

Demonstration

Materials *electrolysis apparatus, matches* **Time** 10 minutes

Use an electrolysis apparatus to show students that hydrogen can be obtained by passing an electric current through water. (If you are not familiar with the electrolysis setup and procedure, ask a physical science teacher to show you or to do the demonstration for the class.) At the end of the demonstration, emphasize that more energy is used in producing the electricity needed for electrolysis than is provided by the hydrogen. **learning modality: visual**

Answers to Self-Assessment

Caption Question

Figure 8 The dam is built at a naturally narrow point of the river.

☑ *Checkpoint*

Biomass fuels are renewable and can be used to make other fuels. Using biomass materials to produce alcohol and methane can be expensive, and though they are renewable, it takes time for them to grow.

Ongoing Assessment

Writing Have each student briefly describe the two different ways in which biomass materials can be used as fuels.

 Students can save their work in their portfolios.

3 Assess

Section 2 Review Answers

1. Energy from the sun
2. Two advantages of solar energy are that it does not cause pollution and that it is renewable. One disadvantage is that it is available only during the day or when the sun is shining. Another problem is that solar energy is spread out over Earth's surface, so energy for power must be collected over a wide area.
3. Active solar systems convert solar energy to thermal energy and then use fans and pumps to distribute the heat. Passive solar systems convert solar energy to thermal energy but do not distribute it.
4. *Any three:* wood, leaves, food wastes, manure, sugar-cane wastes, corn, alcohol, methane
5. Geothermal energy is available only where magma is close to Earth's surface.
6. Accept a variety of responses. Students should support their answers with reasons that take into account the geographic features of their area.

Check Your Progress

CHAPTER PROJECT

Check each group's data table to make sure students are collecting and recording data. Provide some copies of the school's fuel and utility bills so students can determine the amount and actual cost of each type of energy used. If a group is studying energy used for transportation, encourage them to survey other students about transportation to school. They also may need to contact your district's central office or the private company that owns and operates the school buses for information.

Performance Assessment

Skills Check Have each student create a compare/contrast table that includes at least five of the renewable energy sources discussed in this section and identifies one advantage and one disadvantage of each source.

 Portfolio Students can save their tables in their portfolios.

Figure 10 The object fascinating these three astronauts is a bubble of water—the harmless byproduct of the hydrogen fuel cells used on the space shuttle.

Hydrogen Power

This fuel burns cleanly, forming only water as a byproduct. It creates no smoke, smog, or acid rain. It can be handled and transported through pipelines, much like natural gas. This fuel exists on Earth in such large supply that it could be considered an inexhaustible resource.

This ideal-sounding fuel is real—it's hydrogen. However, there is an obstacle. Almost all the hydrogen on Earth is combined with oxygen in the form of water. Pure hydrogen can be obtained by passing an electric current through water. But it takes more energy to obtain the hydrogen than is produced by burning it again.

Scientists aren't ruling out hydrogen as a good fuel for the future. At present, hydroelectric plants decrease their activity when the demand for electricity is low. Instead, they could run at full power all the time, using the excess electricity to produce hydrogen. Similarly, solar power plants often generate more electricity than is needed during the day. This extra electricity could be used to produce hydrogen. If a way can be found to produce hydrogen cheaply, it could someday be an important source of energy.

Section 2 Review

1. What is solar energy?
2. What are some advantages and disadvantages of solar energy?
3. How are active and passive solar heating systems different?
4. List three examples of biomass fuels.
5. What limits the use of geothermal energy?
6. **Thinking Critically** **Predicting** Which of the renewable sources of energy do you think is most likely to be used in your community in 100 years? Give reasons to support your answer.

Check Your Progress

CHAPTER PROJECT

Continue to collect data on how much energy is used in your group's area of the school. Begin to brainstorm ideas for reducing energy usage in this area. For example, is there a way to use some electrical devices for shorter periods of time? (*Hint:* Interviewing some adults who are responsible for the operation of the school building may give you some good ideas. Be sure to check with your teacher before interviewing anyone.)

304

Program Resources

◆ **Unit 3 Resources** 9-2 Review and Reinforce, p. 39; 9-2 Enrich, p. 40

How It Works

Cooking With Sunshine

In the future, will you cook your meals with sunshine instead of electricity? That's certainly a possibility. In this lab, you'll investigate how solar energy can be used to cook food.

Problem

What is the best shape for a solar cooker?

Skills Focus

predicting, designing experiments, forming operational definitions

Suggested Materials

scissors	glue	3 thermometers
3 dowels	tape	marshmallows
3 sheets of aluminum foil		clock or watch
3 sheets of oaktag paper		

Procedure

Part 1 Capturing Solar Energy

1. Read over the entire lab. Then predict which shape will produce the largest temperature increase when placed in the sun.
2. Glue a sheet of aluminum foil, shiny side up, to each sheet of oaktag paper. Before the glue dries, gently smooth out any wrinkles in the foil.
3. Bend one sheet into a V shape. Bend another sheet into a U shape. Leave the last sheet flat.
4. Place the aluminum sheets in direct sunlight, using wood blocks or books to hold the U- and V-shapes in position.
5. Tape a dowel to each thermometer. Record the starting temperature on each thermometer.
6. Use the dowels to hold the thermometer bulbs in the center of the aluminum shapes. After 15 minutes, record the final temperature on each thermometer.

Part 2 Designing a Solar Cooker

7. Use the results from Step 6 to design a solar cooker that can toast a marshmallow. Prepare a written description of your plan for your teacher's approval. Include an operational definition of a "well-toasted" marshmallow.
8. After your teacher has approved your plan, test your design by placing a marshmallow on a wooden dowel. Record the time it takes to toast the marshmallow.

Analyze and Conclude

1. What was the role of the aluminum foil in this investigation? What other materials could you have used instead? Explain.
2. Which of the three shapes—V, U, or flat—produced the largest increase in temperature? Propose an explanation for this result.
3. What other variables might have affected your results? Explain.
4. **Apply** What are some possible advantages of a solar cooker based on this design? What are some possible disadvantages?

More to Explore

Try adapting your design to heat water. Show your new design to your teacher before trying it.

Extending the Inquiry

More to Explore Have students use a small volume of water. Encourage them to consider the kind of material to use for the water container.

Safety

Students should wear safety goggles and use caution in handling glass thermometers. Review the safety guidelines in Appendix A.

Program Resources

◆ **Unit 3 Resources** Chapter 9 Real-World Lab blackline masters, pp. 49–50

Media and Technology

 Lab Activity Videotapes
Grade 6, Tape 3

Real-World Lab

How It Works

Cooking With Sunshine

Preparing for Inquiry

Key Concept A solar cooker that focuses the sun's rays in its center works best.

Skills Objectives Students will be able to
◆ predict which of three designs will produce the greatest temperature increase in a solar cooker;
◆ design an experiment to test how the shape of a solar cooker affects how it functions;
◆ form an operational definition of a "well-toasted" marshmallow.

Time 40 minutes

Advance Planning Identify a sunny area for the solar cookers.

Guiding Inquiry

Introducing the Procedure

◆ Have students work in groups of three.
◆ If needed, review the meaning of "operational definition."

Troubleshooting the Experiment

◆ In Step 3, make sure students have the foil side on the inside of the U or V.
◆ In Step 6, make sure students hold the thermometers with their bulbs at the same distance from the foil.

Expected Outcome

Specific temperatures will vary, but the U-shaped cooker should produce the largest temperature increase and the flat cooker the smallest increase.

Analyze and Conclude

1. The foil reflected the sun's rays. Other reflective materials such as mirrors or shiny metal could be used.
2. The U shape; it reflects the sun's rays into the center of the cooker.
3. Variables include time of day, distance between the thermometer bulbs and the cookers' surface, and air movement.
4. *Advantages:* simple design, ease of use, inexpensive, no polluting fumes. *Disadvantages:* cannot be used on a cloudy day or at night; slow; not efficient for cooking large items.

Hydroelectric Dams: Are They All Here to Stay?

Purpose

Evaluate the benefits and costs of removing hydroelectric dams, and recommend removing, adapting, or relicensing a dam.

Role-Play

Time 40 minutes

◆ After students have read the feature, ask: **Why should people try to protect fish species?** (*Accept a variety of reasons, including the economic value of commercial fishing.*) **Why are hydroelectric dams an important source of energy?** (*They reduce use of fossil fuels, produce electricity at low cost, and don't cause pollution.*)

◆ Point out that there are *three* possible recommendations: relicense the dam, remove it, or find ways to enable fish to bypass it. Let students discuss the issue freely.

◆ Divide the class into small groups, with each group member representing a different viewpoint—for example, the company that owns the dam, local industries that rely on the electricity produced by the dam, fisheries, ecologists, and citizens. Provide time for the groups to discuss the options.

Extend Suggest that students research the costs of electricity produced by hydroelectric dams and by burning fossil fuels. They could also investigate the effectiveness of fish ladders.

You Decide

◆ Students' answers to Identify the Problem and Analyze the Options should use the points in the text.

◆ In response to Find a Solution, students may rely on issues raised in their discussions or present new ideas. Each student should give a well-reasoned rationale for his or her recommendation.

Hydroelectric Dams: Are They All Here to Stay?

There are hundreds of hydroelectric dams on United States rivers. These dams provide electricity for millions of people. Hydroelectric dams provide clean, inexpensive, and renewable energy. They are a good source of power.

Recently, however, people have learned that dams can have negative effects on river ecosystems. Some people have even suggested removing certain dams. But is this wise? When do the benefits of dams outweigh the problems?

The Issues

How Do Dams Affect the Environment? Because dams change water depth and flow, they can alter the temperature of a river. The water may become too cold or too warm for fish that normally live there. A change in temperature can also reduce the number of algae in a river. This affects other organisms in the river food web.

Some species of fish, such as salmon, herring, and menhaden, hatch in rivers but then travel to the ocean. To breed, they must return to the river. Dams can block the movement of these fish populations. For example, the Columbia River Basin, which has more than 50 dams, once contained more than 10 million salmon. Today it is home to only 2 million salmon.

What Are the Effects of Removing Dams? Some people say that the only way to restore ecosystems is to remove dams. However, these dams supply a small but important part of the nation's electricity. Removing them could force the United States to use more nonrenewable fossil fuels. Fossil fuels also produce more pollution than hydroelectric plants.

The reservoirs behind hydroelectric dams supply water for irrigation and drinking. These supplies would be difficult to replace. In addition, a series of dams on a river can reduce flooding downstream during heavy rains.

What Can People Do? Removing dams might restore some river ecosystems. For example, Edwards Dam on the Kennebec River in Maine was removed in 1999 to allow several threatened fish species to spawn. Edwards Dam provided only a small percent of Maine's electric power. This small amount was easier to replace than the power provided by a much larger dam.

There are other ways to protect migrating fish. Fish ladders, for example, are step-like waterways that help fish pass over dams. Fish can even be carried around dams in trucks. Still, these methods are costly and not always successful.

The government issues licenses for hydroelectric dams. In considering license renewals, officials examine environmental impact as well as energy production.

You Decide

1. Identify the Problem
In your own words, explain some of the major issues surrounding hydroelectric dams.

2. Analyze the Options
Examine the pros and cons of removing dams. What are the benefits? What are the costs? Who will be affected by the change?

3. Find a Solution
The license of a nearby dam is up for review. The dam provides electricity, but also blocks the migration of fish. What do you recommend? Explain.

History of Science In November 1997, the Federal Energy Regulatory Commission for the first time refused to renew the license for a hydroelectric dam—the Edwards Dam on the Kennebec River in Maine. The dam produced only a very small amount of electricity, but prevented salmon and other anadromous fish from spawning in the river.

The owners of hydroelectric dams upstream on the Kennebec contributed millions of dollars toward the costs of removing the dam and restoring 17 miles of spawning grounds in exchange for having their deadlines extended to install fish ladders on the upstream dams.

INTEGRATING **CHEMISTRY**

SECTION 3 Nuclear Energy

DISCOVER ··················· ACTIVITY ····

Why Do They Fall?

1. Line up 15 dominoes to form a triangle, as shown.

2. Knock over the first domino so that it falls against the second row of dominoes. Observe the results.

3. Set up the dominoes again, but then remove the dominoes in the third row from the lineup.

4. Knock over the first domino again. Observe what happens.

Think It Over

Inferring Suppose each domino produced a large amount of energy when it fell over. Why might it be helpful to remove the dominoes as you did in Step 3?

Wouldn't it be great if people could use the same method as the sun to produce energy? In a way, they can! The kind of reactions that power the sun involve the central cores of atoms. The central core of an atom that contains the protons and neutrons is called the **nucleus** (plural *nuclei*). The reactions that involve nuclei, called nuclear reactions, involve tremendous amounts of energy. Two types of nuclear reactions are fission and fusion.

Fission Reactions and Energy

Nuclear reactions convert matter into energy. In 1905, Albert Einstein developed a formula that described the relationship between energy and matter. You have probably seen this famous equation, $E = mc^2$. In the equation, the E represents energy and the m represents mass. The c, which represents the speed of light, is a very large number. This equation states that when matter is changed into energy, an enormous amount of energy is released.

Nuclear fission is the splitting of an atom's nucleus into two smaller nuclei. The fuel for the reaction is a large atom that has an unstable nucleus, such as uranium-235 (U-235). A neutron is shot at the U-235 atom at high speed. **When the neutron hits the U-235 nucleus, the nucleus splits apart into two smaller nuclei and two or more neutrons.** The total mass of all these particles is a bit less than the mass of the original nucleus. The small amount of mass that makes up the difference has been converted into energy—a lot of energy, as described by Einstein's equation.

GUIDE FOR READING

◆ What happens during fission and fusion reactions?

◆ How does a nuclear power plant produce electricity?

Reading Tip As you read, create a Venn diagram to compare and contrast nuclear fission and nuclear fusion.

Key Terms nucleus
• nuclear fission
• reactor vessel • fuel rod
• control rod • meltdown
• nuclear fusion

Albert Einstein ▶
in 1930

INTEGRATING CHEMISTRY

SECTION 3 Nuclear Energy

TEKS: 6.2B, C, D, E; 6.3C; 6.4A; 6.9A, C

Objectives

After completing the lesson, students will be able to

◆ describe nuclear fission and nuclear fusion reactions;

◆ explain how a nuclear power plant produces electricity.

1 Engage/Explore

Activating Prior Knowledge

Ask several students to come to the board, draw what they think an atom looks like, and label its parts. Encourage the rest of the class to discuss the drawings and suggest corrections or additions. You can return to the diagrams later in the section.

········ DISCOVER ·········

Skills Focus inferring
Materials *15 dominoes*
Time 10 minutes
Tips Make sure students place the dominoes with less than a domino-length space between rows.
Expected Outcome In Step 2, all 15 dominoes will topple as those in one row fall back against those in the next row. With the third row removed in Step 4, the last two rows will remain standing.
Think It Over Removing the third row would stop the production of energy after a certain point.

READING STRATEGIES

Reading Tip Review the format of a Venn diagram: two overlapping circles with likenesses noted in the overlap area and differences noted in the outer areas. Likenesses should include the use of atomic nuclei to produce energy; differences should include how the nuclei are affected, the amount of energy produced, fuel availability, safety, and pollution produced.

Program Resources

◆ **Unit 3 Resources** 9-3 Lesson Plan, p. 41; 9-3 Section Summary, p. 42
◆ **Guided Reading and Study Workbook** 9-3

2 Facilitate

Fission Reactions and Energy

Building Inquiry Skills: Making Models

Materials *sheet of paper*
Time 5 minutes

Give each student a sheet of paper, and tell the class to think of the paper as the nucleus of a U-235 atom. To model the nucleus splitting into two smaller nuclei and three neutrons, have students tear the paper into five pieces—two larger and three smaller—and label the two larger pieces "smaller nucleus" and the three smaller pieces "neutron." Then have students tear a tiny piece off each "smaller nucleus" and set these tiny pieces aside. Explain that the tiny pieces represent the tiny amount of matter that is converted into energy in a fission reaction. **learning modality: tactile/kinesthetic**

Skills Focus making models

Materials *12 marbles*
Time 10 minutes
Tips Caution students not to walk around during this activity so they do not step on the marbles.
Expected Outcome The single marble represents a neutron being shot at an atom's nucleus. When it strikes the cluster, it scatters the marbles, similar to the breaking apart of the nucleus when it is struck by a neutron.
Extend After students have read about nuclear fusion on pages 310–311, challenge them to adapt this activity to model fusion. **learning modality: tactile/kinesthetic**

308

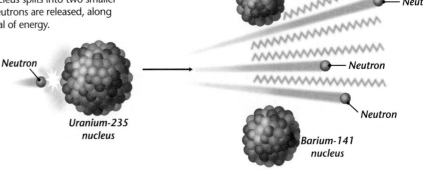

Figure 11 In a nuclear fission reaction, a neutron "bullet" strikes a U-235 nucleus. As a result, the nucleus splits into two smaller nuclei. More neutrons are released, along with a great deal of energy.

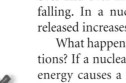

Shoot the Nucleus

In an open area of your classroom, make a model of a nuclear fission reaction. Place a handful of marbles on the floor in a tight cluster, so that they touch one another. Step back about a half-meter from the marbles. Shoot another marble at the cluster.

Making Models What does the marble you shot at the cluster represent? What effect did the marble have on the cluster? How is this similar to a nuclear fission reaction?

Meanwhile, the fission reaction has produced three more neutrons. If any of these neutrons strikes another nucleus, the fission reaction is repeated. More neutrons and more energy are released. If there are enough nuclei nearby, the process continues over and over in a chain reaction, just like a row of dominoes falling. In a nuclear chain reaction, the amount of energy released increases rapidly with each step in the chain.

What happens to all the energy released by these fission reactions? If a nuclear chain reaction is not controlled, the released energy causes a huge explosion. The explosion of an atomic bomb is an uncontrolled nuclear reaction. A few kilograms of matter explode with more force than several thousand tons of a nonnuclear explosive such as dynamite. However, if the chain reaction is controlled, the energy is released as heat, which can be used to generate electricity.

Nuclear Power Plants

Controlled nuclear fission reactions take place inside nuclear power plants. **In a nuclear power plant, the heat released from the reactions is used to change water into steam. As in other types of power plants, the steam then turns the blades of a turbine to generate electricity.** Look at the diagram of a nuclear power plant in Figure 12. In addition to the generator, it has two main parts: the reactor vessel and the heat exchanger.

Reactor Vessel The **reactor vessel** is the section of a nuclear reactor where nuclear fission occurs. The reactor contains rods of U-235, called **fuel rods.** When several fuel rods are placed close together, a series of fission reactions occurs. The reactions are controlled by placing **control rods** made of the metal cadmium between the fuel rods. The cadmium absorbs the neutrons

308

Background

Integrating Science Investigation of the Chernobyl accident revealed two basic causes. First, the reactor was not housed in a containment building and was extremely unstable at low power. This type of reactor is not used commercially in North America or Western Europe because nuclear engineers consider it too unsafe. Second, many of the plant's operators lacked scientific or technical expertise and made major errors when dealing with the initial problem.

The long-term health effects of the Chernobyl disaster are still being studied. Increases in birth defects and thyroid cancer in children have been documented. Other cancers are not expected to increase until 20 or more years after the accident.

released during the fission reactions. As the cadmium control rods are removed, the fission reactions speed up. If the reactor vessel starts to get too hot, the control rods are moved back in place to slow the chain reaction.

Heat Exchanger Heat is removed from the reactor vessel by water or another fluid that is pumped through the reactor. This fluid passes through a heat exchanger. There, the fluid boils water to produce steam, which runs the electrical generator. The steam is condensed again and pumped back to the heat exchanger.

✓ *Checkpoint* How are fission reactions controlled?

The Risks of Nuclear Fission

When it was first demonstrated, people thought that nuclear fission would provide an almost unlimited source of clean, safe energy. Today nuclear power plants generate about 17 percent of the world's electricity. In some places, nuclear power's share is larger. For example, nuclear power generates almost 80 percent of the electricity produced in the state of Vermont. France gets more than 70 percent of its electricity from nuclear power.

In 1986, in Chernobyl, Ukraine, the reactor vessel in a nuclear power plant overheated. The fuel rods generated so much heat that they started to melt, a condition called a **meltdown.** The excess heat increased the steam pressure in the generator. A series of explosions blew parts of the roof off and injured or killed dozens of plant workers and firefighters. Radioactive materials escaped into the environment. Today, the soil in an area the size of Florida remains contaminated with radioactive waste.

Sharpen your Skills

Calculating
ACTIVITY

A single pellet of U-235 the size of a breath mint can produce as much energy as 615 liters of fuel oil. An average home uses 5,000 liters of oil a year. How many U-235 pellets would be needed to supply the same amount of energy?

Figure 12 In a nuclear plant, uranium fuel undergoes fission, producing heat. The heat boils water, and the resulting steam drives the turbines that generate electricity. *Interpreting Diagrams From which part of the power plant is heat released to the environment?*

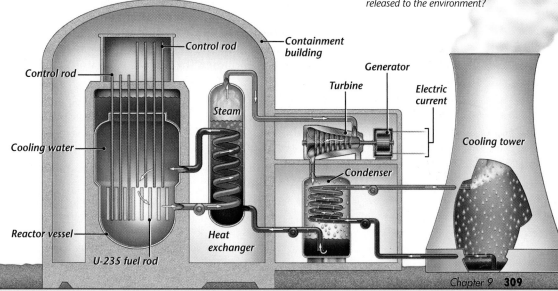

Control rod
Control rod
Cooling water
Reactor vessel
U-235 fuel rod
Containment building
Steam
Heat exchanger
Turbine
Generator
Electric current
Condenser
Cooling tower

Nuclear Power Plants

Sharpen your Skills

Calculating
ACTIVITY

Materials *calculator (optional)*
Time 5 minutes
Tips If needed, help students determine how to calculate the answer (divide 5,000 by 615).
Expected Outcome About 8 (8.13) pellets would be needed.
Extend Suggest that each student estimate how many homes are in his or her neighborhood, then calculate how many pellets would be needed to supply energy to all those homes for a year.
learning modality: logical/ mathematical

The Risks of Nuclear Fission

Building Inquiry Skills: Inferring

Display a large world map, and let volunteers locate Chernobyl (51°N, 30°E, about 130 km north of Kiev). Tell students that the force of the 1986 explosion carried radioactive materials high into the atmosphere, where they spread across the Northern Hemisphere and then settled back to Earth in what is called "fallout." The heaviest fallout occurred in Ukraine, Belarus, Sweden, Norway, Denmark, France, and Switzerland. In addition, Finland, Lithuania, Germany, Poland, the Czech Republic, Slovakia, Austria, Hungary, Italy, and Great Britain suffered moderate fallout. Let students find all these countries on the map. Ask: **What does this tell you about the dangers of nuclear power plants?** *(An accident can affect a huge area.)* **learning modality: visual**

Ongoing Assessment

Oral Presentation Call on students at random to each explain a step in the process of how a nuclear power plant converts nuclear energy to electricity.

Media and Technology

Transparencies "Nuclear Fission," Transparency 45; "A Nuclear Power Plant," Transparency 46

Answers to Self-Assessment

✓ *Checkpoint*
Fission reactions are controlled by placing cadmium control rods between the fuel rods to absorb neutrons.

Caption Question
Figure 12 The cooling tower

Figure 13 One problem with nuclear power is disposal of the used radioactive fuel rods. In this plant in France, the fuel rods are stored in a deep pool of water.

Chernobyl and less serious accidents at other nuclear power plants have led to public concerns about nuclear plant safety.

The danger of a meltdown is a serious concern. However, a meltdown can be avoided by careful planning. A more difficult problem is the disposal of radioactive wastes produced by power plants. Radioactive wastes remain dangerous for many thousands of years. Scientists must find a way to safely store these wastes for a long period of time. Finally, nuclear power has turned out to be a much more costly source of power than was originally expected. Among other things, the safety features required for nuclear plants make the plants very expensive.

☑ *Checkpoint* *What are three problems with using nuclear fission as an energy source?*

The Quest to Control Fusion

A second type of nuclear reaction is fusion. **Nuclear fusion is the combining of two atomic nuclei to produce a single larger nucleus. As shown in Figure 14, two kinds of hydrogen nuclei are forced together in a fusion reaction.** One kind (hydrogen-2) has one proton and one neutron, and the other kind (hydrogen-3) has one proton and two neutrons. The tremendous heat and pressure

Figure 14 In a nuclear fusion reaction, two nuclei combine to form a single larger nucleus. *Interpreting Diagrams What is released during a fusion reaction?*

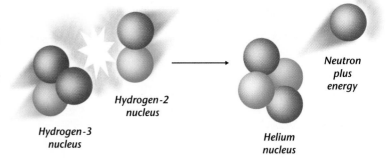

Hydrogen-3 nucleus

Hydrogen-2 nucleus

Helium nucleus

Neutron plus energy

cause them to combine and create a helium nucleus with two protons and two neutrons. This helium nucleus has slightly less mass than the total mass of the two hydrogen nuclei. The difference is converted to energy.

Nuclear fusion would have many advantages as an energy source. Fusion can produce much more energy per atom than nuclear fission. The fuel for a nuclear fusion reactor is also readily available. Water, which is plentiful in Earth's oceans, contains one of the kinds of hydrogen needed for fusion. Fusion should be safer and less polluting than nuclear fission. You can see why scientists are eager to find a way to build a nuclear fusion reactor!

Although some fusion bombs have been exploded, scientists have not yet been able to control a large-scale fusion reaction. The biggest problem is temperature. In the sun, nuclear fusion occurs at 15 million degrees Celsius. Such conditions are almost impossible to control on Earth. No material has been found that can serve as a reactor vessel under the high temperature and pressure of a nuclear fusion reaction. Extremely powerful magnetic fields can contain a fusion reaction. However, it takes more energy to generate these fields than the fusion reaction produces.

Although many more years of research are expected, some scientists believe that they will eventually be able to control fusion reactions. If they succeed, the quest for a clean, cheap energy source may be over at last.

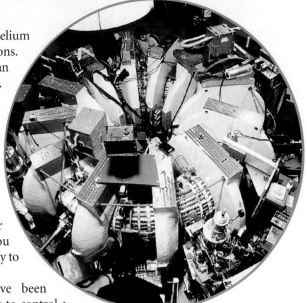

Figure 15 Researchers at Los Alamos National Laboratory in New Mexico are studying fusion as an energy source. This machine creates strong magnetic fields that allow fusion to occur for short periods of time.

 ## Section 3 Review

1. Draw and label a simple diagram of a nuclear fission reaction. Include the following labels: U-235 nucleus, neutrons, smaller nuclei, and energy.
2. How can the energy released in a fission reaction be used to produce electricity?
3. Explain the purpose of control rods.
4. Give two reasons that people have not been able to use nuclear fusion as an energy source.
5. **Thinking Critically Classifying** Is nuclear fission a renewable or nonrenewable energy source? Is nuclear fusion renewable or nonrenewable? Explain.

Check Your Progress
CHAPTER PROJECT

By now you should begin preparing the written report of your findings about energy use in your group's area of the school. Your report should include the major ways energy is used in your chosen area. You should also include recommendations on how energy use might be reduced.

Program Resources

◆ **Unit 3 Resources** 9-3 Review and Reinforce, p. 43; 9-3 Enrich, p. 44

Media and Technology

Transparencies "Nuclear Fusion," Transparency 47

Answers to Self-Assessment

☑ *Checkpoint*

An accident can cause serious damage, injury, and death. Radioactive wastes are difficult to dispose of safely. Nuclear power is costly.

Caption Question

Figure 14 A neutron plus energy

3 Assess

Section 3 Review Answers

1. Students' diagrams should show the U-235 nucleus being struck by one neutron, then splitting to form two smaller nuclei, three neutrons, and energy. (See Figure 16.)
2. The heat energy released by a fission reaction can be used to boil water, producing steam that turns the blades of a turbine to generate electricity.
3. Control rods absorb excess neutrons and control the fission reactions.
4. Fusion reactions cannot be controlled; more energy is needed to produce a fusion reaction than is produced by the reaction itself.
5. Nuclear fission is considered a nonrenewable resource because it depends on uranium, which is a nonrenewable element. Nuclear fusion is considered a renewable resource because Earth's water is abundant and is renewed in natural processes.

Check Your Progress
CHAPTER PROJECT

Encourage students to make their reports concise, focusing on the major points and, when appropriate, using visual displays (such as a neat copy of the data table). Also suggest that they explain how each recommendation would reduce energy use.

Performance Assessment

Skills Check Have each student create a compare-contrast table that compares the advantages and disadvantages of nuclear fission and nuclear fusion as energy sources.

 Students can save their tables in their portfolios.

311

Keeping Comfortable

NOTE: This lab is placed before its related section to allow enough time for students to conduct the test in Part 1, then design and carry out their own experiments.

Preparing for Inquiry

Key Concept Different materials lessen the transfer of heat to different degrees.

Skills Objectives Students will be able to
◆ measure temperature changes of water in a paper cup for use as a baseline;
◆ design an experiment to compare how well different materials maintain water temperature by slowing heat transfer.

Time 40 minutes

Advance Planning CAUTION: *Do not use water hot enough to cause scalding.*

 If using probeware, refer to the *Probeware Lab Manual.*

Guiding Inquiry

Helping Design a Plan
◆ Ask: **Why should you do Part 1 with a paper cup first?** *(To determine a standard for comparing materials)*

Troubleshooting the Experiment
◆ Have students discuss the questions in Step 5 before they write their plans.
◆ Make sure students record temperatures at regular intervals.

Expected Outcome
The most effective material is plastic foam; the least effective is metal.

Analyze and Conclude
1. Temperatures will vary. Heat flowed from the hot water to the cold water, as shown by the temperature changes.
2. *Rooms:* cold water; *outdoor weather:* hot water; *walls:* paper cup
3. *Most effective:* plastic foam. *Least effective:* metal. Plastic foam kept the cold water close to its starting temperature for the longest time, while metal let the starting temperature increase the most.
4. Students should consider other issues, such as the materials' strength, durability, and cost.

Skills Lab

Designing Experiments

Keeping Comfortable

Two ways to use less energy are to keep heat *out* of your home during hot weather, and to keep it *in* during cold weather. In this lab, you will investigate how to do both things.

Problem

How well do different materials stop heat transfer?

Suggested Materials

watch or clock   beakers
ice water   hot water
thermometers or temperature probes
containers and lids made of paper, plastic foam, plastic, glass, and metal

Design a Plan

Part 1 Measuring Temperature Changes

1. Use a pencil to poke a hole in the lid of a paper cup. Fill the cup about halfway with cold water.
2. Put the lid on the cup. Insert a thermometer or temperature probe into the water through the hole. When the temperature stops dropping, place the cup in a beaker. Add hot water to the beaker until the water level is about 1 cm below the lid.
3. Record the water temperature once every minute until it has increased by 5 degrees. Use the time it takes for the temperature to increase 1 degree to measure how well the paper cup prevents heat transfer.

Part 2 Comparing Materials

4. Use the ideas from Part 1 to design a controlled experiment to rank the effectiveness of different materials in preventing heat transfer.

5. Use these questions to help you plan your experiment:
   ◆ What hypothesis will you test?
   ◆ Which materials do you predict will be the best and worst at preventing heat transfer? How will you define these terms?
   ◆ What will your manipulated variable be? What will your responding variable be?
   ◆ What variables do you need to control? How will you control them?
   ◆ What step-by-step procedures will you use?
   ◆ What kind of data table will you use?

6. After your teacher has reviewed your plans, make any necessary changes in your design. Then perform your experiment.

Analyze and Conclude

1. In Part 1, what was the starting temperature of the hot water? What was the starting temperature of the cold water? In which direction did the heat flow? How do you know?
2. If the materials in Part 1 are used to represent your home in very hot weather, which material would represent the rooms in your home? Which would represent the outdoor weather? Which would represent the walls of the building?
3. Which material was most effective at preventing the transfer of heat? Which was the least effective? Explain.
4. **Think About It** Would experiments similar to this one provide you with enough information to choose materials to build a home? Explain.

Design an Experiment

Design an experiment to compare how well the materials would work if the hot water were inside the cup and the cold water were outside. With your teacher's permission, carry out your experiment.

Extending the Inquiry

More to Explore Students' experiments should be similar to those in Part 2.

Program Resources

◆ **Unit 3 Resources** Chapter 9 Skills Lab blackline masters, pp. 51–53
◆ **Probeware Lab Manual** Blackline masters

Safety

Students should use caution in handling the thermometers, hot water, and glass containers. Review the safety guidelines in Appendix A.

Media and Technology

Lab Activity Videotapes Grade 6, Tape 3

DISCOVER •••••••••••••••••••••••••••• ACTIVITY ••••

Which Bulb Is More Efficient?

1. Record the light output (listed in lumens) from the packages of a 60-watt incandescent light bulb and a 15-watt compact fluorescent bulb.

2. Place the fluorescent bulb in a lamp socket.
CAUTION: *Make sure the lamp is unplugged.*

3. Plug in the lamp and turn it on. Hold the end of a thermometer about 8 centimeters from the bulb.

4. Record the temperature after 5 minutes.

5. Turn off and unplug the lamp. When the bulb is cool, remove it. Repeat Steps 2, 3, and 4 with the incandescent light bulb.

Think It Over

Inferring The 60-watt bulb uses about 4 times more energy than the 15-watt bulb. How does the light output of each bulb compare with the energy it uses? How can the difference in efficiency be explained?

Imagine what would happen if the world ran out of fossil fuels today. Much of the electric power that people depend on would disappear. Most buildings would lose their heating and cooling. Forests would disappear as people began to burn wood for heat and cooking. Almost all transportation would stop. Cars, buses, trains, airplanes, and ships would be stranded wherever they ran out of fuel. Since radios, televisions, computers, and telephones depend on electricity, communication would be greatly reduced.

Although fossil fuels may never be completely used up, they will eventually become scarcer and more expensive. Most people think that it makes sense to start planning now to avoid a fuel shortage in the future. **One approach to the problem is to find new sources of energy. The second approach is to make the fuels that are available now last as long as possible while other solutions are being developed.**

Conservation and Efficiency

Reducing energy use is called **energy conservation.** For example, if you walk to the store instead of getting a ride, you are conserving the gasoline needed to drive to the store. Reducing energy use is a solution to energy problems that will help no matter what form of energy is used in the future.

GUIDE FOR READING

◆ What are two ways to make sure there will be enough energy for the future?

◆ How does insulation help conserve energy?

Reading Tip Before you read, list ways to conserve energy. As you read, add to the list.

Key Terms energy conservation • efficiency • insulation

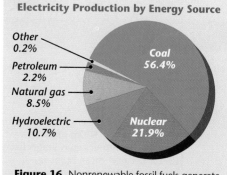

Electricity Production by Energy Source

Other 0.2%
Coal 56.4%
Petroleum 2.2%
Natural gas 8.5%
Nuclear 21.9%
Hydroelectric 10.7%

Figure 16 Nonrenewable fossil fuels generate over two thirds of the nation's electricity.

Chapter 9 **313**

Background

Reading Tip To provide structure and prompt students' thinking, suggest that they list types of energy uses (electricity for lights and appliances, oil or natural gas for heating, gasoline for cars, and so forth) as headings across the top of a page and then list ways to reduce each use below the headings (such as turning off lights and appliances not in use).

Program Resources

◆ **Unit 3 Resources** 9-4 Lesson Plan, p. 45; 9-4 Section Summary, p. 46
◆ **Guided Reading and Study Workbook** 9-4

SECTION
4 Energy Conservation

TEKS: 6.1A; 6.2B, C; 6.3E; 6.4A; 6.9A

Objectives

After completing the lesson, students will be able to

◆ list two ways to ensure that there will be enough energy for the future;

◆ identify things that individuals can do to conserve energy.

1 Engage/Explore

Activating Prior Knowledge

Point out the section's title and ask: **What does the term energy conservation mean?** (*Accept all reasonable responses, such as "not wasting energy."*) **What are some examples of wasting energy?** (*Setting a thermostat too high, leaving lights on in an unoccupied room, running a dishwasher with only a small load, and the like.*)

········· DISCOVER ·········

Skills Focus inferring
Materials *60-watt incandescent light bulb and 15-watt compact fluorescent light bulb in packages, lamp, thermometer, clock or watch*
Time 20 minutes
CAUTION: *Students should use caution when handling the bulbs and lamp plug.*
Tips Compact fluorescent bulbs, widely available in supermarkets and hardware stores, screw into a regular bulb socket.
Expected Outcome The fluorescent bulb will not produce as high a temperature as the incandescent bulb because it uses electricity more efficiently, converting more to light and less to heat.
Think It Over Lumens may vary among bulb brands. Based on 900 lumens for a 60-watt incandescent bulb and 825 lumens for a 15-watt compact fluorescent bulb, the difference is 75 lumens. The incandescent bulb uses more electricity because so much is converted to heat.

2 Facilitate

Conservation and Efficiency

Building Inquiry Skills: Calculating

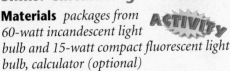

Materials *packages from 60-watt incandescent light bulb and 15-watt compact fluorescent light bulb, calculator (optional)*

Time 10 minutes

Explain that the number of watts printed on a light bulb and its package tells how much electrical energy is needed to light the bulb for one second (1 watt = 1 joule per second). Have students examine the packages and identify the wattage of each bulb. *(Incandescent bulb 60 watts, fluorescent bulb 15 watts)* Ask: **How many times more electrical energy does the incandescent bulb use to produce the same amount of light as the fluorescent bulb?** *(4 times as much)* **What is the expected life of each bulb?** *(Answers will depend on brands of bulbs used; examples: incandescent bulb 1,000 hours, fluorescent bulb 10,000 hours)* **How many incandescent bulbs would you need to equal the life of one fluorescent bulb?** *(10)* **How much would 10 incandescent bulbs cost compared with the cost of one fluorescent bulb?** *($7.50 [10 × 75¢] compared with $20.00; prices may vary)* **How much more than 10 incandescent bulbs would the fluorescent bulb cost over its life?** *($12.50)* **Do you think the fluorescent bulb is worth its higher cost?** *(Accept all answers at this point.)* **According to the fluorescent bulb's package, how much would you save in electricity costs by using that one bulb instead of 10 incandescent bulbs for 10,000 hours?** *($45.00)* **What would your total savings be over the life of the fluorescent bulb?** *($45.00 – $12.50, or $32.50)* **So which type of bulb is better, and why?** *(The fluorescent bulb, because it costs less in the long term and conserves electricity.)* **learning modality: logical/mathematical**

A way to get as much work as possible out of fuels is to use them efficiently. **Efficiency** is the percentage of energy that is actually used to perform work. The rest of the energy is "lost" to the surroundings, usually as heat. People have developed many ways to increase energy efficiency.

Lighting Lights can use as much as 10 percent of the electricity in your home, but much of that electricity is wasted. An incandescent light bulb converts less than 10 percent of the electricity it uses into light. The rest is given off as heat. You can prove this to yourself by holding your hand close to an incandescent light bulb. But don't touch it! Compact fluorescent bulbs, on the other hand, use only about one fourth as much energy to provide the same amount of light.

☑ *Checkpoint* *Which type of light bulb is more energy-efficient?*

SCIENCE & History

Energy-Efficient Devices

Scientists and engineers have developed many technologies that improve energy efficiency and reduce energy use.

1932 Fiberglass Insulation

Long strands of glass fibers trap air and keep buildings from losing heat. Less fuel is used for heating.

1958 Solar Cells

More than 150 years ago, scientists discovered that silicon can convert light into electricity. The first useful application of solar cells was to power the radio on a satellite. Now solar cells are even used on experimental cars like the one below.

| 1930 | 1940 | 1950 |

1936 Fluorescent Lighting

Fluorescent bulbs were introduced to the public at the 100th anniversary celebration of the United States Patent Office. Because these bulbs use less energy than incandescent bulbs, most offices and schools use fluorescent lights.

314

Background

Facts and Figures Energy-efficient devices like those shown in the timeline have helped conserve energy. For example, "superinsulated" homes can use from 70 to 95 percent less energy for heating than homes with conventional insulation. However, the airtight construction of these homes may lead to problems of indoor air pollution.

Because of lighter materials and designs that reduce air drag, the fuel efficiency of passenger cars has improved dramatically, from an average of 6.8 km/L in 1981 to 9.1 km/L in 1994.

The National Appliance Energy Conservation Act sets energy-efficiency standards for refrigerators, washing machines, water heaters, and other appliances. As a result of this law, refrigerators built in the mid-1990s use more than 80 percent less energy than those built in the early 1980s.

Heating and Cooling One method of increasing the efficiency of heating and cooling systems is insulation. **Insulation** is a layer of material that helps block the transfer of heat between the air inside and outside a building. You have probably seen insulation made of fiberglass, which looks like fluffy pink cotton candy. The mat of thin glass fibers traps air. **This layer of trapped air helps keep the building from losing or gaining heat from the outside.** A layer of fiberglass 15 centimeters thick insulates a room as well as a brick wall 2 meters thick or a stone wall almost 6 meters thick!

Buildings lose a lot of heat around the windows. Look at the windows in your school or home. Was the building built after 1980? Have the windows been replaced recently? If so, you will most likely see two panes of glass with space between them. The air between the panes of glass acts as insulation.

In Your Journal

Design an advertisement for one of the energy-saving inventions described in this time line. The advertisement may be a print, radio, or television ad. Be sure that your advertisement clearly explains the benefits of the invention.

1967
Microwave Ovens

The first countertop microwave oven for the home was introduced. Microwaves cook food by heating the water the food contains. The microwave oven heats only the food, not the air, racks, and oven walls as in a conventional oven. Preheating is also not required, saving even more energy.

1997
Smart Roads

The Department of Transportation demonstrated that cars can be controlled by computers. Sensors built into the road control all the cars, making traffic flow more smoothly. This uses less energy.

| 1970 | 1980 | 1990 | 2000 |

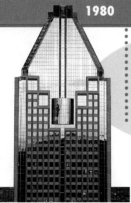

1981
High-Efficiency Window Coatings

Materials that reflect sunlight were first used to coat windows in the early 1980s. This coating reduces the air conditioning needed to keep the inside of the building cool.

Chapter 9 **315**

Answers to Self-Assessment

☑ *Checkpoint*

A compact fluorescent bulb is more energy-efficient.

315

What You Can Do

Real-Life Learning

Create a class list on the board from students' lists they started if they did the Reading Tip on page 313. Pay particular attention to any ideas that are not covered in the text. Encourage students to copy the list so they can use it in the Science at Home activity below.

learning modality: verbal

3 Assess

Section 4 Review Answers

1. Find new sources of energy, and make the fuels we have now last as long as possible.
2. Insulation traps air so heat is not lost to the outside in cold weather and is kept outside in hot weather, reducing use of the building's heating and cooling systems.
3. Several people sharing one car uses less fuel than each person driving separately.
4. The building with only incandescent lights has higher energy bills because incandescent bulbs are less energy-efficient than fluorescent bulbs; most of the electrical energy used by incandescent bulbs is converted to heat, not light.

Science at Home

Encourage students to look for simple energy-saving ideas that they and their family members can implement easily and inexpensively—for example, wrapping an older, less efficient water heater with an insulating material rather than replacing the heater.

Performance Assessment

Oral Presentation Have each student describe one energy-saving idea that he or she will take responsibility for implementing at home.

Figure 17 A single city bus can transport dozens of people, reducing the number of cars on the roads and saving energy. *Applying Concepts How does riding a bus conserve energy?*

Transportation Engineers have improved the energy efficiency of cars by designing better engines and tires. Another way to save energy is to reduce the number of cars on the road. In many communities, public transit systems provide an alternative to driving. Other cities encourage carpooling. If four people travel together in one car, they use much less energy than they would by driving separately. Many cities now set aside lanes for cars containing two or more people.

Cars that make use of electric power can provide more energy savings. For example, a hybrid car has both an electric motor and a gasoline engine. In hybrid cars, the heat energy generated in braking charges a rechargeable battery, which powers the electric motor. Therefore, the hybrid car is more energy-efficient than one that runs only on gasoline.

What You Can Do

You can reduce your personal energy use by changing your behavior in some simple ways.

◆ Keep your home cooler in winter and warmer in summer. Instead of turning up the heat, put on a sweater. Use fans instead of air conditioners.

◆ Use natural light instead of electric lights when possible.

◆ Turn off the lights or television when you leave a room.

◆ Walk or ride a bike for short trips. Ride buses and trains.

◆ Recycle, especially metal products. Recycling an aluminum can uses only 5 percent of the energy making a new can uses!

The items in this list are small things, but multiplied by millions of people they add up to a lot of energy saved for the future.

Section 4 Review

1. What are two ways to make energy resources last longer?
2. Explain how putting insulation in a building conserves energy.
3. How does carpooling conserve energy?
4. **Thinking Critically** **Predicting** An office building contains only incandescent lights. The building next door contains fluorescent lights. Predict which building has higher energy bills. Explain your answer.

316

Science at Home

Saving Energy With an adult family member, conduct an energy audit of your home. Look for places where energy is being lost, such as cracks around windows and doors. Also look for ways to reduce energy use, such as running the dishwasher only when it is full. Together, create a list of energy-saving suggestions for your family. Post the list where everyone can see it.

Program Resources

◆ **Unit 3 Resources** 9-4 Review and Reinforce, p. 47; 9-4 Enrich, p. 48

Answers to Self-Assessment

Caption Question

Figure 17 A bus uses less fuel than all the individual cars that would be driven by the bus passengers.

SECTION 1 Energy and Fossil Fuels

Key Ideas
- A fuel is a substance that provides a form of energy as a result of a chemical change.
- Energy can be converted from one form to another.
- The three major fossil fuels are coal, oil, and natural gas. These fuels release more energy when they are burned than most other substances do.
- Because fossil fuels take hundreds of millions of years to form, they are considered nonrenewable resources.

Key Terms
fuel	nonrenewable resource
energy transformation	petroleum
combustion	refinery
fossil fuel	petrochemical
hydrocarbon	reserves

SECTION 2 Renewable Sources of Energy

Key Ideas
- The sun constantly gives off energy in the form of heat and light. Solar energy can serve directly or indirectly as a renewable energy source.
- Because the sun causes winds and drives the water cycle, wind power and water power are considered indirect forms of solar energy.
- Biomass fuels, geothermal energy, and hydrogen power are other renewable energy sources that are currently in limited use.

Key Terms
renewable resource	hydroelectric power
solar energy	biomass fuel
inexhaustible resource	geothermal energy

SECTION 3 Nuclear Energy

INTEGRATING CHEMISTRY

Key Ideas
- Nuclear reactions include fission reactions and fusion reactions.
- In a fission reaction, the impact of a neutron splits an atom's nucleus into two smaller nuclei and two or more neutrons. In a fusion reaction, two kinds of hydrogen nuclei are forced together. A large amount of energy is released in both processes.
- In a nuclear power plant, the thermal energy released from controlled fission reactions is used to generate electricity.
- Disadvantages of nuclear power include the risk of a meltdown and radioactive waste.

Key Terms
nucleus	fuel rod	meltdown
nuclear fission	control rod	nuclear fusion
reactor vessel		

SECTION 4 Energy Conservation

Key Ideas
- To avoid an energy shortage in the future, people must find new sources of energy and conserve the fuels that are available now.
- Insulation keeps a building from losing heat to, or gaining heat from, the outside.
- Ways to conserve energy use in transportation include making more efficient vehicles, carpooling, and using public transit.

Key Terms
energy conservation	efficiency	insulation

Organizing Information

Compare/Contrast Table Make a table listing an advantage and a disadvantage for each of the following types of energy: coal, petroleum, solar, wind, water, geothermal, nuclear. For example, one advantage of coal is that it produces a large amount of energy. (For tips on making compare/contrast tables see the Skills Handbook.)

Organizing Information

Compare/Contrast Table
Students' tables should include a single advantage and disadvantage for each energy type similar to the examples in the following:

Advantages and Disadvantages of Energy Sources

Energy Type	Advantage	Disadvantage
Coal	Produces large amount of energy; easy to transport	Causes air pollution when burned; difficult to mine
Petroleum	Produces large amount of energy; can be used to produce plastics and other products	Causes air pollution when burned, difficult to find, must be refined
Solar	Free, renewable, does not cause pollution	Not available on cloudy days or at night, is very spread out
Wind	Free, renewable, does not cause pollution	Not available in many places
Water	Free, renewable, does not cause pollution	Most of the suitable rivers in the United States have already been dammed, dams can have negative effect on the environment
Geothermal	Free, renewable, cheap, does not cause pollution	Available in only a few places, drilling deep wells is expensive
Nuclear	Produces huge amount of energy	Creates radioactive waste, risk of meltdown, costly

Program Resources

- **Unit 3 Resources** Chapter 9 Project Scoring Rubric, p. 32
- **Performance Assessment** Chapter 9, pp. 29–31
- **Chapter and Unit Tests** Chapter 9 Test, pp. 44–47

Media and Technology

 Computer Test Bank
Chapter 9 Test

Reviewing Content

Multiple Choice

1. b 2. a 3. c 4. a 5. d

True or False

6. true 7. true 8. renewable 9. solar cells
10. true

Checking Concepts

11. Spilled oil harms fish and birds; spilled gasoline may contaminate groundwater; burning oil contributes to air pollution.

12. As plants die and decay, their remains pile up and are buried by layers of sand, rock, and mud. Over millions of years, heat and pressure change the decaying remains into coal.

13. Solar energy is considered an inexhaustible resource because it will not run out for several billion years.

14. Possible answers include overhangs to shade the windows in summer, positioning the house to receive maximum sunlight in winter, solar cells on the roof to provide electricity, and a backup energy source.

15. Wind can turn a turbine, which rotates an electromagnet to create electricity.

16. Cost and the time it takes to renew the supply of trees limit the use of biomass fuels.

17. Advantages include burning cleanly; creating no smoke, smog, or acid rain; ease of handling and transport; and large fuel supply. Disadvantages include taking more energy to obtain the fuel than is produced by burning it.

18. By placing control rods made of cadmium between the fuel rods to limit chain reactions

19. Energy efficiency is the percentage of energy actually used to perform work; *examples:* insulation, fluorescent light bulbs, window coatings, microwave ovens

20. Responses will vary but should include ways of traveling, preparing meals, and obtaining light and heat.

Critical Thinking

21. *Likenesses:* All form from the remains of organisms, contain hydrocarbons, and produce a large amount of energy when burned. *Differences:* Coal forms from plant

---

Reviewing Content

 Review key concepts online using iText at www.phschool.com

Multiple Choice

Choose the letter of the best answer.

1. Which of the following is *not* a fossil fuel?
   a. coal b. wood
   c. oil d. natural gas

2. An appliance that transfers thermal energy from a cold space inside to a warm space outside is a
   a. refrigerator. b. solar oven.
   c. water heater. d. microwave.

3. Which of the following is *not* a biomass fuel?
   a. methane
   b. gasohol
   c. hydrogen
   d. sugar-cane wastes

4. The particle used to start a nuclear fission reaction is a(n)
   a. neutron.
   b. nucleus.
   c. proton.
   d. atom.

5. A part of a nuclear power plant that undergoes a fission reaction is called a
   a. turbine.
   b. control rod.
   c. heat exchanger.
   d. fuel rod.

True or False

If the statement is true, write true. If it is false, change the underlined word or words to make the statement true.

6. A change of energy from one form to another is called <u>energy transformation</u>.

7. The process of burning a fuel for energy is <u>combustion</u>.

8. Geothermal energy is an example of a <u>nonrenewable</u> energy source.

9. Solar energy is harnessed to run calculators using <u>nuclear fusion</u>.

10. Most of the energy used in the United States today comes from <u>fossil fuels</u>.

Checking Concepts

11. What are some negative impacts of petroleum on the environment?

12. Describe how coal forms.

13. Why is solar energy an inexhaustible resource?

14. Describe three features of a solar home. (Your answer may include passive or active solar systems.)

15. Explain how wind can be used to generate electricity.

16. What factors limit the use of biomass fuels as an energy source?

17. Describe the advantages and disadvantages that hydrogen power would have as a source of energy.

18. How is a nuclear fission reaction controlled in a nuclear power plant?

19. Define *energy efficiency*. Give three examples of inventions that increase energy efficiency.

20. **Writing to Learn** Suppose you had no electricity. Write a journal entry describing a typical weekday, including your meals, classes, and after-school activities. Explain how you might get things done without electricity.

Critical Thinking

21. **Comparing and Contrasting** Discuss how the three fossil fuels are alike and how they are different.

22. **Classifying** State whether each of the following energy sources is renewable or nonrenewable: coal, solar power, methane, hydrogen. Give a reason for each answer.

23. **Making Judgments** Write a short paragraph explaining why you agree or disagree with the following statement: "The United States should build more nuclear power plants to prepare for the future shortage of fossil fuels."

24. **Relating Cause and Effect** Explain the steps by which an electric power plant generates electricity by burning a fossil fuel.

---

remains; oil and natural gas form from the remains of small animals, algae, and protists. Coal is solid, oil is liquid, and natural gas is a gas. Natural gas causes less air pollution than coal and oil.

22. Coal is nonrenewable because it takes so long to form. Solar power is renewable because its supply is unlimited. Methane is renewable because it is produced as wastes decompose. Hydrogen is renewable because it can be obtained from water, which is abundant on Earth.

23. Accept both "agree" and "disagree" responses. Students should support their views with explanations that cite the advantages and disadvantages of nuclear power as an energy source.

24. In a furnace, fossil fuel is burned and thermal energy is released. This energy is used to boil water and make steam. The mechanical energy of moving steam turns turbine blades. The turbine turns the shaft of a generator, producing an electric current.

Applying Skills

The table below shows how the world's energy production changed between 1973 and 1995. Use the information in the table to answer Questions 25–28.

Source of Energy	Energy Units Produced 1973	Energy Units Produced 1995
Coal	1,498	2,179
Gas	964	1,775
Hydroelectric	107	242
Nuclear	54	646
Oil	2,730	3,228
TOTAL Energy Units	5,353	8,070

25. **Interpreting Data** How did total energy production change from 1973 to 1995?
26. **Calculating** What percentage of total world energy production did nuclear power provide in 1973? In 1995?

27. **Classifying** Classify the different types of energy as renewable or nonrenewable. How important was renewable energy in 1995?
28. **Drawing Conclusions** Which energy source was the most important in 1995?

Performance CHAPTER PROJECT Assessment

Present Your Project Have another group review your report for clarity, organization, and detail. Make revisions based on feedback from the other group. As a class, discuss each group's findings. Make a list of suggestions for conserving energy in your school.

Reflect and Record In your project notebook, explain what types of energy use were the hardest to measure. What other information would you have liked to have when making your recommendations? Record your overall opinion of energy efficiency in your school.

Test Preparation
Use these questions to prepare for standardized tests.

Read the passage. Then answer Questions 29–33.

Tides are a source of renewable energy. Along some coasts, great amounts of water move into bays at high tide and flow out to sea again as the tide falls.

A few tidal power plants have been built to take advantage of this regular motion. A low dam across the entrance to a shallow bay holds water in the bay at high tide. As the tide goes out, water flowing past turbines in the dam generates electricity, as in a hydroelectric power plant.

Tidal power will probably never become a major source of energy because only a few coastal areas in the world are suitable for building tidal power plants. Also, a dam across a bay blocks boats and fish from traveling up the river.

29. How many tidal power plants are now in use?
   A only a few   B several dozen
   C zero   D several hundred

30. Tides are an energy source that is
   F widely used throughout the world.
   G renewable.
   H nonrenewable.
   J impossible to use in generating power.

31. Tidal power plants most resemble
   A geothermal power plants.
   B windmills.
   C hydroelectric power plants.
   D water-cooled nuclear power plants.

32. The selection concludes that tidal power
   F will replace other types of power.
   G already produces too much energy.
   H can be developed wherever the tide rises.
   J won't become a major source of energy.

33. A good title for this reading selection would be
   A The Limitless Power of Tides.
   B Tidal Power Blocks Boats.
   C A Minor Source of Renewable Energy.
   D A Major Source of Energy.

Chapter 9 **319**

Applying Skills

25. It increased from 5,353 units to 8,070 units.
26. *1973:* 1%; *1995:* 8%
27. *Renewable:* hydroelectric; *nonrenewable:* coal, gas, nuclear, oil. Renewable energy (hydroelectric power) was not very important to the world's energy production in 1995, representing only 3% of the total energy units produced.
28. oil

Performance CHAPTER PROJECT Assessment

Present Your Project Encourage groups to give each other specific suggestions for improving the reports and to avoid making overly general criticisms. In the whole-class discussion, give each group an opportunity to summarize its findings, then focus on the group's suggestions for reducing energy use. Ask students for their ideas about how the proposal should be organized and presented. You may want to have a group of volunteers compile the final proposal and present it to the entire class for further discussion.

Reflect and Record Specific responses to the questions and issues raised in this paragraph will vary. Allow time for students to share the answers and ideas they recorded.

Test Preparation

29. A **30.** G **31.** C **32.** J **33.** C

Program Resources

- **Inquiry Skills Activity Book** Provides teaching and review of all inquiry skills
- **Prentice Hall Assessment System** Provides standardized test practice
- **Reading in the Content Area** Provides strategies to improve science reading skills
- **Teacher's ELL Handbook** Provides multiple strategies for English language learners

Protecting Desert Wildlife

Focus on Ecology

This four-page feature focuses on the process of scientific inquiry by involving students in a high-interest, magazine-like article about a working scientist, wildlife management biologist Elroy Masters. Using Masters's efforts to protect desert wildlife and habitats as an example, the feature shows how observing, collecting data, and problem solving are key elements of scientific inquiry.

The concept of habitat and scientific methods used to study populations are presented in Chapter 8. However, students do not need to have any previous knowledge of the chapter's content to understand and appreciate this feature.

Scientific Inquiry

Before students read the feature, invite them to preview the pages and the photographs and maps. Then ask: **What kinds of animals does Elroy Masters study?** (*Fish, bighorn sheep, birds, tortoises, bats*) **Where does he work?** (*In the area around Lake Havasu in western Arizona*) **How were you able to determine these things?** (*By looking at the pictures and map and reading the captions*) Confirm this response by emphasizing that students learned these things by observing. Then point out to students that just as they were able to learn about Masters's work by observing the illustrations, scientists learn by observing the world around them.

PROTECTING DESERT WILDLIFE

Elroy Masters likes working outdoors. One day he hikes a mountain trail, looking for desert tortoises. The next morning he may be in a boat on the Colorado River, counting birds along the riverbank. Another day he may be in the Arizona hills, building a water container for thirsty bighorn sheep. Elroy is a biologist working for the federal government's Bureau of Land Management (BLM). His job is to protect wildlife habitat in the desert along the Colorado River between California and Arizona.

"People may come in wanting to run a pipeline across public land or needing to build a road," he explains. "Part of my job is to check out the biological effect of that action on different species of animals and plants. If people are going to build a road where there are a lot of tortoises, we might try to have them work from November to March. Since tortoises hibernate during those months, we reduce the chance of a tortoise getting run over."

Growing up in Arizona, Elroy lived in a farming community. "I was always outdoors. I was able to have animals that a lot of people don't have—chickens, pigeons, ducks, and a horse. I always loved animals. I always hoped for some type of career with them."

Elroy Masters studied biology at Phoenix College and Northern Arizona University. He started working for the Bureau of Land Management when he was still a college student. He now works as a Wildlife Management Biologist. In this photograph, Elroy is about to release a razorback sucker, an endangered species of fish, into the Colorado River.

320

Background

Ecology is the study of how living things interact with each other and with the nonliving things in their environment. Environmental science is the study of how humans affect these interactions.

Environmental science is an applied science in which problem solving is a key element. Because environmental problems are so complex, environmental scientists must be knowledgeable in many disciplines: biology, chemistry, geology, physics, meteorology, geography, economics, mathematics, sociology, natural resource management, law, and politics. Environmental science is thus a truly interdisciplinary study.

Today, Elroy and his co-workers make surveys of desert animals. They count the animals in different areas and make maps of their habitats. They locate where the animals live, what they eat, and where they build their nests and raise their young. Elroy uses that information to protect the animals when natural events or human activities threaten them.

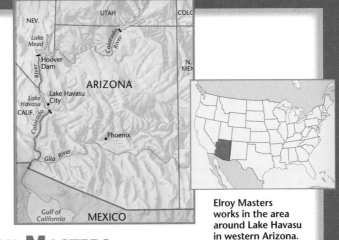

Elroy Masters works in the area around Lake Havasu in western Arizona.

TALKING WITH ELROY MASTERS

Q *What wildlife do you protect?*

A One of the neatest animals we deal with is the desert bighorn sheep. In an average summer, it can get as hot as 120 degrees here. Sometimes the heat lasts for weeks. But with the number of people living around the river, the animals are no longer able to travel to water. So we go up into the mountains to construct catchments (containers)

to collect water and store it. That way the sheep can stay in the mountains without trying to cross freeways to get to water.

We fly in big storage tanks that hold about 10,000 gallons of water. We bury them in the ground or put them on a platform. We use paint to mask them into the color of the scenery. We sometimes build a dam or put out a metal sheet to catch drizzle rain.

A catchment can hold 10,000 gallons of water (right). It is buried in the ground. The drinking container provides water for desert bighorn sheep (below), mule deer, and other wildlife.

321

- ◆ Ask students: **What is a wildlife biologist?** (*A scientist who studies living things in their environment*) You may want to share the information in Background on the previous page.
- ◆ After students read the introductory text on pages 320–321, ask: **What is a habitat?** (*A specific place where an organism lives and that provides the things the organism needs; if students are not familiar with the term, explain it for them.*) **Is the entire desert a single habitat?** (*no*) **Why not?** (*A desert has many different kinds of "specific places" where organisms live, such as sandy flatlands, rocky hills, and riverbanks. Different types of organisms live in different specific places, or habitats.*)
- ◆ Ask: **What is the major purpose of the surveys that Elroy conducts?** (*To collect information about the desert animals' habitats and behaviors*) **Why is that information important to him?** (*Knowing where the animals live and what they need in order to survive helps him know what can threaten the animals.*) **Once Elroy knows the animals' needs and how they are being threatened, what does he have to do next?** (*Figure out a way to protect the animals from these threats*) Confirm this response by emphasizing that Elroy has to solve problems. Point out that collecting data and problem solving are two important aspects of a scientist's work.
- ◆ Have students read the first section of the interview on this page. Then ask: **What is the bighorn sheep's habitat?** (*The desert mountains*) **What threat to the sheep did Elroy identify?** (*The sheep were unable to get to the river for water because human settlements and highways blocked their route.*) **How did the scientists solve this problem?** (*They supplied water for the sheep by building catchments in the mountains where the sheep live.*) **Why do you think the catchments are camouflaged to match the scenery?** (*To make the sheep and other wild animals less afraid of the artificial structures; to make the tanks look like a natural and attractive part of the desert landscape*)

- After students read the first question and answer on this page, ask: **What does Elroy mean when he says that a group of sheep in his area "aren't doing as well as expected"?** (*Students should be able to infer that many of the sheep are being killed by mountain lions.*) **How would Elroy know that?** (*From counting how many sheep there are in the group from one season or year to the next, from finding carcasses of sheep killed by lions, from seeing a lion track the sheep, and other observations*)

- After students read the second question and answer, ask: **What is a population?** (*Confirm all answers that include the idea of a group of organisms of the same kind, or species, that live in the same area. If necessary, define the term for students.*) **Why does Elroy talk about "two different populations" of desert tortoises?** (*The two groups of desert tortoises live on opposite sides of the river, so they are considered different populations.*)

- After students read the third question and answer, pose the following question: **Imagine you're conducting a survey to find out how many desert tortoises live in one particular habitat, but you don't see any tortoises above ground. What could you do to estimate the size of the tortoise population?** (*Based on the text alone, students should be able to infer that they could count the number of tortoise burrows they find. Some students may also suggest counting the separate sets of tortoise tracks they see on the ground.*) Explain that these are the methods actually used by biologists who study animals in the wild.

Q *What else are you doing to protect the bighorn sheep?*

A We're going to work with the Fish and Wildlife Department to capture and transplant bighorn sheep to a mountain range in my area. There are already sheep and some mountain lions here. But the sheep aren't doing as well as we expected. We want to bring in some bighorn sheep that are used to lions. We hope these lion-savvy sheep will teach the sheep in our area how to avoid lions. To catch the sheep, we'll use a helicopter. We'll shoot a net over the sheep and a couple of guys will jump out to secure the animals and then bring them to our herd.

The Colorado River valley is home to the Southwestern willow flycatcher and the desert tortoise.

Q *What other animals are you responsible for protecting?*

A I work a lot with desert tortoises. I'm responsible for two different populations, one on either side of the river. The tortoises live in the drier, hilly areas away from the river. Any time we go out into the field, we try to collect data. We keep track of where they've been and where they feed.

Q *How do you find the tortoises?*

A We have maps that indicate their habitat. Based on the habitat, we'll go out, walk around, and look under rocks and boulders to see if we can find a burrow. The tortoises are good diggers. They find a good boulder and go underground 10 or 12 feet. That's where they'll spend the winter.

Southwestern willow flycatcher

Desert tortoise

Q *Do you also work with birds?*

A Right now we're working with the Southwestern willow flycatcher. It's a small bird that depends on thick riparian (riverbank) vegetation to build nests and breed. The flycatcher is a migratory bird. Each spring, the birds fly to Arizona from Central America and Mexico. In the early summer months, we go out to find how many are breeding. We're trying to learn what's needed to prevent flycatchers from becoming extinct. We need to survey and protect the remaining stands of habitat. The flycatchers like to nest in thick stands of willow. But they will also build nests in another tree, salt cedar. The birds don't prefer it, but sometimes salt cedar is the only vegetation remaining, so they use it.

Q *What's threatening the riverbank plants?*

A The low water level in the river—due to human use—is a big threat. So is fire. During summer months, there are large numbers of recreational boats. Careless boaters can cause fires. Some fires get pretty big along the river and destroy a lot of the habitat where the birds nest and raise their young.

Q *Can you see the benefits of your work?*

A Yes, I see it especially in riverbank zones where areas are protected so that vegetation and trees can grow back. This year we did a new bird count in one area. Species that hadn't been seen in a while, like tanagers, showed up. Some of the migratory birds are already stopping in young cottonwood trees. That's the best gauge I've had—seeing birds returning to these new trees.

There are also quick results with the water catchments in the hills. We put the water in a year ago. They're aimed at bighorn sheep and mule deer. But now we've also got a lot of different birds—doves and quails— that come into the area.

Elroy Masters also works with populations of the California leaf-nosed bat. This bat has large ears and a leaf-shaped, turned-up nose. The bats are threatened by the loss of their habitat.

In Your Journal

Elroy Masters and his co-workers "survey" the wildlife in their area in order to learn how to protect them. Think of a wild animal that lives in a park or open area near you—squirrels, frogs, birds, even insects. Work out a step-by-step plan to draw a simple map marking the places where the animal is found.

323

◆ After students read about the birds and riverbank plants, draw their attention to the bat photograph and its caption. Ask: **What common problem threatens the survival of willow flycatchers, riverbank plants, and leaf-nosed bats in Elroy's area?** (*Loss of habitat*) **Why do you think the flycatchers' habitat is being lost?** (*Willows are being destroyed as people build along the river; accept other reasonable answers.*) **What causes habitat loss along riverbanks?** (*Lower water levels and fires—both caused by human activities*) **What do you think could destroy the bats' habitat?** (*Accept all responses without comment, then share the information in Background below.*)

◆ After students read the last question and answer, ask: **How do you think Elroy and his co-workers feel when their work is successful?** (*Satisfied, glad, relieved*) **Why do they feel that way?** (*They were able to use their knowledge and problem-solving skills to help wild animals survive.*)

In Your Journal This activity is suitable for students to do either individually or in cooperative learning groups of three or four students each. Have students share their plans with the rest of the class. Also encourage students to carry out their plans, if feasible, and share their maps and other findings with the class. (CAUTION: *Students should visit their areas with an adult. Remind students not to try to touch wild animals.*)

Background

The California leaf-nosed bat (*Macrotus californicus*) does not hibernate or migrate and cannot reduce its body temperature. To remain active year-round, the bats must have warm daytime roosts, which they find in caves, mine tunnels, and buildings.

Roosting areas are destroyed when large numbers of people visit caves, old mines, and "ghost town" buildings and when old mine entrances are sealed to prevent injury to people. New land development also reduces the bats' habitat. Bats that roost in occupied buildings are usually exterminated or kept from re-entering by blocking the entrances.

10 Solid Earth

Sections	Time	Student Edition Activities	Other Activities	
CHAPTER PROJECT **Cut-Away Earth** p. 325 TEKS: 6.14	Ongoing (2–3 weeks)	TEKS: 6.3C Check Your Progress, pp. 329, 347 Present Your Project, p. 351	TE	Chapter 10 Project Notes, pp. 324–325
1 Inside Earth pp. 326-329 TEKS: 6.14 10.1.1 Describe the conditions and forces that geologists study. 10.1.2 Explain what seismic waves are and how geologists use them to study Earth's structure. 10.1.3 List and describe the layers of Earth's interior and their characteristics.	1 period/ $\frac{1}{2}$ block	TEKS: 6.2B, C, D, E; 6.3C **Discover** How Can Scientists Find Out What's Inside Earth?, p. 326	TE	Demonstration, p. 328
2 Minerals pp. 330–339 TEKS: 6.14A 10.2.1 Explain the characteristics that a material must have in order to be considered a mineral. 10.2.2 List and describe the properties by which minerals are identified. 10.2.3 Explain two ways in which minerals form. 10.2.4 Describe how people use minerals.	2 periods/ 1 block	TEKS: 6.2B, C, D, E; 6.3C; 6.4A **Discover** How Do Minerals Break Apart?, p. 330 **Sharpen Your Skills** Inferring, p. 333 **Math Toolbox,** Calculating Density, p. 335 Science at Home, p. 337 **Skills Lab: Observing** Mineral I.D., pp. 338-339	TE TE	Building Inquiry Skills: Classifying, p. 332 Building Inquiry Skills: Comparing and Contrasting, p. 335
3 Rocks and the Rock Cycle pp. 340–348 TEKS: 6.14A 10.3.1 List and describe the three major groups of rocks. 10.3.2 Explain how geologists classify rocks. 10.3.3 Explain what igneous, sedimentary, and metamorphic rocks are and describe how they are formed. 10.3.4 Explain how the rock cycle changes rock.	2 periods/ 1 block	TEKS: 6.1A; 6.2B, C, D, E; 6.4A **Discover** What Is Earth's Crust Made Of?, p. 340 **Real-World Lab: How It Works** Rock Recycling, p. 348	TE TE TE TE LM	Building Inquiry Skills: Comparing and Contrasting, p. 341 Building Inquiry Skills: Making Models, p. 343 Demonstration, p. 344 Using the Visuals, p. 346 10, "Making Models of Sedimentary Rocks"
Study Guide/Chapter Assessment pp. 349–351	1 period/ $\frac{1}{2}$ block	PLM Provides blackline masters for Probeware labs	ISAB	Provides teaching and review of all inquiry skills

Key: **CTB** Computer Test Bank
CUT Chapter and Unit Tests
ELL Teacher's ELL Handbook

CHAPTER PLANNING GUIDE

 The Resource Pro® CD-ROM provides flexibility for planning the instruction for any type of schedule.

Program Resources	Assessment Strategies	Media and Technology
UR Chapter 10 Project Teacher Notes, pp. 2–3 UR Chapter 10 Project Overview and Worksheets, pp. 4–7	TE Performance Assessment: Present Your Project, p. 351 TE Check Your Progress, pp. 329, 347 UR Chapter 10 Project Scoring Rubric, p. 8	Science Explorer at www.phschool.com Student Edition on Audio CD, English-Spanish, Chapter 10
UR 10-1 Section Lesson Plan, p. 9 UR 10-1 Section Summary, p. 10 UR 10-1 Review and Reinforce, p. 11 UR 10-1 Enrich, p. 12	SE Section 1 Review, p. 329 TE Ongoing Assessment, pp. 327 TE Performance Assessment, p. 329	Earth Science Videodisc, Unit 2, Side 1, "A Trip Through the Earth" Videotape Grade 6, Unit 4, "A Trip Through the Earth" Transparency 48, "Earth's Interior"
UR 10-2 Section Lesson Plan, p. 13 UR 10-2 Section Summary, p. 14 UR 10-2 Review and Reinforce, p. 15 UR 10-2 Enrich, p. 16 UR Skills Lab blackline masters, pp. 21–23	SE Section 2 Review, p. 337 TE Ongoing Assessment, pp. 331, 333, 335 TE Performance Assessment, p. 337	Earth Science Videodisc, Unit 3, Side 1, "What A Gem!" Videotape Grade 6, Unit 4, "What A Gem!" Lab Activity Videotapes, Tape 3 Transparency 49, "Mohs Hardness Scale"
UR 10-3 Section Lesson Plan, p. 17 UR 10-3 Section Summary, p. 18 UR 10-3 Review and Reinforce, p. 19 UR 10-3 Enrich, p. 20 UR Real-World Lab blackline masters, pp. 24–25	SE Section 3 Review, p. 347 TE Ongoing Assessment, pp. 341, 343, 345 TE Performance Assessment, p. 347	Lab Activity Videotapes, Tape 3 Transparency 50, "The Rock Cycle"
ELL Provides multiple strategies for English language learners GRSW Provides worksheets to promote student comprehension of content RCA Provides strategies to improve science reading skills	SE Chapter 10 Study Guide/Assessment, pp. 349–351 PA Chapter 10 Assessment, pp. 32–34 CUT Chapter 10 Test, pp. 52–55 CTB Chapter 10 Test PHAS Provides standardized test preparation	Chapter 10 Computer Test Bank, Chapter 10 Test

GRSW Guided Reading and Study Workbook
ISAB Inquiry Skills Activity Book
LM Laboratory Manual

PA Performance Assessment
PHAS Prentice Hall Assessment System
PLM Probeware Lab Manual

RCA Reading in the Content Area
SE Student Edition

TE Teacher's Edition
UR Unit Resources

Student Edition Activities Planner

ACTIVITY	Time (minutes)	Materials — Quantities for one work group	Skills
Section 1			
Discover, p. 326	10	**Nonconsumable** spherical object	Posing Questions
Section 2			
Discover, p. 330	10	**Consumable** clay, plastic knife **Nonconsumable** ruler, rolling pin	Observing
Sharpen Your Skills, p. 333	10	**Nonconsumable** glass marble, emery board, penny, paperclip	Inferring
Math Toolbox, p. 335	10	No special materials are required.	Calculating
Science at Home, p. 337	home	**Consumable** ice cube, teaspoon of salt **Nonconsumable** charcoal, penny, glass marble	Classifying
Skills Lab, p. 338–339	40	**Consumable** vinegar **Nonconsumable** samples of quartz, pyrite, hematite, calcite, talc, magnetite, or halite, hand lens, penny, iron nail, scissors, magnet, hardness point kit (optional), streak plate, plastic dropper	Observing, Creating Data Tables, Classifying
Section 3			
Discover, p. 340	10	**Nonconsumable** 3 rocks, hand lens	Forming Operational Definitions
Try This, p. 342	10	**Nonconsumable** rock samples, hand lens	Classifying
Real-World Lab, p. 348	40	**Nonconsumable** 10 rocks, hand lens, computer (optional)	Observing, Creating Data Tables, Classifying, Inferring

A list of all materials required for the Student Edition activities can be found on pages T43–T49. You can obtain information about ordering materials by calling 1-800-848-9500 or by accessing the Science Explorer Internet site at **www.phschool.com**.

Texas Essential Knowledge and Skills

(6.1) Scientific processes. The student conducts field and laboratory investigations using safe, environmentally appropriate, and ethical practices. *(Section 3)*
The student is expected to:
(A) demonstrate safe practices during field and laboratory investigations.

(6.2) Scientific processes. The student uses scientific inquiry methods during field and laboratory investigations. *(Sections 1, 2, 3)*
The student is expected to:
(B) collect data by observing and measuring;
(C) analyze and interpret information to construct reasonable explanations from direct and indirect evidence;
(D) communicate valid conclusions; and
(E) construct graphs, tables, maps, and charts using tools including computers to organize, examine, and evaluate data.

(6.3) Scientific processes. The student uses critical thinking and scientific problem solving to make informed decisions. *(Project; Sections 1, 2)*
The student is expected to:
(C) represent the natural world using models and identify their limitations.

(6.4) Scientific processes. The student knows how to use a variety of tools and methods to conduct science inquiry. *(Sections 2, 3)*
The student is expected to:
(A) collect, analyze, and record information using tools including beakers, petri dishes, meter sticks, graduated cylinders, weather instruments, timing devices, hot plates, test tubes, safety goggles, spring scales, magnets, balances, microscopes, telescopes, thermometers, calculators, field equipment, compasses, computers, and computer probes.

(6.14) Science concepts. The student knows the structures and functions of Earth systems. *(Project; Sections 1, 2, 3)*
The student is expected to:
(A) summarize the rock cycle.

Take It to the Net

 Interactive text at www.phschool.com

Science Explorer comes alive with iText.

- **Complete student text** is accessible from any computer with Internet access or a CD-ROM drive.

- **Animations, simulations, and videos** enhance student understanding and retention of concepts.

- **Self-tests and online study tools** assess student understanding.

- **Teacher management tools** help you make the most of this valuable resource.

STAY CURRENT with **SCIENCE NEWS**®

Find out the latest research and information about rocks and minerals at **www.phschool.com**.

Go to **www.phschool.com**. Select Texas on the navigation bar. Click on the Science icon. Then click on <u>Science Explorer</u> under PH@school.

Cutaway Earth

TEKS: 6.3C; 6.14

When most students think of what's under the surface of Earth, they generally think of a static ball of dirt and rock, unchanging through time. In this chapter, they will be introduced to the concepts of layers of Earth and plate tectonics. The Chapter 10 Project will reinforce their understanding of Earth's interior and its physical composition and features.

Purpose Students will make sketches of their three-dimensional model of Earth's interior. Then, within a group they will come to a final design for a model of Earth and build it to scale. In doing so, they will gain a better understanding of the structure of Earth.

Skills Focus After completing the Chapter 10 Project, students will be able to
- apply the concepts learned in the chapter to a model of Earth's interior;
- interpret data to make their model to scale;
- design and make a model of Earth's interior;
- communicate the features of their model in a presentation to the class.

Project Time Line The entire project will require about three weeks. Depending on how much class time students can spend working on the project each day, about two days may be required for each of the following phases.
- Make individual sketches of a possible three-dimensional model of Earth's interior.
- Take the sketches to a group meeting, in which all sketches can be considered in thinking about a final design.
- Discuss with the group possible materials in making the model.
- Experiment with possible materials and decide which might work best.
- Revise individual sketches to show the composition, temperature, and pressure of Earth's layers.
- Take the second set of sketches to a group meeting, come to a consensus on a model design, and construct the model.

10 Solid Earth

This rock formation in northern Argentina is part of Earth's outer layer, the crust.

WEB ACTIVITY
www.phschool.com

1 **Inside Earth**
Discover How Can Scientists Find Out What's Inside Earth?

2 **Minerals**
Discover How Do Minerals Break Apart?
Skills Lab Mineral I.D.

3 **Rocks and the Rock Cycle**
Discover What Is Earth's Crust Made Of?
Real-World Lab Rock Recycling

- Make a presentation to the class, explaining what the model shows about the features of Earth's interior.

For more detailed information on planning and supervising the chapter project, see Chapter 10 Project Teacher Notes, pages 2–3 in Unit 4 Resources.

Suggested Shortcuts You can make this project shorter and less involved in one of the following ways.

- Have students make their individual sketches and then design a model in their groups. Then invite the class as a whole to decide on a final design, incorporating the best aspects of all the groups' plans. Finally, have volunteers make the actual model in their free time.
- Have students individually complete the two worksheets. The final product would be a detailed sketch of Earth's interior by each student.

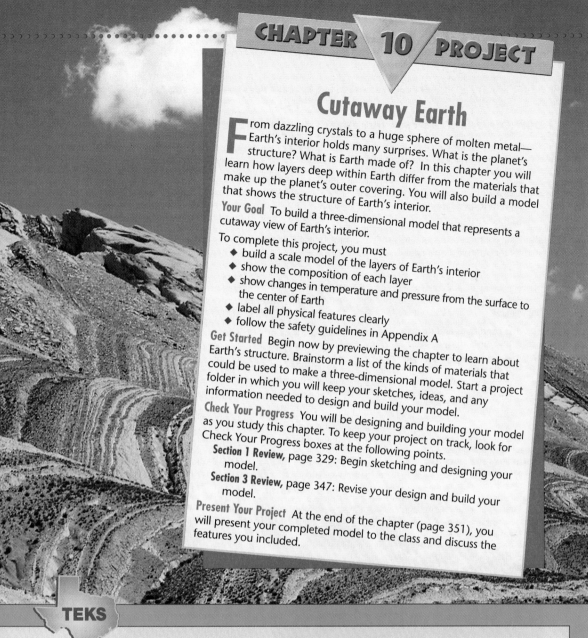

CHAPTER 10 PROJECT

Cutaway Earth

From dazzling crystals to a huge sphere of molten metal—Earth's interior holds many surprises. What is the planet's structure? What is Earth made of? In this chapter you will learn how layers deep within Earth differ from the materials that make up the planet's outer covering. You will also build a model that shows the structure of Earth's interior.

Your Goal To build a three-dimensional model that represents a cutaway view of Earth's interior.

To complete this project, you must

◆ build a scale model of the layers of Earth's interior
◆ show the composition of each layer
◆ show changes in temperature and pressure from the surface to the center of Earth
◆ label all physical features clearly
◆ follow the safety guidelines in Appendix A

Get Started Begin now by previewing the chapter to learn about Earth's structure. Brainstorm a list of the kinds of materials that could be used to make a three-dimensional model. Start a project folder in which you will keep your sketches, ideas, and any information needed to design and build your model.

Check Your Progress You will be designing and building your model as you study this chapter. To keep your project on track, look for Check Your Progress boxes at the following points.

Section 1 Review, page 329: Begin sketching and designing your model.

Section 3 Review, page 347: Revise your design and build your model.

Present Your Project At the end of the chapter (page 351), you will present your completed model to the class and discuss the features you included.

 TEKS

In addition to process TEKS, this chapter addresses these concept TEKS as they relate to the chapter's topics.

(6.14) The student knows the structures and functions of Earth systems.
The student is expected to:
(A) summarize the rock cycle.

Program Resources

◆ **Unit 4 Resources** Chapter 10 Project Teacher Notes, pp. 2–3; Chapter 10 Project Overview and Worksheets, pp. 4–7

Media and Technology

Student Edition on Audio CD
English-Spanish, Chapter 10

 **WEB ACTIVITY** **www.phschool.com**

You will find an Internet activity, chapter self-tests for students, and links to other chapter topics at this site.

◆ Challenge groups to make a detailed, color poster of Earth's interior instead of a model.

Possible Materials A variety of materials could be used for the model. These include papier-mâché, modeling clay, chicken wire, cardboard, and wood blocks. Groups may also think of other materials to use. Also provide paints, paint brushes, and permanent markers.

Launching the Project To introduce this project, show students a large world globe and ask: **If the inside of this globe reflected Earth's interior as well as it reflects Earth's surface, what would it show when cut in half?** *(Students might mention dirt, water, and rock.)* Tell them that in this chapter, they will learn that Earth's interior has several layers, each with different characteristics. Explain that in this project, students will work in groups to make a model of Earth's interior. Then ask: **What kinds of materials are good for making three-dimensional models?** *(Students might mention a variety of materials, including clay and papier mâché.)* Then mention that they should be thinking of such materials in order to contribute to a group design for a model of Earth's interior. To help students get started, pass out Chapter 10 Project Student Overview and Worksheets, pages 4–7 in Unit 4 Resources. You may also wish to pass out the Chapter 10 Project Scoring Rubric, page 8, at this time.

Performance Assessment

Use the Chapter 10 Project Scoring Rubric on page 8 in Unit 4 Resources to assess students' work. Students will be assessed on

◆ how well they make their sketches and plan their models;
◆ how well they incorporate the required features and create an attractive model of Earth's interior;
◆ how effectively they present and explain the model to the class;
◆ how well they work in the group and how much they contribute to the group's effort.

TEKS: 6.2B, C, D, E; 6.3C; 6.14

Objectives

After completing the lesson, students will be able to

◆ describe the conditions and forces that geologists study;

◆ explain what seismic waves are and how geologists use them to study Earth's structure;

◆ list and describe the layers of Earth's interior and their characteristics.

1 Engage/Explore

Activating Prior Knowledge

Ask students to describe situations in which they have dug below the ground surface or observed others doing so. They might mention digging a garden or observing a backhoe digging at a construction site. Ask: **What did you observe below the surface?** *(Most students will describe dirt and rock.)* **If you could dig to the center of Earth, what kind of material would you expect to see?** *(Some students might mentions dirt, rock, water, or oil. Accept all reasonable responses.)*

DISCOVER

Skills Focus posing questions

Materials *spherical object*

Time 10 minutes

Tips Make sure the surface layers of the spherical objects are opaque. Try to provide students with spherical objects in a variety of materials.

Expected Outcome Student may suggest that they are able to directly observe the surface features of the sphere and measure its mass and circumference. Characteristics that cannot be directly observed and measured may include the structure and compostion of its interior.

Think It Over Answers will vary depending on the questions posed. Most questions about Earth's surface can be answered based on direct observation, whereas those about Earth's deep interior must be answered by indirect evidence.

326

SECTION 1 Inside Earth

DISCOVER •••••••••••••••••••••••••• ACTIVITY

How Can Scientists Find Out What's Inside Earth?

1. Your teacher will give you a spherical object, such as a sports ball. You can think of the sphere as a model of planet Earth.

2. Carefully observe your sphere. What characteristics of the sphere can you observe and measure directly?

3. What characteristics of the sphere cannot be directly observed and measured?

Think It Over

Posing Questions In your notebook, list several questions that you have about Earth. Which of these questions could you answer based on direct observation? Which questions would need to be answered based on indirect evidence?

GUIDE FOR READING

◆ What conditions and forces do geologists study?

◆ What are the major layers of Earth's interior?

Reading Tip As you read, make a list of Earth's layers. Write a sentence about each layer.

Key Terms rock • crust
• geology • geologist
• seismic wave • inner core
• outer core • mantle
• lithosphere

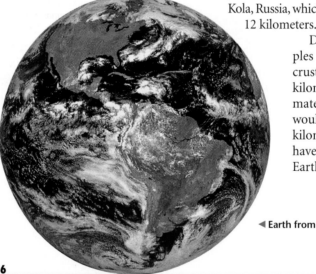

◀ Earth from space

Y ou probably already know something about Earth's surface. Beneath the buildings, grass, and roads around your home and school there is a layer of soil and rock. **Rock** is the material that makes up Earth's hard outer surface. A layer of solid rock called the **crust** surrounds Earth's surface like the tough shell of a walnut.

But what's inside Earth? Scientists have drilled deep holes into the crust to study the rocks below the surface. The scientists use a drill with diamond teeth that cuts a thin cylinder of rock called a core. The core is then brought to the surface. For example, equipment carried by the drillship *JOIDES Resolution* drilled about two kilometers into the crust beneath the ocean floor. On land, scientists have drilled the "superdeep" borehole in Kola, Russia, which reached a depth of approximately 12 kilometers.

Drilling helps scientists obtain samples of the rock that makes up the crust, which ranges from about 5 to 40 kilometers in thickness. But to sample material from Earth's center, you would need to drill down nearly 6,400 kilometers! Fortunately, scientists also have other ways of learning about Earth's interior.

326

READING STRATEGIES

Reading Tip Students' lists should include the crust, mantle, outer core and inner core. Typical sentences about the layers might include the following: The crust is a layer of solid rock that surrounds Earth's surface, The inner core consists of hot, solid metal. The outer core is made of melted iron and nickel. The mantle is a hot but mostly solid layer surrounding the core.

Compare/Contrast Table Suggest that students construct a three-column table to summarize information about Earth's layers. In the first column students should list Earth's layers. In the second column, they can describe how each layer is like any of the other layers. In the third column, they can describe how each layer differs from the other layers.

The Science of Geology

Learning about Earth's interior is one goal of the science of geology. **Geology** is the study of planet Earth, including Earth's surface and interior. Scientists who study Earth and the processes that have shaped Earth over time are called **geologists.** Geologists also study the physical and chemical characteristics of minerals and rocks.

Why do geologists study Earth's interior? They want to know what materials make up Earth. They try to determine how those materials are arranged beneath the surface. **Geologists study physical conditions, such as temperature and pressure, inside Earth. Geologists also study the forces inside Earth that affect the surface.** You will learn about some of these forces in this chapter and in Chapter 11.

You know that drilling has provided geologists with some data on Earth's crust. But most of what geologists know about the interior below the crust is based on indirect evidence. Suppose a friend or relative gave you a birthday gift in a wrapped box. You might try tapping and shaking it to obtain indirect evidence of its content. Based on this evidence, you might be able to infer what was in the box.

In a similar way, geologists use indirect evidence from seismic waves to learn about Earth's interior. **Seismic waves** are vibrations that travel through Earth every time an earthquake shakes the ground. As seismic waves travel through Earth, they may be slowed down, bent, or reflected by different structures inside Earth. Geologists have recorded these different paths taken by seismic waves. From this evidence, they have inferred Earth's composition and structure.

☑ *Checkpoint* What is a geologist?

Figure 1 Geologists' work often takes them into the field. **(A)** This geologist is using a rock hammer to obtain a sample of rock. **(B)** These geologists are observing red-hot, molten lava near Mt. Kilauea volcano in Hawaii. *Posing Questions If you were a geologist, what questions would you ask about the rocks in each photo?*

Answers to Self-Assessment

Caption Question

Figure 1 Photo A: Students may ask how the rocks formed, what they are made of, and how old they are. Photo B: Students may ask what the rocks are made of and how hot the lava is.

☑ *Checkpoint*

A geologist studies Earth and the processes that have shaped it over time.

---

2 Facilitate

The Science of Geology

Including All Students

To help students who have not mastered written English, have pairs of students of differing abilities work together to list general subjects or specific things that geologists study. As a class, review and add to the lists. **learning modality: verbal**

Real-Life Learning

Encourage students to prepare a list of questions they would like answered by a professional geologist, such as questions about the training required to become a geologist or what it is like being one. Then have students pose their questions in a letter to a geologist sent by mail or the internet. Students can read their letters and responses to the class. **learning modality: verbal**

Using the Visuals: Figure 1

Ask students: **What are the geologists in each photograph doing?** *(Collecting a rock sample and observing molten lava)* **Why might the geologists be doing these activities?** *(Accept all reasonable responses. Students might suggest that geologists collect rocks to study their physical and chemical characteristics, and observe lava to find out how volcanoes form.)* **learning modality: visual**

Ongoing Assessment

Oral Presentation Have students describe two ways in which geologists learn about Earth's interior.

Earth's Interior

Demonstration

Materials *hard-boiled egg, knife*

Time 5 minutes

Slice a hard-boiled egg in half crosswise. Hold up the cross-section for students to see. Ask students to compare what they see to the layers of Earth. Ask: **Which part of the egg is like Earth's core? Mantle? Crust?** *(The yolk is like the core; the white is like the mantle; the shell is like the crust.)* Ask: **How are the layers of the egg different from the layers of Earth?** *(Earth's core has two layers, but you can't see two layers in the egg yolk.)* **learning modality: visual**

Using the Visuals: Figure 3

Provide students with calculators. Have them use the thickness of Earth's layers shown to determine the total radius of Earth. Suggest they use the maximum thickness of the crust (6,390 km) in their calculations. Then have students calculate the percentage of Earth's radius represented by all layers shown in the diagram, again using the maximum thickness of the crust in their calculations. *(Crust, 0.6%; lithosphere, 1.6%; mantle, 45%; outer core, 35%; inner core, 19%)* **learning modality: logical/mathematical**

Figure 2 The Canadian Shield covers a large part of northern North America. It is a region where the rock that makes up much of Earth's crust can often be seen at the surface.

Earth's Interior

If you could slice Earth in half, you would see that the planet is made up of layers like an onion. Each layer completely surrounds the layer beneath it. **The major layers that make up Earth are the inner core, outer core, mantle, and lithosphere. The lithosphere includes the crust and the uppermost part of the mantle.** These layers differ in composition or physical conditions. For example, temperature and pressure increase with depth beneath Earth's surface. You may be surprised to learn that the center of Earth is as hot as the surface of the sun!

Core As you can see in Figure 3, the dense core forms the center of Earth. The core is divided into two layers. The **inner core** is a sphere of hot, solid metal. Surrounding the inner core is the liquid **outer core.** The core is extremely hot—hot enough to melt the metal in the outer core. But pressure in the inner core is so great that it remains solid.

Most scientists accept the hypothesis that both parts of the core are made of iron and nickel. But some scientists also have found data suggesting that the density of Earth's core is a bit less than it would be if the core were made only of iron and nickel. Therefore, they hypothesize that the core also contains less-dense elements such as oxygen, sulfur, and silicon. Scientists must seek additional data before they decide whether to accept either hypothesis—or develop a new hypothesis about the composition of Earth's core.

Scientists hypothesize that circulation of molten metal within Earth's core helps to create a magnetic field. As a result, Earth has an immense magnetic field surrounding it, just as there is a magnetic field around a bar magnet. Earth's magnetic field is still not completely understood. But the fact that Earth has a magnetic field explains why a compass works as it does. The poles of the magnetized needle on the compass align themselves with Earth's magnetic field.

☑ *Checkpoint* *What type of material makes up Earth's core?*

Background

Facts and Figures The first convincing evidence of Earth's layering was presented in 1909 by Yugoslavian seismologist Andrija Mohorovičić. After carefully examining recordings of seismic waves, called seismograms, Mohorovičić discovered a boundary separating rocks of the crust from those of a different composition in the underlying mantle. This boundary was named in his honor the *Mohorovičić discontinuity,* or *Moho* for short.

A few years later, the boundary between the mantle and core was discover by German seismologist Beno Gutenberg, also based on seismic wave evidence. Although the boundary between the inner and outer core was identified earlier, it was not accurately located until the early 1960s as a result of seismic waves generated from underground nuclear testing conducted in Nevada.

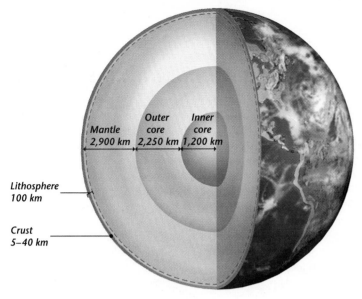

Mantle 2,900 km   Outer core 2,250 km   Inner core 1,200 km

Lithosphere 100 km

Crust 5–40 km

Figure 3 Parts of Earth's crust are covered with ice. But scientists estimate that the temperature of the core could be as hot as 5000° C. Pressure also increases greatly between the crust and Earth's center. *Interpreting Diagrams Which layer of Earth's interior is the thickest?*

Mantle Surrounding the core is a thick layer called the **mantle.** The mantle is made of hot but mostly solid material. Mantle material is less dense than the material that makes up the core. In a few places, volcanoes have brought up material from a depth of about 150 kilometers in the mantle.

Toward the upper part of the mantle is a layer of soft but solid material a few hundred kilometers thick. Over time, this material can flow very slowly, like road tar softened by the heat of the sun.

Lithosphere and Crust Like a giant golf ball, Earth has a rigid outer covering—the **lithosphere.** The crust is the thin, rock layer of the lithosphere that forms Earth's surface. The lithosphere also includes the uppermost part of the mantle down to a depth of about 100 kilometers.

 Section 1 Review

1. What do geologists study about Earth's interior?
2. Describe the characteristics and structure of the different layers of Earth.
3. **Thinking Critically Inferring** The outer core is liquid, and the lithosphere is solid. What can be inferred about the temperature of the mantle, which contains a layer that can flow slowly?
4. **Thinking Critically Posing Questions** What questions would you want to answer before developing a new hypothesis about the composition of the core?

Check Your Progress **CHAPTER PROJECT**

Begin by drawing a sketch of your three-dimensional model of Earth. Think about how you will show the thicknesses of Earth's different layers at the correct scale. What materials can you use for building your model? Experiment with materials that might work well for showing the physical composition of Earth's layers.

Program Resources

◆ **Unit 4 Resources** 10-1 Review and Reinforce, p. 11; 10-1 Enrich, p. 12

Media and Technology

 Transparencies "Earth's Interior," Transparency 48

Earth Science Videodisc Unit 2, Side 1, "A Trip Through the Earth"   Chapter 1

Answers to Self-Assessment

Caption Question

Figure 3 The mantle is the thickest layer.

✓ *Checkpoint*

Earth's core is made up of the elements iron and nickel.

---

3 Assess

Section 1 Review Answers

1. Geologists study physical conditions inside Earth and the forces inside Earth that affect the surface.

2. The inner core is solid while the outer core is liquid. The mantle is a thick layer surrounding the core. It is made of hot but mostly solid material that is less dense than the material of the core. Its upper part consists of soft, but solid, material that can flow. The lithosphere is the rigid outer covering of Earth that includes the crust and uppermost mantle.

3. The temperature of the mantle is cooler than the outer core, but hotter than the lithosphere.

4. Accept all reasonable responses. Students may pose questions asking how temperature and pressure vary from the outer core to the inner core, or how the melting point of different elements in the core might be affected by changing temperature and pressure.

Check Your Progress **CHAPTER PROJECT**

To help you identify students having difficulty grasping the concepts related to Earth's interior, review student sketches of models. Clarify any misconceptions before the group meeting. Then, during the group meeting, encourage participation by all members. Have students brainstorm a list of possible materials for the model, then rule out unsuitable materials through experimentation with materials on the list.

Performance Assessment

Drawing Have students make a poster that shows Earth sliced in half to reveal its layers. Students should label and briefly describe the crust, mantle, inner core, and outer core.

TEKS: 6.2B, C, D, E; 6.3C; 6.4A; 6.14A

Objectives

After completing the lesson, students will be able to

♦ explain the characteristics that a material must have in order to be considered a mineral;

♦ list and describe the properties by which minerals are identified;

♦ explain two ways in which minerals form;

♦ describe how people use minerals.

1 Engage/Explore

Activating Prior Knowledge

Ask students to name any minerals they can think of. *(Some students may know that gemstones and precious metals are minerals, and name diamond, ruby, gold, and silver. They may also mention dietary minerals, such as iron and zinc.)* Ask: **What do you think makes a substance a mineral?** *(Accept all reasonable responses. Some students may know that minerals are solid and made of crystals.)*

••••••• DISCOVER •••••••

Skills Focus observing
Materials *clay, ruler, rolling pin, plastic knife*
Time 10 minutes
Tips Make sure students hold the second cube in such a way that they pull perpendicular to the plane of each layer rather than parallel to it.
Expected Outcome The first cube pulls apart along an irregular surface and models fracture, whereas the second cube pulls apart along its flat layers and models cleavage.
Think It Over Minerals break apart along irregular surfaces and along flat surfaces.

DISCOVER •••••••••••••••••••••••••••••••• ACTIVITY

How Do Minerals Break Apart?

1. Mold some clay into a cube about 3 cm on a side.

2. Roll an equal amount of clay into a sheet about 0.5 cm thick. Cut the sheet of clay into six squares about 3 cm on a side.

3. Assemble the squares to form a second cube made up of layers of clay. Gently press the layers so that they hold together.

4. Holding the first cube between your fingers, pull it apart into two pieces.

5. Hold the second cube so that the layers are vertical and perpendicular to your body. Then pull the second cube apart.

6. Compare the surfaces along which the two cubes came apart. How are they similar? How are they different?

Think It Over
Observing The two cubes are models of two groups of minerals that break apart in different ways. Based on your observations, what might be two ways that minerals can break apart?

GUIDE FOR READING

♦ What is a mineral?

♦ What are some properties of minerals?

♦ How do minerals form?

Reading Tip Before you read, use the section headings to make an outline. Leave space in your outline to take notes.

Key Terms mineral • crystal • streak • luster • cleavage • fracture • density • magma • lava • vein • gemstone

You have probably seen a sieve in your kitchen at home. A sieve is made of wire mesh. Particles can pass through the sieve only if they are smaller than the openings in the mesh. Now imagine a sieve that can separate different molecules. This sieve allows some molecules to pass, but traps or absorbs others. If you're wondering whether there really are any materials that can do this—meet the zeolites!

Zeolites are a group of materials that can act like a sieve to separate molecules of different sizes. Zeolites are useful for many purposes. In your home, you might find zeolites in water purifiers, water softeners, and deodorizers. Some cities add zeolites to their landfills to absorb polluting liquids. Oil refineries and other industries use zeolites to speed up chemical changes.

Figure 4 The light-colored crystals are natrolite, which is one of the zeolite minerals.

READING STRATEGIES

Reading Tip Help students preview the section to identify the main headings. Also point out subheadings, which give clues to the main ideas that fall under the main headings. Outlines may begin as shown here.

I. What Is a Mineral?
  A. Solid
  B. Naturally Occuring
  C. Crystal Structure
  D. Definite Chemical Composition
II. Identifying Minerals

What Is a Mineral?

You can find zeolites on Earth's surface. Zeolites sometimes occur in areas where geologists think there was once a lake. Millions of years ago, material from a volcano filled in the lake bed. Then chemicals in the lake water changed some of the volcanic material into hard, glassy particles—zeolites. But what are these particles? Zeolites are minerals.

Minerals come in many colors and shapes. Minerals can be as rare as a precious diamond. Or they can be as common as halite, which you know as table salt. Geologists have identified more than 3,000 different minerals. But all of these minerals share certain characteristics. **A mineral is a solid, inorganic material that forms naturally on or beneath Earth's surface. Almost all minerals have a crystal structure. Each mineral also has a definite chemical composition.** The example of halite may help you to understand these characteristics of minerals.

Solid If you pour some halite into the palm of your hand, you can see that it is made up of small, solid particles. Recall that a solid is a material with a definite volume and a definite shape. Minerals generally remain solid under ordinary conditions on Earth's surface. But high temperatures inside Earth can cause minerals deep beneath the surface to melt.

Inorganic Halite is inorganic. A material that is inorganic did not arise from a living thing. Unlike halite, coal is not a mineral, because coal is formed from the remains of plants that lived millions of years ago.

Naturally Occurring A substance that is naturally occurring is the result of processes that take place in the natural world. For example, halite often occurs naturally in areas once occupied by seas. Deposits of halite were left behind when the sea water evaporated. Materials made by people, such as cement, plastic, glass, and steel, are not minerals.

Wulfenite

Coal

Figure 5 A substance must be naturally occurring to be a mineral. The yellow crystals of the mineral wulfenite (left) form thin, rectangular plates. Coal (right) is not considered a mineral because it is formed from once-living things. *Comparing and Contrasting How are the samples of wulfenite and coal similar? How are they different?*

---

2 Facilitate

What Is a Mineral?

Including All Students
Content Mastery

Explain to students that, in order to be classified as a mineral, a substance must meet five criteria. Write the numbers one through five on the board and, beside each number, have a different student volunteer write one characteristic of a mineral. Tell students that, even if a substance meets four of the five characteristics, it is not a mineral.
learning modality: verbal

Ongoing Assessment

Writing and Drawing Have students create a poster that describes and illustrates what a mineral is.

Program Resources

◆ **Unit 4 Resources** 10-2 Lesson Plan, p. 13; 10-2 Section Summary, p. 14
◆ **Guided Reading and Study Workbook** 10-2

Answers to Self-Assessment

Caption Question

Figure 5 Wulfenite and coal are similar in that they are both solid substances that formed naturally. Apart from the obvious difference in color, they differ in that wulfenite has a crystal structure and formed from inorganic materials, but coal lacks a crystal structure and formed from the remains of once-living things.

What Is a Mineral?, continued

Building Inquiry Skills: Classifying

Provide students with samples of coal such as lignite, or brown coal, which contains obvious organic materials. Have them examine the samples with a hand lens and sketch what they see. Then ask: **Is coal a mineral? Why or why not?** *(It is not a mineral. Since it contains plant remains, it is not inorganic.)* **learning modality: visual**

Using the Visuals: Figure 6

Ask students: **What minerals are shown in the photographs?** *(Sphalerite, microcline feldspar, and quartz)* **In what state do these minerals occur?** *(solid)* **If these minerals were to melt under high temperatures, would they still be minerals? Why or why not?** *(They would no longer be minerals because they would be liquid.)* **learning modality: visual**

Using the Visuals: Figure 7

Ask students to describe what a cube is. Make sure they understand that a cube is a solid shape in which the length, width, and height are equal. Then ask: **How might you identify a crystal of halite?** *(By its cubic crystal shape, or by the fact that, when broken, its pieces have a cubic shape)* **How would you expect the shape of two different crystals of halite to compare?** *(Both would be cubic in shape.)* **learning modality: visual**

Language Arts Connection

Some student may be familiar with the use of the term *crystal* meaning clear, brilliant glass or objects such as bowls and goblets made of such glass. Differentiate between this usage and the use of *crystal* as a natural shape formed by the repeating pattern of the atoms of a mineral. **learning modality: verbal**

Figure 6 Each of these minerals has its own combination of crystal structure and chemical composition. The red crystals of sphalerite (left) contain zinc and sulfur. Microcline feldspar (middle) is made up of potassium, aluminum, silicon, and oxgen. Quartz (right) is a compound made of silicon dioxide.

Microcline feldspar

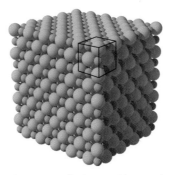

Figure 7 Halite has a cubic crystal structure. A mineral's crystal structure remains the same even when the mineral is broken into pieces.

Crystal Structure If you look at Figure 7, you can see that the atoms in halite line up in a regular way. The atoms that make up a mineral line up in a pattern that repeats over and over again. The repeating pattern of a mineral's atoms forms a solid called a **crystal.** Halite crystals are cubic, that is, shaped like a cube. You can break a large piece of halite into smaller pieces. But the smaller halite pieces still have a cubic crystal structure.

Other minerals have crystal structures that differ from halite's structure. Geologists classify crystals according to the number of faces, or sides, on the crystal. They also measure the angle at which the faces meet. But all the crystals of a particular mineral have the same crystal structure.

Definite Chemical Composition What does it mean to say that a mineral has a definite chemical composition? Every mineral is made up of certain elements in definite proportions. For example, the mineral halite is made up of one atom of sodium for every atom of chlorine. Other minerals can be compounds of several elements. A few minerals are made up of only one element. Copper, silver, gold, and sulfur sometimes occur naturally in a pure form. These pure elements are also considered minerals.

✓ *Checkpoint* *What characteristics do all minerals share?*

332

Identifying Minerals

Suppose that you are a geologist exploring a cave. In the cave, you find crystals of a mineral you have never seen before. To learn about this new mineral you test to determine its properties. A mineral's properties are the characteristics of the mineral that make it different from other minerals. **Some properties of minerals include hardness, color, streak, luster, how a mineral breaks apart, and density.** Geologists use a variety of tests to determine a mineral's properties.

Hardness Talc is a mineral that is so soft, you can scratch it with a fingernail. But nothing can scratch the hardest mineral, diamond. To classify minerals according to their hardness, geologists use the Mohs hardness scale. The scale was invented nearly 200 years ago by a German geologist named Friedrich Mohs.

There are ten minerals on the Mohs scale. Talc, the first and softest mineral on the scale, has a hardness of 1. As you can see in Figure 8, the scale continues up to diamond, with a hardness of 10.

Geologists use a scratch test to determine the hardness of minerals on the Mohs scale. The scratch test compares the hardness of a mineral sample with the minerals on the scale. If you tested the hardness of a piece of halite, you would find that halite can scratch gypsum. Halite, however, cannot scratch calcite. Therefore, halite's hardness is between the hardness of gypsum and calcite, or between 2 and 3 on the Mohs scale.

Mohs Hardness Scale

Mineral	Rating	Testing Method
Talc	1	Softest known mineral. It flakes easily when scratched by a fingernail.
Gypsum	2	A fingernail can easily scratch it.
Calcite	3	A fingernail cannot scratch it, but a copper penny can.
Fluorite	4	A steel knife can easily scratch it.
Apatite	5	A steel knife can scratch it.
Feldspar	6	Cannot be scratched by a steel knife, but it can scratch window glass.
Quartz	7	Can scratch steel and hard glass easily.
Topaz	8	Can scratch quartz.
Corundum	9	Can scratch topaz.
Diamond	10	Hardest known mineral. Diamond can scratch all other substances.

Sharpen your Skills

Inferring

Your teacher will give you a glass marble, an emery board, a penny, and a paper clip. Carefully try to scratch the marble and the penny with one end of the paper clip. Next, using the penny, try to scratch the marble and the paper clip. Then try to scratch the marble, the penny, and the paper clip using the emery board. Based on your observations, arrange the four materials in order from softest to hardest.

Figure 8 The Mohs hardness scale rates the hardness of minerals on a scale of 1 to 10. Minerals on the scale can only scratch minerals that are rated lower on the scale. *Drawing Conclusions* You find a mineral that can be scratched by a steel knife, but not by a copper penny. What is this mineral's hardness on the Mohs scale?

Identifying Minerals

Sharpen your Skills

Inferring

Materials *glass marble, emery board, penny, paperclip*
Time 10 minutes
Tips Divide students into pairs, pairing students of differing abilities.
Expected Outcome The paper clip scratches the penny but not the marble. The penny does not scratch the marble or the paper clip. The emery board scratches the marble, penny, and paper clip. Therefore, the materials in order from softest to hardest are: copper (penny), steel (paper clip), glass (marble), emery board.
Extend Have students test other materials in the classroom such as wood, chalk, and other metals, then place these materials in the correct position on their list based on their relative hardness.
learning modality: tactile/ kinesthetic

Using the Visuals: Figure 8

Ask students to compare the hardness of topaz and corundum. *(Topaz, which has a hardness of 8, is softer than corundum, which has a harness of 9.)* Then ask: **Which of these two minerals will diamond scratch?** *(Both)* Which will feldspar scratch? Explain your answer. *(Neither; feldspar is softer than both minerals, so it will not scratch them.)*
learning modality: visual

Media and Technology

 Transparencies "Mohs Hardness Scale," Transparency 49

Answers to Self-Assessment

Caption Question
Figure 8 Greater than 3 but less than 6

✓ Checkpoint

All minerals are solid, are inorganic, are formed naturally on Earth, have a crystal structure, and have a definite chemical composition.

Ongoing Assessment

Oral Presentation Have students describe how they would go about determining the hardness of an unknown mineral.

Identifying Minerals, continued

Using the Visuals: Figure 9

Have students examine the photograph of quartz and use it to list some of the colors in which quartz occurs. *(Possible responses include clear, black, pink, purple, yellow, orange, brown, and white.)* Ask: **How might you distinguish black quartz from another black mineral, such as hornblende?** *(By comparing another property, such as density, crystal shape, or hardness)* **learning modality: visual**

Using the Visuals: Figure 10

After students have examined Figure 10, ask them: **What are the three types of luster shown?** *(metallic, satiny, and earthy)* **How would you describe each of these lusters?** *(Accept all reasonable responses. Students might describe metallic luster as shiny like a metal, satiny luster as smooth and only somewhat reflective, and earthy luster as dull or like dirt.)* **How might you expect glassy luster and pearly luster to appear?** *(Possible response: shiny like glass and milky like a pearl)* Have students describe the luster of the minerals shown in Figures 9 and 11. *(Possible responses: quartz, glassy; azurite, glassy; mica, pearly)* Refer to the **ELL Handbook** for additional teaching strategies. **learning modality: visual**

Figure 9 Quartz (left) occurs in a variety of colors. Azurite (right) is a mineral that is easily identified by its blue color.

Quartz

Azurite

Color, Streak, and Luster You may have heard the expression, "You can't judge a book by its cover." Well, you usually can't always judge a mineral by its color alone. Different forms of the same mineral may have different colors. Quartz, for example comes in a variety of colors. There are some minerals, however, that can be easily identified by color. One example is azurite, which is always bright blue.

Geologists test a mineral's streak to tell it apart from minerals with the same color. **Streak** is the color of a mineral's powder. Geologists determine a mineral's streak by rubbing the mineral on an unglazed piece of tile called a streak plate. A mineral's streak often differs from the color of a sample of that mineral. For example, gold and pyrite are both yellow minerals. Yet gold has a yellow streak, while pyrite's streak is greenish brown to black. The streak test can help you find out whether you have real gold or pyrite—also known as "fool's gold."

Geologists also use a property called luster to tell minerals apart by their appearance. **Luster** is the way a mineral reflects light from its surface. Some of the many terms used to describe luster include glassy, pearly, silky, metallic, and earthy.

Figure 10 A mineral's luster is the way its surface reflects light. Pyrite (left) has a metallic luster. One type of gypsum, called satin spar (middle), has a satiny luster. *Applying Concepts What word could you use to describe the luster of limonite (right)?*

Pyrite

Satin spar

Limonite

334

Background

Facts and Figures Fluorescence, or the tendency of a mineral to glow when exposed to ultraviolet light, is caused by impurities in the minerals known as activators. Activators respond to invisible ultraviolet light by giving off visible light in a variety of colors including yellow, green, orange, red, and blue. The mineral scheelite, for example, has a distinctive bluish-white fluorescence. This property led geologists using ultraviolet lamps in a search for scheelite to discover many commercially valuable deposits of tungsten during World War II. Since samples of a single mineral may fluoresce in several colors, and different minerals exhibit similar fluorescent colors, minerals cannot be identified by fluorescence alone.

Figure 11 Minerals that split apart evenly along flat surfaces have cleavage; minerals that break in an irregular way have fracture. Mica (left), which has cleavage, splits into thin sheets. However, quartz (right), which has fracture, breaks into irregular pieces that look like chipped glass.

Cleavage and Fracture Observing how a mineral breaks apart can also help a geologist identify the mineral. Some minerals split apart easily along flat surfaces. These minerals have a property called **cleavage.** Muscovite, a common type of mica, has cleavage. You can easily split apart muscovite into paper-thin, translucent layers using a pocketknife.

Many minerals lack cleavage. Instead, these minerals form irregular surfaces when they break apart. These minerals have the property called **fracture.** Minerals that have fracture can break apart in several ways. When quartz fractures, it looks like the surface of a thick piece of glass that has been chipped. Other minerals with fracture may produce rough, jagged surfaces.

Density Another property that geologists use to identify a mineral is density. You may recall from Chapter 2 that **density** is a measurement of how much mass is contained in a given volume. The density of a cubic centimeter of quartz, for example, is about 2.6 times the density of the same volume of water. But the density of a cubic centimeter of gold is 19.3 times the density of the same volume of water.

Other Properties of Minerals Minerals have a variety of other properties that geologists can use to identify them. For example, a mineral that contains iron may be magnetic. Minerals that contain carbon react with certain acids. A drop of vinegar reacts with the carbon in calcite, forming carbon dioxide gas. The gas bubbles up from the surface of the calcite. Some minerals glow with bright colors when placed under ultraviolet light. Such minerals are said to be fluorescent.

Quartz and a few other minerals have electrical properties. Their crystals vibrate if they come in contact with an electric current. Because of these properties, quartz crystals are used in microphones, radio transmitters and watches.

☑ *Checkpoint* *What are cleavage and fracture?*

Math TOOLBOX

Calculating Density

To calculate the density of a mineral, divide the mass of a sample by its volume.

$$\text{Density} = \frac{\text{Mass}}{\text{Volume}}$$

Suppose you have a sample of quartz, a common rock-forming mineral. The sample you have has a mass of 13 grams and a volume of 5 cubic centimeters. What is the density of that sample?

Math TOOLBOX

Calculating Density

Tips Explain to students that the unit of measure for density is grams/cubic centimeter, so no unit conversion is necessary in this example.

Expected Outcome density = 13 grams ÷ 5 cubic centimeters = 2.6 grams/cubic centimeter

Extend Ask students: **If the density of a cubic centimeter of quartz is about 2.6 times the density of the same volume of water, what is the density of water?** *(2.6 grams/cubic centimeter ÷ 2.6 = 1.0 grams/cubic centimeter)*

Building Inquiry Skills: Comparing and Contrasting

Materials *samples of calcite, galena, and pyrite of approximately the same volume*

ACTIVITY

Time 15 minutes

Explain to students that they can determine the relative densities of mineral samples of approximately the same volume by hefting, or lifting, them. Minerals that are more dense will seem heavier when hefted than those that are less dense. Have students take turns hefting samples of the minerals calcite, galena, and pyrite, and then place them in order from most dense to least dense mineral. Students should place the minerals in the following order: galena, pyrite, calcite. **learning modality: tactile/kinesthetic**

Answers to Self-Assessment

Caption Question

Figure 10 Answers may vary. Students will likely describe the luster as "earthy."

☑ *Checkpoint*

Cleavage is the mineral property of splitting apart easily along flat surfaces. Fracture is the mineral property of forming irregular surfaces when broken.

Ongoing Assessment

Writing Have students describe the mineral properties of color, streak, and luster.

How Minerals Form

Addressing Naive Conceptions

Some students may think that synthetic substances used in jewelry like cubic zirconium and plastics that are shaped or cut like gemstones are minerals. Remind students that, in order to be a mineral, a substance must form naturally on or beneath Earth's surface, which these substances do not since they are manufactured by people. **learning modality: logical/mathematical**

How People Use Minerals

EXPLORING

Texas Minerals

Have students take turns reading aloud the captions in the feature. Then make a class list of the minerals mentioned and their uses. Ask students: **Without which of these minerals would your home probably not have interior walls?** *(gypsum, which is used to make sheetrock or wallboard)* **Oil to heat the school?** *(sulfur and clay minerals)* Have students name other products they might find in and around the classroom and school that consist of or depend on the minerals on the list. Students might mention fertilizers used to grow grass in the school yard, salts used in the kitchen, and ceramic building materials. Refer to the **ELL Handbook** for additional teaching strategies. **learning modality: verbal**

Figure 12 One way minerals can form is by evaporation of solutions that contain mineral-forming material. These gypsum crystals, which formed by evaporation, look like the petals of a rose.

Figure 13 Some gemstones have become popular as birthstones—one for each month. However, one of the birthstones shown below—the pearl—is not a mineral because it is formed inside a living thing.

How Minerals Form

Have you ever made a tray of ice cubes in your home freezer? If you have, you already know something about how minerals can form. Some minerals form when a substance "freezes"—that is, changes from the liquid state to the solid state.

In general, there are two ways that minerals can form. **Many minerals form when molten material cools and hardens inside Earth or on the surface. Other minerals form when materials dissolved in water come out of solution.** Molten material inside Earth is called **magma.** Formed in the mantle, hot, liquid magma rises through the crust toward the surface. Molten material that reaches the surface is called **lava.**

When magma and lava cool and harden, crystals form. Large crystals form if cooling takes place slowly. Small crystals form if the cooling is rapid. For example, feldspar minerals form by slow cooling of magma deep beneath Earth's surface. Crystals of feldspar are large—they can range from several centimeters to a meter across. But lava that cools and hardens on the surface often forms such small crystals that you need a microscope to see them.

Sometimes, mineral-forming material dissolves in hot water beneath the surface. The water is heated by the heat of Earth's interior. As these solutions cool, the mineral-forming material comes out of solution, forming crystals of different minerals. Minerals that form from solutions often occur underground in narrow bands called **veins.** Sometimes, veins contain pure elements such as copper, silver, and gold.

Minerals can also form when a solution evaporates on Earth's surface. Halite and gypsum are two common minerals that are formed by this process.

How People Use Minerals

A **gemstone** is a mineral that is valued for its beautiful color, hardness, and glassy luster. Gemstones may be cut into gems for use in jewelry. Some gemstones are used to make fine machine parts. But minerals have many other uses.

Minerals are probably most important as the source of metals. Everything that's made of metal—from car engines to eyeglass frames—began as minerals inside Earth.

Minerals that do not contain metals are also very important in everyday life. Some medicines, building materials, electronic parts, and chemicals used in agriculture and industry contain minerals. Many useful minerals are mined in Texas. Look at *Exploring Texas Minerals* to learn what some of these minerals are and how they are used.

336

EXPLORING Texas Minerals

A mineral does not have to be a precious metal or gemstone to be of economic value. These Texas minerals have many uses.

▲ **Salt** Texas has large underground deposits of halite (sodium chloride) along the Gulf Coast.

▲ **Sulfur** Sulfur often occurs in Texas in areas where salt and oil are also found. Sulfur is used in fertilizers, medicines, petroleum refining, and many chemical processes.

▼ **Gypsum** Widely mined in Texas, gypsum goes into building materials such as the "sheetrock" used to surface inside walls.

▲ **Clay minerals** Clay minerals, which are found in Texas, are used in many kinds of ceramics and in building materials such as bricks. A clay called fuller's earth is used in refining oils and fats used in foods.

Section 2 Review

1. Define *mineral* in your own words.
2. How could you use the Mohs hardness scale to identify a mineral?
3. What is a mineral's streak? How can streak be helpful in identifying a mineral?
4. Describe two ways in which minerals can form.
5. **Thinking Critically Applying Concepts** Petroleum (oil) is a naturally occurring substance from inside Earth. Can petroleum be considered a mineral? Explain.

Science at Home

Pick the Mineral Gather at least three of the following materials: an ice cube, a piece of charcoal, a teaspoon of salt, and a penny. Then give family members your definition of a mineral. Ask family members to decide, based on your definition, which materials are, or contain, minerals. Discuss their choices based on what you have learned about minerals.

---

3 Assess

Section 2 Review Answers

1. Possible response: A mineral is a solid, is inorganic, is formed naturally on Earth, has a crystal structure, and has a definite chemical composition.

2. Possible response: You could scratch the mineral using minerals or objects of known hardness on the Mohs hardness scale, then estimate the mineral's relative hardness based on the results of your scratch tests.

3. Streak is the color of a mineral's powder. Since a mineral's streak often differs from the color of a sample of the mineral, it can be used to tell minerals of the same color apart.

4. Some minerals form when molten material cools and hardens on or inside Earth. Others form when materials dissolved in water come out of solution.

5. No. Petroleum is not a mineral because it is a liquid and is formed from organic material.

Science at Home

Students can extend the activity by challenging family members to a mineral scavenger hunt. Suggest that each person try to identify and list as many minerals in their home as possible. Then family members can compare lists and cross off any entries that do not meet the criteria of what a mineral is. The person who correctly identifies the most minerals is the winner.

 ACTIVITY

Performance Assessment

Drawing Have students use markers, colored pencils, or paints to create a three-stage diagram showing one way in which large mineral crystals can form.

Portfolio Students can save their diagrams in their portfolios.

Mineral I.D.

Preparing for Inquiry

Key Concept Individual minerals have a unique set of properties that can be used to identify them.

Skills Objectives Students will be able to

◆ observe the properties of minerals;
◆ create a data table to record observations;
◆ classify minerals based on their properties.

Time 40 minutes

Advance Planning Before class, collect enough minerals to supply each student group with a full set of 6 minerals. Paint each sample with a small patch of white correction fluid and, using a marker, label them with the appropriate letters. For all mineral sets, you might wish to make the identities of samples A–E consistent (for example, A, calcite; B, pyrite; C, talc; D, quartz; E, halite) and vary the identity of sample F (for example, F, either magnetite or hematite). Fill small dropper bottles with vinegar. Gather several field guides to rocks and minerals so they can be available for students to refer to during class.

Guiding Inquiry

Introducing the Procedure

◆ Ask: **What mineral property is the easiest to observe?** The most difficult to observe? (*Students will most likely suggest that color is the easiest to observe and hardness is the most difficult.*)
◆ Ask: **Which mineral property do you think will be the most useful in identifying minerals? Why?** (*Accept all reasonable responses. Students may suggest that hardness is most useful because it is quantifiable.*)

Mineral I.D.

In this lab, you will use a variety of tests to determine the properties of several minerals.

Problem

How can the properties of minerals be used to classify them?

Materials

samples of quartz, pyrite, hematite, calcite, talc, magnetite, or halite
hand lens   hardness point kit (optional)
copper penny   streak plate
iron nail   plastic dropper
scissors   vinegar
magnet

Procedure

1. Make a data chart like the one below to organize your observations.
2. Your teacher will give you 6 mineral samples labeled A through F.
3. Observe the color of each mineral and record the mineral's color in your chart.
4. Using the hand lens, carefully observe the size of the crystals in each mineral. Minerals with large crystals have a coarse texture. Minerals with small or hard-to-see crystals have a fine texture. Record what you observe.
5. Now observe the luster of your mineral. Is it metallic or nonmetallic? Would you describe your nonmetallic minerals as having a glassy, pearly, silky, or earthy luster? Record your observations in your data chart.
6. Try to scratch Mineral A with your fingernail. If a scratch appears, record this in your table. If your fingernail does not scratch Mineral A, try the penny, then the iron nail, and then the scissors. Record the softest material that can first scratch each mineral. (You may also use hardness points to determine the hardness of each mineral.)

DATA CHART

Sample	Color (dark, light, or mixed colors)	Crystal Size (fine or coarse-grained)	Luster	Hardness	Streak	Magnetic	Reaction to Vinegar
A							
B							
C							
D							
E							
F							

Troubleshooting the Experiment

◆ Demonstrate how to use the streak plate. Make sure students press down on the mineral hard enough to leave a line of powder on the plate.
◆ Remind students to refer to Mohs Hardness Scale on page 333 as they attempt to determine the relative hardness of each mineral.

Expected Outcome

In students' data tables, observations for color, crystal size, and luster may vary with the mineral samples used. Students should note the following characteristic properties: quartz, hardness 7; pyrite, hardness 6–6.5, greenish or brownish black streak; hematite, hardness 5.5–6.5, red or reddish brown streak; calcite, hardness 3, bubbles in vinegar; talc, hardness 1; magnetite, hardness 6, black streak, magnetic; halite, hardness 2.5.

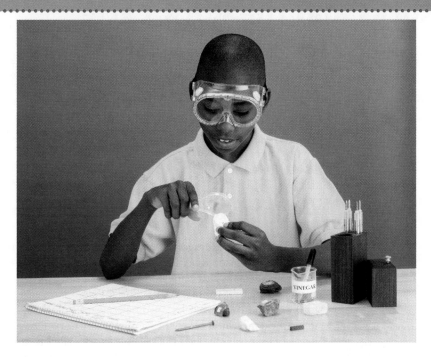

Analyze and Conclude

7. To test the streak of a mineral, push down on the mineral as you rub it across the streak plate. Observe the color of the streak and record it in your data chart.
8. Hold a magnet next to each mineral. Record the results.
9. Calcite will fizz as it reacts with the acid in the vinegar to produce tiny bubbles of carbon dioxide gas. To test for the mineral calcite, place 3 drops of vinegar on each of your minerals. Record the results.
10. Wash your hands when you are finished.

Analyze and Conclude

1. Use your chart to examine and evaluate your data. Did any of your minerals have the same color? How useful is color in determining a mineral's identity?
2. Classify your minerals in two groups according to crystal size. How do you think each group of minerals formed?

3. Did any of your minerals have a glassy or sparkly luster? Why do you think that minerals with a glassy or sparkly luster are important to people?
4. How would knowing the hardness of a mineral help you decide how the mineral could be used?
5. Was streak color ever different from the color of the mineral? How could streak be useful in identifying minerals that are the same color?
6. **Think About It** What physical property was most useful in classifying minerals? Why?

More to Explore

The different properties of your mineral samples can help you identify them. Use a field guide to rocks and minerals to identify the specific name of each mineral sample.

Analyze and Conclude

1. Answers will vary. Quartz, calcite, talc, and halite often have similar white or clear coloring. Students may not find color to be very distinctive and thus not particularly useful in identifying minerals.
2. Grouping of minerals will vary. Small crystals form when lava cools quickly on Earth's surface, whereas large crystals form when magma cools slowly below the surface.
3. Quartz often has a glassy or sparkly luster. Students might suggest that this luster is attractive and thus the mineral could be used for decorative purposes, such as in jewelry, or to make glass.
4. Answers will vary. Students might suggest that hardness indicates how durable a mineral is, which affects how it can be used.
5. The streak colors of pyrite and hematite often differ from the colors of the minerals. Different minerals of the same color may have different streak colors, which can be used to tell them apart.
6. Answers will vary. Students should justify their choice of most useful physical property.

Extending the Inquiry

More to Explore Students can compare results and characteristic properties they used to identify the minerals. Provide additional minerals such as hornblende, biotite, and galena for students to identify, or invite them to bring in for identification minerals they may have collected.

Program Resources

◆ **Unit 4 Resources** Chapter 10 Skills Lab blackline masters, pp. 21-23

Media and Technology

 Lab Activity Videotapes
Grade 6, Tape 3

Safety

Remind students to wash their hands after handling the mineral samples. Review the safety guidelines in Appendix A.

TEKS: 6.1A; 6.2B, C, D, E; 6.4A; 6.14A

Objectives

After completing the lesson, students will be able to

◆ list and describe the three major groups of rocks;

◆ explain how geologists classify rocks;

◆ explain what igneous, sedimentary, and metamorphic rocks are and describe how they are formed;

◆ explain how the rock cycle changes rock.

1 Engage/Explore

Activating Prior Knowledge

Ask students: **How do you think rocks and minerals are related?** (*Some students may realize that rocks are made up of minerals.*) Once they make the connection between rocks and minerals, encourage students to recall how minerals form and use this information to suggest ways in which rocks form. (*Students should infer that, like minerals, some rocks form when magma and lava cool and when materials dissolved in water come out of solution.*)

⋯⋯⋯ DISCOVER ⋯⋯⋯

Skills Focus forming operational definitions

Materials *rock samples, hand lens*

Time 10 minutes

Tips Each set of three rocks should consist of one igneous, one metamorphic, and one sedimentary rock, such as granite, quartzite, and sandstone. If examples from each group are not available, any three rocks that differ noticeably in color, texture, and composition may be used.

Expected Outcome Students' descriptions and sketches should reflect the colors and textures of their samples.

Think It Over Answers should accurately reflect the rock samples provided. Students' definitions should indicate that rocks consist of one or more minerals or sediments.

DISCOVER ⋯⋯⋯⋯⋯⋯⋯⋯⋯⋯⋯⋯⋯⋯⋯ ACTIVITY ⋯

What Is Earth's Crust Made Of?

1. Your teacher will give you three different rocks.

2. Observe each rock under a hand lens. In your notebook, describe the color or colors that you see in the rocks. Also describe any shapes or patterns in the rocks.

3. Make a sketch of each of your rocks.

Think It Over

Forming Operational Definitions Are your rocks made up of one material or several materials? How can you tell? How are the rocks similar? How are they different? Based on your observations, how would you define "rock"?

GUIDE FOR READING

◆ What are the three major groups of rocks?

◆ How do different kinds of rocks form?

◆ What is the rock cycle?

Reading Tip Before you read, rewrite the section headings as questions. As you read, write answers to the questions.

Key Terms rock • texture • grain • igneous rock • intrusive rock • extrusive rock • sedimentary rock • sediment • erosion • deposition • metamorphic rock • rock cycle

Figure 14 The Painted Wall in the Black Canyon of the Gunnison in Colorado is a sheer rock cliff more than 750 meters high.

340

There is a huge dragon climbing out of the Black Canyon of the Gunnison River in Colorado. The dragon has jaws like an alligator, a twisting body, and a tail. But this dragon is not a fire-breathing monster. It is a bright pattern on a cliff that forms one side of the Black Canyon. Because of colorful patterns in the rock, this cliff is called the Painted Wall. The pattern shaped like a dragon is actually a thick vein of rock called pegmatite. Veins of bright pink and white pegmatite stand out against the dark purple-gray rocks that make up most of the canyon.

Building Blocks of the Crust

Like many kinds of rock, pegmatite is a mixture of several minerals. Recall from Section 1 that rock forms Earth's crust. **Rock** is a solid material made up of one or more minerals or other substances, including the remains of once-living things. Some rocks contain material that comes from plants or animals. For example, clam shells can be found in some rocks. Other rocks are made up of only one mineral. One such rock is "rock salt," which is made up only of the mineral halite.

You may be surprised to learn that most of Earth's rocks are made up of about 20 common minerals. These minerals are called rock-forming minerals.

READING STRATEGIES

Reading Tip Students' questions will vary. Typical questions might include these: "How are rocks classified?" "What is an igneous rock?" "How do metamorphic rocks form?" "What are the different kinds of sedimentary rocks?" "What is the rock cycle?" Answers will vary, depending on the questions posed.

Study and Comprehension As students read about each of the three major groups of rocks, suggest that they write the name of each group and then below it list examples of rocks in that group.

Slate *Fine-grained*

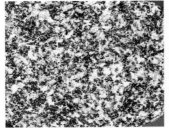
Diorite *Coarse-grained*

Flint *No visible grain*

Figure 15 The size, shape, and pattern of a rock's grains determine its texture.

Conglomerate *Rounded grain*

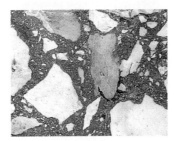
Breccia *Jagged grain*

Classifying Rocks

Geologists classify rocks based on the rocks' color, texture, composition, and how the rocks formed.

Color The color of a rock depends on the colors of the minerals that make up the rock. The color of the minerals, in turn, reflects their chemical composition. For example, certain rocks made up of minerals that are rich in silicon and aluminum are often light in color. But other rocks made up of minerals rich in iron and magnesium tend to be dark in color. As with minerals, classifying a rock just by color is not always helpful. For one thing, weather can change the color of a rock's outer surface over time.

Texture Usually, the word "texture" means how a surface feels to the touch. But to a geologist, **texture** refers to the size, shape, and arrangement of a rock's grains. A **grain** is one of the particles that make up a rock. A grain can be made up of crystals of a mineral. Or a grain can be a piece of another rock.

Geologists use several terms to describe a rock's texture. A rock with a coarse-grained texture has large grains. A rock with a fine-grained texture has small grains. You can see examples of different rock textures in Figure 15.

Composition How do geologists determine a rock's composition? First, they try to identify the minerals the rock contains. Identifying the minerals can be quite easy if the rock is made up of large crystals. But it can be much harder to identify small crystals. One method is to make a slice of rock called a "thin section." A geologist can prepare a thin section by cutting and grinding a rock. Finally, the rock becomes so thin that light shines through. By viewing the thin section under a microscope, a geologist can identify the minerals in the thin section.

Program Resources

- **Unit 4 Resources** 10-3 Lesson Plan, p. 17; 10-3 Section Summary, p. 18
- **Guided Reading and Study Workbook** 10-3

Building Blocks of the Crust

Including All Students

Encourage groups of interested students to research rock-forming minerals and make a poster-sized list to display for the class. **cooperative learning**

Classifying Rocks

Building Inquiry Skills: Comparing and Contrasting

Materials *coarse-grained and fine-grained sandpaper, hand lens*
Time 10 minutes

To reinforce students' understanding of coarse-grained and fine-grained textures, allow them to touch and examine sandpaper that is very coarse-grained and sandpaper that is very fine-grained. Have students compare and contrast the two textures of sandpaper. Elicit from students that the coarser paper is coated with grains that both look larger and feel rougher. **learning modality: tactile/kinesthetic**

Using the Visuals: Figure 15

On the board, create a two-column table with column heads "Fine-grained" and "Coarse-grained". Have students examine the photographs, and then take turns classifying one of the rocks pictured and writing it in the appropriate column of the table. *(Fine-grained: slate, flint; coarse-grained: diorite, conglomerate, breccia)* When completed, students can suggest an appropriate title for the table. **learning modality: visual**

Ongoing Assessment

Writing Have students explain in their own words what characteristics geologists use to classify rocks.

Igneous Rock

▼ *Granite*

▲ *Basalt*

Figure 16 Two common igneous rocks are basalt and granite. Basalt (above) is a dark, extrusive rock that makes up much of the oceanic crust. Granite (right) is a light-colored intrusive rock that is common in continental crust.

TRY THIS

To See or Not to See

Learn about the difference ACTIVITY in texture between intrusive and extrusive rocks.

1. Obtain samples of igneous rocks from your teacher.
2. Observe the rocks carefully with a hand lens.
3. Can you see separate crystals of rock-forming minerals, or are the crystals too small to see?
4. Separate your rocks into two piles: those with a coarse-grained texture and those with a fine-grained texture.

Classifying Which samples are intrusive rocks? Which are extrusive rocks? How do you know?

How Rock Forms Geologists also classify rocks based on how the rocks form. **Geologists classify rocks into three major groups: igneous, sedimentary, and metamorphic.** As you will see, the rocks in each of these groups are formed in a different way.

Igneous Rock

The pegmatite in the Black Canyon is an igneous rock. **Igneous rock forms when magma or lava cools and hardens.** Pegmatite is formed when hot, liquid magma rises through cracks in rock deep beneath the surface. The magma cools very slowly underground, producing the large crystals often found in pegmatite.

Geologists further classify igneous rocks according to whether the rocks formed above or beneath Earth's surface. Igneous rock formed from magma beneath the surface is called **intrusive rock.**

One common intrusive rock is granite, often made up of the minerals quartz, feldspar, mica, and hornblende. If you look at the picture of granite in Figure 16, you can see the crystals of these minerals. Granite forms much of the continental crust—the part of the crust that makes up Earth's continents.

When igneous rock forms from lava on the surface, it is called **extrusive rock.** A type of rock called basalt is probably the most common extrusive rock on Earth. Basalt is a dark, dense rock made up of several minerals. Basalt forms much of the oceanic crust—the part of the crust that makes up the ocean floor. Basalt forms as a result of volcanic activity. You will learn more about igneous rocks and volcanic activity in Chapter 11.

☑ *Checkpoint* *What are two ways in which igneous rocks can form?*

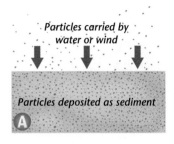

Particles carried by water or wind

Particles deposited as sediment

A

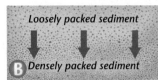

Loosely packed sediment

Densely packed sediment

B

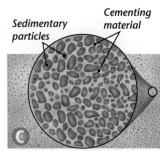

Sedimentary particles

Cementing material

C

Figure 17 Sedimentary rocks form through the erosion, deposition, compaction, and cementation of sediments. **(A)** Water or wind deposits sediment. **(B)** The heavy sediments press down on the layers beneath. **(C)** Dissolved minerals flow between the particles and cement them together.
Relating Cause and Effect What conditions are necessary for sedimentary rock to form?

Sedimentary Rock

Another group of rocks arises from bits and pieces of rock and other substances. **Sedimentary rock forms when particles of rock and other materials are pressed and stuck together.** Geologists use the term **sediment** for particles of rock or material from living things. The sand and gravel on a beach and the mud on a riverbank are sediment. Seashells, leaves, twigs, and other remains of animals or plants are also sediment. All these different kinds of sediment can become sedimentary rock.

Have you ever watched rushing water from a heavy rain wash soil and gravel down a slope? If so, you have seen the beginning of the process that forms sedimentary rock. First, **erosion** moves sediment from place to place on Earth's surface. Flowing water, waves, wind, and ice can all cause erosion. Second, sediment is laid down in a process called **deposition.** For example, deposition occurs when water slows down or stops moving. The sediment sinks out of the water and comes to rest.

Slowly, thick layers of sediment build up. The weight of the layers above presses down on the layers below. This process, called compaction, squeezes the layers of sediment together. Another process, called cementation, glues the sediment together. Cementation can occur in several ways. Sometimes, cementation occurs when water dissolves some of the sediment. The solution then forms mineral crystals that cement the sediment particles together. Compaction and cementation may continue for millions of years. Eventually, the sediment changes to sedimentary rock.

There are three major kinds of sedimentary rock: clastic rock, organic rock, and chemical rock. Each type of sedimentary rock forms in a different way.

Figure 18 The sedimentary rock conglomerate is made up of sediment particles of different sizes that have been pressed and cemented together.

Sedimentary Rock

Using the Visuals: Figure 17

Refer students to diagram A, and ask: **Where do the particles carried by water or wind come from?** *(Water or wind eroded them from another place on Earth's surface.)* **What might cause the particles to be deposited?** *(Water or wind slows down and stops moving, causing the particles to be dropped.)* Have students name and describe the process taking place in diagram B. *(The process is compaction, which occurs when the weight of sediment layers above press down on the layers below, squeezing the sediment particles together.)* Then ask: **In diagram 3, what acts as the "glue" that cements the sediment particles together?** *(Mineral crystals)* **learning modality: visual**

Building Inquiry Skills: Making Models

Materials *sediment such as sand, gravel, and small shells, plastic container, petroleum jelly, spoon, white glue*

ACTIVITY

Time 20 minutes

Challenge students to use the materials provided to model how sedimentary rocks form. Instruct them to sketch their models during the various stages of "rock formation" and be sure to label the processes shown. Allow glue used in the models to dry overnight, then have students share their models and sketches with the class. **learning modality: tactile/kinesthetic**

Program Resources

◆ **Laboratory Manual** 10 "Making Models of Sedimentary Rocks"

Answers to Self-Assessment

Caption Question

Figure 17 For sedimentary rocks to form, there must be particles of rock and other materials deposited, compacted, and cemented.

☑ Checkpoint

They can form as magma cools beneath Earth's surface or when lava cools on the surface of Earth.

Ongoing Assessment

Oral Presentation Call on various students to describe ways in which igneous rocks and sedimentary rocks are alike and different.

Sedimentary Rock,
continued

Demonstration

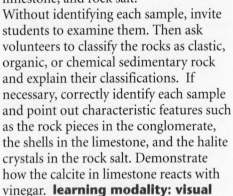

Obtain samples of conglomerate, organic limestone, and rock salt. Without identifying each sample, invite students to examine them. Then ask volunteers to classify the rocks as clastic, organic, or chemical sedimentary rock and explain their classifications. If necessary, correctly identify each sample and point out characteristic features such as the rock pieces in the conglomerate, the shells in the limestone, and the halite crystals in the rock salt. Demonstrate how the calcite in limestone reacts with vinegar. **learning modality: visual**

Using the Visuals: Figure 20

Ask students: **If you found coquina on the top of a mountain, what could you infer about the environment at that location? Explain your answer.** *(The environment must have changed. Since coquina forms from the shells and skeletons of ocean organisms, the rocks on the mountain must have formed in an ocean environment.)* **What was the environment like when the gypsum was deposited?** *(The area was covered by a lake.)* **learning modality: visual**

Figure 19 These colorful layers of sandstone in Utah are examples of clastic sedimentary rocks.

Figure 20 Some sedimentary rocks, such as the gypsum that covers this dry lake bed, form when dissolved minerals come out of solution.

Clastic Rock Can a sedimentary rock be like a gelatin dessert with pieces of fruit mixed in? The answer is yes, if the rock is a clastic rock. Pieces of rock that have been pressed and stuck together are called clastic rock. One common clastic rock is conglomerate. Conglomerate is made up of rounded pieces of rock. It may contain sand and pebbles, or even large rocks and boulders. Another clastic rock, sandstone, is made up of grains of sand cemented together by dissolved quartz.

Organic Rock Sedimentary rock formed from the remains of plants and animals is called organic rock. One of the most common rocks is limestone. Limestone is formed from the shells and skeletons of animals that lived in ancient seas. The shells and skeletons are made up of the mineral calcite. Some of the calcite dissolves in water as a result of a chemical change. The dissolved calcite cements the shells and skeletons together to form limestone.

Coal is an organic rock formed from the remains of plants that lived in swamps millions of years ago. Over time, thick layers of plant remains were changed to coal.

Chemical Rock A chemical rock is formed when dissolved minerals come out of solution and form crystals. Deposits of chemical rock are often found in areas that were once covered by water. The chemical rock was formed as water containing dissolved minerals evaporated. Halite, or rock salt, is an example of a common chemical rock.

344

Background

Integrating Science Sedimentary rocks are particularly important in the interpretation of Earth's history. Sedimentary rocks may form on Earth's land surface or underwater. These rocks often provide clues to past surface environments. For example, sedimentary rocks often contain horizontal layers called *strata*. *Ripple marks* are small waves of sand formed by moving air or water. *Mud cracks* are just what their name implies, and they suggest that the sediment was deposited in an alternately wet and dry environment. Sediment deposited on sand dunes in beaches and deserts often include *cross-bedding*, strata inclined at a steep angle.

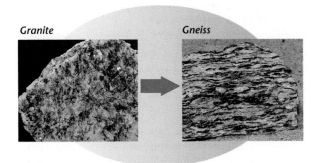

Figure 21 Heat and pressure can change any rock into metamorphic rock. For example, granite becomes gneiss, and sandstone changes to quartzite.
Observing What evidence of heat or pressure can you see in the gneiss and quartzite?

Metamorphic Rock

Sometimes, sediment buries rock deep beneath the surface. The weight of thick layers of sediment pushes the rock down toward the heat of Earth's mantle. **Heat and great pressure deep beneath Earth's surface can change rock to metamorphic rock.** Sometimes, heat from a volcano causes nearby rock to become metamorphic rock.

A metamorphic rock is different from the rock that formed it. For example, a rock's texture changes as it becomes metamorphic rock. Chemical reactions may also occur that change the minerals in the rock.

Any kind of rock can become a metamorphic rock. For example, the igneous rock granite can become the metamorphic rock, gneiss. You know that granite is made up of large crystals. When granite changes to gneiss, the crystals are flattened into parallel rows called bands. Therefore, gneiss is a metamorphic rock with a banded texture.

Other metamorphic rocks do not have bands. Their texture is nonbanded. For example, the sedimentary rock sandstone can become quartzite, a nonbanded metamorphic rock. Look at Figure 21 to see how gneiss and quartzite differ from the rocks from which they formed.

✓ *Checkpoint* *What are metamorphic rocks and how are they formed?*

Real-Life Learning

Have pairs of students brainstorm and list specific places where sedimentary rocks are currently forming. Provide students with maps and globes for inspiration, and encourage them to include local and distant locations on their lists. Have them also record whether clastic, organic, or chemical rocks are likely forming at each location. For example, student lists may include organic rocks forming in the Pacific Ocean, chemical rocks forming in the Great Salt Lake, and clastic rocks forming below the Mississippi River. **learning modality: verbal**

Metamorphic Rock

Using the Visuals: Figure 21

Ask students to first describe how granite and sandstone form. (*Granite forms when magma cools below the surface. Sandstone forms when sediment is eroded, deposited, compacted, and cemented.*) Then have them describe the events that would transform granite into gneiss and sandstone into quartzite. (*Granite and sandstone get buried deep beneath the surface, and the heat and pressure at that depth cause gneiss and quartzite to form.*) Ask: **What might happen to quartzite if it became deeply buried?** (*Heat and pressure might change it into another metamorphic rock.*) **learning modality: visual**

Answers to Self-Assessment

Caption Question

Figure 21 Evidence includes the crystals flattened into bands in the gneiss and the altered texture of the quartzite.

✓ *Checkpoint*

Metamorphic rocks are rocks whose texture and minerals have been changed by heat and pressure deep beneath Earth's surface.

Ongoing Assessment

Writing Students can write a short paragraph describing how metamorphic rocks form.

The Rock Cycle

Including All Students

Challenge students to describe other natural cycles. These might include the cycle of seasons, the cycle of night and day, the water cycle, and the carbon-oxygen cycle. Point out that these cycles are continuous, with no beginning or end, just as the rock cycle is continuous. **learning modality: verbal**

Using the Visuals: Figure 23

Materials *index cards, markers or colored pencils*
Time 20 minutes

Have students write the following on four index cards: lava, basalt, quartzite, sandstone. Then have them use a different color marker or pencil to classify each material as an igneous rock, a sedimentary rock, a metamorphic rock, or a molten material. Instruct students to arrange their cards in one order in which the materials might have formed as part of the rock cycle. They can take turns explaining to a partner how their arrangement represents a possible pathway in the rock cycle. **learning modality: visual**

The Rock Cycle

Earth's rocks are not as unchanging as they seem. **Forces inside Earth and at the surface produce a rock cycle that builds, destroys, and changes the rocks in the crust.** The **rock cycle** is a series of processes on and beneath Earth's surface that slowly change rocks from one kind to another.

Figure 23 shows that the rock cycle can follow many different pathways. Here is one possible pathway: the igneous rock granite formed beneath the surface millions of years ago. Then, the forces of mountain building slowly pushed the granite upward, forming a mountain. Slowly, water and weather wore away the granite through the process of erosion. These granite particles became sand, carried by streams to the ocean.

Over millions of years, layers of sandy sediment piled up on the ocean floor. Slowly, the sediments were pressed together and cemented to form sandstone, a sedimentary rock.

Over time, more and more sediment piled up on the sandstone. As the sandstone became deeply buried, pressure on the rock increased. The rock became hot. Heat and pressure changed the rock's texture from gritty to smooth. After millions of years, the sandstone changed into the metamorphic rock quartzite.

Metamorphic rock does not end the rock cycle. Sometimes, forces inside Earth push all three types of rock many kilometers beneath the surface. There the heat of Earth's interior melts the rock. This molten material can form new igneous rock.

Figure 22 The Bitterroot Mountains in Idaho began as a great mass of intrusive igneous rock deep beneath the surface. Over time, some of the rock changed to metamorphic rock. As forces inside Earth pushed the rock above the surface, erosion began to sculpt the rock into mountains.
Predicting What type of rock might begin to form next in the Bitterroot Mountains?

346

Erosion

IGNEOUS ROCK

SEDIMENTARY ROCK

Volcanic activity

Melting

Heat and pressure

Melting

Heat and pressure

Erosion

MOLTEN MATERIAL

METAMORPHIC ROCK

Melting

Figure 23 Igneous, sedimentary, and metamorphic rocks change continuously through the rock cycle. *Interpreting Diagrams What steps in the rock cycle could change a sedimentary rock into an igneous rock?*

Section 3 Review

1. Briefly describe how rocks in the three major groups are formed.
2. How are the ways that intrusive and extrusive rocks form similar? How are they different?
3. What are four ways in which geologists classify rocks?
4. **Thinking Critically** **Inferring** A geologist finds a coarse-grained rock with crystals arranged in rows. What can the geologist infer about how this rock formed and what group it belongs to?
5. **Thinking Critically** **Applying Concepts** What rock comes before quartzite in the rock cycle? What rock or rocks could come just after quartzite in the rock cycle? Explain your answer.

Check Your Progress

Draw a revised sketch of your model. How will you show Earth's crust? How will your three-dimensional model show the composition, temperature, and pressure of layers beneath the crust? Revise your list of materials. Construct your model, including all the required features. Be sure to label the features on your model.

CHAPTER PROJECT

Chapter 10 **347**

Program Resources

◆ **Unit 4 Resources** 10-3 Review and Reinforce, p. 19; 10-3 Enrich, p. 20

Media and Technology

Transparencies "The Rock Cycle," Transparency 50

Answers to Self-Assessment

Caption Questions

Figure 22 As erosion and deposition continue, sedimentary rock may form.

Figure 23 Answers will vary. A typical answer might be that a sedimentary rock could become deeply buried, where it melts to form molten material. That material could, through volcanic activity, cool and harden to form igneous rock.

Section 3 Review Answers

1. Igneous rocks form when magma or lava cools and hardens. Sedimentary rocks form when particles of rock and other materials are compacted and cemented together. Metamorphic rocks form when heat and pressure inside Earth change rocks.
2. Both form when molten material cools and hardens. Intrusive rocks form from magma beneath the surface, whereas extrusive rocks form from lava on the surface.
3. Geologists classify rocks based on the rocks' color, texture, composition, and how the rocks formed.
4. Since the rows represent a banded texture, the geologist can infer that the rock formed from a coarse-grained rock that was subjected to heat and pressure and is therefore a metamorphic rock.
5. Answers will vary. A typical answer might describe the change by heat and pressure of the sedimentary rock sandstone into the metamorphic rock quartzite, and then a change by melting into magma and by cooling into an igneous rock such as granite.

Check Your Progress

CHAPTER PROJECT

Review students' designs for their models and provide then with feedback. Encourage them to use materials that worked best in their experiments. Then, once they have incorporated any needed changes in their materials or design, have them begin building the base of their models. Once completed, check to make sure students clearly label the features of their models.

Performance Assessment

Oral Presentation Call on students at random and name one of the three major groups of rocks. Then challenge the student to describe a path in the rock cycle that might lead to the formation of the same type of rock.

Rock Recycling

Preparing for Inquiry

Key Concept Properties of rocks can be used to classify rock samples as igneous, sedimentary, or metamorphic, and to infer how they formed through the rock cycle.

Skills Objectives Students will be able to

♦ observe the properties of rocks;

♦ create a data table to record observations;

♦ classify rocks based on their properties

♦ infer how rocks formed through the rock cycle.

Time 40 minutes

Advance Planning Before class, gather enough rocks to supply each student group with a full set of 10 samples. Provide samples that include all three major rock groups and a variety of textures. Paint each sample with a small patch of white correction fluid and, using a marker, label them with the appropriate letters. For all rock sets, you might wish to make the identities of samples A–J consistent. *Computer use is optional.*

Guiding Inquiry

Introducing the Procedure

♦ Ask: **Why is a hand lens helpful in observing the texture of rocks?**
(*Individual grains of fine-grained rocks are too small to be seen with the naked eye.*)

Troubleshooting the Experiment

♦ Demonstrate how to examine a rock sample and record observations in a data table using a sample not included in the students' samples.

Expected Outcome

Students should use the observed properties to classify the samples as igneous, sedimentary, or metamorphic.

I n this lab, you will identify the rock group to which different rocks belong and infer how they could have formed through the rock cycle.

Problem

How can rocks be classified by how they formed?

Materials

10 rocks   hand lens   computer (optional)

Procedure

1. Copy the data table into your notebook or create a data table on the computer.

2. Your teacher will give you 10 rocks for this activity. The rocks are labeled A through J.

3. Carefully observe each rock using the hand lens. Record the color and crystal size of each rock in your data table.

4. Carefully observe the rocks again. Look for clues that a rock formed from molten material. Is one glassy? Does one have bubbles? Does one have large crystals distributed randomly? Record your observations.

5. Look for clues that show that a rock was formed from particles of other rocks. Is one layered as if made from fine silt? Can it be scratched with your fingernail? Is one made of sand particles? Is one made of many kinds and sizes of pebbles and minerals cemented together? Does one contain fossil shells? Record your observations.

6. Look for clues that show whether the rock formed under heat and pressure. Do the rock's grains look melted and interlocked? Does one have flat layers of crystals in colored bands? Does one look as if the original tiny particles have been pressed together and hardened in layers? Does one look as if tiny sand particles have been heated so that larger crystals could grow? Record your observations.

7. Complete your data table by filling in the rock group for each rock.

8. Wash your hands when you are finished.

Analyze and Conclude

1. Which properties were most useful in classifying each type of rock?

2. Which rock was easiest to classify? Which was hardest to classify? Explain.

3. **Think About It** Choose one rock from each group and arrange them according to one possible pathway in the rock cycle. (*Hint:* Think about the ways rocks are formed.) Be prepared to explain your choices to another person. What inferences did you make to arrange your rocks according to the steps in the rock cycle?

More to Explore

Using a field guide to rocks and minerals, find several rocks that are formed from another kind of rock. Create a display showing several of these rock cycle pathways to share with your class.

Sample	Color (dark, medium, light, or mixed colors)	Crystal Size (fine, medium, or coarse-grained)	Other Observations (Record clues of how the rock formed)	Rock Group (igneous, metamorphic, sedimentary)
A				
B				
C				
D				

DATA TABLE

Extending the Inquiry

More to Explore Have several copies of field guides to rocks and minerals available for students to use in identifying their samples. Encourage students to share results and resolve differences.

Analyze and Conclude

1. Answers will vary. Students might suggest that texture or composition were most useful in classifying rock type.

2. Answers will vary. Students should explain why certain rocks were easiest and hardest to classify.

3. Answers will vary, depending on the rocks chosen. Students may suggest that inferring the type of rock helped in arranging the rocks according to steps in the rock cycle.

Safety

Remind students to wash their hands after handling the rock samples. Review the safety guidelines in Appendix A.

SECTION 1 **Inside Earth**

Key Ideas

◆ Geologists study Earth and the processes that have shaped Earth over time. They study the minerals and rocks that make up Earth, physical conditions inside Earth, and the forces inside Earth that affect the surface.

◆ Earth's interior is divided into the crust, the mantle, the outer core, and the inner core. The crust and the rigid uppermost part of the mantle are called the lithosphere.

Key Terms

rock	inner core
crust	outer core
geology	mantle
geologist	lithosphere
seismic wave	

 SECTION 2 **Minerals**

Key Ideas

◆ A mineral is a solid, inorganic material that forms naturally on or beneath Earth's surface. A mineral generally has a definite chemical composition and a crystal structure.

◆ Some of the properties of minerals include hardness, color, luster, density, and how the mineral breaks apart.

◆ Many minerals form when molten material cools and hardens. Other minerals form when materials dissolved in water come out of solution.

Key Terms

mineral	fracture
crystal	magma
streak	lava
luster	vein
density	gemstone
cleavage	

SECTION 3 **Rocks and the Rock Cycle**

Key Ideas

◆ The three major groups of rocks are igneous, sedimentary, and metamorphic.

◆ Rocks can be formed when magma or lava hardens, when sediments are cemented and compacted together, or when heat and pressure change rock deep beneath Earth's surface.

◆ The series of processes on and beneath Earth's surface that change rocks from one type to another is called the rock cycle.

Key Terms

rock	sedimentary rock
texture	sediment
grain	erosion
igneous rock	deposition
intrusive rock	metamorphic rock
extrusive rock	rock cycle

Organizing Information

Cycle Diagram Copy the cycle diagram onto a sheet of paper. This diagram shows one possible pathway through the rock cycle. Place these descriptions on the diagram in the correct order: Sedimentary rock, Metamorphic rock, Melting, and Igneous rock. Then add a title. (For help in making cycle diagrams, see the Skills Handbook.)

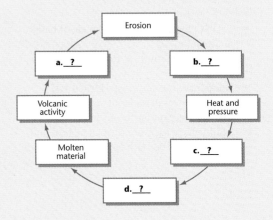

Organizing Information

Organizing Information
Possible title: Pathway of the Rock Cycle
a. Igneous rock
b. Sedimentary rock
c. Metamorphic rock
d. Melting

Program Resources

◆ **Unit 4 Resources** Chapter 10 Real-World Lab blackline masters, pp. 24–25
◆ **Unit 4 Resources** Chapter 10 Project Scoring Rubric, p. 8
◆ **Performance Assessment** Chapter 10, pp. 32–34
◆ **Chapter and Unit Tests** Chapter 10 Test, pp. 52–55

Media and Technology

 Computer Test Bank
Chapter 10 Test

 Lab Activity Videotapes
Grade 6, Tape 3

Reviewing Content
Multiple Choice
1. d 2. d 3. b 4. d 5. b

True or False
6. crust 7. true 8. minerals 9. true
10. metamorphic rocks

Checking Concepts
11. Answers will vary. Possible responses include the physical conditions inside Earth, the forces inside Earth that shape the surface, and the physical and chemical characteristics or rocks and minerals.
12. The outer core is a layer of hot liquid iron and nickel. In contrast, the inner core is a sphere of hot solid iron and nickel.
13. One way geologists have gained indirect evidence of Earth's interior is from seismic waves. As these earthquake vibrations travel through Earth, geologists have recorded the paths they take and used this evidence to infer Earth's composition and structure.
14. Temperature increases between the crust and the core to as much as 5000°C.
15. Scientists hypothesize that circulation of molten metal within Earth's core helps to create Earth's magnetic field.
16. Answers will vary. Possible responses include hardness, color, streak, luster, how a mineral breaks apart, and density.
17. Answers will vary, depending on the rocks chosen.

Thinking Critically
18. Liquid: outer core; solid: crust, lithosphere, inner core; liquid and solid: mantle
19. The size of the crystals tells you how quickly they formed. Large crystals formed more slowly than small crystals.
20. A clastic sedimentary rock forms as a result of erosion and deposition of pieces of rock, followed by compaction and cementation.
21. Both sandstone and quartzite are light-colored rocks. Sandstone is a sedimentary rock formed from grains of sand cemented together, whereas quartzite is a metamorphic rock formed when heat and pressure change sandstone.

Reviewing Content

 Review key concepts online using iText at www.phschool.com

Multiple Choice
Chose the letter of the answer that best completes each statement.

1. Earth's rigid outer layers make up the
   a. inner core.
   b. outer core.
   c. mantle.
   d. lithosphere.
2. To learn the structure of Earth's interior, geologists study
   a. the magnetic compass.
   b. the luster of minerals.
   c. sedimentary rocks.
   d. seismic waves.
3. The hardest mineral in the Mohs hardness scale is
   a. talc.   b. diamond.
   c. quartz.   d. calcite.
4. How is halite formed?
   a. cooling of magma   b. cooling of lava
   c. sea-floor spreading d. evaporation
5. An example of an igneous rock is
   a. gneiss.   b. basalt.
   c. marble.   d. limestone.

True or False
If the statement is true, write true. If it is false, change the underlined word or words to make the statement true.

6. Earth's <u>inner core</u> is largely made of basalt and granite.
7. Pearly is an example of the <u>luster</u> of a mineral.
8. <u>Rocks</u> have specific crystal structures.
9. <u>Erosion</u> moves particles of sediment from place to place on Earth's surface.
10. <u>Sedimentary rocks</u> are formed by heat and pressure deep beneath Earth's surface.

Checking Concepts
11. What are two aspects of Earth that geologists study?
12. How is the outer core different from the inner core?
13. Describe one way in which geologists have gained indirect evidence about Earth's interior.
14. Describe how temperature changes between the crust and the center of Earth.
15. What is one explanation of Earth's magnetic field?
16. Name four properties of minerals that are used to tell them apart.
17. Writing to Learn Use five index cards and write the names of five rocks, one on each card. On the other side write the rock group each belongs to, a description of how each rock was made, and from what types of particles it was made. Have a classmate read each description and see if he or she can guess the name of the rock.

Thinking Critically
18. Classifying Classify these layers of Earth as liquid or solid: crust, lithosphere, mantle, outer core, inner core.
19. Inferring What does the size of a mineral's crystals tell you about how it was formed?
20. Relating Cause and Effect Describe the processes that occur to form a clastic sedimentary rock such as sandstone.
21. Comparing and Contrasting How are sandstone and quartzite similar? How are they different?
22. Predicting What will form if a sedimentary rock melts?
23. Applying Concepts Is there an end to the rock cycle? Explain your answer.

22. When a sedimentary rock melts, magma forms.
23. Answers will vary. Students should recognize that, as long as Earth and its processes exist, the rock cycle will continue.

Applying Skills
24. Talc
25. Quartz
26. Calcite
27. It is feldspar, since feldspar is harder than calcite and thus can scratch it, and is softer than quartz and thus can be scratched by it.

Applying Skills

You are given a number of minerals to identify. All of them can be found on the Mohs hardness scale. Using the information below, answer Questions 24–27.

Mineral	Rating	Testing Method
Talc	1	Flakes easily when scratched by a fingernail.
Calcite	3	A copper penny scratches it, but not a fingernail.
Feldspar	6	Cannot be scratched by a steel knife. Scratches window glass.
Quartz	7	Can scratch steel and hard glass easily.

24. Predicting Which mineral could be most easily turned into a powder?

25. Inferring This mineral cannot be scratched by a fingernail, a copper penny, or a steel knife. It can scratch hard glass and a piece of steel. What is it?

26. Inferring This mineral can be scratched by a steel knife and a copper penny, but not a fingernail. Identify the mineral.

27. Drawing Conclusions This mineral can scratch calcite, but it can be scratched by quartz. What is the mineral and how did you determine the answer?

Performance ▼ CHAPTER PROJECT Assessment

Present Your Project Now you are ready to explain your model of Earth's interior to your class. Label your model to indicate the physical features you have included.

Reflect and Record In your journal, write about the easiest and hardest parts of this project. What other materials could you have used? How many times did you revise your design?

Performance ▼ CHAPTER PROJECT Assessment

Present Your Project As each group presents its model to the class, assess how well the model reflects Earth's layers and their composition. Also, assess how accurately the model was built to scale and how accurately it reflects the temperature and pressure changes within Earth. Encourage all group members to participate in the presentation by asking each student questions.

Reflect and Record Encourage students to explain why they found certain parts of the project easiest and hardest. Students should compare the materials they used to create their models with those used by other groups and evaluate which were most effective. Have them not only report on the number of revisions but summarize their design revision process.

Test Preparation

Test Preparation

28. C **29.** G **30.** D **31.** F

Test Preparation

Use these questions to prepare for standardized tests.

A rock's texture gives clues to how the rock was formed. Use the information below to answer Questions 28–31.

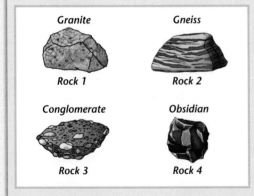

Granite — Rock 1
Gneiss — Rock 2
Conglomerate — Rock 3
Obsidian — Rock 4

28. Which of the rocks is a sedimentary rock made up of other rocks that have been cemented together?
  A Rock 1 **B** Rock 2
  C Rock 3 **D** Rock 4

29. Which rock appears to be a banded metamorphic rock?
  F Rock 1 **G** Rock 2
  H Rock 3 **J** Rock 4

30. Which rock formed from molten material that cooled quickly, giving the rock a glassy texture?
  A Rock 1 **B** Rock 2
  C Rock 3 **D** Rock 4

31. Which rock is an igneous rock made up of large crystals of several different minerals?
  F Rock 1 **G** Rock 2
  H Rock 3 **J** Rock 4

Program Resources

- **Inquiry Skills Activity Book** Provides teaching and review of all inquiry skills
- **Prentice Hall Assessment System** Provides standardized test practice
- **Reading in the Content Area** Provides strategies to improve science reading skills
- **Teacher's ELL Handbook** Provides multiple strategies for English language learners

Earthquakes and Volcanoes

Sections	Time	Student Edition Activities		Other Activities
CHAPTER PROJECT **Volcanoes and People** p. 353 TEKS: 6.6C	Ongoing (2–3 weeks)	TEKS: 6.2E; 6.3D Check Your Progress, pp. 365, 383, 390 Present Your Project, p. 393	TE	Chapter 11 Project Notes, pp. 352–353
1 Plate Tectonics pp. 354–357 TEKS: 6.6C 11.1.1 Explain the theory of plate tectonics.	2 periods/ 1 block	TEKS: 6.2B, C; 6.4A **Discover** How Slow Can It Flow?, p. 354 **Sharpen Your Skills** Predicting, p. 355 **Science at Home,** p. 357	TE	Building Inquiry Skills: Making Models, p. 356
2 Earth's Crust in Motion pp. 358–367 TEKS: 6.6C 11.2.1 Describe how stress forces affect rock. 11.2.2 Describe the types of faults, why faults form, and where they occur. 11.2.3 Describe how uplift and movement along faults changes Earth's surface.	3 periods/ 1½ blocks	TEKS: 6.1A; 6.2B, C, E; 6.3C; 6.4A **Discover** How Does Stress Affect Earth's Crust?, p. 358 **Try This** It's a Stretch, p. 359 **Sharpen Your Skills** Measuring, p. 363 **Skills Lab: Making Models** Modeling Movement Along Faults, pp. 366–367	TE TE TE TE	Demonstration, p. 361 Building Inquiry Skills: Comparing and Contrasting, p. 362 Real-Life Learning, p. 363 Inquiry Challenge, p. 364
3 Measuring Earthquakes pp. 368–373 TEKS: 6.6C 11.3.1 Describe how the energy of an earthquake travels through Earth. 11.3.2 Identify the different kinds of seismic waves. 11.3.3 Name the scales used to measure the strength of an earthquake.	2–3 periods/ 1–1½ blocks	TEKS: 6.2B, C **Discover** How Do Seismic Waves Travel Through Earth? p. 368 **Try This** Recording Seismic Waves, p. 370 **Science at Home,** p. 373	TE TE	Building Inquiry Skills: Observing, p. 369 Demonstration, p. 372
4 Volcanic Activity pp. 374–385 TEKS: 6.6C 11.4.1 Describe what happens when a volcano erupts. 11.4.2 Explain how the two types of volcanic eruptions differ depending on the characteristics of magma. 11.4.3 Identify types of volcanic activity other than eruptions. 11.4.4 Identify some hazards of volcanoes.	4 periods/ 2 blocks	TEKS: 6.2A, B, C, D, E; 6.3C; 6.4A **Discover** What Are Volcanic Rocks Like?, 374 **Try This** Gases in Magma, p. 375 **Real-World Lab: How It Works,** Gelatin Volcanoes, pp. 384–385	TE TE TE LM	Building Inquiry Skills: Inferring, pp. 375, 382; Comparing and Contrasting, p. 376; Interpreting Maps, p. 379; Inquiry Challenge, p. 377 Demonstration, p. 382 11, "Predicting Lava Flows"
5 Volcanic Landforms pp. 386–390 TEKS: 6.6C 11.5.1 Identify landforms formed from magma that hardens beneath the surface. 11.5.2 Identify landforms that lava and other volcanic materials create on Earth's surface.	2 periods/ 1 block	TEKS: 6.2B, C, E; 6.3C **Discover** How Can Volcanic Activity Change Earth's Surface?, p. 386 **Try This** Map in a Pan, p. 388		
Study Guide/Chapter Assessment pp. 391–393	1 period/ ½ block	PLM Provides blackline masters for Probeware labs	ISAB	Provides teaching and review of all inquiry skills

Key: **CTB** Computer Test Bank
CUT Chapter and Unit Tests
ELL Teacher's ELL Handbook

CHAPTER PLANNING GUIDE

 The Resource Pro® CD-ROM provides flexibility for planning the instruction for any type of schedule.

Program Resources	Assessment Strategies	Media and Technology
UR Chapter 11 Project Teacher Notes, pp. 26–27 **UR** Chapter 11 Project Student Materials, pp. 28–31	**SE** Performance Assessment: Present Your Project, p. 393 **TE** Check Your Progress, pp. 365, 383, 390 **UR** Chapter 11 Project Scoring Rubric, p. 32	Science Explorer at www.phschool.com Student Edition on Audio CD, English-Spanish, Chapter 11
UR 11-1 Section Lesson Plan, p. 33 **UR** 11-1 Section Summary, p. 34 **UR** 11-1 Review and Reinforce, p. 35 **UR** 11-1 Enrich, p. 36	**SE** Section 1 Review, p. 357 **TE** Ongoing Assessment, p. 355 **TE** Performance Assessment, p. 357	Earth Science Videodisc Unit 3, Side 1, "Everything on Your Plate"; "Journey to the Bottom of the Sea" Videotape Grade 6, Unit 4, "Everything on Your Plate"; "Journey to the Bottom of the Sea" Transparency 51, "Earth's Plates and Pangaea"
UR 11-2 Section Lesson Plan, p. 37 **UR** 11-2 Section Summary, p. 38 **UR** 11-2 Review and Reinforce, p. 39 **UR** 11-2 Enrich, p. 40 **UR** Skills Lab blackline masters, pp. 53–55	**SE** Section 2 Review, p. 365 **TE** Ongoing Assessment, pp. 359, 361, 363 **TE** Performance Assessment, p. 365	Earth Science Videodisc Unit 3, Side 1, "Why Worry?" Videotape Grade 6, Unit 4, "Why Worry?" Lab Activity Videotapes, Tape 3 Transparency 52, "Shearing, Tension, and Compression"; 53, "Strike-Slip, Normal, and Reverse Faults"
UR 11-3 Section Lesson Plan, p. 41 **UR** 11-3 Section Summary, p. 42 **UR** 11-3 Review and Reinforce, p. 43 **UR** 11-3 Enrich, p. 44	**SE** Section 3 Review, p. 373 **TE** Ongoing Assessment, pp. 369, 371 **TE** Performance Assessment, p. 373	Earth Science Videodisc Unit 2, Side 2, "Waves in the Earth" Videotape Grade 6, Unit 4, "Waves in the Earth" Transparency 54, "Earthquakes and Seismic Waves"
UR 11-4 Section Lesson Plan, p. 45 **UR** 11-4 Section Summary, p. 46 **UR** 11-4 Review and Reinforce, p. 47 **UR** 11-4 Enrich, p. 48	**SE** Section 4 Review, p. 383 **TE** Ongoing Assessment, pp. 377, 379, 381 **TE** Performance Assessment, p. 383	Transparency 55, "Locating the Epicenter"; 56, "Exploring a Volcano"
UR 11-5 Section Lesson Plan, p. 49 **UR** 11-5 Section Summary, p. 50 **UR** 11-5 Review and Reinforce, p. 51 **UR** 11-5 Enrich, p. 52 **UR** Real-World Lab blackline masters, pp. 56–57	**SE** Section 5 Review, p. 390 **TE** Ongoing Assessment, pp. 387, 389 **TE** Performance Assessment, p. 390	Earth Science Videodisc Unit 2, Side 2, "Flying Over America" Videotape Grade 6, Unit 4, "Flying Over America" Lab Activity Videotapes, Tape 3 Transparency 57, "Exploring Volcanic Mountains"
ELL Provides multiple strategies for English language learners **GRSW** Provides worksheets to promote student comprehension of content **RCA** Provides strategies to improve science reading skills	**SE** Chapter 11 Study Guide/Assessment, pp. 391–393 **PA** Chapter 11 Assessment, pp. 35–37 **CUT** Chapter 11 Test, pp. 56–59 **CTB** Chapter 11 Test **PHAS** Provides standardized test preparation	Chapter 11 Computer Test Bank, Chapter 11 Test

GRSW Guided Reading and Study Workbook
ISAB Inquiry Skills Activity Book
LM Laboratory Manual

PA Performance Assessment
PHAS Prentice Hall Assessment System
PLM Probeware Lab Manual

RCA Reading in the Content Area
SE Student Edition

TE Teacher's Edition
UR Unit Resources

Student Edition Activities Planner

ACTIVITY	Time (minutes)	Materials Quantities for one work group	Skills
Section 1			
Discover, p. 354	20	**Consumable** honey, masking tape, damp cloths or paper towels **Nonconsumable** spoon, plate, metric ruler, books or blocks, stopwatch or clock	Forming Operational Definitions
Sharpen Your Skills, p. 355	10	No special materials are required	Predicting
Science at Home, p. 357	20; over 3 weeks	**Nonconsumable** ruler, calendar, calculator (optional)	Measuring
Section 2			
Discover, p. 358	5	**Nonsumable** popsicle stick	Predicting
Try This, p. 359	10	**Nonconsumable** plastic putty	Classifying
Sharpen Your Skills, p. 363	10	**Consumable** masking tape **Nonconsumable** small weight, spring scale, sandpaper	Measuring
Skills Lab, pp. 366–367	40	**Consumable** modeling compound in two or more colors **Nonconsumable** marking pen, plastic butter knife	Making Models, Inferring, Classifying
Section 3			
Discover, p. 368	10	**Conconsumable** spring toy	Observing
Try This, p. 370	10	**Consumable** paper strip 1 m long **Nonconsumable** large book, pencil, pen	Observing
Science at Home, pp. 373	15	**Nonconsumable** towels, books of varying weights	Making Models
Section 4			
Discover, p. 374	5–10	**Nonconsumable** samples of pumice and obsidian, hand lens	Developing Hypotheses
Try This, p. 375	10–15	**Consumable** 10 g baking soda, 65 mL water, 6 raisins, 65 mL vinegar **Nonconsumable** 1- or 2-liter plastic bottle	Making Models
Real-World Lab, p. 384–385	40	**Consumable** unflavored gelatin mold in bowl, aluminum pizza pan, red food coloring in water, unlined paper **Nonconsumable** plastic cup, plastic knife, tray, plastic syringe (10 cc), three small cardboard oatmeal boxes, rubber gloves	Developing Hypotheses, Making Models, Observing
Section 5			
Discover, p. 386	10–15	**Consumable** tape, balloon, damp sand, straw **Nonconsumable** box	Making Models
Try This, p. 388	20	**Consumable** modeling clay, water, food coloring **Nonconsumable** plastic pan, metric ruler, clear plastic sheet, marking pencil	Making Models

A list of all materials required for the Student Edition activities can be found on pages T43–T49 You can obtain information about ordering materials by calling 1-800-848-9500 or by accessing the Science Explorer internet site at **www.phschool.com**.

Texas Essential Knowledge and Skills

(6.1) Scientific processes. The student conducts field and laboratory investigations using safe, environmentally appropriate, and ethical practices. *(Section 2)*

The student is expected to:

(A) demonstrate safe practices during field and laboratory investigations.

(6.2) Scientific processes. The student uses scientific inquiry methods during field and laboratory investigations. *(Project; Sections 1, 2, 3, 4, 5)*

The student is expected to:

(A) plan and implement investigative procedures including asking questions, formulating testable hypotheses, and selecting and using equipment and technology;

(B) collect data by observing and measuring;

(C) analyze and interpret information to construct reasonable explanations from direct and indirect evidence;

(D) communicate valid conclusions; and

(E) construct graphs, tables, maps, and charts using tools including computers to organize, examine, and evaluate data.

(6.3) Scientific processes. The student uses critical thinking and scientific problem solving to make informed decisions. *(Project; Sections 2, 4, 5)*

The student is expected to:

(C) represent the natural world using models and identify their limitations; and

(D) evaluate the impact of research on scientific thought, society, and the environment.

(6.4) Scientific processes. The student knows how to use a variety of tools and methods to conduct science inquiry. *(Sections 1, 2, 4)*

The student is expected to:

(A) collect, analyze, and record information using tools including beakers, petri dishes, meter sticks, graduated cylinders, weather instruments, timing devices, hot plates, test tubes, safety goggles, spring scales, magnets, balances, microscopes, telescopes, thermometers, calculators, field equipment, compasses, computers, and computer probes.

(6.6) Science concepts. The student knows that there is a relationship between force and motion. *(Project; Sections 1, 2, 3, 4, 5)*

The student is expected to:

(C) identify forces that shape features of the Earth including uplifting, movement of water, and volcanic activity.

Take It to the Net

 Interactive text at www.phschool.com

Science Explorer comes alive with iText.

- **Complete student text** is accessible from any computer with Internet access or a CD-ROM drive.

- **Animations, simulations, and videos** enhance student understanding and retention of concepts.

- **Self-tests and online study tools** assess student understanding.

- **Teacher management tools** help you make the most of this valuable resource.

STAY CURRENT with **SCIENCE NEWS®**

Find out the latest research and information about earthquakes and volcanoes at **www.phschool.com**.

Go to **www.phschool.com**. Select Texas on the navigation bar. Click on the Science icon. Then click on <u>Science Explorer</u> under PH@school.

Volcanoes and People

TEKS: 6.2E; 6.3D; 6.6C

When students first consider volcanoes, they will undoubtedly think of fiery eruptions and the death, injury, and destruction they cause. As significant as those effects are, other aspects of volcanoes are also important, including their influence on the art, history, and literature of the people living near them, important products obtained or produced from volcanic materials, and the effects of volcanic activity on soil fertility and agriculture. This project encourages students to consider such aspects as well.

Purpose This project will give students an opportunity to investigate a variety of ways in which people have been affected by volcanoes. Student groups will each choose a specific volcanic region and a particular topic for research. Based on their research, the group will prepare a multimedia documentary about the volcanic region for presentation to the rest of the class.

Skills Focus After completing the Chapter 11 Project, students will be able to
◆ classify the type of volcano chosen for the project;
◆ draw conclusions from a variety of source materials about the volcano's effects on people living near it;
◆ communicate how the volcano has affected the people living in a volcanic region in a documentary presentation, using a variety of media.

Project Time Line The project requires two to three weeks to complete. Each group should first choose a volcanic region and investigate possible topics related to its effects on people in the area. After choosing one topic, group members should research information on that topic and take relevant, well-organized notes. (Chapter 11 Project Worksheet 2 on page 31 in Unit 4 Resources reviews how to take research notes.) Students then should create a storyboard showing each step in the presentation, including the media materials that will be used. Posters,

CHAPTER 11 Earthquakes and Volcanoes

Kilauea volcano is on Hawaii, the largest of the Hawaiian Islands.

WEB ACTIVITY www.phschool.com

SECTION 1 Plate Tectonics
Discover How Slow Can It Flow?

SECTION 2 Earth's Crust in Motion
Discover How Does Stress Affect Earth's Crust?
Skills Lab Modeling Movement Along Faults

SECTION 3 Measuring Earthquakes
Discover How Do Seismic Waves Travel Through Earth?

SECTION 4 Volcanic Activity
Discover What Are Volcanic Rocks Like?
Real-World Lab Gelatin Volcanoes

SECTION 5 Volcanic Landforms
Discover How Can Volcanic Activity Change Earth's Surface?

352

transparencies, videos, and other media should then be prepared and the entire documentary rehearsed before presentation to the class. See Chapter 11 Project Teacher Notes on pages 26–27 in Unit 4 Resources for directions.

Possible Materials
◆ Provide a variety of materials for students to use in their research, including encyclopedias, nonfiction library books, magazine articles, and films on videocassette and CD-ROM. If students have access to the Internet, supervise their use of that source.

◆ Also provide index cards for taking notes and self-stick removable tags for flagging appropriate information in books.
◆ When students are ready to prepare their multimedia materials, supply a variety of materials and devices—poster paper, art supplies, acetate sheets for making overhead transparencies, video cameras, and tape recorders for taping songs, background music, or sound effects. Also let students use materials and devices from home.

CHAPTER 11 PROJECT

Volcanoes and People

The frequent eruptions of Mount Kilauea can be spectacular. And they can be dangerous. Yet volcanoes and people have been closely connected throughout history, not only in Hawaii, but around the world. People often live near volcanoes because of the benefits they offer, from rich soil to minerals to hot springs. In your chapter project, you will research how volcanoes have affected the people living in a volcanic region.

Your Goal To make a documentary about life in a volcanic region.

Your project must

♦ describe the type of volcano you chose and give its history

♦ focus on one topic, such as how people have benefited from living near the volcano or how people show the volcano in their art and stories

♦ use a variety of media in your documentary presentation

Get Started Brainstorm with a group of other students which geographic area you would like to learn about. Your teacher may suggest some volcanic regions for you to check out. What research resources will your group need? Start planning what media you want to use to present your documentary. You might consider video, computer art, overhead transparencies, a rap song, a skit, or a mural. Be creative!

Check Your Progress You'll be working on this project as you study this chapter. To keep your project on track, look for Check Your Progress boxes at the following points.

Section 2 Review, page 365: Select the topic and region you will investigate and begin collecting information.

Section 4 Review, page 383: Use storyboards to organize your materials.

Section 5 Review, page 390: Prepare your visuals and narration.

Present Your Project At the end of the chapter (page 393), practice your presentation, and then present your documentary to your class.

 TEKS

In addition to process TEKS, this chapter addresses these concept TEKS as they relate to the chapter's topics.

(6.6) The student knows that there is a relationship between force and motion. The student is expected to:
(C) identify forces that shape features of the Earth including uplifting, movement of water, and volcanic activity.

353

Program Resources

♦ **Unit 4 Resources** Chapter 11 Project Teacher Notes, pp. 26–27; Chapter 11 Project Overview and Worksheets, pp. 28–31

WEB ACTIVITY www.phschool.com

You will find an Internet activity, chapter self-tests for students, and links to other chapter topics at this site.

Media and Technology

Student Edition on Audio CD
English-Spanish, Chapter 11

Launching the Project

To introduce the project, suggest that students preview Science & History on pages 380–381. Then ask: **What are some ways that each of these volcanoes may have affected the people living nearby?** (*Accept all responses at this time, and encourage creative thinking.*)

Allow time for students to read the project description on page 353 and the Chapter 11 Project Overview on pages 28–29 in Unit 4 Resources. Encourage discussion of the topics students could focus on and the types of source materials they could use for their research. Also answer any initial questions that students may have.

Emphasize that although they may divide responsibilities among group members so only some prepare the visuals, *all* members of the group should take part in planning the visuals and be prepared to answer questions about them.

Distribute Chapter 11 Project Worksheet 1 on page 30 in Unit 4 Resources, which lists a number of volcanoes and specific topics that students might want to consider as subjects for the project. Allow students to choose any volcanic region they wish, so long as they are able to find adequate source material for their research.

Performance Assessment

The Chapter 11 Project Scoring Rubric on page 32 in Unit 4 Resources will help you evaluate how well students complete the Chapter 11 Project. You may want to share the scoring rubric with students so they are clear about what will be expected of them. Students will be assessed on

♦ their ability to identify the type of volcano they have chosen and summarize its history;

♦ how well they have focused both their research and their presentation on a single topic related to the volcano's effect on people living in the area;

♦ their creativity in making use of a variety of media to support the narrative part of their presentation;

♦ how well they present their documentary to the rest of the class.

TEKS: 6.2B, C; 6.4A; 6.6C

Objective

After completing the lesson, students will be able to

◆ explain the theory of plate tectonics.

1 Engage/Explore

Activating Prior Knowledge

Show students a map of the Atlantic Ocean, showing the coastlines of North and South America, Europe, and Africa. Ask them which pieces might fit together like a jigsaw puzzle. *(The coastlines of Africa and South America do fit together.)* If you have a map that shows the continental shelf, the fit will be even better.

········· **DISCOVER** ·········

Skills Focus forming operational definitions

Materials *spoon, plate, honey, masking tape, metric ruler, books or blocks, stopwatch or clock, damp cloths or paper towels*

Time 20 minutes

Tips Refrigerate the honey if possible. Students should prop up the plates using books or blocks. Provide damp cloths or paper towels to clean up any spilled honey. Write the equation for calculating speed on the board: Speed = Distance ÷ Time. Ask: **What distance will you use to complete the calculation?** *(4 cm)* Divide the class into groups of two or three. Allow students to complete their calculations and compare results.

Think It Over You can tell an object is moving if it changes position over a period of time. If the object moves too slowly, you need to observe it over longer periods of time. The growth of hair and the movement of the hour hand on a clock are too slow to see.

DISCOVER •••••••••••••••••••••••••••••• **ACTIVITY** ••••

How Slow Can It Flow?

1. Put a spoonful of honey on a plate.

2. Using a ruler, place a piece of tape 4 cm away from the edge of the honey.

3. Lift one side of the plate just high enough that the honey is visibly flowing.

4. Reduce the angle of the plate a small amount so that the honey appears to be barely moving. Prop up the plate at this angle.

5. Time how long it takes the honey to flow to the tape. Use this information to calculate the speed of the honey.

Think It Over
Forming Operational Definitions
How can you tell that an object is moving if it doesn't appear to be moving at first glance? Can you think of some other examples of motion that are too slow to see?

GUIDE FOR READING

◆ What is the theory of plate tectonics?

Reading Tip As you read, make a list of main ideas and supporting details about plate tectonics

Key Terms plates • Pangaea
• plate tectonics
• plate boundaries

Y ou may be surprised to learn that Earth's lithosphere can move. After all, you know that the lithosphere is made up of solid rock! In fact, the lithosphere is broken into a number of large pieces called **plates.** The plates completely cover Earth's surface and even extend under the oceans.

The plates are made up of oceanic crust and continental crust. A few plates are made mainly of oceanic crust. Each plate also includes the part of the lithosphere that lies beneath it. Most of the United States is located on the North American plate.

Earth's Moving Plates

The plates move very slowly—at rates of several centimeters per year. That's about as fast as your fingernails grow! As the plates move, the continents also move, or "drift," over Earth's surface.

Looking at a world map, you may have observed that the coastlines of the continents on both sides of the Atlantic Ocean seem to match. People have noticed this remarkable fact for centuries. In the early 1900s, a German scientist named Alfred Wegener also saw that some continents seemed to fit together like pieces of a jigsaw puzzle. Wegener developed a hypothesis to explain this observation.

Figure 1 This jagged valley in Iceland marks the line where two of Earth's plates meet.

354

READING STRATEGIES

Reading Tip Students' list will vary. A sample main idea would be that the theory of plate tectonics states that Earth's plates are in constant, slow motion. A supporting detail would be that plate motion results from the movement of material in the upper mantle.

Study and Comprehension Have students scan the section text for vocabulary terms in boldface type. Suggest that they write down each term and then, as they read, record each term's meaning in their own words.

260 million years ago

Present

According to Wegener's hypothesis, the fit of the continents was not the result of chance. Wegener found evidence that the continents that existed millions of years ago moved together. As these continents collided, they formed a great landmass, or "supercontinent," called **Pangaea** (pan JEE uh). Millions of years after Pangaea formed, it slowly broke apart. The continents then moved to their present positions. You can compare a map of Pangaea with a modern world map in Figure 2.

The Theory of Plate Tectonics

During much of the twentieth century, geologists did not accept the idea of continental drift. Wegener had not been able to explain how continental drift occurred. But during the 1960s, several geologists proposed a new theory—the theory of **plate tectonics** (tek TAHN iks). They based the theory on new information about Earth's lithosphere and the interior of the planet.

Figure 2 The supercontinent Pangaea began to break apart about 225 million years ago. *Observing How have North America and South America moved in relation to Africa and Europe?*

Figure 3 The black outlines show the boundaries of some of Earth's plates.

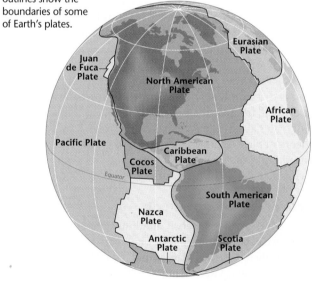

Sharpen your Skills

Predicting
ACTIVITY

Los Angeles, on the Pacific Plate, is slowly moving northwest. San Francisco, on the North American plate, is slowly moving southeast. These two cities are moving toward each other at a rate of about 5 cm/yr. If the two cities are now 554,000 m apart, how long will it take for the two cities to be next to each other?

Program Resources

◆ **Unit 4 Resources** 11-1 Lesson Plan, p. 33; 11-1 Section Summary, p. 34
◆ **Guided Reading and Study Workbook** 11-1

Media and Technology

 Transparencies "Earth's Plates and Pangaea," Transparency 51

Answers to Self-Assessment

Caption Question

Figure 2 North America and South America have moved west, separating from Africa and Europe.

---

2 Facilitate

Earth's Moving Plates

Using the Visuals: Figure 2

On the lefthand map, point out ancient Australia to the northwest of ancient Antarctia. Ask: **How has Australia's position changed over time?** *(Australia moved north.)* **learning modality: visual**

The Theory of Plate Tectonics

Sharpen your Skills

Predicting

Materials *none*
Time 10 minutes
Tips Write the formula for speed on the board: Speed = Distance ÷ Time. Ask: **How does distance depend on time?** *(A greater distance takes a greater time.)* **How does time depend on speed?** *(A greater speed means less time for a certain distance.)* Write the formula for time on the board (Time = Distance ÷ Speed) Remind students that all distances in the equation must first be changed to the same unit. Guide students' calculations using these steps:
554,000 m × 100 cm/m = 55,400,000 cm
Time = 55,400,000 cm ÷ 5 cm/yr
Time = 11,080,000 yr
Extend Give students a map of California and ask them to find San Francisco and Los Angeles. Have them try to figure out where the fault runs based on the information in the text.

Ongoing Assessment

Writing Have students explain what Pangaea is.

Theory of Plate Tectonics, continued

Including All Students

To help students who have not mastered written English, have pairs of students of differing abilities work together to summarize what they have read about the theory of plate tectonics. Students can take turns reading their summaries aloud to their partners. **learning modality: verbal**

EXPLORING

Plate Tectonics

Have volunteers take turns reading aloud the captions of *Exploring Plate Tectonics.* Then elicit from students the three different ways in which plates interact: they collide, they pull apart, and they slide past each other. Refer to the **ELL Handbook** for additional teaching strategies. **learning modality: verbal**

Effects of Plate Movement

Building Inquiry Skills: Making Models

Materials *wood blocks, masking tape, marker*

Time 10 minutes

Challenge small groups of students to use wood blocks to model all the different ways that plates interact in *Exploring Plate Tectonics* on pages 356–357. Students should use masking tape and a marker to label each block as either oceanic crust or continental crust. Check to make sure each group correctly models the movement associated with oceanic-continental collision, continental-continental collision, oceanic-oceanic divergence, continental-continental divergence, and the transform boundary of two continental plates. **learning modality: tactile/kinesthetic**

EXPLORING Plate Tectonics

The movement of Earth's plates produces features on Earth's continents and on the ocean floor.

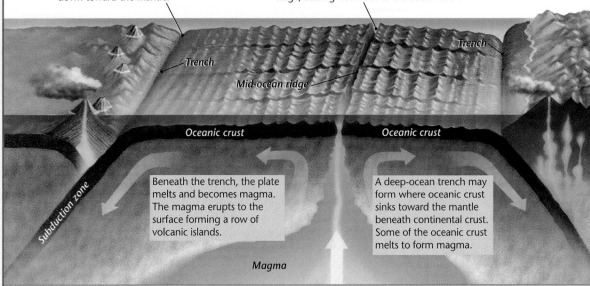

When two plates of oceanic crust collide, one plate sinks beneath the other. One of the plates is pushed beneath the deep-sea trench down toward the mantle.

Sea-floor spreading occurs as oceanic plates pull apart along the mid-ocean ridge, a mountain range that winds through Earth's oceans. Lava erupts through narrow cracks along the ridge, adding new rock to the ocean floor.

Trench

Trench

Mid-ocean ridge

Oceanic crust

Oceanic crust

Subduction zone

Beneath the trench, the plate melts and becomes magma. The magma erupts to the surface forming a row of volcanic islands.

A deep-ocean trench may form where oceanic crust sinks toward the mantle beneath continental crust. Some of the oceanic crust melts to form magma.

Magma

The theory of plate tectonics states that Earth's plates are in constant, slow motion. The theory explains how Earth's plates form and move. It also explains how plates interact, producing volcanoes, mountain ranges, earthquakes, and features of the ocean floor.

What causes the plates to move? Scientists think that plate motion is the result of the movement of material in the upper mantle. Recall from Chapter 10 that beneath the lithosphere is a layer of material in the mantle that can flow slowly. According to the theory of plate tectonics, the plates of the lithosphere float on this layer. As the material in the upper mantle moves, it drags the overlying plates across Earth's surface.

Effects of Plate Movement

Like the covering of a baseball, the lithosphere has seams, or cracks, between the different pieces. The cracks between the plates of the lithosphere are called **plate boundaries.** Along plate boundaries, the plates slide past each other, pull apart, or move together.

356

Background

History of Science In the 1960s, Harry Hess proposed the hypothesis of sea-floor spreading. His hypothesis stated that rising volcanic material along a mid-ocean ridge pushed the older hardened rock away from the ridge in two directions. This movement, in turn, acted like a conveyor belt for the floating continents. Hess's discovery led to

an understanding of how the continents moved.

Earth's continents and other landmasses also move as the plates that carry them move toward or away from each other. When plates collide or split apart, new land features, such as mountains, form.

In some places on Earth's surface, two plates slide past each other, moving slowly in opposite directions. One effect of this movement is frequent earthquakes.

A rift valley froms when two pieces of continental crust pull apart. Over millions of years, the rift valley could widen and sink below sea level, forming a new ocean.

If two plates carrying continental crust collide, neither plate sinks beneath the other. Instead, the plates slowly fold and pile on top of each other, forming a mountain range.

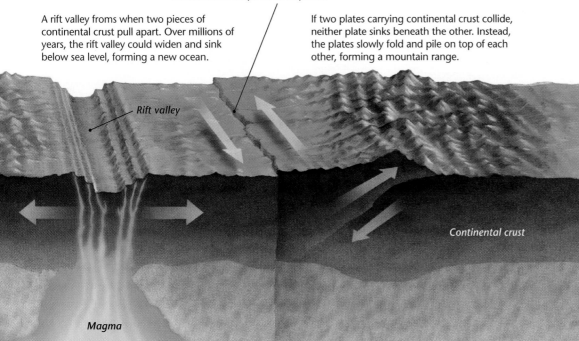

Rift valley

Magma

Continental crust

These movements produce spectacular changes in Earth's surface. For example, the Andes mountains formed where the Nazca plate slides beneath the South American plate. In *Exploring Plate Tectonics*, you can see how plate movements change Earth's surface.

Section 1 Review

1. What does the theory of plate tectonics explain?
2. What are Earth's plates and what are they made of?
3. What was Alfred Wegener's hypothesis about Pangaea?
4. What do scientists think is the cause of plate motion?
5. **Thinking Critically Relating Cause and Effect** Describe how new features of Earth's surface result from the movement of Earth's plates.

Science at Home

Measuring Slow Motion Have each member of your family measure the length of the white part at the end of one fingernail. Write down the results (and which finger you used) and mark your calendar for a date in exactly three weeks. On that day, measure the new length of the white part of the same fingernail. Then calculate the speed, in millimeters per day, at which your fingernail grew. Discuss with your family how your results compare with the typical speed with which continents move.

Media and Technology

Earth Science Videodisc
Unit 3, Side 1, "Everything on Your Plate"
Chapter 6

Earth Science Videodisc
Unit 3, Side 1, "Journey to the Bottom of the Sea"
Chapter 5

Program Resources

◆ **Unit 4 Resources** 11-1 Review and Reinforce, p. 35; 11-1 Enrich p. 36

3 Assess

Section 1 Review Answers

1. The theory of plate tectonics explains how Earth's plates form, move, and interact.
2. Earth's plates are large pieces of the lithosphere made up of solid rock.
3. Wegener's hypothesized that the continents collided and formed a great landmass called Pangaea millions of years ago.
4. Scientists think that plate motion is the result of the movement of material in the upper mantle, which drags the overlying plates along.
5. Answers will vary. Students should indicate that, when plates collide, trenches, volcanoes, or mountain ranges form. When plates pull apart, mid-ocean ridges, rift valleys, or new oceans form.

Science at Home

Materials *metric ruler*
Tips Encourage students to involve at least one or two family members of different ages. Students should record the measurements in millimeters. Suggest that students and family members take measurements of more than one finger in case a particular fingernail breaks during the three-week period. Students should find that fingernail growth rate is similar to the rate of movement of Earth's plates.

Performance Assessment

Drawing Have students draw a simple diagram to show what takes place at plate boundaries.

SECTION 2 Earth's Crust in Motion

TEKS: 6.1A; 6.2B, C, E; 6.3C; 6.4A; 6.6C

Objectives

After completing the lesson, students will be able to
- describe how stress forces affect rock;
- describe the types of faults, why faults form, and where they occur;
- describe how uplift and movement along faults changes Earth's surface.

1 Engage/Explore

Activating Prior Knowledge

Encourage any students who have experienced an earthquake to describe the event—where they were at the time, how they first became aware that an earthquake was occurring, what happened to buildings and objects around them, how they felt during and after the quake, and so on. If students have not experienced an earthquake, let them relate what they have learned from television reports, movies, newspaper and magazine articles, and other sources.

•••••• DISCOVER ••••••

Skills Focus predicting
Materials *popsicle stick*
Time 5 minutes
Tips In Step 2, advise students to increase the pressure on the stick slowly and gradually. In Step 3, caution students to maintain a firm grip on one end of the popsicle stick as they release the pressure so the stick does not fly off into the air and cause injury.
Expected Outcome When students release the pressure in Step 3, the stick will spring back to straighten. As they continue bending in Step 4, the stick will break.
Think It Over The crust will break.

DISCOVER •••••••••••••••••••••••••• ACTIVITY

How Does Stress Affect Earth's Crust?

1. Put on your goggles.
2. Holding a popsicle stick at both ends, slowly bend it into an arch.
3. Release the pressure on the popsicle stick and observe what happens.
4. Repeat Steps 1 and 2. This time, however, keep bending the ends of the popsicle stick toward each other. What happens to the wood?

Think It Over
Predicting Think of the popsicle stick as a model for part of Earth's crust. What do you think might eventually happen as the forces of plate movement bend the crust?

GUIDE FOR READING

- How do stress forces affect rock?
- Why do faults form and where do they occur?
- How do uplift and fault movements affect Earth's surface?

Reading Tip Before you read, use the headings to make an outline about stress in the crust, faults, and mountain building.

Key Terms earthquake
- stress • shearing • tension
- compression • fault
- strike-slip fault
- normal fault • hanging wall
- footwall • reverse fault
- fold • plateau

You are sitting at the kitchen table eating breakfast. Suddenly you notice a slight vibration, as if a heavy truck were rumbling by. At the same time, your glass of orange juice jiggles. Dishes rattle in the cupboards. After a few seconds, the rattling stops. Later, when you listen to the news on the radio, you learn that your region experienced a small earthquake. Earthquakes are a reminder that Earth's crust can move.

Stress in the Crust

An **earthquake** is the shaking and trembling that results from the movement of rock beneath Earth's surface. The movement of Earth's plates creates powerful forces that squeeze or pull the rock in the crust. These forces are examples of **stress,** a force that acts on rock to change its shape or volume. (Volume is the amount of space an object takes up.) Because stress is a force, it adds energy to the rock. The energy is stored in the rock until the rock either breaks or changes shape.

Figure 4 Stress in the crust folded this rock like a sheet of ribbon candy.

READING STRATEGIES

Reading Tip Encourage student to allow space in their outlines for adding details as they read. Students can use their completed outlines as a study guide.

I. Earth's Crust in Motion
  A. Stress in the Crust
  B. Types of Stress
  C. Kinds of Faults
  D. Friction Along Faults
  E. Mountain Building and Uplift
    1. Mountains Formed by Faulting
    2. Mountains Formed by Folding
    3. Anticlines and Synclines
    4. Plateaus

Types of Stress

Three different kinds of stress occur in the crust—shearing, tension, and compression. **Shearing, tension, and compression work over millions of years to change the shape and volume of rock.** These forces cause some rocks to become brittle and snap. Other rocks tend to bend slowly like road tar softened by the heat of the sun.

Stress that pushes a mass of rock in two opposite directions is called **shearing.** Shearing can cause rock to break and slip apart or to change its shape.

The stress force called **tension** pulls on the crust, stretching rock so that it becomes thinner in the middle. The effect of tension on rock is somewhat like pulling apart a piece of warm bubble gum. Tension occurs where two plates are moving apart.

The stress force called **compression** squeezes rock until it folds or breaks. One plate pushing against another can compress rock like a giant trash compactor.

Any change in the volume or shape of Earth's crust is called deformation. Most changes in the crust occur so slowly that they cannot be observed directly. But if you could speed up time so a billion years passed by in minutes, you could see the deformation of the crust. The crust would bend, stretch, break, tilt, fold, and slide. The slow shift of Earth's plates causes this deformation.

☑ *Checkpoint* *How does deformation change Earth's surface?*

Figure 5 Deformation pushes, pulls, or twists the rocks in Earth's crust. *Relating Cause and Effect* *Which type of deformation tends to shorten part of the crust?*

It's a Stretch

You can model the stresses that create faults.

1. Knead a piece of plastic putty until it is soft.
2. Push the ends of the putty toward the middle.
3. Pull the ends apart.
4. Push half of the putty one way and the other half in the opposite direction.

Classifying Which types of stress do Steps 2, 3, and 4 represent?

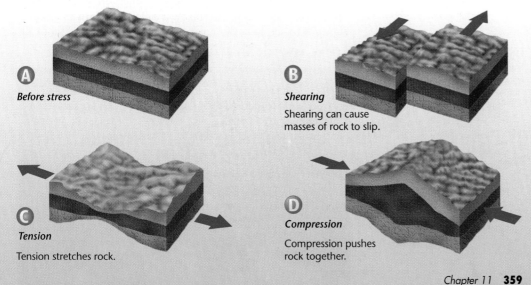

A *Before stress*

B *Shearing*
Shearing can cause masses of rock to slip.

C *Tension*
Tension stretches rock.

D *Compression*
Compression pushes rock together.

Program Resources

◆ **Unit 4 Resources** 11-2 Lesson Plan, p. 37; 11-2 Section Summary, p. 38
◆ **Guided Reading and Study Workbook** 11-2

Media and Technology

 Transparencies "Shearing, Tension, and Compression," Transparency 52

Answers to Self-Assessment

☑ *Checkpoint*

It causes it to bend, stretch, break, tilt, fold, and slide.

Caption Question

Figure 5 Compression is the type of deformation that may shorten part of the crust by pushing it together.

---

2 Facilitate

Stress in the Crust

Including All Students

If students did the Discover activity, ask: **When you bent the popsicle stick the first time and held it in an arch shape, what was happening?** (*Energy—the "push" applied by the hands—was being transferred to the stick and stored in it.*) **What would have happened if you had suddenly let go of one end of the bent stick, and why?** (*The stick would have sprung back to its original shape because the stored energy was quickly released.*) **Where did this stored energy go?** (*It was released as energy in the form of heat.*) **learning modality: logical/ mathematical**

Types of Stress

Skills Focus classifying
Materials *plastic putty*
Time 10 minutes
Tips After students soften the putty in Step 1, tell them to form it into a tube shape before they do each subsequent step.
Expected Outcome Step 2 represents compression, Step 3 represents tension, and Step 4 represents shearing.
Extend Let students repeat the activity with a stiffer material, such as modeling clay, and compare the results.
learning modality: tactile/ kinesthetic

Ongoing Assessment

Oral Presentation Ask each student to explain with the aid of a diagram how the directions of force differ in compression, tension, and shearing.

Kinds of Faults

Including All Students

The San Andreas fault is 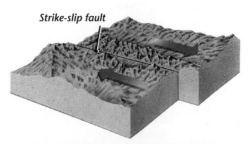 particularly interesting because the deformations it produces in surface features are so clearly visible. Encourage students who need additional challenges to look through books and magazines to find photographs of such deformations and make multiple photocopies for the class to examine. Using evidence in the photographs, students could locate and mark the fault line in each photograph and draw arrows to indicate the directions in which the two opposing rock slabs moved. **learning modality: visual**

Using the Visuals: Figures 7 and 8

Draw students' attention to the hanging wall and footwall in the figures. Point out that, in the case of both the normal fault and reverse fault, the hanging wall is located *above* the fault and the footwall is located *below* the fault. Help students to remember this distinction by suggesting they think of the hanging wall like a picture that *hangs above* them. They can think of the footwall like their foot, which *steps below* them. **learning modality: visual**

Figure 6 A strike-slip fault that is clearly visible at the surface is the San Andreas Fault in California.

Figure 7 A normal fault created the Sandia Mountains in New Mexico.

Key
Force deforming the crust ➡
Movement along the fault ➤

360

Kinds of Faults

If you try to break a caramel candy bar in two, it may only bend and stretch at first. Like a candy bar, many types of rock can bend or fold. But beyond a certain limit, even these rocks will break. And it takes less stress to snap a brittle rock than it does to snap one that can bend.

When enough stress builds up in rock, the rock breaks, creating a fault. A **fault** is a break in the crust where slabs of crust slip past each other. The rocks on both sides of a fault can move up or down or sideways. **Faults usually occur along plate boundaries, where the forces of plate motion compress, pull, or shear the crust so much that the crust breaks.** There are three main types of faults: strike-slip faults, normal faults, and reverse faults.

Strike-Slip Faults Shearing creates strike-slip faults. In a **strike-slip fault,** the rocks on either side of the fault slip past each other sideways with little up-or-down motion. Figure 6 shows the type of movement that occurs along a strike-slip fault. A strike-slip fault that forms the boundary between two plates is called a transform boundary. The San Andreas fault in California is an example of a strike-slip fault that is a transform boundary.

Normal Faults Tension forces in Earth's crust cause normal faults. In a **normal fault,** the fault is at an angle, so one block of rock lies above the fault, while the other block lies below the fault. The half of the fault that lies above is called the **hanging wall.** The half of the fault that lies below is called the **footwall.** Look at Figure 7 to see how the hanging wall lies above the footwall.

When movement occurs along a normal fault, the hanging wall slips downward. Tension forces create normal faults where plates diverge, or pull apart. For example, normal faults occur along the Rio Grande rift valley in New Mexico, where two pieces of Earth's crust are diverging.

Reverse Faults Compression forces produce reverse faults. A **reverse fault** has the same structure as a normal fault, but the blocks move in the opposite direction. Look at Figure 8 to see how the rocks along a reverse fault move. As in a normal fault, one side of a reverse fault lies at an angle above the other side. The rock forming the hanging wall of a reverse fault slides up and over the footwall. Reverse faults produced part of the Appalachian Mountains in the eastern United States.

A type of reverse fault formed the majestic peaks in Glacier National Park in Montana shown in Figure 8. Over millions of years, a huge block of rock slid along the fault, moving up and over the surface rock. Parts of the overlying block then wore away, leaving the mountain peaks.

✓ *Checkpoint* *What are the three types of fault? What force of deformation produces each?*

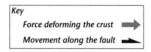

Key
Force deforming the crust →
Movement along the fault →

Footwall   Hanging Wall

Reverse fault

Figure 8 A reverse fault formed Mt. Gould in Glacier National Park. *Applying Concepts Did the hanging wall or footwall slide up and across to form this mountain?*

Media and Technology

 Transparencies "Strike-Slip, Normal, and Reverse Faults," Transparency 53

Answers to Self-Assessment

✓ *Checkpoint*
The three types of faults are strike-slip faults, produced by shearing; normal faults produced by tension; and reverse faults produced by compression.

Caption Question
Figure 8 The hanging wall slipped up and across. If the footwall had moved up, the fault would be called a normal fault.

Demonstration

Content Mastery *ACTIVITY*

To help students visualize the movement associated with the different types of faults, use your hands to model fault movement for them. Tell students to imagine that your hands represent the crust on either side of a fault. First, position your open hands with your fingers pointing toward each other. Lay the fingers of one hand over the fingers of the other hand and move your hands away from each other. Ask: **What type of fault am I modeling?** *(A normal fault)* Have students identify the hand representing the hanging wall (upper hand) and the footwall (lower hand). Next, position your hands as described above, but move them toward each other. Ask: **What type of fault am I modeling now?** *(A reverse fault)* Lastly, position the edges of your open hands against each other with your palms down, your fingers pointing away from your body, and your thumbs tucked below. Slide one hand away from your body and the other hand toward your body. Ask students to identify the fault modeled. *(A strike slip fault)* **learning modality: visual**

Ongoing Assessment

Drawing Provide each student with poster paper and markers and have them create a poster showing the three types of faults.

Friction Along Faults

Integrating Physics

Before students read about friction, invite them to define the term in their own words. *(Students' definitions will vary but should include the idea of resistance as one surface rubs against another.)* Ask: **What are some examples of low friction that you've experienced?** *(Students may mention slipping on ice or a polished floor.)* **What are some examples of high friction?** *(Sliding a heavy box across a concrete floor is one example.)* **What are some examples of times when people use high friction to their advantage?** *(Students may mention using sandpaper to smooth rough wood, wearing rubber-soled sneakers on a slippery gym floor, and filing fingernails.)* **learning modality: logical/mathematical**

Building Inquiry Skills: Comparing and Contrasting

Materials *two ceramic tiles, each with one side glazed and the other side unglazed*

ACTIVITY

Time 5 minutes

Use the following activity to help students understand how the amount of friction affects movement along a fault. Let each student rub two ceramic tiles together in different combinations—the two glazed surfaces against each other, the glazed surface of one tile against the unglazed surface of the other tile, and the two unglazed surfaces against each other—and compare how the tiles move each time. Ask: **When did the tiles move most easily?** *(When the two smooth sides were rubbed against each other)* **When were they hardest to move?** *(When the two rough sides were rubbed together)* **What do you think would happen if the unglazed sides were so rough that they caught on each other when you tried to slide them?** *(At first the tiles would not move, but with more pressure they would jerk free and slide abruptly.)* **How do these tiles show what happens along a fault?** *(The rougher the rock faces along the fault are, the more difficult it is for the blocks to slip and slide past each other. A strong earthquake occurs when the blocks suddenly break free from each other and move abruptly.)* **learning modality: tactile/kinesthetic**

Figure 9 The San Andreas fault extends from the Salton Sea in southern California to the point in northern California where the plate boundary continues into the Pacific Ocean.

Friction Along Faults

 INTEGRATING PHYSICS How rocks move along a fault depends on how much friction there is between the opposite sides of the fault. Friction is the force that opposes the motion of one surface as it moves across another surface. Friction exists because surfaces are not perfectly smooth.

Where friction along a fault is low, the rocks on both sides of the fault slide by each other without much sticking. Where friction is moderate, the sides of the fault jam together. Then from time to time they jerk free, producing small earthquakes. Where friction is high, the rocks lock together and do not move. In this case, stress increases until it is strong enough to overcome the friction force. A powerful quake results.

The San Andreas fault forms a transform boundary between the Pacific plate and the North American plate. In many places along the San Andreas fault, friction is high and the plates lock. Stress builds up until an earthquake releases the stress and the plates slide past each other.

Mountain Building and Uplift

The forces of plate movement can build up Earth's surface. **Over millions of years, fault movement can cause uplift, changing a flat plain into a towering mountain range or plateau.**

Mountains Formed by Faulting When normal faults uplift a block of rock, a fault-block mountain forms. You can see a diagram of this process in Figure 10. How does this process begin?

Figure 10 Two normal faults can form fault-block mountains, such as the Teton Range near the border of Wyoming and Idaho.

Normal faults

Key
Movement along normal faults ➡

362

Background

History of Science The San Andreas fault played a major role in the formulation of a hypothesis to explain how earthquakes are generated. Following the 1906 San Francisco earthquake, geologist H.F. Reid of Johns Hopkins University analyzed the San Andreas fault. Reid found that in the half century leading up to the 1906 earthquake, there was a relative displacement of about 3 m for widely separated points on opposite sides of the fault. From this information, Reid deduced the earthquake-generation mechanism in which rocks store energy as they are deformed until the stored energy overcomes friction and the rocks abruptly slip. This slippage results in the sudden release of the stored energy as seismic waves. Because this slippage allows the deformed rock to spring back to its original shape, Reid termed the process *elastic rebound*.

Where two plates move away from each other, tension forces create many normal faults. When two of these normal faults form parallel to each other, a block of rock is left lying between them. As the hanging wall of each normal fault slips downward, the block in between moves upward. When a block of rock lying between two normal faults slides downward, a valley forms.

If you traveled by car from Salt Lake City to Los Angeles you would cross the Great Basin, a region with many ranges of fault-block mountains separated by broad valleys, or basins. This "basin and range" region covers much of Nevada and western Utah.

Mountains Formed by Folding Under certain conditions, plate movement causes the crust to fold. Have you ever skidded on a rug that wrinkled up as your feet pushed it across the floor? Much as the rug wrinkles, rock stressed by compression may bend slowly without breaking. **Folds** are bends in rock that form when compression shortens and thickens part of Earth's crust.

The collisions of two plates can cause compression and folding of the crust. Some of the world's largest mountain ranges, including the Himalayas in Asia and the Alps in Europe, formed when pieces of the crust folded during the collision of two plates. Such plate collisions also lead to earthquakes, because folding rock can fracture and produce faults.

Individual folds can be only a few centimeters across or hundreds of kilometers wide. You can often see small folds in the rock exposed where a highway has been cut through a hillside.

Sharpen your Skills

Measuring

You can measure the force of friction.

1. Place a small weight on a smooth, flat tabletop. Use a spring scale to pull the weight across the surface. How much force is shown on the spring scale? (*Hint*: The unit of force is newtons.)

2. Tape a piece of sandpaper to the tabletop. Repeat Step 1, pulling the weight across the sandpaper.

Is the force of friction greater for a smooth surface or for a rough surface?

Figure 11 Compression forces cause folds in Earth's crust. **(A)** Some mountains are made up of folded rock. **(B)** The satellite image shows folded mountains west of Harrisburg, Pennsylvania.

Sharpen your Skills

Measuring

Materials *small weight, spring scale, sandpaper, masking tape*

Time 10 minutes

Tips If necessary, let students first practice using the spring scale by weighing several small objects and reading the measurements on the scale. Remind them to calibrate the scale to zero when no weight is added. Point out that when they do the activity, they must read the measurement while they are pulling the weight across the surface.

Expected Outcome The force of friction (the scale reading) is greater for a rough surface.

Extend Students could repeat the activity with other materials taped to the surface, such as waxed paper, aluminum foil, and a terrycloth towel. **learning modality: logical/mathematical**

Mountain Building and Uplift

Real-Life Learning

Encourage students to look for actual examples of rock folds. (Draw students' attention to Figure 12 on the next page.) Roadways cut through rocky hillsides often have exposed folds. Tell students to note the locations of the folds they find and to sketch the fold patterns they see. In a follow-up class session, let students share their observations and drawings. **learning modality: visual**

Ongoing Assessment

Writing Have students write a brief explanation, in their own words, of why earthquakes are so common—and so often violent—along the San Andreas fault.

Mountain Building and Uplift, continued

Inquiry Challenge

Challenge students to use any simple materials **ACTIVITY** available in the classroom to model the folding process that produces anticlines and synclines. *(Students can use any material that buckles and folds when compressed, such as a stack of several sheets of construction paper of different colors to represent different rock layers. To model an anticline, lay the stack on a desktop and push the two short ends toward each other; the stack will bend upward in the middle. To model a syncline, lay the stack across a space between two desks and push the ends; the stack will bend downward in the middle.)*
learning modality: tactile/ kinesthetic

Cultural Diversity

Display a detailed regional map that includes South Dakota and also shows the locations of Indian reservations in the Black Hills area. (Map 4, "The North Central States," in The National Geographic Society's *Close-Up: U.S.A.* map set is an excellent choice.) Let students first locate the Black Hills along the boundary between South Dakota and Wyoming. Explain that since ancient times, Native Americans living in that region have regarded the Black Hills as a sacred place. However, the Black Hills were taken from the native peoples when valuable minerals, including gold, were discovered there. Invite students to locate and name the present-day Indian reservations in the area and find out the name of the Native American tribe living there. *(The Pine Ridge and Rosebud reservations are home to the Oglala Sioux.)* Encourage interested students to find out more about the history of this area and how the type of geology there made it easy for people to find gold and other minerals. Students could also find pictures and descriptions of famous tourist attractions in the Black Hills, including the Mount Rushmore National Memorial and the Crazy Horse Memorial on Thunderhead Mountain.
learning modality: visual

Anticlines and Synclines Geologists use the terms anticline and syncline to describe upward and downward folds in rock. You can compare anticlines and synclines in the diagram in Figure 12. A fold in rock that bends upward into an arch is an anticline. A fold in rock that bends downward in the middle to form a bowl is a syncline. Anticlines and synclines are found on many parts of Earth's surface where compression forces have folded the crust.

One example of an anticline is the Black Hills of South Dakota. The Black Hills began to form about 65 million years ago. At that time, forces in Earth's crust produced a large dome-shaped anticline. Over millions of years, a variety of processes wore down and shaped the rock of this anticline into the Black Hills.

You may see a syncline where a valley dips between two parallel ranges of hills. But a syncline may also be a very large feature, as large as the state of Illinois. The Illinois Basin is a syncline that stretches from the western side of Indiana about 250 kilometers across the state of Illinois. The basin is filled with soil and rock that have accumulated over millions of years.

Figure 12 (A) Over millions of years, compression and folding of the crust produce anticlines, which arch upward, and synclines, which dip downward. (B) The folded rock layers of an anticline can be seen on this cliff on the coast of England.

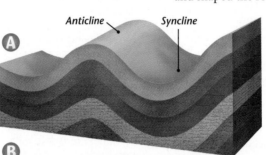

Anticline   Syncline

364

Background

Facts and Figures Anticlines and synclines usually occur one after another in a series. Upward and downward folds may also form roughly elliptical features called domes and basins.

Anticlines and synclines are classified based on their orientation. When the sides of the folds both dip at the same angle, the fold is called *symmetrical.* When one side is steeper than the other, the fold is called *asymmetrical.* If folding continues, the rock layers may fall back on one another, like a flattened letter S. Such a fold is described as *recumbent.* Recumbent folds are known as *nappes,* from the French word for "tablecloth." An *isoclinal* fold has collapsed to the point that the rock layers lie parallel to one another.

Plateaus Uplift, the force that raises mountains, can also raise plateaus. A **plateau** is a large area of flat land elevated high above sea level. Some plateaus form when vertical faults push up a large, flat block of rock. Like a fancy sandwich, a plateau consists of many different flat layers, and is wider than it is tall.

Forces deforming the crust uplifted the Colorado Plateau in the "Four Corners" region of Arizona, Utah, Colorado, and New Mexico. The Colorado Plateau is a roughly circular area of uplifted rock more than 500 kilometers across. This vast slab of rock once formed part of a sea floor. Today, much of the plateau lies more than 1,500 meters above sea level.

Figure 13 The flat land on the horizon is the Kaibab Plateau, which forms the North Rim of the Grand Canyon in Arizona. The Kaibab Plateau is part of the Colorado Plateau.

Section 2 Review

1. What are the three main types of stress in rock?
2. Describe the movements that occur along each of the three types of faults.
3. How does Earth's surface change as a result of movement along faults?
4. **Thinking Critically** **Predicting** If plate motion compresses part of the crust, what landforms will form there in millions of years? Explain.

Check Your Progress
CHAPTER PROJECT

Start by selecting the volcanic region you will study. Possible topics to investigate are myths and legends about volcanoes, the importance of volcanic soils, mineral resources from volcanoes, tourism, and geothermal power. Choose the topic that interests you the most. Begin your research and take notes on the information you collect.

Program Resources

◆ **Unit 4 Resources** 11-2 Review and Reinforce, p. 39; 11-2 Enrich, p. 40

3 Assess

Check Your Progress
CHAPTER PROJECT

To avoid duplication, check each group's choice of a volcanic region. You may want to allow two groups to choose the same region so long as they focus on different specific topics. Other possible topics besides those suggested in this Check Your Progress are listed on Chapter 11 Project Worksheet 1. You may also distribute Chapter 11 Project Worksheet 2 at this time, which provides support for helping students take notes as they do their research.

Performance Assessment

Skills Check To evaluate students' understanding of different types of faults and their ability to represent those concepts in a model, have each student use two dry kitchen sponges to show the movements involved in strike-slip, normal, and reverse faulting and explain the processes as they demonstrate them.

Modeling Movement Along Faults

Preparing for Inquiry

Key Concept The directions of stress forces are different for strike-slip, normal, and reverse faults.

Skills Objectives Students will be able to
- make a simple model to show block movements in a strike-slip fault, a normal fault, and a reverse fault;
- infer how faulting can change the land surface;
- classify deformations in surface features caused by different types of faults.

Time 40 minutes

Guiding Inquiry

Invitation Remind students of the three fault models you made with your hands in the Demonstration, page 361. Ask: **What was different about the directions of movement in the three types of faults?** *(In the strike-slip fault, movement was sideways and in opposite directions; in the normal fault, the hanging wall moved down; in the reverse fault, the hanging wall moved up.)*

Introducing the Procedure

Tell students that in this activity, they will be using blocks of clay to represent blocks of Earth's crust. Ask: **How will blocks of clay more closely resemble real blocks of rock than my hands did?** *(They can show several layers of rock and the actual shape of the hanging wall and footwall.)*

Troubleshooting the Experiment

Have students first cover the desktop with a sheet of waxed paper or plastic to protect it.
- In Step 2, make sure students cut the squares in half from one side to the opposite side, not from corner to corner.
- In Step 4, if any students cut the block straight down instead of at an angle,

---

MODELING MOVEMENT ALONG FAULTS

Faults are cracks in Earth's crust where masses of rock move over, under, or past each other. In this lab, you will make a model of the movements along faults.

Problem

How does the movement of rock along the sides of a fault vary for different types of faults?

Materials

Modeling compound in two or more colors
Marking pen
Plastic butter knife

Procedure

1. Roll some modeling compound into a sheet about 0.5 centimeter thick and about 6 centimeters square. Then make another sheet of the same size and thickness, using a different color.

2. Cut each square in half and stack the sheets on top of each other, alternating colors.
   CAUTION: *To avoid breaking the plastic knife, do not press too hard as you cut.* The sheets of modeling compound stand for different layers of rock. The different colors will help you see where similar layers of rock end up after movement occurs along the model fault.

3. Press the layers of modeling compound together to form a rectangular block that fits in the palm of your hand.

4. Use the butter knife to slice carefully through the block at an angle, as shown in the photograph.

5. Place the two blocks formed by the slice together, but don't let them stick together.

6. Review the descriptions and diagrams of faults in Section 1. Decide which piece of your block is the hanging wall and which is the footwall. Using the marking pen, label the side of each block. What part of your model stands for the fault itself?

7. What part of the model stands for the land surface? Along the top surface of the two blocks, draw a river flowing across the fault. Also draw an arrow on each block to show the direction of the river's flow. The arrow should point from the footwall toward the hanging wall.

8. Make a table that includes the headings Type of Fault, How the Sides of the Fault Move, and Changes in the Land Surface.

Type of Fault	How the Sides of the Fault Move	Changes in the Land Surface

---

have them press the two pieces firmly back together and recut the block.
- In Step 6, the hanging wall is the block with the larger surface area on top and the footwall is the lower block. The fault is the cut between the two blocks.
- In Step 7, the land surface is the top surface of the two blocks. Make sure students draw the arrows to show the river flowing *toward* the fault on the surface of the footwall and *away from* the fault on the surface of the hanging wall.
- In Step 9, the blocks should be moved sideways, with no up or down movement. In Step 10, the upper block should be moved down. In Step 11, the upper block should be moved up.

9. Using your blocks, model the movement along a strike-slip fault. Record your motion and the results on the data table.
10. Repeat Step 9 for a normal fault.
11. Repeat Step 9 for a reverse fault.

Analyze and Conclude

Refer to your data table to draw a chart that will help you answer Questions 1 through 4.

1. On your chart, show the direction in which the sides of the fault move for each type of fault.
2. On your chart, show how movement along a strike-slip fault is different from movement along the other two types of fault.
3. Add to your chart a column that shows how the river on the surface might change for each type of fault.
4. Assuming that the river is flowing from the footwall toward the hanging wall, which type of fault could produce small waterfalls in the surface river? (*Hint:* Recall how you tell which block is the hanging wall and which block is the footwall.)
5. If you could observe only the land surface around a fault, how could you tell if the fault is a strike-slip fault? A normal fault?
6. If you slide the hanging wall of your fault model upward in relation to the footwall, what type of fault forms? If this movement continues, where will the slab of rock with the hanging wall end up?

7. From an airplane, you see a chain of several long, narrow lakes along a fault. What type of fault would cause these lakes to form?
8. **Think About It** In what ways does the model help you picture what is happening along a fault? In what ways does the model not accurately reflect what happens along a fault? How is the model still useful in spite of its inaccuracies?

More to Explore

On Earth's surface, individual faults do not exist all by themselves. With one or more of your classmates, combine your models to show how a fault-block mountain range or a rift valley could form. (*Hint:* Both involve normal faults.) How could you combine your models to show how reverse faults produce a mountain range?

Sample Data Table		
Type of Fault	How Hanging Wall Moves	Changes in the Land Surface
Strike-slip fault	sideways	Riverbed is broken and moved sideways.
Normal Fault	down	Downstream part of river drops below upstream part.
Reverse fault	up	Downstream part of river may form a lake where it meets hanging wall.

Safety

Students should handle the knife carefully during this activity. Review the safety guidelines in Appendix A.

Program Resources

◆ **Unit 4 Resources** Chapter 11 Skills Lab blackline masters, pp. 53–55

Expected Outcome

In Step 9, the riverbed will be displaced horizontally in a zig-zag shape. In Step 10, the downstream part of the river on the surface of the upper block will be displaced downward so it is lower than the upstream part. In Step 11, the downstream part will be displaced upward so it is higher than the upstream part.

Analyze and Conclude

1. *Strike-slip fault:* The walls move sideways. *Normal fault:* The hanging wall moves downward. *Reverse fault:* The hanging wall moves upward.
2. Students' charts should indicate that there is no upward or downward movement along a strike-slip fault.
3. *Strike-slip fault:* The continuous line of the riverbed would be broken and displaced horizontally. *Normal fault:* The downstream part of the river would drop below the upstream part, creating a waterfall at the fault. *Reverse fault:* The downstream part of the river would be thrust above the upstream part; water would collect at the fault to form a lake.
4. A normal fault
5. A strike-slip fault would be indicated by sideways displacement of a feature where it crossed the fault. A normal fault would be indicated by a break in the feature where the two blocks slipped past each other at the fault; the part of the feature on the surface of the hanging wall would be lower than the part on the surface of the footwall.
6. A reverse fault; above the footwall
7. A reverse fault or strike-slip fault
8. The model demonstrates actual rock movements. The model's fault is much more regular and smooth than real faults between rock surfaces, so the model's movements involve far less friction and are less abrupt and "jerky." The model enables you to see block movements that are hidden underground in real faulting.

Extending the Inquiry

More to Explore Encourage students to model fault-block mountains and rift valleys. They can refer to Figure 10, Page 362, for fault-block mountains and *Exploring Plate Tectonics*, pages 356–357, for a rift valley.

TEKS: 6.2B, C; 6.6C

Objectives

After completing the lesson, students will be able to

◆ describe how the energy of an earthquake travels through Earth;

◆ identify the different kinds of seismic waves;

◆ name the scales used to measure the strength of an earthquake.

1 Engage/Explore

Activating Prior Knowledge

Ask: **What kinds of waves have you observed?** *(Students will probably mention ocean waves and waves in a lake, pond, swimming pool, or even a bathtub.)* **How do waves move in water?** *(They will probably say that the waves move outward from a "push" on the water.)*

········ **DISCOVER** ········

Skills Focus observing
Materials *spring toy*
Time 10 minutes
Tips Advise students to hold both ends of the spring securely as they make the waves. If they have difficulty observing differences in the two wave types, let them repeat each step several times. If you add sticky paper strips to the spring toy, it makes the motion easier to observe.
Expected Outcome In Step 2, the coils will move forward and backward along the spring in a straight line. In Step 3, the coils will move sideways.
Think It Over In Step 2, the coils move forward and back as a wave moves from the compressed end of the spring to the other end in a straight line. In Step 3, the coils move from side to side as a wave moves in a bulge from the jerked end of the spring to the other end.

How Do Seismic Waves Travel Through Earth?

1. Stretch a spring toy across the floor while a classmate holds the other end. Do not overstretch the toy.

2. Gather together about 4 coils of the spring toy and release them. In what direction do the coils move?

3. Once the spring toy has stopped moving, jerk one end of the toy from side to side once. In what direction do the coils move? Be certain your classmate has a secure grip on the other end.

Think It Over
Observing Describe the two types of wave motion that you observed in the spring toy.

GUIDE FOR READING

◆ How does the energy of an earthquake travel through Earth?

◆ What are the different kinds of seismic waves?

◆ What are the scales used to measure the strength of an earthquake?

Reading Tip Before you read, rewrite the headings in the section as *what, how,* or *why* questions. As you read, look for answers to these questions.

Key Terms focus • epicenter
• P waves • S waves
• surface waves • seismograph
• magnitude • Mercalli scale
• Richter scale
• moment magnitude scale

Earth is never still. Every day, worldwide, there are about 8,000 earthquakes. Most of them are too small to notice. But when an earthquake is strong enough to rattle dishes in kitchen cabinets, people sit up and take notice. "How big was the quake?" and "Where was it centered?" are two questions just about everyone asks after an earthquake.

To know where an earthquake was centered, you need to know where it began. Earthquakes always begin in rock below the surface. Most earthquakes begin in the lithosphere within 100 kilometers of Earth's surface. An earthquake starts at one particular point. The **focus** (FOH kus) is the point beneath Earth's surface where rock that is under stress breaks, triggering an earthquake. The point on the surface directly above the focus is called the **epicenter** (EHP uh sen tur).

Seismic Waves

If you have ever played a drum, you know that the sound it makes depends on how hard you strike it. Like a drumbeat, an earthquake produces vibrations called waves. These waves carry energy as they travel outward through solid material. During an earthquake, seismic waves race out from the focus in all directions. Seismic waves are vibrations that travel through Earth carrying the energy released during an earthquake. The seismic waves move like ripples in a pond. Look at Figure 14 to see how seismic waves travel outward in all directions from the focus.

READING STRATEGIES

Reading Tip Encourage students to say their question to themselves silently to see if they have chosen appropriate verbs. Questions may include, "What are seismic waves?" and "How are seismic waves detected?" You may wish to have students write their questions in their notebooks and answer the questions after reading the section.

Vocabulary Students may wonder where the terms *seismic, seismograph, seismologist,* and *seismology* came from. Encourage students to look up the origin of the root word *seism. (From* seismos, *the Greek word for earthquake, derived from* seiein, *meaning "to shake")* Also discuss the meanings of the suffixes -graph *("a device that writes or records"),* -ology *("the study of" something),* and -ologist *("a person who studies" something).*

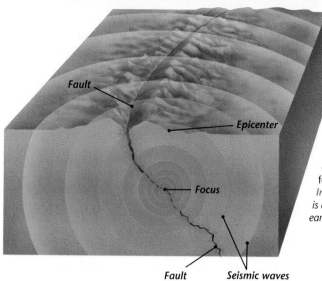

Fault

Epicenter

Focus

Fault   Seismic waves

Figure 14 An earthquake occurs when rocks fracture at the focus, deep in Earth's crust. *Interpreting Diagrams* What point is directly above the focus of the earthquake?

Seismic waves carry the energy of an earthquake away from the focus, through Earth's interior, and across the surface. The energy of the seismic waves that reach the surface is greatest at the epicenter. The most violent shaking during an earthquake, however, may occur kilometers away from the epicenter. The types of rock and soil around the epicenter can affect where and how much the ground shakes. For example, seismic waves in solid rock transmit their energy to the soil. The loose soil shakes more violently than the surrounding rock.

There are three categories of seismic waves: P waves, S waves, and surface waves. An earthquake sends out two types of waves from its focus: P waves and S waves. When these waves reach Earth's surface at the epicenter, surface waves develop.

Primary Waves The first waves to arrive are primary waves, or P waves. **P waves** are earthquake waves that can compress and expand the ground like an accordion. P waves cause buildings to contract and expand. Look at Figure 15 to compare P waves and S waves.

Secondary Waves After P waves come secondary waves, or S waves. **S waves** are earthquake waves that vibrate from side to side as well as up and down. They shake the ground back and forth. When S waves reach the surface, they shake structures violently. Unlike P waves, which travel through both solids and liquids, S waves cannot move through liquids.

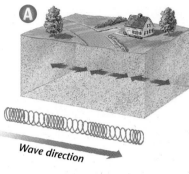

Wave direction

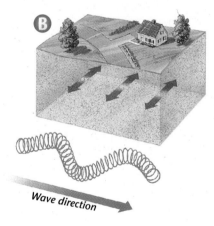

Wave direction

Figure 15 **(A)** In P waves, the particles of the crust vibrate forward and back along the path of the wave. **(B)** In S waves, the particles of the crust vibrate from side to side and up and down.

Answers to Self-Assessment

Caption Question

Figure 14 the epicenter

Seismic Waves

Building Inquiry Skills: Observing

Materials *dishpans or other wide, shallow containers; water; pebbles*
Time 10 minutes

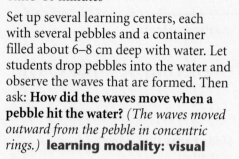

Set up several learning centers, each with several pebbles and a container filled about 6–8 cm deep with water. Let students drop pebbles into the water and observe the waves that are formed. Then ask: **How did the waves move when a pebble hit the water?** (*The waves moved outward from the pebble in concentric rings.*) **learning modality: visual**

Using the Visuals: Figure 14

Draw students' attention to the pattern of seismic waves shown in the diagram and ask: **How are seismic waves like the waves you made when you dropped pebbles into water?** (*Seismic waves also move outward in concentric rings.*) **How are they different?** (*Seismic waves move outward three-dimensionally in all directions, whereas the water waves moved only on the surface. Seismic waves move through solid materials.*) **learning modality: visual**

Including All Students

Remind students of their experience creating waves with the spring toy in the Discover activity. Ask: **When the wave moved straight ahead along the spring, which type of earthquake wave did it model?** (*a P wave*) **When the spring moved from side to side, which type of wave did it model?** (*an S wave*) **When you used the spring, where was the focus of the model earthquake?** (*At the end that was compressed and jerked*) **learning modality: logical/ mathematical**

Ongoing Assessment

Writing Have each student describe the major difference between P waves and S waves.

Seismic Waves, continued

Building Inquiry Skills: Inferring

After students read about surface waves, ask: **Why do you think surface waves produce more severe ground movements than P waves and S waves do?** (*Students should infer that because the surface consists of loose soil, sand, gravel, mud, small rocks, and the like rather then solid rock, it is susceptible to greater movement as the particles shift and slide.*) **learning modality: logical/mathematical**

Detecting Seismic Waves

TRY THIS

Skills Focus observing
Materials *large book, pencil, paper strip 1 m long, pen*
Time 10 minutes
Tips Make sure students hold the pencil and rolled strip *parallel* to the book and tabletop.
Expected Outcome The pen will first draw a straight line, then a jagged back-and-forth line as the book is jiggled. The line's spikes will be larger with stronger jiggling.
Extend Encourage students to try different types of "earthquakes"—long, slow movements; strong, abrupt movements; a strong quake followed by calm and then a smaller quake (an aftershock); and so forth. **learning modality: kinesthetic**

Using the Visuals: Figure 16

After students have studied the figure and read the caption, ask: **Which type of seismograph did you model in Try This?** (*A mechanical seismograph*) **What similarities do you see between the real seismograph record (also called a seismogram) and the marks you made on the paper strip?** (*Students should mention the back-and-forth jiggles in the line and the different sizes of the spikes caused by different strengths of the movements.*) **learning modality: visual**

Recording Seismic Waves

ACTIVITY

You and two classmates can simulate a seismograph.

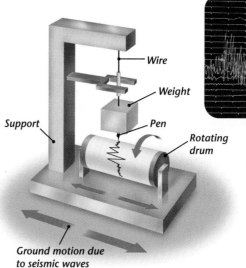

1. Place a big book on a table.
2. With one hand, hold a pencil with a strip of paper about one meter long wound around it.
3. In your other hand, hold a pen against the paper.
4. As you hold the pen steady, have one student slowly pull on the paper so it slides across the book.
5. After a few seconds, have the other student jiggle the book for 10 seconds—first gently, then strongly.

Observing How did the line on the paper change when the earthquake began? When it grew stronger?

Surface Waves When P waves and S waves reach the surface, some of them are transformed into surface waves. **Surface waves** move more slowly than P waves and S waves, but they can produce severe ground movements. Some surface waves make the ground roll like ocean waves. Other surface waves shake buildings from side to side.

☑ *Checkpoint* *What are the three types of seismic waves?*

Detecting Seismic Waves

To record and measure the vibrations of seismic waves, geologists use instruments called seismographs. A **seismograph** (SYZ muh graf) records the ground movements caused by seismic waves as they move through the Earth.

Until recently, scientists used mechanical seismographs. As shown in Figure 16, a mechanical seismograph consists of a heavy weight attached to a frame by a spring or wire. A pen connected to the weight rests its point on a rotating drum. When the drum is still, the pen draws a straight line on paper wrapped around the drum. During an earthquake, seismic waves cause the drum to vibrate. Meanwhile, the pen stays in place and records the drum's vibrations. The height of the jagged lines drawn on the seismograph's drum is greater for a more severe earthquake.

Today, scientists use electronic seismographs that work according to the same principle as the mechanical seismograph. The electronic seismograph converts ground movements into a signal that can be recorded and printed.

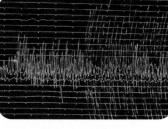

Wire
Weight
Support
Pen
Rotating drum
Ground motion due to seismic waves

Figure 16
The mechanical seismograph records seismic waves. The record made by a seismograph shows the arrival times of different types of seismic waves.

The Mercalli Scale

Earthquake Intensity	Earthquake Effects
I–II	Almost unnoticeable
III–IV	People notice vibrations like those from a passing truck. Unstable objects disturbed.
V–VI	Dishes and windows rattle. Books knocked off shelves. Slight damage.
VII–VIII	People run outdoors. Moderate to heavy damage.
IX–X	Buildings jolted off foundations or destroyed. Cracks appear in ground and landslides occur.
XI–XII	Severe damage. Wide cracks appear in ground. Waves seen on ground surface.

Figure 17 An earthquake in 1997 damaged the tower of this city hall in Foligno, Italy (left). The Mercalli scale (right) uses Roman numerals to rank earthquakes by how much damage they cause. *Applying Concepts How would you rate the damage to the Foligno city hall on the Mercalli scale?*

Measuring Earthquakes

When geologists want to know the size of an earthquake, they must consider many factors. As a result, there are at least 20 different measures for rating earthquakes, each with its strengths and shortcomings. Three ways of measuring earthquakes, the Mercalli scale, the Richter scale, and the moment magnitude scale, are described here. **Magnitude** is a measurement of earthquake strength based on seismic waves and movement along faults.

The Mercalli Scale Early in the twentieth century, geologists developed the **Mercalli scale** to rate earthquakes according to their intensity. An earthquake's intensity is the strength of ground motion in a given place. The Mercalli scale is not a precise measurement. But the 12 steps of the Mercalli scale describe how earthquakes affect people, buildings, and the land surface. The same earthquake can have different Mercalli ratings because it causes different amounts of damage at different locations.

The Richter Scale The **Richter scale** was originally a rating of the size of seismic waves as measured by a type of mechanical seismograph. The Richter scale was developed in the 1930s. Geologists all over the world used this scale for about 50 years. Eventually, electronic seismographs replaced the mechanical seismographs used for the Richter scale. The Richter scale provides accurate measurements for small, nearby earthquakes. But the scale does not work well for large or distant earthquakes.

Media and Technology

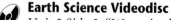 **Earth Science Videodisc**
Unit 2 Side 2, "Waves in the Earth"

Chapter 9

Answers to Self-Assessment

✓ Checkpoint
The three types of seismic waves are P waves, S waves, and surface waves.

Caption Question
Figure 17 The damage would probably rate VII–VIII.

Measuring Earthquakes

Including All Students

Students may wonder how the Mercalli and Richter scales got their names. Explain that the scales were named after the men who developed them—Italian volcanologist Giuseppe Mercalli and American seismologist Charles Richter. Then ask: **How are the Mercalli scale and the Richter scale similar?** *(Both describe the "strength" of an earthquake.)* **How are they different?** *(The Mercalli scale describes an earthquake's strength in terms of its effects—to what extent people notice it and the amount of damage it causes. The Richter scale describes an earthquake's strength in terms of the size of its seismic waves; it is a precise measurement.)* **On which scale would an earthquake's strength vary from one place to another, and why?** *(The Mercalli scale; the amount of shaking that people would feel and the damage to objects would be greater in a place closer to the quake's epicenter and less in a place farther away, so the intensity ratings in the two places would be different.)* **learning modality: verbal**

Building Inquiry Skills: Classifying

Direct students to examine the photograph of the 1906 San Francisco earthquake in Figure 19 on the next page. Ask: **Where do you think this earthquake rated on the Mercalli scale?** *(Probably IX or X)* Ask volunteers to find photographs of other areas damaged by earthquakes, including moderate quakes as well as severe ones, and make photocopies of the pictures for the class to examine. Let students try to estimate each quake's Mercalli rating based on evidence they see in the photograph. *(Students may have some difficulty differentiating between categories VII–VIII and IX–X and between categories IX–X and X–XII. Accept all reasonable responses.)* **learning modality: visual**

Ongoing Assessment

Drawing Have each student draw and label a simple diagram explaining how a mechanical seismograph works.

Locating the Epicenter

Demonstration

Time 10–15 minutes
Do the following activity in a roomy area such as a gym. Choose two students to roleplay a P wave and an S wave. Position both students at a starting point, and position a third student some distance away to represent a seismograph. When you say "Earthquake!" the two students should start walking toward the third student, with the "P wave" student taking long forward strides and the "S wave" student taking shorter steps in a waddling gait to represent the side-to-side vibration of S waves. After a few seconds, say "Stop" and ask: **Which wave is closer to the seismograph?** *(The P wave)* Repeat the activity with six students roleplaying three pairs of P and S waves. Assign a number to each pair, and have all three pairs start walking at your signal. Say "One, stop," "Two, stop," and "Three, stop" at intervals. Have the students who are observing compare the distances between the P-wave and S-wave students in the three pairs. Ask: **Are all three distances the same?** *(No)* **How do they vary?** *(The P and S students who were walking for the shortest time are the closest together, while the P and S students who were walking for the longest time are the farthest apart.)* **How would this difference help a geologist tell how far away an earthquake's epicenter is?** *(If the S waves arrive at a seismograph a very short time after the P waves, the epicenter is close to the seismograph; the longer the interval between the arrival times of the P and S waves, the farther away the epicenter is.)* **learning modality: kinesthetic**

Integrating Mathematics

Ask: **Why would drawing only two circles not be enough to locate the earthquake's epicenter?** *(Two circles would intersect at two points, not one, and identify two possible epicenters. If students have difficulty visualizing this, let them lay a sheet of tracing paper over the map in Figure 20, trace each circle in a different color, and mark the two points where each pair of circles intersect.)* **learning modality: logical/mathematical**

Earthquake Magnitudes	
Earthquake	**Moment Magnitude**
San Francisco, California, 1906	7.7
Southern Chile, 1960	9.5
Anchorage, Alaska, 1964	9.2
Loma Prieta, California, 1989	7.2
Northridge/ Los Angeles, California, 1994	6.7
Izmit, Turkey, 1999	7.4

Figure 18 The table lists the moment magnitudes for some of the twentieth century's biggest earthquakes.

The Moment Magnitude Scale Today, geologists use the **moment magnitude scale,** a rating system that estimates the total energy released by an earthquake. **The moment magnitude scale can be used to rate earthquakes of all sizes, near or far.** You may hear news reports that mention the Richter scale. But the magnitude number they quote is almost always the moment magnitude for that earthquake.

To rate an earthquake on the moment magnitude scale, geologists first study data from modern electronic seismographs. The data show what kinds of seismic waves the earthquake produced and how strong they were. The data also help geologists infer how much movement occurred along the fault and the strength of the rocks that broke when the fault slipped. Geologists combine all this information to rate the earthquake on the moment magnitude scale.

Earthquakes with a magnitude below 5.0 on the moment magnitude scale are small and cause little damage. Those with a magnitude above 5.0 can produce great destruction. A magnitude 6.0 quake releases 32 times as much energy as a magnitude 5.0 quake, and nearly 1,000 times as much as a magnitude 4.0 quake.

✓ *Checkpoint* What are three scales for measuring earthquakes?

Locating the Epicenter

Geologists use seismic waves to locate an earthquake's epicenter. Seismic waves travel at different speeds. P waves arrive first at a seismograph, with S waves following close behind. To tell how far the epicenter is from the seismograph, scientists measure the difference between the arrival times of the P waves and S waves.

Figure 19 In terms of magnitude, the 1906 San Francisco earthquake was not the strongest of the century. But it toppled buildings and caused fires that devastated the city.

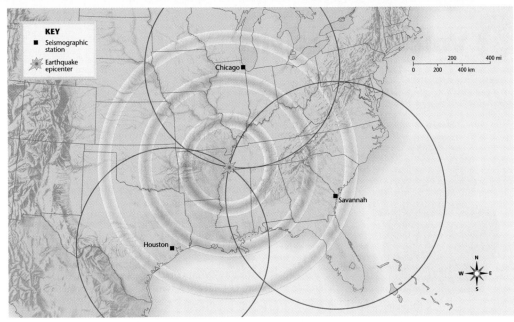

KEY

■ Seismographic station

✴ Earthquake epicenter

Chicago

Savannah

Houston

Figure 20 The map shows how to find the epicenter of an earthquake using data from three seismographic stations. *Measuring Use the map scale to determine the distances from Savannah and Houston to the epicenter. Which is closer?*

The farther away an earthquake is, the greater the time between the arrival of the P waves and the S waves.

 INTEGRATING MATHEMATICS Geologists then draw at least three circles using data from different seismographs set up at stations all over the world. The center of each circle is a particular seismograph's location. The radius of each circle is the distance from the seismograph to the epicenter. The point where the three circles intersect is the location of the epicenter. If you look at Figure 20, you can see why two circles would not give enough information to pinpoint the epicenter.

Section 3 Review

1. How does the energy from an earthquake reach Earth's surface?
2. Describe the three types of seismic waves.
3. What system do geologists use today for rating the magnitude of an earthquake?
4. **Thinking Critically Relating Cause and Effect** Describe how energy released at an earthquake's focus, deep inside Earth, can cause damage on the surface many kilometers from the epicenter.

Science at Home

Toppling Towers Show your family how an earthquake can affect two structures—one with more weight on top, the other with more weight on the bottom. Make a model of a fault by placing two small, folded towels side by side on a flat surface. Pile a stack of books on the fault by placing the light books on the bottom and the heaviest ones on top. Then, gently pull the towels in opposite directions until the pile topples. Repeat the process, but this time with the heavier books on the bottom. Discuss with your family which makes a more stable structure.

Chapter 11 **373**

Answers to Self-Assessment

☑ *Checkpoint*

Three scales for measuring earthquakes are the Mercalli scale, the Richter scale, and the moment magnitude scale.

Caption Question

Figure 20 Houston (about 800 km compared with about 900 km for Savannah)

Section 3 Review Answers

1. Seismic waves carry the energy of an earthquake away from the focus. Some of those waves reach the surface and become surface waves.
2. *P waves:* Travel straight outward from the focus; compress and expand the ground; move through solids and liquids; are the fastest-moving seismic waves. *S waves:* Vibrate from side to side and up and down as they travel; move only through solids. *Surface waves:* Move along the surface; move more slowly than P and S waves; can produce severe ground movements.
3. Data from electronic seismographs, are used to rate the strength of earthquakes on the moment magnitude scale.
4. P waves, S waves, and surface waves can all cause damaging ground movements at the surface many kilometers from epicenter. In addition, the types of rock and soil around an epicenter can affect how much the ground shakes.

Science at Home

Tips Tell students to make a tall stack of about 10 books—first with several light books such as paperbacks on the bottom, several medium-size books next, and several large, heavy books (such as dictionaries, and cookbooks) on top, then reversing the order. Demonstrate the procedure in class. With the heavier books on top, the stack will topple when the towels are pulled in opposite directions. With the heavier books at the bottom, the stack will wobble, but stand.

Performance Assessment

Drawing Have each student draw and label a sketch, without referring to Figures 14 or 15, showing an earthquake's focus underground, its epicenter on the surface, the different motions of P waves and S waves moving outward from the focus, and surface waves moving outward from the epicenter.

TEKS: 6.2A, B, C, D, E; 6.3C; 6.4A; 6.6C

Objectives

After completing the lesson, students will be able to

- describe what happens when a volcano erupts;
- explain how the two types of volcanic eruptions differ depending on the characteristics of magma;
- identify types of volcanic activity other than eruptions;
- identify some hazards of volcanoes.

1 Engage/Explore

Activating Prior Knowledge

Ask students: **What does lava look like when it comes out of a volcano?** *(Based on photographs or videos they have seen, students may describe lava as red-hot and thick or gooey.)* **What else comes out of a volcano when it erupts?** *(Students may mention steam and dark clouds of volcanic dust. Accept all responses without comment at this time.)*

• • • • • • • • DISCOVER • • • • • • • •

Skills Focus developing hypotheses
Materials *samples of pumice and obsidian, hand lens*
Time 5–10 minutes
Tips Help students with the correct pronunciations of *pumice* (PUHM is) and *obsidian* (ob SID ee un).
Expected Outcome The obsidian is smooth and glassy, whereas the pumice is rough and porous. (CAUTION: Advise students to handle the obsidian with care because it sometimes has sharp edges that can cut the skin.)
Think It Over The lava that produced the pumice had more gas (air) in it than the lava that produced the obsidian. Obsidian formed when lava cooled very quickly.

SECTION
4 Volcanic Activity

▶ DISCOVER • ACTIVITY • • • •

What Are Volcanic Rocks Like?

Pumice ▼

▲ Obsidian

Volcanoes produce lava, which hardens into rock. Two of these rocks are pumice and obsidian.

1. Observe samples of pumice and obsidian with a hand lens.

2. How would you describe the texture of the pumice? What could have caused this texture?

3. Observe the surface of the obsidian. How does the surface of the obsidian differ from pumice?

Think It Over
Developing Hypotheses What could have produced the difference in texture between the two rocks? Explain your answer.

▶ GUIDE FOR READING

- What happens when a volcano erupts?
- How do the two types of volcanic eruptions differ?
- What are some hazards of volcanoes?

Reading Tip Before you read, preview *Exploring a Volcano* on page 376. Write a list of any questions you have about how a volcano erupts.

Key Terms magma chamber
• pipe • vent • lava flow • crater
• silica • pahoehoe • aa
• pyroclastic flow • active
• dormant • extinct • geyser
• geothermal energy

374

In Hawaii, there are many myths about Pele (PAY lay), the fire goddess of volcanoes. In these myths, Pele is the creator and the destroyer of the Hawaiian islands. She lives in the fiery depths of erupting volcanoes. According to legend, when Pele is angry, she releases the fires of Earth through openings on the mountainside. Evidence of her presence is "Pele's hair," a fine, threadlike rock formed by lava. Pele's hair forms when lava sprays out of the ground like water from a fountain. As it cools, the lava stretches and hardens into thin strands.

How Magma Reaches Earth's Surface

Where does this hot, molten lava come from? Lava begins as magma in the mantle. There, magma forms in the asthenosphere, which lies beneath the lithosphere. The materials of the asthenosphere are under great pressure.

Magma Rises Because liquid magma is less dense than the surrounding solid material, magma flows upward into any cracks in the rock above. Magma rises until it reaches the surface, or until it becomes trapped beneath layers of rock.

Figure 21 Pele's hair is a type of rock formed from lava. Each strand is as fine as spun glass.

▶ READING STRATEGIES

Reading Tip Suggest that students write their questions on a sheet of paper, leaving space below each question to write the answer as they read the section. Questions may include, "How do side vents form?" and "How far can lava flow before it hardens?"

After students have answered their own questions, have pairs of students exchange questions to answer. Encourage students who pose questions that are not answered in the text to do research in the library or, with supervision, on the Internet to find the answers.

Figure 22 Molten lava from Kilauea volcano in Hawaii.

A Volcano Erupts Just like the carbon dioxide trapped in a bottle of soda pop, the dissolved gases trapped in magma are under tremendous pressure. You cannot see the carbon dioxide gas in a bottle of soda pop because it is dissolved in the liquid. But when you open the bottle, the pressure is released. The carbon dioxide forms bubbles, which rush to the surface.

As magma rises toward the surface, the pressure decreases. The dissolved gases begin to separate out, forming bubbles. A volcano erupts when an opening develops in weak rock on the surface. **During a volcanic eruption, the gases dissolved in magma rush out, carrying the magma with them.** Once magma reaches the surface and becomes lava, the gases bubble out.

Inside a Volcano

All volcanoes have a pocket of magma beneath the surface and one or more cracks through which the magma forces its way. You can see these features in *Exploring a Volcano.* Beneath a volcano, magma collects in a pocket called a **magma chamber.** The magma moves through a **pipe,** a long tube in the ground that connects the magma chamber to Earth's surface. Molten rock and gas leave the volcano through an opening called a **vent.** Often, there is one central vent at the top of a volcano. However, many volcanoes also have other vents that open on the volcano's sides. A **lava flow** is the area covered by lava as it pours out of a vent. A **crater** is a bowl-shaped area that may form at the top of a volcano around the volcano's central vent.

☑ *Checkpoint* *How does magma rise through the lithosphere?*

Gases in Magma

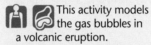 This activity models the gas bubbles in a volcanic eruption.

1. In a 1- or 2-liter plastic bottle, mix 10 g of baking soda into 65 mL of water.
2. Put about six raisins in the water.
3. While swirling the water and raisins, add 65 mL of vinegar and stir vigorously.
4. Once the liquid has stopped moving, observe the raisins.

Making Models What happens after you add the vinegar? What do the raisins and bubbles represent? How is this model similar to the way magma behaves in a volcano?

Answers to Self-Assessment

☑ *Checkpoint*

Liquid magma in the asthenosphere is less dense than the rock in the lithosphere above it, so it flows upward through cracks in the rock. It continues upward until it reaches the surface or is trapped beneath layers of rock.

---

2 Facilitate

How Magma Reaches Earth's Surface

Building Inquiry Skills: Inferring

Materials *2 clear, capped, plastic bottles of soda water; hand lens*
Time 5 minutes

Have one student closely watch a bottle with the hand lens while a partner slowly uncaps it. Students can then switch places and repeat with the second bottle. Ask students what happened and why. *(Bubbles formed. At some point, enough pressure was released to allow the carbon dioxide gas to come out of solution.)* **What do you think releases the pressure on gases trapped in magma?** *(When magma reaches Earth's surface, it is no longer confined to a limited space.)* **learning modality: visual**

Skills Focus making models
Materials *1- or 2-liter plastic bottle, 10 g baking soda, 65 mL water, 6 raisins, 65 mL vinegar*
Time 10–15 minutes
Expected Outcome The vinegar reacts with the baking soda solution to produce carbon dioxide gas. Bubbles of gas adhere to the raisins, causing the raisins to rise to the surface, where the bubbles pop. The raisins sink again, and the cycle repeats. The raisins represent magma; the bubbles represent gases trapped in the magma. In this model, the raisins and gas bubbles are not under great pressure, as magma and gases are in a real volcano. Also, magma, unlike raisins, doesn't go up and down in a volcano, but rather goes up and out.
Extend Students could repeat the activity using raisins and clear carbonated soda.
learning modality: tactile/ kinesthetic

Ongoing Assessment

Writing Have students describe what happens when a volcano erupts.

EXPLORING
a Volcano

After students have examined the diagram and read the captions on their own, call on students in turn to describe the movement of magma during an eruption, starting with the magma chamber and moving upward through the pipe to the vent and then out onto the surface in a lava flow. Make sure students notice the side vent as well. Ask: **Why would magma flow to a side vent?** *(A crack in the rock layers might offer less resistance to the magma's flow than the magma-filled main pipe.)* Point out the two bodies of magma to the right and left of the pipe just above the magma chamber. Ask: **What happened to the magma there?** *It flowed sideways away from the pipe, then smaller amounts flowed upward from those bodies.)* Refer to the **ELL Handbook** for additional teaching strategies. **learning modality: visual**

Characteristics of Magma

Building Inquiry Skills: Comparing and Contrasting

Materials *2 small paper cups, molasses, small paper cup with warmed molasses, small paper cup with chilled molasses*
Time 15 minutes

ACTIVITY

Give each student an empty cup and an identical cup half-filled with molasses at room temperature. Let students pour the molasses from one cup to the other, observing its rate of flow. Let students repeat the pouring activity and compare the flow rate of warmed molasses and then the chilled molasses with the flow rate of the room-temperature molasses. Ask: **How did the temperature of the molasses affect its thickness?** *(The lower the molasses' temperature, the thicker it was.)* Emphasize that although magma is thousands of degrees hotter than the molasses used in this activity, its thickness also varies with temperature. **learning modality: tactile/ kinesthetic**

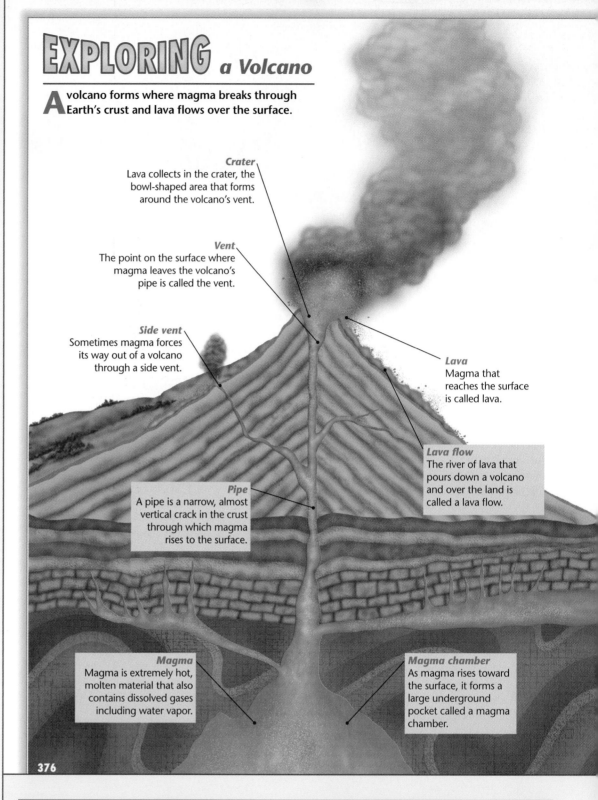

EXPLORING a Volcano

A volcano forms where magma breaks through Earth's crust and lava flows over the surface.

Crater
Lava collects in the crater, the bowl-shaped area that forms around the volcano's vent.

Vent
The point on the surface where magma leaves the volcano's pipe is called the vent.

Side vent
Sometimes magma forces its way out of a volcano through a side vent.

Lava
Magma that reaches the surface is called lava.

Lava flow
The river of lava that pours down a volcano and over the land is called a lava flow.

Pipe
A pipe is a narrow, almost vertical crack in the crust through which magma rises to the surface.

Magma
Magma is extremely hot, molten material that also contains dissolved gases including water vapor.

Magma chamber
As magma rises toward the surface, it forms a large underground pocket called a magma chamber.

376

Background

Integrating Science Students may wonder how geologists are able to determine what the inside of a volcano is like when they cannot observe it directly. Some evidence is indirect. For example, geologists can determine that magma is present underground by measuring delays in the arrival times of seismic waves from faroff earthquakes.

Other evidence is more direct. The erosion of some ancient volcanoes has exposed their "roots," enabling geologists to examine the dikes and pipes that once linked underground magma chambers to the surface vents. Also, magma sometimes breaks off pieces of the mantle as it rises. These fragments, called ultramafic nodules, are found in lava flows. The composition of these nodules provides support for geologists' theories about Earth's interior.

Characteristics of Magma

The force of a volcanic eruption depends partly on the amount of gas dissolved in the magma. But gas content is not the only thing that affects an eruption. How thick or thin the magma is, its temperature, and its silica content are also important factors.

Some types of magma are thick and flow very slowly. Other types of magma are fluid and flow almost as easily as water. Magma's temperature partly determines whether it is thick or fluid. The hotter the magma, the more fluid it is.

The amount of silica in magma also helps to determine how easily the magma flows. **Silica,** which is a material that is formed from the elements oxygen and silicon, is one of the most abundant materials in Earth's crust and mantle. The more silica magma contains, the thicker it is.

Magma that is high in silica produces light-colored lava that is too sticky to flow very far. When this type of lava cools, it forms the rock rhyolite, which has the same composition as granite. Pumice and obsidian, which you observed if you did the Discover activity, also form from high-silica lava. Obsidian forms when lava cools very quickly, giving it a smooth, glossy surface. Pumice forms when gas bubbles are trapped in cooling lava, leaving spaces in the rock.

Magma that is low in silica flows readily and produces dark-colored lava. When this kind of lava cools, rocks such as basalt are formed.

Figure 23 Rhyolite (top) forms from high-silica lava. Basalt (bottom) forms from low-silica lava. When this type of lava cools, it sometimes forms six-sided columns like the ones in the picture.

Inquiry Challenge

ACTIVITY

Materials *fluids of different thicknesses, jars with secure tops, board covered with waxed paper, other materials of students' choice*
Time 15 minutes

Ask students: **What are some thick liquids?** *(Examples include maple syrup, hand lotion, shampoo, and liquid detergent.)* **What are some thin liquids?** *(Water, milk, juice, vinegar, and so forth)* Then challenge students with the following question: **How could you test how thick or thin a liquid is and compare it with another liquid?** *(Students' ideas will vary. They could put a small amount of each liquid in a jar, turn the jar over, and observe how quickly the liquid flows to the other end. They also could pour liquids down an inclined surface, such as a board, and time its flow rate. Accept other ideas as well.)* Allow time for students to test their ideas and report their results to the rest of the class.
learning modality: logical/ mathematical

Media and Technology

Transparencies "Locating the Epicenter," Transparency 55; "Exploring a Volcano," Transparency 56

Ongoing Assessment

Drawing Have each student draw a simple cross-sectional diagram of a volcano and label the magma chamber, pipe, vent, crater and lava without referring to the diagram on page 376.

377

Types of Volcanic Eruptions

A volcano's magma influences how the volcano erupts. **The silica content of magma helps to determine whether the volcanic eruption is quiet or explosive.**

Quiet Eruptions A volcano erupts quietly if its magma flows easily. In this case, the gas dissolved in the magma bubbles out gently. Thin, runny lava oozes quietly from the vent. The islands of Hawaii and Iceland were formed from quiet eruptions. On the Big Island of Hawaii, lava pours out of the crater near the top of Mount Kilauea (kee loo AY uh). Lava also flows out of long cracks on the volcano's sides. Quiet eruptions like the ones that regularly take place on Mount Kilauea have built up the Big Island over hundreds of thousands of years. In Iceland, lava usually emerges from gigantic fissures many kilometers long. The fluid lava from a quiet eruption can flow many kilometers from the volcano's vent.

Quiet eruptions produce two different types of lava: pahoehoe and aa. **Pahoehoe** (pah HOH ee hoh ee) is fast-moving, hot lava. The surface of a lava flow formed from pahoehoe looks like a solid mass of wrinkles, billows, and ropelike coils. Lava that is cooler and slower-moving is called **aa** (AH ah). When aa hardens, it forms a rough surface consisting of jagged lava chunks. Figure 24 shows how different these types of lava can be.

☑ *Checkpoint* **What types of lava are produced by quiet eruptions?**

Figure 24 Both pahoehoe and aa can come from the same volcano. **(A)** Aa hardens into rough chunks. **(B)** Pahoehoe flows easily and hardens into a rippled surface. *Inferring What accounts for the differences between these two types of lava?*

378

Figure 25 Mount St. Helens erupted at 8:30 A.M. on May 18, 1980. **(A)** A large bulge that had formed on the north side of the mountain crashed downward.

(B) As the mountainside collapsed, bottled-up gas and magma inside began to escape.

(C) Shattered rock and pyroclastic flows blasted out sideways from the volcano.

(D) The blast traveled outward, leveling the surrounding forest and causing mudflows that affected a wide area around the volcano.

Explosive Eruptions If its magma is thick and sticky, a volcano erupts explosively. The thick magma does not flow out of the crater and down the mountain. Instead, it slowly builds up in the volcano's pipe, plugging it like a cork in a bottle. Dissolved gases cannot escape from the thick magma. The trapped gases build up pressure until they explode. The erupting gases push the magma out of the volcano with incredible force.

The explosion breaks the lava into fragments that quickly cool and harden into pieces of different sizes. The smallest pieces are volcanic ash—fine, rocky particles as small as a grain of sand. Cinders are pebble-sized particles. Larger pieces, called bombs, may range from the size of a baseball to the size of a car. A **pyroclastic flow** (py roh KLAS tik) occurs when an explosive eruption hurls out ash, cinders, and bombs as well as gases.

Look at Figure 25 to see the 1980 eruption of Mount St. Helens in the state of Washington. It was one of the most violent explosive eruptions that has ever occurred in the United States.

✓ *Checkpoint* **What causes an explosive eruption?**

Social Studies CONNECTION

In A.D. 79, Mount Vesuvius in Italy erupted. A thick layer of ash from Vesuvius buried the Roman city of Pompeii. Beginning in the 1700s, about half of the buried city was dug out, and scientists now know a great deal about daily life in Pompeii, a bustling city that was home to 20,000 people.

In Your Journal

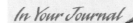

Research Pompeii to find out what scientists have learned about daily life in the city. Write a paragraph summarizing your findings.

Provide students with maps (particularly relief maps) of western North America. Have them locate Mount St. Helens and identify the mountain range of which Mount St. Helens is a part. *(The Cascade Range)* Ask: **What other mountain peaks in the Cascade Range are or were likely volcanoes in the past?** *(Students should identify Mount Hood, Mount Rainier, and Mount Shasta.)* **learning modality: visual**

ACTIVITY

Social Studies CONNECTION

Display a large map of the Mediterranean region, and let students find Mount Vesuvius and Pompeii in Italy. You may wish to provide various source materials for students to use for their research.

In Your Journal Provide photographs showing excavated areas of Pompeii and artists' illustrations depicting daily life in the city. Encourage students to use these pictures to help them imagine what life in Pompeii was like. **learning modality: verbal**

Including All Students

Content Mastery

Write the term *pyroclastic* on the board, and draw a line between the two word parts. Choose volunteers to find the meaning of each part in a dictionary. *(pyro: "fire"; clastic: "made of fragments")* Ask: **Why is pyroclastic a good word for a volcanic explosion?** *(The lava is fiery and is broken into pieces.)* **learning modality: verbal**

Answers to Self-Assessment

✓ *Checkpoint*
Quiet eruptions produce two types of lava: pahoehoe (a fast-moving, hot lava) and aa (a cooler, slower-moving lava).

Caption Question
Figure 24 The temperature of the lava and the speed at which it flows.

✓ *Checkpoint*
Magma that is thick and sticky causes a volcano to erupt explosively.

Ongoing Assessment

Oral Presentation Ask students to describe the major differences between quiet and explosive volcanic eruptions.

Stages of a Volcano

SCIENCE & History

Focus students' attention on the introductory statement that volcanic eruptions "have greatly affected the land and the people around them." Ask: **How do you think each of these eruptions affected the people in the area?** (*Some eruptions killed people; people lost their homes and possessions; they may have had to evacuate the area; crops were destroyed when fields were covered with ash and other volcanic materials; and so forth.*)

In Your Journal Provide age-appropriate resource books so students can research these eruptions. Also remind students that if their group has chosen one of these volcanoes as the subject of its chapter project, they can add this research to their report. Refer to the **ELL Handbook** for additional teaching strategies. **learning modality: verbal**

Including All Students

Ask: **What are some signs that a volcano may be about to become active?** (*Accept all reasonable responses. Students will probably mention steam and other gases escaping from vents, bulges in the mountainside, a changing water level in a crater lake, and small earthquakes in the area.*) **learning modality: verbal**

Stages of a Volcano

The activity of a volcano may last from less than a decade to more than 10 million years. Most long-lived volcanoes, however, do not erupt continuously. Geologists often describe volcanoes with terms usually reserved for living things, such as sleeping, awakening, alive, and dead. An **active,** or live, volcano is one that is erupting or has shown signs that it may erupt in the near future. A **dormant,** or sleeping, volcano is like a sleeping bear. Scientists expect a dormant volcano to awaken in the future and become active. However, there may be thousands of years between eruptions. An **extinct,** or dead, volcano is unlikely to erupt again.

The Power of Volcanoes

Within the last 150 years, major volcanic eruptions have greatly affected the land and people around them.

1883 Indonesia

The violent eruption of Krakatau volcano threw 18 cubic kilometers of ash skyward. The blast was heard 5,000 kilometers away.

1912 Alaska, U.S.A.

Today, a river in Alaska cuts through the thick layer of volcanic ash from the eruption of Mount Katmai. Mount Katmai blasted out almost as much ash as Krakatau.

1850   1900

1902 Martinique

Mount Pelée, a Caribbean volcano, erupted a burning cloud of hot gas and pyroclastic flows. Within two minutes of the eruption, the cloud had killed the 29,000 residents of St. Pierre, a city on the volcano's flank. Only two people survived.

Background

Facts and Figures Of the six volcanic eruptions presented in the time line on these pages, two—Krakatau in 1883 and Mount Pelèe in 1902—are among the five most destructive volcanic eruptions since 1700. The remaining three are Unzen, Japan, in 1792; Mt. Tambora, Indonesia, in 1815; and Nevada del Ruiz, Colombia, in 1985.

As evidence of a volcano's varying hazards, 80,000 of the 92,000 people killed as a result of the 1815 Mt. Tambora eruption died not from the volcanic activity itself but from starvation afterward. Ninety percent of Krakatau's 36,000 victims were killed by a tsunami. Pyroclastic flows claimed about 30,000 lives in the Mount Pelée eruption. Mudflows killed about 25,000 people in the Nevada del Ruiz eruption. Clearly, lava flows and collapsing cones are not the only volcanic hazards.

Monitoring Volcanoes

To tell if a volcano is becoming active, geologists use a variety of instruments to detect slight surface changes caused by magma moving underground. Changes in and around a volcano usually give warning a short time before the volcano erupts. Geologists monitor the local magnetic field, water level in a volcano's crater lake, and any gases escaping from a volcano. They take the temperature of underground water to see if it is getting hotter—a sign that magma may be nearing the surface.

Geologists also monitor the many small earthquakes that occur in the area around a volcano before an eruption. The movement of magma into the magma chamber and through the volcano's pipe triggers these quakes.

In Your Journal

People have written eye-witness accounts of famous volcanic eruptions. Research one of the eruptions in the time line. Then write a letter describing what someone observing the eruption might have seen.

1991 Philippines

Mount Pinatubo was dormant for hundreds of years before erupting in June 1991. Pinatubo spewed out huge quantities of ash that rose high into the atmosphere and also buried the surrounding countryside.

1950 — **2000**

1980 Washington, U.S.A.

When Mount St. Helens exploded, it blasted one cubic kilometer of rock fragments and volcanic material skyward. The eruption was not unexpected. For months, geologists had monitored releases of ash, small earthquakes, and a bulge on the mountain caused by the buildup of magma inside.

1995
Montserrat

For more than two years, eruptions of volcanic ash from the Soufrière Hills volcano poured down on this small Caribbean island. Geologists anxiously waited for the eruption to run its course, not knowing whether it would end in a huge explosion.

Chapter 11 **381**

Program Resources

◆ **Laboratory Manual** 11, "Predicting Lava Flows"

Monitoring Volcanoes

Building Inquiry Skills: Applying Concepts

Prompt students to recall what they learned about seismographs in the previous section by asking: **What is a seismograph?** *(A seismograph is a device used to record and measure the vibrations of seismic waves.)* Then ask: **How might a seismograph be used to detect signs of a possible volcanic eruption?** *(Accept all reasonable responses. Students might suggest that an increase in the frequency or magnitude of earthquakes near a volcano as indicated by seismic waves recorded by a seismograph would suggest a possible volcanic eruption.)* **learning modality: logical/mathematical**

Ongoing Assessment

Oral Presentation Ask each student to identify at least four ways in which geologists can determine that a volcano may erupt in the near future.

Other Types of Volcanic Activity

Integrating Technology

Invite students to consider the problems and benefits involved in the use of geothermal energy by asking: **Why are the steam and water sometimes difficult to access?** *(They may be far underground, so deep wells must be drilled.)* **What dangers are involved?** *(Steam could rupture pipes and injure workers.)* **What are the advantages of geothermal energy?** *(It is a nonpolluting, renewable energy source.)* **learning modality: logical/mathematical**

Volcano Hazards

Building Inquiry Skills: Inferring

Materials *sealed plastic bag containing ash and cinders from a fire, hand lens*

ACTIVITY

Time 10 minutes

Advance Preparation Prepare one bagged sample for each group of four students. Seal the bag securely with tape or staples. *(CAUTION: Warn students not to open the bags, as the fine dust could be inhaled.)*

Let students examine the sample both with and without a hand lens and note the varying sizes of the particles. Encourage students to draw circles and dots on a sheet of plain paper to represent the particle sizes they see. Then ask: **Why would the smallest ash particles be hazardous?** *(People and animals can breathe them in; plants coated with ash die; ash can clog automobile engines and other machinery; and so forth.)* **What is the difference between volcanic ash and ash formed from burning wood or paper?** *(Volcanic ash does not form as a result of burning. It forms when gases from an explosive eruption blasts lava into small fragments that quickly cool and harden. Volcanic ash is made up of small, glassy particles of pyroclastic material that range in size from very fine dust to particles the size of sand grains.* **learning modality: visual**

Figure 26 Old Faithful, a geyser in Yellowstone National Park, erupts about every 33 to 93 minutes. That's how long it takes for the pressure to build up again after each eruption.

Other Types of Volcanic Activity

Hot springs and geysers are two examples of volcanic activity that do not involve the eruption of lava. These features may occur in any volcanic area—even around an extinct volcano.

A hot spring forms when groundwater heated by a nearby body of magma rises to the surface and collects in a natural pool. (Groundwater is water that has seeped into the spaces among rocks deep beneath Earth's surface.) Water from hot springs may contain dissolved gases and other substances from deep within Earth.

Sometimes, rising hot water and steam become trapped underground in a narrow crack. Pressure builds until the mixture suddenly sprays above the surface as a geyser. A **geyser** (GY zur) is a fountain of water and steam that erupts from the ground.

INTEGRATING TECHNOLOGY In volcanic areas, water heated by magma can provide a clean, reliable energy source called **geothermal energy.** The people of Reykjavik, Iceland, pipe this hot water directly into their homes for warmth. Geothermal energy is also a source of electricity in Iceland as well as northern California and New Zealand. Steam from deep underground is piped into turbines. Inside a turbine, the steam spins a wheel in the same way that blowing on a pinwheel makes the pinwheel turn. The moving wheel in the turbine turns a generator that changes the energy of motion into electrical energy.

Volcano Hazards

The time between volcanic eruptions may span hundreds of years. So people living near a dormant volcano may be unaware of the danger. Before 1980, the people who lived, worked, and vacationed in the region around Mount St. Helens viewed it as a peaceful mountain. Few imagined the destruction the volcano would bring when it awakened from its 123-year slumber.

Although quiet eruptions and explosive eruptions involve different volcano hazards, both types of eruption can cause damage far from the crater's rim. **During a quiet eruption, lava flows pour from vents, setting fire to and then burying everything in their path. During an explosive eruption, a volcano can belch out hot, burning clouds of volcanic gas, ash, cinders, and bombs.**

Background

Facts and Figures The explosive eruption of Mount St. Helens on May 18, 1980, destroyed the north face of the mountain and lowered its overall elevation by about 400 m. The eruption flattened stands of timber like matchsticks, leaving the trees stripped of branches. About 60 people died—in many cases as a result of the heat, ash, and gases of the pyroclastic flow that accompanied the eruption.

Mount St. Helens is one of 15 major volcanoes in the Cascade Range. Eight volcanoes in this group have erupted within the last several centuries. For example, Mount St. Helens was active as recently as 1857. Scientists think that several other volcanoes in the Cascade Range could also become active again, including Mount Baker, Mount Rainier, Mount Hood, Mount Shasta, and Lassen Peak.

(A)

(B)

Figure 27 (A) Mudflows were one of the hazards of Mt. Pinatubo's 1991 eruption. (B) People around Mt. Pinatubo wore masks to protect themselves from breathing volcanic ash.

Volcanic ash can bury entire towns, damage crops, and clog car engines. If it becomes wet, the heavy ash can cause roofs to collapse. If a jet plane sucks ash into its engine, the engine may stall. Eruptions can also cause landslides and avalanches of mud, melted snow, and rock. Figure 27 shows some effects of mud and ash from Mount Pinatubo's eruption. When Mount St. Helens erupted, gigantic mudflows carried ash, trees, and rock fragments 29 kilometers down the nearby Toutle River.

Section 4 Review

1. What are the stages that lead up to a volcanic eruption?
2. Compare and contrast quiet and explosive eruptions.
3. Describe some of the hazards posed by volcanoes.
4. **Thinking Critically** **Drawing Conclusions** A geologist times a passing lava flow at 15 kilometers per hour. The geologist also sees that lava near the edge of the flow is forming smooth-looking ripples as it hardens. What type of lava is this? What type of magma produced it? Explain your conclusions.

Check Your Progress

CHAPTER PROJECT

By now you should have collected information about what it's like to live in a volcanic region. Do you need to do more research? Now begin to plan your presentation. One way to plan a presentation is to prepare storyboards. In a storyboard, you sketch each major step in the presentation on a separate sheet of paper. Decide who in your group is presenting each portion.

Program Resources

◆ **Unit 4 Resources** 11-4 Review and Reinforce, p. 42; 11-4 Enrich, p. 43

---

3 Assess

Section 4 Review Answers

1. Magma deep underground flows upward through cracks in rock. As the magma rises, the pressure decreases, and dissolved gases in the magma begin to separate out and form bubbles. When an opening develops in weak rock on the surface, the gases and magma erupt out of the volcano.

2. Quiet eruptions occur if the magma is thin and runny. The gases dissolved in the magma bubble out gently, and the lava oozes from the vent. Explosive eruptions occur if the magma is thick and sticky. The magma slowly collects in the volcano's neck and plugs it, trapping the gases. Pressure builds up until the gases explode, pushing the magma out of the volcano with great force.

3. Hazards include lava flows; hot, burning clouds of gas; cinders and bombs; volcanic ash; and landslides and mudflows. Accept other reasonable answers as well.

4. Pahoehoe; produced by thin lava. The speed is high, and smooth ripples are characteristic of pahoehoe.

Check Your Progress

CHAPTER PROJECT

Discuss the storyboarding technique with the entire class to make sure each group knows what to do. Instruct students to include in their storyboards notes about the media materials they plan to use. Review each group's storyboard to make sure it includes all the required elements and to provide any help that students may need in organizing the information they have collected.

Performance Assessment

Drawing Have each student draw and label a sketch to identify the parts of a volcano and describe what happens underground to cause an eruption.

Gelatin Volcanoes

Preparing for Inquiry

Key Concept Magma inside a volcano generally flows vertically to form dikes.

Skills Objectives Students will be able to

♦ develop a hypothesis about how magma flows inside a volcano;

♦ make a model volcano to test their hypothesis;

♦ observe how "magma" flows inside their model.

Time 40 minutes

Advance Planning

Gelatin molds: At least five hours before students will do this lab, make a gelatin mold for each student group. You can use bowls ranging from $2\frac{1}{2}$ cups to 2 quarts in capacity. For a $2\frac{1}{2}$-cup bowl (such as a plastic margarine container), mix one 7-oz envelope of unflavored gelatin with $\frac{1}{2}$ cup of room-temperature water. Add $1\frac{1}{2}$ cups of boiling water and stir until the gelatin is completely dissolved. Add $\frac{1}{3}$ cup of cold water. Refrigerate the mold for 3–5 hours or until set. Also make a test mold in a smaller container. After 3 hours, check the hardness of the test mold by removing it from its container. If it is not completely set, refrigerate the large molds for at least another 2 hours. You may want to practice removing one mold from its bowl beforehand to make sure you can demonstrate the technique successfully to the class.

Pizza pan: Use an aluminum pizza pan with holes punched in it with a nail at 2.5-cm intervals. Drive the nail *downward* through the tray so the upper surface stays smooth and the gelatin mold will not snag on the holes' edges.

Syringe: Use plastic bird-feeding syringes, which will pass through the holes in the pizza pan and pierce the gelatin by at least 1 cm.

Layered volcano (Design an Experiment): Fill a bowl only half full with gelatin solution, and set aside the rest at room temperature. Add the second layer to the bowl after the first layer has been refrigerated for two hours.

Real-World Lab

How It Works

Gelatin Volcanoes

Does the magma inside a volcano move along fractures, or through tubes or pipes? How does the eruption of magma create features such as dikes and sills? You can use a gelatin volcano model and red-colored liquid "magma" to find answers to these questions.

Problem

How does magma move inside a volcano?

Skills Focus

developing hypotheses, making models, observing

Materials

plastic cup	tray or shallow pan

plastic knife

aluminum pizza pan with holes punched at 2.5-cm intervals

unflavored gelatin mold in bowl

red food coloring and water

plastic syringe, 10 cc

3 small cardboard oatmeal boxes

rubber gloves

unlined paper

Procedure

1. Before magma erupts as lava, how does it travel up from underground magma chambers? Record your hypothesis.

2. Remove the gelatin from the refrigerator. Loosen the gelatin from its container by briefly placing the container of gelatin in a larger bowl of hot water.

3. Place the pizza pan over the gelatin so the mold is near the center of the pizza pan. While holding the pizza pan against the top of the mold, carefully turn the mold and the pizza pan upside down.

4. Carefully lift the bowl off the gelatin mold to create a gelatin volcano.

5. Place the pizza pan with the gelatin mold on top of the oatmeal boxes as shown in the photograph.

6. Fill the syringe with the red water ("magma"). Remove air bubbles from the syringe by holding it upright and squirting out a small amount of water.

7. Insert the tip of the syringe through a hole in the pizza pan near the center of the gelatin volcano. Inject the magma into the gelatin very slowly. Observe what happens to the magma.

8. Repeat Steps 6 and 7 as many times as possible. Observe the movement of the magma each time. Note any differences in the direction the magma takes when the syringe is inserted into different parts of the gelatin volcano. Record your observations.

9. Look down on your gelatin volcano from above. Make a sketch of the positions and shapes of the magma bodies. Label your drawing "Top View."

10. Carefully use a knife to cut your volcano in half. Separate the pieces and examine the cut surfaces for traces of the magma bodies.

11. Sketch the positions and shapes of the magma bodies on one of the cut faces. Label your drawing "Cross Section."

Alternative Materials Instead of a pizza pan, each group could use a pegboard square. Use pegboard with holes 5 mm in diameter. Cut the pegboard into squares about 10 cm wider than the tops of the bowls.

Guiding Inquiry

Invitation To introduce the terms *dike* and *sill*, have students preview Figure 28 and the first paragraph on page 387. Then ask: **What are dikes and sills made of?** (Hardened magma) **What is the major difference between a dike and a sill?** (Dikes are vertical; sills are horizontal.)

Introducing the Procedure

Have students read the entire procedure and examine the picture of the lab set-up. Ask if they have any questions before they begin.

Troubleshooting the Experiment

♦ Demonstrate the mold-removal process described in steps 2–5.

♦ Have students wear rubber gloves in steps 6–8 to keep their hands from being stained by the food coloring.

Analyze and Conclude

1. Describe how the magma moved through your model. Did the magma move straight up through the center of your model volcano or did it branch off in places? Explain why you think the magma moved in this way.
2. What knowledge or experience did you use to develop your hypothesis? How did the actual movement compare with your hypothesis?
3. Were there differences in the direction the magma flowed when the syringe was inserted in different parts of the gelatin volcano?
4. **Apply** How does what you observed in your model compare to the way magma moves through real volcanoes?

Design an Experiment

Plan to repeat the experiment using a mold made of two layers of gelatin. Before injecting the magma, predict what effect the layering will have on magma movement. Record your observations to determine if your hypothesis was correct. What volcanic feature is produced by this version of the model? Can you think of other volcanic features that you could model using gelatin layers?

Safety

Students should take care with the compass point in this activity. Review the safety guidelines in Appendix A.

Program Resources

◆ **Unit 4 Resources** Chapter 11 Real-World Lab blackline masters, pp. 56–57

Media and Technology

 Lab Activity Videotapes
Grade 6, Tape 3

◆ In Step 6, have students lightly tap the syringe before they squirt water out.
◆ Before students begin injecting colored water in Step 7, make sure they have put a tray under the pizza pan to catch any water that drains out of the mold.
◆ If colored water dribbles down the syringe in steps 7 and 8, students can wrap a folded paper towel around it.
◆ In Step 10, make sure students cut the volcano in half *from top to bottom*, not across its diameter.

Expected Outcome

With a slow, steady injection rate, the colored water will create thin, vertical dikes inside the gelatin.

Analyze and Conclude

1. The magma spread vertically from the point of injection into a fan-shaped dike that gradually grew until it broke through the surface of the volcano. With repeated injections, dikes may have branched off into other vertical planes. The magma moved in this way because there was upward pressure on it from the syringe.
2. Answers will vary. Students should base their answers on what they have already learned about how magma flows through a volcano and how dikes are formed in a vertical or near-vertical plane.
3. When injected into the center, the magma flowed radially outward in any direction. When injected near the edge, magma flowed to the closest surface point, following a path of least resistance.
4. The colored water flowed vertically in the direction of least resistance, much like a flow of magma in an actual volcano.

Extending the Inquiry

Design an Experiment Horizontal sills will form along the joint between the layers. Students might also be able to model dome mountains or batholiths, which are discussed in Section 5 on pages 387–388.

SECTION
5 Volcanic Landforms

TEKS: 6.2B, C, E; 6.3C; 6.6C

Objectives

After completing the lesson, students will be able to

◆ identify landforms formed from magma that hardened beneath the surface;

◆ identify landforms that lava and other volcanic materials create on Earth's surface.

1 Engage/Explore

Activating Prior Knowledge

Ask students: **What shape is a volcano?** Choose several volunteers to come to the board and draw what they think a volcano looks like. (*Students will most likely draw cone-shaped mountains.*) **Are all volcanoes shaped like this?** (*Accept all responses without comment at this time.*)

DISCOVER

Skills Focus making models

Materials *tape, balloon, straw, box, damp sand*

Time 10–15 minutes

Tips Make sure the box is large enough for the balloon to fit when it is fully inflated. Tell students to inflate the balloon slowly in Step 5.

Expected Outcome As the balloon is inflated, a dome will form in the sand.

Think It Over The sand represents Earth's crust. The balloon represents a filling magma chamber.

DISCOVER
ACTIVITY

How Can Volcanic Activity Change Earth's Surface?

1. Use tape to secure the neck of a balloon over one end of a straw.

2. Place the balloon in the center of a box with the straw protruding.

3. Partially inflate the balloon.

4. Put damp sand on top of the balloon until it is covered.

5. Slowly inflate the balloon more. Observe what happens to the surface of the sand.

Think It Over

Making Models This activity models one of the ways in which volcanic activity can cause a mountain to form. What do you think the sand represents? What does the balloon represent?

GUIDE FOR READING

◆ What landforms are formed from magma that hardened beneath the surface?

◆ What landforms does lava create on Earth's surface?

Reading Tip As you read, make a table comparing volcanic landforms. Include what formed each landform—lava, ash, or magma—as well as its characteristics.

Key Terms volcanic neck
• dike • sill • batholith
• shield volcano • cinder cone
• composite volcano • caldera

olcanoes have created some of Earth's most spectacular landforms. For example, the perfect volcanic cone of Mt. Fuji in Japan and the mysterious profile of Ship Rock rising above the grasslands of New Mexico are famous around the world.

Some volcanic landforms, like Mt. Fuji, arise when lava flows build up mountains and plateaus on Earth's surface. Other volcanic landforms, like Ship Rock, are the result of the buildup of magma beneath the surface.

Landforms From Magma

Sometimes magma forces its way through cracks in the upper crust, but fails to reach the surface. There the magma cools and hardens into rock. Eventually, the forces that wear away Earth's surface—such as flowing water, ice, or wind—may strip away the layers of rock above the magma and expose it. **Features formed by magma include volcanic necks, dikes, and sills, as well as batholiths and dome mountains.**

386

◀ Ship Rock, New Mexico

READING STRATEGIES

Reading Tip Columns in students' tables should have the heads *Landform, Shape,* and *How It Forms.* Under *Landform,* students should list shield volcanoes, cinder cone volcanoes, composite volcanoes, lava plateaus, calderas, volcanic necks, dikes, sills, batholiths, and dome mountains.

Volcanic neck

Dike

Sill

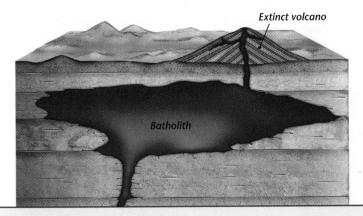

Figure 28 Magma that hardens beneath the surface may form volcanic necks, dikes, and sills.
Compare and Contrast What is the difference between a dike and a sill?

Volcanic Necks, Dikes, and Sills A volcanic neck looks like a giant tooth stuck in the ground. A **volcanic neck** forms when magma hardens in a volcano's pipe. The softer rock around the pipe wears away, exposing the hard rock of the volcanic neck. Ship Rock in northwestern New Mexico is an example of a volcanic neck. Magma that forces itself across rock layers hardens into a **dike.** On the other hand, when magma squeezes between layers of rock, it forms a **sill.**

Batholiths Large rock masses called batholiths form the core of many mountain ranges. A **batholith** (BATH uh lith) is a mass of rock formed when a large body of magma cools inside the crust. The diagram in Figure 29 shows how a batholith looks when it forms. Over millions of years, uplift may slowly push the batholith toward the surface. Gradually, the layers of rock above the batholith wear away. As uplift continues, erosion shapes the batholith itself into a mountain range.

Extinct volcano

Batholith

Figure 29 A batholith forms when magma cools inside the crust.

2 *Facilitate*

Landforms From Magma

Building Inquiry Skills: Inferring

Ask students: **If magma is rising through the upper crust, why would it fail to reach the surface?** *(It might become trapped under a solid rock layer, or there might not be enough pressure to keep forcing the magma up. Accept other reasonable responses.)* **learning modality: logical/mathematical**

Using the Visuals: Figures 28 and 29

Have students examine and compare the two figures. Then ask: **Could the land surface in Figure 29 eventually look similar to that of Figure 28? If so, what series of events must occur?** *(Accept all reasonable responses. Students should recognize that if in Figure 29 the magma in the volcano's pipe were to harden and become exposed at the surface due to the wearing away of the rock layers above it, a volcanic neck would form similar to that of Figure 28. Dikes and sills might also be exposed at the surface.)* Have students identify areas of magma in Figure 29 that, when hardened, will likely form dikes and sills. **learning modality: visual**

Program Resources

◆ **Unit 4 Resources** 11-5 Lesson Plan, p. 49; 11-5 Section Summary, p. 50
◆ **Guided Reading and Study Workbook** 11-5

Answers to Self-Assessment

Caption Question

Figure 28 A dike cuts across rock layers while a sill squeezes between rock layers.

Ongoing Assessment

Writing Have students name and describe four landforms formed from hardened magma.

Landforms From Magma, continued

Including All Students

After students have read about dome mountains, ask: **Where have you seen a bulging landform like this before?** *(In the Discover activity at the beginning of this section, when the inflated balloon made the sand bulge upward)* Review with students that the balloon in the model represented rising magma and the sand represented layers of rock in the upper crust. **learning modality: visual**

Landforms From Lava and Ash

Skills Focus making models

Materials *plastic pan, modeling clay, metric ruler, water, food coloring, clear plastic sheet, marking pencil*

Time 20 minutes

Tips To insure consistent positioning of the plastic sheet, instruct students to mark on the sheet the corners of the pan in Step 3.

Expected Outcome Students' topographic maps and contour lines should accurately represent the shape, slope, and elevation of their model volcano.

Extend Have students repeat the activity using a model volcano of different shape, slope, and elevation. **learning modality: visual**

Map in a Pan

1. In a plastic pan with a flat bottom, mold a volcano out of clay that is lower than the top of the container.
2. Fill the pan to a depth of 1 cm using water colored with a few drops of food coloring.
3. Place a clear plastic sheet over the container and trace the outline of the pan with a marking pencil.
4. Looking straight down into the pan, trace the outline the water makes around the edges of the clay model.
5. Add another 1 cm of water, then replace the plastic sheet exactly as before and trace the water level again.
6. Repeat Step 5 several times to complete your topographic map.

Making Models How does your topographic map of the volcano compare with the clay model?

Figure 30 Thick layers of lava formed the Columbia Plateau.

Dome Mountains Other, smaller bodies of magma can create dome mountains. A dome mountain forms when rising magma is blocked by horizontal layers of rock. The magma forces the layers of rock to bend upward into a dome shape. Eventually, the rock above the dome mountain wears away, leaving it exposed. This process formed the Black Hills in South Dakota.

✓ *Checkpoint* How can magma cause a dome mountain to form?

Landforms From Lava and Ash

Rock and other materials formed from lava create a variety of landforms including shield volcanoes, composite volcanoes, cinder cone volcanoes, and lava plateaus. Look at *Exploring Volcanic Mountains* on page 389 to see the similarities and differences among these features.

Shield Volcanoes At some places on Earth's surface, thin layers of lava pour out of a vent and harden on top of previous layers. Such lava flows gradually build a wide, gently sloping mountain called a **shield volcano.** Shield volcanoes rising from a hot spot on the ocean floor created the Hawaiian Islands.

Cinder Cone Volcanoes A volcano can also be a **cinder cone,** a steep, cone-shaped hill or mountain. If a volcano's lava is thick and stiff, it may produce ash, cinders, and bombs. These materials pile up around the vent in a steep, cone-shaped pile. For example, Paricutín in Mexico erupted in 1943 in a farmer's cornfield. The volcano built up a cinder cone about 400 meters high.

Composite Volcanoes Sometimes, lava flows alternate with explosive eruptions of ash, cinder, and bombs. The result is a composite volcano. **Composite volcanoes** are tall, cone-shaped mountains in which layers of lava alternate with layers of ash. Examples of composite volcanoes include Mount Fuji in Japan and Mount St. Helens in Washington state.

Lava Plateaus Instead of forming mountains, some eruptions of lava form high, level areas called lava plateaus. First, lava flows out of several long cracks in an area. The thin, runny lava travels far before cooling and solidifying. Again and again, floods of lava flow on top of earlier floods. After millions of years, these layers of lava can form high plateaus. One example is the Columbia Plateau, which covers parts of Washington, Oregon, and Idaho.

Background

Facts and Figures Shield volcanoes derive their name from the shape of a warrior's shield. Over roughly one million years, five shield volcanoes, including Mauna Loa, slowly built up the island of Hawaii. Rising about 5,000 meters from the ocean floor, and another 4,000 meters above sea level, Mauna Loa and its companion Mauna Kea, overall, are higher than Mount Everest. Shield volcanoes also formed Midway Island and the Galapagos Islands.

Composite volcanoes, also called stratovolcanoes because of their layering, produce the most violent eruptions. Most active composite volcanoes are located in the Ring of Fire.

Cinder cones are small in comparison with shield volcanoes and composite volcanoes. They often form on or near larger volcanoes. Because loose volcanic cinders remain stable on a slope of 30–40 degrees, cinder cones have very steep slopes.

EXPLORING Volcanic Mountains

Volcanic activity is responsible for building up much of Earth's surface. Lava from volcanoes cools and hardens into three types of mountains.

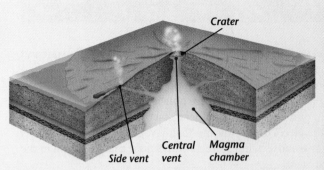

Crater

Side vent

Central vent

Magma chamber

Shield Volcano
Repeated lava flows during quiet eruptions gradually build up a broad, gently sloping volcanic mountain known as a shield volcano.

▲ Mauna Loa is one of the shield volcanoes that built the island Hawaii.

Cinder Cone Volcano
When cinders erupt explosively from a volcanic vent, they pile up around the vent, forming a cone-shaped hill called a cinder cone.

▲ Sunset Crater is an extinct cinder cone in Arizona.

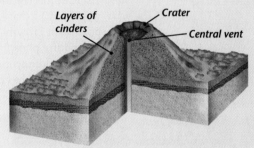

Layers of cinders

Crater

Central vent

Composite Volcano
Layers of lava alternate with layers of ash, cinders, and bombs in a composite volcano, which has both quiet and explosive eruptions.

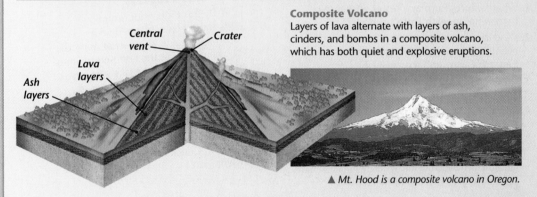

Central vent

Crater

Lava layers

Ash layers

▲ Mt. Hood is a composite volcano in Oregon.

Chapter 11 **389**

Media and Technology

 Transparencies "Exploring Volcanic Mountains," Transparency 57

 Earth Science Videodisc
Unit 2, Side 2, "Flying Over America"

Chapter 7

Answers to Self-Assessment

☑ *Checkpoint*

When rising magma is blocked by horizontal rock layers, it forces the layers to bend upward in a dome shape, creating dome mountains.

EXPLORING
Volcanic Mountains

After students have examined the visual essay, ask: **How do the shapes of these mountains differ?** *(The cinder cone volcano is very steep-sided. The composite volcano is also steep-sided but has a wider base. The shield volcano has a very gradual slope and is not as high as the other two.)* **What causes these differences?** *(The type of material that erupts from each volcano; pyroclastic materials—ash, cinders, and bombs— seem to create a steeper slope.)* Refer to the **ELL Handbook** for additional teaching strategies. **learning modality: visual**

Soils from Lava and Ash

 Integrating Environmental Science

Obtain (or ask students to find) photographs of the area around Mount St. Helens soon after the 1980 eruption and at intervals in the years afterward. (A good source is *Mount St. Helens, Eruption and Recovery of a Volcano* by Rob Carson, Sasquatch Books, 1990.) Let students examine the photographs to find evidence of regrowth in the area— first of small, scattered "settler" plants, then of wider areas of larger plants and saplings, and finally stands of maturing trees. Ask: **Where do you think the new plants came from?** *(Accept all reasonable answers. Examples: Seeds blew in from other, undamaged areas. Tree roots that were not destroyed grew new sprouts.)* **Were plants the only organisms that returned to the area? Why?** *(No, animals returned too because the regrowth provided food, shelter, and the like.)* **learning modality: visual**

Ongoing Assessment

Drawing Have each student draw cross-sectional views of the three volcano types, label each with its name, and add a brief explanation of how it is formed.

 Students could save their sketches in their portfolios.

3 Assess

Section 5 Review Answers

1. Volcanic necks, dikes, sills, batholiths, dome mountains
2. Magma forces its way upward through cracks in the crust, but overlying rock layers keep the magma from reaching the surface. The magma forces the rock layers to bend upward into a dome shape. When the rock layers wear away, the dome is exposed.
3. Students should describe shield volcanoes, cinder cone volcanoes, composite volcanoes, lava plateaus, and calderas using information from pages 388–390.
4. Thin, runny lava flows out of several long, horizontal cracks and travels far in all directions before cooling and hardening. Over time, layers of lava build up, forming a plateau.
5. A huge eruption can empty a volcano's magma chamber. Without magma to support it, the top of the mountain collapses inward, forming a caldera.

Check Your Progress

CHAPTER PROJECT

Suggest that group members display the visuals to one another from across the room to check whether they are readable at a distance. Provide tape recorders, video cameras, and a separate, quiet area for making the recordings without disturbing others. *Computer use is optional.*

Performance Assessment

Oral Presentation Call on students to name one of the landforms discussed in this section and explain how it is formed.

Figure 31 Crater Lake in Oregon fills the caldera formed after an eruption that destroyed the top 2,000 meters of Mount Mazama nearly 7,000 years ago. *Developing Hypotheses Develop a hypothesis to explain the formation of Wizard Island, the small island in Crater Lake.*

Calderas Enormous eruptions may empty the main vent and the magma chamber beneath a volcano. The mountain becomes a hollow shell. With nothing to support it, the top of the mountain collapses inward. The huge hole left by the collapse of a volcanic mountain is called a **caldera** (kal DAIR uh). The hole is filled with the pieces of the volcano that have fallen inward, as well as some lava and ash. In Figure 31 you can see a large caldera in the United States.

Soils From Lava and Ash

INTEGRATING ENVIRONMENTAL SCIENCE The lava, ash, and cinders that erupt from a volcano are initially barren. Over time, however, the hard surface of the lava flow breaks down to form soil. As soil develops, plants are able to grow. Some volcanic soils are among the richest soils in the world. Saying that soil is rich means that it's fertile, or able to support plant growth. Volcanic ash also breaks down and releases potassium, phosphorus, and other materials that plants need. Why would anyone live near an active volcano? People settle close to volcanoes to take advantage of the fertile volcanic soil.

Section 5 Review

1. What features form as a result of magma hardening beneath Earth's surface?
2. Describe how a dome mountain can eventually form out of magma that hardened beneath Earth's surface.
3. Describe five landforms formed from lava and ash.
4. Describe the process that creates a lava plateau.
5. **Thinking Critically Relating Cause and Effect** Explain the formation of a volcanic landform that can result when a volcano uses up the magma in its magma chamber.

Check Your Progress

CHAPTER PROJECT

By this time, your group should have planned your documentary and know what materials you will need. Put the finishing touches on your presentation. Make sure any posters, overhead transparencies, or computer art will be easy for your audience to read. If you are using video or audio, make your recordings now. Revise and polish any narrative, rap, or skit. (*Hint:* Check the length of your presentation.)

Answers to Self-Assessment

Caption Question

Figure 31 Wizard Island is a small cinder cone that formed after the collapse of Mount Mazama. Accept all reasonable hypotheses.

Program Resources

◆ **Unit 4 Resources** 11-5 Review and Reinforce, p. 51; 11-5 Enrich, p. 52

SECTION 1 Plate Tectonics

Key Ideas

◆ According to the theory of plate tectonics, the movement of Earth's plates produces volcanoes, mountain ranges, earthquakes, and features of the ocean floor.

Key Terms

plates
Pangaea
plate tectonics
plate boundaries

 SECTION 2 Earth's Crust in Motion

Key Ideas

◆ Stresses on Earth's crust produce compression, tension, and shearing in rock.
◆ Faults are cracks in Earth's crust that result from stress.
◆ Faulting, folding, and uplift cause mountains to form on Earth's surface.

Key Terms

earthquake
stress
shearing
tension
compression
fault
strike-slip fault
normal fault
hanging wall
footwall
reverse fault
fold
plateau

 SECTION 3 Measuring Earthquakes

Key Ideas

◆ Seismic waves carry the energy of an earthquake from the focus to the surface.
◆ Earthquakes produce P waves, S waves, and surface waves.
◆ The scales used to measure earthquakes include the moment magnitude scale, the Mercalli scale, and the Richter scale.

Key Terms

focus
epicenter
P waves
S waves
surface waves
seismograph
magnitude
Mercalli scale
Richter scale
moment magnitude scale

 SECTION 4 Volcanic Activity

Key Ideas

◆ An eruption occurs when gases trapped in magma rush through an opening at the Earth's surface, carrying magma with them.
◆ Volcanoes can erupt quietly or explosively, depending on the silica content of the magma.
◆ Volcano hazards include pyroclastic flows, avalanches of mud, damage from ash, lava flows, flooding, and deadly gases.

Key Terms

magma chamber
pipe
vent
lava flow
crater
silica
pahoehoe
aa
pyroclastic flow
active
dormant
extinct
geyser
geothermal energy

 SECTION 5 Volcanic Landforms

Key Ideas

◆ Magma that hardens beneath the surface forms batholiths, dome mountains, dikes, and sills, which are eventually exposed by erosion.
◆ Lava and other volcanic materials on the surface create shield volcanoes, cinder cones, composite volcanoes, and plateaus.

Key Terms

volcanic neck
dike
sill
batholith
shield volcano
cinder cone
composite volcano
caldera

 Organizing Information

Compare/Contrast Table On a separate piece of paper, make a table comparing shield volcanoes, cinder cones, composite volcanoes, and lava plateaus. Your table should compare these volcanic landforms in terms of volcanic material, shape, and structure. Then complete your table and add a title. For more on compare/contrast tables, see the Skills Handbook.

Chapter 11 **391**

Organizing Information

Compare/Contrast Table Sample title: Landforms Formed From Lava Sample table:

Landforms	Material	Shape	Structure
Shield volcanoes	lava	broad, gently sloping mountains	thin layers of lava around central and side vents
Cinder cones	ash, cinders, and bombs	steep, cone-shaped hills or mountains	layers of cinders around central vent
Composite volcanoes	lava, ash, cinders, and bombs	tall, cone-shaped mountains	layers of lava alternating with layers of ash, cinders and bombs
Lava plateaus	lava	high, level areas	layers of lava

Program Resources

◆ **Unit 4 Resources** Chapter 11 Project Scoring Rubric, p. 32
◆ **Performance Assessment** Chapter 11, pp. 35–37
◆ **Chapter and Unit Tests** Chapter 11 Test, pp. 56–59

Media and Technology

Computer Test Bank
Chapter 11 Test

Reviewing Content

Multiple Choice

1. c 2. b 3. c 4. d 5. a

True or False

6. true 7. normal faults 8. focus
9. P waves 10. composite volcano

Checking Concepts

11. Pangaea was the great landmass formed millions of years ago when the continents moved together.

12. Where two plates move away from each other, tension forces create many normal faults. When two normal faults form parallel to each other, a block of rock is left lying between them. As the hanging wall of each normal fault slips downward, the block in between moves upward, forming a fault-block mountain.

13. Compression forms folded mountains. Compression shortens and thickens the crust so it bends slowly without breaking. If the fold bends upward into an arch, the fold is called an anticline. If the fold bends downward to form a bowl, the fold is called a syncline.

14. An earthquake occurs when rock along a fault suddenly breaks at a point beneath the surface called the focus. This releases the stress stored in the rock as seismic waves. The seismic waves travel outward from the focus in all directions. They reach the surface at the epicenter.

15. Both the moment magnitude scale and the Richter scale measure earthquake strength. The Richter scale rates the size of seismic waves as measured by a mechanical seismograph. The moment magnitude scale estimates the total energy released by an earthquake. The Richter scale provides accurate measurements for small, nearby earthquakes but does not work well for large or distant earthquakes. The moment magnitude scale can be used to rate earthquakes of all sizes and at all distances.

16. Aa; It forms from cooler, slower-moving lava.

17. Plateaus form when vertical faults push up large, flat blocks of rock. They can also form when thin, runny lava floods an area again and again, forming lava plateaus.

Reviewing Content

 Review key concepts online using iText at www.phschool.com

Multiple Choice

Choose the letter of the answer that best completes each statement.

1. Earth's lithosphere is broken into large pieces called
   a. plateaus.   b. continents.
   c. plates.   d. faults and folds.
2. Shearing is the force in Earth's crust that
   a. squeezes the crust together.
   b. pushes the crust in opposite directions.
   c. forces the crust to bend and fold.
   d. stretches the crust apart.
3. When the hanging wall of a fault slips down with respect to the footwall, the result is a
   a. reverse fault.   b. syncline.
   c. normal fault.   d. strike-slip fault.
4. Geologists use the difference in the arrival times of P waves and S waves at a seismograph to determine
   a. the magnitude of the earthquake.
   b. the depth of the earthquake's focus.
   c. the strength of the surface waves.
   d. the distance to the epicenter.
5. A quiet volcanic eruption would most likely produce
   a. pahoehoe lava flows. b. a cinder cone.
   c. a caldera.   d. pyroclastic flows.

True or False

If the statement is true, write true. If it is false, change the underlined word or words to make the statement true.

6. Plates pull apart, come together, or slide past each other along <u>plate boundaries</u>.
7. Rock uplifted by <u>strike-slip faults</u> creates fault-block mountains.
8. An earthquake's <u>epicenter</u> is located deep underground.
9. As <u>S waves</u> move through the ground, they cause it to compress and then expand.
10. A volcano formed by explosive eruptions of lava and ash is called a <u>shield volcano</u>.

Checking Concepts

11. What was Pangaea?
12. Explain the process that forms a fault-block mountain.
13. What type of stress in the crust results in the formation of folded mountains? Explain your answer.
14. Describe what happens along a fault beneath Earth's surface when an earthquake occurs.
15. Explain how the moment magnitude and Richter scales of earthquake measurement are similar and how they are different.
16. While observing a lava flow from a recently active volcano, you notice an area of lava with a rough, chunky surface. What type of lava is this and how does it form?
17. What are two different ways in which plateaus can form?
18. **Writing to Learn** Suppose you are a newspaper reporter in 1980. You have been assigned to report on the eruption of Mount St. Helens. Write a news story describing your observations.

Thinking Critically

19. **Predicting** If two plates made of continental crust crash together, what changes in Earth's surface might result?
20. **Classifying** How would you classify a fault in which the hanging wall has slid up and over the footwall?
21. **Comparing and Contrasting** Compare and contrast P waves and S waves.
22. **Comparing and Contrasting** Compare and contrast faulting and folding. What types of stress in the crust are involved? How do faulting and folding change Earth's surface?
23. **Applying Concepts** Describe the "life cycle" of a volcano from the time the volcano forms until it becomes extinct.
24. **Making Generalizations** How might a volcanic eruption affect the area around a volcano, including its plant and animal life?
25. **Relating Cause and Effect** What is a caldera and how does a caldera form?

---

18. Students' news stories should include a brief description of the nature of the violent eruption consistent with that of a compostite volcano and with the information on page 379.

Thinking Critically

19. Colliding continental plates will compress the crust, likely creating folds and reverse faults that result in mountains forming.
20. It should be classified as a reverse fault.

21. Both P waves and S waves are seismic waves sent out from the earthquake's focus deep under ground. P waves arrive first at a seismograph. They compress and expand the ground like an accordion. P waves travel through both solids and liquids. S waves arrive second at a seismograph. They vibrate from side to side and up and down. S waves cannot move through liquids.

Applying Skills

The graph shows the seismograph record for an earthquake. The y-axis of the graph shows the up-and-down shaking in millimeters at the seismograph station. The x-axis shows time in minutes.

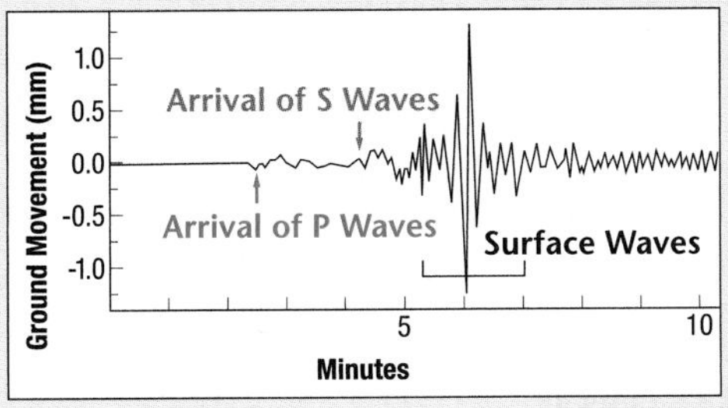

26. **Interpreting Diagrams** In what order do the seismic waves arrive at the seismograph station? Which type of seismic wave produces the largest ground movement?
27. **Interpreting Diagrams** What is the difference in arrival times for the P waves and S waves?
28. **Predicting** What would the seismograph record look like several hours after this earthquake? How would it change if an aftershock occurred?
29. **Drawing Conclusions** If the difference in arrival times for P waves and S waves is 5 minutes longer at a second seismograph station than at the first station, what can you conclude about the location of the second station?

Performance Assessment (Chapter Project)

Present Your Project Rehearse your documentary with your group before presenting it to the class. All group members should be able to answer questions about the visuals.

Reflect and Record In your journal evaluate how well your documentary presented the information you collected. How could you have improved your presentation? As you watched the other documentaries, did you see any similarities between how people in different regions live with volcanoes?

Test Preparation

Use these questions to prepare for standardized tests.

Use the diagram of a fault to answer Questions 30–34.

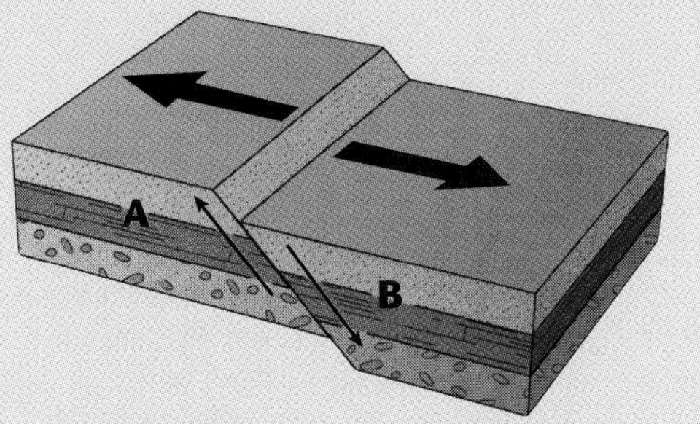

30. The rock on the side of the fault labeled B is the
    A footwall. **B** shearing wall.
    C hanging wall. **D** seismic wall.
31. The rock on the side of the fault labeled A is the
    F hanging wall. **G** strike-slip wall.
    H reverse wall. **J** footwall.
32. The thick arrows in the diagram stand for forces in Earth's crust pulling apart the two slabs of rock. This force is called
    A shearing. **B** compression.
    C elevation. **D** tension.
33. In the fault shown, the footwall
    F does not move.
    G moves down relative to the hanging wall.
    H moves up relative to the hanging wall.
    J slides sideways along the hanging wall.
34. The fault in the diagram is a(n)
    A normal fault. **B** strike-slip fault.
    C reverse fault. **D** inactive fault.

22. Faulting involves the breaking of the crust due to shearing, tension, and compression, whereas folding involves bending of the crust due to compression. Both change Earth's surface by causing mountain building and uplift.
23. A volcano forms when magma rises toward the surface and erupts through an opening that develops in weak rock. While erupting, the volcano is active, or live. It will not likely erupt continuously, but will become dormant periodically until it awakens and erupts again. Eventually, the volcano will become extinct, at which point it is not likely to erupt again.

Program Resources

- **Inquiry Skills Activity Book** Provides teaching and review of all inquiry skills
- **Prentice Hall Assessment System** Provides standardized test practice
- **Reading in the Content Area** Provides strategies to improve science reading skills
- **Teacher's ELL Handbook** Provides multiple strategies for English language learners

24. Land, plants, and animals near a volcano can be damaged or killed by flowing lava and the fires it sets, and by hot, burning clouds of gas, ash cinders, and bombs. Ash and mudflows can bury towns and land surfaces. Eventually, volcanic materials can form fertile soils, able to support plants.
25. A caldera is a huge hole left by the collapse of a volcanic mountain. When eruptions empty the main vent and magma chamber, the resulting hollow area can collapse, forming a caldera.

Applying Skills

26. P waves arrive first, then S waves, and finally surface waves. Surface waves produce the largest ground movement.
27. approximately 1 minute and 50 seconds
28. The up-and-down spikes of the waves would be much less jagged, perhaps almost smooth. If an aftershock occurred, the spikes would resume again.
29. The second station is farther away from the earthquake's epicenter.

Performance Assessment (Chapter Project)

Present Your Project You may want to provide time for groups to practice their presentations. Inform students how much time each group will have for its presentation. Tell them that if their practice presentation runs too long, they should find ways to cut its length without jeopardizing its content or flow.
Reflect and Record Give students time to record their thoughts individually, then encourage them to discuss their ideas with the other members of their group. Let students respond to the last question in a whole-class discussion. Emphasize the similarities that students identify by listing them on the board or an overhead transparency.

Test Preparation

30. C **31.** J **32.** D **33.** H **34.** A

CHAPTER 12 Fresh Water

Sections	Time	Student Edition Activities		Other Activities

CHAPTER PROJECT

Every Drop Counts
p. 395 TEKS: 6.14B

Ongoing (2–3 weeks)

TEKS: 6.1B; 6.2B, C, D, E
Check Your Progress, pp. 402, 415, 422
Present Your Project, p. 431

TE — Chapter 12 Project Notes, pp. 394–395

---

1 The Water Cycle
pp. 396–403 TEKS: 6.8B; 6.14B

12.1.1 Identify how Earth's water is distributed among saltwater and freshwater sources.
12.1.2 Describe how Earth's water moves through the water cycle.
12.1.3 Give examples of how people and other living things use water.

2 periods/ 1 block

TEKS: 6.1A; 6.2B, C, D, E; 6.3C, D; 6.4A
Discover Where Does the Water Come From?, p. 396
Sharpen Your Skills Calculating, p. 397
Try This Tabletop Water Cycle, p. 398
Real-World Lab: You and Your Environment Water From Trees, p. 403

TE — Including All Students, p. 398
TE — Real-Life Learning, pp. 399, 401
TE — Cultural Diversity, p. 400

---

2 Surface Water
pp. 404–411 TEKS: 6.14B

12.2.1 Describe a river system and how water flows into it.
12.2.2 Identify conditions that cause floods and how floods can be controlled.
12.2.3 Explain how ponds and lakes form.
12.2.4 Describe pond and lake habitats.
12.2.5 Explain how icebergs are formed.

3 periods/ 1½ blocks

TEKS: 6.2B, C; 6.3C; 6.4A
Discover What's in Pond Water?, p. 404
Try This The Knuckle Divide, p. 405
Science at Home, p. 411

TE — Integrating Technology, p. 407
TE — Building Inquiry Skills: Comparing and Contrasting, p. 408
TE — Integrating Life Science, p. 408
TE — Including All Students, pp. 409, 410

---

3 Ground Water
pp. 412–417 TEKS: 6.14B

12.3.1 Describe springs and how water moves through underground layers of soil and rock.
12.3.2 Explain what an aquifer is and how people obtain water from an aquifer.

3 periods/ 1½ blocks

TEKS: 6.1A; 6.2B, C, D, E; 6.3C
Discover Where Does the Water Go?, p. 412
Sharpen Your Skills Drawing Conclusions, p. 413
Try This An Artesian Well, p. 414
Real-World Lab: Careers in Science Soil Testing, pp. 416–417

LM — 12, "Field Testing a Body of Fresh Water"

---

4 INTEGRATING LIFE SCIENCE
Wetland Systems
pp. 418–422 TEKS: 6.5B

12.4.1 Identify parts of a wetland system.
12.4.2 Compare the properties of a wetland system to the properties of its parts.
12.4.3 Explain why wetland systems are important.

2 periods/ 1 block

TEKS: 6.2B, C, E; 6.3C
Discover Wet or Dry?, p. 418
Sharpen Your Skills Making Models, p. 421

TE — Building Inquiry Skills: Designing Experiments, p. 419
TE — Including All Students, p. 421

---

5 Water Resources
pp. 423–428 TEKS: 6.14B

12.5.1 Describe conditions that can result in a water shortage and list sources of fresh water for the future.
12.5.2 Explain how water can be conserved.

1 period/ ½ block

TEKS: 6.2B, C; 6.3C, D, E; 6.4A
Discover Can You Reach a Balance?, p. 423
Sharpen Your Skills Predicting, p. 425
Science at Home p. 427

TE — Integrating Technology, p. 424

Study Guide/Chapter Assessment
pp. 429–431

1 period/ ½ block

PLM — Provides blackline masters for Probeware labs

ISAB — Provides teaching and review of all inquiry skills

Key: **CTB** Computer Test Bank
CUT Chapter and Unit Tests
ELL Teacher's ELL Handbook

CHAPTER PLANNING GUIDE

 The Resource Pro® CD-ROM provides flexibility for planning the instruction for any type of schedule.

Program Resources	Assessment Strategies	Media and Technology
UR Chapter 12 Project Teacher Notes, pp. 58–59 UR Chapter 12 Project Student Materials, pp. 60–63	SE Performance Assessment: Present Your Project, p. 431 TE Check Your Progress, pp. 402, 415, 422 UR Chapter 12 Project Scoring Rubric, p. 64	🌐 Science Explorer at www.phschool.com 🎧 Student Edition on Audio CD, English-Spanish, Chapter 12
UR 12-1 Section Lesson Plan, p. 65 UR 12-1 Section Summary, p. 66 UR 12-1 Review and Reinforce, p. 67 UR 12-1 Enrich, p. 68 UR Real-World Lab blackline masters, pp. 85–86	SE Section 1 Review, p. 402 TE Ongoing Assessment, pp.397, 399, 401 TE Performance Assessment, p. 402	💿 Earth Science Videodisc Unit 2, Side 2, "What's in Our Tap?" 📼 Videotape Grade 6, Unit 4, "What's in Our Tap?" 📼 Lab Activity Videotapes, Tape 3 📽 Transparency 58, "Exploring the Water Cycle"
UR 12-2 Section Lesson Plan, p. 69 UR 12-2 Section Summary, p. 70 UR 12-2 Review and Reinforce, p. 71 UR 12-2 Enrich, p. 72	SE Section 2 Review, p. 411 TE Ongoing Assessment, pp. 405, 407, 409 TE Performance Assessment, p. 411	
UR 12-3 Section Lesson Plan, p. 73 UR 12-3 Section Summary, p. 74 UR 12-3 Review and Reinforce, p. 75 UR 12-3 Enrich, p. 76 UR Real-World Lab blackline masters, pp. 87–89	SE Section 3 Review, p. 415 TE Ongoing Assessment, p. 413 TE Performance Assessment, p. 415	📼 Lab Activity Videotapes, Tape 3 📽 Transparency 59, "Underground Layers" 📽 Transparency 60, "Wells and Springs"
UR 12-4 Section Lesson Plan, p. 77 UR 12-4 Section Summary, p. 78 UR 12-4 Review and Reinforce, p. 79 UR 12-4 Enrich, p. 80	SE Section 4 Review, p. 422 TE Ongoing Assessment, pp. 419, 421 TE Performance Assessment, p. 422	
UR 12-5 Section Lesson Plan, p. 81 UR 12-5 Section Summary, p. 82 UR 12-5 Review and Reinforce, p. 83 UR 12-5 Enrich, p. 84	SE Section 5 Review, p. 427 TE Ongoing Assessment, p. 425 TE Performance Assessment, p. 427	💿 Life Science Videodisc Unit 2, Side 2, "Xeriscape" 📼 Videotape Grade 6, Unit 4, "Xeriscape" 📽 Transparency 61, "Conserving Water"
ELL Provides multiple strategies for English language learners GRSW Provides worksheets to promote student comprehension of content RCA Provides strategies to improve science reading skills	SE Chapter 12 Study Guide/Assessment, pp. 429–431 PA Chapter 12 Assessment, pp. 38–40 CUT Chapter 12 Test, pp. 60–63 CTB Chapter 12 Test PHAS Provides standardized test preparation	📖 Chapter 12 💽 Computer Test Bank, Chapter 12 Test

GRSW Guided Reading and Study Workbook
ISAB Inquiry Skills Activity Book
LM Laboratory Manual

PA Performance Assessment
PHAS Prentice Hall Assessment System
PLM Probeware Lab Manual

RCA Reading in the Content Area
SE Student Edition

TE Teacher's Edition
UR Unit Resources

Student Edition Activities Planner

ACTIVITY	Time (minutes)	Materials — Quantities for one work group	Skills
Section 1			
Discover, p. 396	15	**Consumable** ice, water **Nonconsumable** pitcher, clear drinking glass	Inferring
Sharpen Your Skills, p. 397	20; 20	**Consumable** water **Nonconsumable** 1-liter clear plastic bottle, large bowl, 5 cups, permanent marker, plastic graduated cylinder, calculator, plastic dropper	Calculating
Try This, p. 398	20; 20	**Consumable** water, sand, plastic wrap **Nonconsumable** flat-bottomed clear container, small jar, rubber band, small rock, lamp	Making Models
Real-World Lab, p. 403	20; 20	**Consumable** 3 plastic sandwich bags, 3 twist ties **Nonconsumable** 3 small pebbles, balance, computer (optional)	Observing, Calculating, Inferring
Section 2			
Discover, p. 404	20	**Consumable** pond water **Nonconsumable** plastic petri dish, hand lens, microscope, eyedropper, slide and cover slip	Classifying
Try This, p. 405	10	**Consumable** paper towel, water **Nonconsumable** spoon	Making Models
Science at Home, p. 411	home	**Consumable** milk or juice carton, tap water, salt **Nonconsumable** freezer, large bowl, ruler	Making Models
Section 3			
Discover, p. 412	10	**Consumable** dry sand, water **Nonconsumable** pebbles, clear jar, ruler	Observing
Sharpen Your Skills, p. 413	10	No special materials are required.	Drawing Conclusions
Try This, pp. 414	20	**Consumable** newspaper, modeling clay, moist sand, plastic straw, water **Nonconsumable** loaf pan, funnel, scissors	Making Models
Real-World Lab, pp. 416–417	40	**Consumable** 100 mL sand, 100 mL powdered potter's clay, 3 squares of cheesecloth, 300 mL water **Nonconsumable** hand lens, stopwatch, 3 rubber bands, 3 large plastic funnels or cut-off plastic soda bottle tops, 3 100-mL beakers, 100 mL pebbles	Observing, Measuring, Drawing Conclusions
Section 4			
Discover, pp. 418	10–15	**Consumable** water, 2 paper cups **Nonconsumable** 2 dry kitchen sponges, pan	Observing
Sharpen Your Skills, p. 421	10–15	**Consumable** water **Nonconsumable** loaf pan, damp soil, watering can, sponge	Making Models
Section 5			
Discover, p. 423	15	**Consumable** water **Nonconsumable** large measuring cup, plastic dropper, 2 small bowls, spoon, stopwatch	Predicting
Sharpen Your Skills, p. 425	5, 5	**Nonconsumable** large measuring cup	Predicting
Science at Home, pp. 427	home	**Consumable** toothpaste, water, tape, toothbrush	Comparing and Contrasting

A list of all materials required for the Student Edition activities can be found on pages T43–T49. You can obtain information about ordering materials by calling 1-800-848-9500 or by accessing the Science Explorer Internet site at **www.phschool.com**.

Texas Essential Knowledge and Skills

(6.1) Scientific processes. The student conducts field and laboratory investigations using safe, environmentally appropriate, and ethical practices. *(Project; Sections 1, 3)*
The student is expected to:
(A) demonstrate safe practices during field and laboratory investigations; and
(B) make wise choices in the use and conservation of resources and the disposal or recycling of materials.

(6.2) Scientific processes. The student uses scientific inquiry methods during field and laboratory investigations. *(Project; Sections 1, 2, 3, 4, 5)*
The student is expected to:
(B) collect data by observing and measuring;
(C) analyze and interpret information to construct reasonable explanations from direct and indirect evidence;
(D) communicate valid conclusions; and
(E) construct graphs, tables, maps, and charts using tools including computers to organize, examine, and evaluate data.

(6.3) Scientific processes. The student uses critical thinking and scientific problem solving to make informed decisions. *(Sections 1, 2, 3, 4, 5)*
The student is expected to:
(C) represent the natural world using models and identify their limitations;
(D) evaluate the impact of research on scientific thought, society, and the environment; and
(E) connect Grade 6 science concepts with the history of science and contributions of scientists.

(6.4) Scientific processes. The student knows how to use a variety of tools and methods to conduct science inquiry. *(Sections 1, 2, 5)*
The student is expected to:
(A) collect, analyze, and record information using tools including beakers, petri dishes, meter sticks, graduated cylinders, weather instruments, timing devices, hot plates, test tubes, safety goggles, spring scales, magnets, balances, microscopes, telescopes, thermometers, calculators, field equipment, compasses, computers, and computer probes.

(6.5) Scientific concepts. The student knows that systems may combine with other systems to form a larger system. *(Section 4)*
The student is expected to:
(B) describe how the properties of a system are different from the properties of its parts.

(6.8) Science concepts. The student knows that complex interactions occur between matter and energy. *(Section 1)*
The student is expected to:
(B) explain and illustrate the interactions between matter and energy in the water cycle and in the decay of biomass such as in a compost bin.

(6.14) Science concepts. The student knows the structures and functions of Earth systems. *(Project; Sections 1, 2, 3, 5)*
The student is expected to:
(B) identify relationships between groundwater and surface water in a watershed.

Take It to the Net

 Interactive text at www.phschool.com

Science Explorer comes alive with iText.

- **Complete student text** is accessible from any computer with Internet access or a CD-ROM drive.
- **Animations, simulations, and videos** enhance student understanding and retention of concepts.
- **Self-tests and online study tools** assess student understanding.
- **Teacher management tools** help you make the most of this valuable resource.

STAY CURRENT with **SCIENCE NEWS**®

Find out the latest research and information about Earth's waters at **www.phschool.com**.

Go to **www.phschool.com**. Select Texas on the navigation bar. Click on the Science icon. Then click on <u>Science Explorer</u> under PH@school.

Every Drop Counts

TEKS: 6.1B; 6.2B, C, D, E; 6.14B

Opening a faucet is so routine that many students are unaware of how often they run water in the home. Equally as significant, they are probably unaware of the total amount of water used, as most of it swirls down the drain.

Purpose In this project, students will measure how much water they themselves use during a week, how much water is used in their homes during the same week, and how much water is used in another type of building in a week. Gathering this information should give students a greater understanding of the importance of water and water resources.

Skills Focus After completing the Chapter 12 Project, students will be able to
◆ interpret data collected from a home water meter and from another building in their community;
◆ create data tables about home water use;
◆ calculate how much water is used in their home and in another building during a one-week period;
◆ graph the data collected about household water use;
◆ communicate the results of the project in a presentation to the class.

Project Timeline The entire project will require at least two weeks. See Chapter 12 Project Teacher Notes on pages 58–59 in Unit 4 Resources for hints and detailed directions. Also distribute to students Chapter 12 Project Student Materials and Scoring Rubric on pages 60–64 in Unit 4 Resources.

Early in the project, allow class time for students to discuss how to make their data tables. Although students will be making their measurements at home through the week, they will need some class time for you to check their progress.

You may want students to begin immediately looking for an appropriate nonresidential building to study. Tell students they should ask parents and other adults for suggestions. Often parents will know someone who could help students gain access to a building manager or building records. Allow the second week

CHAPTER 12 Fresh Water

Hikers in California's Yosemite National Park are awed by its thundering waterfalls.

WEB ACTIVITY

www.phschool.com

394

of the project for the gathering of this information, as well as for the preparation of student presentations.

Suggested Shortcuts If the project seems too long or involved for your students, you could have them do only the home study for one or two weeks, eliminating the monitoring of a second building. As an alternative, you could ask for a small group of student volunteers to monitor a nonresidential building and report to the class.

A further shortcut would be to simply have students monitor their own water use over several days. This would eliminate the cooperation of family members but would still fulfill the purpose of the project.

Possible Materials Students need nothing more than paper and pencil to collect the data for the project. In presenting their results at the end of the project, some students may want to use poster board to mount their graphs or other visual aids.

CHAPTER 12 PROJECT

Every Drop Counts

With an almost deafening roar, water rushes over this waterfall and plunges into the rocky pool below. Every day, hundreds of thousands of liters of water flow over the falls. How do you think this amount compares with the amount of water that flows out of your faucets at home each day?

In this chapter, you will explore the many ways that living things depend on Earth's water. To learn how water is used in your own home and community, you will design a method for tracking water use over a one-week period.

Your Goal To monitor water use in your home and in another building in your community for one week.

To complete the project you will

- ◆ track your personal water use at home
- ◆ determine the total amount of water used in your home
- ◆ find out how much water is used by a business, school, hospital, or other building in your community

Get Started Begin now by brainstorming the ways you use water at home. Use this list to create a data table in which you will record each time you perform these activities during the week.

Check Your Progress You'll be working on this project as you study this chapter. To keep your project on track, look for Check Your Progress boxes at the following points.

Section 1 Review, page 402: Calculate your total water use.
Section 3 Review, page 415: Investigate water use at another building in your community.
Section 4 Review, page 422: Make graphs of the water-use data for your household and your community.

Present Your Project At the end of the chapter (page 431), you will share your water-use data with your class and discuss the information with your classmates.

TEKS

In addition to process TEKS, this chapter addresses these concept TEKS as they relate to the chapter's topics.

(6.5) The student knows that systems may combine with other systems to form a larger system. The student is expected to:
(B) describe how the properties of a system are different from the properties of its parts.
(6.8) The student knows that complex interactions occur between matter and energy. The student is expected to:
(B) explain and illustrate the interactions between matter and energy in the water cycle and in the decay of biomass such as in a compost bin.

(6.14) The student knows the structures and functions of Earth systems. The student is expected to:
(B) identify relationships between groundwater and surface water in a watershed.

395

Program Resources

- ◆ **Unit 4 Resources** Chapter 12 Project Teacher Notes, pp. 58–59; Chapter 12 Project Student Materials, pp. 60–63

Media and Technology

Student Edition on Audio CD
English-Spanish, Chapter 12

WEB ACTIVITY — www.phschool.com

You will find an Internet activity, chapter self-tests for students, and links to other chapter topics at this site.

Launching the Project To introduce this project to students, ask: **What are some of the ways you and your family use water daily in and around the home?** *(Flushing toilets, taking baths and showers, brushing teeth, cleaning dishes, washing clothes, watering the lawn, washing the car, and so on)* Write students' suggestions on the board. Then challenge students to estimate how many liters of water each of them uses in a day. After students have shared their estimates, tell them that in this country residential water use averages about 300 L per person per day. Encourage students to compare this average with their own water use to estimate if they use more or less than the average.

Finally, have students read the description of the project in their text and in the Chapter 12 Project Overview on pages 60–61 in Unit 4 Resources. Encourage students to come up with their own ideas of how they could accomplish the tasks involved.

Performance Assessment

The Chapter 12 Project Scoring Rubric on page 64 of Unit 4 Resources will help you evaluate how well students complete the Chapter 12 Project. Students will be assessed on

- ◆ how completely and accurately they collect data from their homes and a second building,
- ◆ how thorough and interesting their class presentations are,
- ◆ their participation in their groups.

By sharing the Chapter 12 Project Scoring Rubric with students at the beginning of the project, you will make it clear to them what they are expected to do.

TEKS: 6.1A; 6.2B, C, D, E; 6.3C, D; 6.4A;
6.8B; 6.14B

Objectives

After completing the lesson, students will
be able to

◆ identify how Earth's water is
distributed among saltwater and
freshwater sources;

◆ describe how Earth's water moves
through the water cycle;

◆ give examples of how people and other
living things use water.

1 Engage/Explore

Activating Prior Knowledge

Invite a student volunteer to describe a
rainstorm. Ask: **Where does the water
come from that falls as rain?** *(from clouds)*
How does the water get into the clouds?
*(Some students may know that water vapor
in the atmosphere condenses to form
clouds.)* Continue this line of questioning,
guiding students through the water cycle
to put the parts together to form a cycle.

· · · · · · · DISCOVER · · · · · · ·

Skills Focus inferring
Materials *ice, water,*
pitcher, clear drinking glass
Time 15 minutes

Tips Add enough ice to a pitcher of
water to make the water very cold, thus
ensuring that droplets will quickly form
on the outer surface of the glass. Advise
students to be careful not to spill the
water onto the outside of the glass when
pouring from the pitcher. Once students
have completed the activity, you may
want to spend time exploring their
misconceptions about this phenomenon.

Think It Over Some students may
correctly infer that the water droplets
come from water vapor in the air
condensing on the cold surface of the
glass. Some students, however, will
propose that the water somehow came
from inside the glass.

396

SECTION 1 The Water Cycle

DISCOVER · · · · · · · · · · · · · · · · · · ACTIVITY

Where Does the Water Come From?

1. Fill a glass with ice cubes and water, being careful not to spill
any water. Set the glass aside for 5 minutes.

2. Observe the outside of the glass and the surface it was
sitting on.

Think It Over

Inferring Where did the water on the outside of the glass come
from? How do you think it got there?

GUIDE FOR READING

◆ How is Earth's water
distributed among saltwater
and freshwater sources?

◆ How does Earth's water
move through the water
cycle?

◆ How do people and other
living things use water?

Reading Tip As you read,
use the headings to make an
outline showing how water is
important and where it is
found.

Key Terms water vapor
• groundwater • water cycle
• evaporation • transpiration
• precipitation • irrigation

Why do you think Earth is often called the "water
planet"? Perhaps an astronaut suggested this name.
From space, an astronaut can see that there is much
more water than land on planet Earth. Oceans cover nearly 71
percent of Earth's surface.

Water on Earth

Figure 1 shows how Earth's water is distributed. **Most of Earth's
water — roughly 97 percent — is salt water that is found in
the oceans. Only 3 percent is fresh water.** Of that 3 percent,
about three quarters is found in the huge masses of ice near the
North and South Poles. A fraction more is found in the atmosphere. Most water in the atmosphere is invisible **water vapor,**
the gaseous form of water. Less than 1 percent of the water on
Earth is fresh water that is available for humans to use.

Oceans To explore where Earth's water is found, you can take
an imaginary boat trip around the world. Your journey starts in
Miami, Florida. From here, you can sail completely around the
world without ever going ashore. Although people have given
names to regions of the ocean, these regions are all connected,
forming a single world ocean.

First you sail southeast across the Atlantic Ocean toward
Africa. Swinging around the continent's southern tip, you enter
the smaller but deeper Indian Ocean. Next, you head east across
the Pacific Ocean, the longest part of your trip. This vast ocean,
dotted with islands, covers an area greater than all the land on
Earth put together.

396

READING STRATEGIES

Reading Tip Encourage students to preview
the section, noting the two levels of headings
that appear. Students can use these headings
as the first two levels of their outlines.
Student outlines may begin as follows:

I. Water on Earth
    A. Oceans
    B. Ice
    C. Rivers and Lakes
    D. Below Earth's Surface

II. The Water Cycle
    A. Water Evaporates
    B. Clouds Form
    C. Water Falls as Precipitation
III. How Do People Use Water?
    A. Agriculture
    B. Industry
    C. Transportation
    D. Recreation
IV. Water and Living Things

Ice How can you get back to Miami? You could sail all the way around South America. But watch out for icebergs! These floating chunks of ice are made of fresh water. Icebergs in the southern Pacific and Atlantic oceans have broken off the massive sheets of ice that cover most of Antarctica. You would also find icebergs in the Arctic Ocean around the North Pole.

Rivers and Lakes To see examples of fresh water in rivers and lakes, you'll have to make a side trip inland. Sail north past Nova Scotia, Canada, to the beginning of the St. Lawrence Seaway. Navigate through the series of locks along the St. Lawrence River. Suddenly the river widens and you enter Lake Ontario, one of North America's five Great Lakes. Together, the Great Lakes contain nearly 20 percent of all the water in the world's freshwater lakes.

Below Earth's Surface When rain or snow falls, some of the water soaks into the ground. This water trickles down through spaces between the particles of soil and rock. Eventually the water reaches a layer that it cannot move through. Water that fills the cracks and spaces in underground soil and rock layers is called **groundwater.** Far more fresh water is located underground than in all Earth's rivers and lakes. You will learn more about groundwater in Section 3.

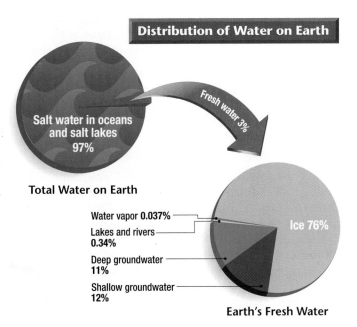

Distribution of Water on Earth

Fresh water 3%

Salt water in oceans and salt lakes 97%

Total Water on Earth

Water vapor **0.037%**
Lakes and rivers **0.34%**
Deep groundwater **11%**
Shallow groundwater **12%**
Ice **76%**

Earth's Fresh Water

Figure 1 Most of Earth's water is salt water. Of the freshwater sources shown in the bottom circle graph, only the water in lakes, rivers, and shallow groundwater is available for human use.

Sharpen your Skills

Calculating

This activity shows how Earth's water is distributed.

ACTIVITY

1. Fill a one-liter plastic bottle with water. This represents the total water on Earth.

2. First, measure 97 percent, or 970 milliliters (mL), of the water and pour it into a large bowl. This represents the salt water in Earth's oceans and salt lakes.

3. Next, you will demonstrate how the remaining fresh water is divided. Label five cups to match the fresh-water sources in Figure 1. Calculate how much of the remaining 30 mL of water you should pour into each cup to represent the percentage of Earth's fresh water found there.

4. Use a plastic graduated cylinder to measure out the amount of water for each cup. Use a plastic dropper to approximate amounts that are too small to measure accurately.

Which cups contain water that is available for humans to use? How does the amount of water in these cups compare to the original one liter?

---

2 Facilitate

Water on Earth

Using the Visuals: Figure 1

Students may have difficulty interpreting these circle graphs. Focus their attention first on the upper graph. Ask: **What does this circle graph tell you?** (*Salt water makes up almost all of the water on Earth.*) **How is the lower graph related to the upper graph?** (*The lower graph represents all the water in the smaller wedge of the upper graph.*) **learning modality: logical/mathematical**

Sharpen your Skills

Calculating

Materials *water, 1-liter clear plastic bottle, large bowl, 5 cups, permanent marker, plastic graduated cylinder, calculator, plastic dropper*

ACTIVITY

Time 30 minutes

Tips Students should pour 97% of 1000 mL, or 970 mL, into the bowl. As students proceed, ask them to examine the lower circle graph in Figure 1. Explain that the 3%, or 30 mL, remaining in the bottle represents 100% of the fresh water on Earth. Then have them use the circle graph and a calculator to calculate the amount of water to be placed in each of the five cups. (*Ice: 76% of 30 mL, or about 22 mL; Shallow Groundwater: 3.6 mL; Deep Groundwater: 3.3 mL; Lakes and Rivers: about 0.1 mL; and Water Vapor: about 0.01 mL.*)

Expected Outcome Students should conclude that only the water in the two cups labeled Lakes and Rivers and Shallow Groundwater is available for human use.

Extend Repeat steps 3 and 4 with a full bottle representing Earth's total fresh water. **learning modality: tactile/ kinesthetic**

Ongoing Assessment

Skills Check Have students make a circle graph of the water available for human use, using Figure 1. Students may estimate the relative sizes of the wedges.

The Water Cycle

Including All Students

To reinforce students' understanding of transpiration, invite students to examine a small plant, such as a geranium, out of soil. Ask: **Through which part does a plant take in water?** *(through its roots)* Help students trace the path that water takes through a plant: from the roots up through the stem and branches to the leaves. Transpiration takes place on the underside of leaves, through openings called stomata. **learning modality: kinesthetic**

Skills Focus making models

Materials *flat-bottomed clear container, water, small jar (such as a baby-food jar), sand, plastic wrap, rubber band, small rock, lamp (if direct sunlight is not available)*

Time 20 minutes for setup; 20 minutes an hour later for conclusion

Tips Be sure the top of the jar does not come into contact with the plastic wrap. The plastic wrap should be a little loose and hanging over the edges of the bowl.

Expected Outcome After about one hour, small drops of water should be evident on the inside surface of the plastic wrap. Also, the sand may be moist from drops of water falling from the plastic wrap. Students should infer that they have modeled the processes of evaporation, condensation, and precipitation, as well as land, a body of water, and the atmosphere.

Extend Ask students to make a labeled drawing of their model, using arrows and labels to show the processes that occur and the source of the energy that drives those processes. **learning modality: kinesthetic**

Tabletop Water Cycle

In this activity you will build a model of the water cycle.

1.   Put on your goggles. Pour enough water into a flat-bottomed bowl to cover the bottom. Fill a small jar with sand and place it in the bowl.

2. Loosely cover the top of the bowl with plastic wrap. Secure with a rubber band.

3. Place a rock on top of the plastic, directly over the jar.

4. Place the bowl in direct sunlight or under a lamp. After one hour, observe the bowl and plastic wrap.

Making Models What features of the water cycle are represented in your model?

The Water Cycle

Water is recycled through the water cycle. The **water cycle** is the continuous process by which water moves through the living and nonliving parts of the environment. **In the water cycle, water moves from bodies of water, land, and living things on Earth's surface to the atmosphere and back to Earth's surface.** The sun is the source of energy that drives the water cycle.

Water Evaporates Water moves continuously through the water cycle. The cycle has no real beginning or end. You can follow a water molecule through one complete cycle in *Exploring the Water Cycle* on the facing page.

Think about a molecule of water floating near the surface of an ocean. The sun is shining and the air is warm. Soon, the molecule has absorbed enough heat energy to change state. It evaporates and becomes water vapor. **Evaporation** is the process by which molecules at the surface of a liquid absorb enough energy to change to the gaseous state. Although the water comes from the salty ocean, it becomes fresh through the process of evaporation. The salt remains in the ocean.

Large amounts of water evaporate constantly from the surfaces of oceans and large lakes. In addition, small amounts evaporate from the soil, puddles, and even from your skin. A significant amount of water is given off by plants. Plants draw in water from the soil through their roots. Eventually the water is given off through the leaves as water vapor in a process called **transpiration.**

Clouds Form Once a water molecule has found its way into the atmosphere, warm air carries it upward. Higher up, the air tends to become much colder. Cold air holds less water vapor than warm air. Some of the water vapor cools and condenses into liquid water. Condensed droplets of water clump together around tiny dust particles in the air, forming clouds.

Water Falls as Precipitation As more water vapor condenses, the water droplets in a cloud eventually become so heavy that they fall back to Earth. Water that falls to Earth as rain, snow, hail, or sleet is called **precipitation.** Most water molecules probably spend only about 10 days in the atmosphere before falling back to Earth. Most precipitation falls directly into the oceans. Water in the ocean may stay there for many years before evaporating, thus continuing the cycle.

When precipitation falls on land, some of the water evaporates again immediately. Some runs off the surface of the land into rivers and lakes. From there, it may eventually evaporate or flow back into the ocean. Some water trickles down into the ground and forms groundwater. Groundwater may move underground

---

until it reaches a river, lake, or ocean. Once groundwater reaches the surface, it can continue through the cycle by evaporating again.

Precipitation is the source of all fresh water on and below Earth's surface. The water cycle renews the usable supply of fresh water on Earth. For millions of years, the total amount of water on Earth has remained fairly constant. In the world as a whole, the rates of evaporation and precipitation are balanced.

☑ *Checkpoint* *List three places from which water evaporates.*

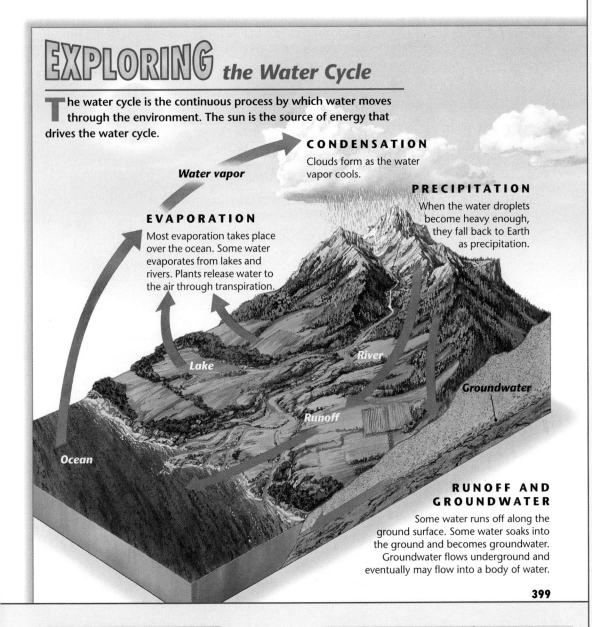

EXPLORING the Water Cycle

The water cycle is the continuous process by which water moves through the environment. The sun is the source of energy that drives the water cycle.

CONDENSATION
Clouds form as the water vapor cools.

Water vapor

PRECIPITATION
When the water droplets become heavy enough, they fall back to Earth as precipitation.

EVAPORATION
Most evaporation takes place over the ocean. Some water evaporates from lakes and rivers. Plants release water to the air through transpiration.

Lake

River

Groundwater

Runoff

Ocean

RUNOFF AND GROUNDWATER
Some water runs off along the ground surface. Some water soaks into the ground and becomes groundwater. Groundwater flows underground and eventually may flow into a body of water.

399

Media and Technology

Transparencies "Exploring the Water Cycle," Transparency 58

Answers to Self-Assessment

☑ *Checkpoint*
Water evaporates from oceans, lakes, and rivers.

EXPLORING
the Water Cycle

After students have examined the illustration, ask: **What are the three processes in the water cycle?** *(Evaporation, condensation, and precipitation)* **Which process begins the cycle?** *(Students might mention evaporation, because that is the first shown on the illustration).* Help students understand that a cycle has no beginning or no end, and that one process is no more important than the others. Point out that the water cycle is continuous and has been continuous for billions of years. Refer to the **ELL Handbook** for additional teaching strategies. **learning modality: visual**

Real-Life Learning

To make students aware of where water is found in your local area, give each student an outline map of your state. Then ask students to draw and label any ocean and the major rivers and lakes that are found there. Provide access to almanacs and atlases, and give students one or two days to complete their maps. **learning modality: tactile/kinesthetic**

 Students can save their maps in their portfolios.

Ongoing Assessment

Skills Check Have each student make a cycle diagram that shows the steps in the water cycle.

How Do People Use Water?

Invite student volunteers to read aloud to the class the annotations to the time line. Have a world map available for students to use to locate the various sites. For each method of irrigation, encourage students to draw conclusions about the environment in which it was used and how well the technology worked. Ask: **Do you think all these methods are used somewhere in the world today?** *(Students' responses will vary. Each method is still used today at some place.)*

In Your Journal 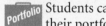 Give students time to research one of the irrigation techniques discussed in the feature. Students can find out more about the techniques by looking under *irrigation* in an encyclopedia or by doing a library computer search for *irrigation* or *agriculture* and for the various countries listed in the feature. Once students have written their letters, encourage volunteers to read theirs aloud to the class. Refer to the **ELL Handbook** for additional teaching strategies. **learning modality: verbal**

Portfolio Students can save their letters in their portfolios.

Cultural Diversity

Note for students that *paddy* is the Malay word for wet rice. The growing of wet rice, or paddy farming, provides the staple food in much of China and Southeast Asia. Ask some students to prepare a report to the class on this agricultural method, complete with pictures and a flow chart showing the process. **cooperative learning**

ACTIVITY

How Do People Use Water?

The water people use at home is just a small percentage of all the water used in the United States. **In addition to household purposes, people use water for agriculture, industry, transportation, and recreation.**

Agriculture Has your family ever had a garden? If so, you know that growing fruits and vegetables requires water. On a large farm, a constant supply of fresh water is essential.

However, some parts of the United States don't receive enough regular rainfall for agriculture. In such areas, farmland must be irrigated. **Irrigation** is the process of supplying water to areas of land to make them suitable for growing crops. In the United States, more water is used for irrigating farmland than for any other single purpose.

Water and Agriculture

Plants require a steady supply of water to grow. How have farmers throughout history provided their crops with water? This time line shows some methods developed in different parts of the world.

2000 B.C. Egypt

Egyptian farmers invented a way to raise water from the Nile River. The device, called a *shaduf,* acted as a lever to make lifting a bucket of water easier. The farmers then emptied the water into a network of canals to irrigate their fields. The *shaduf* is still in use in Egypt, India, and other countries.

| 3000 B.C. | 2000 B.C. | 1000 B.C. |

3000 B.C. China

One of the oldest known methods of irrigation was developed for growing rice. Farmers built paddies, or artificial ponds with raised edges. The farmers flooded the paddies with water from a nearby stream. This ancient technique is still widely used throughout Southeast Asia.

700 B.C. Assyria

Sennacherib, king of the ancient nation Assyria, surrounded the capital city of Nineveh with fruit trees, cotton, and exotic plants. To help irrigate the plantations, he built a 10-kilometer canal and a stone aqueduct to transport water from the nearby hills.

400

Background

Facts and Figures In the early twentieth century, the settlers of the Great Plains used windmills to provide the water to irrigate their crops. But most of those windmills could raise water less than 10 m. With the advent of deep-well drilling and modern pumps, farmers of the 1930s began to reach groundwater much deeper underground. Modern farmers on the Great Plains no longer use ditches in irrigating their fields.

That method loses too much water to evaporation, seepage, and runoff—50–60 percent of the total. Instead, many farmers use center-pivot sprinkler systems. The water is pumped underground in pipes to a central pivot and then out through a long, turning "boom" with sprinklers along its length. The result is a circular field of crops. The center-pivot method wastes only 20–30 percent of the water.

Industry Think about the objects in a typical school locker. Did you know that water is needed to produce all these objects? Even though water is not part of the final products, it plays a role in the industrial processes that created them.

Industries use water in many other ways. For example, power plants and steel mills both need huge volumes of water to cool down hot machinery. Water that is used for cooling can often be recycled, or used again for another purpose.

Transportation Oceans and rivers have been used for transporting people and goods since ancient times. If you look at a map of the United States, you will notice that many large cities are located on the coasts. Ocean travel led to the growth of such port cities. In early America, rivers also served as natural highways.

In Your Journal

Find out more about one of these agricultural techniques. Imagine that you are a farmer seeing the method in action for the first time. Write a letter to a friend describing the new technique. What problem will it solve? How will it improve your farming?

A.D. 1870 United States

When homesteaders arrived on the dry Great Plains of the central United States, they had to rely on water stored underground. Windmills provided the energy to pump the groundwater to the surface. The farmers dug ditches to carry the water to irrigate their fields.

A.D. 1   **A.D. 1000**   **A.D. 2000**

A.D. 1200 Mexico

To grow crops in areas covered by swampy lakes, the Aztecs built raised plots of farmland called *chinampas*. They grew maize on fertile soil scooped from the lake bottom. A grid of canals kept the crops wet and allowed the farmers to navigate boats between the *chinampas*.

Present Israel

Irrigation is the key to survival in desert regions. Today, methods such as drip irrigation ensure that very little water is wasted when crops are watered. Holes in the pipe allow water to drip directly onto the soil around the roots of each plant.

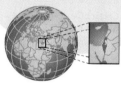

Chapter 12 **401**

3 Assess

Section 1 Review Answers

1. Most fresh water is found in the huge masses of ice near the poles.

2. Liquid water evaporates from Earth's surface to become water vapor. Clouds form as water vapor rises and cools. Water droplets condense, and then fall back to Earth as precipitation. That water eventually evaporates again, continuing the process.

3. Precipitation is the source of all fresh water on and below Earth's surface. The water cycle renews the supply of fresh water on Earth because when water evaporates, impurities, such as salt, are left behind.

4. The major uses are for household purposes, agriculture, industry, transportation, and recreation.

5. Cutting down trees would reduce the amount of evaporation in an area because trees draw in water from the soil and give it off as water vapor in the process of transpiration.

Check Your Progress ▸ CHAPTER PROJECT

As you review students' data tables at this point, make sure each has kept a daily record of water use. Also, check that students have listed most or all of the uses shown in Figure 2. To calculate the total amount of water used in the home over the week, most students should have recorded readings of a water meter. Students without access to a water meter should have made estimates based on their daily records. At this stage, encourage students to identify another type of building to monitor.

Performance Assessment

Oral Presentation Divide the class into small groups and challenge each group to list ways people use water locally for one of the water-use categories in the text and report to the class.

Water Used in the Home

Task	Water Used (liters)
Showering for 5 minutes	95
Brushing teeth	10
Washing hands	7.5
Flushing standard toilet	23
Flushing "low-flow" toilet	6
Washing one load of laundry	151
Running dishwasher	19
Washing dishes by hand	114

Figure 2 Many common household activities involve water.

Recreation Do you like to swim in a neighborhood pool? Catch fish from a rowboat in the middle of a lake? Walk along a beach collecting seashells? Or maybe just sit on the edge of a dock and dangle your feet in the water? Then you know some ways that water is used for recreation. And if you brave the winter cold to ski, snowboard, or skate, you are enjoying water in its frozen form.

Water and Living Things

INTEGRATING LIFE SCIENCE Here's a riddle for you: What do you and an apple have in common? You both consist mostly of water! In fact, water is a large part of every living thing. Water makes up nearly two thirds of your body. That water is necessary to keep your body functioning. You know that if you exercise vigorously outdoors on a hot day, your body can rapidly lose water through perspiration. That's why athletes such as bicycle racers and marathon runners must make sure to drink plenty of water before, during, and after their events.

Water is essential for living things to grow, reproduce, and carry out other important processes. For example, plants use water, plus carbon dioxide and energy from the sun, to make food in a process called photosynthesis. Animals and many other living things depend on the food made by plants. They may eat the plants directly or eat other organisms that eat plants.

Another way that living things use water is as a home. An organism's habitat is the place where it lives and that provides the things it needs to survive. Both fresh water and salt water provide habitats for many different types of living things.

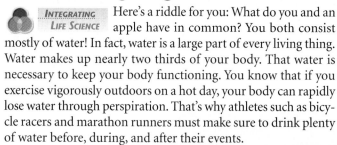

Section 1 Review

1. Where is most of the fresh water on Earth found?

2. Describe the general path of water as it moves through the water cycle.

3. How does the water cycle renew Earth's supply of fresh water?

4. What are five major ways that people in the United States use water?

5. Thinking Critically Relating Cause and Effect How might cutting down trees affect the amount of evaporation in an area?

Check Your Progress ▸ CHAPTER PROJECT

Use Figure 2 to estimate the water used for some common activities. Then determine how much water your family used during the week. You can do this by reading your water meter, estimating based on your personal water use, or having your family members record their usage. (*Hint:* Convert all amounts to liters.) Complete your water-use data table by calculating the total amount of water you used during the week.

Program Resources

◆ **Unit 4 Resources** 12-1 Review and Reinforce, p. 67; 12-1 Enrich, p. 68
◆ **Unit 4 Resources** Chapter 12 Real-World blackline masters, Lab, pp. 85–86

You and Your Environment

Water from Trees

Trees play many important roles in the environment—they keep the soil from washing away, remove carbon dioxide from the air, and produce oxygen. Trees are also a vital part of the water cycle. In this lab you will discover how trees help to keep water moving through the cycle.

Problem

How much water do the leaves on a tree give off in a 24-hour period?

Skills Focus

observing, calculating, inferring

Materials

3 plastic sandwich bags   balance
3 small pebbles   3 twist ties
computer (optional)

Procedure

1. Copy the data table into your notebook or create a spreadsheet on the computer.
2. Place the sandwich bags, twist ties, and pebbles on a balance. Determine their total mass to the nearest tenth of a gram.
3. Select an outdoor tree or shrub with leaves that are within your reach.
4. Put one pebble into a sandwich bag and place the bag over one of the tree's leaves as shown. Fasten the twist tie around the bag, forming a tight seal around the stem of the leaf.
5. Repeat Step 4 with the other plastic bags on two more leaves. Leave the bags in place for 24 hours.
6. The following day, examine the bags and record your observations in your data table.

7. Carefully remove the bags from the leaves and refasten each twist tie around its bag so that the bag is closed tightly.
8. Place the three bags, including pebbles and twist ties, on the balance. Determine their total mass to the nearest tenth of a gram.
9. Subtract the original mass of the bags, ties, and pebbles that you found in Step 2 from the mass you found in Step 8.

Analyze and Conclude

1. Based on your observations, how can you account for the difference in mass?
2. What is the name of the process that caused the results you observed? Explain the role of that process in the water cycle.
3. A single birch tree may transpire as much as 260 liters of water in a day. How much water would a grove of 1,000 birch trees return to the atmosphere in a year?
4. **Apply** Based on what you learned from this investigation, what is one reason that people may be concerned about the destruction of forests around the world?

More to Explore

Find another type of tree and repeat this experiment. What might account for any differences in the amount of water the two trees transpire?

DATA TABLE

Starting mass of bags, ties, and pebbles	
Mass of bags, ties, and pebbles after 24 hours	
Difference in mass	

Sample Data Table

Starting mass of bags, ties, and pebbles	Mass of bags, ties, and pebbles after 24 hours	Difference in mass
41.3 g	42.9 g	1.6 g

Safety

Caution students to avoid plants such as poison ivy and poison oak. Instruct them to carry out the activity in secure, familiar places. Review the safety guidelines in Appendix A.

Media and Technology

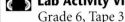
Lab Activity Videotapes
Grade 6, Tape 3

You and Your Environment

Water From Trees

Preparing for Inquiry

Key Concept Plants play an important role in the water cycle through the process of transpiration.

Skills Objectives Students will be able to
- observe the product of transpiration in leaves;
- calculate the mass of the water transpired by leaves in 24 hours;
- infer the important role plants play in the water cycle.

Time 20 minutes for setup; 20 minutes the next day for completion

Advance Planning Ask volunteers to scout around the school for trees or shrubs with large leaves. Make a rough map of the locations of these plants.

Alternative Materials If no trees or shrubs are available, potted plants such as geraniums can be used in the classroom. *Computer use is optional.*

Guiding Inquiry

Invitation Ask: **How are trees part of the water cycle?** (*Trees draw in water from the soil and give it off as water vapor through the process of transpiration.*)

Introducing the Procedure
Have students read through the complete procedure. Then ask: **Why should you be sure to make a tight seal around the stem of each leaf?** (*Making a tight seal ensures that nothing can get into or out of the bag during the 24 hours.*)

Analyze and Conclude
1. Water evaporated from the leaves.
2. Transpiration; it adds water vapor to the atmosphere.
3. 94,900,000 liters
4. The loss of transpiration could decrease the amount of water vapor in the atmosphere.

Extending the Inquiry

More to Explore Possible reasons include variation in leaf size and structure or variations in air temperature

SECTION 2 Surface Water

TEKS: 6.2B, C; 6.3C; 6.4A; 6.14B

Objectives

After completing the lesson, students will be able to

♦ describe a river system and how water flows into it;

♦ identify conditions that cause floods and how floods can be controlled;

♦ explain how ponds and lakes form;

♦ describe pond and lake habitats;

♦ explain how icebergs are formed.

1 Engage/Explore

Activating Prior Knowledge

Encourage students to describe some of the lakes and ponds they have seen. Ask questions such as, **How large is the lake?** and **What types of plants and animals live in or around it?**

▪▪▪▪▪▪▪ DISCOVER ▪▪▪▪▪▪▪

Skills Focus classifying
Materials *pond water,* ACTIVITY
plastic petri dish, hand lens, microscope, eyedropper, slide and cover slip
Time 20 minutes
Tips Collect water from a local pond, making sure you obtain some bottom mud and suspended particles. (As an alternative, you can prepare a hay infusion or use prepared slides.) *To prepare the slide:* Use an eyedropper to place a drop of pond water on the slide. Hold one edge of the cover slip on the slide and drag it toward the water drop. Let the slip's other edge down slowly to avoid trapping air bubbles.
Expected Outcome Students should see larger organisms with the hand lens and a greater variety with the microscope.
Think It Over Students could use movement or the consumption of smaller particles as criteria for deciding whether items are alive. Students should recognize that pond water contains a variety of living and nonliving things.

SECTION 2 Surface Water

DISCOVER ▪▪▪▪▪▪▪▪▪▪▪▪▪▪▪▪▪▪▪▪ ACTIVITY

What's in Pond Water?

1. Using a hand lens, observe a sample of pond water.

2. Make a list of everything you see in the water. If you don't know the name of something, write a short description or draw a picture.

3. Your teacher has set up a microscope with a slide of pond water. Observe the slide and add any new items to your list. Wash your hands with soap when you are done.

Think It Over

Classifying Use one of these systems to divide the items on your list into two groups: moving/still, living/nonliving, or microscopic/visible without a microscope. What does your classification system tell you about pond water?

GUIDE FOR READING

♦ What is a river system?

♦ What conditions can cause a flood?

♦ How do ponds and lakes form?

Reading Tip Before you read, use the section headings to make an outline. Leave space to take notes as you read.

Key Terms tributary
• watershed • divide • levee
• reservoir

Standing on a bridge in Albuquerque, New Mexico, you look through your binoculars at the waters of the Rio Grande—the "Big River." The name fits this broad, deep stretch of water. But 700 kilometers upstream, the Rio Grande looks very different. The river begins as trickles of melting snow high in the San Juan Mountains in Colorado. As more water joins the river, it carves deep, narrow canyons out of the rock.

By the time it reaches Albuquerque the river has grown wider. It continues into Texas, winding back and forth across the dusty desert valley. In places, the river is so shallow that it may even dry up during the summer. When the Rio Grande finally empties into the Gulf of Mexico, it is sluggish and heavy with mud.

River Systems, Watersheds, and Divides

If you were hiking in the San Juan Mountains, you could observe the path of the runoff from melting snow. As you followed one small stream downhill, you would notice that the stream reached a larger stream and joined it. You could then continue along this stream until it flowed into a small river. Eventually this path would lead you to the Rio Grande itself.

Tributaries are the smaller streams and rivers that feed into a main river. **A river and all its tributaries together make up a river system.** The tributaries flow toward the main river following a downhill path due to the pull of gravity.

READING STRATEGIES

Reading Tip On the chalkboard, write *I. River Systems.* Then ask volunteers to find the two headings that would be under this main heading. Student outlines may begin as follows:
I. River Systems
   A. Watersheds
   B. Divides
II. River and Floods

Program Resources

♦ **Unit 4 Resources** 12-2 Lesson Plan, p. 69; 12-2 Summary, p. 70

♦ **Guided Reading and Study Workbook** 12-2

Watersheds Just as all the water in a bathtub flows toward the drain, all the water in a river system drains into the main river. The land area that supplies water to a river system is called a **watershed.** Watersheds are also called drainage basins.

A river can flow into another, larger river. When rivers join another river system, the areas they drain become part of the largest river's watershed. You can identify a river's watershed on a map by drawing an imaginary line around the region drained by all its tributaries. Some watersheds are very small. By contrast, the watershed of the Mississippi River covers more than 3 million square kilometers!

Divides One watershed is separated from another by a ridge of land called a **divide.** Streams on each side of the divide flow in different directions. The Continental Divide, the longest divide in North America, follows the line of the Rocky Mountains. West of the Continental Divide, water either flows toward the Pacific Ocean or into the dry Great Basin. Between the Rocky Mountains and the Appalachian Mountains, water flows toward the Mississippi River or directly into the Gulf of Mexico.

✓ *Checkpoint* Into what ocean do rivers east of the Appalachian Mountains flow?

The Knuckle Divide

Make your hand into a fist **ACTIVITY** and put it on a paper towel, knuckles facing up. With your other hand, dribble water from a spoon so that it falls onto your knuckles. Observe how the water flows over your hand.

Making Models How are your knuckles similar to a mountain range on land? What parts of your hand represent a watershed?

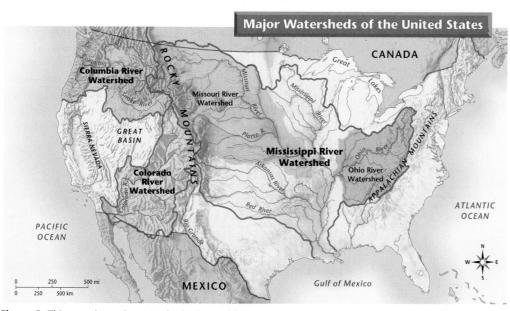

Major Watersheds of the United States

Figure 3 This map shows the watersheds of several large rivers in the United States.
Interpreting Maps Name four tributaries of the Mississippi River. Which tributary has the largest watershed?

Answers to Self-Assessment

Caption Question

Figure 3 Four tributaries of the Mississippi are the Missouri, Arkansas, Red, and Ohio rivers. The Missouri River has the largest watershed.

✓ *Checkpoint*

Rivers east of the Appalachian Mountains flow into the Atlantic Ocean.

---

2 Facilitate

River Systems, Watersheds, and Divides

Using the Visuals: Figure 3

Content Mastery

Point out that the map on this page shows *geographic* features such as rivers and mountains, not *political* features such as states, cities, and roads. Display a large political map of the United States. Choose volunteers to come to the large map and locate the rivers and mountain ranges shown on the text map. Ask: **What function do the Rocky Mountains and the Appalachian Mountains play in the major U.S. watersheds?** (*They are the major divides that separate these watersheds.*) Have students locate on the large map additional rivers and try to identify their possible watersheds. Ask: **Is our area in any of these rivers' watersheds? Which river?** (*Answers will vary depending on your location.*)
learning modality: visual

TRY THIS

Skills Focus making models **ACTIVITY**

Materials *paper towel, water, spoon*

Time 10 minutes

Tips Advise students to dribble the water *slowly* and to make sure it falls on the *tops* of their knuckles, not on either side.

Expected Outcome The water will flow from the tops of the knuckles to the hollows between them and to the back of the hand on one side and the spaces between the fingers on the other side. The knuckles are similar to a mountain range in that the water flows downward from them in different directions on two sides. The back of the hand and the fingers represent two different watersheds, and the knuckles represent a divide. **learning modality: tactile/kinesthetic**

Ongoing Assessment

Writing Have students briefly describe the terms watershed and divide in their own words.

Rivers and Floods

Real-Life Learning

Students who directly experienced the Midwest floods of 1997 or who have been personally affected by other floods (such as the flooding in California and the Southeast due to the heavy rains caused by El Niño of 1997-1998) may be uneasy or even upset by the text descriptions on this page and the next. First concentrate objectively on the physical causes of flooding described in the text. Then go on to discuss the safety precautions that should be followed in the event of a flood. Pamphlets with flood-safety guidelines may be available from your state or regional Red Cross chapter or FEMA (Federal Emergency Management Agency) office. Try to obtain such pamphlets for students to review. If students live in a flood-prone area, encourage them to copy the precautions to take home and review with their family members. **learning modality: verbal**

Rivers and Floods

Spring floods occur frequently on rivers in the Midwest, but the floods of 1997 were far worse than usual. The residents of Fargo, North Dakota, had already used a million sandbags, and the Red River of the North was still rising! As the flood waters rose, people piled the sandbags higher around their houses, hoping no water would break through. People moved their belongings to their attics, then watched as water flowed through their homes.

The Red River floods went on for weeks, fed by rain and melting snow. A spring blizzard added more snow. Other nearby rivers also flooded. Parts of North Dakota, South Dakota, and Minnesota were declared a disaster area. Weary residents just waited for the waters to recede so they could start to repair the damage.

What caused the Red River to flood so badly? **A flood occurs when the volume of water in a river increases so much that the river overflows its channel.** As rain and melting snow added more and more water, the river gained in speed and strength. Recall that as the speed of a river increases, so does the amount of energy it has. A flooding river can uproot trees and pluck boulders from the ground. As it overflows onto its floodplain, the powerful water can even wash away bridges and houses.

Throughout history, people have both feared and welcomed floods. Ancient Egyptians, for instance, called their fertile cropland "the gift of the Nile." Deposition from regular floods left a layer of rich soil on each side of the river, creating a green strip of good land in the middle of the desert. But floods can also destroy farms, towns, and crops. In the United States, 20 million people live in places where flooding is likely. Even in the last century, floods have killed millions of people around the world, many of them in the heavily populated flood plains of China, Bangladesh, and India.

Figure 4 These people are working together to protect their community during a flood.

Background

Facts and Figures The Red River floods that devastated parts of North Dakota and Minnesota in the spring of 1997 resulted from a combination of factors. Throughout the previous winter, 13 massive storms had buried the area with record snowfalls. When the spring thaw arrived, unusually high temperatures melted the snow in days, causing rapid runoff into the Red River and its tributaries. Levees protected some towns but worsened flooding in other towns downriver.

The Red River's valley is one of the flattest on Earth, which allows floodwaters to spread out extensively. In one area close to the Canadian border, the river overflowed its 55-m channel to stretch nearly *65 km* across its valley.

The Red River flows north into Canada. Ice jams in the north slowed water flow, causing river levels to swell further.

Can Floods Be Controlled?

 INTEGRATING TECHNOLOGY For as long as people have lived on flood plains, they have tried to control floods. Building dams is one method of flood control. A dam is a barrier across a river that may redirect the flow of a river to other channels or store the water in an artificial lake. Engineers can open the dam's floodgates to release water in dry seasons. Dams work fairly well to control small floods. During severe floods, however, powerful flood waters can wash over the top of a dam or break through it.

Sediment deposits actually build a natural defense against floods. As a river overflows onto its flood plain, it slows down, depositing the heavier sediments alongside the channel. Over time, these deposits build up into long ridges called **levees.** These natural levees help keep the river inside its banks. People sometimes build up the natural levees with sandbags or stone and concrete to provide further protection against floods.

But building up levees can sometimes backfire. These walls prevent the natural channel-widening process that rivers normally undergo as their volume increases. As a result, during a flood, the water has nowhere to go except downstream. Although built-up levees can work well to prevent small floods, they often make heavy flooding worse for areas farther downstream. The full power of the surge of flood water is passed on to flood the downstream areas.

Bodies of Fresh Water

While water in streams and rivers is always on the move, the water in lakes and ponds is still, or standing, water. Although there is no definite rule to determine whether a body of water is called a pond or a lake, ponds are generally smaller and shallower than lakes. Sunlight usually reaches to the bottom of all parts of a pond. Most lakes have parts where the water is too deep for sunlight to reach all the way to the bottom.

Ponds and lakes form when water collects in hollows and low-lying areas of land. Rainfall, melting snow and ice, and runoff supply water to ponds and lakes. Others are fed by rivers or groundwater. Eventually, water may flow out of a pond or lake into a river, or evaporate from its surface.

Figure 5 A flood can be disastrous for residents of a flooded area. *Making Generalizations Explain how floods can be both harmful and helpful to people.*

Chapter 12 **407**

Answers to Self-Assessment

Caption Question

Figure 5 *Harm:* injury or death of people and livestock, destruction of buildings and crops, and loss of freshwater supplies, electricity, transportation, and communication. *Help:* deposition of nutrient-rich silt

Can Floods Be Controlled?

Integrating Technology

ACTIVITY

Have each group of students set up a stream trough or a long, high-sided tray with a 6-cm-deep layer of mixed sand, gravel, and small pebbles on the bottom. Instruct students to create a narrow, slightly curving river channel about 4 cm deep into the layers. With the trough or tray at a fairly steep angle, students should pour a steady stream of water into the upper end of the river. Ask students: **Does the water stay within the channel?** *(yes)* **What would happen if you had poured more water more quickly?** *(The channel would overflow, causing a flood.)* Invite students to repeat the activity, this time using clay to build levees along the upper and middle sections of the river and pouring more water into the upper end to simulate flood conditions. Ask: **What happened when the water reached the levees?** *(The water flowed downstream, but the water level was very high. Some students may see floods in upper sections if the levee breaks.)* **What happened when the water reached the part of the river that had no levees?** *(The land became flooded.)* **learning modality: tactile/kinesthetic**

Bodies of Fresh Water

Real-Life Learning

If there are lakes or ponds in your area, invite volunteers to describe these bodies of water and, if possible, identify the source or sources of the water in them. **learning modality: visual**

Ongoing Assessment

Writing Have each student summarize, in a two-column format, the hazards and benefits of flooding described in the text, adding others they think of on their own.

EXPLORING

a Pond

After students have read the text in the visual essay, ask: **What are some different habitats that are described?** *(The shore, the shallow water near shore, the bottom of the pond, the surface, and the deeper waters)* Encourage volunteers to summarize how conditions vary in the different habitats. Also encourage students to name other pond organisms they know from personal experience or their reading. Refer to the **ELL Handbook** for additional teaching strategies. **learning modality: verbal**

Building Inquiry Skills: Comparing and Contrasting

Materials *pond algae, pond plants, hand lens*
Time 10 minutes

 Provide specimens of common pond algae, such as *Spirogyra* or *Cladophora,* and plants, such as pondweeds, for students to examine. Then ask: **How are the algae and plants different?** *(The plants have stems, leaves, and roots, whereas the algae do not have any similar structures.)* **How are they alike?** *(They both are green and able to carry out photosynthesis.)* Emphasize that plants and algae are vital to pond habitats because they produce food and oxygen through photosynthesis. **learning modality: visual**

Integrating Life Science

Point out the text information about temporary ponds that appear in the spring and dry up in the summer. Then ask: **What types of organisms could find temporary homes in a spring pond?** *(Frogs, birds, flying insects, and other animals that could leave the pond when it dried up; plants whose seeds could survive dry conditions)* **What is the importance of temporary ponds?** *(They provide habitats for organisms that require water during part of their lifecycles.)* **learning modality: logical/ mathematical**

EXPLORING a Pond

Many organisms live in the different habitats within a pond. From the shallow edges to the muddy bottom, conditions in each habitat vary in important ways.

Some of the most important pond dwellers are the smallest. Microscopic algae are the pond's basic food producers.

The roots of water lilies cling to the pond bottom, while their leaves, on long flexible stems, float on the surface. Sponges live under the leaves. Dragonflies pause on top to rest.

Sunfish and perch live in both the weedy shallows and the deeper waters of the pond. A slender-bodied pickerel waits among the duckweed to grab a meal of insects at the water's edge.

Ponds

INTEGRATING LIFE SCIENCE Compared to a tumbling mountain stream, a pond seems still and peaceful at first glance. Silvery minnows glide smoothly below the surface. A dragonfly touches the water, then whirs away. Lily pads with broad, green leaves and waxy, white blossoms float on the surface. This quiet pond is actually a thriving habitat, supporting a wide diversity of living things.

If you have ever waded in a pond, you know that the muddy bottom is often covered with weeds. Because the water is shallow enough for sunlight to reach the bottom, plants grow throughout a pond. Plantlike organisms called algae also live in the pond. As the plants and algae use sunlight to make food through photosynthesis, they also produce oxygen. Animals in the pond use the oxygen and food provided by plants and algae. You can see some common pond organisms in *Exploring a Pond.*

408

Background

Integrating Science Lakes and ponds are characterized by specific zones. Lakes have three major zones (see Background, page 410); ponds have two.

The shallow water along the edge of a pond is called the *littoral zone.* More photosynthesis occurs in the littoral zone than anywhere else in the pond, partly because nutrients wash into the pond from the land and feed the algae and plants there.

The open water away from the shore is called the *limnetic zone.* Free-floating photosynthetic bacteria and algae and animallike protists inhabit the limnetic zone, as well as animals, such as fish.

The shore is edged with grasses and trees that require a lot of water, such as willows and maples. These plants provide shelter and nesting places for red-winged blackbirds and other birds.

Frogs lay eggs in the shallow water near shore. They hatch in the water as tadpoles and move to the land as adults.

Snails find food on the soft bottom of the pond. Crayfish lie buried in the mud, waiting for bits of food to drift down.

Not all ponds exist year-round. For example, some ponds in the northern and western United States appear only in the spring, when runoff from spring rains and melting snow collects in low areas. The ponds dry up by midsummer as the shallow water quickly evaporates in the heat.

Ponds in colder climates often freeze over during the winter. Recall that ice floats because it is less dense than liquid water. As a result, ice forms on the surface of the pond, while the living things survive in the liquid water below.

☑ *Checkpoint* *Why can plants grow throughout a pond?*

Lakes

Suppose you suddenly found yourself on a sandy beach. Waves break on the shore. The water stretches as far as your eye can see. Gulls screech overhead. Where are you? Although you might think you're at the ocean, this immense body of water could

Answers to Self-Assessment

☑ *Checkpoint*

The water in a pond is shallow enough so that sunlight reaches all areas.

Lakes

Including All Students

Materials *cup of water, ice cube*
Time 5–10 minutes

Give each student a small cup of water and an ice cube. Ask students to predict what will happen when they put the ice cube in the cup. (*The cube will float.*) Let students test their predictions. Then ask: **What would have happened if ice were more dense than water?** (*The cube would have sunk to the bottom of the cup.*) **How does the lower density of ice enable lake organisms to survive through the winter?** (*Ice that forms on the lake's surface floats on the water, and shields the organisms in the water below from the cold.*)
learning modality: logical/mathematical

Ongoing Assessment

Oral Presentation Have students pretend to be one of the organisms that lives in a pond and describe their habitat and activities.

Lakes, continued

Integrating Life Science

To help students understand the complex relationships among organisms in a lake habitat, ask: **What feeding relationships are identified in the text?** *(Loons and kingfishers eat fish; worms and mollusks feed on food particles that drift down; large, bony fish eat tiny bottom dwellers and fish and birds at the surface.)* **Why are plants and algae important to a lake habitat?** *(They carry out photosynthesis, which produces food and oxygen that other organisms depend on.)* Challenge students to draw a food chain that illustrates one set of feeding relationships that exists in a lake habitat. **learning modality: visual**

Including All Students

Have each group of students use the stream trough or tray with the river they created on page 407 to simulate different types of lake formation. To simulate melting ice sheets that created depressions that became lakes, have them let an ice cube melt on a flat surface in the tray. Ask: **Does a depression form where the ice melted?** *(Yes)* **What would you expect to happen if more ice melted in this same place?** *(The depression would deepen. Some of the melted water would soak into the ground, some would evaporate, and some would lie in the depression.)* To simulate creating a reservoir, have students use an eraser or other hard object to dam the river, tilt the tray, and pour a steady stream of water into the upper end of the river. Ask: **What happened when the water reached the dam?** *(The land above the dam flooded.)* **How could you keep the reservoir from becoming too large or the river below the dam from drying up?** *(Occasionally open the dam and let some water continue down the river.)* **learning modality: tactile/kinesthetic**

Figure 6 Standing water is found in lakes and ponds. **(A)** The cold waters of Crater Lake in Oregon fill the hollow of an ancient volcano. **(B)** Water lilies float in a Colorado pond. *Interpreting Photographs In which of these bodies of water does sunlight reach the bottom? Give evidence to support your answer.*

actually be a lake! You could be on a beach in Indiana, on the shore of Lake Michigan.

Although most lakes are not as large as Lake Michigan, they are generally bigger and deeper than ponds. Most lakes are deep enough that sunlight does not reach all the way to the bottom. A lake bottom may consist of sand, pebbles, or rock. The bottom of a pond is usually covered with mud and algae.

Lake Formation Lakes form in many ways. For example, a cutoff river meander may become an oxbow lake. Ice sheets that melted at the end of the Ice Age created depressions that became lakes. Some lakes were created by movements of Earth's crust. Such movements created the deep valleys in central Africa that lie below Lake Tanganyika and Lake Victoria. Other lakes are the result of volcanoes. An erupting volcano can cause a flow of lava or mud that blocks a river and forms a lake. Some lakes, like the one in Figure 6, form in the empty craters of volcanoes.

People can also create a lake by building a dam across a river. The lake may be used for supplying drinking water, for irrigating fields, and for boating and fishing. A lake that stores water for human use is called a **reservoir.** One of the largest reservoirs in the United States is Lake Mead in Nevada, behind Hoover Dam on the Colorado River.

Lake Habitats Like a pond, a lake provides habitats for many different kinds of organisms. In the shallow water near shore, the wildlife is similar to that in a pond. Water beetles scurry over the slippery, moss-covered rocks. Loons and kingfishers pluck fish from the open water.

INTEGRATING LIFE SCIENCE

410

But unlike a pond, sunlight does not reach the bottom at the center of a lake. Without sunlight, plants cannot live in the deep water. As a result, fewer other organisms live in the chilly, dark depths of the lake. A few worms and mollusks do live on the bottom. They feed on food particles that drift down from the surface. The deep waters of lakes are also the home of large, bony fish such as pike and sturgeon. These fish eat the tiny bottom dwellers. They also swim to the surface to feed on fish and even small birds.

Icebergs

You may be surprised to learn that 76 percent of Earth's fresh water exists as ice frozen in glaciers. A glacier is a mass of ice and snow that moves slowly over land. When a glacier reaches the seacoast, icebergs form. With a loud roar, large chunks break off, or calve, and float away. Although icebergs are found in the salty ocean, remember that they consist of fresh water.

In the North Atlantic and Arctic oceans, about 10,000 new icebergs form every year. Many of these icebergs calve from Greenland's continental glacier. As they drift south, the icebergs break into chunks as big as houses. They begin to melt in the warmer water.

The ocean around Antarctica is filled with even larger icebergs. Flat-topped pieces calve from the edges of the glaciers along the coast. In 1995, a giant iceberg broke off Antarctica's Larsen Ice Shelf. Scientists flying over the new iceberg reported that it was about 70 kilometers long and 25 kilometers wide—more than half the size of the state of Rhode Island!

Figure 7 If you could see an entire iceberg at once, how would it look? An artist created this composite photograph to reveal the hidden part of the iceberg.

Section 2 Review

1. What bodies of water make up a river system?
2. Why do floods occur?
3. Explain how ponds and lakes form.
4. Give three examples of typical pond organisms. Describe where in a pond each is found.
5. Where do icebergs form?
6. **Thinking Critically Relating Cause and Effect** How is the depth of the water in the middle of a lake related to the variety of living things there?

Science at Home

Homemade Iceberg With a family member, make a model iceberg. Fill the cut-off bottom of a milk or juice carton with water and freeze. When the water has frozen, peel the carton away from the iceberg. Add salt to a large bowl of water to create an "ocean." Float the iceberg in the bowl. Help your family member use a ruler to measure how much of the iceberg's thickness is above the surface of the water and how much is below. Use these measurements to explain why icebergs can be dangerous to ships.

Chapter 12 **411**

Program Resources

◆ **Unit 4 Resources** 12-2 Review and Reinforce, p. 71; 12-2 Enrich, p. 72

Answers to Self-Assessment

Caption Question

Figure 6 The pond; the water lilies are evidence that the body of water is shallow.

Icebergs

Including All Students

Point out the word *calve* used for the breaking-off of icebergs from glaciers. Ask: **What is a calf?** (*A baby cow*) **What does it mean for a cow to calve?** (*To give birth to a calf*) **Why is the word "calve" a good one to use for the process of icebergs forming?** (*The glacier "gives birth" to an iceberg when it breaks off and floats away.*) **limited English proficiency**

3 Assess

Section 2 Review Answers

1. A river system is made up of a river and all the smaller rivers and streams that feed into it.
2. Floods occur because rainfall or melting snow increases the volume of water so much that the river overflows its channel.
3. Ponds and lakes form when water collects in hollows and low-lying areas.
4. Students may name any three of the organisms and habitats presented in *Exploring a Pond* on pages 408–409.
5. Where a glacier reaches the sea, large chunks break off as icebergs.
6. The variety of living things declines in deeper water where there is not enough sunlight for plants. Without plants, fewer other organisms can live in deep water.

Science at Home

Materials *empty milk or juice carton, tap water, freezer, large bowl, salt, ruler*
Tips Tell students to use about one teaspoonful of salt for each quart of water to make the "ocean." Students and their family members can calculate the percentages of ice above and below water. These calculations will be easier if the measurements are made in metric units.

Performance Assessment

Skills Check Have students create a compare/contrast table that summarizes the similarities and differences between a lake and a pond.

411

TEKS: 6.1A; 6.2B, C, D, E; 6.3C; 6.14B

Objectives

After completing the lesson, students will be able to

♦ describe springs and how water moves through underground layers of soil and rock;

♦ explain what an aquifer is and how people obtain water from an aquifer.

1 Engage/Explore

Activating Prior Knowledge

Show the class a bottle of spring water you have purchased. Ask: **What was the original source of this water?** (*Students may mention wells, springs, or other sources.*) **Where does the water in springs and wells come from?** (*Students may be unsure or may suggest an underground supply; some may know the term "aquifer." Acknowledge all responses without comment at this time.*)

• • • • • DISCOVER • • • • •

Skills Focus observing
Materials *pebbles, clear jar, ruler, dry sand, water*
Time 10 minutes
Tips A plastic jar is preferable to avoid the danger of broken glass. Advise students to add the water slowly.
Expected Outcome The water will seep through the sand and collect at the bottom of the jar.
Think It Over The water fills the spaces between the pebbles.

SECTION 3 **Groundwater**

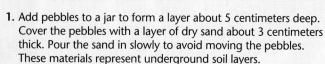
DISCOVER • ACTIVITY

Where Does the Water Go?

1. Add pebbles to a jar to form a layer about 5 centimeters deep. Cover the pebbles with a layer of dry sand about 3 centimeters thick. Pour the sand in slowly to avoid moving the pebbles. These materials represent underground soil layers.

2. Sprinkle water onto the sand to simulate rainfall.

3. Looking through the side of the jar, observe the path of the water as it soaks through the layers. Wash your hands when you are finished with this activity.

Think It Over
Observing Describe what happens when the water reaches the bottom of the jar.

GUIDE FOR READING

♦ How does water move through underground layers of soil and rock?

♦ How do people obtain water from an aquifer?

Reading Tip As you read, create a flowchart that shows one possible path of water from a cloud to a well.

Key Terms pore • permeable • impermeable • saturated zone • water table • unsaturated zone • aquifer • spring • recharge • artesian well

412

When you were younger, did you ever dig a hole in the ground hoping to find a buried treasure? Though you probably never found a trunk full of gold, you could have found a different kind of treasure without even realizing it. If you continued to dig deeper, past tangled grass roots and small stones, you would have noticed the soil begin to feel heavier and wetter. If you dug deep enough, the bottom of your hole would have started to fill up with water. You would have "struck groundwater!" In the days before pipes and public water systems, such a discovery was like finding a treasure. A usable source of fresh water enabled people to build a house or farm and settle on that land. Today, many people still rely on the water underground to meet their water needs.

Underground Layers

Where does this underground water come from? Like the water in rivers, lakes, and glaciers, it comes from precipitation. Recall what can happen to precipitation when it falls. It can evaporate right away, run off the surface, or soak into the ground. The water that soaks in trickles downward, following the pull of gravity.

If you pour water into a glass full of pebbles, the water trickles down around the pebbles until it reaches the bottom of the glass. Then the water begins to fill up the spaces between the pebbles. **In the same way, water underground trickles down between particles of soil and through cracks and spaces in layers of rock.**

READING STRATEGIES

Reading Tip Point out that many different flowcharts are possible. After students have read the section, encourage them to compare their flowcharts. Sample flowchart steps: raindrop to ground to groundwater to well.

Vocabulary Write the terms *permeable* and *impermeable* on the board. Explain that the root *perme* comes from a Latin word meaning "to pass through." Then ask what the suffix *-able* means. (*"Capable of being" something*) Challenge students to find the meaning of *permeable*. (*"Capable of being passed through"; correct students if they say "capable of passing through."*) Ask what the prefix *im-* means. (*"not"*) Again, challenge students to find the meaning of *impermeable*. (*Not capable of being passed through*)

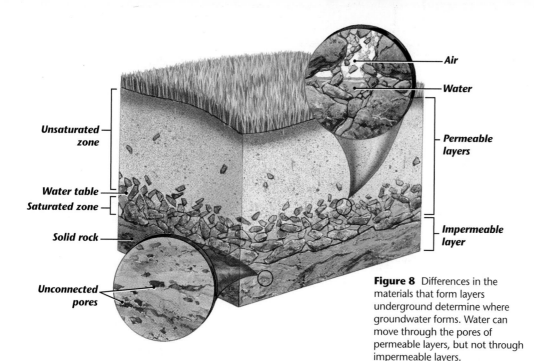

Figure 8 Differences in the materials that form layers underground determine where groundwater forms. Water can move through the pores of permeable layers, but not through impermeable layers.
Interpreting Diagrams What is the difference between the saturated and unsaturated zone?

Labels on figure: Air, Water, Permeable layers, Impermeable layer, Unsaturated zone, Water table, Saturated zone, Solid rock, Unconnected pores

Different types of rock and soil have different-sized spaces, or **pores,** between their particles. How easily water moves through the material depends not only on the size of the pores, but also on whether the pores are connected to each other. Materials that allow water to easily pass through, or permeate, are called **permeable.** Sand and gravel are permeable materials.

As water soaks down through permeable rock, it eventually reaches layers of material that it cannot pass through. These materials have few or no pores or cracks for the water to flow through. Materials that water cannot pass through easily are called **impermeable.** Clay and granite are impermeable materials.

Once water reaches an impermeable layer, it is trapped. It can't soak any deeper. Instead, the water begins to fill up the spaces above the impermeable material. The area of permeable rock or soil that is totally filled, or saturated, with water is called the **saturated zone.** The top of the saturated zone is the **water table.** Knowing the depth of the water table in an area tells you how deep you must dig to reach groundwater.

Soil and rock layers above the water table contain some moisture, too. But here the pores contain air as well as water. They are not saturated with water. Therefore, the layer of rocks and soil above the water table is called the **unsaturated zone.**

☑ *Checkpoint* *Give an example of a permeable material other than sand or gravel.*

Sharpen your Skills

Drawing Conclusions ACTIVITY

You have just bought some land and need to dig a well. By drilling a number of holes on your property, you learn that there is a layer of impermeable granite rock located approximately 12 meters underground. If the saturated zone is 3 meters thick, how deep should you dig your well? (*Hint:* Dra... diagram may b...

Underground Layers

Using the Visuals: Figure 8
Content Mastery

Point out the two circular insets and ask: **What is different about the pores in the two pictures?** (*The pores in the top-right picture are larger and are connected to one another; the pores in the bottom-left picture are smaller and are not connected.*) **Which picture represents a permeable rock layer?** (*The top-right picture*) **In this picture, how do the pores differ above and below the water table?** (*Above, the pores contain both air and water; below, the pores contain only water.*) **learning modality: visual**

Sharpen your Skills

Drawing Conclusions

Time 10 minutes **ACTIVITY**
Tips Before students attempt to solve the problem, ask: **Where is the saturated zone located, on top of the impermeable layer or below it?** (*on top of it*)
Expected Outcome The depth of the well should be at least 9 m. Some students may realize that making it exactly 9 m deep may cause it to run dry in drought conditions or if too much water is withdrawn. Accept answers ranging from somewhat more than 9 m to somewhat less than 12 m.
Extend Encourage students to make a simple three-dimensional model showing the saturated zone, the impermeable layers,

Groundwater
p. 413 – 416

learning ...hematical

Program Resources

◆ **Unit 4 Resources** 12-3 Lesson Plan, p. 73; 12-3 Section Summary, p. 74
◆ **Guided Reading and Study Workbook** 12-3

Media and Technology

 Transparencies "Underground Layers," Transparency 59

Answers to Self-Assessment

Caption Question

Figure 8 The pores in the saturated zone are filled with water, whereas in the unsaturated zone, the pores contain air as well as water.

☑ *Checkpoint*
Other permeable materials include soil, porous rock such as sandstone, foam rubber, plastic foam, and cloth.

Ongoing Assessment

Drawing Have each student make a simple sketch of an underground water supply, without referring to Figure 8, and label its features with the terms *pores, permeable materials, impermeable materials, saturated zone, water table,* and *unsaturated zone.*

Aquifers

Skills Focus making models

Materials *newspaper, loaf pan, modeling clay, moist sand, funnel, plastic straw, scissors, water*

Time 20 minutes

Tips Before students begin, slowly add a little water to the sand to moisten it. Make extra clay available for students to stop any leaks that occur. Also provide paper towels so students can remove any water that overflows the funnel.

Expected Outcome Water will flow from the funnel into the sand layer at the high end, downhill through the sand layer, and then up the straw at the low end. The layers of clay and sand represent impermeable and permeable layers under ground. The water represents rain or other precipitation. The flow of the water downhill through the sand layer represents real water movement in an aquifer. The model is like a real aquifer in that water moves through a permeable layer. It is different because water would fall as precipitation and soak through permeable material until it reaches a layer of impermeable rock.

Extend Ask students: **What do you think would happen if you cut the straw below the water level of the funnel?** Suggest that students test their predictions. *(Cutting the straw below the water level will produce a gushing artesian well.)* **learning modality: tactile/ kinesthetic**

Including All Students

Choose a volunteer to find the derivation of the word "aquifer" in a dictionary. *(From the Latin* aqua, *meaning "water")* Ask: **What other English words do you know that have "aqua" in them?** *(Examples include aquarium, the colors aqua and aquamarine, the astrological sign Aquarius, aquatic, and aqueduct.)* **What non-English words for** *water* **do you know that are similar to** *aqua?* *(Students may suggest the Spanish word* agua.*)* **limited English proficiency**

An Artesian Well

In this activity you will build a model of an artesian well. Before you start, cover your desk or table with newspaper.

1. Cover the bottom of a loaf pan with clay. Pile the clay higher at one end.

2. Cover the clay with about 4 cm of moist sand.

3. Cover the sand with a thin sheet of clay. Seal the edges of the clay tightly against the sides of the pan.

4. Push a funnel into the high end so that the bottom of the funnel is in the sand.

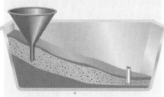

5. Insert a short piece of plastic straw through the clay and into the sand layer at the low end. Remove the straw, discard it, and then insert a new piece of straw in the same hole.

6. Slowly pour water into the funnel. Do not let the water overflow the funnel.

7. Observe the level of water in the straw. Wash your hands after this activity.

Making Models What real-world feature does each part of your model represent? How is your model like a real artesian well? How is it different?

Aquifers

Any underground layer of rock or sediment that holds water is called an **aquifer.** Aquifers can range in size from a small underground patch of permeable material to an area the size of several states. The huge Ogallala aquifer lies beneath the plains of the midwest, stretching from South Dakota to Texas. Millions of people obtain their drinking water from this underground storehouse. The Ogallala aquifer also provides water for crops and livestock.

Maybe you picture groundwater as a large, still pool beneath Earth's surface. In fact, the water is actually in motion, seeping through the layers of rock. How fast it moves depends largely on how steeply the aquifer slopes and how permeable the rocks are. Groundwater in some aquifers moves only a few centimeters a day. At that rate, the water moves about 10 meters a year—less than the length of a typical classroom. Groundwater may travel hundreds of kilometers and stay in an aquifer for thousands of years before coming to the surface again.

☑ *Checkpoint* *What factors affect how fast water moves in an aquifer?*

Bringing Groundwater to the Surface

Look at Figure 9 and notice how the level of the water table generally follows the shape of the underground rock layers. The depth of the water table can vary greatly even over a small area of land. Heavy rain or lots of melting snow raise the level of the water table. The level falls in dry weather.

Where the water table meets the ground surface, groundwater bubbles or flows out of cracks in the rock in places called **springs.** The groundwater may feed a stream or pond, or form a wetland. People can also bring groundwater to the surface.

Wells Since ancient times, people have brought groundwater to the surface for drinking and other everyday uses. **People can obtain groundwater from an aquifer by drilling a well below the water table.** Locate the well near the center of Figure 9. Because the bottom of the well is in the saturated zone, the well contains water. Notice the level of the bottom of the dry well in the diagram. Because this well does not reach below the water table, water cannot be obtained from it.

Long ago, people dug wells by hand. They lined the sides of the well with brick or stone to keep the walls from collapsing. To bring up water, they lowered and raised a bucket. Today, most wells are dug with well-drilling equipment. Pumps bring up the groundwater.

Pumping water out of an aquifer lowers the water level near the well. If too much water is pumped out too fast, the well may

---

Background

In Texas, aquifers provide more than half of the state's water for both irrigation and municipal use. For example, the Edwards aquifer provides water for the city of San Antonio and many other communities in South Central Texas.

Taking more groundwater from an aquifer than can be naturally recharged is known as *aquifer depletion.* The Ogallala aquifer, which underlies the Panhandle, is threatened with depletion largely due to the pumping of water for irrigation.

To protect aquifers from depletion, the Texas Water Development Board has established 16 water-planning areas throughout the state. Each area must develop a regional water plan involving conservation, managing future demand for water, and coping with droughts.

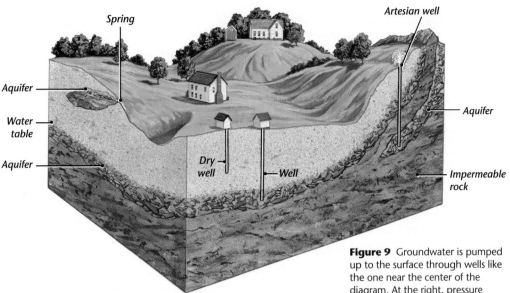

Spring

Artesian well

Aquifer

Water table

Aquifer

Dry well

Well

Aquifer

Impermeable rock

Figure 9 Groundwater is pumped up to the surface through wells like the one near the center of the diagram. At the right, pressure causes water to spurt from an artesian well. Where an aquifer meets the ground surface, at the left, a spring may form. *Interpreting Diagrams Why does the dry well not contain any water?*

run dry. It will be necessary either to dig deeper to reach the lowered water table, or to wait for rainfall to refill the aquifer. New water that enters the aquifer from the surface is called **recharge.**

Artesian Wells In some aquifers, groundwater is trapped between two layers of impermeable rock or sediment. This water is under great pressure from the weight of the water above it. If the top layer of rock is punctured, the pressure sends water spurting up through the hole. Water flows without pumping from a well dug in such an aquifer. A well in which water rises because of pressure within the aquifer is called an **artesian well** (ahr TEEZH uhn).

 Section 3 Review

1. Describe what happens to water that soaks into the ground.
2. Why is it important to know the depth of an aquifer before drilling a well?
3. Draw a cross section of the ground that includes the following labeled features: permeable layer, saturated zone, unsaturated zone, impermeable layer, and water table.
4. **Thinking Critically Inferring** During the winter, a small spring flows on your property. Every summer, the spring dries up. What might be the reason for the change?

Check Your Progress **CHAPTER PROJECT**
By now you should have chosen a building in your community to monitor. How will you determine the amount and type of water usage there? Are the building's water uses different from the water uses in your home? Be sure to check with your teacher before contacting anyone at the site. (*Hint:* A building manager often has information about water use. You may find it helpful to write down your questions before you interview the person.) Prepare a second data table and record this building's water-use data.

Program Resources

◆ **Laboratory Manual** 12, "Field Testing a Body of Fresh Water"
◆ **Unit 4 Resources** 12-3 Review and Reinforce, p. 75; 12-3 Enrich, p. 76

Media and Technology

 Transparencies "Wells and Springs," Transparency 60

Answers to Self-Assessment

☑ *Checkpoint*

How fast the water moves in an aquifer depends on how steeply the aquifer slopes and how permeable the rocks are.

Caption Question

Figure 9 The dry well does not reach below the water table.

Bringing Groundwater to the Surface

Using the Visuals: Figure 9

Call students' attention to the two wells in the figure. Ask: **Why is the one well dry?** (*The well does not reach to the water table.*) **How could that well become a working well?** (*It could be dug deeper, or it could pump water if the water table rose.*)
learning modality: visual

3 Assess

Section 3 Review Answers

1. The pull of gravity causes water to trickle down between particles of soil and through cracks and spaces in rock until it reaches impermeable materials.
2. Without knowing the depth of the aquifer, the drillers don't know how deep they must drill the well to be below the water table.
3. Students' drawings should show the layers in the following sequence from top to bottom: permeable layer; within the permeable layer—unsaturated zone, water table, saturated zone; impermeable layer.
4. The water table must fall below the level of the spring in summer and rise above it in winter. Factors such as precipitation and human water use could also affect the depth of the water table.

Check Your Progress **CHAPTER PROJECT**
Review student's choices of buildings. Help students decide whom might be best to contact to get the needed information. Lead a roleplay interview or phone call with students so they can practice.

Performance Assessment

Writing or Drawing Have each student write a paragraph or draw and label a sketch to explain why water flows from an artesian well without needing to be pumped.

415

Soil Testing

Preparing for Inquiry

Key Concept Different soil materials have different permeabilities.

Skills Objectives Students will be able to
- measure how quickly water flows through sand, clay, and pebbles;
- interpret data to conclude that the sizes of a material's particles and the spaces between them determine its permeability.

Time 40 minutes

Advance Planning At least one day before students do the lab, gather sufficient materials for each group. If funnels are not available, cut the tops off plastic soda bottles, or let students do this. Have them cover the rough edge with masking tape to avoid cutting themselves.

Guiding Inquiry

Invitation After distributing the sand, clay, and pebbles, have students look at and feel them. Ask: **Which material would let water pass through it the quickest? Which do you think would hold water best?** Write their hypotheses on the board, and discuss these responses when students complete the lab.

Introducing the Procedure
- After students read the help-wanted ad, ask: **Which would be a good location for a well—in soil that lets water pass through it easily, or in soil that does not let water pass through?** *(Soil that lets water pass through easily)*
- After students read the instructions, ask: **Why should the layers of sand, clay, and pebbles be the same depth?** *(The depth is a variable that should be controlled; making the layers different depths could affect the results.)*

Real-World Lab

Careers in Science

SOIL TESTING

In what type of soil is it best to site a well? This is a question that hydrologists, scientists who study groundwater, need to answer before new houses or other buildings can be constructed. In this lab, you will compare different soil types to learn more about their water-holding properties.

HELP WANTED

Hydrologists to conduct soil tests for new housing development. Homes will have private wells. Engineers must test soil permeability to select best locations. Please send resumé and references to

Problem

How fast does water move through sand, clay, and pebbles?

Skills Focus

observing, measuring, drawing conclusions

Materials (per group)

hand lens   3 beakers, 100-mL
sand, 100 mL   water, 300 mL
stopwatch   pebbles, 100 mL
3 rubber bands
powdered potter's clay, 100 mL
3 squares of cheesecloth
3 large funnels or cut-off plastic soda bottle tops

Procedure

1. Copy the data table into your notebook.

2. Use a hand lens to observe each of the three material samples closely. Record your observations in your data table.

3. Place a piece of cheesecloth over the bottom of each funnel or bottle top and secure it with a rubber band.

4. Place the sand in one funnel, the pebbles in another, and the clay in another. Be sure that there is at least 5 cm of space above the material in each funnel.

5. Place each funnel on top of a beaker.

6. Slowly pour 100 mL of water into the funnel containing the sand. Do not let the water overflow the funnel.

7. Start the stopwatch when the water begins to flow or drip out of the bottom of the funnel.

DATA TABLE		
Material	Observations	Time for Water to Stop Dripping
Sand		
Clay		
Pebbles		

Program Resources

- **Unit 4 Resources** Chapter 12 Real-World Lab blackline masters, pp. 87–89

Media and Technology

Lab Activity Videotapes
Grade 6, Tape 3

Safety

Have students wear safety goggles. Review the safety guidelines in Appendix A.

8. Stop the stopwatch when the water stops dripping out of the funnel or after 5 minutes. Record the time to the nearest second in your data table.

9. Repeat Steps 6 through 8 with the pebbles and then with the clay. When you are finished with this activity, dispose of your materials according to your teacher's instructions. Wash your hands thoroughly with soap.

Analyze and Conclude

1. Through which material did water move the fastest? The slowest?

2. What can you conclude about the permeability of the three materials?

3. Based on your observations of each sample, suggest an explanation for the differences in their permeability.

4. Based on the results of this lab, would you expect to get more water from a well dug in sand, pebbles, or clay? Explain.

5. **Apply** Why might gardeners and landscapers need to know about the permeability of different soil types?

More to Explore

Which of the soil samples that you tested do you think the soil of the grounds at your school most resembles? Design an experiment to test your hypothesis. With your teacher's permission, carry out your experiment.

Sample Data Table

Material	Observations	Time for Water to Stop Dripping
Sand	small grains, irregular shapes, whitish to brownish	9 minutes
Pebbles	large pieces, smooth shapes, various colors	2 minutes
Clay	tiny particles, regular shapes, tannish color	greater than 15 minutes

Troubleshooting the Experiment

◆ In Step 1, suggest that students make the Observations section of their tables larger so they have more room to record.

◆ If necessary, demonstrate how to make sure the beaker is filled exactly to the 100-mL mark in Step 6. Also remind students to stop pouring the water if it comes close to overflowing the funnel.

Expected Outcome

Times will vary. Sample data might show that it takes about 9 minutes for 100 mL of water to flow through sand, 2 minutes to flow through pebbles, and 15 minutes to flow through clay.

Analyze and Conclude

1. The fastest through pebbles, the slowest through clay

2. A layer of pebbles is the most permeable, a layer of clay the least permeable, and a layer of sand somewhere between those two.

3. The sizes of the particles and of the spaces between them determine a material's permeability. Clay is least permeable because it has the smallest particles and the smallest spaces. Pebbles are the most permeable because they are the largest particles and have the largest spaces between them.

4. You would get more water from a well dug in pebbles because there are larger pores that can hold more water, and the water moves through the pebbles faster into the well as water is pumped out.

5. Some plants may survive and grow best in sandy soils that let water drain away from their roots, while other plants grow best in clay soils that hold water.

Extending the Inquiry

More to Explore Students should be able to estimate the soil's permeability by observing whether water is absorbed after a rain or pools on top. Each group could test an actual sample and compare results with the data using sand, pebbles, and clay.

SECTION 4 Wetland Systems

TEKS: 6.2B, C, E; 6.3C; 6.5B

Objectives

After completing the lesson, students will be able to

♦ identify parts of a wetland system;

♦ compare the properties of a wetland system to the properties of its parts;

♦ explain why wetland systems are important.

1 Engage/Explore

Activating Prior Knowledge

Write the terms *marsh*, *swamp*, and *bog* on the board, and ask: **What is similar about all three of these areas?** (*All are wet—but the water is not as deep as in a pond or lake.*) Then have students define each term in their own words. Encourage responses that identify differences between the three types of wet areas, but do not correct students' definitions or comment on their accuracy at this time.

DISCOVER

Skills Focus observing
Materials *2 dry kitchen sponges, water, pan, 2 paper cups*
Time 10–15 minutes
Tips Make sure sponges are completely dry when students begin.
Expected Outcome The damp sponge will absorb water immediately, whereas water will run off the dry sponge at first.
Think It Over The damp sponge absorbs water faster. The dry sponge models dry land. The damp sponge models the behavior of wetlands: they soak up excess water and help prevent flooding.

418

SECTION 4 Wetland Systems

DISCOVER ·· ACTIVITY

Wet or Dry?

1. Soak a kitchen sponge under water. Then squeeze out the water until the sponge is just damp.

2. Place the damp sponge next to a dry sponge in a pan. The sponges represent areas of wet and dry land.

3. Pour water into two paper cups until each is half full.

4. Hold one cup in each hand so that the cups are about 10 centimeters above the pan. Pour the water onto both sponges at the same time.

Think It Over
Observing Which of the sponges absorbs water faster? How are your observations related to what might happen in areas of wet and dry land?

GUIDE FOR READING

♦ What are the parts of a wetland system?

♦ How do the properties of a wetland system differ from the properties of its parts?

♦ How are wetland systems important?

Reading Tip Before you read, write a short description of what you think a wetland is. As you read, add details and examples to your description.

Key Terms wetland • system

An Oregon marsh ▼

What image does the word *wetland* bring to mind? Do you think of a shallow pond filled with plants and animals? Or do you imagine a swamp with knobby cypress trees growing in still water?

A **wetland** is an area of land that is covered with a shallow layer of water during some or all of the year. Wetlands form in places where water is trapped in low areas or where groundwater seeps onto the surface of the land.

There are many different types of wetlands. Marshes, swamps, and bogs are three common types of freshwater wetlands. You can compare two types of wetlands in Figure 10. Wetlands along the coast usually contain both fresh and salt water.

What Is a Wetland System?

A wetland is not simply water and land. It includes many other parts that make up the total wetland system. A **system** is a group of parts that work together as a whole. More exactly, a wetland is an ecosystem—a system made up of all of the living things in a given area and their physical environment.

As in all ecosystems, the two main parts of a wetland system are the abiotic factors and the biotic factors. Recall from Chapter 8 that abiotic factors are the nonliving parts of an ecosystem. The living parts of an ecosystem are called biotic factors. The parts interact in many ways, affecting each other and changing the system as a whole. As you learn about the parts of a wetland ecosystem, you can better understand how they work together.

418

READING STRATEGIES

Reading Tip Students may say that a wetland is a swamp or a place where the land never becomes dry. To provide a structured format for adding details and examples, have students write the description at the top of a sheet of paper and, below that list the following topics in a column, with space between the items for

recording additional information as they read: *Definition of wetland, Types of wetlands, Characteristics of wetlands, Importance of wetlands,* and *Typical organisms.* Encourage students to review their original descriptions after reading the section and revise them, if necessary.

Abiotic Parts of a Wetland System

The abiotic factors, or nonliving parts, of an ecosystem include the water, temperature, soil, oxygen, and sunlight. Each of these factors affects the types of life an ecosystem can support.

The layer of water covering a wetland can range from several centimeters to a few meters deep. The amount of precipitation and the temperature range greatly affect the amount of water available. Recall that water on Earth is part of the global water cycle. The water in the wetland ecosystem moves from the plants, animals, and land into the atmosphere through evaporation and transpiration, then falls back to the wetland as precipitation. This continuous cycling of water allows the wetland to maintain itself over a long time period.

The types of rock and soil as well as the slope and drainage of the land also help determine the type of wetland you will find. In some wetlands water flows through slowly; in others there is no drainage at all. Impermeable layers of rock or clay can prevent surface water from seeping into the ground.

The level of oxygen in the air, water, and ground is different for each wetland. Due to the lack of movement of water in many wetlands, there is often little oxygen. This affects the kinds of organisms that live there. The sunlight provides the energy that warms the air and water in a wetland, and enables plants to carry on photosynthesis. The sunlight also provides the energy for the water cycle.

Biotic Parts of a Wetland System

The biotic factors in an ecosystem include all of its producers, consumers, and decomposers. These organisms interact with each other and with the wetland's abiotic factors.

Producers The producers in a wetland ecosystem capture the energy of sunlight through photosynthesis and store it as chemical energy in food. The types of producers that exist in a particular wetland depend on the abiotic factors of the wetland.

Figure 10 Freshwater wetlands come in many forms. **(A)** In Montana, colorful flowers dot a bed of velvety moss in an alpine bog. **(B)** Spanish moss hangs from cypress trees in a swamp in Caddo Lake State Park, Texas.
Comparing and Contrasting How are these two environments similar? How are they different?

Program Resources

◆ **Unit 4 Resources** 12-4 Lesson Plan, p. 77; 12-4 Section Summary, p. 78
◆ **Guided Reading and Study Workbook** 12-4

Answers to Self-Assessment

Caption Question

Figure 10 The land in both is covered with shallow water. Swamps are wooded, and bogs are mossy.

2 Facilitate

What is a Wetland System?

Using the Visuals: Figure 10

After students examine the photographs in Figure 10 and the photograph of the marsh on page 418 and read the caption and the text describing the types of wetlands, have students review their earlier definitions (Activating Prior Knowledge on page 418). Suggest that they correct their definitions, if necessary, to reflect the differences shown and discussed here. **learning modality: verbal**

Abiotic Parts of a Wetland System

Building Inquiry Skills: Designing Experiments

After students have read about the abiotic factors of a wetland system, divide the class into groups of three or four. Challenge each group to design an experiment to find out how a change in an abiotic factor affects a wetland system. Help students recall the major steps to be completed: develop a hypothesis, describe the experimental design, control variables, record and interpret data, and draw a conclusion. Monitor the groups' experimental designs for safety and logic. Then encourage groups to conduct their experiments and report their results and conclusions to the class. **learning modality: logical/mathematical**

Portfolio Students can save their experiment descriptions, data, sketches, and conclusions in their portfolios.

Ongoing Assessment

Oral Presentation Call on students at random to explain why a wetland is a system and to identify examples of wetland systems.

Biotic Parts of a Wetland System

Real-Life Learning

Have students work in small groups to research a wetland system in your community or region. Then have them share their findings with the class in a written or oral presentation accompanied by drawings and/or photos. Encourage students to include in their presentation the type of wetland, its location, descriptions of its abiotic and biotic factors, and an explanation of how these factors interact with each other. **cooperative learning**

Properties of Wetland Systems

Using the Visuals: Figure 11

Tell students that the wetland system shown on these pages is a part of the Everglades. Ask: **What particular type of wetland is shown? How do you know?** *(A marsh; it is covered mostly with grass.)* To develop the concept that the properties of a wetland system differ from the properties of its individual parts, have students identify various habitats shown in this marsh. *(Trees, grasses, water, mud under the water)* Then have them discuss how the properties of these habitats vary. **learning modality: visual**

A great variety of plant life finds a place to grow and thrive in wetlands. For example, certain grasses and tall grasslike plants such as cattails can be found in a marsh. Trees that tolerate wet soils are found in swamps. Cypress trees grow in southern swamps in the United States. Willow and dogwood trees are found in northern parts of the country. Sphagnum moss often grows in a bog where the water is acidic. Over time layers of partly decayed moss compress to form a blackish-brown material called peat.

Consumers The consumers found in a wetland depend on the type of producers that thrive there. As in a pond, you will find waterfowl, frogs, turtles, raccoons, snakes, muskrats, and a variety of insects in many wetlands. In southern regions of the United States you can also find alligators and armadillos.

Birds nest in and around wetlands, feeding on the plants and insects there. Waterfowl rely on wetlands to provide temporary shelter as they migrate. Wetlands provide breeding grounds and nurturing waters for young organisms to develop. Many other animals find food and shelter among the wetland plants.

Figure 11 Many unusual species live in the freshwater wetland habitats of the Everglades.

Roseate spoonbills

Great egret

Snowy egret

Little blue heron

Sawgrass

Anhinga

Florida panther

420

Background

Facts and Figures Since the mid-1980s, the rate of wetland loss in the United States has slowed to less than an estimated 36,000 hectares a year. This is less than a quarter of the rate of loss only a few decades earlier. Wetlands may be developed only if an equal area of wetlands is restored. In addition, there are now many initiatives aimed at increasing the number and quality of wetlands. Many programs offer farmers financial incentives to restore wetlands on their property.

Decomposers Decomposers such as bacteria and fungi break down the wastes and remains from the plants and animals. Dead leaves and other plant and animal material serve as natural fertilizer, adding nitrogen, phosphates and other nutrients to the water and soil.

Properties of Wetland Systems

The properties of a wetland ecosystem differ from the properties of its individual parts. Like all ecosystems, a wetland transforms energy, provides different habitats and niches for the organisms that live there, and maintains itself over time. A wetland captures an enormous amount of energy from sunlight. Living things use this energy directly to grow and reproduce. But incoming energy also affects the abiotic parts of a wetland. For example, sunlight warms the water, causing it to evaporate and to continue the water cycle.

Each part of the wetland offers different habitats and niches for living things. Some organisms may live on the wetland's trees, shrubs, and grasses. Others may live in the water, or beneath the water in a layer of mud.

Sharpen your Skills

Making Models
ACTIVITY

In one end of a loaf pan, build a sloping hill of damp soil. Add water to the other end of the pan to form a lake. Use a watering can to sprinkle water onto the hill to simulate rain. Observe the result. Next, empty the water out of the pan and rebuild the hill. Push a sponge into the soil across the bottom of the hill. Again, add water and sprinkle "rain." What happened to the soil with and without the sponge? What does the sponge represent in your model?

Everglades palm

White-tailed deer

Flamingos

Raccoon

Purple gallinule

American alligator

Chapter 12 **421**

The Everglades: A Unique Wetland System

Sharpen your Skills

Making Models
Materials *loaf pan, damp soil, watering can, water, sponge* ACTIVITY
Time 10–15 minutes
Tips Provide a large bucket for collecting used water. Remind students to avoid pouring muddy water down the drain.
Expected Outcome The "rain" will carry soil down the hillside and into the water. The sponge will cause soil to be trapped. The sponge represents the roots of plants. **learning modality: tactile/kinesthetic**

Importance of Wetlands

Including All Students

Have students investigate threats to the Everglades. Then let students work in small groups to create public service radio announcements, television spots, newspaper or transit ads, or educational skits designed to increase public awareness of the importance of the Everglades and threats to its survival. Give each group an opportunity to present its product to the rest of the class. **cooperative learning**

Ongoing Assessment

Writing Have students write a paragraph defining and describing freshwater wetlands.

3 Assess

Section 4 Review Answers

1. Abiotic factors may include water, temperature, soil, oxygen, and sunlight. Biotic factors may include any living things that could be found in a wetland system.

2. Answers will vary. Sample answer: If the number of producers in a wetland system decreases, there will be less food for consumers, so their numbers will also decrease.

3. By absorbing extra runoff from heavy rains; by acting like giant sponges, storing water, and gradually releasing it

4. Answers might include the number of farmers affected and their projected losses, possible commercial uses of the restored Everglades (such as wildlife tours) and their projected revenues, and possible replacements for current agricultural practices or crops.

Check Your Progress ▸ CHAPTER PROJECT

Work with students to choose the type of graph they will use to display their data. Demonstrate how to make circle and bar graphs. Discuss what to show on each axis of a bar graph and what scale to use.

Performance Assessment

Oral Presentation Have students give an imaginary tour of a wetland, describing its characteristics, plants and animals, and importance.

The Everglades

Figure 12 Habitats found in the Everglades include sawgrass marshes, cypress swamps, and mangrove forests.
Interpreting Maps In which area of the park would you expect to find mangrove trees?

Legend:
- Mangrove forests
- Everglades National Park
- Rivers and canals

Map labels: Lake Okeechobee, FLORIDA, Big Cypress Swamp, Naples, Boca Raton, Fort Lauderdale, Miami, Gulf of Mexico, THE EVERGLADES, ATLANTIC OCEAN, Florida Bay, Key Largo, Florida Keys, 0 25 mi, 0 25 km

---

A wetland ecosystem tends to remain stable unless it is disturbed by a change in its abiotic or biotic factors. For example, some bogs slowly dry up over many years. This gradually changes the types of organisms that can live in the bog.

The Everglades: A Unique Wetland System

Water is the key to the Everglades, a unique region of wetlands. A shallow layer of water moves slowly over the gently sloping land from Lake Okeechobee south to Florida Bay. Tall, sharp-edged blades of sawgrass grow in the water. The thick growth of sawgrass gave this region its Native American name, *Pa-hay-okee*, which means "river of grass." Low, tree-covered islands called hammocks are scattered throughout the sawgrass marsh.

As in other wetlands, water means life for many Everglades creatures. Fish and snakes gobble up tiny organisms in the warm, muddy water. Wading birds in a rainbow of colors—pink flamingoes, white egrets, and purple gallinules—stand on skinny legs in the water. A raccoon digs for alligator eggs, unaware of the alligator lying low in the sawgrass nearby.

Importance of Wetland Systems

Wetland ecosystems have important properties that benefit all living things. **Wetlands provide natural filtration and absorb water that might otherwise cause flooding.** As water moves slowly through a wetland, waste materials settle out. The thick network of plant roots traps silt and mud. Wetlands also help control floods by absorbing extra runoff from heavy rains. They act like giant sponges, storing water and gradually releasing it as it drains or evaporates. If wetlands are drained or paved over, the water cannot be absorbed, and flooding may result.

Section 4 Review

1. Give two examples of each: abiotic and biotic parts of a wetland system.
2. Pick one biotic or abiotic part of a wetland system. Explain how a change in this part of the system could change the properties of the wetland system.
3. Explain how wetlands help control floods.
4. **Thinking Critically** **Making Judgments** Some plans to restore the Everglades require millions of dollars and negatively affect local farmers. What information would you need to decide on a plan to save the Everglades?

Check Your Progress ▸ CHAPTER PROJECT

At this point, you should be ready to use the data in your water-use data tables to graph the results of tracking water use in your home and in another building in your community. Think about the type of graph that will best communicate your findings. Decide whether to draw your graphs by hand or to create them on the computer.

422

Program Resources

◆ **Unit 4 Resources** 12-4 Review and Reinforce, p. 79; 12-4 Enrich, p. 80

Answers to Self-Assessment

Caption Question

Figure 12 Along the southern and western coasts; mangroves grow in salt water.

DISCOVER ······························ ACTIVITY····

Can You Reach a Balance?

1. Fill a large measuring cup with water to represent a reservoir. Record the level of the water. One partner, the water supplier, should have a plastic dropper and a small bowl of water. The other partner, the water user, should have a spoon and an empty bowl.

2. Start a stopwatch. For two minutes, the water supplier should add water to the measuring cup one dropperful at a time. Each time the water supplier adds a dropperful of water, the water user should remove one spoonful of water from the reservoir.

3. At the end of two minutes, record the level of water in the cup.

4. Now increase the rate of water use by removing two spoonfuls of water for every dropperful added.

5. After another two minutes, record the level of water in the cup again.

Think It Over
Predicting What changes will you need to make so that the water level in the reservoir stays constant?

H as this ever happened to you? You're eating dinner with your family and you ask someone to pass the rolls. As the basket makes its way around the table, each person takes a roll. By the time it gets to you, there's nothing left in the basket but crumbs!

This scenario is an example of a limited resource, the rolls, being used by many people. The same thing can happen to a river! For example, the Colorado River holds a resource that is precious in the Southwest—water. In this desert region there is little precipitation to provide water for people's needs. As the river flows through five states and into Mexico, it is tapped again and again to provide water for drinking, irrigation, and other uses. The river's mouth at the Gulf of California is now often only a dry riverbed.

GUIDE FOR READING

◆ What conditions can result in a water shortage?

◆ What are some ways industries can conserve water?

Reading Tip Before you read, write an explanation of what you think water conservation means. As you read, add to your explanation.

Key Terms drought • conservation • desalination

Figure 13 Cracks appear in the dry soil of an empty riverbed.

423

READING STRATEGIES

Reading Tip Ask students to write just one or two sentences about water conservation. Students may say that water conservation means not wasting water or not polluting water. Then ask volunteers to share their ideas with the class. After students have read the section, they can discuss how their ideas have changed.

Program Resources

◆ **Unit 4 Resources** 12-5 Lesson Plan, p. 81; 12-5 Section Summary, p. 82
◆ **Guided Reading and Study Workbook** 12-5

Objectives

After completing the lesson, students will be able to

◆ describe conditions that can result in a water shortage and list sources of fresh water for the future;
◆ explain how water can be conserved.

1 Engage/Explore

Activating Prior Knowledge

Begin by eliciting a list of common household uses of water. Write this list on the board. Ask: **How could you use less water for each of these uses?** *(Students should propose ways to conserve water for each use, such as taking shorter showers, not running water while brushing teeth, and not watering the yard in the bright sun.)* Then challenge students to think of reasons why water should not be wasted.

········· DISCOVER ·········

Skills Focus predicting
Materials *large measuring cup, water, plastic dropper, 2 small bowls, spoon, stopwatch*
Time 15 minutes
Tips Use a relatively small plastic dropper in order to accentuate the drop in the level of the water in the cup when the rate is increased in Step 4. Tell students to clean up any water spills, using a sponge or paper towel.
Expected Outcome Students should infer that increased demand will diminish the amount of water if the supply is constant over time. They should also infer that decreasing demand is one way to keep the supply at a constant level.
Think It Over Answers may vary. A typical answer might suggest that the water user must decrease the rate of use by removing a spoonful every two or three dropperfuls, depending on dropper size.

2 Facilitate

Water Supply and Demand

Using the Visuals: Figure 14

After students have studied this figure, have them turn back to the *Science & History* feature on pages 400–401. Point out that Israel is a desert nation. Ask: **How does the irrigation technique used in Israel take into account that most of the country is very dry?** (*One purpose of the technique described is to waste as little water as possible.*) Help students understand that in Israel, the demand for irrigation water is great because the supply is short. **learning modality: verbal**

Integrating Technology

Materials *10 2-L plastic soda bottles, box, concrete block, water*
Time 15 minutes

To model how groundwater can support the weight of the land above it, fill a box with empty plastic bottles with caps on. Have students predict what will happen when you place a concrete block on top of the bottles. Then place the block on the bottles. The bottles will collapse under its weight. Next, fill the bottles with water, screw on the caps tightly, and return them to the box. Again ask students to predict what will happen. This time when you place the block on top of the bottles, they will not collapse. **learning modality: logical/mathematical**

Figure 14 Farmers require large amounts of water to irrigate crops in the dry desert. *Relating Cause and Effect What are two factors that might result in a shortage of water available for irrigation?*

Water Supply and Demand

States along a river such as the Colorado have to decide how much water each one can take from the river. The deserts of Nevada and Arizona are home to some of the fastest-growing cities in the country. As more people move to Las Vegas, Phoenix, and Tucson, these cities need more water. They increase their demand on already scarce water supplies. Meanwhile, farmers claim a large share to irrigate their fields. Mining companies use water to cool down machinery and flush out the mines they dig. The cities, farms, and mines compete for water rights—the legal right to take water from a particular source.

The Southwest is just one of many places in the world where there doesn't seem to be enough water to go around. As you know, the water cycle ensures that water is a renewable resource. However, the water supply in a specific area is only renewed when there is enough time for rainfall to replace what has been used. **A water shortage occurs when there is too little water or too great a demand in an area—or both.**

Drought Places that normally get enough precipitation may experience a few years of scarce rainfall, a condition known as a **drought.** A drought affects the supply of groundwater as well as surface water. Without precipitation to recharge the aquifer, the amount of groundwater in the aquifer decreases. What happens to a well as the level of the water table falls? Imagine trying to drink from a tall glass of milk through a straw the length of a toothpick. When the level of the milk falls below the bottom of the straw, you can no longer reach it to drink. In the same way, when the water table falls below the bottom of a well, the well runs dry.

Aquifer Overuse Even without droughts, the demands of growing populations can result in overuse of aquifers. When water is used up faster than the aquifer can be recharged, the aquifer is depleted, or emptied.

When too much water is pumped out of an aquifer, the ground above the aquifer can sink or collapse. The ground is no longer supported by the pressure of the water inside it. To prevent collapse, engineers can artificially recharge an aquifer. One method is to pump water from wastewater treatment

---

Background

Facts and Figures The Colorado River begins in the mountains of northern Colorado. As it flows southwest, the Colorado River and its tributaries drain land in seven states—Colorado, Wyoming, Utah, Arizona, New Mexico, Nevada, and California. The river continues a short distance through Mexico before reaching its mouth at the Gulf of California. However, so much water is removed from the river upstream for irrigation and urban water supplies, that in years with normal precipitation the Colorado dries up completely before reaching the sea.

Several dams have been built along the Colorado River, creating a series of lakes. Lake Powell is behind the Glen Canyon Dam, Lake Mead is behind the Hoover Dam, Lake Mohave is behind the Parker Dam. The dams create reservoirs, control floods, and generate hydroelectric power.

plants or industrial cooling water into shallow ponds that feed the aquifer. Another method is to inject water down wells directly into the saturated zone. However, because these techniques require expensive equipment and additional water, it is a better solution not to overuse the aquifer.

☑ *Checkpoint* *How can a drought cause a well to run dry?*

Conserving Water

During a water shortage, people often pay more attention to how they use water. They look for ways to avoid wasting water both at home and at work. Using a resource wisely so that it will not be used up is called **conservation.**

In the Home Most people in the United States have access to as much clean, safe water as they want. As a result, it is often easy to use more water than needed without thinking much about it. But as Figure 15 shows, there are some simple things you can do to help conserve water around your home.

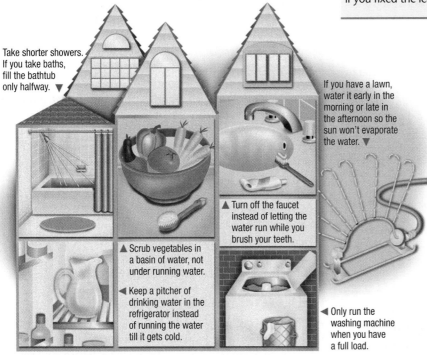

Take shorter showers. If you take baths, fill the bathtub only halfway. ▼

If you have a lawn, water it early in the morning or late in the afternoon so the sun won't evaporate the water. ▼

▲ Turn off the faucet instead of letting the water run while you brush your teeth.

▲ Scrub vegetables in a basin of water, not under running water.

◀ Keep a pitcher of drinking water in the refrigerator instead of running the water till it gets cold.

◀ Only run the washing machine when you have a full load.

Figure 15 There are many simple ways to conserve water around the home. *Developing Hypotheses Which of these ideas do you think would save the most water per day in your home? How could you test your hypothesis?*

Answers to Self-Assessment

☑ *Checkpoint*

A drought can cause the water table to fall below the bottom of the well.

Caption Question

Figure 14 Too little water and too great a demand in an area.

Figure 15 Sample answer: Take shorter showers. Measure the water saved by each idea and then compare.

Conserving Water

Sharpen your Skills

Predicting

Materials *large measuring cup*

Time 5 minutes for setup; 5 minutes for results

Tips Contact a member of your school's custodial staff to find a leaking faucet somewhere in the building. Students can extrapolate from their data how much water would be wasted in a month or year by multiplying by the appropriate number of minutes and days.

Expected Outcome The amount of water that drips into the cup will vary; in general, students will underestimate the amount.

Extend Ask a custodian to fix a leaking school faucet while students watch. Students can then use this knowledge to help fix a leaking faucet at home.

learning modality: logical/ mathematical

Ongoing Assessment

Writing Have each student write a TV news reporter's script for each of the following situations: too great a demand for water results in a water shortage, too little water results in a water shortage. Students should make up the details for each situation.

Conserving Water,
continued

Social Studies
CONNECTION

After students have read the feature, ask: **What is a miller?** *(A person who grinds grain to make flour)* Explain that flowing water can be used to supply energy to run a mill. Then challenge students to come up with their solutions. Students' solutions may vary, but they should each take the following into consideration. Of the four possible uses of water, those of both the fisherman and the miller would not take water from the river. Because the fisherman needs the river to be half full, no more than 5,000 L can be withdrawn per day. The total needed by the grain farmer and the livestock owner add up to 5,100 L per day. Thus, students could assign less water to one or the other of those two in order to keep the river half full or consider reusing the water for washing animals for one of the other purposes.

Extend Have students propose ways by which the grain farmer and livestock owner would not return polluted water to the river. **learning modality: logical/mathematical**

Fresh Water for the Future

Integrating Chemistry

Ask students: **How does the process of distillation produce fresh water from salt water?** *(The saltwater solution evaporates, leaving the salt behind. When the water condenses, it is pure fresh water.)* **How does distillation compare to the water cycle you studied in Section 1?** *(The processes are similar since both include evaporation and condensation.)* Guide students in a comparison of the solar energy that drives the water cycle and the energy used for desalination. Ask: **What is a major drawback in using this method of desalination?** *(The cost of energy, such as electricity, needed to drive the process)* **learning modality: verbal**

Social Studies
CONNECTION

Laws regarding the use of water are a very old concept. Nearly 4,000 years ago in ancient Mesopotamia, now Iraq, a ruler named Hammurabi wrote in his code of laws:

> "If a man neglects the canal so that water floods a neighboring field, he shall repay the loss with his own grain."

In Your Journal

A river carries 10,000 liters of water a day through your village. Imagine that you are a member of the village council. Propose a fair way to assign water rights to the following people. (*Hint:* Think about which uses will return water to the river and which will not.)

◆ grain farmer who wants 4,000 liters a day for watering crops

◆ livestock owner who wants 600 liters a day for washing animals and 500 liters a day for animals to drink

◆ fisherman who needs to keep the river at least half full for the fish to survive

◆ miller who needs 3,500 liters a day to turn his water wheel

Can these suggestions really make a difference? Figure it out. How long do you stand under the shower? For every minute, you use about 18 liters of water. If you stand under the shower for 10 minutes, that's about 180 liters. But if you showered for 5 minutes instead, you would use only 90 liters. And if each student in a class of 25 showered for 5 minutes instead of 10, they would save a total of 2,250 liters of water—enough to fill 22 trash barrels! As you can see, small efforts by many individuals can add up to a lot of water savings.

In Agriculture The biggest use of water in the United States is for agriculture. Farmers have found new ways to use less water. When water is carried into fields in open canals or ditches, much of it is lost through evaporation. Using pipes to carry water reduces the time that water is exposed to the air. Two such methods are sprinkler irrigation and drip irrigation. Sprinkler irrigation sprays water onto crops from overhead pipes. Drip irrigation distributes water through pipes with tiny holes. The water drips directly onto the soil near the plants' roots so that very little is wasted.

In Industry Paper mills, oil refineries, chemical factories, and other industries have made changes in manufacturing processes to use less water. For example, in the 1950s it took about 227,000 liters of water to make 1,000 kilograms of writing paper. By the 1980s, paper mills needed only half that much water to produce the same amount of paper.

New water-saving techniques help industries save money in water costs and meet the requirements of environmental laws. **Reducing water use, recycling water, and reusing water are three major forms of water conservation by industries.** These approaches conserve water while also reducing the amount of wastewater that plants release. For example, some factories that use water to cool machinery are building lagoons on their property. The heated water cools off in the lagoons and then can be used again. Other factories are replacing water-cooling systems with cooling systems that use air. Another change is to use high-pressure water sprays to clean products and equipment instead of dipping the objects in large tanks of water.

Fresh Water for the Future

As the number of people in the world increases, so does the need for water. Where can people find new sources of water for the future? One obvious place would seem to be the other 97 percent of water on Earth—the salt water in the oceans. For thousands of years, people have tried different methods to make salty ocean water drinkable.

Background

Facts and Figures An estimate from the World Resources Institute is that 65–70 percent of water used by people throughout the world is wasted, through leaks, evaporation, runoff, and similar losses. The United States wastes about 50 percent of the water it withdraws. Irrigation accounts for almost 70 percent of world water use; about two-thirds of that is wasted. One way to conserve water is to use treated wastewater for irrigation.

In the typical U.S. home, bathing (including showering), flushing toilets, and washing hands accounts for about 78 percent of water used. Water-saving showerheads and low-flow toilets can prevent a good deal of that waste. In 1994, a federal law mandated that all new toilets sold in the U.S. would use no more than 6 L per flush.

Desalination The process of obtaining fresh water **INTEGRATING CHEMISTRY** from saltwater is **desalination.** One method of desalination, called distillation, is to boil water so that it evaporates, leaving the salt behind. The water vapor is then condensed to produce liquid fresh water. Another method involves freezing the water, which also leaves the salt behind. Still another method is to pump water at high pressure through a very fine filter. The filter separates out pure water and returns saltier water to the ocean.

Desalination is very expensive because of the energy and equipment it requires. In spite of the cost, however, Saudi Arabia, Kuwait, Israel, and other nations in the dry Middle East depend on this technology. A few cities in the United States, such as Santa Barbara, California, have also built desalination plants.

Icebergs Some people think that icebergs are another possible source of fresh water for dry regions. Tugboats could tow a wrapped iceberg from Antarctica to a coastal area of Africa or South America. An iceberg would provide millions of liters of pure water that could be piped to shore as the iceberg melted. However, such plans raise environmental questions: How would a huge mass of ice offshore affect local weather? What would happen to living things as the ice cooled the water around it? These questions need to be answered before icebergs can be seen as a solution to Earth's future water needs.

Figure 16 The ocean is one possible source of drinking water for the future. *Applying Concepts How can ocean water be made suitable for drinking?*

Section 5 Review

1. Describe a situation that could lead to a water shortage in a community.
2. Name three ways that industries can conserve water.
3. Describe the possible effects overpumping might have on an aquifer.
4. Explain how an iceberg might provide drinking water in the future.
5. **Thinking Critically Making Judgments** Do you think communities should be able to limit how often people water their lawns or wash their cars? Why or why not?

Science at Home

Water Use for Brushing Place a stopper over the drain in a sink. Ask a family member to brush his or her teeth over the sink, allowing the water to run until he or she is done. Mark the level of the water in the sink with a small piece of tape. Remove the stopper and let the water drain. Replace the stopper and have the person repeat the brushing, this time turning the water on only when needed. Mark the water level with another piece of tape. Point out the difference in the amount of water used in each case.

Program Resources

◆ **Unit 4 Resources** 12-5 Review and Reinforce, p. 83; 12-5 Enrich, p. 84

Answers to Self-Assessment

Caption Question

Figure 16 Various methods of desalination can make ocean water suitable for drinking.

3 Assess

Section 5 Review Answers

1. Answers may vary. A typical answer might describe a drought or a situation in which there is too great a demand for the supply of water.
2. Reducing water use, recycling water, and reusing water are three major forms of water conservation by industries.
3. The aquifer can be depleted if water is used up faster than the aquifer can be recharged. Overpumping can cause the ground above the aquifer to sink or collapse.
4. Tugboats could tow a wrapped iceberg from Antarctica to a coastal region of Africa or South America and the water could be piped to shore as the iceberg melted.
5. Answers may vary. A typical answer: A community should be able to limit water use in times of shortage but not when water is in good supply.

Science at Home

Encourage students to introduce this activity at home by explaining to family members that water is a precious resource that should not be wasted. Students might do this with more than one family member, making it into a friendly competition about who can conserve the most water. Tell students that if the tape will not stick to the wet sink, they could mark the levels with bar soap.

Performance Assessment

Writing Challenge each student to assume the role of a government official in a region experiencing a severe drought. Because of the water shortage, the official has been asked to recommend a set of regulations limiting water use by homes and businesses. Students should write a brief introduction to the regulations and then list ten specific recommendations.

The Ogallala Aquifer

Purpose To provide students with an understanding of the problems associated with overuse of water resources.

Role-Play

Time a day to prepare; 30 minutes for role-play

Divide students into four groups: (1) a five-member "fact-finding committee" appointed by Congress, (2) a group to argue for more regulations and charges on water use, (3) a group to argue that different water-saving farming practices should be instituted, and (4) a group to argue that current practices should continue. Tell the first group to work out rules and an agenda for a public meeting on water use on the Great Plains. Students in each of the other groups can work together to prepare a presentation to the committee during the public meeting. Then hold the public meeting, using the rules and agenda worked out by the committee members. Encourage students to act the way they think citizens would act in a real public meeting of this kind.

Extend Challenge students to find out whether water shortages are a problem in your area. Suggest that they contact the local water department to ask what plans are in place in case of a drought or some other water problem.

You Decide

Have students individually complete the first two steps before the role-play as a way of preparing themselves for their participation. After the role-play is concluded, students can complete the last step, using what they learned in the role-play for finding a solution to the problem.

 Students can save their letters in their portfolio.

The Ogallala Aquifer

The Ogallala Aquifer lies beneath eight states of the Great Plains. It contains about 4 quadrillion liters of groundwater—about the amount of water in Lake Huron. Rainfall is scarce on the Great Plains. But by pumping water out of the aquifer, farmers can grow cotton, wheat, sorghum, and corn to feed cattle. More than one third of the nation's livestock are raised in this area.

Water in the Ogallala was trapped there during the last Ice Age, about 12,000 years ago. Now, due to the demands of irrigation, water levels are dropping much faster than the aquifer can recharge. In certain parts of the aquifer, water levels have fallen as much as 12 meters since 1980. Farmers recognize that the Ogallala cannot withstand this heavy use for long. However, not all agree on what should be done.

The Issues

Should Water Use Be Regulated? One way to reduce water use might be to charge people for water. But who owns the water and who would determine the cost? In most of the Great Plains, water has been free to anyone who dug a well on their land. To charge for water, local governments would need to construct a public water system as in most cities. This would be a very complex and costly task. Both farmers and consumers would be affected by the charge. Higher costs for growing crops would result in higher supermarket prices for grains and meat.

Should Farmers Change Their Practices? Farmers could switch to crops such as sunflowers and grains that need less water. These crops, however, are less valuable than others for producing food and for feeding livestock. As a result, they would be less profitable than traditional crops. Farmers could use water-saving methods of irrigation. Such methods are expensive to install but eventually save both water and money.

Another possibility is "dryland farming," a method that was used by pioneer farmers. This method involves keeping the soil moist using only rainwater. Because dryland farming depends on the amount of rainfall, it is unpredictable. It may not produce large harvests.

Should Current Use Continue? Many residents of the Great Plains depend on the aquifer for a living. Some people feel that farmers there must continue their present water use in order to compete with farmers elsewhere in the nation and around the world. They feel that people today should not have to suffer in order to preserve the aquifer for future generations. New sources of water may be discovered, or better methods of transporting water to the Great Plains may be developed. Better irrigation techniques that use less water may also be invented. But other people feel that since these possibilities are not certain, water use must be greatly reduced now to save the aquifer.

You Decide

1. Identify the Problem
In your own words, explain the problem facing the farmers on the Great Plains.

2. Analyze the Options
Make a chart of the solutions mentioned. List advantages and drawbacks of each. Who would benefit from each solution? Who would suffer?

3. Find a Solution
As a resident of the Great Plains, write a letter to the newspaper proposing a solution to the Ogallala problem.

Background

The Ogallala is the largest known aquifer in the world. Water from the aquifer is used to irrigate nearly 6 million hectares, or about 20 percent of all cropland in the United States. Each year, about 26 billion m³ of groundwater are pumped from the aquifer. Since 1950, the water table in the Ogallala has dropped an average of 30 m. In some places, the drop has been much greater. For example, the depth to groundwater in Floyd County, Texas, dropped from about 25 m in 1950 to about 75 m in 1984, despite a significant decrease of irrigated land during that time. Throughout the aquifer, water is being pumped out at about eight times the rate that natural recharge occurs. If all pumping ceased, some scientists have estimated it would take at least 1,000 years for the aquifer to recover to be completely recharged.

SECTION 1 The Water Cycle

Key Ideas

- About 97 percent of Earth's water is salt water stored in the oceans. Less than 1 percent is usable fresh water.
- In the water cycle, water evaporates from Earth's surface into the atmosphere. The water forms clouds, then falls as precipitation. Energy from the sun drives the water cycle.
- All living things need water to carry out their life processes.

Key Terms

water vapor   evaporation   precipitation
groundwater   transpiration   irrigation
water cycle

SECTION 2 Surface Water

Key Ideas

- Runoff from precipitation forms streams, which flow together to form rivers. The area drained by a river system is its watershed.
- Ponds and lakes are bodies of standing water that form when fresh water collects in depressions in the land.

Key Terms

tributary   divide   reservoir
watershed   levee

SECTION 3 Groundwater

Key Ideas

- As water soaks into the ground, it moves through the pores between particles of soil and rock. Water moves easily through permeable materials, but does not move easily through impermeable materials.
- People dig wells to obtain groundwater from aquifers.

Key Terms

pore   water table   spring
permeable   unsaturated zone   recharge
impermeable   aquifer   artesian well
saturated zone

SECTION 4 Wetland Systems

INTEGRATING LIFE SCIENCE

Key Ideas

- The two main parts of a wetland ecosystem are the abiotic factors, or nonliving parts, and the biotic factors, or living parts.
- A wetland ecosystem transforms energy, provides different habitats and niches for the organisms, and maintains itself over time.
- Wetland ecosystems provide natural filtration and absorb water that might otherwise cause flooding.

Key Terms

wetland   system

SECTION 5 Water Resources

Key Ideas

- Water is scarce in many places, leading to competition for limited supplies.
- Water shortages can occur when there is too little water or too much demand in an area.
- Industries can conserve water by reducing water use, recycling water, and reusing water.
- Desalination of ocean water and icebergs are two possible future sources of fresh water.

Key Terms

drought   conservation   desalination

Organizing Information

Concept Map Copy the concept map about the water cycle onto a separate piece of paper, then complete it and add a title. (For more on concept maps, see the Skills Handbook.)

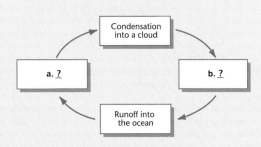

Organizing Information

Concept Map Sample answers may vary. Sample **a.** Evaporation from the ocean **b.** Precipitation onto Earth's surface
Sample title: Path of a Water Molecule

Program Resources

- **Unit 4 Resources** Chapter 12 Project Scoring Rubric, p. 64
- **Performance Assessment** Chapter 12, pp. 38–40
- **Chapter and Unit Tests** Chapter 12 Test, pp. 60–63

Media and Technology

Computer Test Bank
Chapter 12 Test

Reviewing Content
Multiple Choice

1. c 2. b 3. d 4. d 5. c

True or False

6. groundwater 7. fresh water 8. falls
9. true 10. true

Checking Concepts

11. Earth is called the "water planet" because oceans cover nearly 71 percent of Earth's surface.
12. Students should describe the change from liquid to gas involved in evaporation and the change from gas to liquid involved in condensation.
13. More than 97 percent of the total water on Earth is salt water, which is generally not available for human use. About three fourths of the fresh water on Earth is ice, which is mostly unavailable for human use.
14. Plants use the water to make food, and other living things on Earth obtain food either by eating plants or by eating other organisms that eat plants.
15. Students may describe sprinkler irrigation—spraying water onto crops from overhead pipes—or drip irrigation—distributing water through pipes with tiny holes directly onto the soil near the plants' roots.
16. The two major parts of a wetland system are the abiotic factors and the biotic factors.
17. Students' stories should include evaporating and becoming a molecule of water vapor, condensing in the colder air and becoming a molecule of water in a cloud, and returning to the ocean in some form of precipitation.

Thinking Critically

18. Answers may vary. A typical answer might mention the availability of water for industry and transportation of people and goods.
19. The variety of organisms in the center of a pond is much greater because sunlight reaches the bottom. Sunlight does not reach the deep water at the center of a lake, so plants and algae and the organisms that depend on them cannot live there.

430

Reviewing Content

 Review key concepts online using iText at www.phschool.com

Multiple Choice
Choose the letter of the best answer.

1. More than 97 percent of Earth's total water supply is found in
   a. ice sheets.
   b. the atmosphere.
   c. the oceans and salt lakes.
   d. groundwater.
2. The energy that drives the water cycle comes from the
   a. Earth. b. sun.
   c. rain. d. ocean.
3. One process used to obtain fresh water from salt water is
   a. irrigation. b. filtration.
   c. recharge. d. desalination.
4. More than two thirds of Earth's fresh water is found in
   a. rivers and streams.
   b. ponds and lakes.
   c. wetlands.
   d. glaciers and icebergs.
5. Groundwater is stored in
   a. wetlands. b. water tables.
   c. aquifers. d. impermeable layers.

True or False
If the statement is true, write true. If it is false, change the underlined word or words to make the statement true.

6. Most of Earth's liquid fresh water is found in the form of <u>lakes</u>.
7. In the water cycle, precipitation returns <u>salt water</u> to Earth.
8. A drought can cause wells to dry up if the level of the water table <u>rises</u>.
9. Water moves easily through <u>permeable</u> rock layers.
10. Wetland systems help to control <u>flooding</u> by absorbing water.

Checking Concepts

11. Explain why Earth is called the "water planet."
12. Describe two changes that occur during the water cycle.
13. Explain why so little of Earth's water is available for human use.
14. How is the water supplied to plants important for many other living things on Earth?
15. Describe one way that farmers can reduce the amount of water lost during irrigation.
16. What are the two major parts of a wetland ecosystem?
17. **Writing to Learn** Imagine that you are a molecule of water. Write a story about the changes you would experience as you go through the water cycle. Begin in the ocean, then describe each change that occurs, and return to the ocean at the end of your story.

Thinking Critically

18. **Making Generalizations** Explain why towns and cities are often located along bodies of water.
19. **Comparing and Contrasting** How is the variety of organisms you would find in the center of a pond different from those you would find in deep water at the center of a lake?
20. **Classifying** Determine which of the following materials are permeable and which are impermeable: aluminum foil, cotton, plastic wrap, glass, paper towel, and bread.
21. **Problem Solving** What effect would the draining of a wetland have on migrating birds?
22. **Relating Cause and Effect** Describe how one abiotic factor can affect many biotic factors in a wetland system.

---

20. *Permeable:* cotton, paper towel, bread; *impermeable:* aluminum foil, plastic wrap, glass
21. Birds nest in and around wetlands, feeding on the plants and insects there. If the wetland was drained, the plants and insects could not survive. Because the birds could no longer find food and shelter in the area, they may develop a new migration route, or their survival may be threatened.

22. Students should name one abiotic factor—water, temperature, soil, oxygen, or sunlight—and describe its effects on several different types of living things in a wetland system.

Applying Skills

Use the diagram of underground layers to answer Questions 23–25.

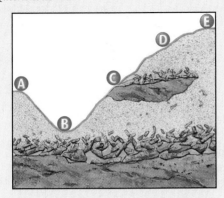

23. **Drawing Conclusions** Would point D or point E be a better location to dig a well? Explain your reasoning.
24. **Inferring** At which location could you obtain groundwater without having to pump it up? What is such a place called?
25. **Predicting** Draw a simple diagram showing how this area might look during a very rainy season.

Performance ▼ Assessment

Present Your Project Now you are ready to share the data you have collected. Present your graph of your water-use data to the class. As a class, discuss any surprising results. How do your findings compare to those of your classmates?

Reflect and Record In your project notebook, reflect on the data collection process. What part of the project was the most difficult? How might you approach this task differently? Write a paragraph summarizing what your class discovered about how water is used in your community. Do you notice any similarities among buildings where a lot of water is used, or among those where little water is used?

Test Preparation

Use these questions to prepare for standardized tests.

Study the circle graph. Then answer Questions 26–29.

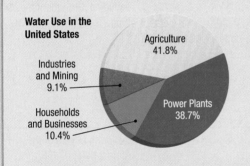

Water Use in the United States
- Agriculture 41.8%
- Industries and Mining 9.1%
- Households and Businesses 10.4%
- Power Plants 38.7%

26. Together the two largest categories of water users represent about what percentage of the total water used in the United States?
    A 19.5 percent   B 49.9 percent
    C 51.1 percent   D 80.5 percent

27. Which of the four categories of water users shown in the graph represents the largest use of water in the United States?
    F agriculture
    G households and businesses
    H industries and mining
    J power plants

28. If the total daily usage of water in the United States is 1,280 billion liters, about how many liters are used each day by power plants?
    A 38.7 billion   B 387 billion
    C 495 billion   D 49,500 billion

29. If farmers were able to reduce their water use by 10 percent, by about how much would total water use decrease in the United States?
    F 1.5 percent   G 4.2 percent
    H 10 percent   J 41.8 percent

Applying Skills

23. Accept Point D or Point E: Point D because the distance down to the saturated zone is less, although Point E has a much larger water supply to draw from.
24. Point C; a spring
25. Students' drawings should show a higher water table and thicker saturated zone. They might show a pond at point B.

Performance ▼ Assessment

Present Your Project To maximize sharing of information and to give students an opportunity to compare their models, try to schedule all the presentations in no more than two class periods or one block, allocating a specific maximum amount of time for each model. If possible, arrange the room with the students forming a large circle so everyone can see each model as it is presented.

Prompt students to identify the specific features in the model by name, explain how the features are formed in nature, and describe the role they play in the river system. Encourage the other students to ask questions about each model as it is presented. Make sure you provide all students with positive feedback about their model. Suggest that students save their models for presentation on Parents' Night or at a science fair.

Reflect and Record Encourage students to use the Chapter 12 Project Scoring Rubric to help assess their models. Suggest that they review their sketches to make sure their models accomplished what they planned. Students might also evaluate the materials they used to make the models for their effectiveness to the application.

Program Resources

- ◆ **Inquiry Skills Activity Book** Provides teaching and review of all inquiry skills
- ◆ **Prentice Hall Assessment System** Provides standardized test practice
- ◆ **Reading in the Content Area** Provides strategies to improve science reading skills
- ◆ **Teacher's ELL Handbook** Provides multiple strategies for English language learners

Test Preparation

26. D 27. F 28. C 29. G

Earth's Atmosphere

Sections	Time	Student Edition Activities	Other Activities
CHAPTER PROJECT ▼ **Watching the Weather** p. 433 TEKS: 6.14C	Ongoing (2 weeks)	TEKS: 6.2B, C, D, E; 6.4B Check Your Progress, p. 437, 456 Present Your Project, p. 459	TE Chapter 13 Project Notes, pp. 432–433
1 The Air Around You pp. 434–439 TEKS: 6.14C 13.1.1 State how the atmosphere is important to living things. 13.1.2 Identify the gases that are present in Earth's atmosphere.	2 periods/ 1 block	TEKS: 6.1A; 6.2A, B, C, D, E; 6.4A **Discover** How Long Will the Candle Burn?, p. 434 **Try This** Breathe In, Breathe Out, p. 436 **Real-World Lab: You and Your Environment** How Clean Is the Air?, pp. 438–439	TE Building Inquiry Skills: Inferring, p. 436
2 INTEGRATING ENVIRONMENTAL SCIENCE **Air Quality** pp. 440–444 TEKS: 6.3D; 6.14C 13.2.1 Name the main sources of air pollution. 13.2.2 Explain how photochemical smog and acid rain form.	2 periods/ 1 block	TEKS: 6.1B; 6.2B, C **Discover** What's On the Jar?, p. 440 **Sharpen Your Skills** Predicting, p. 442 **Science at Home,** p. 443	TE Demonstration, p. 441 TE Integrating Chemistry, p. 442 TE Inquiry Challenge, p. 442 LM 13, "Examining Acid Rain"
3 Air Pressure pp. 445–450 TEKS: 6.14C 13.3.1 Identify some of the properties of air. 13.3.2 Name instruments that are used to measure air pressure. 13.3.3 Explain how increasing altitude affects air pressure and density.	3 periods/ 1½ blocks	TEKS: 6.2B, C, D, E; 6.4A **Discover** Does Air Have Mass?, p. 445 **Try This** Soda-Bottle Barometer, p. 447 **Skills Lab: Measuring** Working Under Pressure, pp. 448–449 **Science at Home,** p. 450	TE Including All Students, p. 446 TE Including All Students, p. 447 TE Real-Life Learning, p. 446
4 Layers of the Atmosphere pp. 451–456 TEKS: 6.3E; 6.14C 13.4.1 Identify and classify the main layers of the atmosphere.	2 periods/ 1 block	TEKS: 6.2B, C **Discover** Is Air There?, p. 451	TE Exploring Layers of the Atmosphere, p. 453 TE Building Inquiry Skills: Making Models, p. 455
Study Guide/Chapter Assessment pp. 457–459	1 period/ ½ block	PLM Provides blackline masters for Probeware labs	ISAB Provides teaching and review of all inquiry skills

Key: **CTB** Computer Test Bank
CUT Chapter and Unit Tests
ELL Teacher's ELL Handbook

CHAPTER PLANNING GUIDE

 The Resource Pro® CD-ROM provides flexibility for planning the instruction for any type of schedule.

Program Resources	Assessment Strategies	Media and Technology
UR Chapter 13 Project Teacher Notes, pp. 90–91 **UR** Chapter 13 Project Overview and Worksheets, pp. 92–95	**SE** Performance Assessment: Present Your Project, p. 459 **TE** Check Your Progress, pp. 437, 456 **UR** Chapter 13 Project Scoring Rubric, p. 96	Science Explorer at www.phschool.com Student Edition on Audio CD, English-Spanish, Chapter 13
UR 13-1 Section Lesson Plan, p. 97 **UR** 13-1 Section Summary, p. 98 **UR** 13-1 Review and Reinforce, p. 99 **UR** 13-1 Enrich, p. 100 **UR** Real-World Lab blackline masters, pp. 113–115	**SE** Section 1 Review, p. 437 **TE** Ongoing Assessment, p. 435 **TE** Performance Assessment, p. 437	Earth Science Videodisc Unit 2, Side 2, "Air Today, Gone Tomorrow" Videotape Grade 6, Unit 4, "Air Today, Gone Tomorrow" Lab Activity Videotapes, Tape 4 Transparency 62, "Gases in Dry Air"
UR 13-2 Section Lesson Plan, p. 101 **UR** 13-2 Section Summary, p. 102 **UR** 13-2 Review and Reinforce, p. 103 **UR** 13-2 Enrich, p. 104	**SE** Section 2 Review, p. 443 **TE** Ongoing Assessment, p. 441 **TE** Performance Assessment, p. 443	Earth Science Videodisc Unit 6, Side 2, "Caution: Breathing May Be Hazardous to Your Health" Videotape Grade 6, Unit 4, "Caution: Breathing May Be Hazardous to Your Health"
UR 13-3 Section Lesson Plan, p. 105 **UR** 13-3 Section Summary, p. 106 **UR** 13-3 Review and Reinforce, p. 107 **UR** 13-3 Enrich, p. 108 **UR** Skills Lab blackline masters, pp. 116–117	**SE** Section 3 Review, p. 450 **TE** Ongoing Assessment, p. 447 **TE** Performance Assessment, p. 450	Physical Science Videodisc Unit 1, Side 1, "Racing Hot Air Balloons" Videotape Grade 6, Unit 1, "Racing Hot Air Balloons" Lab Activity Videotapes, Tape 4 Transparencies 63, "Measuring Air Pressure"; 64, "Density of Air at Two Altitudes"
UR 13-4 Section Lesson Plan, p. 109 **UR** 13-4 Section Summary, p. 110 **UR** 13-4 Review and Reinforce, p. 111 **UR** 13-4 Enrich, p. 112	**SE** Section 4 Review, p. 456 **TE** Ongoing Assessment, pp. 453, 455 **TE** Performance Assessment, p. 456	Earth Science Videodisc Unit 2, Side 2, "A Trip Through the Earth" Videotape Grade 6, Unit 4, "A Trip Through the Earth" Transparency 65, "Layers of the Atmosphere"
ELL Provides multiple strategies for English language learners **GRSW** Provides worksheets to promote student comprehension of content **RCA** Provides strategies to improve science reading skills	**SE** Chapter 13 Study Guide/Assessment, pp. 457–459 **PA** Chapter 13 Assessment, pp. 41–43 **CUT** Chapter 13 Test, pp. 64–67 **CTB** Chapter 13 Test **PHAS** Provides standardized test preparation	Chapter 13 Computer Test Bank, Chapter 13 Test

GRSW Guided Reading and Study Workbook
ISAB Inquiry Skills Activity Book
LM Laboratory Manual

PA Performance Assessment
PHAS Prentice Hall Assessment System
PLM Probeware Lab Manual

RCA Reading in the Content Area
SE Student Edition

TE Teacher's Edition
UR Unit Resources

Student Edition Activities Planner

ACTIVITY	Time (minutes)	Materials *Quantities for one work group*	Skills
Section 1			
Discover, p. 434	15	**Consumable** modeling clay, short candle, matches **Nonconsumable** aluminum pie pan, small glass jar, stopwatch or watch with second hand, large glass jar	Inferring
Try This, p. 436	10	**Consumable** limewater, straw **Nonconsumable** glass	Developing Hypotheses
Real World Lab, pp. 438–439	20,10,10, 10,10	**Consumable** coffee filters **Nonconsumable** vacuum cleaner with intake hose (1 per class), rubber band, thermometer, low-power microscope, computer (optional)	Measuring, Interpreting Data
Section 2			
Discover, p. 440	10	**Consumable** modeling clay, aluminum pan, candle, matches **Nonconsumable** glass jar, oven mitt	Observing
Sharpen Your Skills, p. 442	10	No special materials are required.	Predicting
Science at Home, p. 443	home	**Nonconsumable** flashlight	Observing
Section 3			
Discover, p. 445	10	**Consumable** balloon **Nonconsumable** balance	Drawing Conclusions
Try This, p. 447	15	**Consumable** water, long straw, modeling clay **Nonconsumable** 2-liter soda bottle	Inferring
Skills Lab, pp. 448–449	40,10,10	**Consumable** large rubber balloon, white glue, 12- to 15-cm drinking straw, modeling clay, 10 cm x 25 cm cardboard strip, tape **Nonconsumable** blunt scissors, wide-mouthed glass jar, rubber band, metric ruler, pencil	Measuring, Observing, Inferring
Science at Home, p. 450	home	**Consumable** tap water **Nonconsumable** glass, piece of heavy cardboard	Communicating
Section 4			
Discover, p. 451	10	**Nonconsumable** heavy rubber band, plastic bag, wide-mouthed glass jar	Predicting

A list of all materials required for the Student Edition activities can be found on pages T43–T49. You can obtain information about ordering materials by calling 1-800-848-9500 or by accessing the Science Explorer internet site at **http://www.phschool.com**.

Texas Essential Knowledge and Skills

(6.1) Scientific processes. The student conducts field and laboratory investigations using safe, environmentally appropriate, and ethical practices. *(Sections 1, 2)*

The student is expected to:

(A) demonstrate safe practices during field and laboratory investigations; and

(B) make wise choices in the use and conservation of resources and the disposal or recycling of materials.

(6.2) Scientific processes. The student uses scientific inquiry methods during field and laboratory investigations. *(Project; Sections 1, 2, 3, 4)*

The student is expected to:

(A) plan and implement investigative procedures including asking questions, formulating testable hypotheses, and selecting and using equipment and technology;

(B) collect data by observing and measuring;

(C) analyze and interpret information to construct reasonable explanations from direct and indirect evidence;

(D) communicate valid conclusions; and

(E) construct graphs, tables, maps, and charts using tools including computers to organize, examine, and evaluate data.

(6.3) Scientific processes. The student uses critical thinking and scientific problem solving to make informed decisions. *(Sections 2, 4)*

The student is expected to:

(D) evaluate the impact of research on scientific thought, society, and the environment; and

(E) connect Grade 6 science concepts with the history of science and contributions of scientists.

(6.4) Scientific processes. The student knows how to use a variety of tools and methods to conduct science inquiry. *(Project; Sections 1, 3)*

The student is expected to:

(A) collect, analyze, and record information using tools including beakers, petri dishes, meter sticks, graduated cylinders, weather instruments, timing devices, hot plates, test tubes, safety goggles, spring scales, magnets, balances, microscopes, telescopes, thermometers, calculators, field equipment, compasses, computers, and computer probes; and

(B) identify patterns in collected information using percent, average, range, and frequency.

(6.14) Science concepts. The student knows the structures and functions of Earth systems. *(Project; Sections 1, 2, 3, 4)*

The student is expected to:

(C) describe components of the atmosphere, including oxygen, nitrogen, and water vapor, and identify the role of atmospheric movement in weather change.

Take It to the Net

 Interactive text at www.phschool.com

Science Explorer comes alive with iText.

- **Complete student text** is accessible from any computer with Internet access or a CD-ROM drive.

- **Animations, simulations, and videos** enhance student understanding and retention of concepts.

- **Self-tests and online study tools** assess student understanding.

- **Teacher management tools** help you make the most of this valuable resource.

STAY CURRENT with **SCIENCE NEWS**®

Find out the latest research and information about weather and climate at **www.phschool.com**.

Go to **www.phschool.com**. Select Texas on the navigation bar. Click on the Science icon. Then click on <u>Science Explorer</u> under PH@school.

Watching the Weather

TEKS: 6.2B, C, D, E; 6.4B; 6.14C

Most people make observations about the weather almost every day of their lives, but they might not be very aware of specific weather conditions and how they change. Of course they notice when a storm is raging, but they might not notice the red clouds at sunset that may indicate a storm is coming. Most students may not think much about the conditions that make up the weather. If they think about the weather at all, they may just think of it as good or bad.

Purpose In this project, students will become more aware of the weather and the variables such as temperature, precipitation, and wind speed that make up weather conditions. Students also will develop ways of observing weather variables.

Skills Focus Students will be able to

◆ design and implement a plan for observing and recording daily weather conditions;

◆ look for patterns in their observations that will help them understand the weather and how it changes;

◆ create data tables and other means of displaying their observations for the rest of the class.

Project Time Line The entire project will take a minimum of two weeks. The longer students make and record weather observations, the more likely they are to see trends in their data. On the first day, allow class time for introducing the project and brainstorming how students can use their senses to describe the weather. Students should decide as soon as possible which weather variables they will observe and how they will observe them. Students also must devise a way to record their observations. Additional class time will be necessary during the two-week period to monitor students' progress and give extra guidance to students who are having difficulty. At the end of the project, students will need time to review and organize their data and present their results to the rest of the class. For more detailed information on

CHAPTER **13** Earth's Atmosphere

WEB ACTIVITY www.phschool.com

SECTION 1 The Air Around You
Discover How Long Will the Candle Burn?
Real-World Lab How Clean Is the Air?

SECTION 2 Air Quality
Discover What's On the Jar?

SECTION 3 Air Pressure
Discover Does Air Have Mass?
Skills Lab Working Under Pressure

SECTION 4 Layers of the Atmosphere
Discover Is Air There?

432

planning and supervising the chapter project, see Chapter 13 Project Teacher Notes, pages 90–91 in Unit 4 Resources.

Suggested Shortcuts To reduce the amount of time students spend on the project, you may assign each student or group of students just one weather variable, such as temperature or precipitation, to monitor. Then, at the end of the project, students can pool their results and the whole class can work together to look for patterns in the data.

Possible Materials Each student will need a log for recording his or her observations, but no other materials or equipment are needed. In fact, you should stress to students that they are to rely only on their senses and not instruments such as thermometers or wind vanes. However, students will need to depend on various materials in their environment, such as the school flag or the clothes people are wearing, to observe weather conditions. Urge students to be creative in the materials they use for their observations. Smoke rising from chimneys, for

CHAPTER 13 PROJECT

Watching the Weather

The air is cool and clear—just perfect for a trip in a hot-air balloon. As you rise, a fresh breeze begins to move you along. Where will it take you? Hot-air balloon pilots need to know about the weather to plot their course.

In this chapter, you will learn about the air around you. As you learn about the atmosphere, you will use your senses to collect information about weather conditions. Even without scientific instruments it is possible to make many accurate observations about the weather.

Your Goal To observe weather conditions without using instruments and to look for hints about tomorrow's weather in the weather conditions today.

Your completed project must
- include a plan for observing and describing a variety of weather conditions over a period of two to three weeks
- show your observations in a daily weather log
- display your findings about weather conditions

Get Started Begin by discussing what weather conditions you can observe. Brainstorm how to use your senses to describe the weather. For example, can you describe the wind speed by observing the school flag? Can you describe the temperature based on what clothes you need to wear outside? Be creative.

Check Your Progress You'll be working on this project as you study this chapter. To keep your project on track, look for Check Your Progress boxes at the following points.

Section 1 Review, page 437: Collect and record observations.
Section 4 Review, page 456: Look for patterns in your data.

Present Your Project At the end of the chapter (page 459), use your weather observations to prepare a display for the class.

Hot-air balloons soar into the atmosphere at a balloon festival in Snowmass, Colorado.

TEKS

In addition to process TEKS, this chapter addresses these concept TEKS as they relate to the chapter's topics.

(6.14) The student knows the structures and functions of Earth systems.
The student is expected to:
(C) describe components of the atmosphere, including oxygen, nitrogen, and water vapor, and identify the role of atmospheric movement in weather change.

433

---

example, can reveal the direction and speed of the wind as well as flags flying from poles can.

Launching the Project To help students start thinking of weather variables they might observe, hand out copies of newspaper weather reports. On the chalkboard, have a volunteer list the weather variables given in the reports, such as temperature, humidity, barometric pressure, and wind speed and direction. Then challenge students to think of ways these weather variables could be observed without instruments. For example, ask: **If a thin skin of ice forms on puddles during the day, what does that tell you about the temperature?** *(It has fallen below the freezing point of water.)* **If the school flag is flying straight out from its pole, what does that tell you about the wind?** *(It is blowing at a high speed.)* Urge students to think of other observations that could give them information about weather conditions.

Program Resources

- **Unit 4 Resources** Chapter 13 Project Teacher Notes, pp. 90–91; Chapter 13 Project Overview and Worksheets, pp. 92–95

Media and Technology

 Student Edition on Audio CD
English-Spanish, Chapter 13

WEB ACTIVITY **www.phschool.com**

You will find an Internet activity, chapter self-tests for students, and links to other chapter topics at this site.

433

TEKS: 6.1A; 6.2A, B, C, D, E; 6.4A; 6.14C

Objectives

After completing the lesson, students will be able to
◆ state how the atmosphere is important to living things;
◆ identify the gases that are present in Earth's atmosphere.

1 Engage/Explore

Activating Prior Knowledge

Ask students to recall the fire triangle, which many will have learned about in fire safety demonstrations. After drawing a large triangle on the chalkboard, ask: **What is the fire triangle?** (*A triangle representing the three components needed for fire to burn: fuel, heat, and air*) As students explain, label the sides of the triangle on the chalkboard. Then relate the fire triangle to the composition of air by asking: **What is in air that fire needs to burn?** (*oxygen*) Point out that living things also need oxygen, and oxygen is just one of the components of air they will learn about in this section.

⋯⋯⋯ DISCOVER ⋯⋯⋯

Skills Focus inferring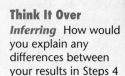
Materials *modeling clay, aluminum pie pan, short candle, matches, small glass jar, stopwatch or watch with second hand, large glass jar*
Time 15 minutes
Tips You can use beakers instead of jars for this activity. You may wish to have students practice using stopwatches before they begin the activity.
Expected Outcome Students should observe that the candle quickly burns out under the small jar and that it burns somewhat longer under the large jar.
Think It Over The gas needed for the candle to burn is oxygen. The candle burned longer under the large jar because the large jar contained more oxygen.

434

DISCOVER ⋯⋯⋯⋯⋯⋯⋯⋯⋯⋯ ACTIVITY

How Long Will the Candle Burn?

1. Put on your goggles.

2. Stick a small piece of modeling clay onto an aluminum pie pan. Push a short candle into the clay. Carefully light the candle.

3. Hold a small glass jar by the bottom. Lower the mouth of the jar over the candle until the jar rests on the pie pan. As you do this, start a stopwatch or note where the second hand is on a clock.

4. Watch the candle carefully. How long does the flame burn?

5. Wearing an oven mitt, remove the jar. Relight the candle and then repeat Steps 3 and 4 with a larger jar.

Think It Over
Inferring How would you explain any differences between your results in Steps 4 and 5?

GUIDE FOR READING

◆ How is the atmosphere important to living things?
◆ What gases are present in Earth's atmosphere?

Reading Tip Before you read, preview Figure 2. As you read, write a sentence about each of the major gases in the atmosphere.

Key Terms weather
• atmosphere • ozone
• water vapor

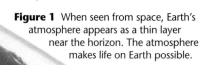

A s you walk home from school, the air is warm and still. The sky is full of thick, dark clouds. In the distance you see a bright flash. A few seconds later, you hear a crack of thunder. As you turn the corner onto your street, raindrops start to fall. You begin to run and reach your home just as the downpour begins. That was close! From the shelter of the entrance you pause to catch your breath and watch the storm.

Importance of the Atmosphere

Does the weather where you live change frequently, or is it fairly constant from day to day? **Weather** is the condition of Earth's atmosphere at a particular time and place. But what is the atmosphere? Earth's **atmosphere** (AT muh sfeer) is the layer of gases that surrounds the planet. To understand the relative size of the atmosphere, imagine that the planet Earth is the size of an apple.

Figure 1 When seen from space, Earth's atmosphere appears as a thin layer near the horizon. The atmosphere makes life on Earth possible.

434

READING STRATEGIES

Reading Tip Make sure students understand how the two parts of Figure 2 are related by pointing out that the table shows the gases that make up the tiny wedge of the circle that is not nitrogen or oxygen. After students have read the section and written their sentences, suggest that they form pairs, read their sentences to each other, and try to identify which gas each sentence describes. Also urge them to work together to resolve any factual errors they detect in each other's sentences. Possible student sentences include the following: The most abundant gas in air is nitrogen. Air is 21 percent oxygen.

Study and Comprehension Before students read the section, have them use the main headings and subheadings to make an outline. Then, as they read the section, have them write down at least one important fact under each heading on their outline.

If you breathe on the apple, a thin film of water will form on its surface. Earth's atmosphere is like that water on the apple—a thin layer of gases on Earth's surface.

Earth's atmosphere makes conditions on Earth suitable for living things. The atmosphere contains oxygen and other gases that you and other living things need to live. In turn, living things affect the atmosphere. The atmosphere is constantly changing, with atoms and molecules of gases moving around the globe and in and out of living things, the land, and the water.

Living things also need warmth and liquid water. By trapping energy from the sun, the atmosphere keeps most of Earth's surface warm enough for water to exist as a liquid. In addition, Earth's atmosphere protects living things from dangerous radiation from the sun. It also prevents Earth's surface from being hit by most meteoroids, or chunks of rock from outer space.

☑ *Checkpoint* *What would conditions on Earth be like without the atmosphere?*

Composition of the Atmosphere

The atmosphere is made up of a mixture of atoms and molecules of different kinds of gases. An atom is the smallest unit of a chemical element that can exist by itself. Molecules are made up of two or more atoms. **Earth's atmosphere is made up of nitrogen, oxygen, carbon dioxide, water vapor, and many other gases, as well as particles of liquids and solids.**

Nitrogen As you can see in Figure 2, nitrogen is the most abundant gas in the atmosphere. It makes up a little more than three fourths of the air we breathe. Each nitrogen molecule consists of two nitrogen atoms.

Gases in Dry Air

Nitrogen (78%)   Oxygen (21%)   All other gases (1%)

Other Gases	Percentage by Volume
Argon	0.93
Carbon dioxide	0.036
Neon	0.0018
Helium	0.00052
Methane	0.00015
Krypton	0.00011
Hydrogen	0.00005

Figure 2 Dry air in the lower atmosphere always has the same composition of gases.
Interpreting Data What two gases make up most of the air?

Program Resources

◆ **Unit 4 Resources** 13-1 Lesson Plan, p. 97; 13-1 Section Summary, p. 98
◆ **Guided Reading and Study Workbook** 13-1

Media and Technology

 Transparencies "Gases in Dry Air," Transparency 62

CONNECTION

The word *atmosphere* comes from two Greek words: *atmos,* meaning "vapor," and *sphaira,* meaning "ball," or "globe." So the atmosphere is the vapors or gases surrounding a globe—in this case, Earth.

In Your Journal

As you read this chapter, write down all the words that end in *-sphere*. Look up the roots of each word in a dictionary. How does knowing the roots of each word help you understand its meaning?

Answers to Self-Assessment

☑ *Checkpoint*

Water could not exist as a liquid on Earth's surface. Earth would also be exposed to meteoroids and dangerous radiation from the sun. There would be no life on Earth without the oxygen and other gases that living things need.

Caption Question

Figure 2 Nitrogen and oxygen

2 *Facilitate*

Importance of the Atmosphere

Language Arts

CONNECTION

Point out that many scientific terms are based on Greek words. Ask: **Why do you think English borrowed many scientific terms from Greek?** *(The Greeks were among the first Western people to study and write about the natural world.*

In Your Journal Other words ending in *-sphere* are terms for the layers of the atmosphere. For each term, have students write the meaning of the prefix. **learning modality: verbal**

Composition of the Atmosphere

Building Inquiry Skills: Making Models

Earth's atmosphere is composed largely of just a few gases, but even gases present in small amounts may be important to life. Also, the gases in Earth's atmosphere are present in the same proportions everywhere below an elevation of about 80 km. To reinforce these concepts, invite students to explain how a cake models the composition of the atmosphere. Provide a simple cake recipe first. Ask: **In what ways are the ingredients in a cake like the gases in Earth's atmosphere?** *(A cake is made up largely of just a few ingredients, especially flour. Ingredients, such as baking powder, included in small amounts may be essential for the cake. The ingredients in the cake are usually in the same proportions.)* **learning modality: logical/mathematical**

Ongoing Assessment

Oral Presentation Call on students at random to state ways that the atmosphere contributes to life on Earth.

Composition of the Atmosphere, continued

Integrating Life Science

The text gives just a short summary of the nitrogen cycle. Divide the class into groups and challenge each group to research the nitrogen cycle further and then make an illustrated flowchart of it. Each student in the group should take responsibility for learning about and illustrating one part of the cycle. Urge groups to share their flowcharts and work together to resolve any discrepancies. Display their best efforts in the classroom. **cooperative learning**

Building Inquiry Skills: Inferring

Materials *tall glass jar, large cake pan, clean steel wool, water, tape*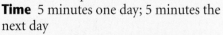

Time 5 minutes one day; 5 minutes the next day

Estimate the amount of oxygen in the atmosphere by having students follow these instructions: Fill a cake pan almost full of water. Push steel wool down into the bottom of a tall glass jar so it will not fall out when the jar is turned over. (**CAUTION:** Remind students to handle glass carefully.) Fill the jar with water, cover the mouth with a hand, and place the jar upside down in the cake pan. Remove the hand and tilt the jar slightly to let out enough water so that the water level in the jar is just above the water level in the pan. Mark the water level in the jar with a piece of tape and leave the jar where it is. Have students check the water level the next day. It should be about one fifth higher than it was. Explain that oxygen in the air combines with iron in steel wool to form rust. Ask: **From this experiment, how can you tell how much oxygen there is in air?** *(About one fifth of the air is used up, so the air must be about one fifth oxygen.)*
learning modality: logical/ mathematical

Breathe In, Breathe Out ACTIVITY

How can you detect carbon dioxide in the air you exhale?

1. Put on your goggles.
2. Fill a glass or beaker halfway with limewater.

3. Using a straw, slowly blow air through the limewater for about a minute. **CAUTION:** *Do not suck on the straw or drink the limewater.*
4. What happens to the limewater?

Developing Hypotheses What do you think would happen if you did the same experiment after jogging for 10 minutes? If you tried this, what might the results tell you about exercise and carbon dioxide?

INTEGRATING LIFE SCIENCE

Nitrogen is essential to living things. Proteins and other complex chemical substances in living things contain nitrogen. You and all other organisms must have nitrogen in order to grow and to repair body cells.

Most living things cannot obtain nitrogen directly from the air. Instead, some bacteria convert nitrogen into substances called nitrates. Plants then absorb the nitrates from the soil and use them to make proteins. To obtain proteins, animals must eat plants or other animals.

Oxygen Most oxygen molecules have two oxygen atoms. Even though oxygen is the second-most abundant gas in the atmosphere, it makes up less than one fourth of the volume. Plants and animals take oxygen directly from the air and use it to release energy from food in a usable form.

Oxygen is also involved in other important processes. Any fuel you can think of, from the gasoline in a car to the candles on a birthday cake, uses oxygen as it burns. Without oxygen, a fire will go out. Burning uses oxygen rapidly. During other processes, oxygen is used slowly. For example, steel in cars and other objects reacts slowly with oxygen to form iron oxide, or rust.

Have you ever noticed a pungent smell in the air after a thunderstorm? This is the odor of ozone, which forms when lightning interacts with oxygen in the air. **Ozone** is a form of oxygen that has three oxygen atoms in each molecule instead of the usual two.

Carbon Dioxide Each molecule of carbon dioxide has one atom of carbon and two atoms of oxygen. Even though the atmosphere contains only a small amount of carbon dioxide, it is essential to life. Plants must have carbon dioxide to produce food. Animals, on the other hand, give off carbon dioxide as a waste product.

When fuels such as coal and gasoline are burned, they release carbon dioxide. Burning these fuels increases the amount of carbon dioxide in the atmosphere. Rising carbon dioxide levels may be raising Earth's temperature.

Figure 3 To burn, these candles need oxygen, one of the gases in the atmosphere. *Predicting What would happen if the candles used up all of the oxygen around them?*

436

Other Gases Oxygen and nitrogen together make up 99 percent of dry air. Carbon dioxide and argon make up most of the other one percent. The remaining gases are called trace gases because only small amounts of them are present.

Water Vapor The composition of the air discussed so far has been for dry air. In reality, air is not dry because it contains water vapor. **Water vapor** is water in the form of a gas. Water vapor is invisible— it is not the same thing as steam, which is made up of tiny droplets of liquid water. Each water molecule contains two atoms of hydrogen and one atom of oxygen.

The amount of water vapor in the air varies greatly from place to place and from time to time. Air above a desert or polar ice sheet may contain almost no water vapor. In tropical rain forests, on the other hand, as much as five percent of the air may be water vapor.

Water vapor plays an important role in Earth's weather. Clouds form when water vapor condenses out of the air to form tiny droplets of liquid water or crystals of ice. If these droplets or crystals become large enough, they can fall as rain or snow.

Particles Pure air contains only gases. But pure air exists only in laboratories. In the real world, air also contains tiny solid and liquid particles of dust, smoke, salt, and other chemicals. Sometimes you can see particles in the air around you, but most of them are too small to see.

Figure 4 This lush vegetation grows in a rain forest in Costa Rica. The percentage of water vapor in the air in a rain forest may be as high as five percent.

Section 1 Review

1. Describe two ways in which the atmosphere is important to life on Earth.
2. What are the four most common gases in dry air?
3. Why are the amounts of gases in the atmosphere usually shown as percentages of dry air?
4. **Thinking Critically** **Applying Concepts** How would the amount of carbon dioxide in the atmosphere change if there were no plants? If there were no animals?

Check Your Progress CHAPTER PROJECT
Have you determined *how*, *where*, and *when*, you will make your observations? Organize a notebook to record them. Think of ways to compare weather conditions from day to day. Make your observations without weather instruments or TV weather reports. (*Hint:* You can estimate how much of the sky is covered by clouds.) For your own safety, do not try to make observations during storms.

Media and Technology

Earth Science Videodisc
Unit 2, Side 2, "Air Today, Gone Tomorrow"

Chapter 2

Answers to Self-Assessment

Caption Question

Figure 3 Their flames would go out.

Program Resources

◆ **Unit 4 Resources** 13-1 Review and Reinforce, p. 99; 13-1 Enrich, p. 100

Skills Focus developing hypotheses
Materials *glass, limewater, straw*
Time 10 minutes
Tips Make sure students are careful not to splash or ingest any of the limewater.
Expected Outcome Students should observe that the limewater becomes cloudy when they blow into it because of carbon dioxide in their breath. After exercise, more carbon dioxide is exhaled, causing the limewater to get cloudier.
Extend Invite students to detect carbon dioxide in carbonated water by adding some of it to the limewater. **learning modality: kinesthetic**

3 Assess

Section 1 Review Answers

1. *Any two:* Provides oxygen and other gases living things need, traps energy from the sun to keep Earth's surface warm, and protects from meteoroids and radiation from the sun
2. Nitrogen, oxygen, argon, carbon dioxide
3. Because the amount of water vapor in air varies greatly
4. Without plants there would be less oxygen and more carbon dioxide; without animals there would be less carbon dioxide and more oxygen.

Check Your Progress CHAPTER PROJECT
Encourage students to observe several different weather variables. They should record the date, time, and place of each observation and also any unusual weather events, such as violent storms.

Performance Assessment

Writing Have students write a paragraph identifying the three most important gases in air for living things, the percentage of each, and why the gas is important.

437

How Clean Is the Air?

Preparing for Inquiry

Key Concept The number of particles in air is affected by the weather.

Skills Objectives Students will be able to
- measure the number of particles in samples collected from the air;
- interpret how the number of particles is affected by weather factors.

Time 20 minutes the first day; 10 minutes a day for four days

Advance Planning If possible, students should collect particle samples outside. If they do, the vacuum cleaner may need an extension cord. However, they should not collect samples outside in wet weather. Instead, have students collect the samples as soon as possible after a rainfall. If you use only one vacuum cleaner, plan sufficient time for each group of students to use it. **Computer use is optional.**

Alternative Materials A portable vacuum cleaner is easier to carry outside than a regular vacuum cleaner. Instead of coffee filters, you can use paper towels for filters, but they are less effective because they let more particles pass through. Avoid using facial tissues because they are too fragile.

Guiding Inquiry

Invitation To help students focus on the key concept, ask: **What does air contain besides gases?** *(particles)* **How do you think weather conditions might affect the number of particles in the air?** *(Rain might wash particles out of the air, and wind might either stir them up or blow them away.)* Save their predictions so students can compare them with their results.

Introducing the Procedure

Have students read through the complete procedure and copy the data table in their notebook. Then ask: **Why do people in some occupations, such as wood-working, wear protective masks?**

How Clean Is the Air?

Sometimes you can actually see the atmosphere! How? Since air is normally transparent, it can only be visible because it contains particles. In this activity, you will use a vacuum cleaner to gather particles from the air.

Problem

How do weather factors affect the number of particles in the air?

Skills Focus

measuring, interpreting data

Materials

coffee filters
rubber band
thermometer
computer (optional)
low-power microscope
vacuum cleaner with intake hose (1 per class)

Procedure

1. Predict what factors will affect the number of particles you collect. How might different weather factors affect your results?

2. In your notebook or on the computer, make a data table like the one below.

3. Place the coffee filter over the nozzle of the vacuum cleaner hose. Fasten the coffee filter securely to the hose with a rubber band. Draw a circle over the filter to show the area over the vacuum nozzle.

4. You will take air samples in the same place each day for five days. If possible, find a place outdoors. Otherwise, you can run the vacuum cleaner out a classroom window. **CAUTION:** *Do not use the vacuum cleaner outdoors on wet or rainy days.* If it is wet or rainy, collect the sample as soon as possible after it stops raining.

5. Hold the vacuum nozzle at least one meter above the ground each time you use the vacuum. Turn on the vacuum. Run the vacuum for 30 minutes.

DATA TABLE

Date and Time	Temperature	Amount of Precipitation	Wind Direction	Wind Speed	Number of Particles

438

(Because they work where there are high levels of particles in the air, and protective masks trap the particles so they do not breathe them in) Mention some devices students may be familiar with, including motor vehicles and furnaces, that have filters to trap particles in the air that flows through them. Tell students that in this lab they will trap particles in the air by running a vacuum cleaner with a filter over the end of the hose.

Troubleshooting the Experiment

- If possible, have students run the vacuum cleaner for 30 minutes each time. However, 20 minutes each time may be enough.

Media and Technology

Lab Activity Videotapes
Grade 6, Tape 4

6. While the vacuum is running, observe the weather conditions. Measure the temperature. Estimate the amount of precipitation, if any, since the previous observation. Note the direction from which the wind, if any, is blowing. Also note whether the wind is heavy, light, or calm. Record your observations.

7. After 30 minutes, turn off the vacuum. Remove the coffee filter from the nozzle. Label the filter with the place, time, and date.

8. Place the coffee filter on the stage of a microscope (40 power). Be sure that the part of the filter that was over the vacuum nozzle is directly under the microscope lens. Without moving the coffee filter, count all the particles you see. Record the number in your data table.

9. Repeat Steps 3–8 each clear day.

Analyze and Conclude

1. Was there a day of the week when you collected more particles?

2. What factors changed during the week that could have caused changes in the particle count?

3. Did the weather have any effect on your day-to-day results? If so, which weather factor do you think was most important?

4. Make a list of some possible sources of the particles you collected. Are these sources natural, or did the particles come from manufactured products?

5. How could you improve your method to get more particles out of the air?

6. **Apply** Identify areas in or around your school where there may be high levels of dust and other particles. What can people do to protect themselves in these areas?

Design an Experiment
Do you think time of day will affect the number of particles you collect? Develop a hypothesis and a plan for testing it. Could you work with other classes to get data at different times of the day? Before carrying out your plan, get your teacher's approval.

Sample Data Table

Date and Time	Temp.	Amt. of Precipitation	Wind Direction	Wind Speed	# of Particles
Oct. 1, 2 P.M.	18°C	none	SW	calm	60
Oct. 2, 2 P.M.	19°C	none	SW	light breeze	55
Oct. 3, 2 P.M.	11°C	1 cm	W	moderate wind	18
Oct. 4, 2 P.M.	12°C	5 cm	W	strong wind	10
Oct. 5, 2 P.M.	13°C	5 cm	W	strong wind	11

Program Resources
◆ **Unit 4 Resources** Chapter 13 Real-World Lab blackline masters, pp. 113–115

Safety
Emphasize the importance of not using the vacuum cleaner around water because of electrical shock. Review the safety guidelines in Appendix A.

◆ Because a vacuum cleaner is noisy, it may be necessary to run it outside of class time.

◆ Explain the importance of controlling other variables besides weather conditions that might influence the number of particles collected, such as proximity to a dusty playing field. Stress that samples should be taken in the same place each day to help control these other variables.

Expected Outcome
Using the microscope, students should be able to see and count the particles collected on the filters. The number of particles may vary greatly from one sample to another.

Analyze and Conclude
1. The particle count may vary from day to day depending on human activities and the weather.

2. The particle count is likely to be higher later in the week as particles given off by motor vehicles and factories and produced by other human activities accumulate in the air. Changing weather conditions also may cause changes in the particle count.

3. Weather factors most likely to affect day-to-day results are wind speed and recent precipitation.

4. Particles can come from many different sources. Natural sources include flowering plants, bare ground, and forest fires. Manufactured products that produce particles include motor vehicles, factories, and power plants.

5. Possible ways to get more particles out of the air include using a more powerful vacuum cleaner or a vacuum cleaner with a wider hose, running the vacuum cleaner longer each time, and using a finer filter.

6. The cafeteria, gymnasium, and shop may have more particles than the classrooms. Playing fields and parking lots may have more particles than lawn areas. Wearing dust masks and using special air filters can help protect people from high levels of particles in the air.

Extending the Inquiry

Design an Experiment Students may hypothesize that more particles will be collected later in the day as particles accumulate in the air. They can test their hypothesis by comparing samples collected at different times of day.

SECTION 2 Air Quality

TEKS: 6.1B; 6.2B, C; 6.3D; 6.14C

Objectives

After completing the lesson, students will be able to

◆ name the main sources of air pollution;

◆ explain how photochemical smog and acid rain form.

1 Engage/Explore

Activating Prior Knowledge

Guide students in recalling weather reports they may have seen or heard that included an air quality index or pollen count. Alternatively, share copies of newspaper weather reports that include these measures. Then ask: **Why do weather reports include warnings about air pollution and pollen in the air?** *(Because high levels of pollution and pollen in the air can make people sick)* **What is the source of pollen in the air?** *(plants)* **What are some sources of pollution in the air?** *(cars and factories)*

········· DISCOVER ·········

Skills Focus observing
Materials *modeling clay, aluminum pan, candle, matches, glass jar*
Time 10 minutes
Tips Before students light their candles, be sure the candles are firmly in place in the modeling clay. When students put their jars near the flame, caution them to avoid touching the wax or wick.
Expected Outcome Students should see black powder collect on the part of the jar just above the flame. In addition to soot, students may see condensation form on the jar from water vapor in the air.
Think It Over The black powder on the jar is soot, which came from the incomplete burning of the wax candle.

SECTION 2 Air Quality

DISCOVER ·······················ACTIVITY

What's On the Jar?

1. Put on your goggles.
2. Put a small piece of modeling clay on an aluminum pan. Push a candle into the clay. Light the candle.
3. Wearing an oven mitt, hold a glass jar by the rim so that the bottom of the jar is just above the flame.

Think It Over
Observing What do you see on the jar? Where did it come from?

GUIDE FOR READING

◆ What are the main sources of air pollution?

◆ How do photochemical smog and acid rain form?

Reading Tip As you read, look for evidence to support this statement: Most air pollution is caused by human activities. What facts support this statement? What facts do not support it?

Key Terms pollutant
• photochemical smog
• temperature inversion
• acid rain

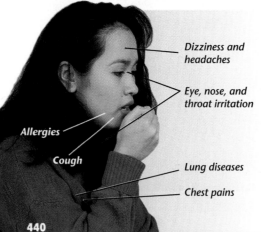

Allergies

Cough

Dizziness and headaches

Eye, nose, and throat irritation

Lung diseases

Chest pains

440

One hundred years ago, the city of London, England, was dark and dirty. Factories burned coal, and most houses were heated by coal. The air was full of soot. In 1905, the term *smog* was created by combining the words *smoke* and *fog* to describe this type of air pollution. Today, people in London burn much less coal. As a result, the air in London now is much cleaner than it was 100 years ago.

Air Pollution

As you are reading this, you are breathing without even thinking about it. Breathing brings air into your lungs, where the oxygen you need is taken into your body. You may also breathe in tiny particles or even a small amount of harmful gases. In fact, these particles and gases are a concern to people everywhere.

If you live in a large city, you probably already know what air pollution is. You may have noticed a brown haze or an unpleasant smell in the air. Even if you live far from a city, the air around you may be polluted. Harmful substances in the air, water, or soil are known as **pollutants**. Figure 5 shows some of the effects of air pollution on human health.

Figure 5 Air pollution can cause many different problems. Some air pollutants are natural, but most are caused by human activities. *Interpreting Photographs* What parts of the body are most affected by air pollution?

READING STRATEGIES

Reading Tip Evidence supporting the statement that air pollution is caused by human activities includes the fact that most air pollution is the result of burning fossil fuels. Evidence contradicting the statement includes the fact that many natural processes add particles to the air. Some particles from natural sources are ocean salt, molds, plant pollen, soil, and ashes from forest fires and volcanoes.

Program Resources

◆ **Unit 4 Resources** 13-2 Lesson Plan, p. 97; 13-2 Section Summary, p. 98
◆ **Guided Reading and Study Workbook** 13-2
◆ **Laboratory Manual** 13, "Examining Acid Rain"

Figure 6 These pollen grains from a ragweed flower have been greatly magnified to show detail. Pollen can cause people who are allergic to it to sneeze.

Some air pollution occurs naturally, but much of it is caused by human activities. **Most air pollution is the result of burning fossil fuels such as coal, oil, gasoline, and diesel fuel.** Almost half of the air pollution from human activities comes from cars and other motor vehicles. A little more than one fourth comes from factories and power plants that burn coal and oil. Burning fossil fuels produces a number of air pollutants, including particles and gases that can form smog and acid rain.

☑ *Checkpoint* *What are two sources of air pollution that you see every day?*

Particles

As you know, air contains particles along with gases. When you draw these particles deep into your lungs, the particles can be harmful. Particles in the air come from both natural sources and human activities.

Natural Sources Many natural processes add particles to the atmosphere. When ocean waves splash salt water against rocks, some of the water sprays into the air and evaporates. Tiny salt particles stay in the air. The wind blows particles of molds and plant pollen. Forest fires, soil erosion, and dust storms add particles to the atmosphere. Erupting volcanoes spew out clouds of dust and ashes along with poisonous gases.

 INTEGRATING HEALTH Even fairly clean air usually contains particles of dust and pollen. Figure 6 shows pollen, a fine, powdery material produced by many plants. The wind carries pollen not only to other plants, but also to people. One type of allergy, popularly called "hay fever," is caused by pollen from plants such as ragweed. Symptoms of hay fever include sneezing, a runny nose, red and itchy eyes, and headaches. Weather reports often include a "pollen count," which is the average number of pollen grains in a cubic meter of air.

Human Activities When people burn fuels such as wood and coal, particles made mostly of carbon enter the air. These particles of soot are what gives smoke its dark color. Farming and construction also release large amounts of soil particles into the air.

Figure 7 These people in Pontianak, Indonesia, are being given dust masks to protect them from smoke caused by widespread forest fires. *Inferring What effects do you think this smoke might have had on the people who live in this area?*

Chapter 13 **441**

2 Facilitate

Air Pollution

Demonstration

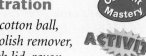

Materials *cotton ball, fingernail polish remover, glass jar with lid, rayon cloth, tape*

Time 5 minutes one day; 5 minutes the next day

Point out that air pollution is bad for clothing and other materials as well as for people. To show students the effect of air pollution on cloth, saturate a cotton ball with fingernail polish remover, which contains acetone, and place it in the bottom of a glass jar. Tape a small piece of rayon to the inside of the jar lid and put the lid on tightly. Place another small piece of rayon beside the jar and leave both overnight. The next day, invite students to compare the two pieces of cloth. Ask: **Why did the cloth in the jar weaken?** *(The fingernail polish produced acetone vapors that attacked fibers in the cloth.)* Add that similar vapors pollute the air over cities. **learning modality: tactile/kinesthetic**

Particles

 Integrating Health

Invite students to learn more about allergies such as hay fever by working in groups to conduct a survey. Each group member should ask family members, friends, and neighbors if they suffer from hay fever or other allergies. Then group members should pool their results and use the data to identify the frequency of such allergies. **cooperative learning**

Ongoing Assessment

Skills Check Have students make a concept map of particles found in the air, including sources and examples.

441

Smog

Predicting

Time 10 minutes
Expected Outcome The amount of pollutants may vary by time of day and day of week. Cars and trucks produce the most pollution during morning and evening rush hours, and factories and plants produce pollutants throughout the workday. Thus, pollution levels are likely to be higher late in the day and on Fridays after pollutants have accumulated.
Extend Have students predict how pollutants vary by season. **learning modality: logical/mathematical**

Temperature Inversion

 Integrating Chemistry

Materials *two small glass bottles, pan of hot water, bowl of ice, matches*
Time 10 minutes

Point out that smog is trapped near the ground when the air near the ground is cooler than the air above it. Demonstrate by placing a small glass bottle in a shallow pan of hot water and another in a bowl of ice. Then drop a smoking match into each bottle. Smoke will rise from the bottle of warm air but not from the bottle of cold air. Ask: **Why does smoke stay in the bottle of cold air?** (*Because cold air is denser than warm air and does not rise*) **learning modality: logical/mathematical**

Acid Rain

Inquiry Challenge

Materials *two saucers, two pennies, tap water, vinegar*
Time 10 minutes one day; 5 minutes the next day

Challenge small groups to brainstorm a way to use the materials to show the effects of acid rain on metal. (*The most likely way is to place each penny on a saucer, cover one penny with vinegar and the other with water, and let them stand overnight.*)
cooperative learning

Sharpen your Skills

Predicting

Are the amounts of pollutants in the air always at the same level, or do they change from time to time? At what time of the day do you think the major sources of air pollution—cars, trucks, power plants, and factories—might produce the most pollution? Overall, do you think there is more air pollution in the morning or in the evening? On Mondays or on Fridays? On what did you base your prediction?

Figure 8 Normally, pollutants rise high in the air and blow away (left). But during a temperature inversion, a layer of warm air traps pollutants close to the ground (right).

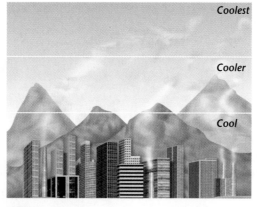

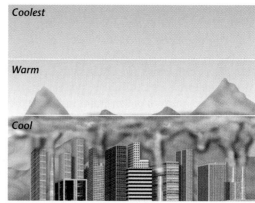

Smog

London-type smog forms when particles in coal smoke combine with water droplets in humid air. Fortunately, London-type smog is no longer common in the United States. Today sunny cities like Los Angeles often have another type of smog. The brown haze that forms in cities is called **photochemical smog**. The *photo-* in photochemical means "light." Photochemical smog is caused by the action of sunlight on chemicals.

INTEGRATING CHEMISTRY Photochemical smog is formed by a complex process. All fossil fuels contain hydrocarbons, which are substances composed of carbon and hydrogen. When fossil fuels are burned, some hydrocarbons are not burned completely and escape into the air. At the same time, the high temperatures that accompany burning cause some of the nitrogen in the air to react with oxygen to form nitrogen oxides. **The nitrogen oxides, hydrocarbons, and other air pollutants then react with one another in the presence of sunlight to form a mix of ozone and other chemicals called photochemical smog.** The ozone in photochemical smog irritates breathing passages, harms plants, and damages rubber, paint, and some plastics.

Temperature Inversion

Normally, air close to the ground is heated by Earth's surface. As the air warms, it rises into the cooler air above it. Pollutants are carried higher into the atmosphere where they blow away. But certain weather conditions cause a condition known as a temperature inversion. During a **temperature inversion,** a layer of warm air prevents the rising air from escaping. The polluted air is trapped and held close to Earth's surface. The smog becomes more concentrated and dangerous.

☑ *Checkpoint* *What happens during a temperature inversion?*

Background

Facts and Figures The 99.9% of the atmosphere that is made up of nitrogen, oxygen, and argon has remained relatively stable for the past 100 million years. Chemical interactions among fewer than 0.1% of molecules in the atmosphere are the cause of all the air quality problems facing us today, including smog and acid rain.

The average pH of rain water is about 5.6, which means that it is weakly acidic. As of 2000, the pH of acid rain in the United States can be as low as about 4.3. To put these values in perspective, consider that tomato juice has a pH of between 4.1 and 4.6, vinegar a pH of between 2.4 and 3.4, and battery acid a pH of 1.

Acid Rain

One result of air pollution is acid rain. The burning of coal that contains a lot of sulfur produces substances composed of oxygen and sulfur called sulfur oxides. **Acid rain forms when nitrogen oxides and sulfur oxides combine with water in the air to form nitric acid and sulfuric acid.**

Rain, sleet, snow, fog, and even dry particles carry these two acids from the air to trees, lakes, and buildings. Rain is naturally slightly acidic, but rain that contains more acid than normal is known as **acid rain.** Acid rain is sometimes strong enough to damage the surfaces of buildings and statues.

As Figure 9 shows, needle-leafed trees such as pines and spruce are especially sensitive to acid rain. It also harms lakes and ponds. Acid rain can make water so acidic that plants, amphibians, fish, and insects can no longer survive in it.

Improving Air Quality

The federal and state governments have passed a number of laws and regulations to reduce air pollution. For example, pollution-control devices are required equipment on cars. Factories and power plants must install filters in smokestacks to remove pollutants from smoke before they are released into the atmosphere.

Air quality in this country has improved over the past 30 years. The amounts of most major air pollutants have decreased. Newer cars cause less pollution than older models. Recently built power plants are less polluting than older power plants.

However, there are now more cars on the road and more power plants burning fossil fuels than in the past. Unfortunately, the air in many cities is still polluted. Many people think that stricter regulations are needed to control air pollution. Others argue that reducing air pollution is expensive.

Figure 9 This scientist is studying trees damaged by acid rain. Acid rain may make tree needles turn brown or fall off. Other factors, such as insects, disease, drought, or very cold weather, can also damage trees.

Section 2 Review

1. How is most air pollution produced?
2. Name two natural and two artificial sources of particles in the atmosphere.
3. How is photochemical smog formed? What kinds of harm does it cause?
4. What substances combine to form acid rain?
5. **Thinking Critically Inferring** Do you think that photochemical smog levels are higher during the winter or during the summer? Explain.

Science at Home

Air Particles It's easy to see particles in the air. Gather your family members in a dark room. Open a window shade or blind slightly, or turn on a flashlight. Can they see tiny particles suspended in the beam of light? Discuss with your family where the particles came from. What might be some natural sources? What might be some human sources?

Building Inquiry Skills: Inferring

Point out that nitrogen dioxide and sulfur dioxide emissions in the U.S. have decreased over the past 30 years. Ask: **How do you think the level of acid in rain has been affected by these trends in air pollutants?** *(Nitrogen dioxide and sulfur dioxide cause acid rain, so the amount of acid in rain probably has decreased as well.)* **learning modality: logical/mathematical**

3 Assess

Section 2 Review Answers

1. By the burning of fossil fuels
2. Natural: ocean salt, molds, plant pollen, forest fires, soil erosion, volcanoes; Artificial: burning of fossil fuels, farming, and construction
3. It forms when nitrogen oxides, hydrocarbons, and other pollutants react in the presence of sunlight. It can irritate breathing passages, harm plants, and damage rubber, paint, and some plastics.
4. Nitrogen oxides, sulfur oxides, and water in the air
5. During the summer, because the production of photochemical smog requires sunlight and the sun's rays are more direct and the hours of daylight are longer then

Science at Home

Materials *flashlight*
Tips Students will see more particles if they stir up dust first. Point out that most particles in the air are too small to be seen without a microscope. Natural sources include plant pollens and molds. Human sources include soot from motor vehicles and soil from farming and construction.

Performance Assessment

Writing Challenge students to write letters to a newspaper to raise peoples' awareness of the causes and dangers of air pollution.

Media and Technology

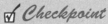

Earth Science Videodisc
Unit 6, Side 2, "Caution: Breathing May Be Hazardous to Your Health"

Chapter 8

Answers to Self-Assessment

☑ *Checkpoint*

A layer of warm air prevents cooler air below it from rising, trapping polluted air close to Earth's surface.

Program Resources

◆ **Unit 4 Resources** 13-2 Review and Reinforce, p. 103; 13-2 Enrich, p. 104

Cars and Clean Air

Purpose

To help students learn ways that pollution from cars can be reduced and make a reasonable judgment about the best ways to do this.

Panel Discussion

Time one day to prepare; 30 minutes for panel discussion

After students have read the feature, ask for volunteers to form a panel to discuss the issues. Have each panel member assume one of the following roles: a car manufacturer, a person who commutes 50 miles a day to work, a person who lives near a busy intersection, a lawmaker, and a public health official. Students should take the point of view of the individual they represent and present relevant facts and opinions for that individual. Following the panel discussion, take a class vote on which methods of reducing pollution seem most effective and whether the methods should be voluntary or enforced.

Extend Challenge students to learn about alternative means of transportation in their community and report on the costs and availability of each.

You Decide

1. Even the least polluting cars cause some air pollution, and there are more cars on the road each year. More cars also mean more traffic jams, which produce more pollution than does driving on the open road. Automobiles pollute the air with particles such as soot and gases that contribute to smog and acid rain.

2. Driving cars that are more efficient and produce less pollution, and driving less

3. Students should illustrate more than one way to help reduce pollution from cars. Their captions should demonstrate that they understand how the solutions address the problem.

Cars and Clean Air

New technology and strict laws have brought cleaner air to many American cities. But in some places the air is still polluted. Cars and trucks still cause about half the air pollution in cities. And there are more cars on the road every year!

Worldwide, there are about 500 million cars. More cars will mean more pollution and more traffic jams. Unfortunately, cars stuck in traffic produce three times as much pollution as cars on the open road. What can people do to reduce air pollution by cars?

The Issues

Can Cars Be Made To Pollute Less?

In the past 20 years, cars have become more fuel-efficient and pollution levels have been lowered. Now engineers are running out of ways to make cars run more efficiently and produce less pollution. But technology does offer other answers.

Some vehicles use fuels other than gasoline. For instance, natural gas can power cars and trucks. Burning natural gas produces less pollution than burning gasoline.

Battery-powered electric cars produce no air pollution. However, the electricity to charge the batteries often comes from power plants that burn oil or coal. So electric cars still produce some pollution indirectly. Car makers have produced a few electric cars, but they are expensive and can make only fairly short trips.

Should People Drive Less?

Many car trips are shorter than a mile—an easy distance for most people to walk. For longer trips, people might consider riding a bicycle. Many cars on the road carry just one person. Some people might consider riding with others in car pools or taking buses or subways.

Are Stricter Standards or Taxes the Answer?

Some state governments have led efforts to reduce pollution. The state of California, for example, has strict anti-pollution laws. These laws set standards for gradually reducing pollutants released by cars. Stricter laws might make some old cars illegal.

Another approach is to make driving more expensive so that people use their cars less. That might mean higher gasoline taxes or fees for using the roads at busy times.

You Decide

1. Identify the Problem
In your own words, explain why automobiles make it hard to improve air quality. What kinds of pollution are caused by automobiles?

2. Analyze the Options
What are some ways to reduce the pollution caused by cars? Should these actions be voluntary, or should governments require them?

3. Find a Solution
How would you encourage people to try to reduce the pollution from cars? Create a visual essay from newspaper and magazine clippings. Write captions to explain your solution.

Background

Young teens tend to see things in all-or-nothing terms. They may think that any method of reducing pollution from cars should be adopted and enforced. Help students appreciate that most methods of reducing pollution from cars have drawbacks by citing these two examples.

Catalytic converters convert unburned hydrocarbons in car exhaust into nonpoisonous gases. These devices have been required by law for many years on all new cars sold in the United States. However, catalytic converters also result in a higher production of sulfuric acid, which contributes to acid rain.

Cars that are more fuel-efficient burn less gas and produce fewer pollutants per mile driven. However, the number of cars on the road and the number of miles people drive every year are both increasing.

SECTION
3 Air Pressure

SECTION
3 Air Pressure

DISCOVER

ACTIVITY

Does Air Have Mass?

1. Use a balance to find the mass of a deflated balloon.

2. Blow up the balloon and tie the neck closed. Do you think the mass of the inflated balloon will differ from the mass of the deflated balloon?

3. Find the mass of the inflated balloon. Compare this mass to the mass of the deflated balloon. Was your prediction correct?

Think It Over
Drawing Conclusions Did the mass of the balloon change after it was inflated? What can you conclude about whether air has mass?

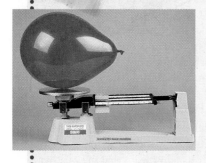

One of the best parts of eating roasted peanuts is opening the jar. When a jar of peanuts is "vacuum packed," most of the air is pumped out, creating low pressure inside. When you break the seal, the "whoosh" you hear is air from the outside rushing into the jar. The "whoosh" is the result of a difference in pressure between the outside of the jar and the inside.

Properties of Air

It may seem to you that air has no mass. However, air consists of atoms and molecules, which have mass. So air must have mass. **Because air has mass, it also has other properties, including density and pressure.**

Density The amount of mass in a given volume of air is its **density**. You can calculate density by dividing mass by volume.

$$Density = \frac{Mass}{Volume}$$

If there are more molecules in a given volume of air, the density is higher. If there are fewer molecules, the density is lower.

Pressure The force pushing on an area or surface is known as **pressure**. A denser substance has more mass per unit volume than a less dense one. So denser air exerts more pressure than less dense air.

To understand pressure, think of carrying a heavy backpack. The weight presses the straps into your shoulders just as the pack does to the hiker in the photo.

GUIDE FOR READING

◆ What are some of the properties of air?

◆ What instruments are used to measure air pressure?

◆ How does increasing altitude affect air pressure and density?

Reading Tip As you read this section, use the headings to make an outline about air pressure.

Key Terms density • pressure • air pressure • barometer • mercury barometer • aneroid barometer • altitude

445

SECTION
3 Air Pressure

TEKS: 6.2B, C, D, E; 6.4A; 6.14C

Objectives

After completing the lesson, students will be able to
◆ identify some of the properties of air;
◆ name instruments that are used to measure air pressure;
◆ explain how increasing altitude affects air pressure and density.

1 Engage/Explore

Activating Prior Knowledge

Introduce students to the concept of air pressure by asking: **Did your ears ever "pop" when you rode in an elevator or airplane?** *(Many students probably have had this experience.)* Explain that as one goes higher, the pressure of the air outside the body decreases while the pressure of the air inside the body, including the ears, stays the same. The popping sensation is air escaping from inside the ears into the throat to even out the pressure. Tell students they will learn more about air pressure and other properties of air in this section.

DISCOVER

Skills Focus drawing conclusions

ACTIVITY

Materials *balance, balloon*
Time 10 minutes
Tips You may want to review how to use the balance before students begin the activity. The larger the balloon, the greater the difference in mass will be. Inflatable balls may be substituted for balloons.
Expected Outcome The balloon should have a greater mass after it is inflated.
Think It Over Students should say that the mass of the balloon increased after it was inflated and conclude from this that air has mass.

2 Facilitate

Properties of Air

Including All Students

Materials *two sink plungers*
Time 5 minutes

To help students appreciate how much pressure air exerts, give pairs of students two sink plungers and show them how to put the plungers together by matching the ends. Then have the students try to pull the plungers apart. Relate this to air pressure by asking: **Why are the plungers hard to pull apart?** (*Because air is pressing on the outside of the two plungers and holding them together*) **learning modality: tactile/kinesthetic**

Measuring Air Pressure

Building Inquiry Skills: Predicting

Reinforce students' understanding of how a mercury barometer works by asking: **Why must there be a vacuum in the tube of a mercury barometer?** (*So the mercury can rise inside the tube*) **What do you predict would happen if the tube was filled with air?** (*The column of mercury would not rise as high because of the pressure from the air in the tube. The barometer would give an incorrect reading.*) **learning modality: verbal**

Real-Life Learning

Materials *copies of newspaper weather reports*
Time 15 minutes

Help students appreciate how barometer readings relate to weather. First, explain that the average air pressure worldwide is 29.9212 inches. A drop of less than an inch can be a sign of a major storm, and a rise of less than an inch a sign of fair weather. Then show students newspaper weather reports for several different days. Have them observe how changes in barometric pressure are related to weather conditions. **learning modality: logical/mathematical**

When you take off a backpack, it feels as if all the pressure has been taken off your shoulders. But has it? The weight of the column of air above you remains, as shown in Figure 10.

Air pressure is the result of the weight of a column of air pushing down on an area. The weight of the column of air above your desk is about the same as the weight of a large school bus!

So why doesn't air pressure crush your desk? The reason is that the molecules in air push in all directions—down, up, and sideways. So the air pushing down on the top of your desk is balanced by the air pushing up on the bottom of the desk.

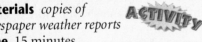

Figure 10 There is a column of air above you all the time. The weight of the air in the atmosphere causes air pressure.

Measuring Air Pressure

Have you ever heard a weather report say that the air pressure is falling? Falling air pressure usually indicates that a storm is approaching. Rising air pressure usually means that the weather is clearing. A **barometer** (buh RAHM uh tur) is an instrument that is used to measure changes in air pressure. **There are two kinds of barometers: mercury barometers and aneroid barometers.**

Mercury Barometers The first barometers invented were mercury barometers. Figure 11 shows how a mercury barometer works. A **mercury barometer** consists of a glass tube open at the bottom end and partially filled with mercury. The space in the tube above the mercury is almost a vacuum—it contains no air. The open end of the tube rests in a dish of mercury. The air pressure pushing down on the surface of the mercury in the dish is equal to the

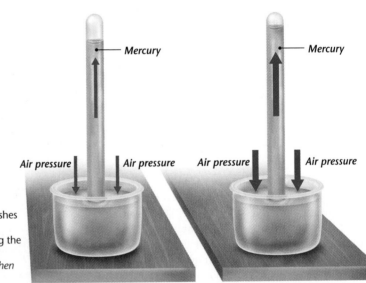
Mercury · Mercury · Air pressure · Air pressure · Air pressure · Air pressure

Figure 11 Air pressure pushes down on the surface of the mercury in the dish, causing the mercury in the tube to rise. *Predicting What happens when the air pressure increases?*

446

Background

History of Science The first mercury barometer was invented in 1643 by an Italian physicist named Evangelista Torricelli. Torricelli was studying why liquids rise only to a certain height in a column. Because mercury is so heavy, he thought it would rise to a lower height than water and be more convenient to study. He filled a long glass tube with mercury, blocked the open end with his finger, and turned the tube upside down in a container of mercury. The mercury in the glass tube went down to about 76 cm. Torricelli experimented with different-sized tubes, but the height of the mercury stayed the same. From this Torricelli concluded that the height of the mercury in the tube was directly related to the pressure of the air on the mercury in the container. Thus, he had invented a way to measure air pressure.

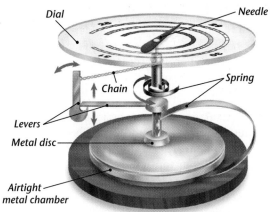

Dial

Needle

Chain

Spring

Levers

Metal disc

Airtight
metal chamber

Figure 12 Changes in air pressure cause the walls of the airtight metal chamber to flex in and out. The needle on the dial indicates the air pressure.

weight of the column of mercury in the tube. At sea level the mercury column is about 76 centimeters high, on average.

When the air pressure increases, it presses down more on the surface of the mercury. Greater air pressure forces the column of mercury higher. What will happen to the column of mercury if the air pressure decreases? The column will fall.

Aneroid Barometers If you have a barometer on a desk or wall at home, it is probably an aneroid barometer. The word *aneroid* means "without liquid." An **aneroid barometer** (AN uh royd) has an airtight metal chamber, as shown in Figure 12. The metal chamber is sensitive to changes in air pressure. When air pressure increases, the thin walls of the chamber are pushed in. When the pressure drops, the walls bulge out. The chamber is connected to a dial by a series of springs and levers. As the shape of the chamber changes, the needle on the dial moves.

Aneroid barometers are smaller than mercury barometers and don't contain a liquid. Therefore, they are portable and often more practical for uses such as airplane instrument panels.

Units of Air Pressure Weather reports use several different units for air pressure. Most weather reports for the general public use inches of mercury. For example, if the column of mercury in a mercury barometer is 30 inches high, the air pressure is "30 inches of mercury" or just "30 inches."

National Weather Service maps indicate air pressure in millibars. One inch of mercury equals approximately 33.87 millibars, so 30 inches of mercury equals approximately 1,016 millibars.

☑ *Checkpoint* *Name two common units used to measure air pressure.*

Soda-Bottle Barometer

Here's how to build a device that shows changes in air pressure.
1. Fill a 2-liter soda bottle one-half full with water.
2. Lower a long straw into the bottle so that the end of the straw is in the water. Seal the mouth of the bottle around the straw with modeling clay.
3. Squeeze the sides of the bottle. What happens to the level of the water in the straw?
4. Let go of the sides of the bottle. Watch the level of the water in the straw.

Inferring Explain your results in terms of air pressure.

Including All Students

Materials *calculator*
Time 10 minutes

Invite students who need additional challenges to do this activity. It will give them a better appreciation of how air pressure is measured. First, tell students that if you laid a quarter on a table, it would exert a pressure of 0.00013 kg per cm^2. Then say that the pressure exerted by the atmosphere at sea level is 1.03 kg per cm^2. Ask: **How many quarters would you need to stack on top of each other for the quarters to exert the same pressure as the air at sea level?** *(1.03 kg ÷ 0.00013 kg = 7,923)* **If six quarters are about 1 cm thick, how high would the stack of quarters be?** *(7,923 ÷ 6 = 1,321 cm, or about 1.3 km)* **learning modality: logical/mathematical**

TRY THIS

Skills Focus inferring
Materials *2-liter soda bottle, water, long straw, modeling clay*

Time 15 minutes
Tips Before students seal the mouth of the bottle with clay, make sure the straw is in the water but not touching the bottom of the bottle.
Expected Outcome When students squeeze the sides of the bottle, the water level rises in the straw. When they let go of the sides, the water level falls in the straw. Students should infer that the water rises in the straw because air pressure increases in the bottle when the sides of the bottle are squeezed.
Extend Ask: **What do you think would happen if you heated the air in the bottle?** *(The air would expand and make the water rise in the straw.)* **learning modality: logical/mathematical**

Media and Technology

 Transparencies "Measuring Air Pressure," Transparency 63

Answers to Self-Assessment

Caption Question

Figure 11 When the air pressure increases, the column of mercury in the tube of a mercury barometer goes up.

☑ *Checkpoint*

Two common units used to measure air pressure are inches and millibars.

Ongoing Assessment

Skills Check Challenge students to make a table comparing and contrasting mercury barometers and aneroid barometers.

Working Under Pressure

Preparing for Inquiry

Key Concept A flexible wall of a sealed container will expand and contract with changes in the pressure of the outside air.

Skills Objectives Students will be able to
◆ measure air pressure with a simple barometer that they construct;
◆ observe daily weather conditions;
◆ infer from their data the kinds of weather conditions that are associated with high and low air pressure.

Time 40 minutes the first day; 10 minutes each day for the next two days

Advance Planning You may wish to have students work in pairs for this activity, because it is easier for two people to assemble the barometer. If possible, bring a commercial aneroid barometer to class to familiarize students with air pressure readings before they begin the activity. You may want to leave the barometer so students can compare their readings with the readings on the commercial barometer. When students record weather conditions during the lab, at a minimum they should record whether the sky is cloudy or fair. You may want them to record additional factors, including temperature. If so, place an outdoor thermometer in a shady location where students can see it from the classroom.

Alternative Materials Students can use beakers instead of wide-mouthed glass jars, rubber dental dams instead of balloons, and rulers instead of cardboard strips.

Guiding Inquiry

Invitation Show students a commercial aneroid barometer and then ask: **How does the aneroid barometer work?** *(Changes in air pressure cause slight movements in or out of the walls of a box, and these movements are measured on a scale.)* Tell students that they will make a barometer that works the same way as a commercial aneroid barometer. However, their barometer will be less accurate.

Increasing Altitude

The air pressure at the top of Alaska's Mount McKinley—more than 6 kilometers above sea level—is less than half the air pressure at sea level. **Altitude,** or elevation, is the distance above sea level, the average level of the surface of the oceans. **Air pressure decreases as altitude increases. As air pressure decreases, so does density.**

Altitude Affects Air Pressure Imagine a stack of ten books. Which book has more weight on it, the second book from the top or the book at the bottom? The second book from the top has only the weight of one book on top of it. The book at the bottom

---

Skills Lab

Measuring

Working Under PRESSURE

Air pressure changes are related to changing weather conditions. In this lab, you will build and use your own barometer to measure air pressure.

Problem

How can a barometer detect changes in air pressure?

Materials

modeling clay   scissors
white glue   tape
pencil   wide-mouthed glass jar
metric ruler   rubber band
large rubber balloon
drinking straw, 12–15 cm long
cardboard strip, 10 cm x 25 cm

Procedure

1. Cut off the narrow opening of the balloon.
2. Fold the edges of the balloon outward. Carefully stretch the balloon over the open end of the glass jar. Use a rubber band to hold the balloon on the rim of the glass jar.
3. Place a small amount of glue on the center of the balloon top. Attach one end of the straw to the glue. Allow the other end to extend several centimeters beyond the edge of the glass jar. This is your pointer.

Balloon
Glue
Straw
High Pressure
Low Pressure
Rubber band
Tape

Introducing the Procedure

Have students read the entire procedure. Then ask: **What part of your barometer is like the flexible sides of the metal box in a commercial aneroid barometer?** *(The balloon stretched across the jar)* Point out that the balloon will expand when the air pressure falls. Ask: **Why does the expanding balloon make the pointer in your barometer fall?** *(Students may think that the pointer should rise, not fall, as the balloon expands.)* Explain that the pointer resting on the jar is like a seesaw. The clay

weights down the free end of the straw. The free end falls when the expanding balloon causes the other end of the straw to rise.

Sample Data Table

Date and Time	Air Pressure	Weather Conditions
April 2, 10:00 A.M.	1	rainy, 24°C
April 2, 2:00 P.M.	2	cloudy, 23°C
April 4, 10:00 A.M.	4	sunny, 18°C
April 4, 2:00 P.M.	5	sunny, 19°C

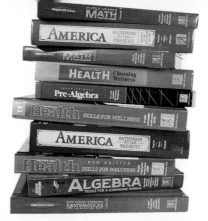

of the stack has the weight of all the other books pressing on it.

Air at sea level is like the bottom book. Recall that air pressure is the weight of the column of air pushing down on an area. Sea-level air has the weight of the whole atmosphere pressing on it. So air pressure is greatest at sea level. Air near the top of the atmosphere is like the second book from the top. There, the air has less weight pressing on it, and thus has lower air pressure.

4. While the glue dries, fold the cardboard strip lengthwise and draw a scale along the edge with marks 0.5 cm apart. Write "High pressure" at the top of your scale and "Low pressure" at the bottom.

5. After the glue dries, add a pea-sized piece of modeling clay to the end of the pointer. Place your barometer and its scale in a location that is as free from temperature changes as possible. Arrange the scale and the barometer as shown in the diagram. Note that the pointer of the straw must just reach the cardboard strip.

6. Tape both the scale and the barometer to a surface so they do not move during your experiment.

7. In your notebook, make a data table like the one at the left. Record the date and time. Note the level of the straw on the cardboard strip.

8. Check the barometer twice a day. Record your observations in your data table.

9. Record the weather conditions for each day.

Analyze and Conclude

1. What change in atmospheric conditions must occur to cause the free end of the straw to rise? What change must occur for it to fall?

2. According to your observations, what kind of weather is usually associated with high air pressure? With low air pressure?

3. If the balloon had a tiny hole in it, what would happen to the accuracy of your barometer?

4. **Think About It** What effect, if any, would a great temperature change have on the accuracy of your barometer?

More to Explore

Compare changes in air pressure shown by your barometer with high and low air pressure readings shown on newspaper weather maps during the same time period. How do your readings compare with the readings in the newspapers?

Troubleshooting the Experiment

◆ Before students cut their balloon, suggest they inflate it to stretch the rubber.

◆ Caution students to avoid making holes in the balloon when they cut it. Once the balloon is in place, they should make sure it does not leak air.

Expected Outcome

When the air pressure outside is low, the higher air pressure inside the jar pushes up on the balloon, causing the pointer to fall. When the air pressure outside is high, it pushes down on the balloon, causing the pointer to rise. Low air pressure is likely to be followed by cloudy or even stormy weather conditions. High air pressure is likely to be followed by fair weather conditions.

Analyze and Conclude

1. Air pressure must rise for the free end of the straw to rise. Air pressure must fall for the free end of the straw to fall.

2. Clear, dry weather usually is associated with high air pressure. Cloudy, wet, or stormy weather usually is associated with low air pressure.

3. A tiny hole in the balloon would cause the barometer not to work because air would leak in or out to equalize the air pressure inside and outside the jar.

4. A great increase in temperature would cause the air inside the barometer to expand and a large decrease in temperature would cause it to contract, affecting the readings.

Extending the Inquiry

More to Explore Students' air pressure readings should agree in general with high and low air pressure readings given in the newspaper. If the readings do not agree, it may be because students' barometers are faulty. Balloons may leak air or not be stretchy enough, or the lumps of clay may be too large. Also, students' barometers are not likely to be accurate enough to reflect minor fluctuations in air pressure. In addition, the readings reported in the newspaper may have been taken at a different time of day when air pressure was lower or higher.

Safety

In Step 2, to reduce chances of the jar breaking, suggest that one student hold the jar while the other stretches the balloon and rubber band over it. Review the safety guidelines in Appendix A.

Program Resources

◆ **Unit 4 Resources** Chapter 13 Skills Lab blackline masters, pp. 116–117

◆ **Inquiry Skills Activity Book** Provides teaching and review of all inquiry skills

Media and Technology

 Lab Activity Videotapes Grade 6, Tape 4

Increasing Altitude

People who live at high altitudes have developed adaptations to the low pressure and density of oxygen in the air around them. Ask: **What kinds of adaptations would allow people to live successfully at high altitudes?** (*A larger chest and lungs would allow a person to take in more air.*) **learning modality: logical/mathematical**

3 Assess

Section 3 Review Answers

1. Air has mass, density, and pressure. Air has these properties because it is composed of molecules.

2. Air presses down on the mercury in the bottom of the barometer, and this forces the mercury up into the sealed tube. The greater the air pressure, the higher the mercury rises and the higher the air pressure reading.

3. Because it has low pressure and density, there are fewer oxygen molecules in each lungful of air.

4. You would expect to see the air pressure increase because the column of air pressing down on the barometer would be taller.

Materials *glass, tap water, piece of heavy cardboard*

Tips Students should fill the glass until the level of water bulges over the rim and then slide the cardboard *completely* over the rim, being careful not to let any air bubbles under the cardboard. Some water may overflow the glass, so students should do this over a sink.

Performance Assessment

Skills Check Call on volunteers to infer why an inflated balloon flies around the room when it is released. (*The force of the air escaping the balloon propels the balloon.*)

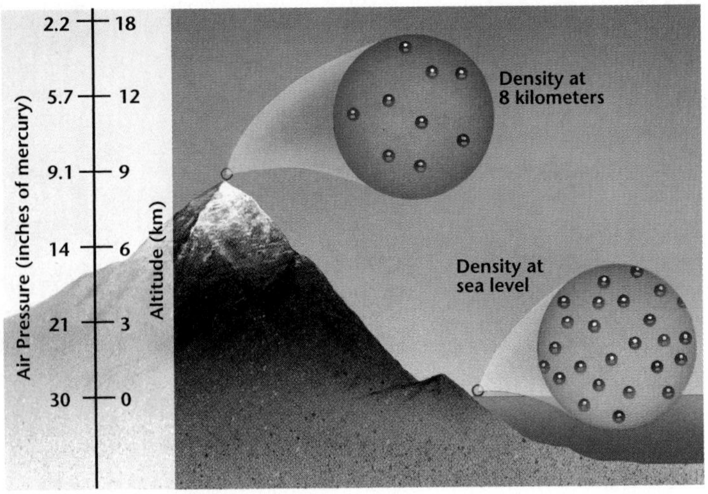

Figure 13 The density of air decreases as altitude increases. Air at sea level has more gas molecules in each cubic meter than air at the top of a mountain.

Altitude Also Affects Density If you were near the top of Mount McKinley and tried to run, you would get out of breath quickly. Why would you have difficulty breathing at high altitudes?

As you go up through the atmosphere, the air pressure decreases. As air pressure decreases, the density of the air decreases. So density decreases as altitude increases, as shown in Figure 13.

Whether air is at sea level or at 6 kilometers above sea level, the air still contains 21 percent oxygen. However, since the air is less dense at a high altitude, there are fewer oxygen molecules to breathe in each cubic meter of air than there are at sea level. You are taking in less oxygen with each breath. That is why you get out of breath quickly.

Section 3 Review

1. What properties does air have? Why does it have these properties?
2. Describe how a mercury barometer measures air pressure.
3. Why is the air at the top of a mountain hard to breathe?
4. **Thinking Critically** **Predicting** What changes in air pressure would you expect to see if you carried a barometer down a mine shaft? Explain.

Science at Home

Under Pressure Here's how you can show your family that air has pressure. Fill a glass to the brim with water. Place a piece of heavy cardboard over the top of the glass. Hold the cardboard in place with one hand as you turn the glass upside down. **CAUTION:** *Be sure the cardboard does not bend.* Now remove your hand from the cardboard. What happens? Explain to your family that the cardboard doesn't fall because the air pressure pushing up on it is greater than the weight of the water pushing down.

Media and Technology

 Transparencies "Density of Air at Two Altitudes," Transparency 64

 Physical Science Videodisc Unit 1, Side 1, "Racing Hot Air Balloons"

Chapter 3

Program Resources

◆ **Unit 4 Resources** 13-3 Review and Reinforce, p. 107; 13-3 Enrich, p. 108

SECTION
4 Layers of the Atmosphere

TEKS: 6.2B, C; 6.3E; 6.14C

DISCOVER · ACTIVITY · · ·

Is Air There?

1. Use a heavy rubber band to tightly secure a plastic bag over the top of a wide-mouthed jar.

2. Gently try to push the bag into the jar. What happens? Is the air pressure higher inside or outside of the bag?

3. Remove the rubber band and line the inside of the jar with the plastic bag. Use the rubber band to tightly secure the edges of the bag over the rim of the jar.

4. Gently try to pull the bag out of the jar with your fingertips. What happens? Is the air pressure higher inside or outside of the bag?

Think It Over

Predicting Explain your observations in terms of air pressure. How do you think differences in air pressure would affect a weather balloon as it traveled up through the atmosphere?

Imagine taking a trip upward into the atmosphere in a hot-air balloon. You begin on a warm beach near the ocean, at an altitude of 0 kilometers.

You hear a roar as the balloon's pilot turns up the burner to heat the air in the balloon. The balloon begins to rise, and Earth's surface gets farther and farther away. As the balloon rises to an altitude of 3 kilometers, you realize that the air is getting colder. As you continue to rise, the air gets colder and colder. At 6 kilometers you begin to have trouble breathing. The air is becoming less dense. It's time to go back down.

What if you could have continued your balloon ride up through the atmosphere? As you rose farther up through the atmosphere, the air pressure and temperature would change dramatically. **The four main layers of the atmosphere are the troposphere, the stratosphere, the mesosphere, and the thermosphere. They are classified according to changes in temperature.**

The Troposphere

You live in the inner, or lowest, layer of Earth's atmosphere, the **troposphere** (TROH puh sfeer). *Tropo-* means "turning" or "changing"; conditions in the troposphere are more variable than in the other layers. The troposphere is where Earth's weather occurs.

GUIDE FOR READING

◆ What are the main layers of the atmosphere and how are they classified?

Reading Tip Before you read, preview *Exploring Layers of the Atmosphere.* Make a list of unfamiliar words. Look for the meanings of these words as you read.

Key Terms troposphere
• stratosphere • mesosphere
• thermosphere • ionosphere
• aurora borealis • exosphere

Objective

After completing this lesson, students will be able to
◆ identify and classify the main layers of the atmosphere.

1 Engage/Explore

Activating Prior Knowledge

Ask: **Did you ever see a shooting star?** *(Most students probably will say yes.)* **What is a shooting star?** *(A meteor burning up because of friction as it falls through Earth's atmosphere)* Point out that most shooting stars are visible from about 50 to 80 km above Earth in a layer of the atmosphere called the mesosphere. This layer protects us from being bombarded by shooting stars and other space debris. The mesosphere is just one of four major layers of the atmosphere students will read about in this section.

· · · · · · · · · DISCOVER  · · · · · · · ·

Skills Focus predicting
Materials *heavy rubber band, plastic bag, wide-mouthed glass jar*
Time 10 minutes
Tips Make sure the rubber band is tight and the plastic bag does not have holes in it. Caution students to push gently on the bag to avoid breaking the bag or the jar.
Expected Outcome Students should find it difficult to push the bag into or pull it out of the jar.
Think It Over Trying to push the bag into the jar decreases the volume and increases the air pressure inside the jar. Trying to pull the bag out of the jar increases the volume and decreases the air pressure inside the jar. As a weather balloon traveled up, it would expand until it burst as the air pressure outside the balloon became lower than the air pressure inside.

READING STRATEGIES

Reading Tip Students lists might include the names of the layers of the atmosphere, as well as terms such as *meteoroid* and *aurora borealis.* Suggest that, as they read and encounter the words on their list, students record their meanings.

Program Resources

◆ **Unit 4 Resources** 13-4 Lesson Plan, p. 109; 13-4 Section Summary, p. 110
◆ **Guided Reading and Study Workbook** 13-4

Media and Technology

 Transparencies "Layers of the Atmosphere," Transparency 65

2 Facilitate

The Troposphere

Building Inquiry Skills: Graphing

Challenge students to calculate the temperature for every 1,000 m above Earth's surface in the troposphere, starting at sea level and ending at 10,000 m. They should assume that the temperature is 15.0°C at sea level and decreases 6.5 Celsius degrees for each 1,000-m increase in altitude. Then have students draw a graph that shows the relationship between altitude and temperature in the troposphere.
learning modality: logical/mathematical

The Stratosphere

Addressing Naive Conceptions

In Section 2, students read that ozone is a harmful chemical in smog. In this section, they read that ozone is a natural component of the atmosphere that protects Earth from ultraviolet solar radiation. Students may wonder if ozone is harmful or not. Explain that the ozone in the stratosphere absorbs, and thus protects us from, too much sunlight. Ozone in this layer occurs naturally. However, ozone in the troposphere harms our health and contributes to photochemical smog. Ozone in this layer is caused by pollution. **limited English proficiency**

The Mesosphere

Building Inquiry Skills: Inferring

Challenge students to explain why there is a temperature reversal between the stratosphere and mesosphere. Ask: **Why is the mesosphere colder than the stratosphere?** (*Because it contains no ozone molecules to absorb solar radiation and convert the radiation into heat*)
learning modality: logical/ mathematical

Figure 14 This weather balloon will carry a package of instruments to measure weather conditions high in the atmosphere.
Applying Concepts Which is the first layer of the atmosphere the balloon passes through on its way up?

Although hot-air balloons cannot travel very high into the troposphere, other types of balloons can. To measure weather conditions, scientists launch weather balloons that carry instruments up into the atmosphere. The balloons are not fully inflated before they are launched. Recall that air pressure decreases as you rise through the atmosphere. Leaving the balloon only partly inflated gives the gas inside the balloon room to expand as the air pressure outside the balloon decreases.

The depth of the troposphere varies from more than 16 kilometers above the equator to less than 9 kilometers above the North and South Poles. Even though it is the shallowest layer of the atmosphere, the troposphere contains almost all of the mass of the atmosphere.

As altitude increases in the troposphere, the temperature decreases. On average, for every 1-kilometer increase in altitude the air gets about 6.5 Celsius degrees cooler. At the top of the troposphere, the temperature stops decreasing and stays constant at about –60°C. Water here forms thin, feathery clouds of ice.

☑ *Checkpoint* Why are clouds at the top of the troposphere made of ice crystals instead of drops of water?

The Stratosphere

The **stratosphere** extends from the top of the troposphere to about 50 kilometers above Earth's surface. *Strato-* is similar to *stratum*, which means "layer" or "spreading out."

The lower stratosphere is cold, about −60°C. You might be surprised to learn that the upper stratosphere is warmer than the lower stratosphere. The upper stratosphere contains a layer of ozone, the three-atom form of oxygen. When the ozone absorbs energy from the sun, the energy is converted into heat, warming the air.

As a weather balloon rises through the stratosphere, the air pressure outside the balloon continues to decrease. The volume of the balloon increases. Finally, the balloon bursts, and the instrument package falls back to Earth's surface.

The Mesosphere

Above the stratosphere, a drop in temperature marks the beginning of the next layer, the **mesosphere.** *Meso-* means "middle," so the mesosphere is the middle layer of the atmosphere. The mesosphere begins 50 kilometers above Earth's surface and ends at 80 kilometers. In the outer mesosphere temperatures approach −90°C.

Background

Facts and Figures You may wish to share the following facts and figures about the mesosphere with students.
♦ The mesosphere is the coldest part of the atmosphere. Temperatures there reach lows that are as cold as the lowest temperatures ever recorded anywhere on Earth.
♦ Oddly, air temperatures in the mesosphere are colder in summer than in winter. Temperatures there also are colder over the equator than over the North and South poles.
♦ The clouds that form in the mesosphere are unlike any other clouds in the atmosphere. They are formed of ice crystals and are called noctilucent clouds because they are visible only at night.

EXPLORING Layers of the Atmosphere

The atmosphere is divided into four layers: the troposphere, the stratosphere, the mesosphere, and the thermosphere. The thermosphere is further divided into the ionosphere and the exosphere.

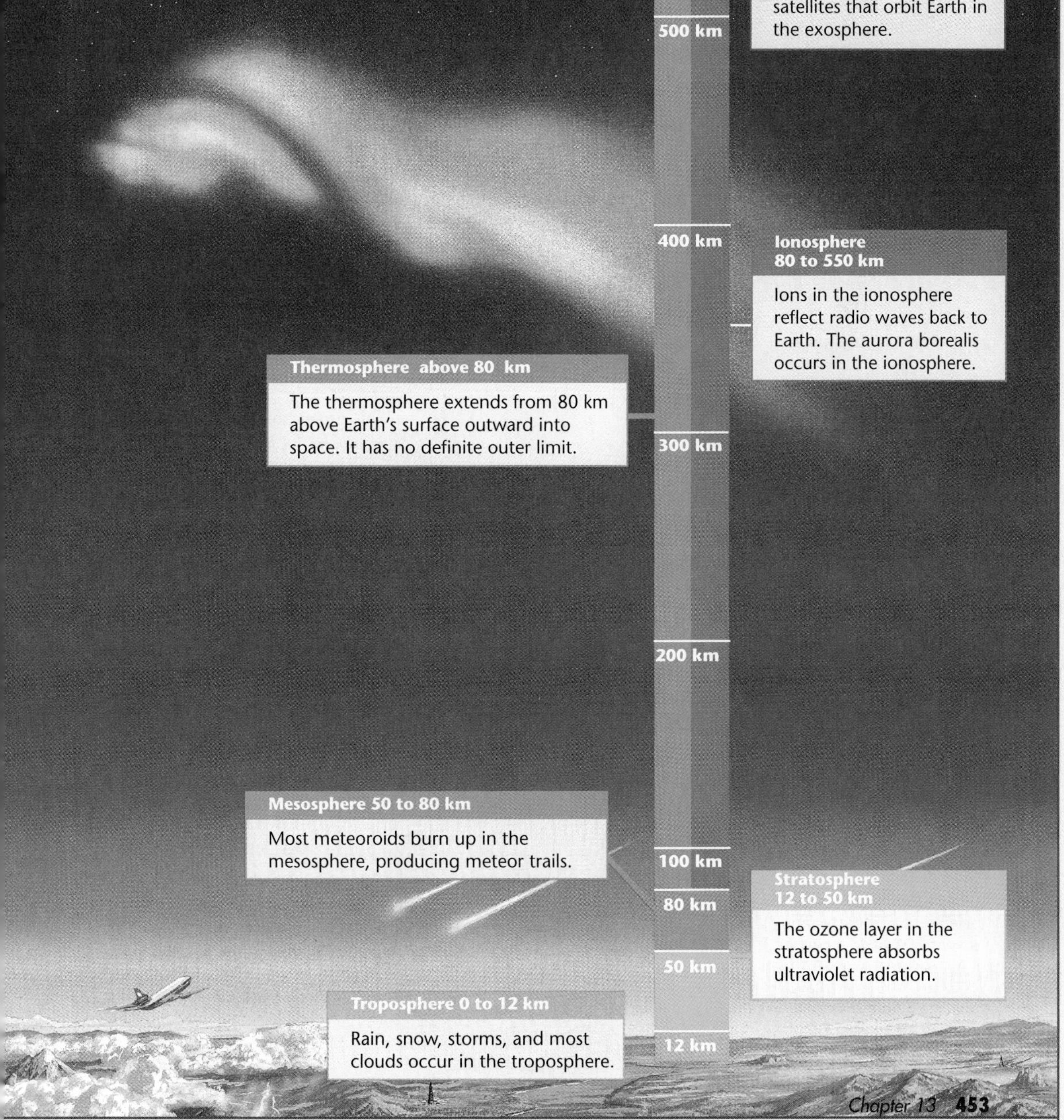

Exosphere above 550 km

Phone calls and television pictures often reach you by way of communications satellites that orbit Earth in the exosphere.

Ionosphere 80 to 550 km

Ions in the ionosphere reflect radio waves back to Earth. The aurora borealis occurs in the ionosphere.

Thermosphere above 80 km

The thermosphere extends from 80 km above Earth's surface outward into space. It has no definite outer limit.

Mesosphere 50 to 80 km

Most meteoroids burn up in the mesosphere, producing meteor trails.

Stratosphere 12 to 50 km

The ozone layer in the stratosphere absorbs ultraviolet radiation.

Troposphere 0 to 12 km

Rain, snow, storms, and most clouds occur in the troposphere.

550 km
500 km
400 km
300 km
200 km
100 km
80 km
50 km
12 km

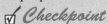

EXPLORING

Layers of the Atmosphere

Materials *posterboard, colored markers, index cards, buttons and other small objects for game pieces*

ACTIVITY

Time 30 minutes

Divide the class into groups and have each group use the information presented in the feature to create a board game. The object of the game should be to get from the ground to the top of the atmosphere. Reaching the objective might involve overcoming various obstacles in the different layers of the atmosphere, such as clouds and storms in the troposphere, very high temperatures in the stratosphere, meteoroids in the mesosphere, electrically charged ions in the ionosphere, and orbiting satellites in the exosphere. To advance through the layers of the atmosphere, players might be required to correctly answer questions about each layer, such as the layer's temperature or height above Earth's surface. Group members should work together to brainstorm the objectives and rules of the game. The actual work of constructing the game board and other parts of the game should be divided up among individual group members. Suggest that the groups exchange games and try them out. Refer to the **ELL Handbook** for additional teaching strategies. **cooperative learning**

Media and Technology

Earth Science Videodisc Unit 2, Side 2, "A Trip Through the Earth"

Chapter 1

Answers to Self-Assessment

Caption Question

Figure 14 The first layer is the troposphere.

☑ *Checkpoint*

Because the temperature at that altitude is always below the freezing point of water

Ongoing Assessment

Writing Challenge students to write a short story describing their imaginary ascent up through the troposphere and stratosphere in a hydrogen balloon. They should describe the conditions they pass through in each layer.

 Students can save their stories in their portfolios.

453

Integrating
Space Science

Stress that the mesosphere protects Earth from meteoroids that are pulled toward the planet by gravity. Tell students that the moon has gravity, too, but no atmosphere to protect it from meteoroids. As a result, meteoroids crash on the moon's surface, forming large depressions called craters. Challenge students to draw labeled diagrams showing what happens to meteoroids that fall toward the moon as compared with those that fall toward Earth. **limited English proficiency**

Point out that exploring the atmosphere is difficult because it requires scientists or their instruments to reach high altitudes. Ask: **What are some ways explorers of the atmosphere have made scientific observations at high altitudes?** *(By climbing to the tops of mountains, ascending in hydrogen balloons, flying kites, and attaching instruments to balloons and satellites)* **What have these explorers learned through these means?** *(That air pressure decreases with altitude, that lightning is a form of electricity, how the sun influences the atmosphere, and the temperature, air pressure, and humidity at various altitudes)*

In Your Journal Ask volunteers to read their paragraphs aloud to the class. The items students would take with them should show they understand how the atmosphere changes with altitude. For example, warm clothing would be necessary above an altitude of just a few kilometers because temperature declines steadily with increasing altitude. Also, a supply of oxygen would be needed above about 7 km. Instruments should include at least a thermometer for measuring changes in temperature and a barometer for measuring changes in air pressure. Refer to the **ELL Handbook** for additional teaching strategies. **learning modality: verbal**

 INTEGRATING SPACE SCIENCE If you watch a shooting star streak across the night sky, you are seeing a meteoroid burn up as it enters the mesosphere. The mesosphere protects Earth's surface from being hit by most meteoroids, which are chunks of stone and metal from space. What you see as a shooting star, or meteor, is the trail of hot, glowing gases the burning meteoroid leaves behind.

☑ *Checkpoint* **What is the depth of the mesosphere?**

The Thermosphere

Near the top of the atmosphere, the air is very thin. The air 80 kilometers above Earth's surface is only about 0.001 percent as dense as the air at sea level. It's as though you took a cubic

SCIENCE & History

Explorers of the Atmosphere

The atmosphere has been explored from the ground and from space.

1746

Franklin's Experiment with Electricity

American statesman and inventor Benjamin Franklin and some friends in Philadelphia experimented with electricity in the atmosphere. To demonstrate that lightning is a form of electricity, Franklin flew a kite in a thunderstorm. However, Franklin did not hold the kite string in his hand, as this historical print shows.

1600	1700	1800

1643

Torricelli Invents the Barometer

Italian physicist and mathematician Evangelista Torricelli improved existing scientific instruments and invented some new ones. In 1643 he invented the barometer, using a column of mercury 1.2 meters high.

1804

Gay-Lussac Studies the Upper Troposphere

French chemist Joseph-Louis Gay-Lussac ascended to a height of about 7 kilometers in a hydrogen balloon to study the upper troposphere. Gay-Lussac studied pressure, temperature, and humidity.

454

Background

Facts and Figures At sea level, an air molecule can travel just a fraction of a centimeter before colliding with another, whereas in the upper thermosphere it can travel as far as 10 km before colliding with another. Because of their very high temperatures, air molecules in the upper thermosphere move at speeds of up to 40,000 km per hour, allowing many to escape into outer space. Therefore, where the thermosphere ends and outer space begins is arbitrary. Air molecules become farther and farther apart as you travel higher above Earth's surface until, somewhere thousands of kilometers above the surface, there are no more air molecules.

meter of air at sea level and expanded it into 100,000 cubic meters at the top of the mesosphere. The outermost layer of the atmosphere, the **thermosphere,** extends from 80 kilometers above Earth's surface outward into space. It has no definite outer limit. The atmosphere does not end suddenly at the outer edge of the thermosphere. Gas atoms and molecules there are so far apart that the air blends gradually with outer space.

The *thermo-* in thermosphere means "heat." Even though the air in the thermosphere is thin, it is very hot, up to 1,800°C. The temperature in the thermosphere is actually higher than the temperature in a furnace used to make steel! But why is the thermosphere so hot? Energy coming from the sun strikes the thermosphere first. Nitrogen and oxygen molecules convert energy from the sun into heat.

In Your Journal

Imagine you were one of the first people to go up into the atmosphere in a balloon. What would you need to take? Find out what the early explorers took with them in their balloons. Write at least two paragraphs about what you would take, and why.

1931

Piccard Explores the Stratosphere

Swiss-Belgian physicist Auguste Piccard made the first ascent into the stratosphere. He reached a height of about 16 kilometers in an airtight cabin attached to a huge hydrogen balloon. Piccard is shown here with the cabin.

1900 ———————————————————— **2000**

1960

First Weather Satellite Launched

TIROS-1, the first weather satellite equipped with a camera to send data back to Earth, was put into orbit by the United States. As later weather satellites circled Earth, they observed cloud cover and recorded temperatures and air pressures in the atmosphere.

1994

Space Shuttle Investigates the Atmosphere

The NASA space shuttle *Atlantis* traveled to a height of 300 kilometers in the thermosphere. *Atlantis* carried the ATLAS–3 research program, which observed the sun's influence on the atmosphere.

Chapter 13 **455**

Answers to Self-Assessment

☑ *Checkpoint*

The mesosphere extends from 50 to 80 km above Earth's surface, so it has a depth of 30 km.

The Thermosphere

Building Inquiry Skills: Making Models

Time 5 minutes

Challenge a group of student volunteers to pretend they are atoms and molecules and to demonstrate the density and speed of atoms and molecules in the atmosphere, first at sea level, then in the thermosphere. (*For sea level, students should stand close together and move very slowly. For the thermosphere, they should stand as far apart as possible and move very quickly.*) Point out that the classroom would have to be much larger for them to be as far apart as atoms and molecules really are in the thermosphere. Ask: **How much larger would the classroom have to be?** (*Almost 100,000 times larger*) **learning modality: kinesthetic**

Including All Students

Content Mastery

To help students whose native language is not English remember that the defining characteristic of the thermosphere is its high temperature, stress that the prefix *thermo-* means "heat." Ask: **What are some other words that start with this prefix?** (*thermometer, thermostat, thermal, thermos*) Have students explain how each of the terms is related to heat. **limited English proficiency**

Ongoing Assessment

Oral Presentation Call on students to describe density, temperature, and pressure of air in the thermosphere as compared with the troposphere. Call on other students to explain why the thermosphere has these characteristics.

The Thermosphere, continued

Integrating Technology

Help students understand why satellites orbit Earth at such high altitudes. First point out that molecules in air create resistance that can slow down objects orbiting Earth. Then ask: **What happens to the density of molecules in air as you go higher above Earth's surface?** *(It decreases.)* **Why do you think satellites orbit Earth at such high altitudes?** *(The lower density of air molecules creates less resistance to slow down orbiting satellites.)* **learning modality: logical/ mathematical**

3 Assess

Section 4 Review Answers

1. Layers of the atmosphere are classified according to changes in temperature.
2. Troposphere—weather occurs here; stratosphere—contains the ozone layer; mesosphere—coldest layer of atmosphere; thermosphere—sun's energy converted to heat here.
3. A glowing light display caused when energy from the sun causes gas molecules to become electrically charged; it occurs in the lower layer of the thermosphere.
4. Because it does not absorb much energy from the sun

Check Your Progress ⛛ CHAPTER PROJECT

Students may observe such trends as cooler temperatures after a storm and fair weather after an increase in air pressure. Some weather variables, such as temperature and wind speed, have a greater range than others, including air pressure.

Performance Assessment

Writing Challenge students to write crossword puzzles using all the bold-faced terms in the section. Then have students exchange puzzles and try to solve their partner's puzzle.

Figure 15 The aurora borealis, seen from Fairbanks, Alaska, creates a spectacular display in the night sky.

Despite the high temperature, however, you would not feel warm in the thermosphere. An ordinary thermometer would show a temperature well below 0°C. Why is that? Temperature is the average amount of energy of motion of each molecule of a substance. The gas molecules in the thermosphere move very rapidly, so the temperature is very high. However, the molecules are spaced far apart in the thin air. And there are not enough of them to collide with a thermometer and warm it very much. So an ordinary thermometer would not detect the molecules' energy.

The Ionosphere The thermosphere is divided into two layers. The lower layer of the thermosphere, called the **ionosphere** (eye AHN uh sfeer), begins 80 kilometers above the surface and ends at 550 kilometers. Energy from the sun causes gas molecules in the ionosphere to become electrically charged particles called ions. Radio waves bounce off ions in the ionosphere and then bounce back to Earth's surface.

The brilliant light displays of the **aurora borealis**—the Northern Lights—also occur in the ionosphere. The aurora borealis is caused by particles from the sun that enter the ionosphere near the North Pole. These particles strike oxygen and nitrogen atoms in the ionosphere, causing them to glow.

The Exosphere *Exo-* means "outer," so the **exosphere** is the **INTEGRATING TECHNOLOGY** outer layer of the thermosphere. The exosphere extends from 550 kilometers outward for thousands of kilometers. When you make a long-distance phone call or watch television, the signal may have traveled up to a satellite orbiting in the exosphere and then back down to your home. Satellites are also used for watching the world's weather and carrying telescopes that look deep into space.

❓ Section 4 Review

1. What property is used to classify the layers of the atmosphere?
2. Describe one characteristic of each of the four main layers of the atmosphere.
3. What is the aurora borealis? In which layer of the atmosphere does it occur?
4. **Thinking Critically Drawing Conclusions** Why is the mesosphere the coldest part of the atmosphere?

Check Your Progress CHAPTER PROJECT

At this point, review your weather log. What do you notice about the weather on one day that might allow you to predict the next day's weather? What weather conditions changed the most from day to day? Continue to record your observations and start thinking about how you will present them.

Background

Facts and Figures Another sphere around Earth, called the magnetosphere, extends above the atmosphere to more than 65,000 km above Earth's surface. It is a magnetic field that traps charged particles from the sun. The trapped particles follow the lines of magnetic force and bounce back and forth from one pole to the other, sometimes breaking through into the ionosphere to produce auroras.

Program Resources

◆ **Unit 4 Resources** 13-4 Review and Reinforce, p. 111; 13-4 Enrich, p. 112

1 The Air Around You

Key Ideas
◆ Earth's atmosphere makes conditions on Earth suitable for living things.
◆ Earth's atmosphere is made up of molecules of nitrogen, oxygen, carbon dioxide, and water vapor, as well as some other gases and particles of liquids and solids.

Key Terms
weather   ozone
atmosphere   water vapor

2 Air Quality
INTEGRATING ENVIRONMENTAL SCIENCE

Key Ideas
◆ Most air pollution results from the burning of fossil fuels such as coal and oil.
◆ Nitrogen oxides, hydrocarbons, and other air pollutants react with one another in the presence of sunlight to form a mix of ozone and other chemicals called photochemical smog.
◆ Acid rain forms when nitrogen oxides and sulfur oxides combine with water in the air to form nitric acid and sulfuric acid.

Key Terms
pollutant   temperature inversion
photochemical smog   acid rain

3 Air Pressure

Key Ideas
◆ Properties of air include mass, density, and pressure.
◆ Air pressure is the result of the weight of a column of air pushing down on an area.
◆ Air pressure is measured with mercury barometers and aneroid barometers.
◆ Air pressure decreases as altitude increases. As air pressure decreases, so does density.

Key Terms
density   barometer   altitude
pressure   mercury barometer
air pressure   aneroid barometer

4 Layers of the Atmosphere

Key Ideas
◆ The four main layers of the atmosphere are classified according to changes in temperature. These layers are the troposphere, the stratosphere, the mesosphere, and the thermosphere.
◆ Rain, snow, storms, and most clouds occur in the troposphere.
◆ Ozone in the stratosphere absorbs energy from the sun.
◆ Most meteoroids burn up in the mesosphere, producing meteor trails.
◆ The aurora borealis occurs in the ionosphere.
◆ Communications satellites orbit Earth in the exosphere.

Key Terms
troposphere   thermosphere   aurora borealis
stratosphere   ionosphere   exosphere
mesosphere

Organizing Information

Concept Map Copy the air pressure concept map onto a separate sheet of paper. Then complete it and add a title. (For more on concept maps, see the Skills Handbook.)

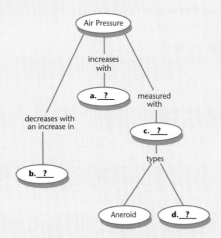

Organizing Information

Concept Map Sample title: Air Pressure **a.** Density **b.** Altitude **c.** Barometers **d.** Mercury

Program Resources

◆ **Unit 4 Resources** Chapter 13 Project Scoring Rubric, p. 96
◆ **Performance Assessment** Chapter 13, pp. 41–43
◆ **Chapter and Unit Tests** Chapter 13 Test, pp. 64–67

Media and Technology

 Computer Test Bank
Chapter 13 Test

Reviewing Content

Multiple Choice

1. d 2. d 3. c 4. b 5. b

True or False

6. true 7. carbon dioxide (Other possible answers: nitrogen oxides, sulfur oxides, soot) 8. acid rain 9. more 10. decreases

Checking Concepts

11. Carbon dioxide is added to the atmosphere through the respiration of animals and the burning of fossil fuels.

12. It is difficult to include water vapor in a graph that shows the percentages of different gases in the atmosphere because the percentage of water vapor varies greatly.

13. Photochemical-type smog is caused by the action of sunlight on chemicals in the air. It forms over sunny cities like Los Angeles today. London-type smog was caused by particles in coal smoke combining with water droplets in humid air. It once blanketed industrial cities like London but is no longer common.

14. Acid rain may make lake and pond water so acidic that many types of plants and animals can no longer live in it. Acid rain may also cause damage to tree needles and the surfaces of buildings and statues.

15. Moving upward from Earth's surface, the layers are troposphere, stratosphere, mesosphere, thermosphere.

16. As you move upward through the troposphere, the temperature decreases by about 6.5°C for each 1,000-meter increase in altitude.

17. Students' letters should demonstrate a thorough understanding of their chosen layer of the atmosphere.

Thinking Critically

18. You would experience a decrease in temperature and also in the pressure and density of the air. You would feel cold unless you dressed appropriately. You would also feel the effects of low oxygen pressure and density. For example, you might be short of breath and tire easily.

Reviewing Content

 Review key concepts online using iText at www.phschool.com

Multiple Choice

Choose the letter of the answer that best completes each statement.

1. The most abundant gas in the atmosphere is
   a. ozone.   b. carbon dioxide.
   c. oxygen.   d. nitrogen.
2. Most air pollution is caused by
   a. dust and pollen.
   b. acid rain.
   c. erupting volcanoes.
   d. the burning of fossil fuels.
3. A barometer is used to measure
   a. temperature.   b. smog.
   c. air pressure.   d. density.
4. The layers of the atmosphere are classified according to changes in
   a. altitude.
   b. temperature.
   c. pressure.
   d. density.
5. The inner layer, or "weather layer," of the atmosphere is called the
   a. mesosphere.
   b. troposphere.
   c. thermosphere.
   d. stratosphere.

True or False

If the statement is true, write true. If it is false, change the underlined word or words to make the statement true.

6. Plants need <u>carbon dioxide</u> from the atmosphere to make food.
7. Burning fuels add <u>nitrogen</u> to the atmosphere.
8. When sulfur and nitrogen oxides mix with water in the air, they form <u>smog</u>.
9. If the mass of a fixed volume of air increases, it becomes <u>less</u> dense.
10. Air pressure <u>increases</u> as you climb from land at sea level to the top of a mountain.

Checking Concepts

11. Name two ways in which carbon dioxide is added to the atmosphere.

12. Explain why it is difficult to include water vapor in a graph that shows the percentages of various gases in the atmosphere.

13. What is the difference between photochemical smog and London-type smog?

14. Describe some of the problems caused by acid rain.

15. List the following layers of the atmosphere in order moving up from Earth's surface: thermosphere, stratosphere, troposphere, mesosphere.

16. Describe the temperature changes that occur as you move upward through the troposphere.

17. **Writing to Learn** You are a scientist who has a chance to join a research mission to explore the atmosphere. To win a place on this mission, write a persuasive letter telling which layer of the atmosphere you want to research and why you chose it.

Thinking Critically

18. **Predicting** Describe the changes in the atmosphere that you would experience while climbing a mountain four or more kilometers high. How might these changes affect you physically?

19. **Applying Concepts** Why can an aneroid barometer be used to measure elevation as well as air pressure?

20. **Relating Cause and Effect** How can burning high-sulfur coal in a power-generating plant harm a forest hundreds of kilometers away?

21. **Classifying** Which sources of air pollution occur naturally, and which are caused by humans?

19. Air pressure decreases as elevation or altitude increases. An aneroid barometer can be calibrated to show the change in air pressure as a change in altitude.

20. Burning high-sulfur coal can produce sulfur oxides and other air pollutants that may lead to the formation of acid rain hundreds of kilometers away, where it might harm a forest.

21. Natural sources of air pollution include molds, dust, pollen, salt from ocean spray, and particles from forest fires, soil erosion, dust storms, and volcanoes. Human sources of air pollution include soot and carbon dioxide and other gases from the burning of fuels, such as wood, coal, oil, and gas, and dust particles from farming and construction.

Applying Skills

The table below shows the temperature at various altitudes above Omaha, Nebraska, on a day in January. Use the table to answer the questions that follow.

Altitude (kilometers)	0	1.6	3.2	4.8	6.4	7.2
Temperature (°C)	0	–4	–9	–21	–32	–40

22. **Graphing** Make a line graph of the data in the table. Put temperature on the horizontal axis and altitude on the vertical axis. Label your graph.
23. **Interpreting Graphs** At about what height above the ground was the temperature –15°C?
24. **Interpreting Graphs** What was the approximate temperature 2.4 kilometers over Omaha?

25. **Calculating** Suppose an airplane was about 6.8 kilometers above Omaha on this day. What was the approximate temperature at 6.8 kilometers? How much colder was the temperature at 6.8 kilometers above the ground than at ground level?

Performance CHAPTER PROJECT Assessment

Present Your Project For your class presentation, prepare a display of your weather observations. Include drawings, graphs, and tables that summarize the weather you observed. Practice presenting your project to your group. Do you need to make any improvements? If so, make them now.

Reflect and Record In your journal, write how you might improve your weather log. What weather conditions would you like to know more about? What factors could you have measured more accurately using instruments?

Test Preparation

Use these questions to prepare for standardized tests.

Study the graph. Then answer Questions 26–29.

Temperature in the Atmosphere

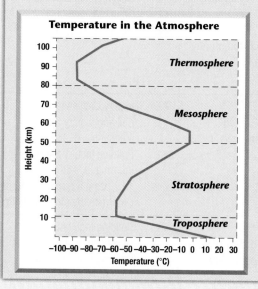

26. Name the layer of the atmosphere that is closest to Earth's surface.
   - **A** thermosphere
   - **B** troposphere
   - **C** stratosphere
   - **D** mesosphere
27. Which layer of the atmosphere has the lowest temperature?
   - **F** thermosphere
   - **G** troposphere
   - **H** stratosphere
   - **J** mesosphere
28. The range of temperatures found in the stratosphere is about ___ Celsius degrees.
   - **A** 100
   - **B** 0
   - **C** 30
   - **D** 60
29. Which of the following best describes how temperature changes as altitude increases in the troposphere?
   - **F** steadily increases
   - **G** increases then decreases
   - **H** steadily decreases
   - **J** decreases then increases

Sample Graph for Question 22

Altitude (km) vs *Temperature (°C)*

Program Resources

- ◆ **Inquiry Skills Activity Book** Provides teaching and review of all inquiry skills
- ◆ **Prentice Hall Assessment System** Provides standardized test practice
- ◆ **Reading in the Content Area** Provides strategies to improve science reading skills
- ◆ **Teacher's ELL Handbook** Provides multiple strategies for English language learners

---

Applying Skills

22. Students' graphs should show a line with a negative slope, that is, a line that slopes downward to the right. See sample graph below.
23. The temperature was -15°C at about 4 kilometers above the ground.
24. At 2.4 kilometers over Omaha, the approximate temperature was -6.5°C.
25. The approximate temperature at 6.8 kilometers above Omaha was -36°C, which was about 36° colder than the temperature at ground level.

Performance CHAPTER PROJECT Assessment

Present Your Project Displays should show how, where, and when observations were made and what scale was used to categorize each weather variable. Encourage students to present their observations in creative ways, such as weather centers, bulletin boards, or newspaper or television weather reports. Students should be prepared to discuss any trends they have identified in their observations.

Reflect and Record Students may be able to improve their weather logs by observing more weather variables or making more frequent or detailed observations. Encourage students to look at other students' logs for additional ideas. Weather factors that are not directly observable, such as temperature and air pressure, could be measured more accurately using instruments.

Test Preparation

26. B 27. F 28. D 29. H

CHAPTER 14 Weather Factors

Sections	Time	Student Edition Activities	Other Activities	
CHAPTER PROJECT **Your Own Weather Station** p. 461 TEKS: 6.14C	Ongoing (2-3 weeks)	TEKS: 6.2A, B, C, D, E; 6.4A, B **Check Your Progress**, p. 471, 480, 490 **Present Your Project**, p. 493	TE	Chapter 14 Project Notes, pp. 460–461
1 Energy in the Atmosphere pp. 462–467 TEKS: 6.14C 14.1.1 State in what form energy travels from the sun to Earth. 14.1.2 Explain what happens to energy from the sun when it reaches Earth.	3–4 periods/ 1½–2 blocks	TEKS: 6.1A; 6.2A, B, C, D, E; 6.4A **Discover** Does a Plastic Bag Trap Heat?, p. 462 **Science at Home**, p. 465 **Skills Lab: Developing Hypotheses** Heating Earth's Surface, pp. 466–467 (Probeware version available)	TE TE	Integrating Physics, p. 463 Exploring Energy in the Atmosphere, p. 464
2 *INTEGRATING PHYSICS* **Heat Transfer** pp. 468–471 TEKS: 6.14C 14.2.1 Describe how temperature is measured. 14.2.2 Explain the three ways heat is transferred.	1 period/ ½ block	TEKS: 6.2B, C, E; 6.4A **Discover** What Happens When Air Is Heated?, p. 468 **Try This** Temperatures at Two Heights, p. 470	TE TE TE	Demonstration, p. 469 Building Inquiry Skills: Calculating, p. 469 Inquiry Challenge, p. 470
3 Winds pp. 472–480 TEKS: 6.14C 14.3.1 Explain what causes winds. 14.3.2 Distinguish between local winds and global winds. 14.3.3 Describe the major global wind belts and where they are located.	3 periods/ 1½ blocks	TEKS: 6.2B, C, E; 6.3C; 6.4A **Discover** Which Way Does the Wind Turn?, p. 472 **Try This** Build a Wind Vane, p. 473 **Real-World Lab: You and Your Community** Where's the Wind?, pp. 474, 475	TE TE TE TE	Demonstration, p. 473 Including All Students, p. 476 Demonstration, p. 477 Including All Students, p. 478
4 Water in the Atmosphere pp. 481–486 TEKS: 6.14C 14.4.1 Describe how relative humidity is measured. 14.4.2 Explain how clouds form. 14.4.3 Describe the main types of clouds.	2–3 periods/ 1–1½ blocks	TEKS: 6.1A; 6.2A, B, C, D; 6.3C **Discover** How Does Fog Form?, p. 481 **Sharpen Your Skills** Interpreting Data, p. 483 **Science at Home**, p. 486	TE TE TE LM	Inquiry Challenge, p. 482 Building Inquiry Skills: Measuring, p. 483 Building Inquiry Skills: Inferring, p. 484 14, "Using a Psychrometer to Determine Relative Humidity"
5 Precipitation pp. 487–490 TEKS: 6.14C 14.5.1 Identify the main types of precipitation. 14.5.2 Describe how precipitation is measured and ways that it might be controlled.	1–2 periods/ ½–1 block	TEKS: 6.2C **Discover** How Can You Make Hail?, p. 487 **Sharpen Your Skills** Calculating, p. 489	TE TE	Building Inquiry Skills: Observing, p. 488 Building Inquiry Skills: Measuring, p. 489
Study Guide/Chapter Assessment pp. 491–493	1 period/ ½ block	PLM Provides blackline masters for Probeware labs	ISAB	Provides teaching and review of all inquiry skills

Key: **CTB** Computer Test Bank
CUT Chapter and Unit Tests
ELL Teacher's ELL Handbook

CHAPTER PLANNING GUIDE

 The Resource Pro® CD-ROM provides flexibility for planning the instruction for any type of schedule.

Program Resources	Assessment Strategies	Media and Technology
UR Chapter 14 Project Teacher Notes, pp. 118–119 **UR** Chapter 14 Project Overview and Worksheets, pp. 120–123	**SE** Performance Assessment: Present Your Project, p. 493 **TE** Check Your Progress, pp. 471, 480, 490 **UR** Chapter 14 Project Scoring Rubric, p. 124	Science Explorer at www.phschool.com Student Edition on Audio CD, English-Spanish, Chapter 14
UR 14-1 Lesson Plan, p. 125 **UR** 14-1 Section Summary, p. 126 **UR** 14-1 Review and Reinforce, p. 127 **UR** 14-1 Enrich, p. 128 **UR** Skills Lab blackline masters, pp. 145–147	**SE** Section 1 Review, p. 465 **TE** Ongoing Assessment, p. 463 **TE** Performance Assessment, p. 465	Earth Science Videodisc Unit 4, Side 2, "Heating the Earth" Videotape Grade 6, Unit 4, "Heating the Earth" Lab Activity Videotapes, Tape 4 Transparency 66, "Energy in the Atmosphere"
UR 14-2 Lesson Plan, p. 129 **UR** 14-2 Section Summary, p. 130 **UR** 14-2 Review and Reinforce, p. 131 **UR** 14-2 Enrich, p. 132	**SE** Section 2 Review, p. 471 **TE** Ongoing Assessment, p. 469 **TE** Performance Assessment, p. 471	Transparency 67, "Types of Heat Transfer"
UR 14-3 Lesson Plan, p. 133 **UR** 14-3 Section Summary, p. 134 **UR** 14-3 Review and Reinforce, p. 135 **UR** 14-3 Enrich, p. 136 **UR** Real-World Lab blackline masters, pp. 148–149	**SE** Section 3 Review, p. 480 **TE** Ongoing Assessment, pp. 473, 477, 479 **TE** Performance Assessment, p. 480	Earth Science Videodisc Unit 2, Side 2, "The Power of Heat" Videotape Grade 6, Unit 4, "The Power of Heat" Lab Activity Videotapes, Tape 4 Transparency 68, "Global Winds"
UR 14-4 Lesson Plan, p. 137 **UR** 14-4 Section Summary, p. 138 **UR** 14-4 Review and Reinforce, p. 139 **UR** 14-4 Enrich, p. 140	**SE** Section 4 Review, p. 486 **TE** Ongoing Assessment, pp. 483, 485 **TE** Performance Assessment, p. 486	Transparency 69, "Clouds"
UR 14-5 Lesson Plan, p. 141 **UR** 14-5 Section Summary, p. 142 **UR** 14-5 Review and Reinforce, p. 143 **UR** 14-5 Enrich, p. 144	**SE** Section 5 Review, p. 490 **TE** Ongoing Assessment, p. 489 **TE** Performance Assessment, p. 490	Earth Science Videodisc Unit 6, Side 2, "What's in Our Tap?" Videotape Grade 6, Unit 4, "What's in Our Tap?"
ELL Provides multiple strategies for English language learners **GRSW** Provides worksheets to promote student comprehension of content **RCA** Provides strategies to improve science reading skills	**SE** Chapter 14 Study Guide/Assessment, pp. 491–493 **PA** Chapter 14 Assessment, pp. 44–46 **CUT** Chapter 14 Test, pp. 68–71 **CTB** Chapter 14 Test **PHAS** Provides standardized test preparation	Chapter 14 Computer Test Bank, Chapter 14 Test

GRSW Guided Reading and Study Workbook
ISAB Inquiry Skills Activity Book
LM Laboratory Manual

PA Performance Assessment
PHAS Prentice Hall Assessment System
PLM Probeware Lab Manual

RCA Reading in the Content Area
SE Student Edition

TE Teacher's Edition
UR Unit Resources

Student Edition Activities Planner

ACTIVITy	Time (minutes)	Materials Quantities for one work group	Skills
Section 1			
Discover, p. 462	10	**Consumable** plastic bag, 2 small pieces of paper, tape **Nonconsumable** 2 thermometers	Measuring
Science at Home, p. 465	home	No special materials required.	Observing
Skills Lab, pp. 466–467	40	**Consumable** 300 mL water, string, 300 mL sand, graph paper **Nonconsumable** 2 thermometers or temperature probes, 2 400-mL beakers, metric ruler, ring stand and ring clamp, lamp with 100-W bulb, clock or stopwatch	Developing Hypotheses, Measuring, Creating Data Tables, Drawing Conclusions
Section 2			
Discover, p. 468	10	**Consumable** aluminum pie plate, thread, candle **Nonconsumable** heavy scissors, hot plate or incandescent light	Inferring
Try This, p. 470	10, 10, 10, 20	**Consumable** graph paper **Nonconsumable** 2 thermometers, metric tape measure, watch or clock	Interpreting Data
Section 3			
Discover, p. 472	10	**Consumable** heavy-duty tape **Nonconsumable** pencil, large smooth ball, marker	Making Models
Try This, p. 473	15	**Consumable** construction paper, soda straw, tape, straight pin **Nonconsumable** scissors, metric ruler, pencil with eraser	Observing
Real-World Lab, pp. 474–475	40	**Consumable** 15 cm x 20 cm corrugated cardboard sheet, round toothpick, 2 wooden coffee stirrers, narrow masking tape **Nonconsumable** pen, wind vane, meter stick, computer (optional)	Measuring, Interpreting Data, Drawing Conclusions
Section 4			
Discover, p. 481	10	**Consumable** hot tap water, 2 ice cubes, cold tap water **Nonconsumable** narrow-necked plastic bottle	Developing Hypotheses
Sharpen Your Skills, p. 483	10	No special materials required.	Interpreting Data
Science at Home, p. 486	home	**Consumable** cold water, ice cubes **Nonconsumable** large glass	Communicating
Section 5			
Discover, p. 487	15	**Consumable** 15 g salt, 50 mL water, 15 mL cold water, crushed ice **Nonconsumable** beaker, stirrer, clean test tube, watch or clock	Inferring
Sharpen Your Skills, p. 489	15	**Nonconsumable** funnel, narrow straight-sided glass jar, metric ruler, calculator	Calculating

A list of all materials required for the Student Edition activities can be found beginning on page T43–T49. You can obtain information about ordering materials by calling 1-800-848-9500 or by accessing the Science Explorer Internet site at **www.phschool.com**.

Texas Essential Knowledge and Skills

(6.1) Scientific processes. The student conducts field and laboratory investigations using safe, environmentally appropriate, and ethical practices. *(Sections 1, 4)*
The student is expected to:
(A) demonstrate safe practices during field and laboratory investigations.

(6.2) Scientific processes. The student uses scientific inquiry methods during field and laboratory investigations. *(Project; Sections 1, 2, 3, 4, 5)*
The student is expected to:
(A) plan and implement investigative procedures including asking questions, formulating testable hypotheses, and selecting and using equipment and technology;
(B) collect data by observing and measuring;
(C) analyze and interpret information to construct reasonable explanations from direct and indirect evidence;
(D) communicate valid conclusions; and
(E) construct graphs, tables, maps, and charts using tools including computers to organize, examine, and evaluate data.

(6.3) Scientific processes. The student uses critical thinking and scientific problem solving to make informed decisions. *(Sections 3, 4)*
The student is expected to:
(C) represent the natural world using models and identify their limitations.

(6.4) Scientific processes. The student knows how to use a variety of tools and methods to conduct science inquiry. *(Project; Sections 1, 2, 3)*
The student is expected to:
(A) collect, analyze, and record information using tools including beakers, petri dishes, meter sticks, graduated cylinders, weather instruments, timing devices, hot plates, test tubes, safety goggles, spring scales, magnets, balances, microscopes, telescopes, thermometers, calculators, field equipment, compasses, computers, and computer probes; and
(B) identify patterns in collected information using percent, average, range, and frequency.

(6.14) Science concepts. The student knows the structures and functions of Earth systems. *(Project; Sections 1, 2, 3, 4, 5)*
The student is expected to:
(C) describe components of the atmosphere, including oxygen, nitrogen, and water vapor, and identify the role of atmospheric movement in weather change.

Take It to the Net

 Interactive text at www.phschool.com

Science Explorer comes alive with iText.

- **Complete student text** is accessible from any computer with Internet access or a CD-ROM drive.

- **Animations, simulations, and videos** enhance student understanding and retention of concepts.

- **Self-tests and online study tools** assess student understanding.

- **Teacher management tools** help you make the most of this valuable resource.

STAY CURRENT with

Find out the latest research and information about weather and climate at **www.phschool.com**.

Go to **www.phschool.com**. Select Texas on the navigation bar. Click on the Science icon. Then click on <u>Science Explorer</u> under PH@school.

Your Own Weather Station

TEKS: 6.2A, B, C, D, E; 6.4A, B; 6.14C

In this chapter, students will learn more about specific weather factors, how they are related, and how they can be measured with instruments. The Chapter 14 Project gives students an opportunity to use instruments to take measurements of each of the weather factors.

Purpose In this project, students will set up a weather station and use instruments to measure weather factors over a two-week period. At the end of the project, students will look for patterns in their data and use them to try to predict the weather. Doing the project will give students a better understanding of weather factors and how they can be used to predict the weather.

Skills Focus After completing this project, students will be able to
◆ plan and create a model weather station;
◆ use their weather station to measure weather factors;
◆ record the data in a weather log;
◆ graph their data and analyze it for trends;
◆ use the trends to try to predict the weather;
◆ compare their predictions with actual weather conditions;
◆ communicate their findings to the rest of the class.

Project Time Line The entire project will take about three weeks. On the first day, introduce the project and hand out the Chapter 14 Project Overview, pages 120–121 in Unit 4 Resources. Allow time for class discussion of the project rules and for students to brainstorm weather factors, how they can be measured, and ways to record the measurements. At this time, you may wish to divide the class into small groups for the project.

Distribute the Chapter 14 Project Worksheet 1, page 122 in Unit 4 Resources, to help students plan their weather station, and Worksheet 2, page 123 in Unit 4 Resources, to show students a way to measure cloud cover. You also may wish to distribute the Chapter 14 Project Scoring Rubric, page 124 in the

14 Weather Factors

WEB ACTIVITY www.phschool.com

① Energy in the Atmosphere
Discover Does a Plastic Bag Trap Heat?
Skills Lab Heating Earth's Surface

② Heat Transfer
Discover What Happens When Air is Heated?

③ Winds
Discover Which Way Does the Wind Turn?
Real-World Lab Where's the Wind?

④ Water in the Atmosphere
Discover How Does Fog Form?

⑤ Precipitation
Discover How Can You Make Hail?

Unit 4 Resources, so students will know what is expected of them.

Give students a day or two to plan their weather station and assemble the instruments and other materials they will need. Allow one class period for students to set up their weather station and practice using the instruments. You may wish to give students enough class time each day over the next two weeks to measure and record weather data. At the end of two weeks, give students a day or two to graph and analyze their data. Finally, set aside a class period at the end of the project for students to

present and discuss their results.

For more information on supervising the chapter project, see Chapter 14 Project Teacher Notes, pages 118–119 in Unit 4 Resources.

Suggested Shortcuts You can streamline the project by having students make and share a single weather station. If you assemble the instruments and materials for the shared weather station yourself, you will save another day or two. If you do the project as a class project, assign different students to make the weather observations each day.

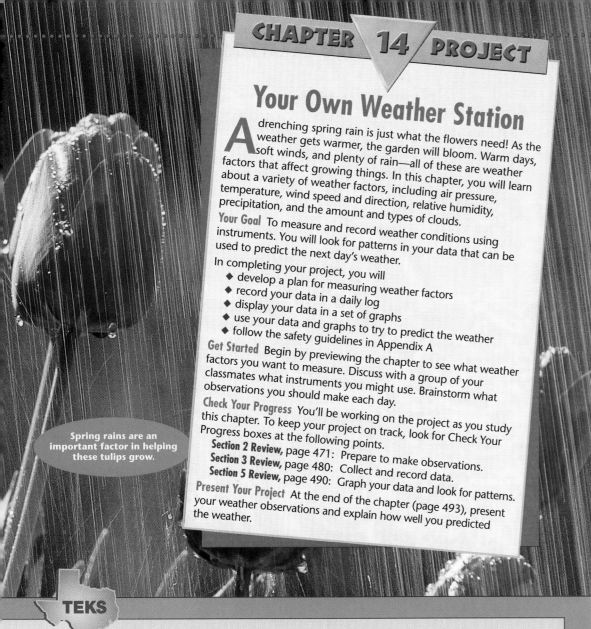

CHAPTER 14 PROJECT

Your Own Weather Station

A drenching spring rain is just what the flowers need! As the weather gets warmer, the garden will bloom. Warm days, soft winds, and plenty of rain—all of these are weather factors that affect growing things. In this chapter, you will learn about a variety of weather factors, including air pressure, temperature, wind speed and direction, relative humidity, precipitation, and the amount and types of clouds.

Your Goal To measure and record weather conditions using instruments. You will look for patterns in your data that can be used to predict the next day's weather.

In completing your project, you will
- develop a plan for measuring weather factors
- record your data in a daily log
- display your data in a set of graphs
- use your data and graphs to try to predict the weather
- follow the safety guidelines in Appendix A

Get Started Begin by previewing the chapter to see what weather factors you want to measure. Discuss with a group of your classmates what instruments you might use. Brainstorm what observations you should make each day.

Check Your Progress You'll be working on the project as you study this chapter. To keep your project on track, look for Check Your Progress boxes at the following points.

Section 2 Review, page 471: Prepare to make observations.
Section 3 Review, page 480: Collect and record data.
Section 5 Review, page 490: Graph your data and look for patterns.

Present Your Project At the end of the chapter (page 493), present your weather observations and explain how well you predicted the weather.

Spring rains are an important factor in helping these tulips grow.

 TEKS

In addition to process TEKS, this chapter addresses these concept TEKS as they relate to the chapter's topics.

(6.14) The student knows the structures and functions of Earth systems.
The student is expected to:
(C) describe components of the atmosphere, including oxygen, nitrogen, and water vapor, and identify the role of atmospheric movement in weather change.

461

Program Resources

- **Unit 4 Resources** Chapter 14 Project Teacher Notes, pp. 118–119; Chapter 14 Project Overview and Worksheets, pp. 120–123

Media and Technology

🎧 **Student Edition on Audio CD**
English-Spanish, Chapter 14

WEB ACTIVITY www.phschool.com

You will find an Internet activity, chapter self-tests for students, and links to other chapter topics at this site.

Possible Materials A weather station requires a sheltered place outdoors, such as the slatted wooden box described in Worksheet 1. Several instruments are needed, including a thermometer, psychrometer, barometer, wind vane, anemometer, and rain gauge. Useful additions are a device for measuring cloud cover (see Worksheet 2) and a chart showing cloud types (or use Exploring Clouds, page 485 in the text).

Students will need commercial thermometers and psychrometers. They can use the barometer they made in the Skills Lab in Chapter 13, pages 448–449 in the text. They also can make their own wind vane (Try This, page 473 in the text), anemometer (Real-World Lab, pages 474–475 in the text), and rain gauge (Sharpen Your Skills, page 489 in the text). However, commercial instruments are more accurate and should be used if possible.

Launching the Project Introduce the project by discussing weather stations. Ask: **If you were going to visit another city, what would you want to know about the weather so you would be prepared?** (*Students may say they would want to know how hot or cold it was and if it was raining or snowing.*) **How could you find out what the weather conditions in the city were?** (*Students may say they would watch a national weather report on television or look at a national weather map in a newspaper.*) Point out that weather information for specific locations is collected and recorded by weather stations. Tell students that in this project they will make a weather station and observe and record weather factors for a location near their school.

Performance Assessment

To assess students' performance in this project, use the Chapter 14 Project Scoring Rubric on page 124 in Unit 4 Resources. Students will be assessed on their
- weather observations and weather log;
- graphical presentation and interpretation of weather data;
- presentation of the results to the class;
- group participation, if they worked in groups.

461

Objectives

After completing the lesson, students will be able to

◆ state in what form energy travels from the sun to Earth;

◆ explain what happens to energy from the sun when it reaches Earth.

1 Engage/Explore

Activating Prior Knowledge

Encourage students to think about the way the sun heats Earth's surface by asking: **Which is cooler on a hot, sunny day, a lawn or a parking lot?** *(a lawn)* Point out that even without trees, a grass-covered surface stays cooler than a surface covered by blacktop. Ask: **Why doesn't the lawn get as hot as the parking lot?** *(Students may not know.)* Tell students that grass absorbs less light than pavement even when both surfaces receive the same amount of sun. As a result, the grass does not get as hot. Add that such differences in the heating of Earth's surface, on a large scale, are the major cause of Earth's weather.

········ **DISCOVER** ········

Skills Focus measuring
Materials

2 thermometers, plastic bag, 2 small pieces of paper, tape

Time 10 minutes

Tips Make sure the bulbs of both thermometers are shaded by the pieces of paper from direct rays of light or both may show equally high temperatures.

Expected Outcome The thermometer in the bag should show a higher temperature.

Think It Over The plastic bag trapped the heat inside it from the sun, and this caused the thermometer in the bag to show a higher temperature.

462

SECTION
1 Energy in the Atmosphere

DISCOVER .... ACTIVITY

Does a Plastic Bag Trap Heat?

1. Record the initial temperatures on two thermometers. (You should get the same readings.)

2. Place one of the thermometers in a plastic bag. Put a small piece of paper in the bag so that it shades the bulb of the thermometer. Seal the bag.

3. Place both thermometers on a sunny window ledge or near a light bulb. Cover the bulb of the second thermometer with a small piece of paper. Predict what you think will happen.

4. Wait five minutes. Then record the temperatures on the two thermometers.

Think It Over

Measuring Were the two temperatures the same? How could you explain any difference?

GUIDE FOR READING

◆ In what form does energy from the sun travel to Earth?

◆ What happens to energy from the sun when it reaches Earth?

Reading Tip Before you read, skim the section for boldfaced words that are unfamiliar to you. As you read, find their meanings and write them down in your notebook.

Key Terms radiation
• electromagnetic waves
• infrared radiation
• ultraviolet radiation
• scattering • greenhouse effect

Think of a sunny summer day. When you get up in the morning, the sun is low in the sky and the air is cool. As the sun rises, the temperature increases. By noon it is quite hot. As you will see in this chapter, heat is a major factor in the weather. The movement of heat in the atmosphere causes temperatures to change, winds to blow, and rain to fall.

Energy from the Sun

 INTEGRATING PHYSICS Nearly all the energy in Earth's atmosphere comes from the sun. This energy travels to Earth as **electromagnetic waves,** a form of energy that can travel through space. Electromagnetic waves are classified according to wavelength, or distance between waves. The direct transfer of energy by electromagnetic waves is called **radiation.**

Most of the energy from the sun reaches Earth in the form of visible light and infrared radiation, and a small amount of ultraviolet radiation. Visible light is a mixture of all of the colors that you see in a rainbow: red, orange, yellow, green, blue, and violet. The different colors are the result of different wavelengths

462

READING STRATEGIES

Reading Tip Suggest that students make a list of unfamiliar boldfaced words and then fill in their meanings as they read.

Study and Comprehension Suggest that students use ROY G. BV to remember the order of colors in the spectrum of visible light, going from longer to shorter wavelengths. The colors represented by the letters are red, orange, yellow, green, blue, and violet.

Program Resources

◆ **Unit 4 Resources** 14-1 Lesson Plan, p. 125; 14-1 Section Summary, p. 126

◆ **Guided Reading and Study Workbook** 14-1

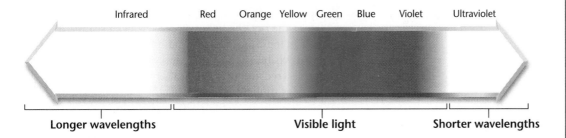

Infrared | Red | Orange | Yellow | Green | Blue | Violet | Ultraviolet

Longer wavelengths | Visible light | Shorter wavelengths

of visible light. Red and orange light have the longest wavelengths, while blue and violet light have the shortest wavelengths.

Infrared radiation is a form of energy with wavelengths that are longer than red light. Infrared radiation is not visible, but can be felt as heat. Heat lamps used to keep food warm in restaurants give off both visible red light and invisible infrared radiation. The sun also gives off **ultraviolet radiation,** which has wavelengths that are shorter than violet light. Sunburns are caused by ultraviolet radiation. This radiation can also cause skin cancer and eye damage.

☑ *Checkpoint* *Which color of visible light has the longest wavelengths?*

Energy in the Atmosphere

Before the sun's rays can reach Earth's surface, they must pass through the atmosphere. The path of the sun's rays is shown in *Exploring Energy in the Atmosphere* on the following page.

Some of the energy from the sun is absorbed within the atmosphere. Water vapor and carbon dioxide absorb some infrared radiation. The ozone layer in the stratosphere absorbs most of the ultraviolet radiation. Clouds, dust, and other gases also absorb energy from the sun.

Some of the sun's rays are reflected. Clouds in the atmosphere act like mirrors, reflecting some solar energy back into space. In addition, dust particles and molecules of gases in the atmosphere reflect light from the sun in all directions.

Figure 1 Electromagnetic waves include infrared radiation, visible light, and ultraviolet radiation.
Interpreting Diagrams *What type of radiation has wavelengths that are shorter than visible light? What type has wavelengths that are longer?*

Chapter 14 **463**

Answers to Self-Assessment

Caption Question

Figure 1 Ultraviolet radiation has wavelengths that are shorter than visible light. Infrared radiation has wavelengths that are longer than visible light.

☑ *Checkpoint*

Red light has the longest wavelengths.

---

2 *Facilitate*

Energy from the Sun

 Integrating Physics

Materials *prism*
Time 5 minutes

Show students a prism and explain that its angled sides bend the different colors in sunlight by different amounts, splitting the light into a rainbow. Demonstrate by placing the prism in sunlight. Then ask: **Where does light have the shortest wavelength and where does light have the longest wavelength?** *(The end with violet light is the shortest, and the end with red light is the longest.)* **learning modality: visual**

Energy in the Atmosphere

Building Inquiry Skills: Inferring

Describe the following hypothetical situation to the class. City A is located where the ozone layer of the stratosphere has become very thin. City B is located where the ozone layer is still relatively thick. Ask: **How do you think the two cities compare in terms of the ultraviolet radiation they receive?** *(City A would get more ultraviolet radiation than City B because less of the ultraviolet radiation would be absorbed by ozone in the stratosphere.)* **learning modality: logical/mathematical**

Ongoing Assessment

Drawing Have students draw a representation of the visible spectrum, showing the different colors of visible light in order by wavelength.

Energy in the Atmosphere, continued

Including All Students

Remind students that the moon, unlike Earth, has no atmosphere. Then ask: **If you were standing on the moon during the day, what color would the sky appear to be?** *(Students may know from photographs that the sky would appear to be black.)* **Why wouldn't the sky appear to be blue?** *(Because without an atmosphere on the moon there are no gas molecules to scatter the light and make it look blue)* **learning modality: logical/mathematical**

EXPLORING

Energy in the Atmosphere

Materials *several sheets of light- and dark-colored construction paper, bandanas or other material for blindfolds*

ACTIVITY

Time 10 minutes

Point out to students that all parts of Earth's surface are not heated equally by energy from the sun. Demonstrate this point by placing several pieces of construction paper in direct sunlight. Use white, black, and at least one or two other light and dark colors. After the papers have been in the sun for at least five minutes, ask volunteers to put on blindfolds. Then rearrange the order of the papers and have the volunteers try to tell which papers are light colored and which are dark colored based on how warm or cool they feel to the touch. Ask: **Why do the dark-colored papers feel warmer than the light-colored papers?** *(Dark-colored surfaces absorb more of the light that strikes them, whereas light-colored surfaces reflect more of the light that strikes them.)* **Which surfaces on Earth do you think reflect more of the sun's light back into space?** *(Light-colored surfaces such as sand or snow)* **Which surfaces absorb more of the sun's light?** *(Dark-colored surfaces such as bare soil or blacktop pavement)* Refer to the **ELL Handbook** for additional teaching strategies. **learning modality: tactile/kinesthetic**

Reflection of light in all directions is called **scattering.** When you look at the sky, the light you see has been scattered by gas molecules in the atmosphere. Gas molecules scatter short wavelengths of visible light (blue and violet) more than long wavelengths (red and orange). Scattered light is therefore bluer than ordinary sunlight, which is why the daytime sky looks blue.

When the sun is rising or setting, light from the sun passes through a greater thickness of the atmosphere than when the sun is higher in the sky. More light from the blue end of the spectrum is removed by scattering before it reaches your eyes. The remaining light from the sun contains mostly red and orange light. The sun looks red, and clouds around it become very colorful.

☑ *Checkpoint* Why would particles from volcanic eruptions make sunsets and sunrises more red?

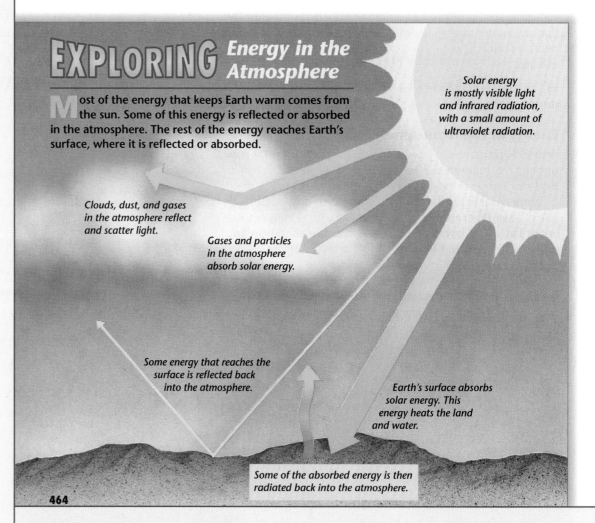

EXPLORING *Energy in the Atmosphere*

Most of the energy that keeps Earth warm comes from the sun. Some of this energy is reflected or absorbed in the atmosphere. The rest of the energy reaches Earth's surface, where it is reflected or absorbed.

Solar energy is mostly visible light and infrared radiation, with a small amount of ultraviolet radiation.

Clouds, dust, and gases in the atmosphere reflect and scatter light.

Gases and particles in the atmosphere absorb solar energy.

Some energy that reaches the surface is reflected back into the atmosphere.

Earth's surface absorbs solar energy. This energy heats the land and water.

Some of the absorbed energy is then radiated back into the atmosphere.

464

Background

Facts and Figures The amount of energy produced by the sun is amazing. An area of the sun's surface the size of a postage stamp gives off enough energy to power 500 60-watt light bulbs. Although only one part in two billion of the total amount of solar energy reaches Earth, this is still a huge amount. If the amount of solar energy reaching Earth in just one hour could be used, it would meet the world's total energy needs for a year. If

the amount of solar energy reaching Earth in a day could be used, it would take 700 billion tons of coal to match it.

A tiny fraction of the sun's energy actually is trapped and used for power. Some solar energy plants collect sunlight with mirrors and focus it with lenses on tubes filled with fluid. The fluid heats up, and the heat is used to boil water into steam that powers electric generators.

Energy at Earth's Surface

Some of the sun's energy reaches Earth's surface and is reflected back into the atmosphere. Some of the energy, however, is absorbed by the land and water and changed into heat.

When Earth's surface is heated, it radiates some of the energy back into the atmosphere as infrared radiation. Most of this infrared radiation cannot travel all the way through the atmosphere back into space. Instead, much of it is absorbed by water vapor, carbon dioxide, methane, and other gases in the air. The energy from the absorbed radiation heats the gases in the air. These gases form a "blanket" around Earth that holds heat in the atmosphere. The process by which gases hold heat in the air is called the **greenhouse effect.**

Have you ever been inside a greenhouse during the winter? Even on a cold day, a greenhouse is warm. Greenhouses trap heat in two ways. First, infrared radiation given off in the interior cannot easily pass through glass and is trapped inside. Second, warm air inside the greenhouse cannot escape because the glass blocks the movement of air. What happens in Earth's atmosphere is similar to the first way that greenhouses trap heat. However, a greenhouse does not provide a perfect model of processes in the atmosphere.

The greenhouse effect is a natural process that keeps Earth's atmosphere at a temperature that is comfortable for most living things. Human activities over the last 200 years, however, have increased the amount of carbon dioxide in the atmosphere, which may be warming the atmosphere.

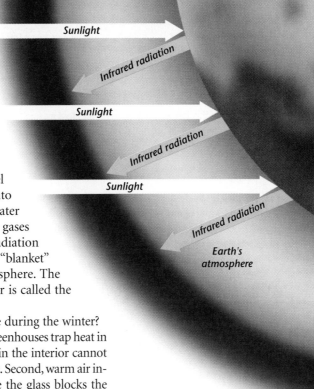

Figure 2 Sunlight travels through the atmosphere to Earth's surface. Earth's surface then gives off infrared radiation. Much of this energy is held by the atmosphere, warming it.

Section 1 Review

1. List three forms of radiation from the sun. How are these alike? How are they different?
2. What happens to the energy from the sun that is absorbed by Earth's surface?
3. Why is the sky blue? Why are sunsets often red?
4. **Thinking Critically Applying Concepts** What might conditions on Earth be like without the greenhouse effect?

Science at Home

Heating by Radiation With an adult family member, explore the role radiation plays in heating your home. Are some rooms warmer and sunnier in the morning? Are other rooms warmer and sunnier in the afternoon? How does opening and closing curtains or blinds affect the temperature of a room? Explain your observations to your family.

Answers to Self-Assessment

☑ *Checkpoint*

The particles would scatter more light from the sun. This would remove more light from the blue end of the spectrum, causing the remaining light to look mostly red.

Energy at Earth's Surface

Real-Life Learning

Ask students if they have ever noticed a difference in the temperature of different rooms in their homes. Students may say that rooms that receive more sunlight are warmer. Then ask if the difference in temperature is the same on sunny days and cloudy days. The difference will likely be greater on sunny days.
learning modality: verbal

3 Assess

Section 1 Review Answers

1. Visible light, infrared radiation, and ultraviolet radiation; they differ in their wavelengths.
2. It is changed into heat.
3. The sky is blue because short-wavelength blue light is scattered more by gas molecules in the atmosphere. Sunsets are often red because the light from the setting sun passes through a greater thickness of the atmosphere than when the sun is higher in the sky, and more blue light is removed by scattering, leaving mostly red light to reach your eyes.
4. Without the greenhouse effect, more infrared radiation radiated back from Earth's surface would escape into space instead of being held in the atmosphere, so Earth's surface would be much colder.

Science at Home

Tips Suggest to students that they try to do this activity on a sunny day, preferably when the furnace or other source of artificial heat is not operating.

Performance Assessment

Oral Presentation Call on students to explain in their own words one of the various things that can happen to sunlight that reaches Earth's atmosphere.

Heating Earth's Surface

Preparing for Inquiry

Key Concept Sand heats and cools more quickly than water.

Skills Objectives Students will be able to
◆ develop hypotheses about how quickly sand and water heat and cool;
◆ measure the temperature of sand and water while they are heating and cooling;
◆ create a data table to record their measurements;
◆ conclude from their data whether sand or water heats and cools more quickly.

Time 40 minutes

Advance Planning To be sure students have enough class time to record temperatures for a full 30 minutes, you may wish to set up the equipment and measure out the sand and water ahead of time. Make sure the sand is dry. Both sand and water should be at room temperature when the lab begins.

Alternative Materials Students can use small wide-mouthed glass jars instead of beakers, as long as both jars are the same size and shape. They also can substitute sugar for sand. If ring stands and clamps are not available, you can substitute two 2-L soda bottles placed about 30 cm apart and connected by a ruler placed across the tops. The thermometers can be suspended from the ruler.

If using probeware, refer to the *Probeware Lab Manual.*

Guiding Inquiry

Invitation To help students formulate hypotheses about the heating and cooling of sand and water, have them recall walking barefoot on a beach. Ask: **Did you ever walk barefoot on the beach on a sunny day? What was the temperature of the sand like?** *(The sand was probably hot.)* **When you reached the water, how did it feel in comparison to the hot sand?** *(much cooler)* **If you ever walked barefoot on the beach after dark, which felt warmer, the sand or the water?** *(the water)*

Skills Lab

Developing Hypotheses

Heating Earth's Surface

In this lab, you will develop and test a hypothesis about how quickly different materials absorb radiation.

Problem

How do the heating and cooling rates of sand and water compare?

Materials

2 thermometers or temperature probes
ring stand and 2 ring clamps
2 beakers, 400 mL   sand, 300 mL
water, 300 mL   lamp with 150-W bulb
metric ruler   clock or stopwatch
string   graph paper

Procedure

1. Do you think sand or water will heat up faster? Record your hypothesis. Then follow these steps to test your hypothesis.
2. Copy the data table into your notebook. Add enough rows to record data for 15 minutes.
3. Fill one beaker with 300 mL of dry sand.
4. Fill the second beaker with 300 mL of water at room temperature.
5. Arrange the beakers beneath the ring stand.
6. Place one thermometer in each beaker. If using temperature probes, see your teacher for instructions.
7. Suspend the thermometers from the ring stand with string. This will hold the thermometers in place so they do not fall.

8. Adjust the height of the clamp so that the bulb of each thermometer is covered by about 0.5 cm of sand or water in a beaker.
9. Position the lamp so that it is about 20 cm above the sand and water. There should be no more than 8 cm between the beakers. **CAUTION:** *Be careful not to splash water onto the hot light bulb.*
10. Record the temperature of the sand and water in your data table.
11. Turn on the lamp. Read the temperature of the sand and water every minute for 15 minutes. Record the temperatures in the Light On column in the data table.
12. Which material do you think will cool off more quickly? Record your hypothesis. Again, give reasons why you think your hypothesis is correct.
13. Turn the light off. Read the temperature of the sand and water every minute for another 15 minutes. Record the temperatures in the Light Off column (16–30 minutes).

DATA TABLE					
Temperature with Light On (°C)			**Temperature with Light Off (°C)**		
Time (min)	Sand	Water	Time (min)	Sand	Water
Start			16		
1			17		
2			18		
3			19		
4			20		
5			21		

Introducing the Procedure

Have students read through the steps of the procedure. Clarify any steps they do not understand. Students should use exactly the same amount of sand as water and place both beakers exactly the same distance from the lamp. Explain that by making these factors the same for both the sand and water, they will be controlling other variables that might affect the outcome of the experiment.

Troubleshooting the Experiment

◆ To reduce the number of setups needed, divide the class into groups and have each group use one setup.
◆ Make sure that each lamp is positioned so it shines evenly on the two beakers. If one beaker receives more direct rays than the other, it may bias the results. Also check that both thermometers are positioned the same distance below the surface and held in an upright position by the string.

Analyze and Conclude

1. Draw two line graphs to show the data for the temperature change in sand and water over time. Label the horizontal axis from 0 to 30 minutes and the vertical axis in degrees Celsius. Draw both graphs on the same piece of graph paper. Use a dashed line to show the temperature change in water and a solid line to show the temperature change in sand.

2. Calculate the total change in temperature for each material.

3. Based on your data, which material had the greater increase in temperature?

4. What can you conclude about which material absorbed heat faster? How do your results compare with your hypothesis?

5. Review your data again. In 15 minutes, which material cooled faster?

6. How do these results compare to your second hypothesis?

7. **Think About It** If your results did not support either of your hypotheses, why do you think the results differed from what you expected?

8. **Apply** Based on your results, which do you think will heat up more quickly on a sunny day: the water in a lake or the sand surrounding it? Which will cool off more quickly after dark?

More to Explore

Do you think all solid materials heat up as fast as sand? For example, consider gravel, crushed stone, or different types of soil. Write a hypothesis about their heating rates as an "If . . . then . . ." statement. With the approval and supervision of your teacher, develop a procedure to test your hypothesis. Was your hypothesis correct?

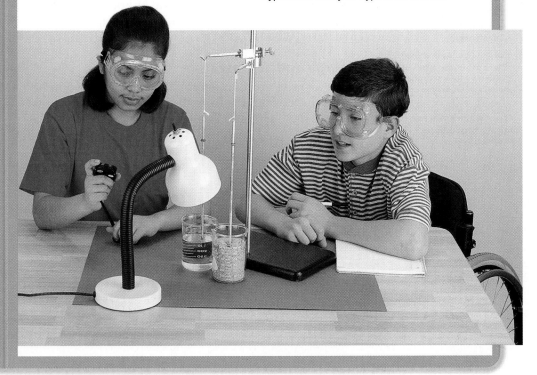

Safety

Caution students to be careful not to touch the light bulb or splash water on it. Review the safety guidelines in Appendix A.

Program Resources

◆ **Unit 4 Resources** Chapter 14 Skills Lab blackline masters, pp. 145–147
◆ **Probeware Lab Manual** Blackline masters

Media and Technology

 Lab Activity Videotapes
Grade 6, Tape 4

Expected Outcome

Students should find that the sand heats and cools more quickly than the water.

Analyze and Conclude

1. Both graphs should rise steadily during the first 15 minutes and then decline steadily during the second 15 minutes. The line for sand temperature should rise and fall more steeply than the line for water temperature, indicating a greater rate of change in temperature for sand than water.

2. Exact answers will vary depending on the specific temperatures recorded. However, the sand should show a greater total change in temperature than the water.

3. The data should show that the sand had a greater increase in temperature.

4. Students should conclude that the sand absorbed heat faster than the water. These results may or may not agree with their hypothesis.

5. The data should show that the sand cooled faster.

6. These results may or may not agree with their second hypothesis.

7. Answers may vary. One possible answer is that they expected both the sand and water to heat and cool at the same rate because there were equal amounts of the two substances.

8. Based on their results, students should say that the sand surrounding a lake will heat up more quickly on a sunny day and cool off more quickly after dark than the water in the lake.

Extending the Inquiry

More to Explore Students may think that solids with a different texture, made of different materials, or having different colors might heat up at different rates than sand. For example, students may think that rock would heat up faster than sand because it is more solid. Students may hypothesize that soil will heat up faster than sand because it is darker in color. They can test their hypothesis by repeating the skills lab and substituting soil or other materials for water.

SECTION 2 Heat Transfer

TEKS: 6.2B, C, E; 6.4A; 6.14C

Objectives

After completing the lesson, students will be able to

◆ describe how temperature is measured;

◆ explain the three ways heat is transferred.

1 Engage/Explore

Activating Prior Knowledge

Introduce students to the concept of heat transfer by helping them recall the shimmery effect produced by heated air rising from hot pavement. Ask: **On a hot sunny day, did you ever see cars, buildings, or other objects appear to shimmer or waver on the other side of a street or parking lot?** (*Most students probably will say yes.*) **What causes this effect?** (*Hot air rising from the pavement*) Explain that the sun heats up the ground more quickly than the air, especially if the surface of the ground is dark colored. The heated air then rises and bends light waves as they pass through it, making objects on the other side shimmer.

·········· DISCOVER ··········

Skills Focus inferring
Materials *aluminum pie plate, heavy scissors, thread, candle or hot plate or incandescent light*
Time 10 minutes
Tips You may want to poke the holes in the flat parts yourself.
Expected Outcome The spiral will spin.
Think It Over The spiral spun because warm air rose from the heat source and pushed against the spiral.

SECTION 2 Heat Transfer

DISCOVER ·· ACTIVITY

What Happens When Air Is Heated?

1. Use heavy scissors to cut the flat part out of an aluminum pie plate. Use the tip of the scissors to poke a small hole in the middle of the flat part.

2. Cut the part into a spiral shape, as shown in the photo. Tie a 30-centimeter piece of thread to the middle of the spiral.

3. Hold the spiral over a source of heat, such as a candle, hot plate, or incandescent light bulb.

Think It Over
Inferring What happened to the spiral? Why do you think this happened?

GUIDE FOR READING

◆ How is temperature measured?

◆ In what three ways is heat transferred?

Reading Tip As you read, make a list of the types of heat transfer. Write a sentence about how each type occurs.

Key Terms thermal energy • temperature • thermometer • heat • conduction • convection

You know that energy from the sun is absorbed by Earth's surface. Some energy is then transferred from the surface to the atmosphere in the form of heat. The heat then moves from place to place within the atmosphere. But how does heat move in the atmosphere?

Energy and Temperature

Gases are made up of small particles, called molecules, that are constantly moving. The faster the molecules are moving, the more energy they have. Figure 3 shows how the motion of

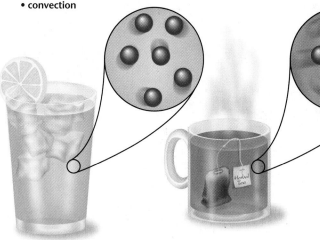

Figure 3 The lemonade is cold, so the molecules move slowly. The herbal tea is hot, so the molecules move faster than the molecules in the lemonade. *Inferring Which liquid has a higher temperature?*

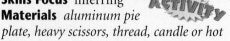

READING STRATEGIES

Reading Tip Student lists should include radiation, conduction, and convection. Their sentences should explain that radiation occurs by direct transfer of heat by one substance touching another, and that convection occurs as the result of the movement of fluids.

Program Resources

◆ **Unit 4 Resources** 14-2 Lesson Plan, p. 129; 14-2 Section Summary, p. 130
◆ **Guided Reading and Study Workbook** 14-2

molecules is related to the amount of energy they hold. The total energy of motion in the molecules of a substance is called **thermal energy.** On the other hand, **temperature** is the *average* amount of energy of motion of the molecules of a substance. That means that temperature is a measure of how hot or cold a substance is.

Measuring Temperature

Ask someone what the weather is like. The answer will probably include the temperature. Temperature is one of the most important elements of weather. **Air temperature is usually measured with a thermometer.** A thermometer is a thin glass tube with a bulb on one end that contains a liquid, usually mercury or colored alcohol.

Thermometers work because liquids usually expand when they are heated and contract when they are cooled. When the air temperature increases, the liquid in the bulb expands and rises up the column. What happens when the temperature decreases? The liquid in the bulb contracts and moves down the tube.

Temperature is measured in units called degrees. The two most common scales are shown in Figure 4. Scientists use the Celsius scale. On the Celsius scale, the freezing point of pure water is 0°C (read "zero degrees Celsius"). The boiling point of pure water is 100°C. Weather reports in the United States use the Fahrenheit scale. On the Fahrenheit scale, the freezing point of water is 32°F and the boiling point is 212°F.

✓ *Checkpoint* *How many degrees Celsius are there between the freezing point of water and the boiling point of water?*

Figure 4 Scientists use the Celsius scale to measure temperature. However, weather reports often use the Fahrenheit scale.
Measuring According to this thermometer, what is the air temperature in degrees Celsius?

How Heat Is Transferred

The energy transferred from a hotter object to a cooler one is referred to as **heat.** You can compare the different types of heat transfer in Figure 5 on page 471. **Heat is transferred in three ways: radiation, conduction, and convection.**

Radiation Have you ever felt the warmth of the sun's rays on your face? You were feeling energy coming directly from the sun as radiation. Recall that radiation is the direct transfer of energy by electromagnetic waves. The heat you feel from the sun or a campfire travels directly to you as infrared radiation. You cannot see infrared radiation, but you can feel it as heat.

Answers to Self-Assessment

Caption Questions

Figure 3 The herbal tea has a higher temperature.

Figure 4 The air temperature is about 20 degrees Celsius.

✓ *Checkpoint*

Between the freezing point of water and the boiling point of water there are 100 Celsius degrees.

2 Facilitate

Energy and Temperature

Demonstration

Materials *glass jar with lid, black and white sheets of construction paper, toothpick, thread, glue, tape, scissors*
Time 15 minutes

 ACTIVITY

Make a radiometer to show students that heat increases the movement of air molecules. Cut four 2-cm squares from white construction paper and four from black construction paper. Glue each black square to a white square. Holding a toothpick vertically, glue one edge of each square to the shaft of the toothpick, like feathers sticking out from the shaft of an arrow. Arrange the squares so that colors alternate between black and white. Tape the end of a piece of thread to one end of the toothpick. Tape the other end of the thread to the inside of a jar lid. Put the lid on the jar, making sure the toothpick dangles freely, and place the jar in sunlight. Soon the toothpick will start to spin. When it does, ask: **What causes the toothpick to spin?** *(The black squares heat up faster than the white squares, and this heats the air molecules close to them. The heated air molecules bounce off the black squares, pushing the toothpick around in a circle.)* **learning modality: visual**

Measuring Temperature

Building Inquiry Skills: Calculating

Materials *calculator*
Time 10 minutes

Help students become more familiar with the Celsius scale by having them convert several Fahrenheit temperatures to their Celsius equivalents, using the formula °C = (°F − 32) × 5/9. **learning modality: logical/mathematical**

Ongoing Assessment

Skills Check Have students compare and contrast the terms *thermal energy, temperature,* and *heat.*

469

How Heat Is Transferred

Inquiry Challenge

Materials *ball*
Time 5 minutes

Challenge students to model the three different types of heat transfer by using a ball to represent heat and students to represent air molecules. Then have students move the ball around the classroom in different ways to model radiation, conduction, and convection. Ask: **How would you move the ball to represent radiation?** *(Toss or roll it.)* **How would you move the ball to represent conduction?** *(Pass it from one student to another.)* **How would you move the ball to represent convection?** *(Have one student walk with it.)*
learning modality: tactile/ kinesthetic

Heat Transfer in the Troposphere

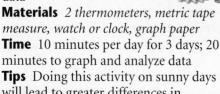

Skills Focus interpreting data
Materials *2 thermometers, metric tape measure, watch or clock, graph paper*
Time 10 minutes per day for 3 days; 20 minutes to graph and analyze data
Tips Doing this activity on sunny days will lead to greater differences in temperatures at the two heights.
Expected Outcome Students should find that the temperature 1 cm above the ground varies more than the temperature 1.25 m above the ground. The ground heats up during the day as it absorbs sunlight. It cools quickly at night as it radiates the heat back into the air. Heat is not effectively transferred through air, so air close to the ground will be more affected by these variations in ground temperature than air farther above the ground.
Extend Have students repeat the activity in a shady location and then compare the data obtained from the two locations. They should find less variation in the shady-location readings. Challenge students to explain why. **learning modality: logical/mathematical**

Temperature Ranges

How much difference do you think there is between air temperatures near the ground and air temperatures higher up? Give reasons for your prediction.

1. Take all of your measurements at a location that is sunny all day.
2. Early in the morning, measure the air temperature 1 cm and 1.25 m above the ground. Record the time of day and the temperature for both locations. Repeat your measurements late in the afternoon.
3. Record these measurements in the morning and afternoon for two more days.
4. Graph your data for each height with temperature on the vertical axis and time on the horizontal axis. Draw both lines on the same piece of graph paper using the same axes. Label both lines.
5. For each day's measurements, calculate the temperature range at both heights. (*Hint:* Find the range by subtracting the lower temperature from the higher temperature for each height and time of day.)

Interpreting Data At which height was the temperature range the widest? How can you explain the difference?

470

Conduction Have you ever walked barefoot on hot sand? Your feet felt hot because heat moved directly from the sand into your feet. When a fast-moving molecule bumps into a nearby slower-moving molecule, it transfers some of its energy. The transfer of heat through the direct contact of molecules within a substance or between substances is **conduction.** The molecules that gain energy can in turn pass the energy along to other nearby molecules. When you walk on hot sand, the fast-moving molecules in the sand transfer heat into the slower-moving molecules in your feet.

The closer together the molecules in a substance are, the more effectively they can conduct heat. Conduction works well in some solids, such as metals, but not as well in liquids and gases. Air and water do not conduct heat very well.

Convection How can you dry your boots over a hot-air vent, even though the furnace is in another room? Air from the furnace carries the heat to your boots. In fluids (liquids and gases), molecules can move from place to place. As the molecules move, they take their heat along with them. The transfer of heat by the movement of a fluid is called **convection.**

☑ *Checkpoint* *Give at least one example each of radiation, conduction, and convection in your daily life.*

Heat Transfer in the Troposphere

Radiation, conduction, and convection work together to heat the troposphere. When Earth's surface absorbs solar energy during the day, the surface of the land becomes warmer than the air. Air near Earth's surface is warmed by radiation and conduction of heat from the surface to the air. However, heat is not easily conducted from one air molecule to another. Only the first few meters of the troposphere are heated by conduction. Thus, the air close to the ground is usually warmer than the air a few meters up.

Convection causes most of the heating of the troposphere. When the air near the ground is heated, the molecules have more energy. Because they have more energy, the molecules move

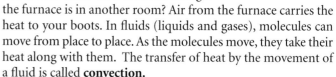

Heat transfer by convection

Background

Facts and Figures The highest air temperature ever recorded near Earth's surface is 58°C (136°F), which was recorded in Libya in northern Africa. The highest average annual air temperature ever recorded is 34°C (94°F), which is the average daytime temperature in Ethiopia in eastern Africa. The highest air temperature ever recorded in the Western Hemisphere is 57°C (134°F), at Death Valley, California.

Program Resources

◆ **Unit 4 Resources** 14-2 Review and Reinforce, p. 131; 14-2 Enrich, p. 132

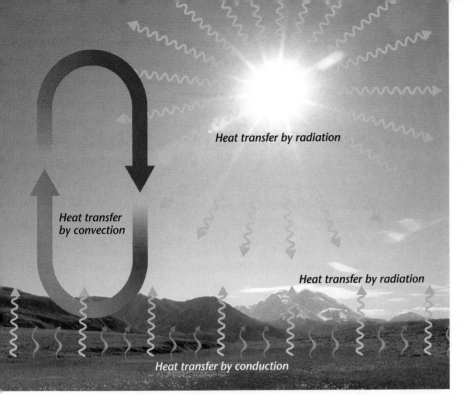

Heat transfer by radiation

Heat transfer by convection

Heat transfer by radiation

Heat transfer by conduction

Figure 5 All three types of heat transfer—radiation, convection, and conduction—occur near Earth's surface.

faster. As the molecules in the heated air move, they bump into each other and move farther apart. The air becomes less dense. Cooler, denser air sinks, forcing the warmer, less dense air to rise.

The upward movement of warm air and the downward movement of cool air form convection currents. Convection currents move heat throughout the troposphere.

 Section 2 Review

1. What is temperature? How is it usually measured?
2. Describe how a thermometer works.
3. Name three ways that heat can be transferred. Briefly explain how the three heat the troposphere.
4. **Thinking Critically** **Applying Concepts** When you light a fire in a fireplace, warm air rises by convection and goes up the chimney. How, then, does a fireplace heat a room? Why do only the people directly in front of the fireplace feel the warmth of the fire?

Check Your Progress **CHAPTER PROJECT**
Gather the instruments you will need to measure the weather factors. (*Hint:* Make sure you know how to take accurate measurements.) Plan when and where to measure weather factors. Be sure to take your measurements at the same location and at the same time of day.

Answers to Self-Assessment

☑ *Checkpoint*

Possible examples might include heat radiating from a campfire, heat being conducted through the bottom of a metal pot on a stove, and heat flowing in convection currents through a house heated by a furnace.

Using the Visuals: Figure 5 *Content Mastery*

Call students' attention to the illustration and have them locate the arrows showing each of the three types of heat transfer. Point out that radiation occurs from Earth's surface as well as from the sun.
learning modality: visual

3 Assess

Section 2 Review Answers

1. Temperature is the average amount of energy of motion in the molecules of a substance. It is usually measured with a thermometer.
2. When the air temperature increases, the liquid in the bulb of a thermometer expands and rises up the column. When the air temperature decreases, the liquid contracts and moves down the column.
3. Heat can be transferred by radiation, conduction, and convection. Air near Earth's surface is warmed by radiation and by conduction of heat from the surface to the air. When the air near the ground is heated, it becomes less dense and rises in convection currents.
4. A fireplace heats a room by radiation. Only people sitting directly in front of the fire feel its warmth because radiation is the direct transfer of energy and does not effectively heat areas of the room out of the direct line of the fireplace.

Check Your Progress **CHAPTER PROJECT**

Check that students have all the instruments they need and know how to use them. Make sure that the place they plan to take their measurements is suitable. Remind students to take their measurements in the same place and at the same time each day.

Performance Assessment

Drawing Have students draw a diagram to show how heat is transferred from Earth's surface to the atmosphere.

TEKS: 6.2B, C, E; 6.3C; 6.4A; 6.14C

Objectives

After completing the lesson, students will be able to

♦ explain what causes winds;

♦ distinguish between local winds and global winds;

♦ describe the major global wind belts and where they are located.

1 Engage/Explore

Activating Prior Knowledge

Introduce students to winds by helping them recall a time when they flew a kite. Ask: **What made the kite fly in the air?** *(the wind)* **What is wind?** *(the movement of air).* Then remind students how hard it can be to hold on to a kite against the force of a strong wind. Stress that even though air is an invisible gas, it still consists of molecules, and their movement, especially at high speeds, can exert a lot of force. Tell students they will learn more about wind in this section.

DISCOVER

Skills Focus making models

Materials *heavy-duty tape, pencil, large smooth ball, marker*

Time 10 minutes

Tips Make sure students spin the ball in a counterclockwise direction before their partner draws on it with the marker. You might want to have students also draw a line from the "South Pole" to the "Equator" to see what direction winds blow in the Southern Hemisphere due to Earth's rotation.

Expected Outcome The lines students draw should veer to the west as the marker goes from the "North Pole" to the "Equator" of the ball.

Think It Over The movement of cold air from Canada to the United States would turn toward the west.

DISCOVER

Which Way Does the Wind Turn?

Do this activity with a partner. Think of the ball as a model of Earth and the marker as representing wind.

1. Using heavy-duty tape, attach a pencil to a large smooth ball so that you can spin the ball from the top without touching it.

2. One partner should hold the pencil. Slowly turn the ball counterclockwise when seen from above.

3. While the ball is turning, the second partner should use a marker to try to draw a straight line from the "North Pole" to the "equator" of the ball. What shape does the line form?

Think It Over

Making Models If cold air were moving south from Canada into the United States, how would its movement be affected by Earth's rotation?

GUIDE FOR READING

♦ What causes winds?

♦ What are local winds and global winds?

♦ Where are the major global wind belts located?

Reading Tip Before you read, preview the illustrations and read their captions. Write down any questions you have about winds. As you read, look for answers to your questions.

Key Terms wind
• anemometer
• wind-chill factor
• local wind • sea breeze
• land breeze • monsoon
• global wind • Coriolis effect
• latitude • jet stream

The highest point in the northeastern United States, at 1,917 meters above sea level, is Mount Washington in New Hampshire. On April 12, 1934, instruments at the weather observatory atop Mount Washington measured a wind speed of 370 kilometers per hour. That's the greatest wind speed ever measured at Earth's surface apart from a fierce storm such as a tornado. What causes this incredible force?

What Causes Winds?

Because air is a fluid, it can move easily from place to place. The force that makes air move is caused by a difference of air pressure. Fluids tend to move from areas of high pressure to areas of low pressure. A **wind** is the horizontal movement of air from an area of high pressure to an area of lower pressure. **All winds are caused by differences in air pressure.**

READING STRATEGIES

Reading Tip Student questions might include: Why does the wind blow? What is a monsoon? How are winds connected to the energy of the sun? Encourage students to record the answers to their questions as they encounter them in their reading.

Vocabulary Urge students to look up the word *doldrums* in a dictionary. In addition to being the name for the equatorial zone of calm winds, students will find that it also means "a period of inactivity or stagnation." Call students' attention to the explanation given in the text for the name *horse latitudes.* Knowing the rather memorable story behind it will help them remember that the *horse latitudes* also are zones of calm.

Most differences in air pressure are caused by unequal heating of the atmosphere. As you learned in the previous section, convection currents form when an area of Earth's surface is heated by the sun's rays. Air over the heated surface expands and becomes less dense. As the air becomes less dense, its air pressure decreases. If a nearby area is not heated as much, the air above the less-heated area will be cooler and denser. The cool, dense air has a higher air pressure so it flows underneath the warm, less dense air. This process forces the warm air to rise.

Measuring Wind

Winds are described by their direction and speed. Wind direction is determined with a wind vane. The wind swings the wind vane so that one end points into the wind. The name of a wind tells you where the wind is coming from. For example, a south wind blows from the south toward the north. A north wind blows to the south.

Wind speed is measured with an **anemometer** (an uh MAHM uh tur). An anemometer has three or four cups mounted at the ends of spokes that spin on an axle. The force of the wind against the cups turns the axle. A speedometer attached to the axle shows the wind speed.

A cool breeze can be very refreshing on a warm day. However, during the winter, a similar breeze can make you feel uncomfortably cold. The wind blowing over your skin removes body heat. The stronger the wind, the colder you feel. The increased cooling that a wind can cause is called the **wind-chill factor.** Thus a weather report may say, "The temperature is 20 degrees Fahrenheit. But with a wind speed of 30 miles per hour, the wind-chill factor makes it feel like 18 degrees below zero."

✓ *Checkpoint* *Toward what direction does a west wind blow?*

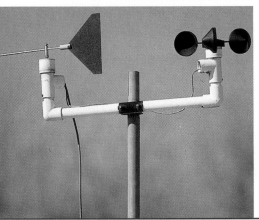

Figure 6 The wind vane on the left points in the direction the wind is blowing from. The anemometer on the right measures wind speed.

TRY THIS

Build a Wind Vane ACTIVITY

1. ✂ Use scissors to cut out a pointer and a slightly larger tail fin from construction paper.
2. Make a slit 1 cm deep in each end of a soda straw.
3. Slide the pointer and tail fin into place on the straw, securing them with small pieces of tape.

4. Hold the straw on your finger to find the point at which it balances.
5. Carefully push a pin through the balance point and into the eraser of a pencil. Move the wind vane back and forth to make sure it can spin freely.
6. Place your wind vane in the center of a magnetic compass to determine the direction the wind is blowing from.

Observing How can you use your wind vane to tell the direction of the wind?

Answers to Self-Assessment

✓ *Checkpoint*

A west wind blows toward the east.

---

2 Facilitate

What Causes Winds?

Demonstration

Materials *pinwheel, lamp with incandescent light bulb* ACTIVITY
Time 10 minutes

Show students how differences in temperature cause air movement by holding a pinwheel over a lamp. First hold the pinwheel over the lamp with the light bulb turned off. The pinwheel will remain stationary. Then hold the pinwheel over the lamp with the light bulb turned on. Once the light bulb gets hot, the pinwheel will start to spin. Ask: **Why did the pinwheel start spinning after the lightbulb was turned on?** (*The hot light bulb heated the air around it, which rose and turned the pinwheel.*)
learning modality: visual

Measuring Wind

TRY THIS

Skills Focus observing ACTIVITY
Materials *scissors, construction paper, metric ruler, soda straw, tape, straight pin, pencil with eraser*
Time 15 minutes
Expected Outcome Students should find when they take their wind vane outside in the wind or blow on it that the wind vane points in the direction from which the wind is coming.
Extend If students set their wind vane in the center of a compass, it will show them whether it is an east, west, north, or south wind. Remind students that winds are named for the direction from which they blow. **learning modality: kinesthetic**

Ongoing Assessment

Drawing Have students make a simple drawing with arrows and labels to show how differences in air temperature cause wind.
 Students can keep their drawings in their portfolios.

You and Your Community

Where's the Wind?

Preparing for Inquiry

Key Concept Obstacles such as buildings can change the speed and direction of the wind.

Skills Objectives Students will be able to

- measure the direction and speed of the wind on all sides of the school building;
- interpret their data to determine which side of the building is less windy than the other sides;
- conclude from the data which side of the building provides the best location for a door.

Time 40 minutes

Advance Planning Follow weather reports when scheduling the lab so students take their measurements on a day when the wind is blowing steadily, not in gusts, and from its usual direction. Students can make the anemometers one day and measure wind speed and direction another day.

Alternative Materials If you do not have a wind vane, students can measure wind direction by observing the direction that flags are flying. Instead of using corrugated cardboard to make the anemometer, students may use a piece of a plastic foam plate. Also, wooden craft sticks may be used in place of wooden stirrers. Adhesive or electrical tape will work as well as masking tape. ***Computer use is optional.***

Guiding Inquiry

Invitation Ask: **Which two factors do you need to know to determine wind patterns?** *(Wind direction and wind speed)* **How can you measure wind direction?** *(With a wind vane or by observing the direction in which objects are blowing in the wind)* **How can you measure wind speed?** *(With an anemometer)* Point out to students that in this lab they will make a simple anemometer. Then they will use a wind vane to measure wind direction and their anemometer to measure wind speed.

Local Winds

Have you ever flown a kite at the beach on a hot summer day? Even if there is no wind inland, there may be a cool breeze blowing in from the water toward the beach. This breeze is an example of a local wind. **Local winds** are winds that blow over short distances. **Local winds are caused by unequal heating of Earth's surface within a small area.** Local winds form only when no winds are blowing from farther away.

Real-World Lab

You and Your Community

Where's the Wind?

Your city is planning to build a new community center. You and your classmates want to be sure that the doors will not be hard to open or close on windy days. You need to know which side of the building will be sheltered from the wind. You decide to measure wind speeds around a similar building.

Problem

How can you determine wind patterns around a building?

Skills Focus

measuring, interpreting data, drawing conclusions

Materials

pen
wind vane
meter stick
corrugated cardboard sheet, 15 cm x 20 cm
computer (optional)
round toothpick
2 wooden coffee stirrers
narrow masking tape

Procedure

1. You'll begin by making a simple anemometer that uses wooden coffee stirrers to indicate wind speed. On your piece of cardboard, draw a curved scale like the one shown in the diagram. Mark it in equal intervals from 0 to 10.

2. Carefully use the pen to make a small hole where the toothpick will go. Insert the toothpick through the hole.

3. Tape the wooden coffee stirrers to the toothpick as shown in the diagram, one on each side of the cardboard.

4. Copy the data table into your notebook or create the data table on the computer.

5. Take your anemometer outside the school. Stand about 2–3 m away from the building and away from any corners or large plants.

474

Making the measurements on all sides of their school building will let them determine wind patterns around it and from this decide on the best location for a door.

Introducing the Procedure
Explain that the second coffee stirrer added to the anemometer provides a balance for the stirrer that measures wind speed. Point out that the numbers on the dial do not represent actual units, such as kilometers per hour. However, they do allow comparison of wind speeds.

Safety

Do not do this lab on a day when there is danger of lightning or high winds. Review the safety guidelines in Appendix A.

Unequal heating often occurs on land that is next to a large body of water. It takes more energy to warm up a body of water than it does to warm up an equal area of land. This means that as the sun heats Earth's surface during the day, the land warms up faster than the water. Therefore the air over the land becomes warmer than the air over the water. The warm air over the land expands and rises, creating a low-pressure area. Cool air blows inland from the water and moves underneath the warm air.

DATA TABLE

Location	Wind Direction	Wind Speed

6. Use the wind vane to find out what direction the wind is coming from. Hold your anemometer so that the card is straight, vertical, and parallel to the wind direction. Observe which number the wooden stirrer is closest to. Record your data.

7. Repeat your measurements on all the other sides of the building. Record your data.

Analyze and Conclude

1. Was the wind stronger on one side of the school building than the other sides? How can you explain your observation?

2. Do your classmates' results agree with yours? What might account for any differences?

3. **Apply** Based on your data, which side of the building provides the best location for a door?

More to Explore

What effect do plants have on the wind speed in an area? Could bushes and trees be planted so that they reduce the wind speed near the doors? What measurements could you make to find out?

475

Sample Data Table

Location	Wind Direction	Wind Speed
East side of building	W	1
South side of building	NW	4
West side of building	W	3
North side of building	SW	6

Program Resources

◆ **Unit 4 Resources** Chapter 14 Real-World Lab blackline masters, pp. 148–149

Media and Technology

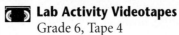 **Lab Activity Videotapes**
Grade 6, Tape 4

Stress the importance of taking all measurements the same distance from the building. Suggest that they select a spot near the middle of each side about 2 to 3 m from the building.

Troubleshooting the Experiment

◆ Have students test their anemometers before they take them outside to measure wind speed. They can use a fan or hair dryer set on low or simply blow on them. They should make sure the coffee stirrers blow freely in the wind and adjust them if necessary.

◆ Check that students are holding their anemometers parallel to wind direction. Otherwise, the wind will be less effective at moving the coffee stirrer and the anemometer will give a reading that is too low.

Expected Outcome

Students will probably find that one side of the building had winds blowing at a lower speed than the other sides. If a west wind was blowing, then the east side of the building probably was the least windy. Students also may find that wind direction is different from one side of the building to another.

Analyze and Conclude

1. Students probably will find that the wind was stronger on the side of the building that the wind was coming from. Students should explain their observations by saying that the building blocked and slowed the wind on the other sides of the building.

2. Classmates' results may or may not agree. Differences could be due to students measuring the wind at somewhat different locations around the building, wind gusts, or slight differences in how the anemometers were made or used.

3. Students should conclude that the best location is the side of the building that has winds with the lowest speed.

Extending the Inquiry

More to Explore Students may say that bushes and trees can block the wind and reduce its speed near the doors. They could find out by determining wind patterns around bushes and trees, as they did around the school building, to see how these obstacles affect wind direction and speed.

Local Winds

Figure 7 (A) During the day, cool air moves from the sea to the land, creating a sea breeze. (B) At night, cooler air moves from the land to the sea.
Forming Operational Definitions
What type of breeze occurs at night?

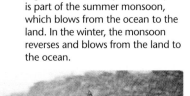

Figure 8 This heavy rain in Nepal is part of the summer monsoon, which blows from the ocean to the land. In the winter, the monsoon reverses and blows from the land to the ocean.

A wind that blows from an ocean or lake onto land is known as a **sea breeze** or a lake breeze. Figure 7A shows a sea breeze.

At night, the situation is reversed. Land cools more quickly than water, so the air over the land becomes cooler than the air over the water. As the warmer air over the water rises, cooler air moves from the land to take its place. The flow of air from land to a body of water is called a **land breeze.**

Monsoons

A process similar to land and sea breezes can occur over wider areas. In the summer in South and Southeast Asia, the land gradually gets warmer than the ocean. A large "sea breeze" blows steadily inland from the ocean all summer, even at night. In the winter, the land cools and becomes colder than the ocean. A "land breeze" blows steadily from the land to the ocean.

Sea and land breezes over a large region that change direction with the seasons are called **monsoons.** The summer monsoon in South Asia and Southeast Asia is very important for the crops grown there. The air blowing from the ocean during the rainy season is very warm and humid. As the humid air rises over the land, the air cools, producing heavy rains that supply the water needed by rice and other crops.

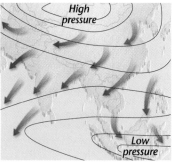

Global Winds

Winds that blow steadily from specific directions over long distances are referred to as **global winds.** Like local winds, global winds are created by unequal heating of Earth's surface. Refer to Figure 9 to see how sunlight strikes Earth's surface. In the middle of the day near the equator, the sun is almost directly overhead. The direct rays from the sun heat Earth's surface intensely. Near the North Pole or South Pole, the sun's rays strike Earth's surface at a lower angle, even at noon. The sun's energy is spread out over a larger area, so it heats the surface less. As a result, temperatures near the poles are much lower than they are near the equator.

Global Convection Currents Temperature differences between the equator and the poles produce giant convection currents in the atmosphere. Warm air rises at the equator, and cold air sinks at the poles. Therefore air pressure tends to be lower near the equator and greater near the poles, causing winds at Earth's surface to blow from the poles toward the equator. Higher in the atmosphere, air flows away from the equator toward the poles. **The movement of air between the equator and the poles produces global winds.**

The Coriolis Effect If Earth did not rotate, global winds would blow in a straight line from the poles toward the equator. Because Earth is rotating, global winds do not follow a straight path. As the winds move, Earth rotates from west to east underneath them, making it seem as if the winds have curved. The way Earth's rotation makes winds curve is called the **Coriolis effect** (kawr ee OH lis). It is named for the French mathematician who studied and explained it in 1835.

In the Northern Hemisphere, all global winds gradually turn toward the right. As you can see in Figure 10, a wind blowing toward the north gradually turns toward the northeast. In other words, a south wind gradually changes to a southwest wind. In the Southern Hemisphere, winds curve toward the left. A south wind becomes an southeast wind, and a north wind becomes a northwest wind.

☑ *Checkpoint* *What happens to a wind blowing toward the south in the Northern Hemisphere? What would you call this wind?*

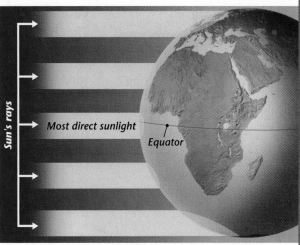

Figure 9 Near the equator, energy from the sun strikes Earth almost directly. Near the poles, the same amount of energy is spread out over a larger area.

Figure 10 As Earth rotates on its axis, the Coriolis effect turns winds in the Northern Hemisphere toward the right. *Interpreting Diagrams Which way do winds turn in the Southern Hemisphere?*

Rotation of Earth

Demonstration

Materials *globe, small flashlight*
Time 5 minutes

Challenge a pair of students to model Earth and the sun using a globe and flashlight. *(One student should hold the globe, and the other student should shine the light on the equator, with the room lights dimmed.)* Call students' attention to the fact that the light is direct and bright over the equator but angled and dim at the poles. Ask: **How do these differences in energy cause global winds?** *(The more concentrated energy falling directly on the equator causes air over the equator to be warmer than air over the poles, leading to the convection currents that cause global winds.)*
learning modality: visual

Answers to Self-Assessment

Caption Questions

Figure 7 A land breeze occurs at night.
Figure 10 In the Southern Hemisphere, winds turn toward the left.

☑ *Checkpoint*

A wind blowing toward the south in the Northern Hemisphere gradually turns toward the right. You would call it a northeast wind.

Ongoing Assessment

Drawing Have students make a sketch in their journals to show how the Coriolis effect influences global winds.

Global Wind Belts

Including All Students

Materials *globe*
Time 10 minutes

Give students who need extra help a chance to spin a globe in a west to east direction while moving their finger over its surface from north to south. Ask: **How does the path you traced on the globe model global winds?** *(The path of global winds curves to the right in the same way.)* Then have students use the globe to locate a city or country that interests them. Ask: **Which major wind belt flows over that location?** *(Answers will vary depending on locations students choose.)* Suggest that students find the latitude of their location to determine which global wind belt flows over it.
learning modality: kinesthetic

Social Studies
CONNECTION

Make sure students realize that for the time period in question, ships had sails and depended on the wind to move. Suggest that they refer to the illustration on page 479 when doing this feature. From the figure, students should be able to identify which winds they would have used to sail east *(prevailing westerlies)* and which they would have used to sail west *(trade winds).*

In Your Journal Students should see from the figure on page 479 that making use of the trade winds to go west requires a more southern route across the Atlantic. They should write in their letter that the journey west takes almost twice as many weeks because the southern route is less direct and longer.
learning modality: verbal

Social Studies
CONNECTION

From colonial days to the late 1800s, American merchants traded new ships, lumber, cotton, tobacco, and furs for manufactured goods, such as textiles, from England. The eastbound voyage in the early 1800s took about three weeks. However, the westbound passage took almost twice as long—five to six weeks.

In Your Journal

Imagine that you are a sea captain making the voyage to England and back to America. Your family doesn't understand why your journey home takes almost twice as long as your journey to England. Write a letter to your family explaining why you have to travel farther south to take advantage of the prevailing winds on your return voyage.

Global Wind Belts

The Coriolis effect and other factors combine to produce a pattern of calm areas and wind belts around Earth. The calm areas include the doldrums and the horse latitudes. **The major global wind belts are the trade winds, the prevailing westerlies, and the polar easterlies.** As you read about each area, find it in *Exploring Global Winds.*

Doldrums Near the equator, the sun heats the surface strongly. Warm air rises steadily, creating an area of low pressure. Cool air moves into the area, but is warmed rapidly and rises before it moves very far. There is very little horizontal motion, so the winds near the equator are very weak. Regions near the equator with little or no wind are called the doldrums.

Horse Latitudes Warm air that rises at the equator divides and flows both north and south. **Latitude** is the distance from the equator, measured in degrees. At about 30° north and south latitudes, the air stops moving toward the poles and sinks. In each of these regions, another belt of calm air forms. Hundreds of years ago, sailors becalmed in these waters ran out of food and water for their horses and had to throw the horses overboard. Because of this, the latitudes 30° north and south of the equator are called the horse latitudes.

Trade Winds When the cold air over the horse latitudes sinks, it produces a region of high pressure. This high pressure causes surface winds to blow both toward the equator and away from it. The winds that blow toward the equator are turned west by the Coriolis effect. As a result, winds in the Northern Hemisphere between 30° north latitude and the equator blow generally from the northeast. In the Southern Hemisphere between 30° south latitude and the equator, the winds blow from the southeast. These steady easterly winds are called the trade winds. For hundreds of years, sailors relied on them to carry cargoes from Europe to the West Indies and South America.

Figure 11 The bark *Patriot*, built in 1809, carried goods to many parts of the world.
Applying Concepts How much effect do you think the prevailing winds have on shipping today?

Background

Integrating Science Like global winds, the surface currents of oceans are deflected by the Coriolis effect. They flow to the right in the Northern Hemisphere and to the left in the Southern Hemisphere.

The prevailing winds blow the surface waters of the oceans and contribute to the deflection of ocean currents caused by the Coriolis effect. For example, the prevailing westerlies, which blow across most of the United States, help make the Gulf Stream the largest, strongest surface current in the North Atlantic Ocean. The Gulf Stream flows from the Caribbean Sea northeast along the east coast of the United States until it reaches North Carolina. Then it veers off into the Atlantic Ocean. Eventually the Gulf Stream reaches the western coast of Europe, where its warm waters bring relatively mild, humid weather.

EXPLORING Global Winds

A series of wind belts circles Earth. Between the wind belts are calm areas where air is rising or falling.

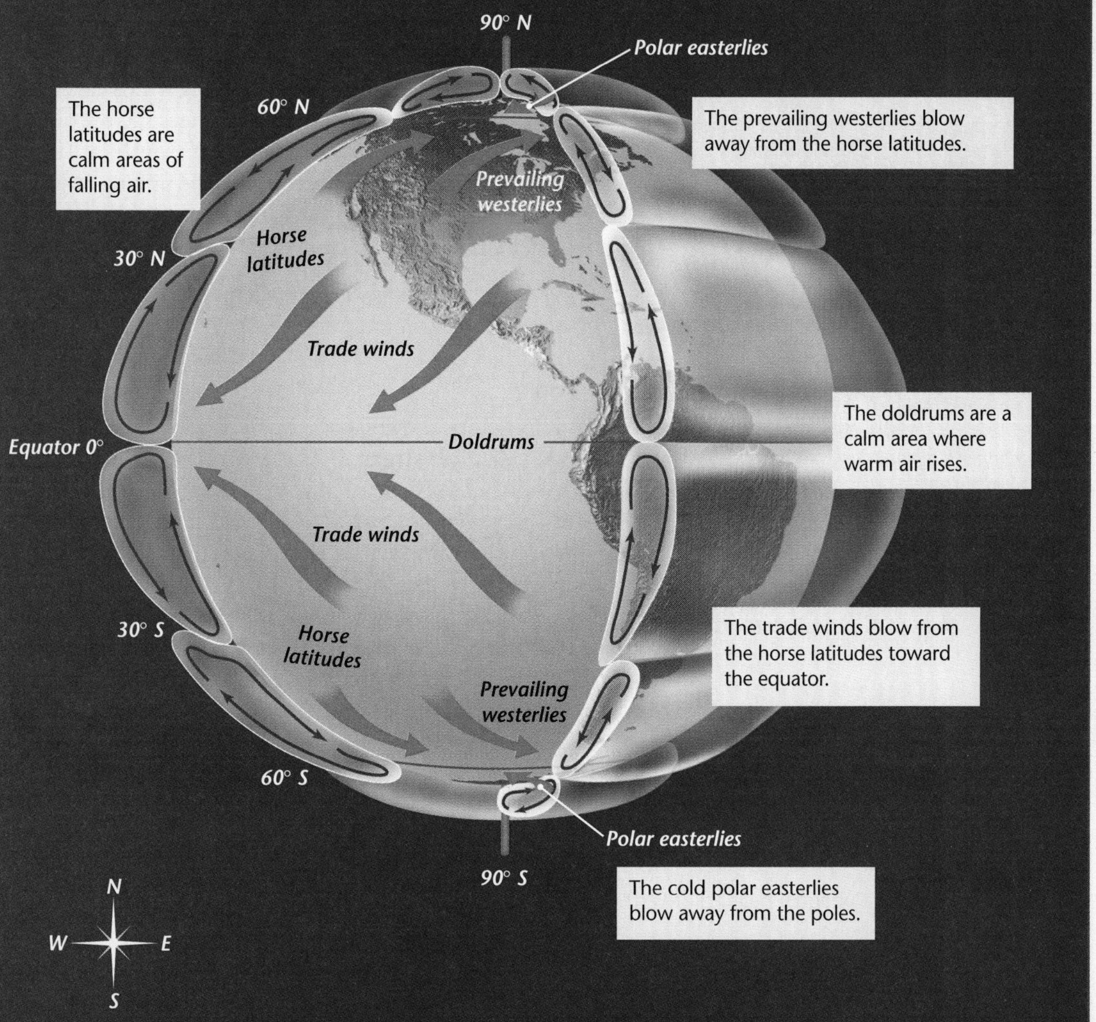

90° N

Polar easterlies

60° N

The horse latitudes are calm areas of falling air.

The prevailing westerlies blow away from the horse latitudes.

Prevailing westerlies

Horse latitudes

30° N

Trade winds

Equator 0°

Doldrums

The doldrums are a calm area where warm air rises.

Trade winds

The trade winds blow from the horse latitudes toward the equator.

30° S

Horse latitudes

Prevailing westerlies

60° S

Polar easterlies

90° S

The cold polar easterlies blow away from the poles.

N
W   E
S

Media and Technology

Transparencies "Global Winds," Transparency 68

Answers to Self-Assessment

Caption Question

Figure 11 Answers may vary. The most likely answer is that prevailing winds have little effect on shipping today because ships no longer depend on the winds to move.

EXPLORING
Global Winds

Make sure students understand that the spin of the planet in the figure is from left to right, or counterclockwise as seen from the North Pole. Check to see that students understand how the two different types of arrows are used in the diagram. Ask: **What do the small blue arrows pointing straight north or straight south represent?** (*The general direction of convection currents in the atmosphere due to unequal heating*) **What do the large red arrows represent?** (*The direction in which global winds blow because of the Coriolis effect*)

Tell students to assume they are planning a sailing trip from California to the tip of South America. Have them use the figure to trace with a finger the route they would take. Ask: **Which winds would help speed you on your way?** (*In the Northern Hemisphere the trade winds and in the Southern Hemisphere the prevailing westerlies*) **Which winds would slow you down?** (*In the Northern Hemisphere the prevailing westerlies and in the Southern Hemisphere the trade winds*)

Students may not understand why the two major global wind belts in each hemisphere blow in opposite north/south directions, even though both are turned in the same east/west direction by Earth's rotation. Explain that they blow in opposite directions because the convection currents that produce them flow in opposite directions. Point out in the figure how, in the Northern Hemisphere, the convection currents in the region of the prevailing westerlies flow to the north, whereas in the region of the trade winds, the convection currents flow to the south. Refer to the **ELL Handbook** for additional teaching strategies. **learning modality: visual**

Ongoing Assessment

Oral Presentation Call on students at random to explain in their own words similarities and differences between the prevailing westerlies and the trade winds.

Jet Streams

Building Inquiry Skills: Inferring

Point out that the jet stream follows the boundary between the prevailing westerlies and polar easterlies. Ask: **Why do you think the jet stream is farther south in the winter?** *(As the sun's direct rays move south, the global wind belts also shift south.)* **learning modality: logical/mathematical**

3 Assess

Section 3 Review Answers

1. Unequal heating of air above Earth's surface causes winds because the warm air rises and cool air moves in to take its place.

2. Both local and global winds are caused by unequal heating of Earth's surface. Local winds cover small areas; global winds circle the globe. Local winds often change direction; global winds do not.

3. The major wind belts are trade winds, prevailing westerlies, and polar easterlies. Students' drawings should show the winds as pictured on page 479.

4. The pilot should set a course to the southeast because Earth's rotation will result in the plane going west relative to cities on the ground.

Check Your Progress
CHAPTER PROJECT

Check that students continue to take accurate measurements. Make sure they are recording all the measurements in their weather log, including the units for each measurement.

Performance Assessment

Writing/Drawing Have students write a paragraph explaining what causes global winds and why they flow in the direction they do. Have them accompany their explanation with a clearly labeled diagram.

Figure 12 By traveling east in a jet stream, pilots can save time and fuel.
Predicting What would happen if a plane flew west in a jet stream?

Prevailing Westerlies In the mid-latitudes, winds that blow toward the poles are turned toward the east by the Coriolis effect. Because they blow from the west to the east, they are called prevailing westerlies. The prevailing westerlies blow generally from the southwest between 30° and 60° north latitudes and from the northwest between 30° and 60° south latitudes. The prevailing westerlies play an important part in the weather of the United States.

Polar Easterlies Cold air near the poles sinks and flows back toward lower latitudes. The Coriolis effect shifts these polar winds to the west, producing winds called the polar easterlies. The polar easterlies meet the prevailing westerlies at about 60° north and 60° south latitudes, along a region called the polar front. The mixing of warm and cold air along the polar front has a major effect on weather changes in the United States.

☑ *Checkpoint* In what region do the polar easterlies meet the prevailing westerlies?

Jet Streams

About 10 kilometers above Earth's surface are bands of high-speed winds called **jet streams.** These winds are hundreds of kilometers wide but only a few kilometers deep. Jet streams blow from west to east at speeds of 200 to 400 kilometers per hour. As jet streams travel around Earth, they wander north and south along a wavy path.

Airplanes are aided by a jet stream when traveling east. Pilots can save fuel and time by flying east in a jet stream. However, airplanes flying at jet stream altitudes are slowed down when traveling west against the jet stream winds.

Section 3 Review

1. How does the unequal heating of Earth's surface cause winds?
2. How are local winds and global winds similar? How are they different?
3. Name and draw the three major wind belts.
4. **Thinking Critically Applying Concepts** Imagine you are flying from Seattle to San Francisco, which is almost exactly due south of Seattle. Should the pilot set a course due south? Explain your answer.

Check Your Progress
CHAPTER PROJECT

Check with your teacher to be sure you are using the weather instruments correctly. Are you recording units for each measurement? Collect and record measurements each day.

Answers to Self-Assessment

☑ *Checkpoint*

The polar easterlies meet the prevailing westerlies at about the 60° north and 60° south latitudes.

Caption Question

Figure 12 If a plane flew west in a jet stream, it would be slowed down by the winds flowing east.

Program Resources

◆ **Unit 4 Resources** 14-3 Review and Reinforce, p. 135; 14-3 Enrich, p. 136

SECTION

4 Water in the Atmosphere

TEKS: 6.1A; 6.2A, B, C, D; 6.3C; 6.14C

DISCOVER .... ACTIVITY

How Does Fog Form?

1. Fill a narrow-necked plastic bottle with hot tap water. Pour out most of the water, leaving about 3 cm at the bottom. **CAUTION:** *Avoid spilling hot water. Do not use water that is so hot that you cannot safely hold the bottle.*

2. Place an ice cube on the mouth of the bottle. What happens?

3. Repeat Steps 1 and 2 using cold water instead of hot water. What happens?

Think It Over

Developing Hypotheses How can you explain your observations? Why is there a difference between what happens with the hot water and with the cold water?

---

uring a rainstorm, the air feels moist. On a clear, cloudless day, the air may feel dry. As the sun heats the land and oceans, the amount of water in the atmosphere changes. Water is always moving between the atmosphere and Earth's surface.

As you learned in Chapter 12, this movement of water between the atmosphere and Earth's surface is called the water cycle. This cycle is shown in Figure 13. Water vapor enters the air by evaporation from the oceans and other bodies of water. **Evaporation** is the process by which water molecules in liquid water escape into the air as water vapor. Water vapor is also added to the air by living things. Water enters the roots of plants, rises to the leaves, and is released as water vapor.

As part of the water cycle, some of the water vapor in the atmosphere condenses to form clouds. Rain and other forms of precipitation fall from the clouds toward the surface. The water then runs off the surface, or moves through the ground, back into the oceans, lakes, and streams.

GUIDE FOR READING

◆ How is relative humidity measured?

◆ How do clouds form?

◆ What are the three main types of clouds?

Reading Tip Before you read, write a definition of "cloud." Revise your definition as you read about clouds.

Key Terms evaporation • humidity • relative humidity • psychrometer • condensation • dew point • cumulus • stratus • cirrus

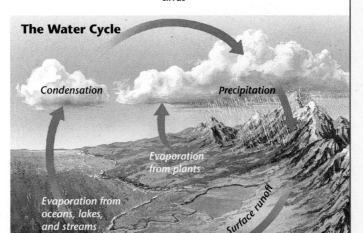

The Water Cycle

Condensation

Precipitation

Evaporation from plants

Evaporation from oceans, lakes, and streams

Surface runoff

Figure 13 In the water cycle, water moves from lakes and oceans into the atmosphere and falls back to Earth.

Chapter 14 **481**

READING STRATEGIES

Reading Tip Encourage students to base their initial definition of "cloud" on what they have observed or experienced. Their revised definition should describe a cloud as consisting of drops of liquid water or ice crystals in the air.

Program Resources

◆ **Unit 4 Resources** 14-4 Lesson Plan, p. 137; 14-4 Section Summary, p. 138
◆ **Guided Reading and Study Workbook** 14-4

---

1 Engage/Explore

Objectives

After completing the lesson, students will be able to

◆ describe how relative humidity is measured;

◆ explain how clouds form;

◆ describe the main types of clouds.

Activating Prior Knowledge

Help students recall seeing water vapor condense out of the air. Ask: **Have you ever noticed when you take a shower that the bathroom mirror clouds up?** *(Most students will have had this experience.)* **Do you know what causes this?** *(Students may say it is caused by moisture in the air from the shower.)* Explain that when warm moist air from the shower comes into contact with the cool surface of the mirror, the air cools and can hold less water vapor. As a result, water vapor condenses on the mirror. Point out that clouds form the same way: water vapor condenses when warm moist air cools in the atmosphere.

.... DISCOVER ....

Skills Focus developing ACTIVITY hypotheses

Materials *narrow-necked plastic bottle, hot tap water, 2 ice cubes, cold tap water*

Time 10 minutes

Tips Make sure students let the bottle cool before repeating Steps 1 and 2 with cold water.

Expected Outcome Fog will form in the bottle when it contains hot water but not when it contains cold water.

Think It Over Fog forms in the bottle when warm moist air rises from the surface of the hot water and condenses as it cools near the ice cube. This does not occur when there is cold water in the bottle because the cold water does not produce warm moist air.

2 Facilitate

Humidity

 Integrating Life Science *Content Mastery*

Help students appreciate how evaporation can cool the body by asking: **Did you ever step out of a swimming pool on a hot day and feel cold, even though the air was warmer than the water?** *(Most students will have experienced this.)* **Why did you feel cold?** *(As the water evaporated, it took heat from the body.)* Then help students appreciate the effect of high relative humidity on evaporative cooling. Ask: **What happens when you exercise on a hot, humid day?** *(You get wet with sweat, but the sweat doesn't evaporate and cool you down.)* **learning modality: verbal**

Measuring Relative Humidity

Inquiry Challenge

Materials *human hair, drinking straw, tape, glue, clay, shoebox, or other materials of students' choice* **ACTIVITY**
Time 20 minutes for setup; 5 minutes for later observations

Tell students that human hair shrinks when the humidity is low and stretches when the humidity is high. Then challenge students to use a human hair to indicate changes in humidity. One way students might do this is by setting a shoebox on one of its long sides and taping one end of a drinking straw to the inside of this long side. The unattached end of the straw should be close, but not touching, the inside of a short side of the shoebox. Then attach a long human hair to the straw and to the inside of the opposite (top) long side of the shoebox so it suspends the unattached end of the straw, making it a pointer. Plug this end of the straw with a little clay so the hair remains taut. Students can calibrate this hair hygrometer by observing the straw pointer move up and down with changes in humidity. **learning modality: logical/mathematical**

Humidity

Humidity is a measure of the amount of water vapor in the air. The percentage of water vapor in the air compared to the maximum amount the air could hold is the **relative humidity.** For example, at 10°C, 1 cubic meter of air can hold a maximum of 8 grams of water vapor. If there actually were 8 grams of water vapor in the air, then the relative humidity of the air would be 100 percent. If the air held 4 grams of water vapor, the relative humidity would be half, or 50 percent. The amount of water vapor that the air can hold depends on its temperature. Warm air can hold more water vapor than cool air.

INTEGRATING LIFE SCIENCE "It's not the heat, it's the humidity." What does this common expression mean? Even on a hot day, you can still feel comfortable if the air is dry. Evaporation of moisture from your skin removes heat and helps to keep your body's temperature comfortable. You feel less comfortable on a hot day if the relative humidity is high. When the relative humidity is high, evaporation slows down. Evaporation therefore has less cooling effect on your body.

Measuring Relative Humidity

Relative humidity can be measured with a psychrometer. A **psychrometer** (sy KRAHM uh tur) has two thermometers, a wet-bulb thermometer and a dry-bulb thermometer. The bulb of the wet-bulb thermometer has a cloth covering that is moistened with water. Air is then blown over both thermometers. Because the wet-bulb thermometer is cooled by evaporation, its reading drops below that of the dry-bulb thermometer.

Relative Humidity					
Dry-Bulb Reading (°C)	**Difference Between Wet- and Dry-Bulb Readings (°C)**				
	1	2	3	4	5
10	88	76	65	54	43
12	88	78	67	57	48
14	89	79	69	60	50
16	90	80	71	62	54
18	91	81	72	64	56
20	91	82	74	66	58
22	92	83	75	68	60
24	92	84	76	69	62
26	92	85	77	70	64
28	93	86	78	71	65
30	93	86	79	72	66

Figure 14 A sling psychrometer is used to measure relative humidity. First, find the wet-bulb and dry-bulb temperatures. Then find the dry-bulb temperature in the left column of the table. Find the difference between the wet- and dry-bulb temperatures across the top of the table. The number in the table where these two readings intersect indicates the relative humidity in percent.

Background

Facts and Figures The heat stress index tells you how much hotter it feels because of high humidity. For example, a temperature of 38°C (100°F) combined with a relative humidity of 50% gives a heat stress index of 49°C (120°F). In other words, the humidity makes it feel like it is 11°C (20°F) hotter than it actually is.

The dew point is a good indicator of relative humidity, because the higher the temperature at which water vapor starts condensing out of the air, the more saturated the air must be. When the dew point is 27°C (80°F) or higher, humidity is extremely high. When the dew point is around 10°C (50°F), humidity is moderate. When the dew point is below 4°C (40°F), humidity is very low.

If the relative humidity is high, the water on the wet bulb will evaporate slowly and the wet-bulb temperature will not change much. If the relative humidity is low, the water on the wet bulb will evaporate rapidly and the wet-bulb temperature will drop. The relative humidity can be found by comparing the temperatures of the wet-bulb and dry-bulb thermometers in a table like the one in Figure 14.

☑ *Checkpoint* **What is the difference between humidity and relative humidity?**

How Clouds Form

What do clouds remind you of? They can look like people, animals, countries, and a thousand other fanciful forms. Of course, not all clouds are fluffy and white. Storm clouds can be dark and cover the whole sky.

Clouds of all kinds form when water vapor in the air becomes liquid water or ice crystals. The process by which molecules of water vapor in the air become liquid water is called **condensation.** How does water condense? As you know, cold air can hold less water vapor than warm air. As air cools, the amount of water vapor it can hold decreases. Some of the water vapor in the air condenses to form droplets of liquid water.

The temperature at which condensation begins is called the **dew point.** If the dew point is below the freezing point, the water vapor may change directly into ice crystals. When you look at a cloud, you are seeing millions of tiny ice crystals or water droplets.

For water vapor to condense, tiny particles must be present so the water has a surface on which to condense. Most of these particles are salt crystals, dust from soil, and smoke. Sometimes water vapor condenses onto solid surfaces, such as blades of grass, instead of particles. Water that condenses from the air onto a cold surface is called dew. Frost is ice that has been deposited directly from the air onto a cold surface.

Clouds form whenever air is cooled to its dew point and particles are present. But why does the air cool? If air is warmed near the ground, it

Figure 15 Dew forms when water vapor condenses out of the air onto a solid surface, such as this flower.

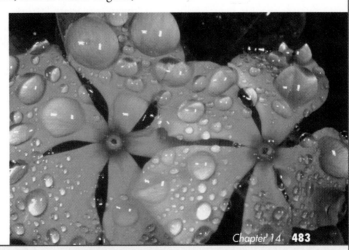

Chapter 14 **483**

Sharpen your Skills

Interpreting Data

Time 10 minutes
Tips Remind students to **ACTIVITY** subtract the wet-bulb reading from the dry-bulb reading and then find the difference between the two in the table.
Expected Outcome The first value for relative humidity is 64%, the second is 91%; relative humidity is increasing.
Extend Use the table to help students understand the relationship between temperature and relative humidity. Ask: **When the difference between wet- and dry-bulb readings is small, is the relative humidity high or low?** *(high)* **How is this relationship affected by air temperature?** *(The higher the air temperature, the higher the relative humidity for a given difference between wet- and dry-bulb readings.)* **learning modality: logical-mathematical**

How Clouds Form

Building Inquiry Skills: Measuring

Materials *beaker, room-temperature water, ice cubes, stirring rod, thermometer* **ACTIVITY**
Time 10 minutes

Have students find the dew point in the classroom. Have them fill a beaker with room-temperature water and measure and record the water temperature. Then have them add a few ice cubes to the beaker and stir the ice water. As soon as moisture condenses on the outside of the beaker, have students measure and record the temperature of the water again. This temperature represents the dew point in the classroom. Ask: **Would the dew point be the same if you did this experiment on a different day?** *(Probably not, because the dew point depends on the temperature and relative humidity)* **learning modality: logical/mathematical**

Ongoing Assessment

Writing Have students explain in their own words how temperature, humidity, and dew point are related.

Answers to Self-Assessment

☑ *Checkpoint*

Humidity is a measure of the amount of water vapor in the air. Relative humidity is the percentage of water vapor in the air compared to the maximum amount the air could hold.

Building Inquiry Skills: Inferring

Materials *water, gallon bottle with cap, bicycle pump*

Time 10 minutes

 Show students how clouds form by making a cloud in a bottle. Explain that air gets warmer when compressed and cooler when allowed to expand. Cover the bottom of a gallon bottle with a few centimeters of water. Use a nail to punch holes in the cap, overlapping the holes to make an opening about 0.5 cm in diameter. Place the cap on the bottle and push the nozzle of a bicycle pump into the opening. Have a volunteer push down on the pump two or three times. Quickly release the cap, and a cloud will form inside the bottle. Ask: **Why did a cloud form inside the bottle?** *(Pumping air into the bottle compressed and warmed the air in the bottle, so it picked up moisture from the water. Letting air out of the bottle let the air in the bottle expand and cool, so it could hold less water. Water condensed out of the air, forming a cloud.)* **learning modality: logical/mathematical**

Types of Clouds

Including All Students

Help students become more familiar with the distinctive shapes of the main cloud types. Find and bring to class several drawings or photographs of different types of clouds. Challenge students to identify the types of clouds shown in the pictures. Ask: **How can you tell which of the three main types a cloud is?** *(by its shape)* **learning modality: visual**

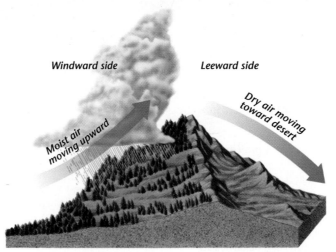

Figure 16 Humid air cools as it is blown up the side of a mountain. *Predicting What happens when water vapor condenses out of the air?*

becomes less dense and rises in a convection current. When the rising air expands and becomes cooler, clouds may form.

When wind strikes the side of a hill or mountain, the air is forced upward. As the air rises along the slope, the air cools. Rain or snow falls on the windward side of the mountains, the side facing the on-coming wind.

By the time the air reaches the other side of the mountains, it has lost much of its water vapor. The air is cool and dry. The land on the leeward side of the mountains—downwind—is in a rain shadow. Just as very little light falls in a sun shadow, very little rain falls in a rain shadow. Not only has the air lost its water vapor while crossing the mountains, but the air has also grown warmer while flowing down the mountainside. This warm, dry air often creates a desert on the leeward side of the mountains.

☑ *Checkpoint* **Why are the tops of some mountains almost always covered by clouds?**

Types of Clouds

As you know, clouds come in different shapes. **Meteorologists classify clouds into three main types: cumulus, stratus, and cirrus.** Clouds are also classified by their altitude. Each type of cloud is associated with a different type of weather.

Clouds that look like fluffy, rounded piles of cotton are called **cumulus** (KYOO myuh lus) clouds. The word *cumulus* means "heap" or "mass." Cumulus clouds form less than 2 kilometers above the ground, but may grow in size and height until they extend upward as much as 18 kilometers. Cumulus clouds usually indicate fair weather. Towering clouds with flat tops, called cumulonimbus clouds, often produce thunderstorms. The suffix *-nimbus* comes from a Latin word meaning "rain."

Clouds that form in flat layers are called **stratus** (STRAT us) clouds. *Strato* means "spread out." Stratus clouds usually cover all or most of the sky. As stratus clouds thicken, they may produce drizzle, rain, or snow. They are then called nimbostratus clouds.

Wispy, feathery clouds are called **cirrus** (SEER us) clouds. Cirrus clouds form only at high levels, above about 6 kilometers, where temperatures are very low. As a result, cirrus clouds are made of ice crystals.

Background

Facts and Figures The amount of water contained in a cloud may surprise students. A scientist with the National Center for Atmospheric Research, named Margaret LeMone, actually estimated the weight of a small cumulus cloud. The cloud was about 1,000 m wide, 1,000 m long, and 1,000 m high. Based on other studies of clouds of the same type, LeMone assumed that the cloud contained about 0.5 g of water per cubic meter. Given the size of the cloud, she concluded that it contained a total of 500 million g of water. This is about 550 tons of water, or about 100 tons heavier than a fully loaded jumbo jet.

Did you ever notice a ring around the sun or moon? Called halos, these rings are created when light passes through thin high clouds of ice crystals.

EXPLORING Clouds

The main types of clouds are cumulus, stratus, and cirrus. A cloud's name contains clues about its height and structure.

Cirrus clouds
Cirrus, cirrostratus, and cirrocumulus clouds are made up of ice crystals.

Cumulonimbus clouds
Thunderstorms come from cumulonimbus clouds. For this reason cumulonimbus clouds are also called thunderheads.

Nimbostratus clouds
Nimbostratus clouds may produce rain or snow.

Cumulus clouds
Cumulus clouds are usually a sign of fair weather.

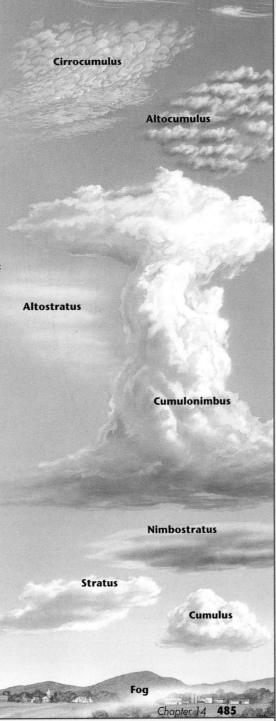

Cirrus

Cirrocumulus

Altocumulus

Altostratus

Cumulonimbus

Nimbostratus

Stratus

Cumulus

Fog

Answers to Self-Assessment

Caption Question

Figure 16 When water vapor condenses out of the air, clouds form.

✓ Checkpoint

When warm, moist air moves upward over a mountain it cools. This causes water vapor to condense out of the air and form clouds.

EXPLORING

Clouds

Extend the information in the Exploring feature by calling students' attention to each of the clouds pictured on the left, and explaining how each type of cloud is formed. This will help students understand why the different cloud types have the shapes and other characteristics they do. Explain that cumulus clouds form during clear weather when warm air rises over small regions of Earth, such as plowed fields or paved parking lots, because these areas are heated more by the sun. Nimbostratus clouds are formed by warm air rising over a wide area, so they tend to cover the whole sky. Cumulonimbus clouds are formed when a lot of hot air rises very fast and towers upward for several kilometers. Strong winds at the bottom of the stratosphere flatten the tops of cumulonimbus clouds to give them their characteristic anvil shape. Cirrus clouds are formed high up in the atmosphere where it is very cold and there is little water vapor, making them thin and wispy. Refer to the **ELL Handbook** for additional teaching strategies. **learning modality: visual**

Building Inquiry Skills: Forming Operational Definitions

Have students play a quiz game called "Name that Cloud." First have students find and list the definitions of basic cloud names (cumulus, stratus, cirrus, nimbus) and cloud prefixes (alto-, nimbo-, cirro-) on a set of index cards. Then have students use the definitions as the basis for the game. Students should provide a definition of a specific cloud type, and their partner must correctly name the cloud. The person with the most correct responses wins the game. **cooperative learning**

Ongoing Assessment

Drawing Have students draw and label each of the three main cloud types.

485

Types of Clouds, continued

3 Assess

Section 4 Review Answers

1. The instrument is a psychrometer. It works by comparing the temperatures on a wet-bulb and a dry-bulb thermometer.
2. For clouds to form, air must be cooled to its dew point and particles must be present in the air.
3. Cumulus clouds look like fluffy, rounded piles of cotton. Stratus clouds form in flat layers. Cirrus clouds are wispy and feathery.
4. Low-level clouds are fog, cumulus, stratus, and nimbostratus. Medium-level clouds are altocumulus and altostratus. High-level clouds are cirrostratus and cirrus.

Science at Home

Materials *large glass, cold water, ice cubes*

Tips Tell students to use cold tap water for the activity, not cold water from the refrigerator, which may be cold enough to make water condense on the outside of the glass without adding ice. Students should explain that the water on the outside of the glass condensed from water vapor in the air. It only appeared after ice was added because water vapor condenses out of the air when the temperature falls below the dew point.

Performance Assessment

Skills Check Have students infer why they can see their breath on a cold day. (*Students should infer that water droplets condense out of their warm, moist breath when it hits the cold air.*)

486

Figure 17 Fog often forms at night over cool lakes.
Predicting What will happen as the sun rises and warms the air above the lake?

Cirrus clouds that have feathery "hooked" ends are sometimes called mare's tails. Cirrocumulus clouds, which look like rows of cotton balls, often indicate that a storm is on its way.

Part of a cloud's name may be based on its height. The names of clouds that form between about 2 and 6 kilometers above Earth's surface have the prefix *alto-*, which means "high." The two main types of these clouds are altocumulus and altostratus.

Clouds that form at or near the ground are called fog. Fog often forms when the ground cools at night after a warm, humid day. The ground cools the air just above the ground to the air's dew point. The next day the heat of the morning sun "burns" the fog off as its water droplets evaporate.

Section 4 Review

1. What instrument is used to measure relative humidity? How does it work?
2. What conditions are needed for clouds to form?
3. Describe each of the three main types of clouds.
4. **Thinking Critically Classifying** Classify each of the following cloud types as low-level, medium-level, or high-level: altocumulus, altostratus, cirrostratus, cirrus, cumulus, fog, nimbostratus, and stratus.

486

Science at Home

Condensation on Glass Fill a large glass half-full with cold water. Show your family members what happens as you add ice cubes to the water. Explain to your family that the water that appears on the outside of the glass comes from water vapor in the atmosphere. Also explain why the water on the outside of the glass only appears after you add ice to the water in the glass.

Answers to Self-Assessment

Caption Question

Figure 17 The fog will "burn" off as its water droplets evaporate.

SECTION 5 Precipitation

TEKS: 6.2C; 6.14C

DISCOVER ••••••••••••••••••••••••••••••••••• ACTIVITY

How Can You Make Hail?

1. Put on your goggles.

2.  Put 15 g of salt into a beaker. Add 50 mL of water. Stir the solution until most of the salt is dissolved.

3. Put 15 mL of cold water in a clean test tube.

4. Place the test tube in the beaker.

5. Fill the beaker almost to the top with crushed ice. Stir the ice mixture every minute for six minutes.

6. Remove the test tube from the beaker and drop an ice chip into the test tube. What happens?

Think It Over

Inferring Based on your observation, what conditions are necessary for hail to form?

In Arica, Chile, the average rainfall is less than 1 millimeter per year. Many years pass with no precipitation at all. On the other hand, the average rainfall on Mount Waialeale on the island of Kauai in Hawaii is about 12 meters per year. That's more than enough to cover a three-story house! As you can see, rainfall varies greatly around the world.

Water evaporates into the air from every water surface on Earth and from living things. This water eventually returns to the surface as precipitation. **Precipitation** (pree sip uh TAY shun) is any form of water that falls from clouds and reaches Earth's surface.

Precipitation always comes from clouds. But not all clouds produce precipitation. For precipitation to occur, cloud droplets or ice crystals must grow heavy enough to fall through the air. One way that cloud droplets grow is by colliding and combining with other cloud droplets. As the droplets grow larger, they fall faster and collect more droplets. Finally, the droplets become heavy enough to fall out of the cloud as raindrops.

Types of Precipitation

In warm parts of the world, precipitation is almost always rain or drizzle. In colder regions, precipitation may fall as snow or ice. **Common types of precipitation include rain, sleet, freezing rain, hail, and snow.**

GUIDE FOR READING

◆ What are the main types of precipitation?

◆ How is rainfall measured?

Reading Tip As you read, make a list of the types of precipitation. Write a sentence describing how each type forms.

Key Terms precipitation • rain gauge • drought

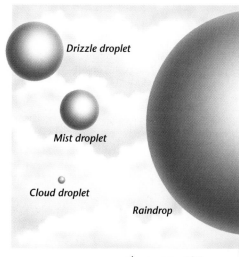

Drizzle droplet

Mist droplet

Cloud droplet

Raindrop

Figure 18 Droplets come in many sizes. Believe it or not, a raindrop has about one million times as much water in it as a cloud droplet.

Chapter 14 **487**

READING STRATEGIES

Reading Tip Student lists should include rain, sleet, freezing rain, hail, and snow. Suggest to students that they save their sentences and use them as a study guide. Tell students that knowing how each type of precipitation forms will help them understand its characteristics.

Program Resources

◆ **Unit 4 Resources** 14-5 Lesson Plan, p. 141; 14-5 Section Summary, p. 142

◆ **Guided Reading and Study Workbook** 14-5

Objectives

After completing the lesson, students will be able to

◆ identify the main types of precipitation;

◆ describe how precipitation is measured and ways that it might be controlled.

1 Engage/Explore

Activating Prior Knowledge

Stimulate students to think about precipitation by asking: **Did you ever hear the expression, "It's raining cats and dogs"?** (Most students will say yes.) **Do you know what it means?** (That it's raining very hard) **Where do you think the expression comes from?** (Students probably will not know.) Explain that the expression may come from old Norse myths, in which cats were identified with rain and dogs with winds. Tell the class they will learn more about rain and other types of precipitation in this section.

•••••••• DISCOVER ••••••••

Skills Focus inferring
Materials *15 g salt, beaker, 50 mL water, stirrer, 15 mL cold water, clean test tube, crushed ice, watch or clock*
Time 15 minutes
Tips The inside of the test tube must be very clean. Have students measure the temperature of the water in the test tube before they add the ice chip. They may be surprised to find it is less than 0°C. (The freezing point of salt water is less than 0°C, the freezing point of fresh water.)
Expected Outcome When the ice chip is dropped into the test tube, the cold water in the test tube will crystalize into ice around it.
Think It Over For hail to form, it must be very cold and there must be particles on which water can crystalize into ice.

2 Facilitate

Types of Precipitation

Building Inquiry Skills: Observing

Materials *transparent plastic lid, dropper, pencil, water*

Time 10 minutes

Have student pairs do this activity to observe how tiny water droplets in clouds merge to form larger drops of water until the drops are heavy enough to fall as precipitation. Students should fill the dropper with water and squeeze many separate drops onto the inside of a transparent plastic lid. Then they should quickly turn the lid over and, holding it in the air by one side, use the point of a pencil from underneath the lid to move the tiny drops of water together. When the drops touch, they will appear to leap together to form larger drops, and when the drops get large enough they will fall like rain. Ask: **What causes the water drops in clouds to move around and bump into each other so they can merge into larger drops?** *(wind and gravity)* **learning modality: tactile/ kinesthetic**

Using the Visuals: Figure 19

Call students' attention to the devastation caused by freezing rain that is shown in photo B. Ask: **How did freezing rain cause this kind of damage?** *(The weight of the accumulated ice broke tree branches and downed power lines.)* **How would the street pictured in the photo look if, instead of freezing rain, the same amount of snow or hailstones had fallen?** *(Snow is lighter than ice so it probably would not have broken branches or power lines, although it might have blocked the street. Hailstones, depending on their size, might have broken twigs and small branches and even the windshield of the car, but it probably would not have blocked the street with large branches or downed power lines.)* **learning modality: visual**

Figure 19 **(A)** Snowflakes form in clouds that are colder than 0°C. **(B)** Freezing rain coats objects with a layer of ice. **(C)** Hailstones are formed inside clouds during thunderstorms.

Rain The most common kind of precipitation is rain. Drops of water are called rain if they are at least 0.5 millimeter in diameter. Precipitation made up of smaller drops of water is called mist or drizzle. Mist and drizzle usually fall from nimbostratus clouds.

Sleet Sometimes raindrops fall through a layer of air below 0°C, the freezing point of water. As they fall, the raindrops freeze into solid particles of ice. Ice particles smaller than 5 millimeters in diameter are called sleet.

Freezing Rain At other times raindrops falling through cold air near the ground do not freeze in the air. Instead, the raindrops freeze when they touch a cold surface. This is called freezing rain. In an ice storm, a smooth, thick layer of ice builds up on every surface. The weight of the ice may break tree branches onto power lines, causing power failures. Freezing rain and sleet can make sidewalks and roads slippery and dangerous.

Hail Round pellets of ice larger than 5 millimeters in diameter are called hailstones. Hail forms only inside cumulonimbus clouds during thunderstorms. A hailstone starts as an ice pellet inside a cold region of a cloud. Strong updrafts in the cloud carry the hailstone up and down through the cold region many times. Each time the hailstone goes through the cold region, a new layer of ice forms around the hailstone. Eventually the hailstone becomes heavy enough to fall to the ground. If you cut a hailstone in half, you can often see shells of ice, like the layers of an onion. Because hailstones can grow quite large before finally falling to the ground, hail can cause tremendous damage to crops, buildings, and vehicles.

488

Background

History of Science For centuries people have tried to increase the amount of precipitation that falls. From praying and dancing to sending up explosives into clouds, they have searched for ways to make rain. It wasn't until the 1940s, however, that Vincent Schaefer discovered how to make rain by seeding clouds. He discovered that a grain of dry ice dropped into a cloud led to the formation of millions of ice crystals, often leading to precipitation. Shortly after this discovery, Bernard Vonnegut discovered that silver iodide led to the production of even more ice crystals than dry ice. Since then, no other process has been found that is better at making rain than their cloud-seeding method. Rainmaking companies still use this method in many parts of the world.

Snow Often water vapor in a cloud is converted directly into ice crystals called snowflakes. Snowflakes have an endless number of different shapes and patterns, all with six sides or branches. Snowflakes often join together into larger clumps of snow in which the six-sided crystals are hard to see.

☑ *Checkpoint* *How do hailstones form?*

Measuring Precipitation

Meteorologists measure rainfall with a rain gauge. A **rain gauge** is an open-ended can or tube that collects rainfall. The amount of rainfall is measured by dipping a ruler into the water or by reading a marked scale. To increase the accuracy of the measurement, the top of a rain gauge may have a funnel that collects ten times as much rain as the tube alone. The funnel collects a greater depth of water that is easier to measure. But to get the actual depth of rain, it is necessary to divide by ten.

Snowfall is measured using a ruler or by melting collected snow and measuring the depth of water it produces. On average, 10 centimeters of snow contains about the same amount of water as 1 centimeter of rain. Of course, light, fluffy snow contains far less water than heavy, wet snow.

Collecting funnel

1 centimeter of rain

10 centimeters in measuring tube

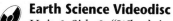
Measuring tube $\frac{1}{10}$ *area of funnel*

Figure 20 A rain gauge measures the depth of rain that falls.
Observing How much rain was collected in the measuring tube of this rain gauge?

Sharpen your Skills

Calculating

ACTIVITY

Make your own rain gauge by putting a funnel into a narrow, straight-sided glass jar. Here's how to calculate how much more rain your funnel collects than the jar alone.

1. First measure the diameter of the top of the funnel and square it.
   Example: 4 × 4 = 16

2. Then measure the diameter of the top of the jar and square it.
   Example: 2 × 2 = 4

3. Divide the first square by the second square.
   Example: $\frac{16}{4} = 4$

4. To find the actual depth of rain that fell, divide the depth of water in the jar by the ratio from Step 3.
   Example: $\frac{8 \text{ cm}}{4} = 2 \text{ cm}$

Building Inquiry Skills: Measuring

Materials *shallow pan, flour, sieve*

ACTIVITY

Time 10 minutes to collect raindrops; 10 minutes to compare sizes

On a day when it is raining and there is no danger of lightning, challenge students to catch raindrops and estimate their size. Have each student hold a shallow pan containing a smooth layer of flour out in the rain for a second or two, just long enough for several raindrops to land in the pan and form little lumps in the flour. After at least 15–20 minutes when the lumps have dried, have students pour the flour through a sieve to separate the lumps. Ask: **How big are the raindrops you caught?** *(Students should estimate the size of the raindrops from the size of the lumps. The bigger the lumps, the larger the raindrops.)* **learning modality: visual**

Measuring Precipitation

Sharpen your Skills

Calculating

Time 15 minutes

ACTIVITY

Tips Explain that the amount of rain collected in the jar is the amount that fell over an area the size of the funnel opening. The calculations show how much smaller the area of the jar opening is than the area of the funnel opening. The total amount of rain collected must be reduced by this ratio to show how much would have fallen into the jar alone. Note that Figure 20, has a different ratio.

Expected Outcome Students should work through the calculations to make sure they also get a final answer of 2 cm.

Extend Ask: **What is the actual depth of the rain that fell if the diameter of the top of the funnel is 6 cm and the depth of water in the jar is 8 cm?** *(8 cm ÷ (36/4) = 0.89 cm)* **learning modality: logical/mathematical**

Ongoing Assessment

Drawing Have students draw diagrams showing how rain, sleet, and freezing rain form.

Media and Technology

Earth Science Videodisc
Unit 6, Side 2, "What's in Our Tap?"

Chapter 6

Answers to Self-Assessment

☑ *Checkpoint*

Hailstones form when pellets of ice inside cumulonimbus clouds are carried up and down many times, each time adding a new layer of ice, until they become heavy enough to fall to the ground.

Caption Question

Figure 20 Though one cm of rain fell into the gauge, 10 cm were collected.

Controlling Precipitation

Point out that rain-making technology could not be developed until scientists discovered how rain actually forms in clouds. In the early 1900s, a scientist named Alfred Wegener hypothesized that almost all precipitation, even rain, starts out as ice crystals. Explain that the condensation of water alone is a much slower process, and this is why Wegener believed correctly that it could not account for most precipitation. Ask: **How does Wegener's hypothesis relate to the cloud-seeding technology?** *(Clouds are seeded with crystals of dry ice and silver iodide because this quickly leads to the formation of ice crystals large enough to fall as precipitation.)* **learning modality: verbal**

3 Assess

Section 5 Review Answers

1. Rain, sleet, freezing rain, hail, and snow
2. rain gauge
3. Cloud droplets or ice crystals must grow heavy enough to fall through the air.
4. Cumulonimbus clouds produce hail.
5. The can with the larger diameter would collect more rain. However, the depth of the water in the two cans would be the same.

Check Your Progress   CHAPTER PROJECT

Suggest that students experiment with different types of graphs to display their weather data. Also require that they graph all or most of the weather factors on the same graph so they can see how the weather factors change together. This will help them see patterns in the data.

Performance Assessment

Skills Check Have students make a table comparing and contrasting the five common types of precipitation.

Figure 21 The corn in this photo was damaged by a long drought. *Applying Concepts How can cloud seeding be used to reduce the effect of droughts?*

Controlling Precipitation

In some regions, there may be periods that are much drier than usual. Long periods of unusually low precipitation are called **droughts.** Droughts can cause great hardship. In the farming regions of the Midwest, for example, droughts may cause entire crops to fail. The farmers suffer from lost income and consumers suffer from high food prices. In some less-developed countries, droughts can cause widespread hunger, or famine.

 INTEGRATING TECHNOLOGY In recent years, scientists have been trying to produce rain during droughts. The most common method is called cloud seeding. In cloud seeding, tiny crystals of dry ice (solid carbon dioxide) and silver iodide are sprinkled into clouds from airplanes. Many clouds contain supercooled water droplets, which are actually below 0°C. The droplets don't freeze because there aren't enough particles around which ice crystals can form. Water vapor can condense on the particles of silver iodide, forming rain or snow. Dry ice works by cooling the droplets even further, so that they will freeze without particles being present.

Cloud seeding has also been used with some success to clear fog from airports. Dry ice is sprinkled into the fog, causing ice crystals to form. This removes some of the fog so pilots can see the runways. Unfortunately, cloud seeding clears only cold fogs, so its use for this purpose is limited.

Section 5 Review

1. Name the five common types of precipitation.
2. What device is used to measure precipitation?
3. What must happen before precipitation can fall from a cloud?
4. What kind of cloud produces hail?
5. **Thinking Critically Applying Concepts** If two open cans of different diameters were left out in the rain, how would the amount of water they collected compare? How would the depth of water in the cans compare?

490

Check Your Progress   CHAPTER PROJECT

Now you should be ready to begin graphing your weather data. Look for patterns in your graphs. Use your data to predict what the next day's weather will be. Compare your predictions with what actually happens the next day. Are you able to predict the weather with confidence?

Answers to Self-Assessment

Caption Question

Figure 21 Cloud seeding can be used to lessen the effect of droughts by sprinkling clouds with particles around which water droplets can condense to form rain.

Program Resources

◆ **Unit 4 Resources** 14-5 Review and Reinforce, p. 143; 14-5 Enrich, p. 144

SECTION 1 Energy in the Atmosphere

Key Ideas

◆ Energy from the sun travels to Earth as electromagnetic waves—mostly visible light, infrared radiation, and ultraviolet radiation.

◆ When Earth's surface is heated, it radiates some of the energy back into the atmosphere in the form of longer-wavelength radiation.

Key Terms

electromagnetic waves   ultraviolet radiation
radiation   scattering
infrared radiation   greenhouse effect

SECTION 2 Heat Transfer

INTEGRATING PHYSICS

Key Ideas

◆ Temperature of the air is typically measured with a thermometer.

◆ Three forms of heat transfer—radiation, conduction, and convection—work together to heat the troposphere.

Key Terms

thermal energy   thermometer   conduction
temperature   heat   convection

SECTION 3 Winds

Key Ideas

◆ All winds are caused by differences in air pressure, which are the result of unequal heating of Earth's surface.

◆ Local winds are caused by unequal heating of Earth's surface within a small area.

◆ The movement of air between the equator and the poles produces global winds.

Key Terms

wind   monsoon
anemometer   global wind
wind-chill factor   Coriolis effect
local wind   latitude
sea breeze   jet stream
land breeze

SECTION 4 Water in the Atmosphere

Key Ideas

◆ Relative humidity is the percentage of water vapor in the air compared to the amount of water vapor the air could hold. It can be measured with a psychrometer.

◆ Clouds of all kinds form when water vapor in the air becomes liquid water or solid ice.

◆ Meteorologists classify clouds into three main types: cumulus, stratus, and cirrus.

Key Terms

evaporation   psychrometer   cumulus
humidity   condensation   stratus
relative humidity   dew point   cirrus

SECTION 5 Precipitation

Key Ideas

◆ Common types of precipitation include rain, sleet, freezing rain, hail, and snow.

◆ Rain is measured with a rain gauge.

◆ Scientists have used cloud seeding to produce rain and to clear fog from airports.

Key Terms

precipitation
rain gauge
drought

Organizing Information

Concept Map Construct a concept map about winds on a separate sheet of paper. Be sure to include the following terms: local winds, global winds, monsoons, sea breezes, land breezes, prevailing westerlies, polar easterlies, tradewinds, and the two types of monsoon. (For more on concept maps, see the Skills Handbook.)

Chapter 14 **491**

Organizing Information

Concept Map Answers will vary. A typical concept map is shown below.

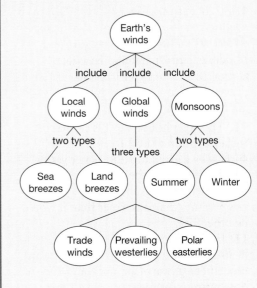

Program Resources

◆ **Unit 4 Resources** Chapter 14 Project Scoring Rubric, p. 124

◆ **Performance Assessment** Chapter 14 pp. 44–46

◆ **Chapter and Unit Tests** Chapter 14 Test pp. 68–71

Media and Technology

 Computer Test Bank
Chapter 14 Test

Reviewing Content

Multiple Choice

1. a 2. b 3. b 4. c 5. c

True or False

6. visible light 7. greenhouse effect
8. true 9. anemometer 10. true

Checking Concepts

11. The greenhouse effect is caused by the absorption of heat from Earth's surface by carbon dioxide, water vapor, and other gases in the atmosphere. It keeps Earth's atmosphere at a temperature that is warmer than it would be otherwise.

12. Convection causes most of the heating of the troposphere as the upward movement of warm air and the downward movement of cool air form convection currents.

13. Like local land and sea breezes, monsoons occur because of unequal heating of land and nearby bodies of water. Unlike local land and sea breezes, monsoons occur over a wide region and change direction with the seasons.

14. Warm air rises at the equator and flows toward the poles. Cold air sinks at the poles and spreads out toward the equator. The movement of air between the equator and the poles produces global winds.

15. When wind strikes the windward side of a mountain range, it is forced upward. As air rises, it becomes cooler. Since cool air can hold less water vapor than warm air, the moisture in the air often precipitates as snow or rain on the windward side of the mountain, leaving little to fall on the leeward side.

16. Clouds usually form high in the air instead of at Earth's surface because the air must be cold for water vapor to condense and form clouds and air at high altitudes usually is colder than air near the surface.

17. Sleet forms when raindrops fall through a layer of air below 0°C and freeze into small particles of ice. Hail forms when an ice pellet in a cumulonimbus cloud is carried up and down through the cold region of the cloud by strong updrafts, each time gathering another layer of ice until the

Reviewing Content

 Review key concepts online using iText at www.phschool.com

Multiple Choice

Choose the letter of the best answer.

1. Energy from the sun travels to Earth's surface by
   a. radiation.
   b. convection.
   c. evaporation.
   d. conduction.

2. Rising warm air transports heat energy by
   a. conduction.
   b. convection.
   c. radiation.
   d. condensation.

3. A psychrometer is used to measure
   a. rainfall.
   b. relative humidity.
   c. temperature.
   d. humidity.

4. Clouds form because water vapor in the air
   a. warms.   b. conducts.
   c. condenses.   d. evaporates.

5. Rain, sleet, and hail are all forms of
   a. evaporation.
   b. condensation.
   c. precipitation.
   d. convection.

True or False

If the statement is true, write true. If it is false, change the underlined word or words to make the statement true.

6. Infrared radiation and <u>ultraviolet radiation</u> make up most of the energy Earth receives from the sun.

7. The process by which gases hold heat in the atmosphere is called the <u>wind-chill factor</u>.

8. Water molecules in liquid water escape into the atmosphere as water vapor in the process of <u>evaporation</u>.

9. The instrument used to measure wind speed is a <u>thermometer</u>.

10. Clouds that form near the ground are called <u>fog</u>.

Checking Concepts

11. What causes the greenhouse effect? How does it affect Earth's atmosphere?

12. What form of heat transfer is most important in heating the troposphere?

13. What are monsoons? How are they like land and sea breezes? How are they different?

14. Describe how the movements of hot air at the equator and cold air at the poles produce global wind patterns.

15. Why are deserts often found on the leeward side of mountain ranges?

16. Why do clouds usually form high in the air instead of near Earth's surface?

17. Describe sleet, hail, and snow in terms of how each one forms.

18. **Writing to Learn** Imagine you are a drop of water in the ocean. Write a diary describing your journey through the water cycle. How do you become a cloud? What type of conditions cause you to fall as precipitation? Use descriptive words to describe your journey.

Thinking Critically

19. **Relating Cause and Effect** What circumstances could cause a nighttime land breeze in a city near the ocean?

20. **Problem Solving** If you use a psychrometer and get the same reading on both thermometers, what is the relative humidity?

21. **Comparing and Contrasting** How are hail and sleet alike? How are they different?

22. **Classifying** Classify the different types of clouds by the kind of weather associated with each type.

23. **Relating Cause and Effect** What is the source of the energy that powers Earth's winds?

hailstone is heavy enough to fall to the surface. Snow forms when water vapor in a cloud is converted directly into ice crystals.

18. Students' diary entries will vary, but they should reflect students' knowledge of the water cycle and include the terms *evaporation*, *condensation*, and *precipitation*.

Thinking Critically

19. A nighttime land breeze in a city near the ocean would be caused by the land cooling off more quickly than the water at night so that as

warm air rose over the water, cool air would flow from the land to take its place.

20. The relative humidity is 100 percent because since both temperatures were the same, the water on the wet bulb must not have been able to evaporate, which would happen only when the relative humidity is that high.

21. Hail and sleet are both frozen rain. Sleet is smaller than 5 millimeters in diameter, while hail is larger than 5 millimeters in diameter. Sleet forms anytime rain falls through a layer of air below 0°C; hail forms only inside

Applying Skills

Use the table below to answer Questions 24–27.

Average Monthly Rainfall

Month	Rainfall	Month	Rainfall
January	1 cm	July	49 cm
February	1 cm	August	57 cm
March	1 cm	September	40 cm
April	2 cm	October	20 cm
May	25 cm	November	4 cm
June	52 cm	December	1 cm

24. **Graphing** Use the information in the table to draw a bar graph that shows the rainfall each month at this location.
25. **Calculating** What is the total amount of rainfall each year at this location?
26. **Classifying** Which months of the year would you classify as "dry"? Which months would you classify as "wet"?

27. **Drawing Conclusions** The place represented by the rainfall data is in Southeast Asia. What do you think accounts for the extremely heavy rainfall that occurs during some months?

Performance CHAPTER PROJECT **Assessment**

Present Your Project Develop a way to present your findings to the class. For example, you could put your graphs and predictions on a poster. Are your graphs neatly drawn and easy to understand? Practice your presentation and make any needed improvements.

Reflect and Record How could you improve the accuracy of your observations? What did you learn about how easy or difficult it is to predict the weather?

Test Preparation

Use these questions to prepare for standardized tests.

Study the graph. Then answer Questions 28–31.

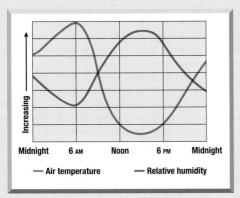

— Air temperature   — Relative humidity

28. The greatest change in air temperature occurred during the period from
   A midnight to 6 A.M.
   B 6 A.M. to noon.
   C noon to 6 P.M.
   D 6 P.M. to midnight.

29. The graph indicates that as air temperature increases, relative humidity
   F increases.
   G sometimes increases and sometimes decreases.
   H decreases.
   J stays about the same.

30. Condensation is most likely to occur at approximately
   A 6 A.M.   B noon.
   C 3 P.M.   D 6 P.M.

31. Assuming that the amount of water vapor in the air stayed constant through the day, one could infer from the graph that
   F cool air can hold more water vapor than warm air.
   G cool air can hold less water vapor than warm air.
   H cool air and warm air can hold the same amount of water vapor.
   J cool air cannot hold water vapor.

---

cumulonimbus clouds during thunderstorms when layers of ice form around ice pellets as they are carried up and down through cold regions of a cloud.
22. Cumulus clouds are associated with fair weather. Cumulonimbus clouds are associated with thunderstorms. Nimbostratus clouds are associated with drizzle, mist, rain, or snow.
23. Earth's winds are powered by unequal heating of Earth's atmosphere by the sun.

Program Resources

- ◆ **Inquiry Skills Activity Book** Provides teaching and review of all inquiry skills
- ◆ **Prentice Hall Assessment System** Provides standardized test practice
- ◆ **Reading in the Content Area** Provides strategies to improve science reading skills
- ◆ **Teacher's ELL Handbook** Provides multiple strategies for English language learners

---

Applying Skills

24. Student's graphs should have one axis labeled "Month" and the other axis labeled "Average Monthly Rainfall (centimeters)." The bars should range from 1 centimeter in height (January, February, March, and December) to 57 centimeters in height (August).
25. 253 centimeters
26. *Dry:* January, February, March, April, November, and December; *Wet:* May, June, July, August, September, and October
27. Monsoons

Performance CHAPTER PROJECT **Assessment**

Present Your Project Make sure students have clearly-drawn graphs or other visuals to use for their presentations. Advise them to include in their presentations a description of when and where their measurements were made and the instruments that were used. They also should include a discussion of any patterns they see in their data.

Reflect and Record If students used instruments they made themselves, they may be able to improve the accuracy of their observations by using commercial instruments. Students probably will find that it is difficult to predict the weather because some of the patterns they observe in their data may not be significant for prediction. Help students focus on the most significant factors for predicting the weather, including air pressure, clouds, and wind direction.

Test Preparation

28. B 29. H 30. A 31. G

Weather Patterns

Sections	Time	Student Edition Activities		Other Activities
CHAPTER PROJECT ▼ **The Weather Tomorrow** p. 495 TEKS: 6.14C	Ongoing (2–3 weeks)	TEKS: 6.2B, C, E; 6.4B Check Your Progress, p. 502, 518, 525 Present Your Project, p. 529	TE	Chapter 15 Project Notes, pp. 494–495
1 Air Masses and Fronts pp. 496–502 TEKS: 6.14C 15.1.1 Identify the major types of air masses that affect the weather in North America. 15.1.2 Name and describe the main types of fronts. 15.1.3 Describe cyclones and anticyclones.	2–3 periods/ 1–$\frac{1}{2}$ blocks	TEKS: 6.2B, C **Discover** How Do Fluids of Different Densities Behave?, p. 496 **Sharpen Your Skills** Classifying, p. 501	TE TE TE TE	Inquiry Challenge, p. 499 Including All Students, p. 499 Demonstration, p. 500 Including All Students, p. 501
2 Storms pp. 503–514 TEKS: 6.14C 15.2.1 List the main kinds of storms and explain how they form. 15.2.2 Describe measures people can take to ensure safety in a storm.	3 periods/ 1$\frac{1}{2}$ blocks	TEKS: 6.2B, C, D; 6.3C, D, E **Discover** Can You Make a Tornado?, p. 503 **Try This** Lightning Distances, p. 504 **Science at Home,** p. 511 **Real-World Lab: Careers in Science** Tracking a Hurricane, pp. 512–513	TE TE	Demonstration, p. 504 Including All Students, p. 505
3 ● *INTEGRATING HEALTH* **Floods** pp. 515–518 TEKS: 6.14C 15.3.1 Identify the causes of flooding. 15.3.2 Explain how people can protect themselves in a flood.	1 period/ $\frac{1}{2}$ block	TEKS: 6.2B, C; 6.3C; 6.4A **Discover** What Causes Floods?, p. 515 **Sharpen Your Skills** Communicating, p. 516	TE	Using the Visuals: Figure 15, p. 517
4 Predicting the Weather pp. 519–526 TEKS: 6.14C 15.4.1 Explain how technology helps forecasters predict the weather. 15.4.2 Describe the types of information shown on weather maps. 15.4.3 Describe El Niño and its effects.	3 periods/ 1$\frac{1}{2}$ blocks	TEKS: 6.2B, C, D **Discover** What's the Weather?, p. 519 **Sharpen Your Skills** Interpreting Data, p. 522 **Skills Lab: Interpreting Data** Reading a Weather Map, p. 526	TE TE TE LM	Inquiry Challenge, p. 521 Building Inquiry Skills: Calculating, p. 524 Exploring Newspaper Weather Maps, p. 525 15, "Investigating Weather Maps"
Study Guide/Chapter Assessment pp. 527–529	1 period/ $\frac{1}{2}$ block	PLM Provides blackline masters for Probeware labs	ISAB	Provides Teaching and review of all inquiry skills

Key: **CTB** Computer Test Bank
CUT Chapter and Unit Tests
ELL Teacher's ELL Handbook

CHAPTER PLANNING GUIDE

 The Resource Pro® CD-ROM provides flexibility for planning the instruction for any type of schedule.

Program Resources	Assessment Strategies	Media and Technology
UR Chapter 15 Project Teacher Notes, pp. 150–151 UR Chapter 15 Project Student materials, pp. 152–155	SE Performance Assessment: Present Your Project, p. 529 TE Check Your Progress, pp. 502, 518, 525 UR Chapter 15 Project Scoring Rubric, p. 156	Science Explorer at www.phschool.com Student Edition on Audio CD, English-Spanish, Chapter 15
UR 15-1 Section Lesson Plan, p. 157 UR 15-1 Section Summary, p. 158 UR 15-1 Review and Reinforce, p. 159 UR 15-1 Enrich, p. 160	SE Section 1 Review, p. 502 TE Ongoing Assessment, pp. 497, 499, 501 TE Performance Assessment, p. 502	Transparencies 70, "North American Air Masses"; 71, "Cold Front"; 72, "Warm Front"; 73, "Occluded Front"
UR 15-2 Section Lesson Plan, p. 161 UR 15-2 Section Summary, p. 162 UR 15-2 Review and Reinforce, p. 163 UR 15-2 Enrich, p. 164 UR Real-World Lab blackline masters, pp. 173–175	SE Section 2 Review, p. 511 TE Ongoing Assessment, pp. 505, 507, 509 TE Performance Assessment, p. 511	Earth Science Videodisc, Unit 4, Side 2, "Violent Storms" Videotape Grade 6, Unit 4, "Violent Storms" Lab Activity Videotapes, Tape 4 Transparency 74, "Clouds and Winds in a Hurricane"
UR 15-3 Section Lesson Plan, p. 165 UR 15-3 Section Summary, p. 166 UR 15-3 Review and Reinforce, p. 167 UR 15-3 Enrich, p. 168	SE Section 3 Review, p. 518 TE Ongoing Assessment, p. 517 TE Performance Assessment, p. 518	
UR 15-4 Section Lesson Plan, p. 169 UR 15-4 Section Summary, p. 170 UR 15-4 Review and Reinforce, p. 171 UR 15-4 Enrich, p. 172 UR Skills Lab blackline masters, pp. 176–177	SE Section 4 Review, p. 525 TE Ongoing Assessment, pp. 521, 523 TE Performance Assessment, p. 525	Earth Science Videodisc, Unit 4, Side 2, "Never Put Up the Umbrella Until It Starts to Rain" Videotape Grade 6, Unit 4, "Never Put Up the Umbrella Until It Starts to Rain" Lab Activity Videotapes, Tape 4 Transparency 75, "Weather Map"; 76, "Newspaper Weather Map"
ELL Provides multiple strategies for English language learners GRSW Provides worksheets to promote student comprehension of content RCA Provides strategies to improve science reading skills	SE Chapter 15 Study Guide/Assessment, pp. 527–529 PA Chapter 15 Assessment, pp. 47–49 CUT Chapter 15 Test, pp. 72–75 CTB Chapter 15 Test PHAS Provides standardized test preparation	Chapter 15 Computer Test Bank, Chapter 15 Test

GRSW Guided Reading and Study Workbook
ISAB Inquiry Skills Activity Book
LM Laboratory Manual

PA Performance Assessment
PHAS Prentice Hall Assessment System
PLM Probeware Lab Manual

RCA Reading in the Content Area
SE Student Edition

TE Teacher's Edition
UR Unit Resources

Student Edition Activities Planner

ACTIVITY	Time (minutes)	Materials — Quantities for one work group	Skills
Section 1			
Discover, p. 496	10	**Consumable** cardboard divider, red food coloring, 1 L warm water, 100 mL table salt, blue food coloring, 1 L cold water **Nonconsumable** plastic shoe box	Developing Hypotheses
Sharpen Your Skills, p. 501	home	No special materials are required.	Classifying
Section 2			
Discover, p. 503	10	**Consumable** water, liquid dish detergent **Nonconsumable** large plastic jar with lid, penny or marble	Observing
Try This, p. 504	10	**Nonconsumable** watch or stopwatch, calculator	Calculating
Science at Home, p. 511	home	No special materials are required.	Communicating
Real-World Lab, pp. 512–513	40	**Consumable** tracing paper **Nonconsumable** ruler; red, blue, green, and brown pencils	Interpreting Data, Predicting
Section 3			
Discover, p. 515	10	**Consumable** water **Nonconsumable** cup, funnel, basin	Inferring
Sharpen Your Skills, p. 516	10	No special materials are required. Computer use is optional.	Communicating
Section 4			
Discover, p. 519	10	**Nonconsumable** local newspaper weather report	Observing
Sharpen Your Skills, p. 522	10	No special materials are required.	Interpreting Data
Skills Lab, p. 526	30	No special materials are required.	Interpreting Data, Drawing Conclusions

A list of all materials required for the Student Edition activities can be found on pages T43–T49. You can obtain information about ordering materials by calling 1-800-848-9500 or by accessing the Science Explorer Internet site at **www.phschool.com**.

(6.2) Scientific processes. The student uses scientific inquiry methods during field and laboratory investigations. *(Project; Sections 1, 2, 3, 4)*

The student is expected to:

(B) collect data by observing and measuring;

(C) analyze and interpret information to construct reasonable explanations from direct and indirect evidence;

(D) communicate valid conclusions; and

(E) construct graphs, tables, maps, and charts using tools including computers to organize, examine, and evaluate data.

(6.3) Scientific processes. The student uses critical thinking and scientific problem solving to make informed decisions. *(Sections 2, 3)*

The student is expected to:

(C) represent the natural world using models and identify their limitations;

(D) evaluate the impact of research on scientific thought, society, and the environment; and

(E) connect Grade 6 science concepts with the history of science and contributions of scientists.

(6.4) Scientific processes. The student knows how to use a variety of tools and methods to conduct science inquiry. *(Project; Section 3)*

The student is expected to:

(A) collect, analyze, and record information using tools including beakers, petri dishes, meter sticks, graduated cylinders, weather instruments, timing devices, hot plates, test tubes, safety goggles, spring scales, magnets, balances, microscopes, telescopes, thermometers, calculators, field equipment, compasses, computers, and computer probes; and

(B) identify patterns in collected information using percent, average, range, and frequency.

(6.14) Science concepts. The student knows the structures and functions of Earth systems. *(Project; Sections 1, 2, 3, 4)*

The student is expected to:

(C) describe components of the atmosphere, including oxygen, nitrogen, and water vapor, and identify the role of atmospheric movement in weather change.

Take It to the Net

 Interactive text at www.phschool.com

Science Explorer comes alive with iText.

- **Complete student text** is accessible from any computer with Internet access or a CD-ROM drive.

- **Animations, simulations, and videos** enhance student understanding and retention of concepts.

- **Self-tests and online study tools** assess student understanding.

- **Teacher management tools** help you make the most of this valuable resource.

STAY CURRENT with **SCIENCE NEWS**®

Find out the latest research and information about weather and climate at **www.phschool.com**.

Go to **www.phschool.com**. Select Texas on the navigation bar. Click on the Science icon. Then click on <u>Science Explorer</u> under PH@school.

The Weather Tomorrow

TEKS: 6.2B, C, E; 6.4B; 6.14C

Predicting the weather is something that interests most people because the weather influences so many things that we do. In this chapter, students will learn what causes changes in the weather and how the information recorded on weather maps can be used to make weather predictions.

Purpose In this project, students will get a chance to predict the weather and then evaluate how well they have done compared with the actual weather and with professional forecasts.

Skills Focus After completing this project, students will be able to

♦ interpret the symbols in newspaper weather maps;

♦ compare weather maps from day to day to find patterns in the weather;

♦ predict the weather for tomorrow based on the weather today;

♦ draw weather maps to show their weather predictions;

♦ compare their own predictions with professional forecasts and the next day's weather.

Project Time Line The entire project will take at least two weeks. Students should start collecting newspaper weather maps immediately. They should also read about weather maps in Section 4, paying special attention to *Exploring Newspaper Weather Maps* on page 525. As soon as students have finished reading Section 1 on air masses and fronts, they can start analyzing their weather maps. They should be looking for patterns in the weather by comparing the maps from day to day. Check students' progress at this point and give extra guidance to any students who are having problems.

Students should continue collecting and comparing weather maps over the next week or so. Check their progress when they finish Section 3 by having them predict the next day's weather at their own location and two other locations of their choice that are at least 1,000 km apart. Students should draw a weather map to show their predictions. After a week of

A lightning bolt tears through the dark sky.

WEB ACTIVITY
www.phschool.com

SECTION 1 Air Masses and Fronts
Discover How Do Fluids of Different Densities Behave?

SECTION 2 Storms
Discover Can You Make a Tornado?
Real-World Lab Tracking a Hurricane

SECTION 3 Floods
Discover What Causes Floods?

SECTION 4 Predicting Weather Change
Discover What's the Weather?
Skills Lab Reading a Weather Map

494

predicting the weather, have students compare their predictions to the weather maps and professional forecasts.

When students have finished reading the chapter, give them a day or two to organize their presentations. They should display their newspaper weather maps and the weather maps they made to predict the weather. They should also include commentary, written or oral, about the patterns they observed in the weather and how they made their predictions.

For more detailed information on planning and supervising the chapter project, see Chapter 15 Project Teacher Notes, pages 150–151 in Unit 4 Resources.

Suggested Shortcuts You can reduce the scope of the project by requiring students to select just one location instead of three. Another shortcut is to have students work in groups. If you do, make sure groups divide tasks in such a way that each student makes a significant contribution. Urge groups to divide tasks according to students' specific abilities and interests, if possible.

This chapter project can also be done as a class project. Spend a few minutes at the beginning of

The Weather Tomorrow

When the sky turns dark and threatening, it's not hard to predict the weather. A storm is on its way. But wouldn't you rather know about an approaching storm before it actually arrives?

In this chapter you will learn about weather patterns, including the kinds of patterns that cause strong thunderstorms like this one. As you work through this chapter, you will get a chance to make your own weather forecasts and compare them to the forecasts of professionals. Good luck!

Your Goal To predict the weather for your own community and two other locations in the United States.

To complete the project you will
◆ compare weather maps for several days at a time
◆ look for repeating patterns in the weather
◆ draw maps to show your weather predictions

Get Started Begin by previewing Section 4 to learn about weather maps and symbols. Start a project folder to hold daily national weather maps from your local newspaper and a description of the symbols used on the maps. Choose two locations in the United States that are at least 1,000 kilometers away from your community and from each other.

Check Your Progress You'll be working on this project as you study this chapter. To keep your project on track, look for Check Your Progress boxes at the following points.

Section 1 Review, page 502: Collect weather maps and look for patterns.

Section 3 Review, page 518: Predict the next day's weather.

Section 4 Review, page 525: Compare your predictions to professional forecasts and to the actual weather.

Present Your Project At the end of the chapter (page 529), you will present your weather maps and discuss how well you predicted the weather.

TEKS

In addition to process TEKS, this chapter addresses these concept TEKS as they relate to the chapter's topics.

(6.14) The student knows the structures and functions of Earth systems.
The student is expected to:
(C) describe components of the atmosphere, including oxygen, nitrogen, and water vapor, and identify the role of atmospheric movement in weather change.

495

Program Resources

◆ **Unit 4 Resources** Chapter 15 Project Teacher Notes, pp. 150–151; Chapter 15 Project Overview and Worksheets, pp. 152–155

Media and Technology

Student Edition on Audio CD
English-Spanish, Chapter 15

WEB ACTIVITY www.phschool.com

You will find an Internet activity, chapter self-tests for students, and links to other chapter topics at this site.

---

class each day reviewing with students that day's newspaper weather map. If possible, make an overhead transparency of the map so you can point out details on the map as you discuss it. Also spend a few minutes each day comparing that day's weather map with the weather map from the day before. At the end of a week, have students start trying to predict the next day's weather.

Possible Materials Newspaper weather maps are readily available and easy to work with as long as students always use the same source so the maps have the same format. This makes them easier to compare and creates less confusion. A good source for weather maps regardless of where you live is *USA Today*.

Launching the Project Introduce students to weather maps by handing out copies of a national weather map showing today's weather. Have students find their own state on the map, and then challenge them to use the map to learn as much as they can about their state's weather. For example, ask: **What does the map tell you about the temperature in our state today?** Make sure all the students know how to find this and other weather factors for their state on the map. If necessary, call their attention to the map key and point out the relevant symbols and numbers on the map. Tell students they will be collecting and comparing maps like this one for the Chapter 15 Project. They will use the maps to learn how weather changes and how to predict tomorrow's weather from weather conditions today. Point out, however, that students will make their weather predictions without using the weather forecasts that are often included in weather information in newspapers and on radio and television.

Performance Assessment

To assess students' performance in this project, use the Chapter 15 Project Scoring Rubric on page 156 of Unit 4 Resources.
Students will be assessed on
◆ their collection and interpretation of weather maps;
◆ their weather predictions;
◆ their class presentation;
◆ their group participation, if they worked in groups.

Objectives

After completing the lesson, students will be able to

♦ identify the major types of air masses that affect the weather in North America;

♦ name and describe the main types of fronts;

♦ describe cyclones and anticyclones.

1 Engage/Explore

Activating Prior Knowledge

Help students recall the properties of air they learned about in Chapter 14. Ask: **Which is denser, warm air or cold air?** *(cold air)* **What do you think would happen if a large mass of cold air came into contact with a large mass of warm air?** *(The cold air would sink and the warm air would rise.)* Tell students that large masses of cold and warm air often do meet in the atmosphere. Point out that the meeting of large air masses with different temperatures causes most of our weather.

DISCOVER

Skills Focus developing hypotheses

Materials *cardboard divider, plastic shoe box, red food coloring, 1 L warm water, 100 mL table salt, blue food coloring, 1 L cold water*

Time 10 minutes

Tips The more salt students use, the denser the cold water will be and the more obvious the outcome.

Expected Outcome The red water and the blue water will not mix. Instead, they will form separate layers, with the blue water on the bottom and the red water on top.

Think It Over Students should hypothesize that the cold air mass would move underneath the warm air mass and the warm air mass would rise.

496

SECTION
1 Air Masses and Fronts

DISCOVER · ACTIVITY · · · ·

How Do Fluids of Different Densities Behave?

1. Put on your apron. Place a cardboard divider across the middle of a plastic shoe box.

2. Add a few drops of red food coloring to a liter of warm water. Pour the red liquid, which represents low-density warm air, into the shoe box on one side of the divider.

3. Add about 100 mL of table salt and a few drops of blue food coloring to a liter of cold water. Pour the blue liquid, which represents high-density cold air, into the shoe box on the other side of the divider.

4. What do you think will happen if you remove the divider?

5. Now quickly remove the divider. Watch carefully from the side. What happens?

Think It Over

Developing Hypotheses Based on this activity, write a hypothesis stating what would happen if a mass of cold air ran into a mass of warm air.

GUIDE FOR READING

♦ What are the major types of air masses that affect the weather in North America?

♦ What are the main types of fronts?

♦ What are cyclones?

Reading Tip Before you read, use the headings to make an outline about air masses and fronts. Leave space to fill in details as you read.

Key Terms air mass • tropical • polar • maritime • continental • front • occluded • cyclone • anticyclone

496

Listen to the evening news and you may hear a weather forecast like this: "A huge mass of Arctic air is moving our way, bringing freezing temperatures." Today's weather is influenced by air from thousands of kilometers away—perhaps from Canada or the Caribbean Sea. A huge body of air that has similar temperature, humidity, and air pressure throughout it is called an **air mass.** A single air mass may spread over an area of millions of square kilometers and be up to 10 kilometers high.

Types of Air Masses

Scientists classify air masses according to two characteristics: temperature and humidity. Whether an air mass is warm or cold depends on the temperature of the region over which the air mass forms. **Tropical,** or warm, air masses form in the tropics and have low air pressure. **Polar,** or cold, air masses form north of 50° north latitude and south of 50° south latitude. Polar air masses have high air pressure.

Whether an air mass is humid or dry depends on whether it forms over water or land. **Maritime** air masses form over oceans. Water evaporates from the oceans, so the air can become very humid. **Continental** air masses form over land, in the middle of continents, and are dry.

READING STRATEGIES

Reading Tip Review with students the outline format. If necessary, provide a model outline on the board to remind students how to arrange numerals and letters. Student outlines might begin as follows:

I. Types of Air Masses
  A. Tropical
    1. Maritime Tropical
    2. Continental Tropical
  B. Polar

Vocabulary Point out to students that the term *cyclone,* as it is used in this section, has a somewhat different meaning than its common usage. Many people use the term *cyclone* to mean a tornado, a type of severe storm students will learn about in Section 2. In this section, the term *cyclone* is used to refer to any large, swirling air mass that has low pressure at the center. Unlike a tornado, a cyclone may cover thousands of kilometers.

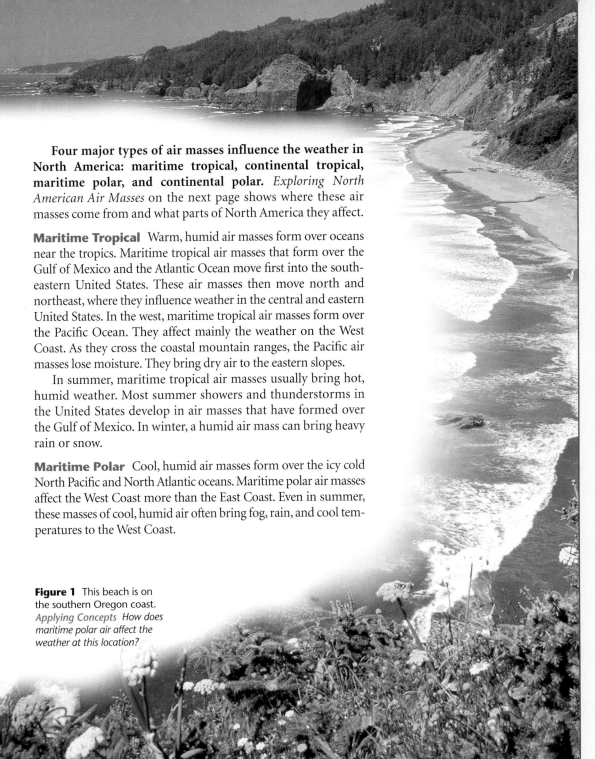

Four major types of air masses influence the weather in North America: maritime tropical, continental tropical, maritime polar, and continental polar. *Exploring North American Air Masses* on the next page shows where these air masses come from and what parts of North America they affect.

Maritime Tropical Warm, humid air masses form over oceans near the tropics. Maritime tropical air masses that form over the Gulf of Mexico and the Atlantic Ocean move first into the southeastern United States. These air masses then move north and northeast, where they influence weather in the central and eastern United States. In the west, maritime tropical air masses form over the Pacific Ocean. They affect mainly the weather on the West Coast. As they cross the coastal mountain ranges, the Pacific air masses lose moisture. They bring dry air to the eastern slopes.

In summer, maritime tropical air masses usually bring hot, humid weather. Most summer showers and thunderstorms in the United States develop in air masses that have formed over the Gulf of Mexico. In winter, a humid air mass can bring heavy rain or snow.

Maritime Polar Cool, humid air masses form over the icy cold North Pacific and North Atlantic oceans. Maritime polar air masses affect the West Coast more than the East Coast. Even in summer, these masses of cool, humid air often bring fog, rain, and cool temperatures to the West Coast.

Figure 1 This beach is on the southern Oregon coast. *Applying Concepts How does maritime polar air affect the weather at this location?*

2 Facilitate

Types of Air Masses

Building Inquiry Skills: Applying Concepts

Some students may need to review concepts covered in earlier chapters to understand the material presented in this section. Review the role evaporation plays in the water cycle. Then ask: **Which type of air mass would you expect to contain more moisture, a maritime air mass or a continental air mass?** (*A maritime air mass, because it forms over the ocean*) **Would a maritime tropical air mass or a maritime polar air mass have more moisture?** (*A maritime tropical air mass, because it is warmer and warm air can hold more moisture than cold air*) **learning modality: verbal**

Including All Students

Help students distinguish among the different types of air masses covered in this section. Challenge them to create crossword puzzles incorporating the terms *tropical, polar, maritime,* and *continental.* After students have created their puzzles, urge them to exchange puzzles with a partner and try to solve them. **limited English proficiency**

Program Resources

- **Unit 4 Resources** 15-1 Lesson Plan, p. 157; 15-1 Section Summary, p. 158
- **Guided Reading and Study Workbook** 15-1

Answers to Self-Assessment

Caption Question

Figure 1 It causes the weather to be cool and humid and often foggy and rainy.

Ongoing Assessment

Writing Have students explain the similarities and differences between polar and tropical air masses and between maritime and continental air masses.

Types of Air Masses, continued

EXPLORING

North American Air Masses

Invite students to apply the information in the feature by having them identify the types of air masses that affect different locations, such as different regions of the United States, different states, or different cities. Include the location where students live. For each location, ask: **What type of air are you likely to find there, and where does it come from?** (*Answers will depend on the locations chosen. For example, northern California receives cool, humid air due to maritime polar air masses from the northern Pacific Ocean.*) Refer to the **ELL Handbook** for additional teaching strategies. **learning modality: visual**

Building Inquiry Skills: Predicting

Point out that when air masses move from where they originate, they tend to be modified by the terrain they pass over. For example, the cold, dry air of continental polar air masses is warmed and moistened when it passes over the Great Lakes. Ask: **How would you predict that the other three North American air masses would be modified by the terrain they usually pass over?** (*Continental tropical air masses would be cooled, maritime polar air masses would be warmed and dried, maritime tropical air masses would be cooled and dried.*) **learning modality: logical/ mathematical**

EXPLORING North American Air Masses

Air masses can be warm or cold, and humid or dry. As an air mass moves into an area, it changes the weather there.

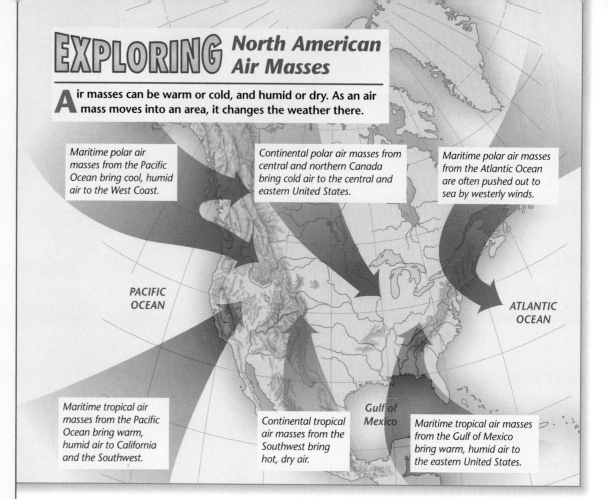

Maritime polar air masses from the Pacific Ocean bring cool, humid air to the West Coast.

Continental polar air masses from central and northern Canada bring cold air to the central and eastern United States.

Maritime polar air masses from the Atlantic Ocean are often pushed out to sea by westerly winds.

PACIFIC OCEAN

ATLANTIC OCEAN

Gulf of Mexico

Maritime tropical air masses from the Pacific Ocean bring warm, humid air to California and the Southwest.

Continental tropical air masses from the Southwest bring hot, dry air.

Maritime tropical air masses from the Gulf of Mexico bring warm, humid air to the eastern United States.

Continental Tropical Hot, dry air masses form only in summer over dry areas of the Southwest and northern Mexico. Continental tropical air masses cover a smaller area than other air masses. They occasionally move northeast, bringing hot, dry weather to the southern Great Plains.

Continental Polar Large continental polar air masses form over central and northern Canada and Alaska. As you would expect, continental polar air masses bring cool or cold air. In winter, continental polar air masses bring clear, cold, dry air to much of North America. Air masses that form near the Arctic Circle can bring bitterly cold weather with very low humidity. In summer, storms may occur when continental polar air masses move south and meet maritime tropical air masses moving north.

☑ *Checkpoint* Where do continental polar air masses come from?

Background

History of Science Up until the early 1900s, scientists thought that storms were caused by low air pressure. This conclusion was based on the fact that storms always seemed to occur in low-pressure areas. Then, in the early twentieth century, a Norwegian meteorologist named Vilhelm Bjerknes and a group of his colleagues deduced that storms are caused by the collision of large air masses that differ from one another in temperature and humidity. Although storms do occur in low-pressure areas, the low pressure is not their cause. Rather, low pressure areas, like storms, are a result of the collision of different air masses. This finding is now accepted as one of the most important principles of modern meteorology, and it is the basic principle underlying weather forecasting today.

How Air Masses Move

Recall that the prevailing westerlies are the major wind belts in the continental United States. The prevailing westerlies generally push air masses from west to east. For example, maritime polar air masses from the Pacific Ocean are blown onto the West Coast, bringing heavy rain or snow. Continental polar air masses from central Canada enter the United States between the Rocky Mountains and the Great Lakes. These cold, dry air masses are then blown east, where they affect the weather of the central and eastern United States.

Fronts

As huge masses of air move across the land and the oceans, they bump into each other. But the air masses do not easily mix. Why don't they? Think about a bottle of oil-and-vinegar salad dressing. The less dense oil floats on top of the more dense vinegar.

Something similar happens when two air masses with different temperatures and densities collide. The area where the air masses meet and do not mix becomes a **front**. The word *front*, which is borrowed from military language, means a battle area where opposing armies meet to fight. When air masses meet at a front, the collision often causes storms and changeable weather. A front may be 15 to 200 kilometers wide and extend as much as 10 kilometers up into the troposphere.

There are four types of fronts: cold fronts, warm fronts, stationary fronts, and occluded fronts. The kind of front that develops depends on the characteristics of the air masses and how they are moving. How does each type of front affect your local weather?

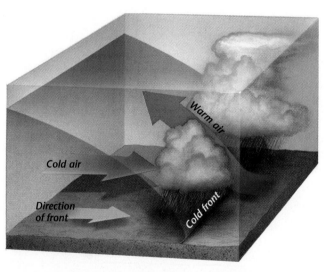

Figure 2 A cold front forms when cold air moves underneath warm air, forcing the warm air to rise.

Inquiry Challenge

Material *world map or globe*

Time 10 minutes

Based on what they have just learned about the movement of air masses in North America, challenge students to infer which types of air masses are likely to affect the weather of Europe. First provide students with a world map or globe, and then ask: **Where do you think air masses come from that move over the European continent?** *(The Atlantic Ocean, northern Eurasia, and the African continent)* **What type of air do you think they bring to Europe?** *(Cool humid air from the Atlantic Ocean, cold dry air from northern Eurasia, and hot dry air from Africa)* **learning modality: logical/mathematical**

Fronts

Including All Students

Materials *red and blue modeling clay*

Time 5 minutes

Give hands-on learners an opportunity to model the formation of warm and cold fronts using wedges of red and blue modeling clay to represent warm and cold air masses, respectively. For each type of front that students model, ask: **In which direction is the front moving?** *(For the cold front, toward the warm air mass; for the warm front, toward the cold air mass)* **learning modality: tactile/kinesthetic**

Answers to Self-Assessment

Checkpoint

Continental polar air masses come from central and northern Canada and Alaska.

Ongoing Assessment

Oral Presentation Call on students to name the four types of air masses that influence weather in North America. Then call on other students to state where each type of air mass forms, whether it is warm or cold, and whether it is humid or dry.

Fronts, continued

500

Using the Visuals: Figure 3

Content Mastery

Help students understand the similarities and differences between warm and cold fronts by having them compare and contrast illustrations of each type of front. Ask: **How does Figures 3, which shows the formation of a warm front, differ from Figure 2, which shows the formation of a cold front?** (In Figure 3, the warm air mass moves up over the cold air mass; in Figure 2, the cold air mass moves underneath the warm air mass.) **How are the two figures similar?** (In both cases, the warm air rises and cools, causing water vapor to condense out of it and form clouds.) **learning modality: visual**

Demonstration

Materials *tall heat-resistant jar or beaker, cold water, pepper, stirrer, container of hot water, food coloring, candle, matches*
Time 15 minutes

Do this demonstration to show students how fronts form. Half-fill a tall, heat-resistant jar or beaker with cold water. Stir pepper into the water until it is mixed throughout. Add food coloring to a container of hot water, mix well, and then gently pour the hot water into the jar of cold water. The two layers of water should remain separate and mix only slightly. Light a candle and hold the jar above it. As the cold water in the bottom of the jar heats up, the pepper will move upward due to convection. However, the pepper will not penetrate the top layer of colored water but instead collect at the "front" between the two layers of water. Ask: **Why doesn't the pepper rise up through the top layer of water?** (Because the top layer of water is warmer and will not mix with the cooler layer of water containing the pepper) **learning modality: visual**

Cold Fronts As you know, cold air is dense and tends to sink. Warm air is less dense and tends to rise. When a rapidly moving cold air mass runs into a slowly moving warm air mass, the denser cold air slides under the lighter warm air. The warm air is pushed upward, as shown in Figure 2. The front that forms is called a cold front.

As the warm air rises, it cools. Remember that warm air can hold more water vapor than cool air. The rising air soon reaches the dew point, the temperature at which the water vapor in the air condenses into droplets of liquid water. Clouds form. If there is a lot of water vapor in the warm air, heavy rain or snow may fall. What will happen if the warm air mass contains only a little water vapor? In this case, the cold front may be accompanied by only cloudy skies.

Cold fronts move quickly, so they can cause abrupt weather changes, including violent thunderstorms. After a cold front passes through an area, cool, dry air moves in, often bringing clear skies and cooler temperatures.

Warm Fronts Clouds, storms, and rain also accompany warm fronts. At a warm front, a moving warm air mass collides with a slowly moving cold air mass. Because cold air is more dense than warm air, the warm air moves over the cold air, as shown in Figure 3. If the warm air is humid, showers and light rain fall along the front where the warm and cold air meet. If the warm air is dry, scattered clouds form. Because warm fronts move more slowly than cold fronts, the weather may be rainy or foggy for several days. After a warm front passes through an area, the weather is likely to be warm and humid. In winter, warm fronts bring snow.

Figure 3 A warm front forms when warm air moves over cold air. *Interpreting Diagrams What kind of weather forms at a warm front?*

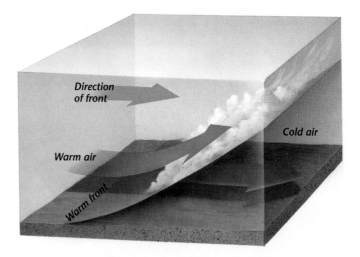
Direction of front
Cold air
Warm air
Warm front

500

Background

Facts and Figures Like fingerprints or snowflakes, no two fronts are exactly alike. For example, the slope of a front can vary considerably, from about 1:100 (1 km of vertical distance covers 100 km of horizontal distance) for a cold front to about 1:200 for a warm front.

The slope of a front is an important determinant of the type of weather the front brings. A cold front with a very steep slope is likely to bring a narrow band of violent storms extending less than 100 km. A warm front with a very gradual slope, on the other hand, is likely to bring cloudy weather but no storms. However, the area affected by the cloudy weather may extend for many hundreds of kilometers.

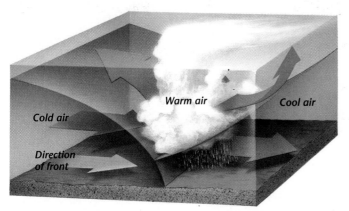

Warm air

Cold air

Cool air

Direction
of front

Figure 4 When a cold air mass and a cool air mass come together, the warm air caught between them is forced upward. The result is an occluded front.

Stationary Fronts Sometimes cold and warm air masses meet, but neither one has enough force to move the other. The two air masses face each other in a "standoff." In this case, the front is called a stationary front. Where the warm and cool air meet, water vapor in the warm air condenses into rain, snow, fog, or clouds. If a stationary front remains stalled over an area, it may bring many days of clouds and precipitation.

Occluded Fronts The most complex weather situation occurs at an occluded front, shown in Figure 4. At an occluded front, a warm air mass is caught between two cooler air masses. The denser cool air masses move underneath the less dense warm air mass and push it upward. The two cooler air masses meet in the middle and may mix. The temperature near the ground becomes cooler. The warm air mass is cut off, or **occluded,** from the ground. As the warm air cools and its water vapor condenses, the weather may turn cloudy and rainy or snowy.

☑ *Checkpoint* *What type of front forms when two air masses meet and neither one can move?*

Cyclones and Anticyclones

If you look at a weather map, you will see areas marked with an "L." The "L" is short for "low," and indicates an area of relatively low air pressure. A swirling center of low air pressure is called a **cyclone,** from a Greek word meaning "wheel."

As warm air at the center of a cyclone rises, the air pressure decreases. Cooler air blows toward this low-pressure area from nearby areas where the air pressure is higher. Winds spiral inward toward the center of the system. Recall that in the Northern Hemisphere, the Coriolis effect deflects winds to the right.

Sharpen your Skills

Classifying

At home, watch the ACTIVITY weather forecast on television. Take note of each time the weather reporter mentions a front. Classify the fronts mentioned or shown as cold, warm, stationary, or occluded. Also note what type of weather is predicted to occur when the front arrives. Is each type of front always associated with the same type of weather?

Answers to Self-Assessment

Caption Question

Figure 3 Clouds, storms, and precipitation form at a warm front.

☑ *Checkpoint*

A stationary front forms when two air masses meet and neither one can move.

Sharpen your Skills

Classifying

Tips Have students continue this activity over several days in order to observe at least three different types of fronts.
Expected Outcome Students should find that all types of fronts are associated with clouds and precipitation. However, cold fronts tend to be associated with more abrupt changes in the weather.
Extend Have students continue to monitor weather changes after the fronts pass through their area. Ask: **What type of weather follows each type of front?** *(Cold and occluded fronts are followed by cool, clear weather, warm fronts by warm, humid weather.)* **learning modality: logical/mathematical**

Cyclones and Anticyclones

Including All Students

Materials *two balloons, pencil, thread, ruler*
Time 5 minutes

Instruct students to inflate two balloons to 10 cm in diameter and tie them to the opposite ends of a pencil with pieces of thread 30 cm long. Then have them hold the pencil level, with the balloons 8 cm from their faces, and blow gently between the balloons. Ask: **Why did the balloons move closer together?** *(Air moving between the balloons caused an area of low pressure between them. The higher air pressure on the outer sides of the balloons then pushed the two balloons closer together.)* Ask: **How is this like a cyclone?** *(In a cyclone, winds blow in toward the center because there is low pressure there.)* **learning modality: tactile/kinesthetic**

Ongoing Assessment

Drawing Have students create drawings to represent a warm front and a cold front. They should label the air masses as "cold" or "warm" and use arrows to indicate the direction the air masses are moving.

501

3 Assess

Section 1 Review Answers

1. temperature and humidity
2. A front is the area where two air masses meet and do not mix. A cold front forms when cold air moves underneath warm air. A warm front forms when warm air moves over cold air. A stationary front forms when a warm and a cold air mass meet but neither can move the other. An occluded front forms when a warm air mass is caught between two cool air masses and cut off from the ground.
3. A swirling center of low air pressure; storms and precipitation
4. Because East Coast maritime polar air masses are blown out to sea by prevailing westerlies
5. Maritime tropical and polar air masses are humid; continental tropical and polar air masses are dry.

Check Your Progress
CHAPTER PROJECT

Check that each student has started to collect weather maps. Comparisons of weather in the three locations should include all the weather factors represented on the maps.

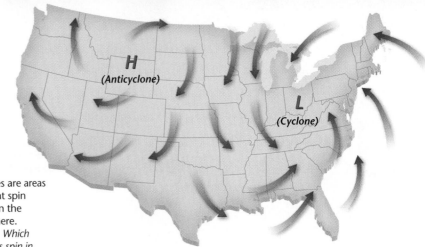

Figure 5 Cyclones are areas of low pressure that spin counterclockwise in the Northern Hemisphere. *Interpreting Maps Which way do anticyclones spin in the Northern Hemisphere?*

Because of this, winds in a cyclone spin counterclockwise in the Northern Hemisphere, as shown in Figure 5.

Cyclones play a large part in the weather of the United States. As air rises in a cyclone, the air cools, forming clouds and precipitation. **Cyclones and decreasing air pressure are associated with storms and precipitation.**

As its name suggests, an anticyclone is the opposite of a cyclone in most ways. **Anticyclones** are high-pressure centers of dry air. Anticyclones are also called "highs"—"H" on a weather map. Winds spiral outward from the center of an anticyclone, moving toward areas of lower pressure. Because of the Coriolis effect, winds in an anticyclone spin clockwise in the Northern Hemisphere. Because air moves out from the center of the anticyclone, cool air moves downward from higher in the troposphere. As the cool air falls, it warms up, so its relative humidity drops. The descending air in an anticyclone causes dry, clear weather.

Section 1 Review

1. What two main characteristics are used to classify air masses?
2. What is a front? Name and describe four types of fronts.
3. What is a cyclone? What type of weather does it bring?
4. Why do maritime polar air masses have more effect on the West Coast than the East Coast?
5. **Thinking Critically Classifying** Classify the four major types of air masses according to whether they are dry or humid.

Check Your Progress
CHAPTER PROJECT

Collect newspaper weather maps for about a week, and arrange them in order. Look carefully at how symbols on the map have moved from one day to the next. What patterns do you see from day to day in different weather factors? How does the weather in your community differ from the weather in the two other locations you selected?

502

Answers to Self-Assessment

Caption Question

Figure 5 Winds in anticyclones spin clockwise in the Northern Hemisphere.

Program Resources

◆ **Unit 4 Resources** 15-1 Review and Reinforce, p. 159; 15-1 Enrich, p. 160

Performance Assessment

Skills Check Have students describe the direction of winds in cyclones and anticyclones in the Southern Hemisphere.

DISCOVER ●●●●●●●●●●●●●●●●●●●●●●●●●●●●●●●● **ACTIVITY** ●●●●

Can You Make a Tornado?

1. Fill a large jar three-quarters full with water. Add a drop of liquid dish detergent and a penny or marble.

2. Put the lid on the jar tightly. Now move the jar in a circle until the water inside begins to spin.

Think It Over

Observing What happens to the water in the jar? Describe the pattern that forms. How is it like a tornado? Unlike a tornado?

Early in 1998, a series of powerful tornadoes roared through central Florida. With winds as high as 210 miles per hour, the tornadoes dropped cars into living rooms, crumpled trailers, and destroyed businesses and school buildings. They were the deadliest tornadoes ever to hit Florida. These tornadoes were not the only violent weather that year. In California the problem was rain. Record rainfalls brought devastating floods and mudslides.

What was causing these disasters? Meteorologists had an answer: El Niño. El Niño is a warm water current in the tropical Pacific Ocean that can affect weather patterns. When water temperatures rise there, they set off a series of events that can influence weather half a world away.

Have you ever experienced a tornado, hurricane, or other severe storm? When rain pours down, thunder crashes, or snowdrifts pile up, it may be hard to think about the actions of air pressure and air masses. Yet these are the causes of severe storms as well as the weather you experience every day.

A **storm** is a violent disturbance in the atmosphere. Storms involve sudden changes in air pressure, which in turn cause rapid air movements. Conditions that bring one kind of storm often cause other kinds of storms in the same area. For example, the conditions that cause thunderstorms can also cause tornadoes.

GUIDE FOR READING

◆ **What are the main kinds of storms? How do they form?**

◆ **What measures can you take to ensure safety in a storm?**

Reading Tip As you read, create a table comparing thunderstorms, tornadoes, hurricanes, and snowstorms. Include temperature, precipitation, and safety rules.

Key Terms storm • lightning • tornado • hurricane • storm surge • evacuate

Figure 6 Tornadoes caused tremendous damage in Florida and other parts of the southeastern United States in 1998.

Chapter 15 **503**

TEKS: 6.2B, C, D; 6.3C, D, E; 6.14C

Objectives

After completing the lesson, students will be able to
◆ list the main kinds of storms and explain how they form;
◆ describe measures people can take to ensure safety in a storm.

1 Engage/Explore

Activating Prior Knowledge

Introduce students to tornadoes and other storms by asking: **Did you ever see a dust devil, a spinning wind that picks up and carries dust, dead leaves, and other debris?** (*Most students probably will say "yes."*) **What did it look like?** (*a funnel*) **What do think causes dust devils?** (*Air swirling in a circle*) Point out that dust devils resemble small tornadoes. Explain that they are caused by hot air rising rapidly from the heated ground. As the hot air rises, the wind blows it into a spinning motion and it picks up loose material. Add that most dust devils last just a few seconds, rise only a few meters, and cause no damage. Tell students that a similar type of air movement also causes tornadoes, as they will learn in this section.

●●●●●●●● **DISCOVER** ●●●●●●●●

Skills Focus observing
Materials *large plastic jar with lid, water, liquid dish detergent, penny or marble*
Time 10 minutes
Tips Tell students not to shake the jar or slosh the water back and forth to create bubbles. Instead, they should swirl the water gently with a circular motion.
Expected Outcome The water should swirl around in the jar like a tornado.
Think It Over Students should say that the water swirls in a funnel-shaped spiral. It is like a tornado because the water spins around in a circle. It is unlike a tornado because it occurs in water instead of air.

2 Facilitate

Thunderstorms

Demonstration

Materials *bottle with plastic cap, copper wire, aluminum foil, plastic comb, wool fabric*
Time 10 minutes

Show the class how lightning occurs with this demonstration. Push a short piece of copper wire through a small hole in the cap of a bottle. Form the bottom end of the wire into a hook and hang a small strip of aluminum foil over it. Put the cap on the bottle with the hook and foil inside. Rub a comb on wool fabric to give it an electrical charge and then touch the comb to the end of the wire protruding from the top of the bottle cap. Students will see the ends of the foil strip move apart from one another. Ask: **Why did the ends of the foil strip move?** *(Students may not know.)* Explain that the foil became charged with electricity, which was transmitted through the wire from the comb, causing the two ends of the foil strip to repel each other. Ask: **How is this like lightning?** *(A charge is built up when particles in clouds rub together, and when the electricity is discharged from one part of the cloud to another or to the ground, lightning occurs.)* **learning modality: visual**

TRY THIS

Skills Focus calculating
Materials *watch with second hand*
Time 10 minutes
Expected Outcome The number of seconds between the lightning flash and the sound of the thunder will depend on how far away the lightning is. If the lightning is very close, the thunder will occur just a split second later. If the lightning is very far away, the thunder may not even be audible. If the length of time between the lightning and thunder is increasing, the storm is moving away from you. If the length of time is decreasing, the storm is moving toward you. **learning modality: logical/mathematical**

504

Figure 7 The anvil shape of this cloud is typical of cumulonimbus clouds that produce thunderstorms. *Applying Concepts Why do cumulonimbus clouds often form along cold fronts?*

TRY THIS

Lightning Distances

Because light travels faster than sound, you see a lightning flash before you hear the clap of thunder. Here's how to calculate your distance from a thunderstorm.
CAUTION: *Do this activity inside a building only.*

1. Count the number of seconds between the moment when you see the lightning and when you hear the thunder.

2. Divide the number of seconds you counted by three to get the distance in kilometers. Example:

$$\frac{15 \text{ s}}{3 \text{ s/km}} = 5 \text{ km}$$

Calculating Wait for another flash of lightning and calculate the distance again. How can you tell whether a thunderstorm is moving toward you or away from you?

504

Thunderstorms

Do you find thunderstorms frightening? Exciting? A little of both? As you watch the brilliant flashes of lightning and listen to long rolls of thunder, you have probably wondered what caused them.

How Thunderstorms Form Thunderstorms are heavy rainstorms accompanied by thunder and lightning. **Thunderstorms form within large cumulonimbus clouds, or thunderheads.** Most cumulonimbus clouds and thunderstorms form when warm air is forced upward at a cold front. Cumulonimbus clouds also form on hot, humid afternoons in the spring and summer. In both cases, the warm, humid air rises rapidly. As the air rises, it cools, forming dense thunderheads. Heavy rain falls, sometimes along with hail.

Thunderstorms produce strong upward and downward winds—updrafts and downdrafts—inside clouds. When a downdraft strikes the ground, the air spreads out in all directions, producing bursts of wind called wind shear. Wind shear has caused a number of airplane accidents during takeoff or landing.

Lightning and Thunder During a thunderstorm, areas of positive and negative electrical charges build up in the storm clouds. **Lightning** is a sudden spark, or energy discharge, as these charges jump between parts of a cloud, between nearby clouds, or between a cloud and the ground. Lightning is similar to the shocks you sometimes feel when you touch a metal object on a very dry day, but on a much larger scale.

What causes thunder? A lightning bolt can heat the air near it to as much as 30,000°C, much hotter than the surface of the sun. The rapidly heated air expands suddenly and explosively. Thunder is the sound of the explosion. Because light travels faster than sound, you see lightning before you hear thunder.

504

Thunderstorm Safety When lightning strikes **INTEGRATING HEALTH** the ground, the hot, expanding air can start forest fires. When lightning strikes people or animals, it acts like a powerful electric shock. Being struck by lightning can cause unconsciousness, serious burns, or even heart failure.

What should you do to remain safe if you are caught outside during a thunderstorm? **During thunderstorms, avoid touching metal objects because they can conduct electricity from lightning into your body.** Lightning usually strikes the tallest nearby object, such as a tree, house, or flagpole. To protect buildings from lightning, people install metal lightning rods at the highest point on a roof. Lightning rods intercept a lightning stroke and conduct the electricity through cables safely into the ground.

In open spaces, such as a golf course, people can be in danger because they are the tallest objects in the area. It is equally dangerous to seek shelter under a tree, because lightning may strike the tree and you at the same time. Instead, find a low area away from trees, fences, and poles. Crouch with your head down and your hands on your knees. If you are swimming or in a boat, get to shore and find shelter away from the water.

If you are inside a house during a thunderstorm, avoid touching telephones, electrical appliances, or plumbing fixtures, all of which can conduct electricity into the house. It is usually safe to stay in a car with a hard top during a thunderstorm because the electricity will move along the metal skin of the car and jump to the ground. However, do not touch any metal inside the car.

☑ *Checkpoint* *Why is lightning dangerous?*

Tornadoes

A tornado is one of the most frightening and destructive types of storms. A **tornado** is a rapidly whirling, funnel-shaped cloud that reaches down from a storm cloud to touch Earth's surface. If a tornado occurs over a lake or ocean, it is known as a waterspout. Tornadoes are usually brief, but can be deadly. They may touch the ground for 15 minutes or less and be only a few hundred meters across, but wind speeds may approach 480 kilometers per hour.

Figure 8 Lightning occurs when electricity jumps within clouds, between clouds, or between a cloud and the ground.

Tornadoes, continued

Call students' attention to the feature and then ask: **What types of storms are described in the feature?** (*Thunderstorms and hurricanes*) Point out that tornadoes are not included, and then ask: **Why might tornadoes have less impact on history?** (*A tornado's path of destruction tends to be narrow and short lived.*) Inform students that there are some notable exceptions to the brief, local nature of most tornadoes. For example, the Great Tri-State Tornado of March 18, 1925, killed almost 700 people in three states, and the Superoutbreak Tornadoes of April 3–4, 1974, killed more than 300 people and injured over 5,500 others in 12 states in 24 hours. Add that, unlike thunderstorms and hurricanes, exactly when and where a tornado will touch down is still difficult to predict. Suggest to students who need an extra challenge that they research other examples of tornadoes, thunderstorms, and hurricanes that had an impact, great or small, on the course of history. Urge them to share what they learn with the rest of the class.

In Your Journal Students' paragraphs will vary depending on the specific event they choose. If they choose the storms that affected the *Mayflower*, for example, they may say that, with advance warning, the settlers might have delayed their landing until the storms had passed and then settled in what is now New York City instead of Plymouth. Refer to the **ELL Handbook** for additional teaching strategies. **learning modality: verbal**

How Tornadoes Form Tornadoes develop in low, heavy cumulonimbus clouds—the same type of clouds that brings thunderstorms. Tornadoes are most likely to occur when thunderstorms are likely—in spring and early summer, often late in the afternoon when the ground is warm. The Great Plains often have the kind of weather pattern that is likely to create tornadoes: a warm, humid air mass moves north from the Gulf of Mexico into the lower Great Plains. A cold, dry air mass moves south from Canada. When the air masses meet, the cold air moves under the warm air, which rises. A squall line of thunderstorms is likely to form, with storms traveling from southwest to northeast. A single squall line can cause 10 or more tornadoes.

Tornadoes occur more often in the United States than in any other country. About 800 tornadoes occur in the United States

SCIENCE & History

Weather That Changed History

Unanticipated storms have caused incredible damage, killed numbers of people, and even changed the course of history.

1281 Japan
In an attempt to conquer Japan, Kublai Khan, the Mongol emperor of China, sent a fleet of ships carrying a huge army. A hurricane from the Pacific brought high winds and towering waves that sank the ships. The Japanese named the storm *kamikaze*, meaning "divine wind."

1620 Massachusetts
English Pilgrims set sail for the Americas in the *Mayflower.* They had planned to land near the mouth of the Hudson River, but turned back north because of rough seas and storms. When the Pilgrims landed farther north, they decided to stay and so established Plymouth Colony.

| 1300 | 1400 | 1500 | 1600 |

1588 England
King Philip II of Spain sent the Spanish Armada, a fleet of 130 ships, to invade England. Strong winds in the English Channel trapped the Armada near shore. Some Spanish ships escaped, but storms wrecked most of them.

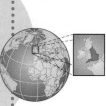

506

Background

Facts and Figures Tornadoes are commonly classified according to the following scale, which is called the Fujita-Pearson Tornado Intensity Scale after its inventors:
F0 Light (under 116 km/h)
F1 Moderate (116–180 km/h)
F2 Considerable (181–253 km/h)
F3 Severe (254–332 km/h)
F4 Devastating (333–419 km/h)

F5 Incredible (over 419 km/h)
The winds of tornadoes have done some amazing things. In Bedfordshire, England, in May of 1950, a tornado is reported to have plucked the feathers off several chickens, who amazingly were otherwise unharmed. Tornadoes also have lifted frogs and fish from ponds and then dropped them elsewhere, leading to the saying, "a tornado may rain frogs."

every year. Weather patterns on the Great Plains, shown on the next page in Figure 9, result in a "tornado alley" that runs from Texas across Oklahoma, Kansas, and Nebraska. However, tornadoes can and do occur in nearly every part of the United States.

☑ *Checkpoint* *Where do tornadoes form?*

Tornado Safety A tornado can level houses on one street, but **INTEGRATING HEALTH** leave neighboring houses standing. Tornado damage comes from both strong winds and flying debris. The low pressure inside the tornado sucks up dust and other objects into the funnel. Tornadoes can move large objects—sheds, trailers, cars—and scatter debris many miles away. One tornado tore off a motel sign in Broken Bow, Oklahoma, and dropped it 30 miles away in Arkansas!

In Your Journal

Some of these events happened before forecasters had the equipment to predict weather scientifically. Choose one of the events in the time line. Write a paragraph describing how history might have been different if the people involved had had accurate weather predictions.

1869 Great Lakes

Learning that more than 1,900 boats had sunk in storms on the Great Lakes in 1869, Congress decided to set up a national weather service, the Army Signal Corps. In 1891, the job of issuing weather warnings and forecasts went to a new agency, the U.S. Weather Bureau.

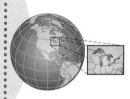

| 1700 | 1800 | 1900 |

1837 North Carolina

The steamship *Home* sank during a hurricane off Ocracoke, North Carolina. In one of the worst storm-caused disasters at sea, 90 people died. In response, the U.S. Congress passed a law requiring seagoing ships to carry a life preserver for every passenger.

1915 Texas

When a hurricane struck the port city of Galveston in 1900, it killed 6,000 people and destroyed much of the city. As a result, a seawall 5 meters high and 16 kilometers long was built. When another hurricane struck in 1915, the seawall greatly reduced the amount of damage.

Chapter 15 **507**

507

Using the Visuals: Figure 9

Use the map in Figure 9 to help students understand why the central part of the United States has so many tornadoes. Ask: **What is the reddish shaded area called?** (*Tornado Alley*) **Why is it called that?** (*More tornadoes occur there than anywhere else in the United States.*) **Why do you think so many tornadoes occur there?** (*Because cold and warm air masses meet there*) **learning modality: visual**

Addressing Naive Conceptions

Ask students if the following statements are true or false: **If you don't have a basement, the safest place in your home in the event of a tornado is the southwest corner.** (*False. The safest place is a small windowless room or closet in the center of the house.*) **If a tornado catches you on the road, it is best to stay in your car.** (*False. A tornado can overturn a car or pick it up and drop it elsewhere. You should leave the car and go to a well-built building or lie flat in a low place with your head covered.*) Based on how students respond, discuss any misconceptions they may hold. For example, if students believe that the safest place in a home without a basement is an outside corner, explain that an outside room is more at risk of damage from the wind, and windows in outside rooms put you at risk of flying glass. **learning modality: verbal**

Hurricanes

Including All Students

Explain to students that hurricanes are given names according to certain rules. They are named alphabetically, alternating between masculine and feminine names. For example, in 1999, the first storm of the season was named Arlene, the second Bret, the third Cindy, and so on. Challenge the class to come up with their own list of names for 15 hurricanes. Give each student a number from 1 to 15 and have the student apply the rules to name the hurricane of that number. **limited English proficiency**

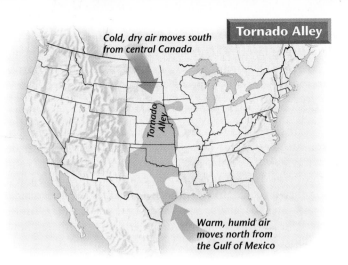

Tornado Alley

Cold, dry air moves south from central Canada

Tornado Alley

Warm, humid air moves north from the Gulf of Mexico

Figure 9 A tornado can cause a lot of damage in a short period of time. The map shows where tornadoes are most likely to occur in the United States.
Interpreting Maps Which states are partially located in "tornado alley"?

What should you do if a tornado is predicted in your area? A "tornado watch" is an announcement that tornadoes are possible in your area. You should watch for approaching thunderstorms. A "tornado warning" is an announcement that a tornado has been seen in the sky or on weather radar. If you hear a tornado warning, move to a safe area as soon as you can. Do not wait until you actually see the tornado.

The safest place to be during a tornado is in the basement of a well-built building. If the building you are in does not have a basement, move to the middle of the ground floor. Stay away from windows and doors that could break and fly through the air. Lie on the floor under a sturdy piece of furniture, such as a large table. If you are outdoors or in a car or mobile home, move to a building or lie flat in a ditch.

☑ *Checkpoint* *What is the difference between a tornado watch and a tornado warning?*

Hurricanes

Between June and November, people who live in the eastern United States hear weather reports much like this: "A hurricane warning has been issued for the Atlantic coast from Florida to North Carolina. Hurricane Michael has winds of over 160 kilometers per hour and is moving north at about 65 kilometers per hour." A **hurricane** is a tropical storm that has winds of 119 kilometers per hour or higher. A typical hurricane is about 600 kilometers across.

Hurricanes also form in the Pacific and Indian oceans. In the western Pacific Ocean, hurricanes are called typhoons. Although hurricanes may be destructive, they bring much-needed rainfall to South Asia and Southeast Asia.

508

How Hurricanes Form A typical hurricane that strikes the United States forms in the Atlantic Ocean north of the equator in August, September, or October. **A hurricane begins over warm water as a low-pressure area, or tropical disturbance.** If the tropical disturbance grows in size and strength, it becomes a tropical storm, which may then become a hurricane.

A hurricane gets its energy from the warm, humid air at the ocean's surface. As this air rises and forms clouds, more air is drawn into the system. As with other storm systems, winds spiral inward toward the areas of low pressure. Inside the storm are bands of very high winds and heavy rains. The lowest air pressure and warmest temperatures are at the center of the hurricane. The lower the air pressure at the center of a storm, the faster the winds blow toward the center. Hurricane winds may be as strong as 320 kilometers per hour.

The Eye of the Hurricane The center of a hurricane is a ring of clouds surrounding a quiet "eye," as shown in Figure 10. If you were in the path of a hurricane, you would notice that the wind gets stronger as the eye approaches. When the eye arrives, the weather changes suddenly. The winds grow calm and the sky may clear. After the eye passes, the storm resumes, but the wind blows from the opposite direction.

How Hurricanes Move Hurricanes last longer than other storms, usually a week or more. Hurricanes that form in the Atlantic Ocean are steered by easterly trade winds toward the Caribbean islands and the southeastern United States. After a hurricane passes over land, it no longer has warm, moist air to draw energy from. The hurricane gradually slows down and loses strength, although heavy rainfall may continue for a number of days.

Figure 10 In a hurricane, air moves rapidly around a low-pressure area called the eye. *Observing Where is the eye of the hurricane in the photograph?*

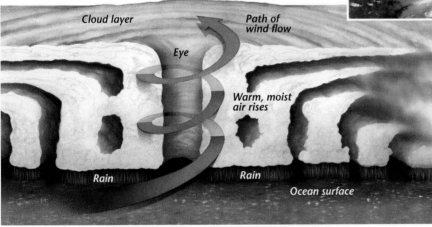

Cloud layer
Path of wind flow
Eye
Warm, moist air rises
Rain
Rain
Ocean surface

If it is hurricane season, have groups of students monitor tropical disturbances, watch for those that develop into hurricanes, and note where the hurricanes reach land. Groups should gather information from newspapers, television, or a supervised Internet search and, at the end of hurricane season, present the information to the class. **cooperative learning**

Using the Visuals: Figure 10

Check to be sure that students understand how the two parts of the figure are related by asking: **In which illustration are you looking down at a hurricane from above?** *(The photograph on the right)* **From which direction are you looking at the hurricane in the drawing?** *(From the side)* **In which direction is the wind blowing in both illustrations?** *(Counterclockwise around the eye of the hurricane)* **learning modality: visual**

Building Inquiry Skills: Problem Solving

Challenge students to solve the following problem. Tell them to assume they have been caught in the path of a hurricane and the eye of the storm is predicted to pass over their town. Now, after two days of high winds and waves and severe thunderstorms with torrential rain, the storm has died down and the sky has cleared. Ask: **Should you assume the storm has passed and start unboarding the windows and cleaning up the debris? Why or why not?** *(No, because this may be a temporary calm due to the eye of the storm. If so, after the eye passes, the storm will return.)* **How could you find out?** *(Listen to weather bulletins on radio or television)* **learning modality: logical/mathematical**

Media and Technology

 Transparencies "Clouds and Winds in a Hurricane," Transparency 74

Answers to Self-Assessment

☑ *Checkpoint*

Tornado watch: tornadoes are possible. Tornado warning: a tornado has been seen in the sky or on weather radar.

Caption Questions

Figure 9 South Dakota, Iowa, Nebraska, Kansas, Missouri, Oklahoma, Texas, New Mexico, Arkansas

Figure 10 In the center of the clouds

Ongoing Assessment

Oral Presentation Call on students at random to name the parts of the country where hurricanes occur. Call on other students to explain in their own words why hurricanes occur only in those places.

Hurricanes, continued

 ### Integrating Health

Divide the class into groups and challenge the groups to brainstorm a list of actions people in hurricane-prone areas should take: (1) at the beginning of hurricane season (*Trim dead branches from trees, learn safe routes inland*); (2) if a hurricane watch is issued (*Keep tuned to radio or television for storm updates, check radio and flashlight for batteries, stock up on canned food*); and (3) if a hurricane warning is issued (*Leave mobile homes, unplug appliances and turn off gas tanks, board up glass windows and doors, listen to radio or television for orders to evacuate and do so immediately when instructed*). When groups have completed their lists, have them share their ideas with the class. **cooperative learning**

Winter Storms

Visual Arts
CONNECTION

Challenge students talented in art to create their own artwork depicting a snowstorm or other storm. Invite them to share their artwork with the class.

In Your Journal Students should comment on how well the words made them see, hear, and feel a snowstorm. **learning modality: visual**

Building Inquiry Skills: Inferring

Towns in the Rocky Mountains get even more snow than Buffalo and Rochester, New York. **Why do you think the high mountain areas of the West receive so much snow?** (*Because warm, moist air from the Pacific Ocean is cooled and drops its moisture as snow when it rises up over the Rocky Mountains*) **How are the Rocky Mountains similar to areas bordering the Great Lakes that receive lake-effect snow?** (*Both areas receive warm, moist west winds that are cooled to produce large amounts of snow.*) **learning modality: logical/mathematical**

Visual Arts
CONNECTION

Weather and storms are favorite subjects for artists. "Snow Storm" is an oil painting by English artist J.M.W. Turner (1775–1851). To convey a mood or feeling, artists choose certain colors and textures. How does Turner's choice of colors enhance the mood of the painting? What texture do you see in the sea and sky? How does the texture support the feeling of the painting?

In Your Journal

Write a paragraph or two about the mood of this painting. Describe how you would feel being out in the wind and waves. Before you begin writing, jot down words that describe what you would see, hear, touch, taste, and smell. Exchange your descriptive writing with a partner to get feedback.

Figure 11 The British artist J.M.W. Turner painted "Snow Storm" in 1842.

Hurricane Damage When a hurricane comes ashore, it brings high waves and severe flooding as well as wind damage. Hurricanes uproot trees, smash buildings, and destroy power lines.

One of the most dangerous features of a hurricane is the storm surge. The low pressure and high winds of the hurricane over the ocean raise the level of the water up to six meters above normal sea level. The result is a **storm surge,** a "dome" of water that sweeps across the coast where the hurricane lands. As the hurricane comes onshore, the water comes with it. Storm surges can cause great damage, washing away beaches and buildings.

Hurricane Safety Until the 1950s, a fast-moving hurricane

INTEGRATING HEALTH could strike with little warning. Since then, advances in communications and satellite tracking have made hurricanes less deadly. People now receive information well in advance of an approaching hurricane.

A "hurricane watch" is an announcement that hurricane conditions are *possible* in your area within the next 36 hours. People should be prepared to **evacuate** (ee VAK yoo ayt), or move away temporarily.

A "hurricane warning" means that hurricane conditions are *expected* within 24 hours. **If you hear a hurricane warning and are told to evacuate, leave the area immediately.** If you must stay in a house, move to the interior of the building, away from windows.

☑ *Checkpoint* What is a storm surge?

Winter Storms

In the winter in the northern United States, much precipitation falls as snow. **Snow falls when humid air cools below 0°C.** Heavy snowfalls can block roads, trapping people in their homes and making it hard for emergency vehicles to move.

Background

Integrating Science Two serious health dangers of winter storms are frostbite and hypothermia. Frostbite is damage to body tissue, usually in the nose, ears, fingers, or toes, due to freezing of the tissue. Symptoms include a loss of feeling and a white appearance in the affected area. If you think you have frostbite, slowly rewarm the affected area and get medical help right away.

Hypothermia is a fall in body temperature below normal. Symptoms include shivering, disorientation, slurred speech, and drowsiness. Hypothermia is a life-threatening emergency. If someone shows signs of hypothermia, seek medical help immediately.

Lake-Effect Snow Two of the snowiest cities in the United States are Buffalo and Rochester in upstate New York. On average, nearly three meters of snow falls on each of these cities every winter. Why do Buffalo and Rochester get so much snow?

Study Figure 12. Notice that Buffalo is located to the east of Lake Erie, and Rochester is located to the south of Lake Ontario. In the fall and winter, the land near these lakes cools much more rapidly than the water in the lakes. Although the water in these lakes is cold, it is still much warmer than the surrounding land and air. When a cold, dry air mass moves from central Canada southeast across one of the Great Lakes, it picks up water vapor and heat from the lake. As soon as the air mass reaches the other side of the lake, the air rises and cools again. The water vapor condenses and falls as snow, most often within 40 kilometers of the lake.

Great Lakes Snow Belts

KEY
Snow belt

Cold, dry air

Lake Superior
Lake Michigan
Lake Huron
Lake Ontario
• Rochester
Detroit
• Buffalo
Lake Erie
Chicago •

0   100   200 mi
0   100   200 km

Figure 12 As cold dry air moves across the warmer water, it picks up water vapor. When the air reaches land and cools, lake-effect snow falls. *Interpreting Maps* Which two cities receive large amounts of snow?

Snowstorm Safety Imagine being out in a snowstorm when the wind suddenly picks up. High winds can blow falling snow sideways or pick up snow from the ground and suspend it in the air. This situation can be extremely dangerous because the blowing snow makes it easy to get lost. Strong winds also cool a person's body rapidly. **If you are caught in a snowstorm, try to find shelter from the wind.** Cover exposed parts of your body and try to stay dry. If you are in a car, the driver should keep the engine running only if the exhaust pipe is clear of snow.

INTEGRATING HEALTH

Section 2 Review

1. What weather conditions are most likely to cause thunderstorms and tornadoes?
2. What is the most common path for the hurricanes that strike the United States?
3. What safety precautions should you take if a tornado is predicted in your area? If a hurricane is predicted in your area?
4. **Thinking Critically Applying Concepts** In the winter, cool, humid air from the Pacific Ocean blows across the cold land of southern Alaska. What kind of storm do you think this causes?

Science at Home

Storm Experiences Interview a family member or other adult about a dramatic storm that he or she has experienced. Before the interview, make a list of questions you would like to ask. For example, how old was the person when the storm occurred? When and where did the storm occur? Write up your interview in a question-and-answer format, beginning with a short introduction.

Chapter 15 **511**

Program Resources

◆ **Unit 4 Resources** 15-2 Review and Reinforce, p. 163; 15-2 Enrich, p. 164

Answers to Self-Assessment

☑ *Checkpoint*

A storm surge is a "dome" of water that sweeps across the coast where a hurricane lands.

Caption Question

Figure 12 Buffalo and Rochester in upstate New York receive large amounts of snow.

Integrating Health

Tell students that the winds of snowstorms make them even more dangerous because they lead to low wind-chill temperatures. Wind chill is how cold it feels because of the wind. For example, if the air temperature is -8°C and the wind is blowing at 50 km/h, the wind-chill temperature is -31°C. Ask: **Why does the wind make you feel colder than the cold air temperature alone?** *(Because it blows the heat away from your body)* **learning modality: logical/mathematical**

3 Assess

Section 2 Review Answers

1. Warm air being forced upward at a cold front to form large cumulonimbus clouds
2. From the Atlantic Ocean westward toward the Caribbean islands and the southeastern United States
3. If a tornado is predicted, go to the basement of a well-built building. If a hurricane is predicted, leave the area immediately.
4. A heavy snowstorm, because the moisture in the cool humid air from the Pacific would condense and fall as snow when it reached the cold land of southern Alaska

Science at Home

Tips Encourage students to tape record or videotape their interview. They might want to present it to the class in the form of a newspaper article or television news report. Suggest that they use drawings or photographs to illustrate their presentation.

ACTIVITY

Performance Assessment

Skills Check Have students make a table comparing and contrasting thunderstorms, tornadoes, hurricanes, and snowstorms.

Tracking a Hurricane

Preparing for Inquiry

Key Concept The path of a hurricane is not always easy to predict, making it difficult to issue hurricane warnings.

Skills Objectives Students will be able to
- interpret data on a map representing the location of a hurricane at repeated intervals;
- interpret additional data in tables to plot the continued path of the hurricane;
- use the data to predict when and where the hurricane will come ashore;
- make a judgement about when and for what area a hurricane warning should be issued.

Time 40 minutes

Advance Planning Students will have to press down hard to mark clearly on the tracing paper with the colored pencils, so have a pencil sharpener and extra pencils on hand. Students may need to trace additional maps, so have extra sheets of tracing paper on hand as well. You may wish to make a copy of the map from the student text as an overhead transparency. Use it to show students how to read latitude and longitude and plot the path of the hurricane.

Alternative Materials Instead of having students use tracing paper to trace the map in their text, you may want to provide each student with a photocopy of the map to mark on directly. If so, make copies of the map in advance.

Guiding Inquiry

Invitation To give the lab a context, point out that today hurricanes cause an average of only 17 deaths each year in the United States. Explain that the relatively low death rate is due to early warnings of when and where hurricanes are coming ashore. Earlier in this century, before the knowledge and technology needed for early warnings were available, the death rate from hurricanes was much higher. Add that one of the main jobs of some meteorologists during hurricane season is to track the storms so warnings can be issued in time to save lives.

Introducing the Procedure
Have students read through the steps of the procedure. Clear up any questions they may have. If necessary, review how to find latitude and longitude. Emphasize to students that they will be plotting the eye of the hurricane as it travels across the water. Ask: **How far on either side of the eye of the hurricane is the storm likely to extend?** *(A typical hurricane is 600 km wide, so the storm may extend 300 km on either side of the eye.)* **Why is this important to know for issuing a hurricane warning?** *(The area affected by the hurricane when it comes ashore will be as wide as the storm, and this is the area for which a hurricane warning should be issued.)*

Tracking a HURRICANE

Hurricane alert! You work at the National Hurricane Center. It is your job to track the paths of hurricanes and try to predict when and where a hurricane is likely to strike land. Then you must decide whether to warn people in the area to evacuate.

Problem

How can you predict when and where a hurricane will come ashore?

Skills Focus

interpreting data, predicting

Materials

ruler
red, blue, green, and brown pencils
tracing paper

Procedure

1. Look at the plotted path of the hurricane on the map. Each dot represents the location of the eye of the hurricane at six-hour intervals. The last dot shows where the hurricane was located at noon on August 30.

2. Predict the path you think the hurricane will take. Place tracing paper over the map below. Using a red pencil, place an X on your tracing paper where you think the hurricane will first reach land. Next to your X, write the date and time you think the hurricane will come ashore.

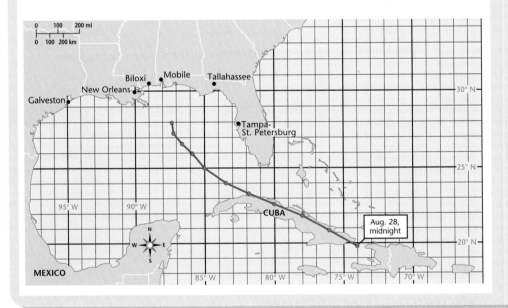

3. Hurricane warnings are issued for an area that is likely to experience a hurricane within 24 hours. On your tracing paper, shade in red the area for which you would issue a hurricane warning.

4. Using the following data table, plot the next five positions for the storm using a blue pencil. Use your ruler to connect the dots to show the hurricane's path.

Date and Time	Latitude	Longitude
August 30, 6:00 P.M.	28.3° N	86.8° W
August 31, midnight	28.4° N	86.0° W
August 31, 6:00 A.M.	28.6° N	85.3° W
August 31, noon	28.8° N	84.4° W
August 31, 6:00 P.M.	28.8° N	84.0° W

5. Based on the new data, decide if you need to change your prediction of where and when the hurricane will come ashore. Mark your new predictions in blue pencil on your tracing paper.

6. During September 1, you obtain four more positions. (Plot these points only after you have completed Step 5.) Based on these new data, mark in green pencil when and where you now think the hurricane will come ashore.

Date and Time	Latitude	Longitude
September 1, midnight	28.8° N	83.8° W
September 1, 6:00 A.M.	28.6° N	83.9° W
September 1, noon	28.6° N	84.2° W
September 1, 6:00 P.M.	28.9° N	84.8° W

7. The next day, September 2, you plot four more positions using a brown pencil. (Plot these points only after you have completed Step 6.)

Date and Time	Latitude	Longitude
September 2, midnight	29.4° N	85.9° W
September 2, 6:00 A.M.	29.7° N	87.3° W
September 2, noon	30.2° N	88.8° W
September 2, 6:00 P.M.	31.0° N	90.4° W

Analyze and Conclude

1. Describe in detail the complete path of the hurricane you tracked. Include where it came ashore and identify any cities that were in the vicinity.

2. How did your predictions in Steps 2, 5, and 6 compare to what actually happened?

3. What was unusual about your hurricane's path?

4. How do you think hurricanes with a path like this one affect the issuing of hurricane warnings?

5. Why do you have to be so careful when issuing warnings? What problems might be caused if you issued an unnecessary hurricane warning? What might happen if a hurricane warning were issued too late?

6. **Think About It** In this activity you only had data for the hurricane's position. If you were tracking a hurricane and issuing warnings, what other types of information would help you make decisions about the hurricane's path?

More to Explore

With your teacher's help, search the Internet for more hurricane tracking data. Map the data and try to predict where the hurricane will come ashore.

Troubleshooting the Experiment

◆ Point out to students that the lines of latitude and longitude on the map are in one-degree increments. Therefore, students will have to estimate where to plot the points because these are given in tenths of a degree of latitude or longitude.

◆ Use an overhead transparency of the map to show students how to plot the first point in the table as an example.

◆ If students think they are plotting incorrectly, advise them that hurricanes can change direction.

Program Resources

◆ **Unit 4 Resources** Chapter 15 Real-World Lab blackline masters, pp. 173–175

Media and Technology

 Lab Activity Videotapes
Grade 6, Tape 4

◆ As the hurricane changes direction, students' maps may become too crowded and difficult to read. If so, suggest that they trace a new map.

Expected Outcome

Students' maps should show that the hurricane changed direction twice, once to the east and then to the west, before finally coming ashore near Biloxi, Mississippi, on September 2.

Analyze and Conclude

1. The hurricane first appeared to be moving north toward southern Louisiana. It then turned east toward central Florida, before reversing direction and heading northwest toward the panhandle of Florida. It continued to move west or northwest until it came ashore near Biloxi, Mississippi.

2. Students' predictions will vary. They are likely to have predicted that the storm would come ashore near Mobile in Step 2, between Tallahassee and Tampa-St. Petersburg in Step 5, and near New Orleans in Step 6. The hurricane actually came ashore somewhat east of New Orleans at Biloxi.

3. The path of the hurricane was unusual because it reversed direction.

4. Hurricanes with a path like this one make it difficult to issue accurate warnings because where the hurricane actually comes ashore is different from where it appears to be headed.

5. You have to be careful when you issue hurricane warnings because unnecessary warnings can disrupt lives, put people in danger, and cause economic losses, whereas warnings that come too late can result in needless loss of life and damage to property.

6. Other types of information that would help you make decisions about the hurricane's path and when and where to issue hurricane warnings would include how fast the hurricane is moving, the speed of its winds, and other indicators of the severity of the storm.

Extending the Inquiry

More to Explore A good Internet site for hurricane tracking data is the National Hurricane Center at **www.nhc.noaa.gov**.

SCIENCE AND SOCIETY

Hurricane Alert: To Stay or Not To Stay?

Purpose To inform students of the pros and cons of evacuation in a hurricane and help them decide whether or not the government should have the power to force people to evacuate.

Role-Play

Time a day to prepare; 15 minutes for role-play

Choose several students to role-play a family discussion in which family members argue over whether or not they should evacuate after a hurricane warning has been issued. Instruct some of the students to take the position that the family should evacuate and others to take the opposite position. Urge students to support their arguments with facts from the feature.

Extend Before the role-play is presented to the class, take a poll of students to see how many would and how many would not evacuate in a hurricane. After the role-play has been presented, take the poll again. Call on any students who changed their minds to explain why.

You Decide

1. The government can order but not enforce evacuations in a hurricane. Some people do not want to evacuate. Other people believe that the government should have the right to force people to evacuate for public safety.

2. Forcing people to evacuate may prevent injuries and save lives by getting people to safety. People who benefit are those who would have been killed or injured had they not been evacuated. People who might be harmed include people who need to protect their homes, businesses, or animals. Government officials might try to increase public awareness of the dangers of not evacuating. Citizens could become better informed about the reasons for evacuating.

3. Make sure students' arguments are well reasoned.

SCIENCE AND SOCIETY

Hurricane Alert: To Stay or Not To Stay?

When a hurricane sweeps in from the ocean, the National Hurricane Center tracks the storm's course. Radio stations broadcast warnings. Sirens blow, and people in the storm path take steps to protect their homes and families.

State and local governments may try to keep people safe by closing state offices, setting up emergency shelters, and alerting the National Guard. As the danger increases, a state's governor can order the evacuation of people from dangerous areas. These actions are meant to protect public safety.

But not everyone wants to evacuate. Some people believe they have the right to stay. And officials cannot make people obey an evacuation order. How much can—or should—the government do to keep people safe?

The Issues

Why Play It Safe? Hurricanes can be extremely dangerous. High winds blow off roofs and shatter windows. Flash floods and storm surges can wash away houses. Even after the storm blows away, officials may need to keep people from returning home because of flooded sewers or broken power lines and gas mains.

In recent years, earlier and more accurate forecasts have saved lives. People now have time to prepare and to get out of the hurricane's path. Emergency officials urge people—especially the elderly, sick, or disabled—to leave early while the weather is still good. Most casualties happen when people are taken by surprise or ignore warnings. Those who decide to stay may later have to be rescued by boat or helicopter. These rescues add to the expense of the storm and may put the lives of rescuers in danger.

Why Ride Out the Storm? People have different reasons for not wanting to evacuate. Some want to protect their homes or businesses. Others don't want to leave pets or farm animals or go to public shelters. Store owners may stay open to sell disaster supplies. In addition, warnings may exaggerate the potential danger, urging people to leave when they might actually be safe. Since leaving can be expensive and disruptive, residents have to carefully evaluate the risks.

Is It a Matter of Rights? Should a government have the power to make people evacuate? Some citizens argue that the government should not tell them what to do as long as they are not harming others. They believe that individuals should have the right to decide for themselves. What do you think?

You Decide

1. Identify the Problem

In your own words, explain the controversy around hurricane evacuations.

2. Analyze the Options

Review and list the pros and cons of forcing people to evacuate. What people benefit? Who might be harmed? What more, if anything, should government officials do? What more could citizens do?

3. Find a Solution

Imagine that the radio has broadcast a hurricane warning. Write a dialogue in which you and members of your family discuss the options and decide whether or not to evacuate.

Background

Many of the severe hurricanes that struck the United States earlier in the twentieth century had high fatality rates. For example, in 1900, a hurricane that struck Texas killed 6,000 people. In 1919, a hurricane that struck the Florida Keys killed 900 people. More recent hurricanes have led to less loss of life, primarily because of early warnings. For example, in 1989, hurricane Hugo killed fewer than 30 people in the United States, even though it was a severe storm. However, recent hurricanes have caused huge amounts of property damage. Hugo, for example, caused an estimated $10.5 billion worth of damage. The increased cost of hurricanes is partly due to an influx of population to the coast. With more houses, businesses, and other types of property along the shore, there is much greater potential for property damage due to hurricanes.

SECTION 3 Floods

DISCOVER

What Causes Floods?

1. Fill a cup with water. Hold a funnel above a basin and pour the water very slowly into the funnel.

2. Refill the cup with the same amount of water you used in Step 1. Hold the funnel above the basin and this time pour the water rapidly into the funnel. What happens?

Think It Over

Inferring How is a funnel like a river valley? What do you think would happen if a large amount of water entered a river valley in a short period of time?

Antelope Canyon in the northern Arizona desert is only a few meters wide in places. On August 12, 1997, a group of 12 hikers entered the dry, narrow canyon. That afternoon a severe thunderstorm dropped several inches of rain on the Kaibeto Plateau, 24 kilometers away. Dry stream channels that drain into Antelope Canyon quickly filled with rainwater. The water rushed into the canyon, creating a wall of water over 3 meters high. Tourists at the top of the canyon watched in horror as the water swept the hikers away. Only one hiker survived.

Are you surprised that floods can occur in a desert? Actually, floods like this are more common in the dry Southwest than in areas with more rain.

GUIDE FOR READING

◆ What causes flooding?

◆ How can people protect themselves in a flood?

Reading Tip As you read, draw a flowchart showing what can happen during a flood and how people should respond to it.

Key Term flash flood

Figure 13 From the top, Antelope Canyon looks like a narrow slit in the ground.

Chapter 15 **515**

INTEGRATING HEALTH

SECTION 3 Floods

TEKS: 6.2B, C; 6.3C; 6.4A; 6.14C

Objectives

After completing the lesson, students will be able to
◆ identify the causes of flooding;
◆ explain how people can protect themselves in a flood.

1 Engage/Explore

Activating Prior Knowledge

Introduce the section by having students apply what they know about watches and warnings to floods. Ask: **What do you think is the difference between a flood watch and a flood warning?** (*Students may say a flood watch means floods are possible and a flood warning means floods have already started to occur.*) **What should people do if a flood watch has been issued?** (*Stay tuned to radio or television.*) **What should people do if a flood warning has been issued?** (*Listen for further instructions, evacuate if ordered to do so.*)

DISCOVER

Skills Focus inferring
Materials *cup, water, funnel, basin*
Time 10 minutes
Tips The funnel should be smaller than the cup so it overflows when students fill it rapidly.
Expected Outcome In Step 1, all the water will flow through the funnel. In Step 2, some of the water will overflow the funnel.
Think It Over The top of the funnel is like a river valley in that it drains a large area. The neck of the funnel is much smaller, like the river channel through which the valley's water flows. The river might overflow its banks, similar to the way the water overflowed the funnel, and this would create a flood.

READING STRATEGIES

Reading Tip A sample flowchart is: rain falls→river rises→land floods→people evacuate. You might want to have students add the words *dam* and *ice jam* to their flowcharts as additional causes of floods.

Study and Comprehension As students read the last two pages of the section, have them summarize flood safety rules in two brief lists, one a list of what *to* do, the other a list of what *not* to do, in a flood.

Program Resources

◆ **Unit 4 Resources** 15-3 Lesson Plan, p. 165; 15-3 Section Summary, p. 166
◆ **Guided Reading and Study Workbook** 15-3

2 Facilitate

Flash Floods

Building Inquiry Skills: Inferring

Point out that flash floods are more likely in hilly areas, such as Antelope Canyon in Arizona, which is described in the text. Ask: **Why do you think flash floods are more likely in hilly areas?** *(Rain water quickly runs off hills and is channeled into narrow valleys and canyons that cannot hold all the water.)* **learning modality: logical/ mathematical**

Flood Safety Measures

Sharpen your Skills

Communicating

Skills Focus
communicating
Time 10 minutes
Tips Invite students to read their announcements to the class. *Computer use is optional.*
Expected Outcome Dangers include high rushing water, uprooted power poles, landslides, mudslides, washed out roads, and contaminated food and drinking water. Steps to follow in case of a flood include moving to higher ground, staying away from flood waters, leaving a flooded car, and boiling water before drinking.
Extend Have interested students use the Internet to contact the National Weather Service at **www.nws.noaa.gov/er/nerfc/ floodinfo.html** for more information on flood safety. **learning modality: verbal**

516

❶ *Heavy rain falls on the plateau.*

❷ *Instead of soaking into the hard soil, the water runs into the canyon.*

❸ *The rainwater is funneled into the narrow canyon and floods it.*

Figure 14 Flash floods occur when large amounts of rain are funneled into a narrow valley. This drawing shows what happened in the Antelope Canyon flood.

Sharpen your Skills

Communicating

On the computer, write a script for a 30-second public service radio announcement in which you tell about the dangers of floods. Include recommended safety steps to follow in case of a flood.

Flash Floods

Although movies feature the violent winds of tornadoes and hurricanes, floods are the most dangerous weather-related events in the United States. **Floods occur when so much water pours into a stream or river that it overflows its banks and covers the land on either side of the channel.** People who live along certain rivers know that melting snow and spring rains are likely to bring floods.

Unexpected floods are the most dangerous. Floods like the Antelope Canyon flood are called flash floods because the water rises very rapidly—"in a flash"—after it begins to rain heavily. A **flash flood** is a sudden, violent flood that occurs within a few hours, or even minutes, of a storm.

Most flash floods are due to large amounts of rain. For example, a line of thunderstorms may remain over an area, dropping heavy rain for several hours or days. Hurricanes or tropical storms bring downpours that quickly fill stream channels. A flash flood can also be caused by a dam breaking, releasing millions of liters of water all at once. Similarly, if ice that has jammed a river breaks free, the sudden rush of water can cause a flash flood.

☑ *Checkpoint* Why are flash floods so dangerous?

Flood Safety Measures

If you've never been in a flood, it's hard to imagine the awesome power of rushing water. What can people do to protect themselves and their homes?

Predicting Floods Advance warnings can help reduce flood damage and loss of life. Weather satellites supply information about snow cover so that scientists can estimate how much water will run into rivers when the snow melts. Radar can track and measure the size of an approaching rainstorm. Scientists check river gauges that measure water levels. With this information, forecasters can predict flood heights at different points along a river. Their goal is to issue warnings early enough to help people prepare and evacuate if necessary.

Background

Facts and Figures Flooding causes almost half of all weather fatalities, and most flood fatalities occur during flash floods. The worst flash flood in United States history was caused by a dam break in Johnstown, Pennsylvania, in May of 1889. A wall of water 12 m high washed over the city, killing 2,200 people.

It isn't dam breaks that cause most flash floods, but heavy rains. One of the worst flash floods in United States history due to heavy rain occurred in Rapid City, South Dakota, in June of 1972. About 38 cm of rain fell in five hours, and the resulting flood killed 238 people. More recently, Shadyside, Ohio, received 10 cm of rain in just two hours. A torrent 12 m high flooded the town, leaving 26 people dead.

①

The car stalls in the water.

②

Moving water pushes against the car.

③

As the water rises, the car begins to float.

④

Sixty centimeters of water can wash a car away.

A "flood watch" is an announcement describing the area in which flooding is possible. Stay alert for more news. A "flood warning" is an announcement that floods have already been reported or are about to occur. It's time to take action!

Emergency Safety What should *you* do in case of a flood? When the danger becomes too great or the water rises too high, people are usually evacuated. **The first rule of flood safety is to move to higher ground and stay away from flood waters.** Don't try to cross streams and rivers that look as if they're flooded. Playing in flood waters may look like fun, but it's dangerous. A few centimeters of fast-moving water can sweep you off your feet. Even the storm drain on a city street can draw you in.

If your family is in a car, the driver shouldn't try to drive on a flooded road. Sometimes less than 60 centimeters of fast-moving water can sweep a car away, as shown in Figure 15. Everyone should leave the car and move to higher ground.

Figure 15 These drawings show what can happen to a car in a flood. *Applying Concepts Why is it dangerous to stay in a car in a flood?*

Chapter 15 **517**

3 Assess

Section 3 Review Answers

1. By pouring so much water into a stream or river that it overflows its banks and covers the land on either side of the channel

2. Move to higher ground, stay away from flood waters, do not try to cross streams and rivers that look flooded, do not play in flood waters, avoid driving on flooded roads, abandon a flooded car and move to higher ground, be careful with food and water that flood waters have touched, and boil water before drinking it to be sure it is safe.

3. A flood watch means flooding is possible, whereas a flood warning means floods have already been reported or are about to occur.

4. Weather satellites, radar, and river gauges

5. Possible answers include a hurricane or tropical storm, a very heavy rain, or melting spring snow.

Check Your Progress
CHAPTER PROJECT

Make sure students use standard weather symbols on their maps. Remind them to include air masses and fronts and to keep in mind the type of weather usually associated with each kind of front.

Performance Assessment

Writing Have students write a list of rules people should follow to ensure safety in a flood.

 Students can save their list of rules in their portfolio.

Figure 16 In the spring of 1997, the Red River of the North flooded regions of North Dakota and Minnesota. A large part of flooded downtown Grand Forks burned down because fire trucks could not get to the scene of the fire or connect to any fire hydrants.

Other Flood Hazards High water is not the only hazard in a flood. Floods can knock down electrical poles and wires, cutting off power supplies. Flood waters can also saturate soil, causing landslides or mudslides. If roads have been flooded or washed away, emergency vehicles such as fire trucks and ambulances may not be able to get through.

Flood waters can wash into wells and water treatment plants, polluting the water. Therefore, be careful with food and water that flood waters have touched. Boil water before drinking it to be sure it is safe.

Section 3 Review

1. How can precipitation cause flooding?

2. How can you stay safe during a flood?

3. What is the difference between a flood watch and a flood warning?

4. Name three tools that supply information used in forecasting floods and providing flood information.

5. Thinking Critically Predicting Describe two weather situations in which you would expect floods to occur.

Check Your Progress
CHAPTER PROJECT

Now you are ready to predict tomorrow's weather. Look at today's weather map. Then predict tomorrow's weather both where you live and in the two other locations you selected. (*Project Hint:* Refer to the weather patterns you have been observing.) Decide what symbols you will need to use. Then, on an outline map of the United States, draw symbols to show what you think tomorrow's weather will be. Continue to make predictions every day for at least a week.

518

Program Resources

◆ **Unit 4 Resources** 15-3 Review and Reinforce, p. 167; 15-3 Enrich, p. 168

DISCOVER

What's the Weather?

1. Look at the weather report in your local newspaper. Note what weather conditions are predicted for your area today, including temperature, precipitation, and wind speed.

2. Look out the window or think about what it was like the last time you were outside. Write down the actual weather conditions where you are.

Think It Over

Observing Does the weather report match what you observe? What is the same? What is different?

For centuries, people have tried to predict the weather. Every nation's folklore includes weather sayings. Many of these sayings are based on long-term observations. Sailors, pilots, farmers, and others who work outdoors are usually careful observers of clouds, winds, and other signs of coming changes in the weather. Here are two examples:

> *Evening red and morning gray
> Will send the traveler on his way;
> Evening gray and morning red
> Will bring down rain upon his head.*
>
> *Red sky in morning,
> sailors take warning;
> Red sky at night, sailor's delight.*

Why do these two weather sayings agree that a red morning sky means bad weather? Recall that in the United States, storms usually move from west to east. Clouds in the west may indicate an advancing low-pressure area, bringing stormy weather. If there are high clouds in the west in the morning, the rising sun in the east turns these clouds red. The reverse is true at sunset. As the sun sets in the west, it turns clouds in the east red. Clouds in the east may indicate that a storm is moving away to the east.

GUIDE FOR READING

- How does technology help forecasters predict the weather?
- What types of information are shown on weather maps?

Reading Tip Before you read, preview Figure 19 and *Exploring Newspaper Weather Maps*. Write a list of any questions you have about weather maps.

Key Terms meteorologist • El Niño • isobar • isotherm

READING STRATEGIES

Reading Tip Urge students to answer their own questions as they read. A sample question might be: How is data on weather maps gathered?

Vocabulary Help students understand the terms *isobar* and *isotherm* by explaining that the prefix *iso-* means "the same", the root *-bar* means "air pressure" (as in *barometer*), and the root *-therm* means "temperature" (as in *thermometer*).

Program Resources

- **Unit 4 Resources** 15-4 Lesson Plan, p. 169; 15-4 Section Summary, p. 170
- **Guided Reading and Study Workbook** 15-4

Objectives

After completing the lesson, students will be able to
- explain how technology helps forecasters predict the weather;
- describe the types of information shown on weather maps.
- describe El Niño and its effects.

1 Engage/Explore

Activating Prior Knowledge

Help students recall occasions when they wanted to know what the next day's or the weekend's weather would be. Ask: **Did you ever wonder how warm or cold it would be the next day so you could plan what to wear to school, or whether it would rain on Saturday and wash out your ball game?** (*Most students will say "yes."*) Point out that the major job of meteorologists, or weather scientists, is predicting the weather. Add that, with modern technology, meteorologists can now predict the weather in the near future quite accurately. Tell students that, in this section, they will learn tips that will also help them predict the weather.

DISCOVER

Skills Focus observing
Materials *local newspaper weather report*
Time 10 minutes
Tips Suggest to students that they consider each of the weather factors reported on in the newspaper before deciding whether or not the actual weather matches the predicted weather.
Expected Outcome The newspaper weather report may or may not match actual conditions, but it probably will be close.
Think It Over The newspaper weather report may match the actual weather in general but not in every detail. For example, the actual temperature may differ from the predicted temperature by a few degrees or showers may be light instead of moderate.

519

2 Facilitate

Weather Forecasting

Real-Life Learning

Call students' attention to the example of weather folklore given in the opening paragraph of the section. Ask: **Do you know any other weather folklore?** *(Students may give familiar examples, such as a groundhog seeing its shadow meaning that there will be six more weeks of winter.)* Point out that long-term weather predictions, such as a groundhog's shadow predicting a longer winter, usually are unreliable. However, short-term predictions, such as the ones in the text, often are reliable because they are based on scientifically valid observations about the weather. Share other examples of reliable weather folklore with students such as the following: "Mackerel sky, mackerel sky, not long wet, not long dry." (High cirrus clouds that look like fish scales usually mean a change in the weather.) "When the sun or moon is in its house, it will rain soon." (The "house" refers to a ring around the sun or moon, which means clouds are thickening and rain is near.) "The north wind does blow, and we will have snow." (A north wind usually brings cold weather and thus a chance for snow.) **learning modality: verbal**

Building Inquiry Skills: Controlling Variables

Stress that today meteorologists rely on information from many different sources to predict the weather. Therefore, it is important to have standard ways of measuring weather factors. For example, wind speed varies with height, so meteorologists set a standard of 10 m above the ground for recording winds. Ask: **How do you think temperature might be standardized?** *(Students may say that temperature varies by time of day so it should be measured at the same time.)* Inform students that the lowest temperature of the day usually occurs near sunrise and the highest temperature between 1:00 and 4:00 p.m. **learning modality: logical/mathematical**

Weather Forecasting

You can make many predictions from your own observations. For example, if a barometer shows that the air pressure is falling, you can expect a change in the weather. Falling air pressure usually indicates an approaching low-pressure area, possibly bringing rain or snow.

You can read weather signs in the clouds too. Cumulus clouds often form on warm afternoons when warm air rises. If you see these clouds growing larger and taller, you can expect them to become cumulonimbus clouds, which may bring a thunderstorm. Thin cirrus clouds high in the sky may indicate that a low-pressure area is approaching.

Even careful weather observers often turn to professional meteorologists for television weather information. You may hear the person who gives the television weather report referred to as a meteorologist. Despite their name, meteorologists don't study meteors. **Meteorologists** (mee tee uh RAWL uh jists) are scientists who study the causes of weather and try to predict it.

Meteorologists interpret information from a variety of sources, including local weather observers, instruments carried by balloons, satellites, and weather stations around the world. They use maps, charts, and computers to analyze the data and to prepare weather forecasts. Meteorologists use radar to track areas of rain or snow, so that forecasters can follow the path of a storm system.

Where do television and radio weather reporters get their information? A lot of weather information comes from the National Weather Service. However, weather forecasts for the general public may not have enough detail to be useful to farmers and pilots. There are also private weather-forecasting services, many of which use advanced, high-technology equipment. Private forecasting services are useful to people who need to answer questions like these: "Will the frost hurt the oranges in my grove?" "Will the airport be fogged in?" "Will the trucks need to spread sand on the roads today?"

☑ *Checkpoint* *Where do meteorologists get weather information?*

Figure 17 These meteorologists are releasing a weather balloon. The box attached to the balloon contains instruments that will record weather data—such as temperature, pressure, and humidity—high in the troposphere.

Background

History of Science Samuel Morse's invention of the telegraph in 1844 revolutionized meteorology. By 1849, scientists at the Smithsonian Institute started gathering weather reports from telegraph operators around the country, and soon the first national weather service was set up. The first weather map showing current conditions based on telegraphed information was published in England in 1851, and the first telegraph system for forecasting severe weather was established in France in 1854.

The United States published its first official weather forecast in 1870. Early weather forecasts were highly inaccurate because they were based on conditions on the ground and not on air masses and fronts.

Warmer   Colder

Weather Technology

Techniques for predicting weather have changed rapidly in recent years. Forecasts for up to five days are now fairly reliable. Meteorologists can also make long-range predictions that were once impossible. **Changes in technology have occurred in two areas: gathering weather data and using computers to make forecasts.**

Weather Balloons and Satellites As you learned in Chapter 13, weather balloons carry instruments high into the troposphere and stratosphere. The instruments measure temperature, air pressure, and humidity.

The first weather satellite was launched in 1960. Cameras on weather satellites in the exosphere can photograph Earth's surface, clouds, storms, and ice and snow cover. These images are then transmitted to meteorologists on Earth, who interpret the information.

Computer Forecasts Computers are widely used to help forecast weather. Instruments can now *INTEGRATING TECHNOLOGY* gather thousands of bits of data about temperature, air pressure, wind speed, and other factors. Computers process large amounts of information quickly to help forecasters make predictions. To make a forecast, the computer starts with weather conditions reported from weather stations over a large area. Conditions reported include wind speed and direction, humidity, sunlight, temperature, and air pressure. Then the computer works through thousands of calculations and makes forecasts for 12 hours, 24 hours, 36 hours, and so on. Each forecast builds on the previous forecast. When new weather data come in, the computer revises its forecasts.

Answers to Self-Assessment

☑ *Checkpoint*

Meteorologists get weather information from local weather observers, instruments carried by balloons, satellites, and weather stations around the world.

Caption Question

Figure 18 You can see temperature, cloud cover, and the location of a storm.

Weather Technology

Inquiry Challenge

Materials *globe, two small balls*
Time 10 minutes

Explain to students that there are two kinds of weather satellites. Geostationary satellites orbit Earth from west to east at a height of about 39,500 km. They always stay above the same spot on Earth's surface. Polar satellites orbit Earth from north to south at a height of about 850 km. They fly over both poles twice a day. Challenge small groups of students to use a globe and two balls, each ball representing one kind of weather satellite, to model how weather satellites orbit Earth. Then ask: **Which type of satellite do you think gets clearer pictures of clouds and other weather factors? Why?** *(Polar satellites, because they orbit at a lower altitude)* **Which type of satellite do you think gets a broader picture of clouds and other weather factors? Why?** *(Geostationary satellites, because they orbit at a higher altitude)* **learning modality: logical/ mathematical**

Integrating Technology

Help students appreciate the role computers play in weather forecasting. Inform students that meteorologists divide the troposphere into about 3,000 grids, and weather data for each grid arrives at the National Weather Service twice a day. Managing all that data to track and forecast the weather requires billions of calculations. The computer used by the National Weather Service can perform over two billion calculations per second. If that work had to be done by hand, it would require more than 123,000 people. Ask: **What is the major role played by computers in weather forecasting?** *(Analyzing huge amounts of information quickly)* **learning modality: verbal**

Ongoing Assessment

Oral Presentation Call on various students to explain in their own words how advances in technology have led to more accurate weather forecasts.

El Niño

Building Inquiry Skills: Communicating

Tell students that weather prediction has become more accurate now that scientists understand how global winds and ocean currents influence weather. Explain that periodic changes in highs and lows over the southern Pacific Ocean modify the trade winds, and changes in the trade winds, in turn, influence ocean currents, leading to an increase in the temperature of the water off the coast of South America. The warm ocean water causes unusually rainy weather along the coast of South America and also, by influencing other ocean currents, indirectly causes unusual weather conditions all over the world. Check students' understanding of the wide-spread influence of El Niño by asking: **How does understanding El Niño help meteorologists predict the weather?** *(Meteorologists can look for changes in ocean currents and, if they occur, anticipate certain unusual weather conditions over a wide area.)* **learning modality: verbal**

Reading Weather Maps

Sharpen your *Skills*

Interpreting Data

Time 10 minutes

Tips Make sure students understand how to read the symbol for wind direction. Explain that when the shaft points down the wind is from the south, when it points left the wind is from the west, and so on.

Expected Outcome Temperature 30°F, wind speed 26–31 mph, wind blowing from the south, air pressure 1016 millibars, 70–80 percent of the sky covered by clouds, snow falling

Extend Ask: **How would you show the same station with a temperature of 34°F, wind direction from the southeast, and sleet falling?** *(Replace 30 with 34, point the shaft halfway between down and right, and replace the star with a triangle containing a solid circle.)* **learning modality: logical/ mathematical**

Sharpen your *Skills*

Interpreting Data

Use the key to Figure 19 to help you answer the questions about this weather station data.

ACTIVITY

30 ● 1016
✳

1. What is the temperature at this station?
2. What is the wind speed?
3. Which way is the wind blowing?
4. What is the air pressure?
5. What percent of the sky is covered by clouds?
6. What type of precipitation, if any, is falling?

El Niño

Some long-term weather patterns may be caused by changes in ocean currents and global winds. Periodically, a warm-water event known as **El Niño** occurs in the tropical Pacific Ocean. During an El Niño event, winds shift and push warm surface water toward the west coast of South America. The warm water replaces the cold water that usually rises from the deep ocean near the coast.

El Niño events occur once every two to seven years. They can cause dramatic climate changes around the Pacific Ocean and in other places. In the winter of 1997 and 1998, a strong El Niño current caused droughts in Asia and Brazil, heavy rains and floods in California and Peru, and tornadoes in Florida and other parts of the southeastern United States.

Scientists have looked for clues and warnings to help predict the return of El Niño. One signal is rising surface temperatures in the tropical part of the Pacific Ocean. Using data gathered during past El Niño events, scientists were able to predict many of the results of the 1997–1998 El Niño.

☑ *Checkpoint* *What evidence do scientists use to predict an El Niño?*

Reading Weather Maps

A weather map is a "snapshot" of conditions at a particular time over a large area. There are many different types of weather maps. Television forecasters often present maps generated by computers from radar information.

Weather Service Maps Data from more than 300 local weather stations all over the country are assembled into weather maps at the National Weather Service. The information collected by a typical reporting station is summarized in the key to Figure 19. The weather map, which has been simplified, includes most of the weather station data shown in the key.

On some weather maps, you see curved lines. These lines connect places where certain conditions—temperature or air pressure—are the same. **Isobars** are lines joining places on the map that have the same air pressure. (*Iso* means "equal" and *bar* means "pressure.") The numbers on the isobars are the pressure readings. Air pressure readings may be given in inches of mercury or in millibars or both. Figure 19 has isobars.

Isotherms are lines joining places that have the same temperature. The isotherm may be labeled with the temperature in degrees Fahrenheit, degrees Celsius, or both.

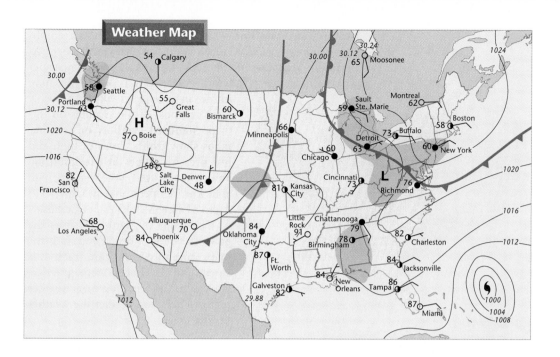

Weather Map

Calgary 54 · Seattle 58 · Portland 63 · Great Falls 55 · Bismarck 60 · Moosonee 65 · Sault Ste. Marie 59 · Montreal 62 · Boston 58 · Buffalo 73 · Detroit 63 · New York 60 · Boise 57 · Minneapolis 66 · Chicago 60 · Cincinnati 73 · Richmond 76 · Salt Lake City 58 · Denver 48 · Kansas City 81 · San Francisco 82 · Los Angeles 68 · Albuquerque 70 · Phoenix 84 · Oklahoma City 84 · Little Rock 91 · Chattanooga 79 · Birmingham 78 · Charleston 82 · Ft. Worth 87 · Galveston 82 · New Orleans 84 · Jacksonville 84 · Tampa 86 · Miami 87

EXPLANATION OF FRONTS

▼▼▼ *Cold Front*
Boundary between a cold air mass and a warm air mass. Brings brief storms and cooler weather.

▲▲▲ *Warm Front*
Boundary between a warm air mass and a cold air mass. Usually accompanied by precipitation.

▲▼ *Stationary Front*
Boundary between a warm air mass and a cold air mass when no movement occurs. Brings long periods of precipitation.

▲▲▲ *Occluded Front*
Boundary on which a warm front has been overtaken by a cold front. Brings precipitation.

Weather	Symbol
Drizzle	⸴
Fog	≡
Hail	△
Haze	∞
Rain	●
Shower	▽
Sleet	⬟
Smoke	⌇
Snow	✳
Thunderstorm	⍐
Hurricane	⌇

Wind Speed (mph)	Symbol
1–2	
3–8	
9–14	
15–20	
21–25	
26–31	
32–37	
38–43	
44–49	
50–54	
55–60	
61–66	
67–71	
72–77	

Cloud Cover (%)	Symbol
0	○
10	◐
20–30	◔
40	◑
50	◑
60	◕
70–80	◕
90	◑
100	●

How Symbols Are Used on a Weather Map

Amount of cloud cover (100%)
Atmospheric pressure (millibars)
Temperature (°F)
38 · 1018
Wind direction (from the southwest)
Wind speed (21–25mph)

Figure 19 This weather map shows data collected from weather stations all over the country. Below the map is an explanation of what the symbols at each city mean.

Using the Visuals: Figure 19

Have students choose partners and quiz each other on the conditions represented by the symbols at several different weather stations shown in the figure. For example, a student might ask his or her partner from which direction the wind is blowing in Miami (*east*), how much cloud cover there is in Seattle (*100%*), or how fast the wind is blowing in Los Angeles (*9–14 mph*). **cooperative learning**

Real-Life Learning

Challenge students to use the symbols in Figure 19 to summarize actual weather conditions in their location. You may either provide students with the relevant data on temperature, wind direction, and other weather factors for your local area or have students read the data from instruments. Ask: **What, if any, weather factors are not included in the key?** (*relative humidity, dew point, and cloud type*) **How could you represent them on a weather map?** (*Students may say that relative humidity and dew point could be represented by numbers placed near the weather station and cloud type by a symbol placed near the weather station.*) **learning modality: visual**

Building Inquiry Skills: Predicting

Content Mastery

Call students' attention to the map in Figure 19 and challenge them to locate the longest cold front. Ask: **Where do you think the cold front will be in a few days?** (*Most likely it will have moved east.*) **As the cold front travels across the country, how do you think it will change the weather?** (*The cold front is likely to bring cloudy, wet, or even stormy weather.*) **learning modality: logical/mathematical**

Program Resources

◆ **Laboratory Manual** 15, "Investigating Weather Maps"

Media and Technology

 Transparencies "Weather Map," Transparency 75

Answers to Self-Assessment

☑ *Checkpoint*

To predict an El Niño, scientists look for evidence of rising surface temperatures in the tropical part of the Pacific Ocean.

Ongoing Assessment

Skills Check Have students interpret data in Figure 19 to find the following weather information: the air pressure in Tampa, Florida (*1016 millibars*); a cyclone, or low pressure system (*between Ohio and West Virginia*); a stationary front (*from Wisconsin to Virginia*); a hurricane (*east of Florida*).

Reading Weather Maps, continued

Using the Visuals: Figure 20

Make sure students understand how the three maps in the figure are related, then ask: **If you had a weather map for Day 4, how do you predict it would differ from the map for Day 3?** *(Chances are the weather systems would be farther east by Day 4.)* **learning modality: logical/mathematical**

Real-Life Learning

Time 20 minutes

Point out that even very detailed weather maps cannot give the precise weather conditions for every location because there are many factors that can modify local conditions. For example, the south side of a hill is likely to be warmer than the north side and an open area is likely to be windier than a wooded area. Ask: **What factors do you think might influence local weather conditions at our school?** *(Factors might include large buildings, open grassy areas, hills, rivers or lakes.)* **learning modality: visual**

The Butterfly Effect

Building Inquiry Skills: Calculating

Materials *calculator*
Time 5 minutes

Help students appreciate how the butterfly effect works with this simple activity. Have students add three numbers, divide the sum by a fourth number, multiply the quotient by a fifth number, and then square the result. Give half the class five numbers written out to three decimal places and give the other half the same numbers rounded to the nearest whole number. Have students compare their results. They will find that answers based on the different sets of numbers diverge more and more with each step in the calculations. Ask: **How does this demonstrate the butterfly effect?** *(Tiny differences in the numbers accumulate into larger differences.)* **learning modality: logical/mathematical**

Newspaper Weather Maps Maps in newspapers are simplified versions of maps produced by the National Weather Service. *Exploring Newspaper Weather Maps* shows a typical newspaper weather map. From what you have learned in this chapter, you can probably interpret most of the symbols on this map. **Standard symbols on weather maps show fronts, areas of high and low pressure, types of precipitation, and temperatures.** Note that the high and low temperatures are given in degrees Fahrenheit instead of Celsius.

The maps in Figure 20 show the path of a winter storm. If you study the maps carefully, you can track this storm and its effects. With practice, you can use information from weather maps to help you predict the weather in your area.

The Butterfly Effect

Even with current technology, weather forecasting is tricky. The main reason is that weather patterns do not follow an orderly, step-by-step process.

A forecast for the weather six days from now is based on forecasts for all the days between now and then. A small change in the weather today can mean a larger change in the weather a week later! This is the so-called butterfly effect. The name refers to a scientist's suggestion that even the flapping of a butterfly's wings causes a tiny disturbance in the atmosphere. This tiny event might cause a larger disturbance that could—eventually—grow into a hurricane.

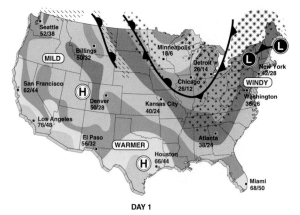

DAY 1

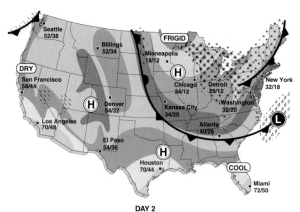

DAY 2

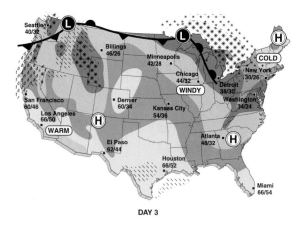

DAY 3

Figure 20 These weather maps show a storm moving from west to east over a three-day period.
Interpreting Diagrams What were the high and low temperatures in Chicago on Day 2? On Day 3?

524

Background

History of Science The butterfly effect was discovered by a theoretical meteorologist at the Massachusetts Institute of Technology named Edward Lorenz. One day in 1961, Lorenz decided to rerun a computer program for weather forecasting that he had been working on. Rather than enter all the numbers to six decimal places, he took a shortcut and entered the numbers to just three decimal places. After many computer calculations, Lorenz was surprised to discover that the results were very different from the results he had obtained earlier using numbers to six decimal places. This showed Lorenz that weather systems and other complex systems are very sensitive to tiny changes in initial conditions. Lorenz's work was the beginning of the mathematical theory of chaos, which is now important in most sciences, in addition to meteorology.

EXPLORING Newspaper Weather Maps

Weather maps in newspapers use symbols to show fronts, high and low pressure areas, and precipitation. Color bands indicate different temperatures.

Areas in the same temperature range are shown in the same color. For example, light green areas have high temperatures in the 40s.

Major low-pressure areas are shown with an "L." High-pressure areas are shown with an "H."

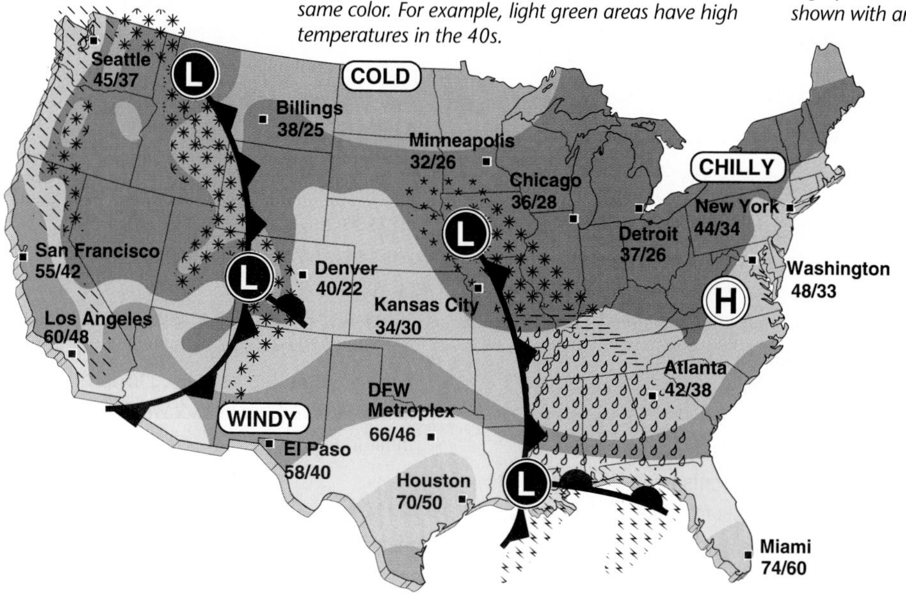

Seattle 45/37 (L)

COLD

Billings 38/25

Minneapolis 32/26

Chicago 36/28

CHILLY

New York 44/34

Detroit 37/26

(L)

San Francisco 55/42

(L)

Denver 40/22

Washington 48/33 (H)

Los Angeles 60/48

Kansas City 34/30

Atlanta 42/38

DFW Metroplex 66/46

WINDY

El Paso 58/40

Houston 70/50

(L)

Miami 74/60

Symbols that look like raindrops or snowflakes show precipitation.

The triangles showing a cold front point in the direction the cold air is moving. The half-circles indicating a warm front show the direction the warm air is moving.

Section 4 Review

1. What kinds of technology do meteorologists use to help predict the weather?

2. Name at least three types of information you could get from a weather map of your area.

3. What lines on a weather map connect points that have the same temperature?

4. **Thinking Critically** **Predicting** If you observe that air pressure is rising, what kind of weather do you think is coming?

Check Your Progress

CHAPTER PROJECT

After a week of predicting the weather, you are ready to compare your predictions to the actual weather that occurred. Then compare your predictions with those made by professional meteorologists. How accurate were your predictions? How accurate were the predictions made by professional meteorologists?

Chapter 15 **525**

Program Resources

◆ **Unit 4 Resources** 15-4 Review and Reinforce, p. 171; 15-4 Enrich, p. 172

Media and Technology

Transparencies "Newspaper Weather Map," Transparency 76

Answers to Self-Assessment

Caption Question

Figure 20 The high temperature in Chicago on Day 2 was 24°F; low was 12°F. On Day 3 the high was 44°F; the low was 32°F.

EXPLORING

Newspaper Weather Maps

Materials *poster board, colored markers*

Time 30 minutes

Challenge pairs of students to produce a brief television weather report based on the weather map shown in the feature. Each pair should interpret the symbols on the map, write a script, and create graphics. Have pairs present their reports to the class. Refer to the **ELL Handbook** for additional teaching strategies.
cooperative learning

3 Assess

Section 4 Review Answers

1. Meteorologists use weather balloons, weather satellites, and computers.
2. Temperature, air pressure, wind speed, wind direction, percent cloud cover, and type of precipitation.
3. isotherms
4. fair weather

Check Your Progress

CHAPTER PROJECT

To compare their predictions with the weather that occurs at each of their three locations, student should compare their own weather maps with the newspaper weather maps showing actual weather conditions for the same days. Most newspaper weather reports also give weather predictions that students can use to compare their own predictions with those made by professional meteorologists.

Performance Assessment

Skills Check Have students interpret the weather map in the Exploring feature on this page to find out weather conditions in Houston. Then have them describe Houston's weather using the symbols in the key to Figure 19.

Reading a Weather Map

Preparing for Inquiry

Key Concept The symbols on weather maps communicate information about weather factors and systems.

Skills Objectives Students will be able to
◆ interpret data on a weather map;
◆ draw conclusions about the type of weather affecting different places.

Time 30 minutes

Advance Planning Make an overhead transparency of the map in the lab to use in class.

Alternative Materials You can use an actual weather map from a newspaper.

Guiding Inquiry

Troubleshooting the Experiment
◆ Make sure students realize how the front changes as it goes across the top of the map.
◆ Explain why two temperatures are given for each city on the map.

Expected Outcome

Students should use the map on page 589 to interpret the map in the lab. In Step 3, the symbols that look like snowflakes represent snow and those that look like raindrops represent rain. In Step 4, half-circles indicate warm fronts and triangles represent cold fronts. In Step 5, H is the symbol for high pressure and L is the symbol for low pressure.

Analyze and Conclude

1. Orange represents the highest temperatures and light purple represents the lowest temperatures.
2. Miami the highest, Billings the lowest
3. It is raining in California and snowing in parts of the Northwest.
4. Three—warm front, cold front, stationary front
5. Two areas of low pressure and two areas of high pressure
6. It is probably winter. The temperatures are fairly low.
7. A cold front; clouds and snow followed by cold, dry weather

---

Reading a Weather Map

In this lab, you will interpret data from a weather map to describe weather conditions in various places.

Problem

How does a weather map communicate data?

Procedure

1. Examine the symbols on the weather map below. For more information about the symbols used on the map, refer to Figure 19 on page 523 and to *Exploring Newspaper Weather Maps* on page 525.
2. Observe the different colors on the weather map.
3. Find the symbols for snow and rain.
4. Locate the warm fronts and cold fronts.
5. Locate the symbols for high and low pressure.

Analyze and Conclude

1. What color represents the highest temperatures? What color represents the lowest temperatures?
2. What city has the highest temperature? What city has the lowest temperature?
3. Where on the map is it raining? Where on the map is it snowing?
4. How many different kinds of fronts are shown on the map?
5. How many areas of low pressure are shown on the map? How many areas of high pressure are shown on the map?
6. What season does this map represent? How do you know?
7. **Think About It** The triangles and semicircles on the front lines show which way the front is moving. What front is moving toward Minneapolis? What kind of weather do you think it will bring?

More to Explore

Compare this weather map with the weather map shown in a television news report. Which symbols on these maps are similar? Which symbols are different?

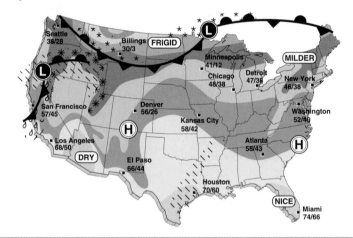

Extending the Inquiry

More to Explore Television weather maps use somewhat different symbols, but students should be able to interpret them with their knowledge of newspaper weather maps.

Air Masses and Fronts

Key Ideas

◆ Four major types of air masses influence the weather in North America: maritime tropical, continental tropical, maritime polar, and continental polar.

◆ When air masses collide, they form four types of fronts: cold fronts, warm fronts, stationary fronts, and occluded fronts.

◆ Cyclones and decreasing air pressure are associated with storms and precipitation.

Key Terms

air mass	maritime	occluded
tropical	continental	cyclone
polar	front	anticyclone

 Storms

Key Ideas

◆ Thunderstorms and tornadoes form within large cumulonimbus clouds. During thunderstorms, avoid touching metal objects.

◆ A hurricane begins over warm water as a low-pressure area. If you hear a hurricane warning and are told to evacuate, leave the area immediately.

◆ Snow falls when humid air cools below 0°C. If you are caught in a snowstorm, try to find shelter from the wind.

Key Terms

storm	tornado	storm surge
lightning	hurricane	evacuate

 Floods

INTEGRATING HEALTH

Key Ideas

◆ Floods occur when so much water pours into a stream or river that it overflows its banks on either side of the channel.

◆ The first rule of flood safety is to move to higher ground and stay away from flood waters.

Key Term
flash flood

Predicting Weather Change

Key Ideas

◆ Meteorologists interpret weather information from local weather observers, instruments carried by balloons, satellites, and weather stations around the world.

◆ Changes in weather technology have occurred in two areas: gathering weather data and using computers to make forecasts.

◆ Standard symbols on weather maps show fronts, areas of high and low pressure, types of precipitation, and temperatures.

Key Terms
meteorologist
El Niño
isobar
isotherm

Organizing Information

Compare/Contrast Table Copy the compare/contrast table about hurricanes and tornadoes onto a separate sheet of paper. Then fill in the empty spaces and add a title. (For more on compare/contrast tables, see the Skills Handbook.)

Type of Storm	Hurricane	Tornado
Where storm forms	Over warm ocean water	a. ?
Size of storm	b. ?	Several hundred meters
How long storm lasts	A week or more	c. ?
Time of year	d. ?	Spring, early summer
Safety rules	Evacuate or move inside a well-built building	e. ?

Organizing Information

Compare/Contrast Table Sample title: Comparing Hurricanes and Tornadoes **a.** In cumulonimbus clouds **b.** Around 600 kilometers **c.** 15 minutes or less **d.** Summer, early fall **e.** Move to the basement of a well-built building

---

Program Resources

◆ **Unit 4 Resources** Chapter 15 Project Scoring Rubric, p. 156
◆ **Performance Assessment** Chapter 15, pp. 47–49
◆ **Chapter and Unit Tests** Chapter 15 Test, pp. 72–75

Media and Technology

Computer Test Bank
Chapter 15 Test

Reviewing Content
Multiple Choice
1. c 2. b 3. d 4. a 5. b

True or False
6. continental tropical 7. stationary front
8. true 9. true 10. isotherms

Checking Concepts
11. temperature and humidity
12. The prevailing westerlies generally push air masses from west to east in the continental United States.
13. A cold front forms when a cold air mass moves underneath a warm air mass, forcing the warm air to rise.
14. Answers may vary. In addition to the dangers of high water to lives and property, floods can knock down electrical poles and cut off power supplies, cause landslides or mudslides, block or wash away roads, pollute drinking water and food.
15. Sources of information that meteorologists use to predict the weather include local weather observers, instruments carried by balloons, satellites, and weather stations around the world.
16. El Niño is a periodic warm water event in which winds shift and push warm water toward the west coast of South America. El Niño can cause dramatic weather changes, including floods, droughts, and tornadoes, over a wide region.
17. **Writing to Learn** Students' descriptions should show that they are familiar with the characteristics of hurricanes, including the heavy rains and high winds that swirl around the calm eye at the center of the hurricane. Their descriptions also should show that they know hurricanes may cover hundreds of kilometers.

Thinking Critically
18. Warm air masses that influence weather in the United States include maritime tropical air masses from the Gulf of Mexico and the Pacific Ocean and continental tropical air masses from the Southwest. Cold air masses that influence weather in the United States include maritime polar air masses from the Atlantic and Pacific Oceans and

Reviewing Content

 Review key concepts online using
iText at www.phschool.com

Multiple Choice
Choose the letter of the answer that best completes each statement.

1. An air mass that forms over an ocean is called
   a. tropical.
   b. continental.
   c. maritime.
   d. polar.
2. Cool, clear weather is usually brought by a
   a. warm front.
   b. cold front.
   c. stationary front.
   d. occluded front.
3. Winds spiraling inward toward a center of low pressure form a(n)
   a. anticyclone.
   b. front.
   c. isobar.
   d. cyclone.
4. Very large tropical storms with high winds are called
   a. hurricanes.   b. tornadoes.
   c. thunderstorms.   d. blizzards.
5. Most flash floods are caused by
   a. hailstorms.   b. heavy rainfall.
   c. high winds.   d. melting snow.

True or False
If the statement is true, write true. If it is false, change the underlined word or words to make it true.

6. Summers in the Southwest are hot and dry because of <u>maritime tropical</u> air masses.
7. A <u>cold front</u> over an area will bring many days of cloudy weather.
8. Foggy, rainy, or humid weather usually follows the passage of a <u>warm front</u> through an area.
9. Low cumulonimbus clouds may bring both thunderstorms and <u>tornadoes</u>.
10. On a weather map, <u>isobars</u> join places on the map with the same temperature.

Checking Concepts
11. What are the basic characteristics used to describe air masses?
12. Describe how wind patterns affect the movement of air masses in North America.
13. How does a cold front form?
14. Describe three hazards associated with floods.
15. What are some of the sources of information that meteorologists use to predict the weather?
16. What is El Niño? How does it influence the weather in certain regions?
17. **Writing to Learn** Imagine you are a meteorologist. Your assignment is to investigate a hurricane by flying into it with a large plane. Describe your experiences in a journal entry. Be sure to include descriptive words. How did the hurricane look? Sound? Feel?

Thinking Critically
18. **Classifying** Classify the major types of air masses that influence weather in the United States in two ways: by temperature and by where they form.
19. **Comparing and Contrasting** Compare and contrast cyclones and anticyclones. What type of weather is associated with each?
20. **Applying Concepts** Would you expect hurricanes to form over the oceans off the northeast and northwest coasts of the United States? Explain.
21. **Relating Cause and Effect** How do differences in air density influence the movement of cold and warm fronts?
22. **Making Judgments** What do you think is the most important thing people should do to reduce the dangers of storms?

continental polar air masses from central and northern Canada. Air masses that form over the water include maritime polar and maritime tropical air masses. Air masses that form over land include continental polar and continental tropical air masses.
19. Cyclones are swirling centers of low pressure air that rotate counterclockwise in the Northern Hemisphere. Anticyclones are swirling centers of high pressure air that rotate clockwise in the Northern Hemisphere. Cyclones are associated with storms and

precipitation whereas anticyclones are associated with dry, clear weather.
20. You would not expect hurricanes to form over the oceans off the northeast and northwest coasts of the United States because the temperature of the water is too cold to provide energy for a hurricane.
21. Warm air is less dense than cold air. When a cold front moves through, it flows underneath warm air. When a warm front moves through, it rises up over cold air.

Applying Skills

Use the map to answer Questions 23–26.

23. **Interpreting Maps** Does the map show a cyclone or an anticyclone? How can you tell?

24. **Interpreting Data** What do the arrows show about the movement of the winds in this pressure center? What else indicates wind direction?

25. **Making Models** Using this diagram as an example, draw a similar diagram to illustrate a high pressure area. Remember to indicate wind direction in your diagram.

26. **Posing Questions** If you saw a pressure center like this on a weather map, what prediction could you make about the weather? What questions would you need to ask in order to make a better prediction?

Performance CHAPTER PROJECT Assessment

Present Your Project Prepare your final report and arrange your maps for presentation. You may want to display each of your maps next to the actual newspaper weather map for that day. Practice your presentation, make any needed changes, and then present your report.

Reflect and Record In your journal, describe what you learned. Are there weather factors on the maps to which you should have paid more attention? Do meteorologists have information that isn't in the newspaper? How could you gather more information to improve your forecasting?

Test Preparation

Use these questions to prepare for standardized tests.

Read the passage. Then answer Questions 27–30.

As Hurricane Andrew roared toward the southern Florida coastline, millions of Florida residents evacuated the area, heading toward safety. It was 1992, and forecasters predicted that Andrew would make landfall sometime in the early morning of August 24. Andrew had been rapidly building speed and strength since it was first classified as a tropical storm on August 17. Andrew quickly advanced to a fierce Category 4 hurricane, with sustained wind speeds estimated at 145 m.p.h. The only type of hurricane that is stronger is a Category 5 hurricane—a very rare event.

Andrew pounded South Florida for several hours. In the end, this hurricane caused over $20 billion in damage to Florida, becoming the most expensive natural disaster in U.S. history to that point.

27. What is the best title for this selection?
   A Category 4 Hurricanes
   B August 24, 1992
   C Hurricane Andrew Pounds Florida
   D Hurricane Andrew Heads North

28. What kind of storm was Andrew before it was classified as a hurricane?
   F tropical storm   G thunderstorm
   H rainstorm   J monsoon

29. Which category of hurricanes has the greatest wind speed?
   A Category 1   B Category 4
   C Category 5   D none of the above

30. Why did Andrew cause so much damage?
   F because it traveled so fast
   G because it traveled in a northward direction
   H because it had very high wind speed
   J because it traveled over water

---

22. Answers may vary. Many students will state the importance of staying informed about conditions during storms by listening to weather reports on radio or television.

Program Resources

◆ **Inquiry Skills Activity Book** Provides teaching and review of all inquiry skills
◆ **Prentice Hall Assessment System** Provides standardized test practice
◆ **Reading in the Content Area** Provides strategies to improve science reading skills
◆ **Teacher's ELL Handbook** Provides multiple strategies for English language learners

---

Applying Skills

23. The map shows a cyclone. You can tell because the air pressure at the center is low and the air is spinning counterclockwise.

24. The winds are spinning in a counterclockwise direction. The low pressure area at the center indicates the winds are spinning inward toward the center.

25. Students' drawings should show a high pressure area surrounded by winds flowing outward from the center in a clockwise direction.

26. If you saw a pressure center like the one depicted on the map on a weather map, you would predict stormy, wet weather. To make a better prediction, you would need to ask about the direction and rate of movement of the pressure center.

Performance CHAPTER PROJECT Assessment

Present Your Project Encourage students to use a variety of formats for presenting their projects, such as television weather reports and bulletin board displays. Advise students to be prepared to explain the patterns they observed in the weather and how they made their predictions.

Reflect and Record Students may find that they should have paid more attention to the movement of air masses and fronts. They probably learned that it is difficult to predict weather accurately. Meteorologists have a great deal more information than what appears in newspapers, including information from weather radar. To improve their forecasting accuracy, students might consider gathering information from local and national television weather reports. These reports may show weather radar images and other information not found in newspapers.

Test Preparation

27. C 28. F 29. C 30. H

Components of the Solar System

Sections	Time	Student Edition Activities		Other Activities
CHAPTER PROJECT **Model of the Solar System** p. 531	Ongoing (3 weeks)	TEKS: 6.2E; 6.3C **Check Your Progress,** pp. 542, 551, 559 **Present Your Project,** p. 573	TE	Chapter 16 Project Notes, pp. 530–531
1 Describing the Solar System pp. 532–537 TEKS: 6.5A; 6.13A 16.1.1 Explain how the heliocentric and geocentric models of the solar system differ. 16.1.2 Identify and explain the two factors that keep planets in their orbits. 16.1.3 Describe what combines to form our solar system.	2 periods/ 1 block	TEKS: 6.1A; 6.2C; 6.3A, C, D, E **Discover** How Do Mass and Speed Affect an Object's Motion?, p. 532 **Try This** A Loopy Ellipse, p. 535 **Science at Home,** p. 537	TE TE	Building Inquiry Skills: Comparing and Contrasting, p. 534 Including All Students, p. 534
2 Characteristics of the Sun pp. 538–543 TEKS: 6.13A 16.2.1 Describe how the sun produces energy. 16.2.2 List and describe the layers of the sun's atmosphere. 16.2.3 Identify features of the sun's surface.	2–3 periods/ 1–$\frac{1}{2}$ blocks	TEKS: 6.1A; 6.2B, C, E; 6.4A **Discover** How Can You Safely Observe the Sun?, p. 538 **Try This** Viewing Sunspots, p. 540 **Real-World Lab: You and Your Environment** Stormy Sunspots, p. 543	TE LM	Demonstration, p. 539 16, "Measuring the Diameter of the Sun"
3 Characteristics of the Inner Planets pp. 544–551 TEKS: 6.13A 16.3.1 Identify the main characteristics of the inner planets.	2 periods/ 1 block	TEKS: 6.1A; 6.2E; 6.3C; 6.4A **Discover** How Does Mars Look From Earth?, p. 544 **Sharpen Your Skills** Graphing, p. 547 **Sharpen Your Skills** Observing, p. 549 **Try This** Remote Control, p. 550	TE TE TE	Integrating Earth Science, p. 545 Building Inquiry Skills: Observing, p. 546, 550 Demonstration, p. 547
4 Characteristics of the Outer Planets pp. 552–561 TEKS: 6.13A 16.4.1 Identify the main characteristics of the gas giant planets. 16.4.2 Compare Pluto and Charon with the other planets.	3 periods/ 1$\frac{1}{2}$ blocks	TEKS: 6.1A; 6.2A, B, C, E; 6.3C; 6.4A **Discover** How Large Are the Outer Planets?, p. 552 **Try This** Model Saturn, p. 555 **Skills Lab: Developing Hypotheses** Speeding Around the Sun, pp. 560–561	TE TE	Building Inquiry Skills: Making Models, p. 554 Building Inquiry Skills: Relating Cause and Effect, p. 558
5 Comets, Asteroids, and Meteors pp. 562–565 TEKS: 6.5A; 6.13A 16.5.1 Identify the characteristics of comets and asteroids. 16.5.2 Describe the formation of meteoroids.	2 periods/ 1 block	TEKS: 6.1A; 6.3C; 6.4B **Discover** Which Way Do Comet Tails Point?, p. 562 **Science at Home,** p. 565		
6 *INTEGRATING TECHNOLOGY* **Traveling in Space** pp. 566–570 TEKS: 6.6A; 6.13B 16.6.1 Explain how rockets travel in space. 16.6.2 List the equipment needed to travel in space.	1 period/ $\frac{1}{2}$ block	TEKS: 6.1A; 6.4A **Discover** How Do Rockets Work?, p. 566 **Try This** Be a Rocket Scientist, p. 568 **Science at Home,** p. 569	TE TE	Demonstration, p. 567 Inquiry Challenge, p. 568
Study Guide/Chapter Assessment pp. 571–573	1 period/ $\frac{1}{2}$ block	**PLM** Provides blackline masters for Probeware labs	ISAB	Provides teaching and review of all inquiry skills

Key: **CTB** Computer Test Bank
       CUT Chapter and Unit Tests
       ELL Teacher's ELL Handbook

CHAPTER PLANNING GUIDE

 The Resource Pro® CD-ROM provides flexibility for planning the instruction for any type of schedule.

Program Resources	Assessment Strategies	Media and Technology
UR Chapter 16 Project Teacher Notes, pp. 178–179 UR Chapter 16 Project Overview and Worksheets, pp. 180–183	SE Performance Assessment: Present Your Project, p. 573 TE Check Your Progress, pp. 542, 551, 559 UR Chapter 16 Project Scoring Rubric, p. 184	Science Explorer at www.phschool.com Student Edition on Audio CD, English-Spanish, Chapter 16
UR 16-1 Section Lesson Plan, p. 185 UR 16-1 Section Summary, p. 186 UR 16-1 Review and Reinforce, p. 187 UR 16-1 Enrich, p. 188	SE Section 1 Review, p. 537 TE Ongoing Assessment, pp. 533, 535 TE Performance Assessment, p. 537	Earth Science Videodisc, Unit 1, Side 1, "For the Love of Astronomy" Videotape Grade 6, Unit 4, "For the Love of Astronomy" Transparency 77, "Planet Motion"
UR 16-2 Section Lesson Plan, p. 189 UR 16-2 Section Summary, p. 190 UR 16-2 Review and Reinforce, p. 191 UR 16-2 Enrich, p. 192 UR Real-World Lab blackline masters, pp. 209–210	SE Section 2 Review, p. 542 TE Ongoing Assessment, pp. 539, 541 TE Performance Assessment, p. 542	Earth Science Videodisc, Unit 1, Side 1, "Sunny Days" Videotape Grade 6, Unit 4, "Sunny Days" Lab Activity Videotapes, Tape 4 Transparency 78, "Exploring the Sun"
UR 16-3 Section Lesson Plan, p. 193 UR 16-3 Section Summary, p. 194 UR 16-3 Review and Reinforce, p. 195 UR 16-3 Enrich, p. 196	SE Section 3 Review, p. 551 TE Ongoing Assessment, pp. 545, 547, 549 TE Performance Assessment, p. 551	Transparency 79, "Characteristics of the Inner Planets"
UR 16-4 Section Lesson Plan, p. 197 UR 16-4 Section Summary, p. 198 UR 16-4 Review and Reinforce, p. 199 UR 16-4 Enrich, p. 200 UR Skills Lab blackline masters, pp. 211–213	SE Section 4 Review, p. 559 TE Ongoing Assessment, pp. 553, 555, 557 TE Performance Assessment, p. 559	Transparency 80, "Characteristics of the Outer Planets"
UR 16-5 Section Lesson Plan, p. 201 UR 16-5 Section Summary, p. 202 UR 16-5 Review and Reinforce, p. 203 UR 16-5 Enrich, p. 204	SE Section 5 Review, p. 565 TE Ongoing Assessment, p. 563 TE Performance Assessment, p. 565	Transparency 81, "A Comet's Orbit"
UR 16-6 Section Lesson Plan, p. 205 UR 16-6 Section Summary, p. 206 UR 16-6 Review and Reinforce, p. 207 UR 16-6 Enrich, p. 208	SE Section 6 Review, p. 569 TE Ongoing Assessment, p. 567 TE Performance Assessment, p. 569	Transparency 82, "Rocket Motion"
ELL Provides multiple strategies for English language learners GRSW Provides worksheets to promote student comprehension of content RCA Provides strategies to improve science reading skills	SE Chapter 16 Study Guide/Assessment, pp. 571–573 PA Chapter 16 Assessment, pp. 50–52 CUT Chapter 16 Test, pp. 76–79 CTB Chapter 16 Test PHAS Provides standardized test preparation	Chapter 16 Computer Test Bank, Chapter 16 Test

GRSW Guided Reading and Study Workbook
ISAB Inquiry Skills Activity Book
LM Laboratory Manual

PA Performance Assessment
PHAS Prentice Hall Assessment System
PLM Probeware Lab Manual

RCA Reading in the Content Area
SE Student Edition

TE Teacher's Edition
UR Unit Resources

Student Edition Activities Planner

ACTIVITY	Time (minutes)	Materials Quantities for one work group	Skills
Section 1			
Discover, p. 532	10	**Nonconsumable** toy trucks, rocks	Predicting
Try This, p. 535	15	**Consumable** white paper, corrugated cardboard **Nonconsumable** 2 pushpins, ruler, pencil, 30-cm string	Predicting
Science at Home, p. 537	home	**Consumable** common materials, such as clay and straws	Making Models
Section 2			
Discover, p. 538	15	**Consumable** thin cardboard, masking tape, white paper **Nonconsumable** binoculars, ring stand, ruler, scissors	Observing
Try This, p. 540	10/day	**Consumable** thin cardboard, masking tape, white paper **Nonconsumable** binoculars, ring stand, ruler, scissors	Interpreting Data
Real-World Lab, p. 543	30	**Consumable** graph paper **Nonconsumable** pencil, straight edge, computer (optional)	Graphing, Interpreting Data
Section 3			
Discover, p. 544	10	**Nonconsumable** compass, ruler	Observing
Sharpen Your Skills, p. 547	15	**Consumable** graph paper **Nonconsumable** colored pencils	Graphing
Sharpen Your Skills, p. 549	20	**Consumable** paper **Nonconsumable** telescope, colored pencils	Observing
Try This, p. 550	15	**Consumable** tape, paper **Nonconsumable** goggles	Inferring
Section 4			
Discover, p. 552	15	**Consumable** lined paper, butcher paper or poster board, string **Nonconsumable** quarter, ruler, compass, push pin	Classifying
Try This, p. 555	20	**Consumable** clear plastic sheet, tape, baking soda, peppercorn, glue (optional) **Nonconsumable** 8-cm plastic foam sphere, ruler, scissors, compass, 5 toothpicks	Making Models
Skills Lab, p. 560–561	45	**Consumable** string, 1.5 m **Nonconsumable** one-hole rubber stopper; plastic tube, 6 cm; stopwatch; meterstick; weight or several washers	Developing Hypotheses
Section 5			
Discover, p. 562	10	**Consumable** 3 10-cm lengths of string **Nonconsumable** modeling clay, pencil, small fan	Inferring
Science at Home, p. 565	home	**Nonconsumable** newspapers or almanacs	Observing
Section 6			
Discover, p. 566	10	**Nonconsumable** balloons, safety goggles	Observing
Try This, p. 568	20	**Consumable** plastic or paper cup, paper tape, film canister with a lid that snaps on inside the canister, water, fizzing antacid table **Nonconsumable** safety goggles	Observing
Science at Home, p. 569	home	No special materials are required.	Communicating

A list of all materials required for the Student Edition activities can be found on pages T43–T49. You can obtain information about ordering materials by calling 1-800-848-9500 or by accessing the Science Explorer Internet site at **www.phschool.com**.

Texas Essential Knowledge and Skills

(6.1) Scientific processes. The student conducts field and laboratory investigations using safe, environmentally appropriate, and ethical practices. *(Sections 1, 2, 3, 4, 5, 6)*
The student is expected to:
(A) demonstrate safe practices during field and laboratory investigations.

(6.2) Scientific processes. The student uses scientific inquiry methods during field and laboratory investigations. *(Project; Sections 1, 2, 3, 4)*
The student is expected to:
(A) plan and implement investigative procedures including asking questions, formulating testable hypotheses, and selecting and using equipment and technology;
(B) collect data by observing and measuring;
(C) analyze and interpret information to construct reasonable explanations from direct and indirect evidence; and
(E) construct graphs, tables, maps, and charts using tools including computers to organize, examine, and evaluate data.

(6.3) Scientific processes. The student uses critical thinking and scientific problem solving to make informed decisions. *(Project; Sections 1, 3, 4, 5)*
The student is expected to:
(A) analyze, review, and critique scientific explanations, including hypotheses and theories, as to their strengths and weaknesses using scientific evidence and information;
(C) represent the natural world using models and identify their limitations;
(D) evaluate the impact of research on scientific thought, society, and the environment; and
(E) connect Grade 6 science concepts with the history of science and contributions of scientists.

(6.4) Scientific processes. The student knows how to use a variety of tools and methods to conduct science inquiry. *(Sections 2, 3, 4, 5, 6)*
The student is expected to:
(A) collect, analyze, and record information using tools including beakers, petri dishes, meter sticks, graduated cylinders, weather instruments, timing devices, hot plates, test tubes, safety goggles, spring scales, magnets, balances, microscopes, telescopes, thermometers, calculators, field equipment, compasses, computers, and computer probes; and
(B) identify patterns in collected information using percent, average, range, and frequency.

(6.5) Scientific concepts. The student knows that systems may combine with other systems to form a larger system. *(Sections 1, 5)*
The student is expected to:
(A) identify and describe a system that results from the combination of two or more systems such as in the solar system.

(6.6) Science concepts. The student knows that there is a relationship between force and motion. *(Section 6)*
The student is expected to:
(A) identify and describe the changes in position, direction of motion, and speed of an object when acted upon by force.

(6.13) Science concepts. The student knows components of our solar system. *(Sections 1, 2, 3, 4, 5, 6)*
The student is expected to:
(A) identify characteristics of objects in our solar system including the Sun, planets, meteorites, comets, asteroids, and moons; and
(B) describe types of equipment and transportation needed for space travel.

Take It to the Net

 Interactive text at www.phschool.com

Science Explorer comes alive with iText.

- **Complete student text** is accessible from any computer with Internet access or a CD-ROM drive.

- **Animations, simulations, and videos** enhance student understanding and retention of concepts.

- **Self-tests and online study tools** assess student understanding.

- **Teacher management tools** help you make the most of this valuable resource.

STAY CURRENT with **SCIENCE NEWS**®

Find out the latest research and information about space science at **www.phschool.com**.

Go to **www.phschool.com**. Select Texas on the navigation bar. Click on the Science icon. Then click on <u>Science Explorer</u> under PH@school.

Model of the Solar System

TEKS: 6.2E; 6.3C

Movies, books, and television shows have given most people a distorted understanding of the sizes of objects and distances between objects in the solar system. The Chapter Project will help students understand that the distances between the planets are very large relative to the sizes of the planets.

Purpose By creating scale models of the solar system, students will begin to understand the vastness of space, including the size of planets and the great distances between them. They will also discover difficulties in scaling the size of objects and distance between objects into the same scale measurements.

Skills Focus After completing the Chapter 16 project, students will be able to
◆ convert large numbers to the established scale;
◆ compare scaled distances and diameters to familiar distances and diameters;
◆ establish scale models to show the actual size of the solar system;
◆ discover why it can be difficult to build a scale model of the solar system's distance.

Suggested Shortcuts Allow students to do the mathematical calculations in groups. Since many distances in the solar system are given in astronomical units, an easy way to establish a scale is to let 1 AU = 1 m. Students can then brainstorm familiar objects that are comparable to the estimated planet sizes. If students have not had much experience with scaling, provide in-class time to assist students. You may decide to allow students to build the models in groups, or as a whole-class project.

Project Time Line This project requires about four weeks. Students will work on a different model each week, and the final week will be reserved for presentation preparation. Models should be completed sequentially, beginning with the planet sizes, then moving to the distance between the planets, and ending with the combination model. Students should complete the appropriate portion

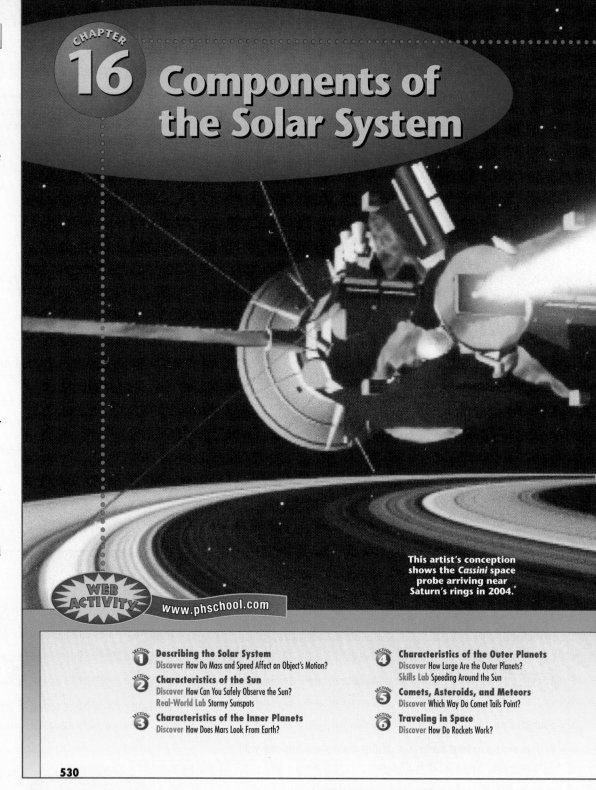

This artist's conception shows the *Cassini* space probe arriving near Saturn's rings in 2004.

WEB ACTIVITY www.phschool.com

1 Describing the Solar System
Discover How Do Mass and Speed Affect an Object's Motion?

2 Characteristics of the Sun
Discover How Can You Safely Observe the Sun?
Real-World Lab Stormy Sunspots

3 Characteristics of the Inner Planets
Discover How Does Mars Look From Earth?

4 Characteristics of the Outer Planets
Discover How Large Are the Outer Planets?
Skills Lab Speeding Around the Sun

5 Comets, Asteroids, and Meteors
Discover Which Way Do Comet Tails Point?

6 Traveling in Space
Discover How Do Rockets Work?

530

of the worksheets and get approval from you before they begin each phase of model building. The project should end with the presentations and a class discussion. Before beginning the project, see Chapter 16 Project Teacher Notes on pages 178–179 in Unit 4 Resources for more details on carrying out the project. Also, distribute the students' Chapter 16 Project Overview and Worksheets and Scoring Rubric on pages 180–184 in Unit 4 Resources.

Possible Materials For model building, students will need meter sticks or metric rulers and calculators. Since models of solar system distance usually involve large numbers, students may also need maps of their local community. Familiar objects such as tennis balls, beach balls, pieces of fruit (grapefruit, orange, etc.), marbles, dried beans, and ball bearings will make good planets, depending on the required diameters.

CHAPTER 16 PROJECT

Model of the Solar System

If you could drive from Earth to the sun at 100 kilometers per hour, your trip would take 170 years. And most distances in the solar system are even greater! The *Cassini* space probe left Earth for Saturn in 1997 traveling much faster than highway speed, but will not arrive at Saturn's rings until 2004. Sizes in the solar system can be huge, too. Compared with some of the other planets in the solar system, Earth is very small. Saturn, for example, is about 10 times Earth's diameter.

In this chapter, you will get to know many of the objects in the solar system. To help you understand the huge distances and sizes, you will design three different scale models of the solar system.

Your Goal To design scale models of the solar system.

To complete this project, you will
- design a model to show the planets' distances from the sun
- design a model to show the planets' sizes relative to the sun
- test different scales to see if you can use the same scale for both size and distance in one model

Get Started Begin by previewing the tables with distances and diameters on pages 545 and 553. Brainstorm with a group of classmates how you will build your models. Prepare a data sheet to record your calculations of scaled-down distances and diameters.

Check Your Progress You will be working on this project as you study this chapter. To keep your project on track, look for Check Your Progress boxes at the following points.

Section 2 Review, page 542: Design a model to show distances.
Section 3 Review, page 551: Design a model to show diameters.
Section 4 Review, page 559: Design one scale model that shows both sizes and distances.

Present Your Project At the end of the chapter (page 573), you will present your design to the class.

 TEKS

In addition to process TEKS, this chapter addresses these concept TEKS as they relate to the chapter's topics.

(6.5) Science concepts. The student knows that systems may combine with other systems to form a larger system. The student is expected to:
(A) identify and describe a system that results from the combination of two or more systems such as in the solar system.

(6.6) Science concepts. The student knows that there is a relationship between force and motion. The student is expected to:
(A) identify and describe the changes in position, direction of motion, and speed of an object when acted upon by force.

(6.13) Science concepts. The student knows components of our solar system. The student is expected to:
(A) identify characteristics of objects in our solar system including the Sun, planets, meteorites, comets, asteroids, and moons; and
(B) describe types of equipment and transportation needed for space travel.

531

Program Resources

- **Unit 4 Resources** Chapter 16 Project Teacher Notes, pp. 178–179; Chapter 16 Project Overview and Worksheets, pp. 180–183

Media and Technology

Student Edition on Audio CD
English-Spanish, Chapter 16

 **WEB ACTIVITY** www.phschool.com

You will find an Internet activity, chapter self-tests for students, and links to other chapter topics at this site.

A video entitled *The Powers of Ten* may help students do their calculations. Also available is a solar system chart that provides relative sizes, distances, orbits, and data about the planets and their place in the galaxy.

Launching the Project When introducing the project, bring in a scale model of an object familiar to all students (e.g., the Statue of Liberty). Ask: **How does the size of this model compare to the real object?** Discuss scaling. Take measurements of features of the model, and compare these to measurements of features on the actual object. If the model is proportional, the scaling should be the same for each measurement taken. Ask: **How big is Earth?** Discuss size. If you travel once around Earth, you would cover about 40,000 km. The United States is about 4,000 km across. It takes at least four or five days to make this journey by car, yet this is only 1/10 the distance around the Earth! Ask: **How could you compare size and distance in space with travel speeds on Earth?** Compare average travel speeds. *(Walking 3.6 km/hr, car 80 km/hr, jet 1,436 km/hr, light 300,000 km/sec)* Since the distance from Earth to the moon is about 386,000 km, it takes about 1.5 sec for light to travel this distance. Ask students how long it would take a jet to fly there.

Give students time to read about the project in their text and in the Chapter Project Overview on pages 180–181 in Unit 4 Resources. Pass out copies of the Project Worksheets on pages 182–183 in Unit 4 Resources.

Performance Assessment

The Chapter 16 Project Scoring Rubric on page 184 of Unit 4 Resources will help you evaluate how well students complete the Chapter 16 Project. Students will be assessed on
- how accurately they did their mathematical calculations;
- how well they selected model scales;
- how well they can discuss the concepts of size and scaling;
- the thoroughness and organization of their presentation.

By sharing the Chapter 16 Project Scoring Rubric with students when they start the project, they will learn what they are expected to do.

SECTION 1 — Describing the Solar System

SECTION 1 — Describing the Solar System

TEKS: 6.1A; 6.2C; 6.3A, C, D, E; 6.5A; 6.13A

Objectives

After completing the lesson, students will be able to

◆ explain how the heliocentric and geocentric models of the solar system differ;

◆ identify and explain the two factors that keep planets in their orbits;

◆ describe what combines to form our solar system.

1 Engage/Explore

Activating Prior Knowledge

Show students a photograph of the night sky that shows stars and the moon. Ask them to identify the objects they see. Then ask: **Where was the sun when this picture was taken?** (*The sun could not be seen from the spot where the picture was taken because it was on the other side of Earth.*) Reinforce the idea that the objects in our solar system are moving.

⋯⋯ DISCOVER ⋯⋯

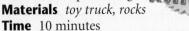

Skills Focus predicting
Materials *toy truck, rocks*
Time 10 minutes
Tips A toy car, roller skate, or skateboard may be substituted for the truck. Remind students to push the truck gently at first. When they add rocks to the truck, students should be careful not to pile them so high that they fall out when the truck is pushed.
Expected Outcome Students should observe that it is harder to stop the truck when the truck is moving faster and when it has more mass.
Think It Over It would be easier to stop the truck if the partner pushed it more slowly. It would be harder to stop the truck if more mass was added.

DISCOVER ⋯⋯⋯⋯⋯⋯⋯⋯ ACTIVITY

How Do Mass and Speed Affect an Object's Motion?

1. Have your partner push a toy truck across the table toward you. Stop the truck with your hands.

2. Repeat Step 1, but have your partner push the truck a little faster. Was it easier or harder to stop the truck than in Step 1?

3. Now add some rocks or other heavy objects to the truck and repeat Step 1. Your partner should push the truck at the same speed as in Step 1. How hard was it to stop the truck this time compared to Step 1?

4. Repeat Step 2 with the rocks still in the truck. How hard was it to stop the truck this time?

Think It Over
Predicting How hard would it be to stop the truck if your partner pushed it more slowly? If you added more mass to the truck?

GUIDE FOR READING

◆ How do the geocentric and heliocentric descriptions of the solar system differ?

◆ What two factors keep the planets in their orbits?

◆ What combines to form our solar system?

Reading Tip As you read, make a list of the evidence that supports the heliocentric system.

Key Terms geocentric system
• heliocentric system
• solar system • ellipse • inertia
• gravity

Have you ever lain outdoors on a starry night, gazing up at the stars? As you watch, the stars seem to move across the sky. The sky seems to be rotating right over your head. In fact, from the Northern Hemisphere, the sky appears to rotate around a point near Polaris, the North Star, once every 24 hours.

Now think about what you see every day. During the day, the sun appears to move across the sky. From here on Earth, it seems as if Earth is stationary and that the sun, moon, and stars are all moving around Earth. But is the sky really moving above you? Centuries ago, before there were space shuttles or even telescopes, there was no easy way to find out.

Figure 1 This photo was made by exposing the camera film for several hours. Each star appears as part of a circle, and all the stars seem to revolve around a single point.

READING STRATEGIES

Reading Tip Students should list such evidence as Galileo's observation of the phases of Venus and the moons of Jupiter. After students have read the section, have them work in groups to compare their lists.

Study and Comprehension As students read the section, have them write brief summaries of the information under each heading. Remind students that summarizing involves stating briefly, in their own words, the main points and key details. In a class discussion, invite volunteers to give oral summaries of the information in the section.

Wandering Stars

When the ancient Greeks watched the stars move across the sky, they noticed that the patterns of most of the stars didn't change. Although the stars seemed to move, they stayed in the same position relative to one another.

As they observed the sky more carefully, the Greeks noticed something surprising. Five points of light seemed to wander among the stars. The Greeks called these objects *planets*, from the Greek word meaning "wandering star." The Greeks made very careful observations of the motions of the five planets they could see. You know these planets by the names the ancient Romans later gave them: Mercury, Venus, Mars, Jupiter, and Saturn.

Greek Ideas: Earth at the Center

When you look up at the sky, you can almost imagine that you are under a rotating dome with the stars pasted on it. The Greeks thought that they were inside a rotating dome they called the celestial sphere. Many ancient Greeks believed that the universe is perfect and has boundaries, and that Earth is stationary in the center of the universe. Because *geo* is the Greek word for Earth, an Earth-centered system is known as a **geocentric** (jee oh SEN trik) **system. A system is a group of parts that work together as a unit. Earth is at the center of the revolving planets in a geocentric system.**

In A.D. 140, the Greek astronomer Ptolemy (TAHL uh mee) explained the motion of the planets in another way. Like the earlier Greeks, Ptolemy believed in a geocentric system with Earth at the center of the system of planets. Ptolemy also thought that the moon, Mercury, Venus, the sun, Mars, Jupiter, and Saturn revolve around Earth.

In Ptolemy's explanation, however, the planets move on little circles that move on bigger circles. Ptolemy thought that this explained why the planets seem to move at different speeds, and even backwards, among the stars. For the next 1,400 years, people believed that Ptolemy's ideas were correct.

☑ *Checkpoint* What is a geocentric system?

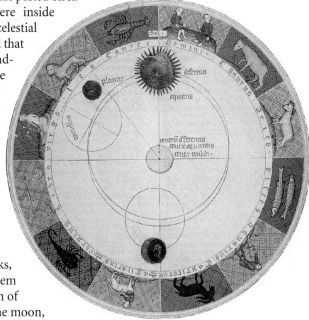

Figure 2 In the 1500s, an astronomy book published this illustration of Ptolemy's system. *Interpreting Diagrams Where is Earth located in this illustration?*

Program Resources

◆ **Unit 4 Resources** 16-1 Lesson Plan, p. 185; 16-1 Section Summary, p. 186
◆ **Guided Reading and Study Workbook** 16-1

Answers to Self-Assessment

Caption Question

Figure 2 Earth is in the center.

☑ *Checkpoint*

A geocentric system is one in which Earth is at the center of a system of revolving planets.

2 Facilitate

Wandering Stars

Building Inquiry Skills: Inferring

Guide students in evaluating what the ancient astronomers knew about stars. Ask: **Why did the Greeks only see five planets?** *(They did not have telescopes and could not see the other planets because they are too dim.)* **learning modality: verbal**

Greek Ideas: Earth at the Center

Cultural Diversity

Remind students that the Romans named the planets they knew after their gods. Tell them that other cultures gave objects in the sky names that were meaningful in those cultures. Ask students from other cultures to give examples of such names from their cultures. **learning modality: verbal**

Using the Visuals: Figure 1

Ask students to infer why exposing the film for several hours produced the circular effect shown in the figure. If they have difficulty, ask: **What is the single point around which the stars seem to revolve?** *(Polaris or the North Star)* Remind students that in the Northern Hemisphere, the stars seem to rotate around a point near the North Star. Leaving the camera shutter open as this rotation occurs produces the circular effect. **learning modality: visual**

Ongoing Assessment

Drawing Have students draw and label a diagram of a geocentric system. The diagram should include the sun, Earth, and at least one other planet.

Copernicus's Idea: Sun at the Center

Building Inquiry Skills: Comparing and Contrasting

Have students diagram Copernicus's heliocentric model and then compare their diagram with the geocentric model in Figure 2. Ask: **How does Earth's motion differ in each system?** (*Geocentric—Earth is not moving; heliocentric—Earth rotates on its axis and revolves around the sun*) **How does the motion of planets differ in each system?** (*Geocentric—planets revolve around Earth; heliocentric—all planets revolve around the sun*) **learning modality: logical/mathematical**

 Students can save their diagrams in their portfolios.

Galileo's Observations

Including All Students

Invite students who need additional challenges to research the phases of Venus in an astronomy textbook or other reference book. Students can draw diagrams to show how the sun, Earth, and Venus are aligned as Venus passes through its phases. Students can present their diagrams to the class. **learning modality: visual**

Copernicus's Idea: Sun at the Center

In the early 1500s, the Polish astronomer Nicolaus Copernicus developed another explanation for the motions of the planets. Copernicus thought that the sun is at the center of the system of planets. His sun-centered system is called a **heliocentric** (hee lee oh SEN trik) **system.** *Helios* is Greek for "sun." **In a heliocentric system, Earth and the other planets revolve around the sun.** Copernicus's explanation included the six planets he knew about: Mercury, Venus, Earth, Mars, Jupiter, and Saturn.

Galileo's Observations

In the 1500s and 1600s, most people still believed Ptolemy's geocentric explanation. However, the Italian astronomer Galileo Galilei, who lived nearly 100 years after Copernicus, thought that the heliocentric explanation was correct.

Galileo was the first scientist to use a telescope to look at objects in the sky. With his telescope, Galileo made two discoveries that supported the heliocentric model. First, Galileo saw four moons revolving around Jupiter. Galileo's observations of Jupiter's moons showed that not everything in the sky revolves around Earth.

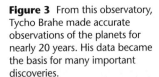
Figure 3 From this observatory, Tycho Brahe made accurate observations of the planets for nearly 20 years. His data became the basis for many important discoveries.

Galileo's observations of Venus also supported Copernicus's heliocentric system. Galileo discovered that Venus goes through phases similar to those of Earth's moon. Galileo reasoned that the phases of Venus could not be explained if Earth were at the center of the system of planets. So Ptolemy's geocentric system could not be correct.

Galileo's evidence gradually convinced others that Copernicus's explanation was correct. Today, people refer to the **solar system** rather than the "Earth system." This shows that people accept Copernicus's idea that the sun is at the center of a system of planets.

☑ *Checkpoint* *What two discoveries made by Galileo supported the heliocentric description of the solar system?*

Brahe and Kepler

Copernicus and Galileo had correctly identified the sun as the center of the solar system. But Copernicus, like Ptolemy, assumed that the orbits of the planets are circles.

Copernicus's ideas were based on observations made by the ancient Greeks. In the late 1500s, Tycho Brahe (TEE koh BRAH uh), a Danish astronomer, made

---

Background

History of Science Johannes Kepler believed the universe contained many profound mathematical patterns and relationships. One of his life-long endeavors was to identify a relationship between the mathematics of the movement of the planets around the sun and the mathematics of musical sound. Kepler compared the mathematics of many aspects of planetary motion to musical harmonies before asserting that he had discovered a clear relationship. In his book *Harmonice Mundi* (The Harmony of the World), Kepler assigned a range of sounds to each planet. Modern scientists do not accept Kepler's musical theories. However, his research may have led him to discover the relationship between the speed of a planet and its distance from the sun, a concept published in the same book.

much more accurate observations. Brahe carefully observed the positions of the planets for almost 20 years.

In 1600, a German mathematician, Johannes Kepler, went to work analyzing Brahe's data. Kepler tried to figure out the shape of the planets' orbits. At first, he assumed that the orbits are circles. When Kepler tried to figure out the exact orbit of Mars, however, no circle fit the observations.

Kepler had discovered that the orbit of each planet is an ellipse. An **ellipse** is an elongated circle, or oval shape. Kepler found that if he assumed that Mars's orbit is an ellipse, his calculations fit Brahe's observations better.

Inertia and Gravity

Kepler had discovered the correct shape of the planets' orbits. But he could not explain why the planets stay in orbit. The English scientist Isaac Newton did. **Newton concluded that two factors—inertia and gravity—combine to keep the planets in orbit.**

Galileo had discovered that a moving object will continue to move until some force acts to stop its motion. This tendency of a moving object to continue in a straight line or a stationary object to remain in place is the object's **inertia.** The more mass an object has, the more inertia it has. An object with greater inertia is more difficult to start or stop.

Isaac Newton picked up where Galileo had left off. Late in his life, Newton told the story of how watching an apple fall from a tree in 1665 had made him think about motion. He hypothesized that the same force that pulls the apple to the ground also pulls the moon toward Earth. This force, called **gravity,** attracts all objects toward one another. The strength of gravity depends on the masses of the objects and the distance between them.

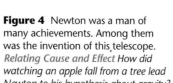

Figure 4 Newton was a man of many achievements. Among them was the invention of this telescope. *Relating Cause and Effect How did watching an apple fall from a tree lead Newton to his hypothesis about gravity?*

A Loopy Ellipse

You can draw an ellipse.

ACTIVITY

1. ✂ Carefully stick two pushpins about 10 cm apart through a sheet of white paper on top of corrugated cardboard.

2. Tie the ends of a 30-cm piece of string together. Place the string around the pushpins.

3. Keeping the string tight, move a pencil around inside the string.

4. Now place the pushpins 5 cm apart. Repeat Step 3.

Predicting How does changing the distance between the pushpins affect the ellipse's shape? What shape would you draw if you used only one pushpin?

Brahe and Kepler

Building Inquiry Skills: Inferring

To help students understand elliptical orbits, diagram a planet and its orbit on the board. Challenge students to infer why scientists record a planet's average distance from the sun. Ask: **In an elliptical orbit, what happens to the distance between the planet and the sun?** *(It changes as the planet revolves.)* Have a volunteer point out where on the diagram the planet is closest and where it is farthest from the sun. Tell students that Earth is closest to the sun in the Northern Hemisphere winter. Ask: **What effect does the distance from the sun have on Earth's temperature?** *(The distance from the sun has little noticeable effect on Earth's temperature.)* **learning modality: visual**

TRY THIS

Skills Focus predicting
Materials *2 pushpins, white paper, corrugated cardboard, ruler, 30-cm string, pencil*
ACTIVITY
Time 15 minutes
Tips Provide students with pieces of cardboard the same size as a sheet of paper. Remind students to keep the string taut when drawing their lines.
Expected Outcome Students should predict that moving the pushpins closer together makes the ellipse more round. If they used only one pushpin, they would draw a circle.
Extend Challenge students to predict the shape of ellipses formed with pushpins 2.5 cm and 7.5 cm apart. Encourage them to test their predictions.
learning modality: tactile/kinesthetic

Answers to Self-Assessment

✓ *Checkpoint*

Four moons revolve around the planet Jupiter. Venus goes through phases similar to those of Earth's moon.

Caption Question

Figure 4 It made Newton think about motion. He hypothesized that the same force that pulled the apple to the ground also pulls the moon toward Earth.

Ongoing Assessment

Writing Have students write a paragraph explaining in their own words the contributions made to the heliocentric model by Copernicus, Galileo, Kepler, and Newton.

Mercury 58,000,000 km
Venus 108,000,000 km
Earth 150,000,000 km
Mars 228,000,000 km

Jupiter
778,000,000 km

Saturn
1,427,000,000 km

Inertia and Gravity

Using the Visuals: Figure 5

As students examine the figure, have them trace the path the planet would take if the sun's gravity disappeared. (*The planet would continue to move in a straight path in the direction it was going when the gravity disappeared.*) **learning modality: visual**

Smaller Systems Inside

Addressing Naive Conceptions

Explain to students that it is difficult to accurately represent the sizes and distances of objects in the solar system on a diagram such as Figure 6. If the sun and the planets were drawn to the same scale as the distances on the diagram, the sun would be a tiny dot about 0.10 mm in diameter and the planets would all be microscopic. On the other hand, if the distances were drawn to the same scale as the sizes of the planets, the diagram would have to be about 1.0 km wide! **learning modality: visual**

Real-Life Learning

In 1982, all of the planets were within 95° of each other as viewed from the sun. This alignment caused some sensationalist newspapers and books to predict earthquakes and global disasters. Assign students to groups of four. Have each group develop an explanation of why this kind of planetary alignment could never cause any noticeable effects on Earth. (*Gravity from the planets is far too weak.*) **cooperative learning**

Building Inquiry Skills: Graphing

To compare the distances between the planets and the sun, students can make a bar graph using the data in Figure 6. The *x*-axis should show the names of the planets and the *y*-axis should show the distance from the sun. Help students choose the intervals for the *y*-axis. They may want to have 1 cm equal 500 million km. **learning modality: logical/ mathematical**

Newton figured out that Earth keeps pulling the moon toward it with gravity. At the same time, the moon keeps moving ahead because of its inertia. The force of Earth's gravity and the inertia of the moon combine to keep the moon in its orbit around Earth.

In the same way, the planets are in orbit around the sun because the sun's gravity pulls on them while their inertia keeps them moving ahead. Therefore, the planets keep moving around the sun and end up in orbit.

Smaller Systems Inside

Since Newton's time, knowledge of the solar system has increased. Newton only knew about six planets—Mercury, Venus, Earth, Mars, Jupiter, and Saturn. Now astronomers know about three more planets—Uranus, Neptune, and Pluto. Just like Earth has a

Figure 5 If there were no force of gravity, inertia would make a planet travel in a straight line. But because gravity pulls the planet toward the sun, the planet actually travels in an elliptical orbit around the sun. *Interpreting Diagrams What would happen if a planet had no inertia?*

Force of gravity

Planet

Actual orbit

Planet's motion without gravity

536

536

Background

Facts and Figures The planets of our solar system have been studied by spacecraft with one exception—Pluto. In 1991, employees of the Jet Propulsion Laboratory met with stamp collectors to view a new series of stamps showing planets and the spacecraft that had explored them. The stamp depicting Pluto said "Not Yet Explored." Challenged by this, JPL employees decided to develop a spacecraft to explore Pluto.

Because of this decision, NASA is now planning a robotic reconnaissance mission to Pluto and its moon Charon called the *Pluto-Kuiper Express*. The plan calls for two vehicles that will be launched around 2001 and fly past Pluto around 2010. If the mission to Pluto is successful, the spacecraft may continue beyond Pluto to the Kuiper Belt of minor planets, called *ice dwarfs*.

 Uranus
2,871,000,000 km

Neptune
4,497,000,000 km

Pluto
5,913,000,000 km

Figure 6 This illustration shows the average distances of the planets from the sun. The sizes of the planets and the sun are not to scale.

moon orbiting around it, many other planets have moons that revolve around them. Each planet and its moons form a small system. These systems combine with each other to form the larger solar system. Astronomers have also identified many other objects in the solar system, such as comets and asteroids, that you will learn about later in this chapter. **The solar system is a large system that consists of a combination of many smaller systems and objects.**

Galileo and Newton used telescopes on Earth to observe the smaller systems that make up the solar system. Astronomers still use telescopes on Earth, but they have also made close-up observations of the planets from space probes sent far into the solar system. Because of such exciting research, our understanding of the solar system continues to change. Who knows what new discoveries will be made in your lifetime!

 ## Section 1 Review

1. How is Copernicus's description of the system of planets different from Ptolemy's description?
2. What two factors act together to keep the planets in orbit around the sun?
3. What smaller systems combine to make the solar system?
4. **Thinking Critically** **Applying Concepts** People usually say that the sun rises in the east, moves across the sky, and sets in the west. Is this description actually correct? Explain.

Science at Home

Heliocentric vs. Geocentric Use materials in your home, such as clay and straws, to make models of Ptolemy's geocentric solar system and Copernicus's heliocentric solar system. Use the models to explain the two hypotheses for a family member. Discuss how Galileo's observations supported Copernicus's idea of a heliocentric solar system.

Program Resources

◆ **Unit 4 Resources** 16-1 Review and Reinforce, p. 187; 16-1 Enrich, p. 188

Media and Technology

 Transparencies "Planet Motion," Transparency 77

Answers to Self-Assessment

Caption Question
Figure 5 The planet would be pulled into the sun.

Section 1 Review Answers

1. Ptolemy thought that Earth was in the center of the system of planets. The other planets, the moon, and the sun all revolve around Earth. Copernicus thought that the sun was in the middle of Earth's orbit, and that the other planets revolved around the sun in circular orbits.
2. Gravity and inertia act together to keep the planets in orbit.
3. Each planet and its moons form small systems that combine to make the solar system.
4. No. Earth is rotating from west to east. This causes the sun to appear to move across the sky in the opposite direction.

Science at Home

Encourage students to be creative in the design of their models, using materials they have on hand. Suggest that students share their models and explanations with family, friends, and classmates by organizing a neighborhood science fair.

Performance Assessment

Skills Check Have students create concept maps that illustrate the relationships among the following: Kepler, Ptolemy, Newton, Galileo, heliocentric, elliptical orbit, geocentric, inertia, and gravity.

SECTION 2 Characteristics of the Sun

TEKS: 6.1A; 6.2B, C, E; 6.4A; 6.13A

Objectives

After completing the lesson, students will be able to
◆ describe how the sun produces energy;
◆ list and describe the layers of the sun's atmosphere;
◆ identify features of the sun's surface.

1 Engage/Explore

Activating Prior Knowledge

Invite students who have gotten sunburned to tell about their experiences. Encourage all students to imagine going outside on a clear, hot day and feeling the warmth of the sun. Then ask: **What do we receive from the sun?** (*Samples: Light, heat*)

DISCOVER .... ACTIVITY

Skills Focus observing
Materials *binoculars, ring stand, ruler, thin cardboard, scissors, masking tape, white paper*
Time 15 minutes
Tips If binoculars are not available, make a pinhole in a sheet of cardboard and project the sun's image through the hole onto the white paper. (If the pinhole is made very small, sometimes larger sunspots will be visible.) CAUTION: *Students must never look directly at the sun.* A small telescope can also be used to project the image. CAUTION: *The image of the sun focused to a point by a small telescope can cause burns and ignite paper.*
Think It Over Students should see a large bright circle. They may also see and draw sunspots.

DISCOVER .... ACTIVITY

How Can You Safely Observe the Sun?

1. Clamp a pair of binoculars to a ring stand.

2. ✂ Cut a hole in a 20-cm by 28-cm sheet of thin cardboard so that it will fit over the binoculars, as shown in the photo. The cardboard should cover one lens, but allow light through the other lens. Tape the cardboard on securely. **CAUTION:** *Never look directly at the sun. You will hurt your eyes if you do.*

3. Use the binoculars to project an image of the sun onto a sheet of white paper. The cardboard will shade the paper. Change the focus and move the paper back and forth until you get a sharp image.

Think It Over
Observing Draw what you see on the paper. What do you see on the surface of the sun?

GUIDE FOR READING

◆ How does the sun get its energy?
◆ What are the layers of the sun's atmosphere?
◆ What are some features of the sun's surface?

Reading Tip As you read, write a sentence defining each boldfaced term in your own words.

Key Terms nuclear fusion
• core • photosphere
• chromosphere • corona
• solar wind • sunspot
• prominence • solar flare

The sun's gravity is by far the most powerful force in the solar system—strong enough to hold all of the planets and comets in orbit! The sun's gravity is so strong because the sun's mass is very large. In fact, 99.8 percent of the mass of the solar system is in the sun.

Like Earth, the sun has an interior and an atmosphere. Unlike Earth, however, the sun does not have a solid surface. The sun is a ball of glowing gas. About three fourths of the sun's mass is hydrogen, one fourth is helium, and very small amounts are other chemical elements.

The Sun's Interior

The interior of the sun is like a giant furnace. Like furnaces in houses, the sun produces energy. But the sun does not get its energy from burning fuels such as oil. **Instead, the sun's energy comes from nuclear fusion.** In the process of **nuclear fusion,** hydrogen atoms join together to form helium. Nuclear fusion occurs only under conditions of extremely high temperature and pressure. The temperature inside the sun's **core,** or center, reaches about 15 million degrees Celsius, high enough for nuclear fusion to occur.

538

READING STRATEGIES

Reading Tip Some sentences that students may write about boldfaced terms may include, "The core is the inner part of the sun." and "The photosphere is the layer of the sun that makes light." After students have written their sentences, have them read aloud their definitions to partners. Encourage partners to discuss their definitions.

Program Resources

◆ **Unit 4 Resources** 16-2 Lesson Plan, p. 189; 16-2 Section Summary, p. 190
◆ **Guided Reading and Study Workbook** 16-2
◆ **Laboratory Manual** 16, "Measuring the Diameter of the Sun"

The total mass of the helium produced by nuclear fusion is slightly less than the total mass of the hydrogen that goes into it. The change in mass occurs because some of the matter is converted into energy, including light and heat. The light and heat gradually move from the core of the sun to its atmosphere and escape into space. Some of this light and heat reach Earth, becoming Earth's main source of energy.

There was enough hydrogen fuel in the core of the sun to last for a total of 10 billion years. The sun is now only about 5 billion years old, so you don't have to worry about the sun "burning out" any time soon!

☑ *Checkpoint* **Where in the sun does nuclear fusion occur?**

The Sun's Atmosphere

The sun's atmosphere has three layers: the photosphere, the chromosphere, and the corona. There are no boundaries between the layers of the sun.

The Photosphere The inner layer of the sun's atmosphere is called the **photosphere** (FOH tuh sfeer). The Greek word *photo* means "light," so *photosphere* means the sphere that makes light. When you look at an image or photograph of the sun, you are looking at the photosphere.

The Chromosphere During a total solar eclipse, the moon blocks light from the photosphere. The photosphere no longer provides the glare that keeps you from seeing the sun's faint, outer layers. At the beginning and end of a total eclipse, you can see a reddish glow just around the photosphere. This glow comes from the middle layer of the sun's atmosphere, the **chromosphere.** The Greek word *chromo* means "color," so the chromosphere is the "color sphere."

The Corona In the middle of a total solar eclipse, the moon also blocks light from the chromosphere. At these times an even fainter layer of the sun becomes visible, as you can see in Figure 7. This outer layer, which looks like a white halo around the sun, is called the **corona,** which means "crown" in Latin. From Earth's surface, the corona is only visible during eclipses or from special telescopes. But astronomers can use telescopes in space to observe the corona all the time and to study how it changes.

Figure 7 During a total solar eclipse, you can see light from the corona, the outer layer of the sun's atmosphere. *Inferring Why is it easiest to photograph the sun's outer layers during a solar eclipse?*

2 Facilitate

The Sun's Interior

Demonstration

Materials *2 large glass jars with lids, 2 plastic thermometers, black plastic, water-proof glue (hot glue works well)*
Time 45 minutes

🔧 Glue black plastic on one-half of the *inside* of each jar. Glue a plastic thermometer to the inside of each jar so it can be read without opening the jar. Fill the jars with cold water, leaving 1.0 cm for expansion, and cap tightly. Take the class outside and place one jar in a shady spot and the other in direct sun propped up so that sunlight fully illuminates the inside of the jar. Read the temperature of each jar every five minutes for thirty minutes. Back in the classroom, have students graph the temperature versus time for each container. Ask: **What happened to the temperature of the jars?** (*The shady jar may have gone up or down slightly; the sunny jar rose several degrees.*) **What caused the temperature to rise?** (*Energy from the sun*) **Where did this energy come from?** (*Nuclear fusion*). **learning modality: logical/mathematical**

The Sun's Atmosphere

Including All Students

Show students color photos of the sun at various stages of an eclipse. Encourage students to point out the photosphere, corona, and chromosphere.
learning modality: visual

Ongoing Assessment

Drawing Have students diagram the sun's interior and atmosphere, then label where nuclear fusion occurs and where the greatest production of light occurs.

539

Features on the Sun

Including All Students

The terms used to describe the sun's features may be difficult or unfamiliar for students whose native language is not English. However, all of the terms are descriptive so students can use word skills to analyze the meaning. Have students separate the terms *sunspot* and *solar flare* into their parts. Allow students to look up the words and word parts in the dictionary. Encourage students to explain how the terms help describe the features of the sun. **limited English proficiency**

Skills Focus interpreting data

Materials *binoculars, ring stand, ruler, thin cardboard, scissors, masking tape, white paper*

Time 10 minutes per day over 10 days

Tips Warn students not to look directly at the sun because sunlight can injure their eyes. Students should identify the variables they must control to get the best data. Suggest students look for sunspots two or three times per day for ten days. Their data tables should include the number of sunspots recorded at each interval as well as the average number of sunspots per day. After the first five days, have students predict how the average number of sunspots will change over the next five days. When their observations are complete, students can draw conclusions about the accuracy of their predictions.

Extend Have students compile class results and evaluate the class average for the number of sunspots observed in a ten-day period. Invite students whose findings vary from those of other students to explain why. **learning modality: logical/mathematical**

TRY THIS

Viewing Sunspots ACTIVITY

You can observe changes in the number of sunspots.

1. Make a data table to record the average number of sunspots you see each day.
2. Decide on a time to look for sunspots each day.
3. View the sun in the way described in the Discover activity. **CAUTION:** *Never look directly at the sun. You will hurt your eyes if you do.*
4. Make and record your observations.

Interpreting Data How much did the average number of sunspots change from day to day?

The corona sends out a stream of electrically charged particles called **solar wind.** Normally Earth's atmosphere and magnetic field block these particles. However, near the North and South poles, the particles can enter Earth's atmosphere, where they hit gas molecules and cause them to glow. The result is rippling sheets of light in the sky called auroras.

☑ *Checkpoint* *During what event could you see the sun's corona?*

Features on the Sun

For hundreds of years, scientists have used telescopes to look at the sun. (To protect their eyes, they used a filter or projected the sun onto a white surface, as in the Discover activity.) The dark spots that they saw on the sun's surface became known as sunspots. The spots seemed to move across the sun's surface, which showed that the sun rotates on its axis, just as Earth does. **Features on or above the sun's surface include sunspots, prominences, and solar flares.**

Sunspots As you can see in Figure 8, sunspots look like small, dark areas on the sun's surface. But in fact, they can be as large as Earth. **Sunspots** are areas of gas on the sun that are cooler than the gases around them. Cooler gases don't give off as much light as hotter gases, which is why sunspots look darker than the rest of the photosphere.

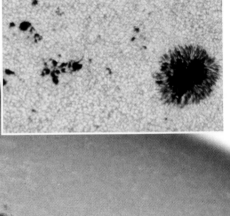

Figure 8 Sunspots are areas of gas on the sun that are cooler than the gas around them. Many of the sunspots in these photos are about as large as Earth.

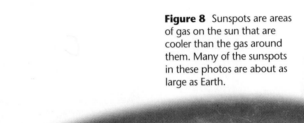

540

Background

Facts and Figures Some scientists think that the sunspot cycle influences weather on Earth. Among the evidence for this is the so-called Little Ice Age, which took place from about 1550 until 1850. During this time, most parts of the world experienced cooler and harsher weather.

The Little Ice Age has been associated with a period of low sunspot activity between 1645 and 1715. This period is called the Maunder minimum after the English astronomer who described it. Sunspots were first detected about 1600, but there are few recorded sightings during the Maunder minimum. Sunspots sightings resumed after 1715.

There is evidence that such times of low sunspot activity occur about every 500 years. Perhaps another Little Ice Age will begin in 2050.

The number of sunspots on the sun varies over a period of 10 or 11 years. Some scientists have hypothesized that short-term changes in climate on Earth may be related to sunspot cycles. Satellites have recently collected data that show that the amount of energy the sun produces changes slightly from year to year. Some scientists think that these increases and decreases, which may be linked to the number of sunspots, may cause changes in Earth's temperature. Scientists need to make more observations in order to test this hypothesis.

EXPLORING *the Sun*

The diameter of the sun (not including the chromosphere and the corona) is 1.4 million kilometers.

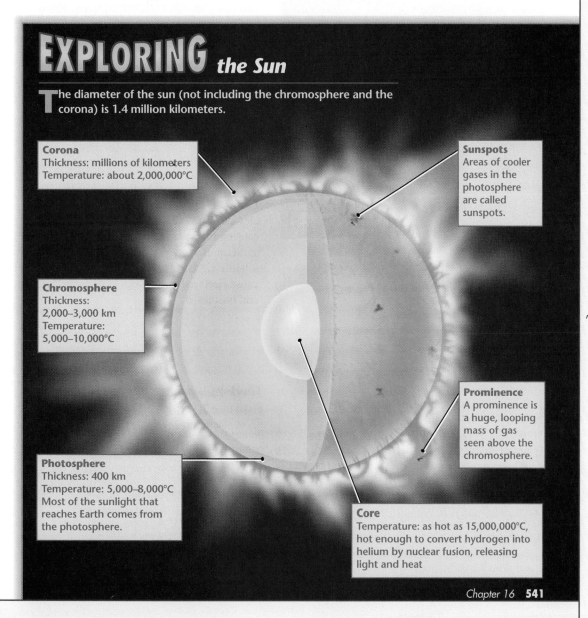

Corona
Thickness: millions of kilometers
Temperature: about 2,000,000°C

Sunspots
Areas of cooler gases in the photosphere are called sunspots.

Chromosphere
Thickness: 2,000–3,000 km
Temperature: 5,000–10,000°C

Photosphere
Thickness: 400 km
Temperature: 5,000–8,000°C
Most of the sunlight that reaches Earth comes from the photosphere.

Prominence
A prominence is a huge, looping mass of gas seen above the chromosphere.

Core
Temperature: as hot as 15,000,000°C, hot enough to convert hydrogen into helium by nuclear fusion, releasing light and heat

Chapter 16 **541**

Media and Technology

Transparencies "Exploring the Sun," Transparency 78

Earth Science Videodisc
Unit 1, Side 1, "Sunny Days"

Chapter 6

Answers to Self-Assessment

☑ *Checkpoint*

You can see the sun's corona during an eclipse.

Have students look up the meanings of the word *corona* and the prefixes *chromo-* and *photo-*. Ask: **Why is the corona called a corona?** (*It surrounds the sun like a crown.*) **Why is the core called a core?** (*Because it's at the center*) **What is the source of light that reaches Earth from the sun?** (*the photosphere*) **What is the source of energy for the light and heat produced by the sun?** (*nuclear fusion*) Explain to students that the chromosphere lies just above the photosphere and has an intense red color when seen during an eclipse.

Extend Challenge students to explain why the surface of the sun is much cooler than the center. Refer to the **ELL Handbook** for additional teaching strategies. **learning modality: visual**

Ongoing Assessment

Drawing Have students draw and label a diagram of the surface of the sun. Diagrams should include a sunspot, a flare, and a prominence. Have students include an explanation of what each solar feature is.

541

3 Assess

Section 2 Review Answers

1. Hydrogen fuel undergoes nuclear [fusi]on and creates helium. Some of the [ener]gy from this process is released as [lig]ht and heat.
2. photosphere, chromosphere, and corona
3. Sunspots are areas of gases on the sun that are cooler than the gases around them. Prominences are reddish loops of gas that link different parts of sunspot regions. Solar flares are explosions that occur when such loops suddenly connect.
4. Sunspots are made up of gases that are cooler than the gases around them. Because of this, they give off less light and thus appear darker.
5. The number of sunspots varies over a 10- to 11-year cycle.
6. The solar wind is a stream of electrically charged particles sent out into space from the corona.
7. A prominence is a loop of gas that links different parts of sunspot regions. A solar flare is an explosion that results when several prominences connect.

⬤ CHAPTER PROJECT

Check Your Progress

If students completed the Building Inquiry Skills activity on page 536, they can use that information here. They can also refer to the Addressing Naive Conceptions strategy on page 536. Suggest that students use lined paper or graph paper to keep their calculations neat and easy to follow. If students are having difficulty finding a good scale, suggest that they try 1: 10,000,000.

Performance Assessment

Writing Have students create a travel brochure for an imaginary vacation trip to the sun. The brochure should include sites to visit, a map, and travel tips.

 Portfolio Students can save their brochures in their portfolios.

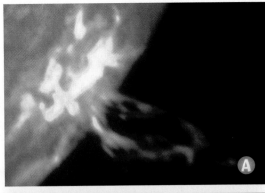

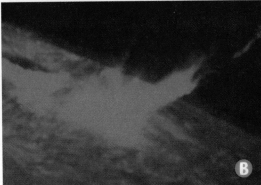

Figure 9 (A) Prominences are huge loops of gas that connect different parts of sunspot regions. (B) Solar flares on the sun release large amounts of energy. *Relating Cause and Effect How can solar flares affect communications on Earth?*

Prominences Sunspots usually occur in pairs or groups. Reddish loops of gas called **prominences** link different parts of sunspot regions. When a group of sunspots is near the edge of the sun as seen from Earth, these loops can stick out over the edge of the sun. If an eclipse hides the sun's photosphere, astronomers are able to see these loops. Prominences are about the same temperature as the sun's chromosphere, about 10,000 degrees Celsius.

Solar Flares Sometimes the loops in sunspot regions suddenly connect, releasing large amounts of energy. The energy heats gas on the sun to millions of degrees Celsius, causing the hydrogen gas to explode out into space. These explosions are known as **solar flares.**

Solar flares can greatly increase the solar wind from the corona, resulting in an increase in the number of particles reaching Earth's atmosphere. These solar wind particles can affect Earth's upper atmosphere, causing magnetic storms. Magnetic storms sometimes disrupt radio, telephone, and satellite signals. Magnetic storms can also cause electrical power problems for homes and businesses.

Section 2 Review

1. How is energy produced in the sun's core?
2. Name the layers of the sun's atmosphere.
3. Describe three features found on or above the surface of the sun.
4. Why do sunspots look darker than the rest of the sun's photosphere?
5. How does the number of sunspots change over time?
6. What is solar wind?
7. **Thinking Critically Comparing and Contrasting** What is the difference between a prominence and a solar flare?

542

⬤ CHAPTER PROJECT

Check Your Progress

Begin by making a table that shows the distances of the planets from the sun. To help visualize the solar system, you can divide all the distances by the same amount: for example, divide all distances by 100,000 or 1,000,000. Record your calculations on your data sheet. Then choose a different scale and repeat your calculations. Which scale makes it easier to see the relative distances between the planets and the sun?

Program Resources

◆ **Unit 4 Resources** 16-2 Review and Reinforce, p. 191; 16-2 Enrich, p. 192

Answers to Self-Assessment

Caption Question

Figure 9 Solar flares increase the solar wind in the corona, which can cause magnetic storms in Earth's upper atmosphere. These storms often disrupt radio, telephone, and television signals.

You and Your Environment

STORMY SUNSPOTS

Problem

How are magnetic storms on Earth related to sunspot activity?

Skills Focus

graphing, interpreting data

Materials

graph paper · pencil · straightedge · computer (optional)

Procedure

1. Use the data in the table to make a line graph of sunspot activity between 1967 and 1997. Create your graph on graph paper or on the computer.
2. On the graph, label the *x*-axis "Year." Use a scale with 2-year intervals, from 1967 to 1997.
3. Label the *y*-axis "Sunspot Number." Use a scale of 0 through 160 in intervals of 10.
4. Graph a point for the Sunspot Number for each year.
5. Complete your graph by connecting the points.

Sunspots			
Year	Sunspot Number	Year	Sunspot Number
1967	93.8	1983	66.6
1969	105.0	1985	17.9
1971	66.6	1987	29.4
1973	38.0	1989	157.6
1975	15.5	1991	145.7
1977	27.5	1993	54.6
1979	155.4	1995	17.5
1981	140.4	1997	23.4

Analyze and Conclude

1. Based on your graph, which years had the highest Sunspot Numbers? The lowest Sunspot Numbers?
2. How often does the cycle of maximum and minimum activity repeat?
3. When was the most recent maximum sunspot activity? The most recent minimum sunspot activity?
4. Compare your sunspot graph with the magnetic storms graph. What relationship can you infer between patterns of sunspot activity and magnetic storms?
5. **Apply** During which years do you think electrical disturbances on Earth were most common?

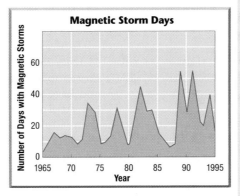

Magnetic Storm Days

Number of Days with Magnetic Storms (y-axis: 0, 20, 40, 60)
Year (x-axis: 1965, 70, 75, 80, 85, 90, 1995)

More to Explore

Using the pattern of sunspot activity you found, predict the number of peaks you would expect in the next 30 years. Around which years would you expect the peaks to occur?

---

5. Electrical disturbances on Earth were probably most common from 1967–1969, 1979–1981, and 1989–1991.

Extending the Inquiry

More to Explore Students add the time it takes to get a repeat to the year of the last maximum (1991). With a repeat of 10–11 years, you expect to get peaks around 2001–2002, 2012–2013 and 2023–2024.

Stormy Sunspots

Preparing for Inquiry

Key Concept Sunspot activity and magnetic storms on Earth can be related by analyzing sunspot activity over time.

Skills Objective Students will be able to
◆ make a graph of sunspot number versus year;
◆ compare a graph of sunspot activity to a graph of number of magnetic storms on Earth during the same time period.

Time 30 minutes

Advance Planning Distribute graph paper and straightedges to the students. *Computer use is optional.*

Guiding Inquiry

Introducing the Procedure

◆ "Sunspot number" is a technical term that represents both the number of sunspot groups and the number of individual sunspots.
◆ Tell students that a magnetic storm is defined as a brief disturbance in Earth's magnetic field.

Troubleshooting the Experiment

◆ Do not allow students to make a bar graph.

Expected Outcome

◆ Students will draw a graph that shows three peaks and three valleys in sunspot activity from 1967–1997.
◆ The sunspot activity valleys seem to coincide with valleys in the magnetic storm days graph.

Analyze and Conclude

1. Highest: 1967–1969, 1979–1981 and 1989–1991; Lowest: 1975–1977, 1985–1987 and 1995–1997
2. Every 10–12 years
3. Maximum: 1989; Minimum: 1995
4. The three sunspot activity valleys (1975, 1985, and 1995) occur at the same time as valleys in magnetic storm days. The three sunspot activity peaks (1970, 1980, and 1990) seem to precede by one or two years a magnetic storm peak (1973, 1982, and 1992).

TEKS: 6.1A; 6.2E; 6.3C; 6.4A; 6.13A

Objective

After completing the lesson, students will be able to

◆ identify the main characteristics of the inner planets.

1 Engage/Explore

Activating Prior Knowledge

Show students a colored drawing of the solar system with the names of the planets covered. Ask: **Which planet is Earth?** *(The third planet from the sun)* Ask students to explain why they guessed that Earth was the third planet. *(Sample: The planet was colored blue, and Earth has water which makes it look blue from space.)* Then invite students to examine the map and point out other planets they think are most like Earth. *(Students should point out the inner planets.)*

DISCOVER

Skills Focus observing
Materials *compass, ruler*
Time 10 minutes
Tips Stress that students should make the small lines dark enough to be seen from a distance. To keep their drawings straight, suggest that they label them as *Original* and *Copied from a Distance.*
Think It Over The partner may see and draw patterns and lines that are not in the original drawing. The view from across the room is not an accurate representation of what the original drawing looked like.

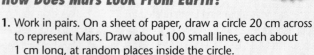
DISCOVER ·· ACTIVITY

How Does Mars Look From Earth?

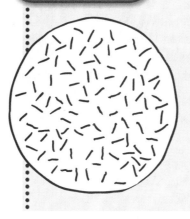

1. Work in pairs. On a sheet of paper, draw a circle 20 cm across to represent Mars. Draw about 100 small lines, each about 1 cm long, at random places inside the circle.

2. Have your partner look at your drawing of Mars from the other side of the room. Your partner should draw what he or she sees.

3. Compare your original drawing with what your partner drew. Then look at your own drawing from across the room.

Think It Over
Observing Did your partner draw any connecting lines that were not actually on your drawing? What can you conclude about the accuracy of descriptions of other planets as observed from Earth?

GUIDE FOR READING

◆ What are the main characteristics of the inner planets?

Reading Tip As you read about each planet, write down the similarities and differences between that planet and Earth.

Key Terms terrestrial planet
• rotation • revolution
• retrograde rotation
• greenhouse effect

Picture a planet whose surface is hot enough to melt lead. How about a planet whose atmosphere has almost entirely leaked away? Some of the four planets closest to the sun have these characteristics. They are called the inner planets.

Earth and the other three inner planets of the solar system—Mercury, Venus, and Mars—are more similar to each other than they are to the five outer planets. **The four inner planets are small and have rocky surfaces.** These planets are often called the **terrestrial planets,** from the Latin word *terra,* which means "Earth." Figure 10 gives a summary of the characteristics of the inner planets. These characteristics include a planet's rotation and revolution. The **rotation** is the spinning motion of a planet about its axis. The **revolution** is the movement of a planet around the sun.

Earth

Our planet's atmosphere extends more than 100 kilometers above Earth's surface. The oxygen you need to live makes up about 20 percent of the gases in Earth's atmosphere. Most of the remaining 80 percent of the atmosphere is nitrogen gas. Earth's atmosphere also contains water vapor and clouds of water droplets. From space, astronauts can usually see between the clouds to Earth's surface.

Most of Earth, about 70 percent, is covered with water. Perhaps the planet should be named "Water" instead of "Earth"! No other planet in our solar system has oceans like Earth's.

544

READING STRATEGIES

Reading Tip Suggest that students use Venn diagrams to compare and contrast each inner planet and Earth. Demonstrate how to use a Venn diagram to compare and contrast two subjects. First, have volunteers read aloud the information about Earth and Mercury in the section. Then draw a Venn diagram on the chalkboard. As students name similarities between Mercury and Earth, such as small size and rocky surface, write these in the overlapping portion of the diagram. Then have students name differences, such as Mercury's lack of moon, and record these in the outer portions of the circles. Instruct students to complete additional Venn diagrams for the remaining planets.

Study and Comprehension Have students work in groups. Each member of the group can read the material on a planet, then teach the rest of the group about that planet.

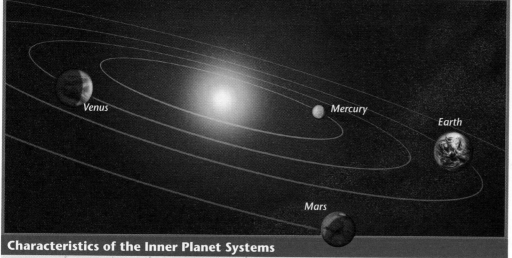

Characteristics of the Inner Planet Systems					
Planet	Diameter (kilometers)	Period of Rotation (Earth days)	Average Distance From the Sun (kilometers)	Period of Revolution (Earth years)	Number of Moons
Mercury	4,878	59	58,000,000	0.24	0
Venus	12,104	243	108,000,000	0.62	0
Earth	12,756	1	150,000,000	1	1
Mars	6,794	1.03	228,000,000	1.9	2

INTEGRATING EARTH SCIENCE As you recall from Chapter 10, Earth has three main layers—a crust, a mantle, and a core. The crust includes the solid rocky surface. Under the crust is the mantle, a layer of hot molten rock. When volcanoes erupt, this hot material rises to the surface. Earth has a dense inner core made up mainly of iron and nickel. The outer core is liquid, but the inner core is solid.

Scientists have been studying Earth for many years. They use what they know about Earth to make inferences about the other planets. For example, when astronomers find volcanoes on other planets, they infer that these planets have or once had hot material inside them. As we continue to learn more about our own planet, scientists will be able to apply that new knowledge to the study of the other planets.

Figure 10 The inner planets take up only a small part of the solar system. The diameter of the entire solar system is more than 25 times the diameter of Mars's orbit.

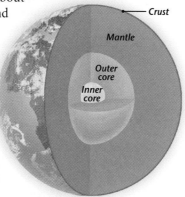

— Crust

Mantle

Outer core

Inner core

Figure 11 Earth has a solid, rocky surface. *Interpreting Diagrams* What are Earth's three main layers?

Answers to Self-Assessment

Caption Question

Figure 11 crust, mantle, and core

Earth

Building Inquiry Skills: Interpreting Data

Content Mastery

To help students interpret the data in Figure 10, ask: **Which planets are most similar in size?** *(Venus and Earth)* Then ask: **How many times does Mercury revolve around the sun during one Earth year?** *(About 4)* Challenge students to make generalizations about a planet's average distance from the sun and its period of revolution. *(The farther from the sun, the longer it takes to complete one period of revolution.)* **learning modality: logical/mathematical**

 Integrating Earth Science

Materials *hard-boiled egg, blunt kitchen knife, paper towel*

Time 10 minutes

Tips Invite students to use hard-boiled eggs to model the layers of Earth. Have them place the eggs on paper towels, then use the knives to slice the shelled eggs crosswise. Ask students to identify what each part of the egg represents. *(Shell—crust; white—mantle; yolk—core)* Ask: **How is the model different from Earth?** *(Earth's outer core is liquid, but the egg yolk is solid.)* Students should take care when using kitchen knives. Make sure students do not eat the eggs. They should wash their hands after disposing of the eggs. **learning modality: tactile/kinesthetic**

Ongoing Assessment

Drawing Have students draw a cross-section of Earth and its atmosphere and label the crust, mantle, outer core, inner core, and atmosphere.

 Students can save their drawings in their portfolios.

Mercury

Help students understand **ACTIVITY** why scientists have difficulty making observations of Mercury. Pair students. Have one student hold a coin about 10 cm in front of a dim desk lamp. The head side of the coin should face away from the bulb. Challenge the other student to determine the date on the coin. Caution the student not to look directly at the light bulb. Ask: **What do you observe about the coin?** *(The brightness of the bulb makes it impossible to see the date.)* Have students explain why this is similar to the problems encountered by scientists who want to observe Mercury's surface features. *(The brightness of the sun makes it hard to see the features of Mercury's surface.)* **learning modality: visual**

Using the Visuals: Figure 12

Show students a photograph of the moon. Point out that Mercury and the moon look very similar. Have students describe the features shared by the moon and Mercury. *(Heavily cratered surface, little atmosphere, no liquid water, little erosion)* Ask: **What difference do you see between the surface of the moon and that of Mercury?** *(Mercury's surface has no maria, which are the smooth, dark areas on the moon where lava flowed.)* **learning modality: verbal**

Figure 12 This photo of Mercury and the closeup view of some of its craters (inset) were taken by the *Mariner 10* space probe. *Inferring Is there a connection between the thin atmosphere on Mercury and the craters on the surface of that planet? Explain.*

Mercury

The planet system closest to the sun is Mercury. Mercury is not much larger than Earth's moon and has no moons of its own. Astronomers have been able to infer that the interior of Mercury is made up mainly of the dense metals iron and nickel.

Exploring Mercury Because Mercury is so close to the sun, people on Earth never get a good view of Mercury. Much of the knowledge that astronomers have about Mercury's surface came from the space probe *Mariner 10* that flew by Mercury in 1974 and 1975. *Mariner 10* photographed only half of Mercury's surface, so astronomers still don't know what the rest of Mercury is like.

Mariner 10's photographs show that, like the moon, Mercury has many flat plains and many craters on its surface. The craters on Mercury have been named for artists, writers, and musicians, including the composers Bach and Mozart.

Mercury's Atmosphere Mercury has an extremely thin atmosphere. Apparently the gases Mercury once had were heated so much that the gas particles moved very fast. Since they were moving so fast, the gas particles escaped from Mercury's weak gravity into space. However, astronomers have detected small amounts of sodium and other gases in Mercury's atmosphere.

Mercury is a planet of extremes. It is so close to the sun that during the day, the side facing the sun reaches temperatures of 430°C. Because Mercury has almost no atmosphere, at night all the heat escapes into space. The temperature drops to –170°C. Mercury thus has a greater range of temperatures than any other planet in the solar system.

☑ *Checkpoint* *Why is it difficult for astronomers to learn about Mercury?*

546

Background

Facts and Figures Until the 1960s, astronomers thought that Mercury's day was the same length as its year. In 1965, observations by Doppler radar showed that Mercury rotates three times in every two Mercury years. Mercury has a very eccentric orbit—sometimes 46 million km from the sun, at other times 70 million km.

Sunrise on Mercury would look strange to someone from Earth. At some places on the planet, the sun would appear to rise, increase in size, then stop, reverse, and stop again before rising again and decreasing in size.

Venus

Whenever you see a bright object in the west after sunset, it is probably Venus. When Venus shines brightly like that, it is known as the "evening star," though of course it really isn't a star. Stars shine with their own light, while Venus shines because it is reflecting light from the sun, just as the other planets and moons do. At other times, you see Venus rise before the sun in the morning. It is then known as the "morning star." At still other times, Venus is too close to the sun in the sky for you to see it from Earth at all.

Venus is so similar in size to Earth that it is sometimes called Earth's twin. Astronomers also think that the density and internal structure of Venus are similar to Earth's. However, in many other ways, Venus is very different from Earth.

Venus's Rotation Venus takes about 7.5 Earth months to revolve around the sun. It takes about 8 months for Venus to rotate on its axis. Venus rotates so slowly that its "day" is longer than its "year." Oddly, Venus rotates from east to west, the opposite direction from most other planets and moons. This type of rotation is called **retrograde rotation,** from the Latin words for "moving backward." One hypothesis proposed by astronomers to explain this unusual rotation is that Venus was struck by a very large object billions of years ago. Such a collision could have caused the direction of its rotation to change.

Sharpen your Skills

Graphing ACTIVITY

Using data in Figure 10 on page 545, make a line graph of the average distances from the sun and the periods of revolution of Mercury, Venus, Earth, and Mars. Describe how the two variables are related. Add data on Jupiter, Saturn, Uranus, Neptune, and Pluto from Figure 19 on page 553 to your graph.

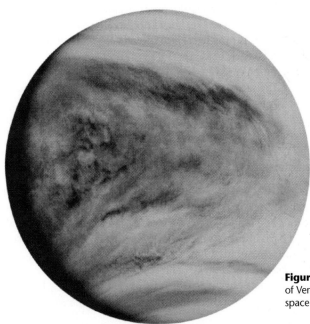

Figure 13 The thick atmosphere of Venus makes the view from space a cloudy one.

Venus

Demonstration

To help students visualize the unusual rotation of Venus, place one globe on a table to represent Earth. Spin the globe so that it turns from west to east. Ask: **How long does it take for Earth to spin once around its axis?** *(24 hours or 1 day)* Place another globe next to the first to represent Venus. Spin the globe very slowly so that it turns from east to west. Invite students to identify the differences between the rotations of Venus and Earth. *(Venus rotates from east to west, Earth from west to east. Venus is slower than Earth. On Venus, the sun "rises" in the west and "sets" in the east.)* **learning modality: visual**

Sharpen your Skills

Graphing

Materials *graph paper, colored pencils* ACTIVITY
Time 15 minutes
Tips Students should set up their graphs with the distances to the planets on the *x*-axis, and the period of revolution on the *y*-axis. Discuss the units. Suggest students use 1 cm = 10,000 km for units of distance and 1 cm = 0.01 year for time.
Expected Outcome Data should form a line with a positive slope. The inner and outer planets must be graphed separately because the same scale will not work for both.
Extend Ask students to predict the relationship between the diameter of a planet and its period of rotation, then create graphs to test their predictions. **learning modality: logical/mathematical**

Media and Technology

 Transparencies "Characteristics of the Inner Planets," Transparency 79

Answers to Self-Assessment

☑ Checkpoint

Mercury is so close to the sun that it is difficult for astronomers on Earth to get a good view of it.

Caption Question

Figure 12 The lack of a thick atmosphere around Mercury allows meteorites to enter the atmosphere and hit the surface of the planet creating many craters.

Ongoing Assessment

Writing Have students describe how sunrise on Venus differs from sunrise on Earth.

Including All Students

To help students who are still mastering English understand the origin of the term *greenhouse effect,* show them a picture of a greenhouse with plants growing inside. Explain that a greenhouse lets in sunlight and prevents convection from carrying heat away. The plants inside stay warm. Pair students who are still mastering English with native speakers, and have them each create flowcharts or sketches that compare the path of light and heat energy in a greenhouse with the path of light and heat energy on Venus.

Extend Have students research possible environmental problems caused by changes in Earth's greenhouse effect.
limited English proficiency

Music
CONNECTION

Recordings of this work are widely available. Check your school or public library for a copy. Holst was trying to musically describe the *astrological* and *mythological* characteristics of these seven planets. Encourage students to listen for *astronomical* connections.
learning modality: auditory/verbal

In Your Journal Students' responses will depend on the pieces they heard. They may suggest the use of specific instruments to give a feel or appearance of a planet. Students may describe the music with words such as *loud, soft, eerie, brash,* or *faraway.*

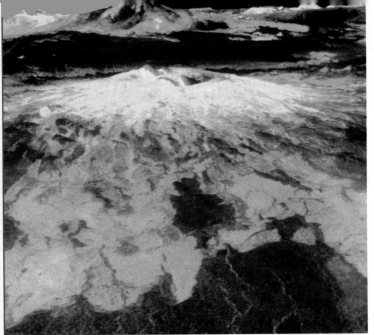

Figure 14 The *Magellan* spacecraft used radar to penetrate Venus's clouds. This three-dimensional image of a volcano on Venus was created by a computer using radar data. The height of the mountains is exaggerated to make them stand out. *Inferring Why must radar be used to photograph the surface of Venus from space?*

Music
CONNECTION

The English composer Gustav Holst, who lived from 1874 to 1934, composed a group of pieces for orchestra entitled *The Planets.* The seven pieces describe musically the planets Mars, Venus, Mercury, Jupiter, Saturn, Uranus, and Neptune.

In Your Journal

Listen to a recording of at least two of the pieces from *The Planets.* How did Holst use music to distinguish the planets from each other? What words would you use to describe what you heard?

548

Venus's Atmosphere The atmosphere of Venus is so thick that every day is a cloudy one. Venus never has a sunny day. From Earth, astronomers see only a smooth cloud cover over Venus all the time.

If you could stand on the surface of Venus, you would quickly be crushed by the weight of its atmosphere. The pressure of Venus's atmosphere is 90 times greater than the pressure of Earth's atmosphere. You could not breathe on Venus because its atmosphere is mostly carbon dioxide. Also, its clouds are partly made of sulfuric acid.

Because Venus is closer to the sun than Earth, it gets more solar energy than Earth does. Ordinary light from the sun can penetrate Venus's atmosphere and hit its surface. The surface heats up and then gives off heat. Carbon dioxide traps this heat in the atmosphere. So Venus's surface becomes hotter and hotter, until it is about 460°C—hot enough to melt lead. This trapping of heat by the atmosphere is called the **greenhouse effect.**

Exploring Venus About 20 spacecraft have visited Venus, more than have visited any other planet. Some have even penetrated its clouds and landed on its surface. The first spacecraft to land and send back information, *Venera 7,* landed in 1970 but transmitted for only 23 minutes. Later spacecraft were more durable and sent back pictures and other data from Venus's surface.

Scientists have learned most of what they now know about the surface of Venus from data collected by the *Magellan* probe.

Background

History of Science Because of Venus's extreme heat, high atmospheric pressure, and clouds of sulfuric acid, it would be almost impossible for astronauts to go there. To gather information about Venus, scientists have sent unmanned space probes. The Soviet Union was the first nation to attempt interplanetary exploration. In 1961, it launched the probe *Venera 1,* which passed within 99,000 km of Venus but did not transmit information. In 1966, the Soviets launched *Venera 3,* the first spacecraft to crash-land on another planet. In 1967, *Venera 4* parachuted a capsule of instruments to the planet's surface. *Venera 7* (1970) detected radioactive isotopes on Venus's surface. In 1975, *Venera 9* sent back the first close-up photographs of the surface of the planet.

The *Magellan* probe reached Venus in 1990, carrying radar instruments. Radar works through clouds, so *Magellan* was able to map Venus's entire surface.

The *Magellan* views are so detailed that computers can be used to figure out what Venus would look like if you could fly just above its surface. Figure 14 shows one of these radar images. Venus is covered with rock, similar to many rocky areas on Earth. Venus has volcanoes with lava flows, many craters, and strange domes not found on other planets.

☑ *Checkpoint* *Why is the surface of Venus so hot?*

Mars

Mars is called the "red planet" because it has a slightly reddish tinge when you see it in the sky. The atmosphere of Mars is mostly carbon dioxide and has only 1 percent the pressure of Earth's atmosphere. You could walk around on Mars, but you would have to wear an airtight suit and carry your own air, like a scuba diver. Mars has clouds but they are very thin compared to the clouds on Earth.

Canals on Mars? In 1877, an Italian astronomer, Giovanni Schiaparelli (sky ah puh REL ee), announced that he had seen long, straight lines on Mars. He called them *canale,* or channels. In the 1890s and the early 1900s, Percival Lowell, an American astronomer, convinced many people that these lines were canals that had been built by intelligent Martians to carry water. Astronomers now know that Lowell was mistaken. There are no canals on Mars that can be seen from Earth.

However, astronomers have found that some water exists on Mars in the form of ice at its north pole, as shown in Figure 15. Mars' south pole has an ice cap made mostly of frozen carbon dioxide. Unlike Earth's ice caps, Mars' polar ice caps are covered by a layer of frozen carbon dioxide during each hemisphere's winter.

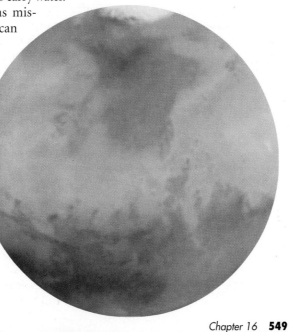

Figure 15 Because of its thin atmosphere and its distance from the sun, Mars is quite cold. Mars has ice caps at both poles.

Sharpen your Skills

Observing

Use a telescope to observe Venus. Draw what you see. Compare and contrast your drawing to the photo in Figure 13 on page 547.

ACTIVITY

Answers to Self-Assessment

Caption Question

Figure 14 Radar must be used to photograph the surface of Venus because of the very thick atmosphere surrounding that planet.

☑ *Checkpoint*

The surface of Venus is so hot because carbon dioxide traps heat inside the atmosphere. This is called the greenhouse effect.

Using the Visuals: Figure 14

Explain to students that radar images are formed when radio waves are bounced off a surface. Have students infer why scientists used radar to get an image of the volcano on Venus. (*They could not see the volcano because the thick atmosphere of Venus blocked the view.*) Explain that the radar-imaging technique exaggerates the heights of objects such as the volcano. Ask students: **Why might astronomers want to use an exaggerated scale when examining an image?** (*Astronomers increase the scale of an image so that they can examine details more clearly.*) Inform students that the colors in the figure are generated by the computer-imaging process. The actual volcano colors vary, and appear more like those of volcanoes on Earth. **learning modality: visual**

Sharpen your Skills

Observing

Materials *telescope, paper, colored pencils*

Time 20 minutes

Tips Partner students experienced at using a telescope with those less experienced.

Expected Outcome Students will only be able to observe and draw the cloudy atmosphere of Venus.

Extend Have students observe and draw any other planets visible. **learning modality: visual**

Mars

Addressing Naive Conceptions

Students' conceptions about the features and history of Mars may be based on science-fiction stories, television shows, and movies. As students complete their reading about Mars, have them prepare a Fact/Fiction sheet to distinguish scientific findings about Mars from science fiction. **learning modality: verbal**

Ongoing Assessment

Skills Check Instruct students to make a Venn diagram comparing the features of Venus's atmosphere with the features of Earth's atmosphere.

Mars, continued

Skills Focus inferring
Materials *tape, paper, goggles*
Time 15 minutes
Tips Perform this activity in a large open area. Make sure that there are no obstacles on which students might trip or hit their heads.
Expected Outcome Simple directions such as "Turn left" or "Take four steps forward" probably worked best. Students would have had to move slowly. This activity is similar to the way NASA engineers moved *Sojourner.* The rover could not move by itself but had to be given directions by remote control. The controller had to be careful not to have *Sojourner* run into anything, and the rover had to move very slowly.
Extend Have students infer difficulties NASA encountered when trying to get the rover to perform tasks on Mars.
learning modality: kinesthetic

Building Inquiry Skills: Observing

Materials *sand, rectangular baking pans, large beaker, bucket for sand disposal*
Time 15 minutes

Place large buckets in strategic locations around the room for sand disposal. Warn students to keep the sand out of the sinks. Have pairs of students build slopes with moist sand in one end of a rectangular metal baking pan. The sand should slope from just below the rim on one end to about the middle of the pan. Have students pour a slow, steady stream of water onto the top of the slope and observe what happens as the water runs down the slope. Have students continue pouring until there is about 1 cm of water in the pan. Ask: **How did the flowing water change the surface of the sand?** *(It formed channels.)* Ask students to infer why scientists believe water once flowed on Mars. *(Channels on Mars look similar to channels formed by flowing water on Earth.)* **learning modality: visual**

Remote Control

How hard is it to explore another planet by remote control?

1. Tape a piece of paper over the front of a pair of goggles. Have your partner put them on.
2. Walk behind your partner and give him or her directions to move to another part of the room. **CAUTION:** *Do not give directions that would cause your partner to walk into a wall or corner, trip on an obstacle, or hit anything.*
3. Trade places and repeat Steps 1 and 2.

Inferring Which verbal directions worked best? How quickly could you move? How is this activity similar to the way NASA engineers moved *Sojourner* on Mars in 1997? How fast do you think the rover could move?

Seasons on Mars Because the axis of Mars is tilted, Mars has seasons just as Earth does. As the seasons change on the dusty surface of Mars, wind storms arise and blow the dust around. Since the dust is blown off some regions, these regions look darker. A hundred years ago, some people thought these regions looked darker because plants were growing there. Astronomers now realize that it is just that wind storms blow dust off the surface.

Exploring Mars The United States has sent many spacecraft to Mars. The first ones, in the 1960s, seemed to show that Mars is barren and covered with craters like the moon. Later spacecraft showed that regions of Mars have giant volcanoes. Astronomers see signs that hot material flowed down the volcanoes in the past, but they don't think the volcanoes are active now.

In 1976, two NASA spacecraft, *Viking 1* and *Viking 2,* landed on Mars. They sent back close-up pictures from Mars's surface. The pictures showed that the rocks look red because they are covered with a rusty dust. Other parts of the *Viking* spacecraft went into orbit around Mars, sending back detailed pictures.

In 1997, *Mars Pathfinder* landed on Mars. As Figure 16 shows, close-up photographs from *Mars Pathfinder* show no oceans or even puddles of water. Photographs taken from space do show evidence that water flowed on Mars millions of years ago.

Figure 16 The surface of Mars is rugged and rocky. The object at the bottom of the photo is the *Mars Pathfinder* lander. You can see the remote-control rover *Sojourner* in the middle of the photo.

Background

Facts and Figures In 1879, Giovanni Schiaparelli discovered another feature of Mars, a large crater he called *Nix Olympica.* Photographs from *Mariner 9* (1971–1972) showed that this crater was the caldera of possibly the largest volcano in the entire solar system, *Olympus Mons.* This volcano is one of several huge volcanoes on a plateau called *Tharsis.* Olympus Mons has ten times the volume of Mauna Kea in Hawaii, the largest volcano on Earth, and at 27 km, is three times as high as Mount Everest. The caldera of Olympus Mons is 85 km across, and the entire volcano covers a circular area 550 km across.

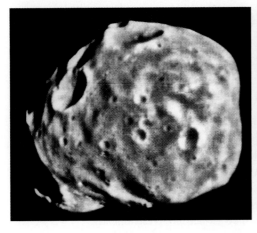

Figure 17 Phobos (left) and Deimos (right) are Mars's two small, crater-covered moons.

Mars Pathfinder carried a microwave-sized remote-control rover, called *Sojourner,* that investigated rocks on Mars. Also in 1997, another probe, *Mars Global Surveyor,* arrived in orbit around Mars, where it began mapping and photographing all of the planet's surface in detail.

Mars's Moons The Mars system has two very small moons that revolve around the planet. Phobos, the larger moon, is only 27 kilometers in diameter, about the distance a car can travel on the highway in 15 minutes. Deimos is even smaller, only 15 kilometers in diameter. Close-up views from space show that, like Earth's moon, Phobos and Deimos are covered with craters.

Section 3 Review

1. What characteristics do all of the inner planets have in common?
2. Why could Earth be called "The Water Planet"?
3. What is Mercury's atmosphere like? Explain.
4. Why can astronomers see the surface of Mars clearly, but not the surface of Venus?
5. How have astronomers been able to study the surface of Venus?
6. **Thinking Critically Relating Cause and Effect** Venus is much farther from the sun than is Mercury. Yet temperatures on Venus are as high as those on the sunny side of Mercury. Explain why.

Check Your Progress CHAPTER PROJECT

Now you will design a model that shows the relative diameters of the planets. Try several different scales to find one for which the smallest planet is clearly visible, but the sun would still fit into your classroom. Convert the sun's and planets' diameters to scaled-down diameters and record your results on your data sheet. Compare your scaled-down diameters to objects you are familiar with, such as coins. Include your comparisons in your data sheet.

Chapter 16 **551**

Program Resources

◆ **Unit 4 Resources** 16-3 Review and Reinforce, p. 195; 16-3 Enrich, p. 196

3 Assess

Section 3 Review Answers

1. They are all small and rocky.
2. About 70 percent of Earth is covered by water. No other planet in the solar system has oceans like Earth's.
3. Mercury has almost no atmosphere. The gases its atmosphere once had were heated so much by the sun that they escaped from Mercury's weak gravity into space.
4. The thin atmosphere of Mars is easy to see through; the very thick atmosphere of Venus is not.
5. Astronomers have been able to study the surface of Venus using unmanned spacecraft and by looking at radar images taken by the *Magellan* probe.
6. Venus's thick atmosphere traps heat due to the greenhouse effect.

Check Your Progress CHAPTER PROJECT

If students have trouble finding a scale that works, suggest they try 1 cm = 10,000 km. At this scale, Mercury would be about the size of a pea, and the sun would be about the size of an easy chair.

Performance Assessment

Skills Check Have students create models of the four inner planets using art supplies and classroom items. Models should include some distinguishing characteristics of each planet. Portfolio Students can save their models in their portfolios.

Characteristics of the Outer Planets

TEKS: 6.1A; 6.2A, B, C, E; 6.3C; 6.4A; 6.13A

Objectives

After completing the lesson, students will be able to

♦ identify the main characteristics of the gas giant planets;

♦ compare Pluto and Charon with the other planets.

1 Engage/Explore

Activating Prior Knowledge

Divide the class into groups of five. Give each student in a group an index card with the name of one outer planet written on it. Have students write three things they think they know about their planets. When they have finished, students can share their cards with the group. Collect the cards and use them to build a list of naive conceptions.

⋯⋯⋯ DISCOVER ⋯⋯⋯

Skills Focus classifying
Materials *quarter, metric*
ACTIVITY
ruler, lined paper, butcher paper or poster board, compass, push pin, and string
Time 15 minutes
Tips A quarter has a diameter of 24 mm. Jupiter and Saturn will be too large to draw with a compass, so use a pin and string for them. CAUTION: *Compasses have sharp points and can cause injury. Warn students to be careful and watch for inappropriate behaviors.* For the best comparison, have students locate the center of each circle in the same place. Students will need large paper, such as poster boards or butcher paper, to fit the larger circles onto one sheet.
Expected Outcome Students' circles should have these diameters: Earth, 24 mm; Jupiter, 264 mm; Saturn, 226 mm; Uranus, 96 mm; Neptune, 94 mm; Pluto, 4 mm.
Think It Over Jupiter, Saturn, Uranus, Neptune, Earth, Pluto; Pluto

552

DISCOVER ⋯⋯⋯⋯⋯⋯⋯⋯⋯⋯⋯⋯⋯⋯⋯⋯⋯⋯ ACTIVITY

How Large Are the Outer Planets?

The table shows the diameters of the outer planets compared to Earth. For example, Jupiter's diameter is 11 times Earth's diameter.

Planet Diameters	
Planet	**Diameter**
Earth	1
Jupiter	11
Saturn	9.4
Uranus	4.0
Neptune	3.9
Pluto	0.17

1. Measure the diameter of a quarter in millimeters. This represents Earth's diameter. Trace the quarter to represent Earth.

2. If Earth were the size of a quarter, calculate how large Jupiter would be. Now draw a circle to represent Jupiter.

3. Repeat Step 2 for each of the other outer planets.

Think It Over
Classifying List the planets in order from largest to smallest. Which outer planet is much smaller than Earth?

GUIDE FOR READING

♦ What are the main characteristics of the gas giant planets?

♦ How are Pluto and Charon different from the other outer planets?

Reading Tip Before you read, preview the photos and captions. Write down any questions you have. Look for answers as you read.

Key Term gas giant

Most of what astronomers know about the outer planet systems has come from NASA space probes. *Voyager 1* and *Voyager 2* reached Jupiter in 1979. *Voyager 1* went on to visit Saturn in 1980. *Voyager 2* also visited Saturn, and then explored Uranus and Neptune. In 1995, the spacecraft *Galileo* dropped a probe into Jupiter's atmosphere.

Characteristics of the Gas Giants

Compared to Earth, some planets are huge. The largest planet, Jupiter, has a diameter that is 11 times Earth's diameter. Jupiter's mass is more than 300 times Earth's mass. If you could put Earth next to Jupiter, Earth would look like a tiny Chihuahua next to an enormous Great Dane.

Jupiter and the other planets farthest from the sun, as seen in Figure 19, are called the outer planets. **The first four outer planets—Jupiter, Saturn, Uranus, and Neptune—are much larger than Earth, and do not have solid surfaces.** These four planets are all so large that they are also called the **gas giants.** The fifth outer planet, Pluto, is small and solid like the terrestrial planets.

Figure 18 If the tiny Chihuahua were Earth's size, the Great Dane would be about half Jupiter's size.

552

READING STRATEGIES

Reading Tip Explain to students that previewing the photos and captions will help them understand what they are about to read. Write the questions below on the board. Suggest students answer the questions as they preview each image and its caption.
♦ How does the picture relate to the caption?

♦ How does the caption help me understand the picture?
♦ What do I already know about the information in the picture and caption?
♦ What else do I want to learn about the subject of this picture?

Compare/Contrast Table Have students make a compare/contrast table to show similarities and differences among the outer planets.

Characteristics of the Outer Planets

Planet	Diameter (kilometers)	Period of Rotation (Earth days)	Average Distance From the Sun (kilometers)	Period of Revolution (Earth years)	Number of Moons
Jupiter	142,800	0.41	778,000,000	12	18
Saturn	120,540	0.43	1,427,000,000	29	18
Uranus	51,200	0.72	2,871,000,000	84	20
Neptune	49,500	0.67	4,497,000,000	165	8
Pluto	2,200	6.4	5,913,000,000	248	1

Figure 19 The outer planets are much farther apart than the inner planets. At this scale, the inner planets are so small and close to the sun that they cannot be shown. *Observing Which outer planet is closest to the sun?*

Atmospheres Because the gas giants have so much mass, they exert a much stronger gravitational force than the terrestrial planets. The strong gravity keeps the giant planets' gases from escaping, so they have deep atmospheres. The composition of their atmospheres is similar to the gases in the sun. They average about 75 percent hydrogen, 24 percent helium, and 1 percent other elements by mass.

None of the giant planets has a well-defined surface. If you could parachute into Jupiter's atmosphere, you would sink into denser and denser gas. You would be crushed by the enormous pressure long before you got to the center, or core, of the planet.

Solid Cores Astronomers think that each of the giant planets has a partly solid core made of rock, ice, frozen carbon dioxide, and other compounds. Each of these cores may have several times as much mass as Earth. But they are buried so deep inside the planets that it has been hard to find out much about them.

✓ *Checkpoint* Why do the gas giants have large atmospheres?

Program Resources

◆ **Unit 4 Resources** 16-4 Lesson Plan, p. 197; 16-4 Section Summary, p. 198
◆ **Guided Reading and Study Workbook** 16-4

Answers to Self-Assessment

Caption Question

Figure 19 Jupiter

✓ *Checkpoint*

The gas giants have so much mass that they exert a strong gravitational force that keeps the planets' gases from escaping.

2 Facilitate

Characteristics of the Gas Giants

Using the Visuals: Figure 19

Have students use their finger to trace the orbits of each planet in the figure. Ask: **Which planet has an orbit that crosses the orbit of another?** *(Pluto crosses the orbit of Neptune.)* Then draw students' attention to the data in the table. Allow them time to evaluate the distances of the planets from the sun. Ask: **Which planet is about twice as far from the sun as Jupiter?** *(Saturn)* **Which planet is about six times as far from the sun as Jupiter?** *(Neptune)* Astronomers have identified more moons orbiting Jupiter, Saturn, and Uranus than are shown in the chart. However, before the moons are recognized officially, additional observations are needed. **learning modality: logical/mathematical**

Building Inquiry Skills: Applying Concepts

Invite students to imagine that they are sending a space probe to examine a gas giant. Encourage them to apply what they know about the planet's structure to describe what the probe would encounter as it approached the visible surface. *(There is no real solid surface, the atmosphere just gets thicker and thicker. Eventually, the combination of heat and pressure would probably cause the probe to fail.)* Ask: **Could the probe penetrate all the way to a solid surface? Explain.** *(Probably not. The solid core is buried deep inside the planet.)* **learning modality: verbal**

Ongoing Assessment

Writing Have students list features that characterize gas giants. *(Large size; far from the sun; partly solid frozen core; dense atmosphere made up mostly of hydrogen and helium)*

Jupiter

Building Inquiry Skills: Making Models

Materials *clear plastic 1-L bottle with lid, water, pepper, funnel or spoon*

Time 10 minutes

If students have completed Chapter 15 *Weather Patterns,* point out the resemblance between the Great Red Spot and a hurricane on Earth. Allow students to model the motion of the Great Red Spot. Pair students. Have each pair fill a clear, plastic bottle half full with water. Using a funnel or a spoon, pour in a spoonful of pepper. Seal the bottle and swirl the water forcefully. Ask: **What happens to the pepper grains?** *(They spin in a large swirl.)* Have students compare the appearance of the spinning pepper to the photographs of the Great Red Spot. *(Both look like giant swirls.)* Challenge students to infer what forces are causing the Giant Red Spot to swirl. Ask: **What kind of data would you need to collect to test your inferences?** *(Sample: Differences in pressure in Jupiter's atmosphere cause the Giant Red Spot. Data that show the pressure of the atmosphere around the Giant Red Spot would be needed to test this inference.)*
learning modality: kinesthetic

Jupiter

Jupiter is the most massive planet in the solar system. In fact, Jupiter is more than 300 times as massive as Earth.

Jupiter's Atmosphere Like all of the gas giant planets, Jupiter has a thick atmosphere made up mainly of hydrogen and helium. Jupiter's atmosphere contains many colorful bands and swirls of thick clouds. An especially interesting feature in Jupiter's atmosphere is its Great Red Spot, a giant area of swirling clouds a few times bigger than Earth. The Great Red Spot, shown in Figure 20, appears to be an ongoing storm similar to a hurricane on Earth.

Jupiter's Moons Recall that the astronomer Galileo discovered four of Jupiter's moons. These moons are named Io (EYE oh), Europa, Ganymede, and Callisto. These four moons are Jupiter's largest. Three of them, Io, Ganymede, and Callisto, are larger than Earth's own moon. Since Galileo's time, astronomers have discovered many more smaller moons revolving around Jupiter.

The *Voyager* and *Galileo* probes sent back images that showed detailed views of Jupiter's moons. Jupiter's moons are very different from one another, as you can see in Figure 21.

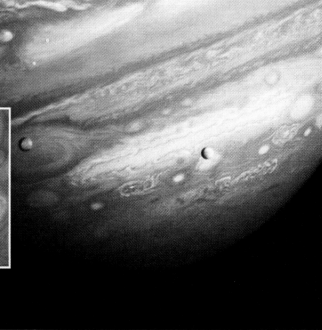

Figure 20 The larger photo of Jupiter was taken by the *Voyager 1* spacecraft. The small objects in front of Jupiter are two of Jupiter's moons, Io (left) and Europa (right). The Great Red Spot, shown in the inset, is a giant storm much larger in size than Earth.

554

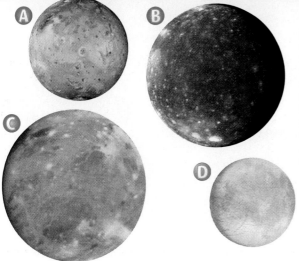

Figure 21 The astronomer Galileo discovered Jupiter's four largest moons. **(A)** Io's surface is covered with large, active volcanoes. **(B)** Callisto's surface is icy and covered with craters. **(C)** Ganymede is the largest of Jupiter's moons. **(D)** Europa's icy crust may have liquid water underneath.
Inferring Why was Galileo able to see only Jupiter's largest moons?

Io is covered with volcanoes. Over a dozen huge volcanoes are erupting all the time, so Io's surface changes from year to year because of the flows of hot material. The sulfur in the flows gives a variety of colors to Io's surface. From space, Io looks something like a giant pizza. In contrast, Europa has an icy crust that may have liquid water underneath.

Ganymede is the largest of Jupiter's moons and has about twice the mass of Earth's moon. Ganymede's surface is icy and partly covered with craters. Other parts of the surface show giant grooves in the ice. Callisto also has an icy surface. It is so heavily cratered that no part of its surface is free of craters.

☑ *Checkpoint* What are Jupiter's four largest moons?

Saturn

The second-largest planet in the solar system is Saturn. Saturn is slightly smaller than Jupiter, but including its beautiful rings it has a greater overall diameter. The *Voyager* probes showed that Saturn, like Jupiter, has a thick atmosphere made up mainly of hydrogen and helium. Saturn's atmosphere also contains clouds and storms, but they are less dramatic than those on Jupiter. Saturn is the only planet that is less dense than water.

Saturn's Rings When Galileo first looked at Saturn with a telescope, he saw something sticking out on the sides, but he didn't know what it was. A few decades later, another astronomer using a better telescope discovered that Saturn had rings around it. Astronomers later found that these rings are made of chunks of ice and rock, each traveling in its own orbit around Saturn. The rings are part of the Saturn system.

Model Saturn

Here's how you can build a scale model of Saturn.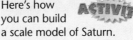

1. Use a plastic foam sphere 8 cm in diameter to represent Saturn.

2. ✂ Use an overhead transparency to represent Saturn's rings. Cut a circle 18 cm in diameter out of the transparency. Cut a hole 9 cm in diameter out of the center of the circle.

3. Stick five toothpicks into Saturn, spaced equally around its equator. Put the transparency on the toothpicks and tape it to them. Sprinkle baking soda on the transparency.

4. Use a peppercorn to represent Titan. Place the peppercorn 72 cm away from Saturn on the same plane as the rings.

Making Models What do the particles of baking soda represent?

TRY THIS

Skills Focus making models

Materials *8-cm plastic foam sphere, clear plastic sheet, ruler, scissors, compass, 5 toothpicks, tape, baking soda, peppercorn, glue (optional)*

Time 20 minutes

Tips You may want to cut circles from the center of the transparencies yourself so that students do not need to use sharp-nosed scissors.

Expected Outcome Students should understand that the particles of baking soda represent the chunks of ice and rock that make up Saturn's rings.

Extend Challenge students to use their model to demonstrate why the rings of Saturn are occasionally invisible from Earth. **learning modality: kinesthetic**

Media and Technology

 Transparencies "Characteristics of the Outer Planets," Transparency 80

Answers to Self-Assessment

Caption Question

Figure 21 The other moons are too small and dim to have been visible through Galileo's telescope.

☑ *Checkpoint*

Io, Callisto, Ganymede, Europa

Ongoing Assessment

Oral Presentation Have students describe what they would see if they stood on the surfaces of Jupiter's four largest moons.

Saturn, continued

Using the Visuals: Figure 23

Have students write sentences describing the distinctive appearance of each of the moons shown in the figure. They should include any features that are visible, such as unusual color or large craters and note similarities to other objects in the solar system.

 Students can save their sentences in their portfolios.

learning modality: visual

Building Inquiry Skills: Comparing and Contrasting

Students can make a compare/contrast table showing the similarities and differences between Saturn and Jupiter. The table should include size, density, appearance, composition, and any other features students wish to include.

learning modality: logical/ mathematical

Visual Arts Connection

The particles in Saturn's rings create an image of a solid surface when viewed from a distance. Artists who paint in the *pointillist* style use tiny dots to create a similar visual effect. One famous painting in this style has over 3,400,000 dots! Computer graphics images are built up in the same way, with hundreds of thousands of tiny colored dots forming the image. Obtain art reference books with examples of pointillist paintings to show to students. Challenge them to create pointillist-style drawings of one of the outer planets.

 Students can save their drawings in their portfolios. **learning modality: visual**

Figure 22 Saturn's rings are made up of ice chunks and rocks of many different sizes. The smaller photo shows that there are actually many small rings. The colors in this photo have been added by a computer. *Observing Why might it be hard to see Saturn's rings when their edges are facing Earth?*

From Earth, it looks as though Saturn has only a few rings, and that they are divided from each other by narrow, dark regions. The *Voyager* spacecraft discovered that each of these obvious rings is divided into dozens of smaller rings. In all, Saturn has hundreds of rings.

Saturn's rings are broad and thin, like a compact disc. Sometimes the rings are tipped so that observers see them at an angle. Occasionally, they are on edge, and then, because they are so thin, astronomers can't see them at all.

In the last few decades, rings have been discovered around the other three gas giants as well. But the rings around Jupiter, Uranus, and Neptune are not as spectacular as Saturn's.

Saturn's Moons Saturn's largest moon, Titan, is larger than Earth's own moon. Titan was discovered in 1665 but was known only as a point of light until the *Voyager*s went by. The probes showed that Titan has an atmosphere so thick that little light can get through it. Astronomers studying Hubble Space Telescope images can barely see Titan's surface.

Four other moons of Saturn are each over 1,000 kilometers in diameter. They are named Tethys (TEE this), Iapetus (eye AP uh tus), Dione, and Rhea. *Voyager* images show craters and canyons on these moons.

☑ *Checkpoint* **What are Saturn's rings made of?**

Figure 23 This image of Saturn and six of its moons combines photos taken by *Voyager 1* and *Voyager 2*.

556

Background

History of Science Like her brother William, Caroline Herschel (1750–1848) was born in Hanover in what is now Germany. William developed an interest in astronomy, even grinding mirrors for his own telescopes. At night, Caroline took notes on William's observations. During the day, she kept house, helped William grind and polish mirrors, and made the difficult computations connected with his observations.

Caroline also made her own observations. In 1786, she became the first woman to discover a comet. After William married in 1788, Caroline continued her studies, discovering seven more comets. William died in 1822, and Caroline returned to Hanover, where she completed the cataloguing of 2,500 nebulae and many star clusters. She died in 1848, two months short of her 98th birthday.

Uranus

Although the gas giant Uranus (YOOR uh nus) is about four times the diameter of Earth, it is still much smaller than Jupiter and Saturn. Uranus is twice as far from the sun as Saturn, so it is much colder. Uranus looks bluish because of traces of methane in its atmosphere.

Discovery of Uranus In 1781, Uranus became the first new planet discovered since ancient times. Astronomer William Herschel, in England, found an object in the sky that did not look like a star. At first he thought it might be a comet. But other astronomers soon calculated its orbit and realized that it was a planet beyond Saturn. The discovery made Herschel famous and started an era of solar system exploration.

Exploring Uranus In 1986, about 200 years after Herschel's discovery, *Voyager 2* arrived at Uranus and sent back our only close-up views of that giant planet. Images from *Voyager 2* show only a few clouds on Uranus's surface, but even these few allowed astronomers to calculate that Uranus rotates in about 17 hours.

Strangely, Uranus's axis is tilted at an angle of about 90° from the vertical, as shown in Figure 24. Viewed from Earth, Uranus is rotating from top to bottom instead of from side to side, the way most of the other planets do. Astronomers think that billions of years ago Uranus was hit by an object that knocked it on its side.

Uranus's Moons Photographs from *Voyager 2* showed that Uranus's five largest moons have icy, cratered surfaces. The craters show that the moons have been hit by rocks from space. Uranus's moons also have lava flows on their surfaces, suggesting that material has erupted from inside each moon. *Voyager 2* images revealed ten moons that had never been seen before. Since then, astronomers have discovered additional moons.

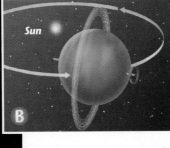

Figure 24 **(A)** This composite image of *Voyager 2* photos includes Uranus and five of its moons. **(B)** Unlike most other planets, Uranus rotates on its side.

Answers to Self-Assessment

Caption Question

Figure 22 The rings are so thin that when their edges face Earth they are nearly invisible.

☑ *Checkpoint*
Ice chunks and rocks

Uranus

Using the Visuals: Figure 24

Some students may think that the axis of rotation of Uranus always points to the sun. Have students lay a pencil over the axis of rotation, then trace the orbit of Uranus by moving the pencil. The pencil should always point to the left edge of the paper. **learning modality: visual**

Language Arts CONNECTION

Explain to students that the planets were supposed to share characteristics of the gods after which they were named. Provide reference books for students. Allow them to work in groups to find out more about the gods the planets were named for. They can try to think of a reason why each planet was given the name it has, both by the Romans and by modern astronomers. (*Sample: Mercury, the fastest moving planet, was named for the swiftest of the gods. Mars, with its distinctive reddish color, was named for the god of war.*)

Extend Have students rename the planets after famous characters from literature or popular culture. Ask them to explain their choices.

In Your Journal Students can consult mythology books and other reference books to read about ancient gods. If students wish to explore the names of bodies other than planets, allow them to research the names of moons of different planets. **learning modality: verbal**

Ongoing Assessment

Writing Have students create two fact sheets about Uranus. The first should include facts known about the planet before the *Voyager* images. The second should include facts learned since the *Voyager* images.

Neptune

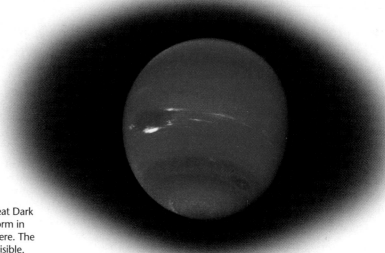

Figure 25 The Great Dark Spot was a giant storm in Neptune's atmosphere. The storm is no longer visible.

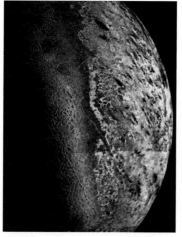

Figure 26 Neptune's largest moon, Triton, is covered with ridges and craters.

Neptune

Neptune is even farther from the sun than Uranus—in fact, it is 30 times Earth's distance from the sun. Unlike Uranus's nearly featureless blue atmosphere, the atmosphere of Neptune contains visible clouds.

Discovery of Neptune The planet Neptune was discovered as a result of a mathematical prediction. Uranus was not quite following the orbit astronomers predicted for it. Astronomers hypothesized that there must be another, unseen planet whose gravity was affecting Uranus's orbit. By 1846, mathematicians in both England and France had calculated the orbit of this new planet. A few months later, an observer in Germany saw an unknown object in the sky. It was the new planet, now called Neptune.

Exploring Neptune In 1989 *Voyager 2* flew by Neptune, where it photographed a Great Dark Spot, as shown in Figure 25, about the size of Earth. Like the Great Red Spot on Jupiter, the Great Dark Spot probably was a giant storm. This storm cannot be seen now. Images from the Hubble Space Telescope taken five years later showed that the Great Dark Spot was gone. Other, smaller spots and regions of clouds on Neptune seem to come and go.

Neptune's Moons Astronomers have discovered eight moons revolving around Neptune. Neptune's largest moon is Triton. The *Voyager* photos show that the region near Triton's south pole is covered with a cap of ice, and that dark material is visible underneath the ice.

☑ *Checkpoint* Before they could see Neptune, what evidence led scientists to conclude that it existed?

Pluto and Charon

Pluto and its single moon Charon are very different from the gas giants. **Pluto and Charon have solid surfaces and masses much less than that of Earth.** In fact, Pluto is less than two thirds the size of Earth's moon. Since Charon is more than half the size of Pluto, astronomers sometimes consider them to be a double planet instead of a planet and a moon.

Pluto and Charon are so far from the sun that they revolve around the sun only once every 248 Earth years. Because Pluto and Charon are so small and far away, astronomers have been unable to learn much about them.

Discovery of Pluto and Charon The American astronomer Clyde Tombaugh discovered Pluto in 1930. He had been searching for a large object he thought might be affecting Neptune's orbit. Tombaugh spent 10 months looking at hundreds of thousands of images before he found Pluto. Charon was not discovered until 1978, by the astronomer James Christy. Christy was studying photographs of Pluto when he noticed that Pluto seemed to have a "bump." The bump turned out to be Charon.

Is Pluto Really a Planet? Pluto is so small that many astronomers do not think it should be called a planet at all. Pluto may be merely the largest of thousands of objects revolving around the sun out beyond Neptune. If astronomers had found these other objects before they found Pluto, they might not have called Pluto a planet.

Figure 27 The space between Pluto and Charon was clearly seen from Earth in 1999, using new telescopes in Hawaii. This photo, taken with the Hubble Space Telescope, clearly shows them as two objects. *Inferring Why do astronomers sometimes call Pluto and Charon a double planet?*

Section 4 Review

1. How are the gas giants similar to each other? How are they different?
2. How is Pluto different from the gas giants?
3. What is the most prominent feature of Jupiter's surface? What causes this feature?
4. Why do astronomers think Uranus may have been hit by another object billions of years ago?
5. **Thinking Critically Predicting** Do you think astronomers have found all of the moons of the outer planets? Explain.

Check Your Progress   CHAPTER PROJECT

Once you have models that show size and distance separately, design another scale model of the solar system. This time, use the same scale for both size and distance. If your chalkboard is the sun, which planets would be in your classroom? Where would the other planets be with respect to your classroom, school grounds, and town?

Discuss with classmates any problems that would come up in building a model using the same scale for both size and distance. Revise your model as needed.

Program Resources

♦ **Unit 4 Resources** 16-4 Review and Reinforce, p. 199; 16-4 Enrich, p. 200

Answers to Self-Assessment

Caption Question

Figure 27 Pluto and Charon are close in size and close together.

☑ *Checkpoint*

Uranus was not following the orbit that scientists predicted. Scientists believed that the gravity of a large object, probably a planet, was affecting Uranus's orbit.

3 Assess

Section 4 Review Answers

1. They are all much larger than Earth, and do not have solid surfaces. They differ in size, number of moons, presence of rings, the tilt of their axes, and the presence of storms in their atmospheres.
2. Pluto is smaller and denser than the gas giants.
3. The Great Red Spot is Jupiter's most prominent feature. It is probably caused by a hurricane-like storm in the atmosphere.
4. Uranus's axis is tilted 90°. This could have been caused by a collision with another object.
5. No. Many of the moons were found only with the help of the *Voyager* photographs. Future probes will probably find other moons that *Voyager* may have missed.

Check Your Progress   CHAPTER PROJECT

By this time, students should have a model showing relative size and a model showing relative distance. The larger the model, the more successful it will be in accurately representing the sizes of the planets. It is difficult to find a suitable scale that will clearly show both sizes and distances between the planets . For example, if the distance to Pluto is made equal to 100 m, then the size of Pluto would be 0.03 mm! Jupiter would be the size of a BB. If the size of Pluto is made 1.00 mm, then the distance to Pluto would be 2.6 km!

Performance Assessment

Drawing Have students draw diagrams of the outer planets that show their relative sizes, order, and at least one distinguishing characteristic of each planet.

 Students can save their diagrams in their portfolios.

Speeding Around the Sun

Preparing for Inquiry

Key Concept Since the pull of gravity is stronger, planets closer to the sun must move faster in order to maintain a stable orbit. Therefore, the length of time it takes a planet to go around the sun is related to the distance of the planet from the sun.

Skills Objectives Students will be able to:

- formulate hypotheses concerning the revolution of a planet around the sun related to its distance from the sun;
- test their hypotheses to determine if they are supported by the available data;
- determine whether their hypotheses should be accepted or rejected based on the results of their tests.

Time 45 minutes

Advance Planning If you have not yet taught the skill of developing a hypothesis, refer to the Skills Handbook. Perform this activity on your own first to become familiar with any problems students may experience in keeping the stopper swinging at various distances from the plastic tube. Use the materials to assemble a sling and test it for safety. Make sure that there is enough open space for groups to work without hitting each other.

Alternative Methods If you are concerned about students hitting one another, carry out the physical aspects of the lab as a demonstration from which students can develop the skill of formulating a hypothesis. In place of the stopper, a tennis ball with rubber bands around it or any other soft object of suitable weight and density that can be safely tied to the end of the string can be used. In place of the plastic tube, a pen tube with smooth ends may be used. Keep these for following years. To ensure that the string will not come out of the tube, tie a washer that does not fit through the tube to the string.

SPEEDING AROUND THE SUN

In this lab, you will make and test a hypothesis about how a planet's distance from the sun is related to its period of revolution.

Problem

How does a planet's distance from the sun affect its period of revolution?

Materials

string, 1.5 m
plastic tube, 6 cm
meter stick
one-hole rubber stopper
stopwatch
weight or several washers

Procedure

1. What do you think is the relationship between a planet's distance from the sun and its period of revolution? Write your hypothesis in the form of an "If . . . then . . ." statement.

2. To test your hypothesis, you need to make a model planet.

   a. Thread the string through the rubber stopper hole. Tie the end of the string to the main part of the string. Pull tightly to make sure that the knot will not become untied.

   b. Thread the other end of the string through the plastic tube and tie a weight to that end. Have your teacher check both knots.

   c. Hold the plastic tube in your hand above your head. Swing the stopper around above your head. Practice keeping the stopper moving at a constant speed. The circle represents the planet's orbit. **CAUTION:** *Stand away from other students. Make sure the swinging stopper will not hit students or objects. Do not let go of the string.*

3. Before you try different distances for your model planet, copy the data table into your notebook.

DATA TABLE				
Distance (cm)	Period of Revolution (seconds)			
	Trial 1	Trial 2	Trial 3	Average
20				
40				
60				

4. Pull the string so the stopper is 20 cm away from the plastic tube. Swing the stopper just fast enough to keep the stopper moving.

560

Guiding Inquiry

Invitation Discuss the difference between a hypothesis and a scientific fact. A hypothesis is an educated statement based on evidence.

Introducing the Procedure

Have students think of the inward pull of the string as gravity. The activity is self-explanatory and should give students a "feel" for the effects of gravity and the increased speed as the orbit gets smaller.

Troubleshooting the Experiment

Students may have to practice keeping the stopper moving at a constant speed. They may try to keep the stopper moving with the same frequency. Tell them to keep the stopper moving just fast enough to keep it up.

Media and Technology

 Lab Activity Videotapes
Grade 6, Tape 4

5. Have your partner time how long it takes for the stopper to make 10 revolutions. Divide by 10 to find the period of revolution. Record this number as Trial 1.

6. Repeat Steps 4–5 two more times. Record your results as Trials 2 and 3. Add the results of the three trials together and divide by three to find the average period of revolution.

7. If you pull the stopper out to 40 cm, do you think the period of revolution will increase or decrease? To find out, pull the stopper out to 40 cm and repeat Steps 4–6.

8. Based on your results in Step 7, do you want to revise your hypothesis? Make any needed changes. Then pull the stopper out to 60 cm and repeat Steps 4–6.

Analyze and Conclude

1. Which object in your model represented the sun? Which represented the planet?

2. What force did the pull on the string represent?

3. When you pulled the stopper out to make the orbit larger, did the string then represent a stronger or weaker force of gravity? Why?

4. What happened to the period of revolution when you made the orbit larger in Steps 7 and 8?

5. Did your observations support your hypothesis? Summarize your conclusions based on your observations.

6. Which planets take less time to revolve around the sun—those closer to the sun or those farther away? Use the model to support your answer.

7. **Think About It** What information did you consider when you made your hypothesis? How did having some experimental data help you modify your hypothesis?

Design an Experiment

Write a hypothesis relating the mass of a planet to its period of revolution. Then, using a stopper with a different mass, modify the activity to test your hypothesis. Before you swing the stopper, have your teacher check your knots.

- Students will see that it takes longer for a revolution when the string is longer.
- Students may have to reformulate their hypotheses from Step 8.
- Some students may ask for more information regarding the planets themselves. The circumference of the orbit increases as distance from the sun increases. As distance from the sun increases, the gravitational pull of the sun on a planet decreases. This means that the planet is traveling more slowly over a greater distance.

Analyze and Conclude

1. The plastic tube represented the sun. The rubber stopper represented the planet.
2. The pull on the string represented the force of gravity.
3. When the orbit was larger, the string represents a weaker force of gravity since the planet is farther away.
4. As the orbit became larger, the period of revolution became longer.
5. Sample: The period increased as predicted by the hypothesis. Observations supported the hypothesis.
6. Planets closer to the sun should take less time to revolve around the sun. When the string was short, the period of revolution was short.
7. Sample: String length determines orbit size, which determines the distance the stopper must travel in one orbit. We predict orbits of greater size will take longer to complete. The data supported the hypothesis.

Extending the Inquiry

Design an Experiment Adding more stoppers to the end of the string, increases the mass of the swinging object. By swinging the increased mass in the same orbit, students will find that planets have the same period at the same distance. They may also notice that the inward pull of the string has to be greater with more stoppers. The force of gravity between the sun and a planet is related to the mass of the planet. The inertia of a planet is also related to its mass. Thus, the effect of increasing the mass is to increase both the pull of the sun's gravity and the ability of the planet to withstand that pull through inertia. The resulting acceleration on the planet is the same, regardless of mass.

Sample Data Table

Distance (cm)	Trial 1 (sec)	Trial 2 (sec)	Trial 3 (sec)	Average (sec)
20	0.4	0.5	0.4	0.43
40	0.6	0.6	0.7	0.63
60	0.8	0.8	0.8	0.80

Safety

Any time there is a swinging stopper, make sure it is in an open space free to swing clear of all students and objects. Make sure that the object on the opposite end of the string from the stopper cannot be pulled through the pen tube. Check the strength of the string to make sure that it will not break. Tell students to wear eye protection throughout the lab. Review the safety guidelines in Appendix A.

SECTION 5 Comets, Asteroids, and Meteors

TEKS: 6.1A; 6.3C; 6.4B; 6.5A; 6.13A

Objectives

After completing the lesson, students will be able to

◆ identify the characteristics of comets and asteroids;

◆ describe the formation of meteoroids.

1 Engage/Explore

Activating Prior Knowledge

Ask students if they have ever seen a shooting star. Invite them to describe what a shooting star looks like. Ask them to speculate about what it is. After the discussion, tell students that in this section, they will investigate the nature of comets, asteroids, and shooting stars, which are actually meteors.

········ DISCOVER ········

Skills Focus inferring
Materials *modeling clay, pencil, 3 10-cm lengths of string, small fan*
Time 10 minutes
Tips You may wish to have more than one fan available and allow two or three students to test their models at the same time.
Expected Outcome The strings point away from the fan, behind the ball of clay.
Think It Over Moving the ball does not change the direction in which the strings point. A comet's tail always points away from the sun.

DISCOVER ···················· ACTIVITY

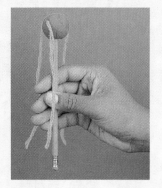

Which Way Do Comet Tails Point?

1. Form a small ball out of modeling clay to represent a comet.

2. ✂ Using a pencil point, push three 10-cm lengths of string into the ball. The strings represent the comet's tail. Stick the ball onto the pencil point, as shown in the photo.

3. 🔥 Hold the ball about 1 m in front of a fan. The air from the fan represents the solar wind. Move the ball toward the fan, away from the fan, and from side to side.
   CAUTION: *Keep your fingers away from the fan blades.*

Think It Over
Inferring How does moving the ball affect the direction in which the strings point? What determines which way the tail of a comet points?

GUIDE FOR READING

◆ What are the characteristics of comets and asteroids?

◆ Where do meteoroids come from?

Reading Tip As you read, make an outline of this section using the headings as the main topics.

Key Terms comet • asteroid • asteroid belt • meteoroid • meteor • meteorite

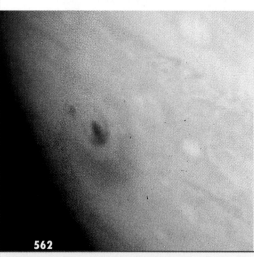

Suppose you could watch a cosmic collision! That's exactly what happened in July 1994. Eugene and Carolyn Shoemaker and David Levy discovered a new comet in 1993 that had previously broken into pieces near Jupiter. In 1994, the fragments returned and crashed into Jupiter. On Earth, astronomers were fascinated to see the huge explosions—some were as large as Earth!

As this story shows, the sun, planets, and moons aren't the only objects in the solar system. There are also millions of smaller objects, most of which are classified as comets and asteroids.

Comet Systems

One of the most glorious things you can see in the night sky is a comet. A bright comet may be visible for days or weeks or months and is well worth seeing. In April 1997, for example, Comet Hale-Bopp and its bright dust tail were clearly visible even without a telescope.

Like each planet, each comet is a small system within the large solar system. You can think of a **comet** as a "dirty snowball" about the size of a mountain on Earth. **Comets are large chunks of ice and dust whose orbits can be very long, narrow ellipses.**

◀ A dark ring on Jupiter caused by comet Shoemaker-Levy 9

562

READING STRATEGIES

Reading Tip Suggest to students that, as they outline, they leave space between the headings to fill in details. The completed outline can be used as a study guide.
I. Comet Systems
  A. Structure
    1. nucleus
    2. coma
    3. tail
  B. Orbit (outline will continue)

Study and Comprehension Provide each student with three note cards, and have them write *comet, asteroid,* and *meteor* on the cards, one term per card. As students read the section, have them list the characteristics of the object on the opposite side of each card. Then have partners take turns using their sets of note cards as flashcards for testing each other's knowledge of comets, asteroids, and meteors.

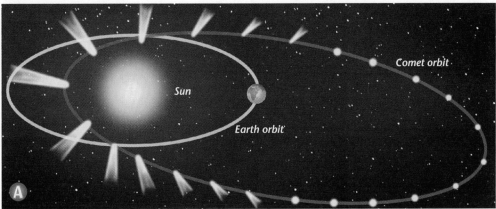

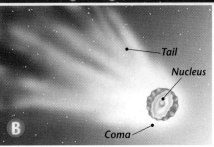

Few comet systems pass near Earth. The ones that do can usually be seen only briefly. When a comet system gets close enough to the sun, the energy in the sunlight turns the ice into gas, releasing dust. The gas and dust form an outer layer called the coma. Figure 28 shows the inner layer of the comet, which is then called the nucleus. The brightest part of a comet, the comet's head, is made up of the nucleus and coma.

Remember that the sun's corona produces a stream of particles called the solar wind. Solar wind pushes the gas from a comet away from the sun. Gas and dust form the comet's tail. The tail looks like hair; in fact, the name *comet* means "long-haired star" in Greek.

A comet's tail can be hundreds of millions of kilometers long and stretch across most of the sky. The material is stretched out very thinly, however, so there actually isn't much mass in the tail of a comet.

In 1705, Edmond Halley, an English astronomer, calculated the orbits of 24 comets that people had observed over hundreds of years. Halley realized that several of the comets seemed to have the same orbit and suggested that they were part of the same comet system. Halley calculated that this comet system appeared about every 76 years, and then predicted that it would reappear in 1758. When this prediction came true, the comet was named Halley's Comet. In 1986, the last time Halley's Comet appeared in our sky, the European Space Agency's *Giotto* spacecraft flew within a few hundred kilometers of it.

☑ *Checkpoint* How did Halley's Comet get its name?

Figure 28 (A) Some comet systems revolve around the sun in very long, narrow orbits. (B) The main parts of a comet system are the nucleus, the coma, and the tail. *Observing What shape is this comet's orbit (A)?*

Program Resources

◆ **Unit 4 Resources** 16-5 Lesson Plan, p. 201; 16-5 Section Summary, p. 202
◆ **Guided Reading and Study Workbook** 16-5

Answers to Self-Assessment

Caption Question

Figure 28 The shape of a comet's orbit is a long, narrow ellipse.

☑ *Checkpoint*

Edmond Halley identified a comet, and calculated that it appeared every 76 years. He predicted the comet would reappear in 1758. When Halley's prediction came true, the comet was named after him.

2 Facilitate

Comet Systems

Using the Visuals: Figure 28

Ask students how the orbit of a comet is different from the orbit of a planet. *(The orbits of most comets are much longer.)* **learning modality: visual**

Building Inquiry Skills: Inferring

As students explore the structure of a comet, have them make inferences about observing comets from Earth. Ask: **Which part of the comet do we see? Why?** *(The coma and tail; they are the brightest parts of the comet.)* **Why would it be difficult to view the nucleus?** *(It is very small and obscured by the coma.)* **learning modality: verbal**

Building Inquiry Skills: Predicting

Ask students to predict whether they are likely to ever have the opportunity to see Halley's comet. *(Probably, for most students)* Encourage students to determine approximately how old they will be at that time. *(Most will be in their 70s.)* **learning modality: logical/ mathematical**

Ongoing Assessment

Writing Have students explain how the coma and tail of a comet are formed.

563

Asteroids

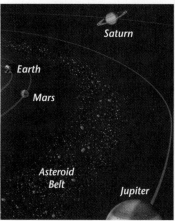

Figure 29 The asteroid belt (left) lies between Mars and Jupiter. Asteroids come in many sizes and shapes, as shown in this artist's depiction (center). NASA's *Galileo* spacecraft photographed the asteroid Gaspra (right) in 1991.

Math TOOLBOX

Frequency

The frequency of an event is how often the event occurs in a given time period. Meteors streak across the sky with a certain frequency during a meteor shower. For example, if you see 1 meteor streak per minute for an hour, the frequency of meteor streaks is 60 streaks per hour. At another time, you might see 1 meteor streak every 10 minutes for an hour. In this case, the frequency of streaks is 6 streaks per hour.

Asteroids

Between 1801 and 1807, astronomers discovered four small objects between the orbits of Mars and Jupiter. They named the objects Ceres, Pallas, Juno, and Vesta. Over the next 80 years, astronomers found 300 more. These objects, called **asteroids,** are too small and too numerous to be considered full-fledged planets. **Most asteroids revolve around the sun between the orbits of Mars and Jupiter.** This region of the solar system, shown in Figure 29, is known as the **asteroid belt.** The asteroid belt is another small system within the solar system.

Astronomers have discovered more than 10,000 asteroids, and more are found every month. Ceres, Pallas, Juno, and Vesta are among the dozen that are over 250 kilometers across.

INTEGRATING EARTH SCIENCE Some asteroids come near the orbit of Earth. Near Earth asteroids could hit Earth. When a large asteroid hit Earth 65 million years ago, it exploded, making a crater 200 kilometers in diameter near the Yucatán Peninsula of Mexico. The explosion almost certainly raised trillions of tons of dust into the atmosphere, blocking the light from the sun for months. Debris from the explosion probably started huge fires that destroyed much of Earth's forests and grass. Scientists hypothesize that as a result many species of organisms, including the dinosaurs, became extinct.

Meteors

Suppose you are outside on a clear night, looking up at the sky. Suddenly, you see a streak of light flashing across the sky. Within seconds, you see another streak. For an hour or so, meteors streak with a frequency of at least one per minute. You are watching a meteor shower. Meteor showers happen regularly, several times a year.

Even when there is no meteor shower, you can see meteors if you are far from city lights and the sky is free of clouds. On average, a meteor streaks overhead with a frequency of one every 10 minutes.

A **meteoroid** is a chunk of rock or dust in space. **Meteoroids usually come from comets or asteroids.** Comets leave dust behind as they move through the solar system. When Earth passes through one of these dust clouds, bits of dust enter Earth's atmosphere.

When a meteoroid enters Earth's atmosphere, friction makes it burn up and produce the streak of light you see in the sky—a **meteor.** If the meteoroid is large, it may not burn up completely. Meteoroids that pass through the atmosphere and hit Earth's surface are called **meteorites.** The craters on the moon and on other objects in the solar system were caused by meteoroids.

Meteorites fall all over Earth. Most of them look just like stones, so nobody notices them. A few meteorites are made almost entirely of iron and nickel, and so are unusually heavy for their size. This makes them more likely to be identified as meteorites than as Earth rocks.

Figure 30 (A) Meteor Crater in Arizona is the best-known meteorite crater on Earth. It was formed when a meteorite hit Earth about 40,000 years ago. (B) Meteoroids make streaks of light, like the one above, as they burn up in the atmosphere.

Section 5 Review

1. What is a comet made of?
2. Where are most asteroids found?
3. What are the main sources of meteoroids?
4. What is the difference between a meteor and a meteorite?
5. **Thinking Critically** **Predicting** Describe what might happen if an asteroid the size of the one that hit Earth 65 million years ago hit Earth today.

Science at Home

Watch a Meteor Shower Meteor showers occur regularly on specific dates. (The Perseids meteor shower, for example, occurs every August 12.) Look in the newspaper or almanac for information about the next meteor shower. With adult family members, go outside on that night and look for meteors. Explain to your family what causes the glow.

Media and Technology

 Transparencies "A Comet's Orbit," Transparency 81

Program Resources

◆ **Unit 4 Resources** 16-5 Review and Reinforce, p. 203; 16-5 Enrich, p. 204

3 Assess

Section 5 Review Answers

1. Chunks of ice and dust
2. In the asteroid belt that lies between Jupiter and Mars
3. Most meteoroids come from comets or asteroids.
4. A meteor is a meteoroid that enters Earth's atmosphere and burns up. A meteorite is a meteoroid that passes through Earth's atmosphere and hits Earth's surface.
5. Effects would vary, depending on whether the object hit on land or water. In either case, the collision would raise huge clouds of dust, blocking light from the sun. Many species of living things could become extinct as a result of the blocked sunlight.

Science at Home

Since they will be outdoors after dark, **ACTIVITY** caution students they should only view a meteor shower with an adult. Meteor showers are more easily seen outside cities, in areas where bright lights do not block the glow from the meteors. Students should explain that the glow is caused by friction caused by Earth's atmosphere heating the rock as it falls.

Performance Assessment

Oral Presentation Have students narrate the life story of an asteroid that orbits close to Earth and eventually hits the ground.

SECTION 6 Traveling in Space

TEKS: 6.1A; 6.4A; 6.6A; 6.13B

Objectives

After completing the lesson, students will be able to

◆ explain how rockets travel in space;
◆ list the equipment needed to travel in space.

1 Engage/Explore

Activating Prior Knowledge

Many students will have watched a space shuttle launch on television or will have seen rockets being launched in news specials, documentaries, or movies. Invite volunteers to describe what happens when a rocket is launched. Ask them to consider the motion of the rocket in their responses. *(Sample: Engines are fired, large clouds of gas come from the rocket boosters, and the rocket or space shuttle pulls away from Earth.)* Ask students what forces are at work when a rocket lifts off from the ground. *(Gas pushed out the bottom of the rocket pushes against the rocket.)*

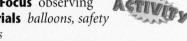 **DISCOVER**

Skills Focus observing **ACTIVITY**
Materials *balloons, safety goggles*
Time 10 minutes
Tips Remind students to try to blow up the balloons to the same size each time so they can compare their results.
Expected Outcome The balloons will move across the room in both trials.
Think It Over The air rushes out the neck of the balloon, and the balloon goes in the opposite direction. The balloon does not need to push against something to move, because it is the action-reaction pair of forces that makes it move, not the push of air off your hand.

SECTION 6 Traveling in Space

DISCOVER ·· ACTIVITY

How Do Rockets Work?

1. Put on your goggles. Blow up a balloon and hold its neck closed with your fingers.

2. Point the balloon toward an area where there are no people. Put your free hand behind the neck of the balloon, so the air will push against your hand. Let go of the balloon.

3. Repeat Steps 1 and 2 without your free hand behind the balloon.

Think It Over
Observing In which direction does the air rush out? In which direction does the balloon go? Does the balloon need to push against something in order to move? Explain your answer.

GUIDE FOR READING

◆ How do rockets travel in space?

◆ What type of equipment is needed in space?

Reading Tip Before you read, rewrite the headings in the section as *how, why,* or *what* questions. As you read, look for answers to those questions.

Key Terms satellite
• geosynchronous orbit

Curiosity about Earth's "neighborhood" in space has led to moon missions, space shuttle missions, space stations, and Mars missions. But without rockets, none of these accomplishments would have been possible.

Transportation in Space

It is not very easy to get into space. It is even more difficult to get back to Earth. Rockets transport astronauts and equipment into space and back.

How Rockets Work A rocket works in much the way that a balloon is propelled through the air by releasing gas. **A rocket moves forward when gases shot out the back of the rocket push it in the opposite direction.** This is because for every force, or action, an equal and opposite force, or reaction, happens. Therefore, the force of the air being forced out the back of a balloon is an action force. An equal force, the reaction, pushes the balloon forward. In a rocket, fuel is burned to make a hot gas. This hot gas is forced out of narrow nozzles in the back of the rocket, propelling the rocket forward.

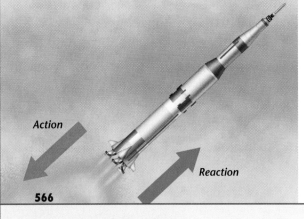

Action

Reaction

566

Figure 31 The force of the rocket engine's hot gas in one direction (action) produces an opposing force (reaction) that propels the rocket forward.

READING STRATEGIES

Reading Tip Suggest students write their how, why, and what questions in columns under those headings. Encourage them to answer the questions based on what they already know, and revise their answers as they read. Questions may include "How does transportation in space work?" and "What are artificial satellites?"

4b Lunar vehicle proceeds to lunar orbit.

3b Third stage ignites.

4a Third stage is discarded.

3a Second stage separates and falls to Earth.

2b Second stage ignites and continues with third stage.

2a First stage separates and falls to Earth.

Figure 32 Multistage rockets have three stages, or sections. *Interpreting Diagrams According to this diagram, which stage, or section, of the rocket reaches the destination? What happens to the other stages?*

Multistage Rockets Early rockets, built by the Chinese around the year 1000, used gunpowder as fuel. But gunpowder burns quickly and explosively. A rocket designed to travel out of Earth's atmosphere needs a different sort of fuel, one that burns slowly and continuously. The American scientist Robert H. Goddard experimented with liquid fuels in the 1920s. He showed that a liquid fuel can provide continuous power.

However, a rocket can carry only so much fuel. Once the fuel is used up, the rocket falls back to Earth. In 1903, the Russian Konstantin Tsiolkovsky came up with the idea of a multistage rocket. As each stage, or section, of a rocket uses up its fuel, the empty fuel container drops off. Then the next stage ignites and continues powering the rocket upward. The development of powerful multistage rockets in the 1950s and 1960s made it possible to send rockets to the moon and farther into space. Figure 32 shows a rocket similar to the one that carried the astronauts to the moon.

In the late 1970s, the National Aeronautics and Space Administration (NASA) developed reusable space shuttles. They are called shuttles because they can go back and forth, or shuttle, between Earth and space. Since the first shuttle was launched in 1981, space shuttles have been the main way that the United States has launched astronauts and equipment into space.

Artificial Satellites

The Soviet Union launched the first artificial satellite into orbit around Earth on October 4, 1957. A **satellite** is any natural or artificial object that revolves around an object in space. This satellite, *Sputnik 1,* revolved around Earth every 96 minutes. Three months later, the United States launched *Explorer 1* into orbit. On April 12, 1961, Yuri Gagarin, a Soviet cosmonaut, orbited Earth, becoming the first person in space.

Third stage

Second stage

First stage

1 Heavy first stage provides thrust for launch.

Transportation in Space

Demonstration

Time 15 minutes
Materials *2 long balloons, nylon fishing line, 2 plastic drinking straws, plastic foam cup, masking tape, scissors*

ACTIVITY

Tips Model a two-stage rocket. Thread the straws on the fishing line and tie the line securely across the room. Cut the top off a cup to make a ring. Inflate one balloon about three quarters full and hold the neck tight so no air can escape. Do not tie the neck. Have a volunteer help you place the neck of the balloon through the plastic foam ring and hold the balloon tightly closed against the ring. Inflate the second balloon so that the round end extends a short way through the ring. After some practice, you will be able to inflate the second balloon so it presses the neck of the first balloon against the ring and holds the first balloon shut. Hold the neck of the second balloon firmly, and tape one balloon to each of the straws on the line. When you release the balloon, the escaping air will propel the balloons down the line. When one balloon runs out of air, it will release the other balloon. **learning modality: visual**

Artificial Satellites

Including All Students

Remind students that something that is artificial is not natural but made by humans. Have students give examples of natural satellites. (*Sample: any moon in the solar system, such as Earth's moon, Charon, Io, Callisto, Ganymede, and Europa.*) **learning modality: verbal**

Answers to Self-Assessment

Caption Question

Figure 32 Only part of the third stage reaches the rocket's destination. As each of the other stages uses up its fuel, the empty fuel container drops off and falls to Earth.

Ongoing Assessment

Oral Presentation Ask students to describe how satellites are launched into orbit.

Artificial Satellites, continued

TRY THIS

Skills Focus observing

ACTIVITY

Materials *plastic or paper cup, paper, tape, film canister with a lid that snaps on inside the canister, water, fizzing antacid tablet, safety goggles*

Time 20 minutes

Tips Caution students not to place sharp objects on the rocket.

Expected Outcome The rocket will lift off and shoot 2 to 5 meters into the air.

Observing Gas pressure builds up inside the canister due to the reaction of the antacid and water. Pressure continues to build until it blows off the lid of the canister and launches the rocket.

Extend Challenge students to design and launch rockets powered by two, three, or more film canisters. **learning modality: logical/mathematical**

Inquiry Challenge

Pair students and have them use physical activity

ACTIVITY

to model how a satellite with a geosynchronous orbit can stay above the same point on Earth. One student turns very slowly in place at about one turn per minute, while the partner walks around the first student in a circle at a rate of one step per second so that the turning student always faces the walking student. There will be only one radius where this will happen. Ask the students to describe what is happening. Now have the walking student move faster and walk in a smaller circle while the turning student turns at the same rate. Ask the students to describe what happens. *(The first case models a geosynchronous orbit. The second case models a low Earth orbit.)* **learning modality: kinesthetic**

568

Be a Rocket Scientist

You can build a rocket.

ACTIVITY

1. Use a plastic or paper cup as the rocket body. Cut out a paper nose cone and tape it to the closed end of the cup.

2. Obtain an empty film canister with a lid that snaps on inside the canister. Go outside to do Steps 3–5.

3. Fill the canister about one-quarter full with water.

4. Put on your goggles. Now add half of a fizzing antacid tablet to the film canister and quickly snap on the lid.

5. Place the canister on the ground with the lid down. Place your rocket over the canister and stand back.

Observing What action happened inside the film canister? What was the reaction of the rocket?

Figure 33 The International Space Station is a cooperative project involving 16 countries, including the United States, Russia, Japan, and Canada. This is an artist's conception of the station in orbit over Florida.

568

Since 1957, thousands of artificial satellites, including space stations, have been launched into orbit. Satellites and space stations are used for communications, navigation, collecting weather data, and research.

Satellites Artificial satellites are used to relay telephone calls, to measure Earth's atmosphere, and to photograph weather systems, crops, and ships. In addition, two dozen Global Positioning Satellites give off signals that a small receiver on Earth can pick up. The receiver can then pinpoint your position on Earth's surface.

Some satellites are in **geosynchronous orbits,** which means they revolve around Earth at the same rate that Earth rotates. Geosynchronous satellites above the equator seem to hover over a given point on Earth. Geosynchronous satellites are used to relay television signals and to map weather patterns.

Space Stations A space station is a large satellite in which people can live for long periods. The first space station, the Soviet Union's *Salyut*, was launched in 1971. In 1973, the United States launched *Skylab*, which carried a series of telescopes and medical, geological, and astronomical experiments. The former Soviet Union, of which Russia was part, launched the *Mir* space station in 1986. Astronauts from many countries visited *Mir* until 2001, when the space station fell out of orbit. Sixteen countries, including the United States and Russia, are now cooperating to build the International Space Station.

✓ *Checkpoint* What is a geosynchronous orbit?

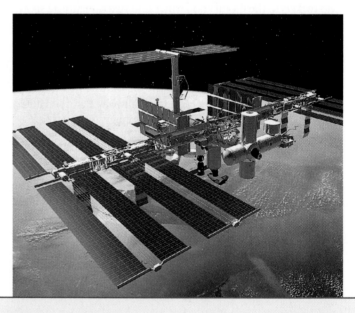

Background

History of Science Artificial satellites used for communications are generally very reliable. However, on May 19, 1998, a satellite called *Galaxy 4* went out of service when its onboard control system failed and the satellite rolled out of position. Its failure interrupted communications systems all over the United States and the Caribbean.

Because a majority of pager companies in the United States relied on *Galaxy 4,* approximately 40 million pager users lost service. In addition, television and radio networks used *Galaxy 4* to transmit feeds to their stations, so these transmissions were interrupted too. The problem also halted the operation of bank automated teller machines and the systems customers use at gas stations to pay with credit cards. To reestablish service, the company that owns *Galaxy 4* had to reposition another satellite.

Figure 34 The Space Shuttle *Discovery* is launched into space by its own rockets as well as by rockets attached to it. *Inferring What is one advantage of a reusable space vehicle?*

Equipment Needed in Space

Astronauts need special equipment such as space suits and computers to work in space. The space suits help them adapt to the changes their bodies experience as they leave Earth. Each suit adjusts air pressure and oxygen levels for the astronaut wearing it. It also includes a helmet, communication system, and parachute.

Once in space, computers monitor the conditions on the shuttle, including air pressure, temperature, and the oxygen in the air. All this information is sent to computers on Earth, linking the shuttle with NASA scientists here.

When the astronauts leave the shuttle to work in space, they must take along a life-supporting environment. Space suits are portable work environments. They supply the oxygen the astronauts need to breathe. They also have built-in radios that allow astronauts to communicate with others. The suits are made of a material that protects astronauts from the sun's radiation and the extreme temperature changes in space.

 Section 6 Review

1. How does a rocket move?
2. What do astronauts need to live and work in space?
3. Which stage of a multistage rocket reaches the final destination?
4. **Thinking Critically** **Applying Concepts** Explain why space suits are among the most important pieces of equipment for an astronaut.

Science at Home

Landmarks in Space Flight Interview someone who remembers the space programs of the 1950s and 1960s. Prepare your questions in advance, such as: How did you feel when *Sputnik* was in orbit? How did you feel when the first Americans went into space? Did you watch any of the rocket launches on television? You may want to record your interview, then write it out in a question-and-answer format.

Answers to Self-Assessment

Caption Question

Figure 34 Reusable vehicles are less expensive.

 Checkpoint

A geosynchronous orbit is one in which a satellite revolves around Earth at the same rate that Earth rotates on its axis.

Equipment Needed in Space

Including All Students

Make sure students understand that much of the equipment astronauts in space need is used to simulate environmental conditions on Earth to which their bodies are adapted. As a class, discuss how environmental conditions in space differ from those on Earth. **learning modality: verbal**

3 Assess

Section 6 Review Answers

1. The rocket's exhaust gases go in one direction and the rocket moves in the opposite direction.
2. A communication system, space suits, navigation equipment, computers, and artificial environments to support life
3. Only part of the third stage of the rocket reaches the final destination.
4. Space suits provide astronauts with the oxygen they need and adjust the air pressure and temperature to appropriate levels.

Science at Home

Students may be able to interview their neighbors, **ACTIVITY** parents, or grandparents about the first moon landing. Encourage students to prepare a list of who, what, when, where, why, and how questions before the interview. Students could also write their interviews as magazine articles. Provide examples of interviews from newspapers and magazines for students to use as a style guide.

Performance Assessment

Drawing Create a poster showing how a space station or satellite is launched into orbit and then used for practical applications on Earth.

Portfolio Students can save their posters in their portfolios.

Space Exploration— Is It Worth the Cost?

Purpose
To discuss the value of space exploration

Panel Discussion

Time 1 day to prepare; 1 hour for panel discussion

Have students discuss space exploration in groups of three or four. Allow them access to books, magazine articles, or supervised access to the Internet to find information on the potential benefits of space exploration.

Once students have had time to discuss the issues in groups, bring them back together and lead a panel discussion on the pros and cons of space exploration. Have each group act as one panel member, representing one point of view and taking turns presenting points in the discussion.

Extend Ask students to come up with several questions concerning space exploration that they could ask their family or community members in order to gain other insights into the space program and its potential benefits. For example, students may not realize how inspiring Armstrong's trip to the moon was when it took place unless they talk to someone who was an adult in the 1960s.

You Decide

Have students complete the first two steps on page 570 before the panel discussion begins as a way to prepare themselves for taking part. After the discussion is concluded, students can complete Step 3 on page 570, using what they learned in the discussion to find solutions to the problem. Students may set priorities for Congress's budget in many different ways. Many will put feeding the poor or researching diseases near the top of the list and space exploration near the bottom.

Space Exploration—Is It Worth the Cost?

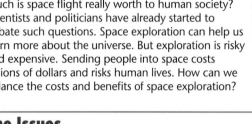

Imagine that your spacecraft has just landed on Mars after a two-month journey from Earth. You've spent years planning for this moment. Canyons, craters, and distant plains stretch out before you. You check your spacesuit and prepare to step out onto the rocky red surface of Mars.

Is such a trip likely? Would it be worthwhile? How much is space flight really worth to human society? Scientists and politicians have already started to debate such questions. Space exploration can help us learn more about the universe. But exploration is risky and expensive. Sending people into space costs billions of dollars and risks human lives. How can we balance the costs and benefits of space exploration?

The Issues

Should Humans Travel Into Space? Many Americans think that Neil Armstrong's walk on the moon in 1969 was one of the great moments in history. Also, learning how to keep people alive in space has led to improvements in everyday life. Safer equipment for firefighters, easier ways to package frozen food, and effective heart monitors have all come out of space program research.

What Are the Alternatives? Space exploration can involve a project to put a person on Mars. It also can involve a more limited use of scientific instruments near Earth, such as the Hubble Space Telescope. Instead of sending people, we could send space probes like *Mars Pathfinder* to other planets.

Is Human Space Exploration Worth the Cost? Scientists who favor human travel into space say that only people can collect certain kinds of information. And using simpler space vehicles that are cheaper to build can also save money. But no one knows if research in space really provides information quicker than research that can be done on Earth. Many critics of space research think that other needs are more important. One United States senator said, "Every time you put money into the space station, there is a dime that won't be available for our children's education or for medical research."

You Decide

1. **Identify the Problem**
   In your own words, list the costs and benefits of space exploration.

2. **Analyze the Options**
   Make a chart of three different approaches to space exploration: sending humans to another planet, doing only Earth-based research, and one other option. What are the benefits and drawbacks of each approach?

3. **Find a Solution**
   Imagine that you are a member of Congress who has to vote on a new budget. There is a fixed amount of money to spend, so you have to decide which needs are most important. Make a list of your top ten priorities. Explain your decisions.

Background

NASA has included a detailed justification of space exploration on their Web site. NASA argues that the basic knowledge about the universe gained through space exploration gives us a better understanding of Earth. Space exploration has allowed applications in satellite communication. Many technological breakthroughs have come as a result of the space program. The space program supports many jobs and is thus good for the economy. The exploration of space serves as an inspiration to people to explore the unknown and push back boundaries. Additional information is available at **www.nasa.gov/** and **www.nss.org/**.

SECTION 1
Describing the Solar System

Key Ideas
- Descriptions of the solar system have changed from a geocentric model to a heliocentric model.
- Newton concluded that two factors—inertia and gravity—combine to keep the planets in orbit.
- Many smaller systems exist within the larger system that is our solar system.

Key Terms
geocentric system   ellipse
heliocentric system   inertia
solar system   gravity

SECTION 2
Characteristics of the Sun

Key Ideas
- The sun's energy comes from nuclear fusion.
- The sun's atmosphere has three layers: the photosphere, the chromosphere, and the corona.
- Features on or above the sun's surface include sunspots, prominences, and solar flares.

Key Terms
nuclear fusion   chromosphere   sunspot
core   corona   prominence
photosphere   solar wind   solar flare

 SECTION 3
Characteristics of the Inner Planets

Key Idea
- Mercury, Venus, Earth, and Mars are small and have rocky surfaces.

Key Terms
terrestrial planet   retrograde rotation
rotation   greenhouse effect
revolution

 SECTION 4
Characteristics of the Outer Planets

Key Ideas
- Jupiter, Saturn, Uranus, and Neptune are much larger than Earth, and are not solid.
- Pluto and Charon have solid surfaces.

Key Term
gas giant

 SECTION 5
Comets, Asteroids, and Meteors

Key Ideas
- Comets are chunks of ice and dust that usually have long, elliptical orbits.
- Most asteroids revolve around the sun between the orbits of Mars and Jupiter.

Key Terms
comet   asteroid belt   meteor
asteroid   meteoroid   meteorite

 SECTION 6
Traveling in Space
INTEGRATING TECHNOLOGY

Key Ideas
- Rockets move forward as gas is pushed from the back of the rocket.
- Astronauts need space suits and computers to survive in space.

Key Terms
satellite   geosynchronous orbit

Organizing Information

Compare/Contrast Table On a separate piece of paper, make a table comparing and contrasting the geocentric and heliocentric systems. Include information on the following: object at the center of the system; objects that move around the center; whom the system was first proposed by; and who supported the system. (For more on compare/contrast tables, see the Skills Handbook.)

Chapter 16 **571**

Organizing Information
Compare/Contrast Table

	Geocentric System	Heliocentric System
Object at center	Earth	sun
Objects that move around center	planets and sun	Earth and other planets
Proposed by	ancient Greek astronomers	Copernicus
Supporters	Ptolemy	Galileo and others

Program Resources

- **Unit 4 Resources** Chapter 16 Project Scoring Rubric, p. 184
- **Performance Assessment** Chapter 16, pp. 50–52
- **Chapter and Unit Tests** Chapter 16 Test, pp. 76–79

Media and Technology

Computer Test Bank
Chapter 16 Test

Reviewing Content
Multiple Choice
1. d 2. d 3. c 4. a 5. c

True or False
6. ellipse 7. true 8. true 9. Jupiter
10. satellite

Checking Concepts
11. Galileo's observations of Venus' phases could not be explained by the geocentric system. His observations of the motions of Jupiter's moons showed that not everything in the sky revolves around Earth.

12. Newton concluded that gravity and inertia keep the planets in the orbits that Kepler found by looking at Brahe's observations.

13. It is usually impossible to see the sun's corona because its faint light is overwhelmed by the bright light of the photosphere and chromosphere.

14. Dark-looking areas of gas on the sun that are cooler than the gases around them

15. Mercury is so hot that the gases in the atmosphere escaped from Mercury's weak gravity.

16. One hypothesis is that Venus was struck by a large object billions of years ago and this collision caused Venus' direction of rotation to change.

17. The terrestrial planets are relatively small and rocky. The gas giants are much larger and lack a solid surface.

18. These astronomers think Pluto should not be a planet because it is so small. They think it may just be the largest of thousands of objects revolving around the sun beyond Neptune.

19. Solar wind pushes the gases in a comet's tail away from the sun.

20. The area served by the satellite would always be able to receive the signal.

21. Students should include descriptions of the terrestrial planet and the gas giant that they visit. High marks should be given for accurate, clearly written descriptions.

CHAPTER 16 ASSESSMENT

Reviewing Content
 Review key concepts online using iText at www.phschool.com

Multiple Choice
Choose the letter of the answer that best completes each statement.

1. Copernicus thought that the solar system was
   a. celestial.
   b. elliptical.
   c. geocentric.
   d. heliocentric.

2. The part of the sun where nuclear fusion occurs is the
   a. photosphere. b. chromosphere.
   c. corona. d. core.

3. Planets with atmospheres composed mostly of carbon dioxide include
   a. Earth and Mercury.
   b. Venus and Mercury.
   c. Venus and Mars.
   d. Mercury and Mars.

4. The Great Red Spot is a huge storm on
   a. Jupiter. b. Neptune.
   c. Saturn. d. Pluto.

5. Most asteroids orbit the sun
   a. between the sun and Mercury.
   b. between Earth and Mars.
   c. between Mars and Jupiter.
   d. between Neptune and Pluto.

True or False
If the statement is true, write true. If it is false, change the underlined word or words to make the statement true.

6. The shape of the orbit of each planet is a <u>circle</u>.
7. Sunspots are regions of <u>cooler</u> gases on the sun.
8. The atmosphere of Venus has <u>higher</u> pressure than the atmosphere of Earth.
9. Aside from the sun, <u>Saturn</u> is the largest source of gravity in the solar system.
10. A <u>meteorite</u> is any natural or manmade object that revolves around an object in space.

Checking Concepts
11. How did Galileo's observations support the idea of a heliocentric system?

12. How did Newton's work on orbits add to the work Kepler had done?

13. Why is it usually impossible to see the sun's corona?

14. What are sunspots?

15. Why does Mercury have only a thin atmosphere?

16. How do astronomers explain that Venus rotates in the opposite direction from most planets and moons?

17. What are the major characteristics of the terrestrial planets? How do they differ from the gas giants?

18. Why do some astronomers think that Pluto should not be called a planet?

19. Why does a comet's tail always stream away from the sun?

20. Why would it be useful to have a satellite that relays television signals in a geosynchronous orbit?

21. Writing to Learn Imagine you are an astronaut on a mission to explore the solar system. Write a trip journal telling the story of your trip from Earth to another terrestrial planet and to a gas giant. Include a description of each planet.

Thinking Critically
22. Relating Cause and Effect How would Earth move if the sun (including its gravity) suddenly disappeared? Explain your answer.

23. Applying Concepts Explain why Venus is hotter than it would be without its atmosphere.

24. Comparing and Contrasting Compare and contrast meteoroids, meteors, and meteorites.

25. Making Generalizations How could the construction of an International Space Station help with the further exploration of the solar system?

Thinking Critically
22. Because of inertia, Earth would continue to move in a straight path in the direction it was going when the sun disappeared.

23. Venus's atmosphere creates a greenhouse effect that traps heat energy from the sun.

24. A meteoroid is a chunk of rock or dust in space. If a meteoroid enters Earth's atmosphere and burns up, a streak of light called a meteor is seen. If a meteoroid hits Earth's surface, it is called a meteorite.

25. Students might suggest that exploration of the solar system may be furthered by combining the technological resources of multiple nations.

Applying Skills

Use the diagram of an imaginary, newly discovered planetary system around Star X to answer Questions 26–28. The periods of revolution of Planets A, B, and C are 75 Earth days, 200 Earth days, and 300 Earth days.

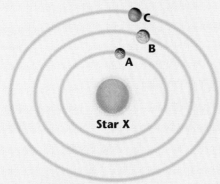

Star X

26. Interpreting Data Which planet in this new planetary system revolves around Star X in the shortest amount of time?

27. Making Models In 150 days, how far will each planet have revolved around Star X? Copy the diagram and sketch the positions of the three planets to find out. How far will each planet have revolved around Star X in 400 days? Sketch their positions.

28. Drawing Conclusions Can Planet C ever be closer to Planet A than to Planet B? Study your drawings to figure this out.

Performance ▼ Assessment
CHAPTER PROJECT

Present Your Project Present your solar system. Explain how you worked with large distances. Display your data tables and your calculations. Show how you checked them for accuracy. Compare the distances in your models to distances inside and outside your classroom.

Reflect and Record In your journal, explain what you would do to improve the model. How effectively did you use computers or calculators to get the data?

Test Preparation
Use these questions to prepare for standardized tests.

Study the table. Then answer Questions 29–32.

Planet	Period of Rotation (Earth days)	Period of Revolution (Earth years)	Average Distance From the Sun (million kilometers)
Mars	1.03	1.9	228
Jupiter	0.41	12	778
Saturn	0.43	29	1,427
Uranus	0.72	84	2,871
Neptune	0.67	165	4,497

29. Which of these planet's orbits is farthest from Earth's orbit?
   A Mars   **B** Jupiter
   C Uranus   **D** Neptune

30. Which planet has a "day" that is most similar in length to a day on Earth?
   F Mars   **G** Jupiter
   H Uranus   **J** Neptune

31. Light takes about 8 minutes and 20 seconds to travel from the sun to Earth, 150 million kilometers away. About how long does it take light to travel from the sun to Jupiter?
   A 10 minutes   **B** 25 minutes
   C 43 minutes   **D** 112 minutes

32. Which one of the following conclusions about planets is supported by the information in the table?
   F As distance from the sun increases, period of rotation increases.
   G As distance from the sun increases, period of revolution increases.
   H As distance from the sun increases, period of revolution decreases.
   J There is no relationship between distance from the sun and period of revolution.

Applying Skills

26. Planet A which takes only 75 days

27. Planet A will have revolved around star X twice. Planet B will have completed three quarters of one revolution. Planet C will have completed only one half of one revolution. In 400 days, planet A will have completed five revolutions and be one third through a sixth; planet B will have completed two revolutions; and planet C will have completed one revolution and be one third through a second.

28. Yes. Planet A and C could be on one side of the star and B on the other. After 300 days, planet A and C are where they began, on the same side of star X, but planet B is on the opposite side of the star.

Performance ▼ Assessment
CHAPTER PROJECT

Present Your Project Students should explain that they scaled all distances by a constant amount to make them manageable. They could have checked their numbers by multiplying the scaled numbers by the reciprocal of their scaling factor to see if they obtained the correct planet sizes. Students should have a good understanding that the sun is very large, that planets vary considerably in size, and that space is mostly "empty space."

Reflect and Record Students might change the scale and present the model in a very large area in order to make the smallest planets visible. Students will reflect that it was not possible to find a scale that was good for comparing the sizes of the planets and the sun with one that was good for showing the distances between the planets and the sun. Since students are dealing with very large numbers with many zeros, they should have found calculators useful in avoiding arithmetic errors.

Test Preparation

29. D **30.** F **31.** C **32.** G

The Mississippi

This interdisciplinary feature presents the central theme of transportation on the Mississippi River by connecting four different disciplines: science, social studies, mathematics, and language arts. The exploration is designed to capture students' interest and help them see how the content they are studying in science relates to other school subjects and to real-world events. The exploration is particularly suitable for team teaching.

1 Engage/Explore

Activating Prior Knowledge

Help students recall what they learned in Chapter 12, Fresh Water, by asking questions such as: **What are the parts of a river system?** *(The main river, its tributaries, and lakes, ponds, and wetlands along the river)* and **How does a river change as it flows from its source to its mouth?** *(Students should identify differences in the river's speed, width, and depth and features such as the flood plain and delta.)* Then ask: **What do you know about the Mississippi River?** *(Accept all responses without comment at this time.)*

Introducing the Unit

Display a large map of the United States, and invite a volunteer to point out the Mississippi River. Ask: **In which direction does the Mississippi flow?** *(From north to south)* Draw students' attention to the map on this page, and have them trace the river's route from its headwaters to its mouth. Ask: **Which states have the Mississippi River as a natural boundary?** *(Minnesota, Wisconsin, Iowa, Illinois, Missouri, Kentucky, Tennessee, Arkansas, Mississippi, and Louisiana)* **What are some of the Mississippi's major tributaries?** *(the Minnesota, Wisconsin, Illinois, Missouri, Ohio, Arkansas, Yazoo, and Red rivers)* **How large is the Mississippi River watershed?** *(It drains about 40 percent of the United States.)*

THE MISSISSIPPI

What would you name a river that—

- *carries about 420 million metric tons of cargo a year,*
- *drains 31 states and 2 Canadian provinces,*
- *looks like a tree that has a thin top trunk and 2 strong branches,*
- *flows at about 18,100 cubic meters of water per second?*

Native Americans called the river *misi sipi*, an Algonquin word meaning "big water," or "father of waters."

Have you ever traveled on a river or lake that feeds into the mighty Mississippi River? Perhaps you have but did not realize it. The map below shows the watershed of this great river. From the west, the Missouri River — the "Big Muddy"— carries soft silt eroded from the Great Plains. The Missouri joins the Mississippi near St. Louis, turning the river's clear water to muddy brown. From the east, the Ohio River flows in from the rocky Appalachian plateau, nearly doubling the volume of water in the river. In all, the huge Mississippi watershed drains about 40 percent of the United States.

The Mississippi River starts at Lake Itasca and flows through 10 states to the Gulf of Mexico. The river is a drainage point for hundreds of tributaries in the vast Mississippi watershed. ▶

The Mississippi River Watershed

574

Program Resources

- **Unit 4 Resources,** Interdisciplinary Exploration: Social Studies, pp. 214–217; Science, pp. 218–219; Mathematics, pp. 221–223; Language Arts, pp. 224–225

A National Trade Route

Since Native Americans settled in villages along the Mississippi around 1,200 years ago, the river has served as a water highway for trade and travel.

In the late 1600s, French explorers, fur traders, and soldiers arrived in the Mississippi Valley. They chose strategic sites for forts and fur-trading posts — Prairie du Chien, St. Louis, and St. Genevieve. At first, traders used canoes, rafts, and flatboats to carry goods downstream. But traveling up the river was difficult. Crews had to use long poles to push narrow keelboats upstream against the current.

▲ St. Anthony Falls is the northernmost point of navigation on the Mississippi.

▲ Crews in flatboats rode the river currents, steering with long oars.

In 1811, the arrival of *The New Orleans,* the first steamboat on the Mississippi River, changed the river forever. Within 40 years, there were hundreds more steamboats and many new river towns. On the upper Mississippi, the city of Minneapolis grew up around flour mills near the falls. Farther downstream, Memphis became a center for transporting cotton. Later, it was a stopping point for showboats and musicians. New Orleans quickly became a world port. It received cotton, tobacco, and sugar cane from southern plantations and exported corn, wheat and indigo to Europe. Imported luxury items, such as soap, coffee, shoes, and textiles, traveled upstream from the port of New Orleans. Up and down the river townspeople eagerly waited for the cry, "Steamboat comin'!"

▲ New Orleans has been a major trading port since its founding in 1718.

Social Studies Activity

Use the map to choose a city on the Mississippi River to learn about. Imagine that you are an early settler in the city. Write a letter to persuade relatives to move to your city. Before writing, learn about the history, founding, and trade of the city. Look for answers to the following questions:

◆ Who founded the city? When was the city founded? Why did settlers decide to move there? Where did they come from?
◆ What part did the Mississippi River play in the city's founding?
◆ What other physical features were important to the city?
◆ Where did the city's name come from?
◆ What products were grown, bought, or sold there?

575

Background

History When Europeans began to explore and settle North America, the Mississippi River played a major role. The first European to see the river was a Spaniard, Hernando de Soto, in 1541. French explorer and fur trader René-Robert Cavelier, Sieur de La Salle, canoed down the length of the river to the Gulf of Mexico. In 1682, he claimed the entire area for France and named it "Louisiana" in honor of the French king.

Early French settlements on the river included New Orleans (1718), St. Louis (1764), and Memphis (1819). In the late 1700s, France, Spain, and the United States fought for control of navigation on the Mississippi, including the right to use the port of New Orleans. In the Louisiana Purchase of 1803, the U.S. purchased from France all the land from the Mississippi River westward to the Rockies.

2 Facilitate

◆ Have students refer to the map on the previous page to find each settlement named in the text. Ask: **Why do you think people chose these places to settle and build a town?** (*The locations provided easy access to the river for travel and transporting goods.*) **How did steamboats change the river?** (*People no longer had to depend on their own strength to move boats.*)
◆ Encourage interested students to create a bulletin board display showing the various types of boats used on the river from earliest times to today.
◆ To extend this exploration, students could construct a time line of important events that have occurred in the Mississippi River valley since early times.

Social Studies Activity

Let students work individually. To provide more choices of cities, suggest that they consult other, more detailed maps of the area. Caution students to choose cities that are large enough to merit entries in encyclopedias or other readily available reference books. If time allows, let students read their letters aloud. **Interdisciplinary Exploration** The following worksheets correlate with this page: Finding Locations on a Map, page 214; Reading a Data Table, page 215; Making a Bar Graph, page 216; and Finding Your Way Around New Orleans, page 217.

3 Assess

Activity Assessment

Evaluate students' research procedures, particularly note-taking and outlining. Make sure their reports are in the form of letters and that they include the type of information that answers the questions on the student page.

2 Facilitate

- Discuss the hazards involved in boating on a river. Ask: **Have you ever gone canoeing on a river or seen a movie of people rafting through river rapids? What can people do to make a river safer for travel and transportation?** (*Accept all reasonable answers. Point out that this page describes one way of "taming" rivers.*)
- Review the diagrams step by step to make sure they understand how a lock operates. You could choose volunteers to read the captions aloud as students examine the illustrations.
- To extend this exploration, suggest that students research the building of the Panama Canal, which includes six pairs of locks. Encourage students to focus on the construction problems posed by the terrain and how engineers solved them. Also have students compare and contrast the locks on the Panama Canal with those on the Mississippi River.

Science Activity

Tell students that the four "L" shapes on the drawing represent modeling wax, which makes the model lock watertight. Interdisciplinary Exploration page 220 provides complete instructions for building the model.
Interdisciplinary Exploration The following worksheets correlate with this page: Traveling the Upper Mississippi, pages 218–219, and Making a Model Lock, page 220.

3 Assess

Activity Assessment

Schedule time for students to demonstrate and explain their models. During these presentations, focus on evaluating students' understanding of the "locking through" process rather than on their skill in building models that operate without flaws such as leaks or sticky gates.

Taming the River

Navigating the sandbars, shallow water, and rocky rapids on the upper Mississippi River was treacherous for captains of ships and barges in the 1800s. To make traveling easier, engineers in the early 1900s built a "water staircase," a series of 29 locks and dams between Minneapolis, Minnesota, and Alton, Illinois, above St. Louis. A lock is an enclosed basin, with gates at each end. Locks allow engineers to raise or lower the water level in a certain area of the river. Between the locks on the upper Mississippi, the river forms wide pools of quiet water, maintaining a channel deep enough for large boats.

Use the diagrams to trace how a boat "locks through" as it travels upstream. This technology allowed boats to travel to cities on the upper Mississippi. ▶

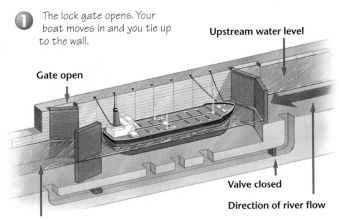

1 The lock gate opens. Your boat moves in and you tie up to the wall.

Upstream water level
Gate open
Valve closed
Direction of river flow
Downstream water level

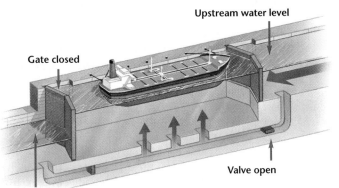

Upstream water level
Gate closed
Valve open
Downstream water level

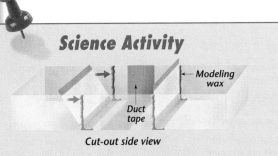

Science Activity

Modeling wax
Duct tape
Cut-out side view

Use a cardboard milk container to build a working model of a lock. Set up your lock following the illustration. Then demonstrate how your lock works, using a cork or pen cap as your ship and sailing it through the lock.

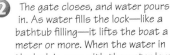

2 The gate closes, and water pours in. As water fills the lock—like a bathtub filling—it lifts the boat a meter or more. When the water in the lock is even with the water level upstream, the gates at the upstream end open. You untie your boat and move out into the river.

If you were going downstream, you would "lock through" in reverse. The water would empty out of the lock, lowering the water level to match the level downstream.

576

Facts and Figures Some students may wonder why the natural topography of the upper Mississippi differed so markedly from that of the lower Mississippi before the locks and dams were constructed. The answer lies in the river's ancient history.

The upper Mississippi is much older than the lower Mississippi. Millions of years ago, the mouth of the ancestral Mississippi was located near what is today Cape Girardeau, Missouri. The river deposited silt in the ocean gulf, over time creating a delta stretching southward more than 1,900 km to the Gulf of Mexico. As the delta built up, the river created a channel through the new land. Today's lower Mississippi winds through these ancient sediments on its way to the ocean.

All Aboard

The whistle blows. The gleaming white steamboat pulls away from the dock just below Fort Snelling, Minnesota. You head downstream toward New Orleans. As you watch the paddlewheel splashing in the water, you think of the old-time steamboats that carried passengers up and down the Mississippi River in the 1800s.

Today you are cruising at a speed of 11.3 kilometers per hour. You want to stay awake until you enter Lock 3 at Red Wing, Minnesota. It's 4:30 P.M. on Monday now. You know that it's about 78.8 kilometers to Red Wing. It should take about 7 hours to reach the lock. So you'll be there at 11:30 P.M. and through the lock by midnight.

As your boat travels along the river, it will follow the schedule you see on this page. The highlight of your trip will be Mark Twain's hometown of Hannibal, Missouri. You will arrive there on Friday.

Look at the Upper Mississippi River schedule to answer the questions below. Distances are given from Fort Snelling.

◆ What is your average speed between Dubuque and Hannibal? Use the following equation:

$$speed = \frac{distance}{time}$$

Round to the nearest tenth.

◆ How long will you spend in Prairie du Chien?
◆ About how long does it take to travel from Prairie du Chien to Dubuque?

MISSISSIPPI RIVERBOAT
SCHEDULE
MAY to SEPTEMBER

UPPER MISSISSIPPI RIVERBOAT SCHEDULE

Port	Arrival Time	Departure Time	Distance From Fort Snelling
Fort Snelling, MN		4:30 P.M. Mon.	0 km
Lock 3, Red Wing, MN	11:30 P.M. Mon.	12:00 midnight	78.8 km
Prairie du Chien, WI	11:00 P.M. Tues.	10:30 A.M. Wed.	337.8 km
Dubuque, IA	6:30 P.M. Wed.	7:00 P.M. Wed.	426.3 km
Hannibal, MO	1:00 A.M. Fri.	———	863.9 km

LOWER MISSISSIPPI RIVERBOAT SCHEDULE

Port	Arrival Time	Departure Time	Distance From Fort Snelling
Hannibal, MO		6 P.M. Fri.	863.9 km
Lock 26 at Alton, IL	a. _?_	b. _?_	1033 km
St. Louis, MO	c. _?_	d. _?_	1070.7 km
Cape Girardeau, MO	6:30 A.M. Sun.	———	e. _?_

Math Activity

Now complete the riverboat schedule for the Lower Mississippi. Your boat will leave Hannibal at 6 P.M. Friday and will travel at a speed of 14.7 kilometers per hour for the rest of the journey.

◆ When will you arrive at Lock 26?
◆ You spend 34 minutes in the lock. When will you depart from Lock 26? Your boat travels on. When will it arrive in St. Louis?
◆ The boat will spend 4 hours in St. Louis and head to Cape Girardeau, arriving at 6:30 A.M. Sunday. How far is it from St. Louis to Cape Girardeau?

577

Background

Integrating Science and Technology
Today, modern versions of the fabled steamboats offer cruises on the Mississippi and several of its major tributaries, including the Illinois, Ohio, Tennessee, and Arkansas rivers. The *Delta Queen, Mississippi Queen,* and *American Queen* offer cruises with a variety of itineraries on the upper and lower Mississippi.

Today's steamboats look like those of Mark Twain's day, but they have hulls of welded steel (not wood), air conditioning, elevators between decks, and electronic navigation aids. They are powered in part by steam engines that turn their colorful paddlewheels. They also have powerful auxiliary diesel engines as well as devices that make steering the big boats much easier than it was 100 years ago.

2 Facilitate

◆ Have students find the ports listed in the schedule on the map on page 574 and trace the riverboat's route. (Cape Girardeau, not shown on the map, is at the river's bend above Cairo.) Point out that on the schedule, each segment of the journey lasts from the departure time listed for one port to the arrival time listed for the next port. Also emphasize that the distances listed in the right column are all from the original departure point at Fort Snelling. To determine whether students understand how to read the schedule, ask: **How far is it from Dubuque to Hannibal?** *(863.9–426.3m, or 437.6 km)* **How long does that part of the trip take?** *(30 hours–from 7:00 P.M. Wednesday to 1:00 A.M. Friday)*

◆ As a whole-class activity, have students work through the three questions in the left column. *(Average speed between Dubuque and Hannibal, 437.6 km ÷ 30 hrs = 14.6 km/hr; time spent in Prairie du Chien, 11.5 hrs; travel time from Prairie du Chien to Dubuque, 8 hrs)*

Math Activity

Let students complete the activity on their own. Remind them that to convert parts of hours expressed as decimal fractions, they must multiply the fraction by 60. **Interdisciplinary Exploration** The following worksheets correlate with this page: Calculating Distances Between Locks, page 221; Graphing Population Changes, page 222; and Paddlewheel Steamboat Cruises, page 223.

3 Assess

Activity Assessment

a. 5:30 A.M. Saturday (169.1 km ÷ 14.7 km/hr = 11.5 hrs from 6 P.M. Friday)
b. 6:04 A.M. Saturday (5:30 + 34 min)
c. 8:40 A.M. Saturday (37.7 km ÷ 14.7 km/hr = 2.6 hrs from 6:04 A.M.)
d. 12:40 P.M. Saturday
e. 1332.4 km from Fort Snelling (261.7 km from St. Louis to Cape Girardeau)

2 Facilitate

- Ask students if they are familiar with Mark Twain and have read any of his books or stories. If so, let them describe the plots and characters briefly.

- After students have read the excerpt, ask: **Have you ever had to walk around your home in the dark? How did you keep from running into things?** (*Students will probably say they already knew the layout from seeing it so many times in the light.*) **Why did Mr. Bixby use the image of a dark hall?** (*To relate the new task to a familiar experience*)

Language Arts Activity

Encourage students to share their responses to the questions posed in the text. (*A river pilot must know the river's shape so well that he can navigate safely even when he cannot see the shore. Mr. Bixby respects the river and is proud of his knowledge of it. You can tell by what he says.*) Ask: **Based on this excerpt, how would you describe Mr. Bixby?** (*Experienced, tough, no-nonsense, forceful, insistent*) **How would you describe the young Mark Twain?** (*Nervous, overwhelmed, unsure of himself, reluctant, somewhat negative*)

- Before students begin writing, ask: **How do you think the excerpt should end?** (*Since students know that Twain did become a river pilot, they should realize that the excerpt would end on a positive note, with Twain resolving to do his best.*) Remind students of the following points: (1) The characters should talk as people would in Mark Twain's time; (2) the dialogue should move the story along and bring it to a natural conclusion; (3) every time the speaker changes, a new paragraph should begin; and (4) the speaker's words should be set off with quotation marks.

Interdisciplinary Exploration The following worksheets correlate with this page: Mississippi River Vocabulary, page 224, and The Mound Builders, page 225.

Mark Three! Mark Twain!

To steer a boat on the Mississippi, early riverboat pilots had to memorize landmarks at every bend and curve of the river, going both upstream and down. They had to know where the channel was deep enough for the boat, where the current was strong, where there were sandbars or sunken logs.

When Samuel Clemens was growing up in the small river town of Hannibal, Missouri, his ambition was to become a Mississippi River steamboat pilot. He was a pilot for a while. Later he became one of America's most famous writers, using the pen name Mark Twain. In the passage below from his book *Life on the Mississippi*, Twain describes a lesson he learned from an experienced pilot, Mr. Bixby.

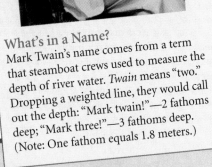

What's in a Name?
Mark Twain's name comes from a term that steamboat crews used to measure the depth of river water. *Twain* means "two." Dropping a weighted line, they would call out the depth: "Mark twain!"—2 fathoms deep; "Mark three!"—3 fathoms deep. (Note: One fathom equals 1.8 meters.)

"My boy," [Bixby said] "you've got to know the shape of the river perfectly. It is all there is left to steer by on a very dark night. Everything else is blotted out and gone. But mind you, it hasn't the same shape in the night that it has in the daytime."

"How on earth am I ever going to learn it, then?"

"How do you follow a hall at home in the dark? Because you know the shape of it. You can't see it."

"Do you mean to say that I've got to know all the million trifling variations of shape in the banks of this interminable [endless] river as well as I know the shape of the front hall at home?"

"On my honor, you've got to know them better than any man ever did know the shapes of the halls in his own house."

"I wish I was dead!"

"Now I don't want to discourage you, but —.... You see, this has got to be learned; there isn't any getting around it.....

The river is a very different shape on a pitch-dark night from what it is on a starlight night. All shores seem to be straight lines, then, and mighty dim ones, too; and you'd run them for straight lines, only you know better.... Then there's your gray mist. You take a night when there's one of these grisly, drizzly gray mists, and then there isn't any particular shape to a shore. A gray mist would tangle the head of the oldest man that ever lived. Well, then, different kinds of moonlight change the shape of the river in different ways. You see —"

"Oh, don't say any more, please! Have I got to learn the shape of the river according to all these five hundred thousand different ways? If I tried to carry all that cargo in my head, it would make me stoop-shouldered."

"No! You only learn the shape of the river; and you learn it with such absolute certainty that you can always steer by the shape that's in your head, and never mind the one that's before your eyes."

Background

History "Mark Twain" is one of the literary world's most famous pen names. Twain himself—in *Life on the Mississippi*, written in 1883—claimed that an older riverboat pilot had used the name for a series of articles and that he (Twain) had borrowed it for a parody. However, most editors and critics do not accept this account, particularly since Clemens first used the pen name 20 years earlier when he was working as a reporter for the Virginia City (Nevada) *Territorial Enterprise*.

Twain never forgot the Mississippi River and his years as a river pilot. As a journalist, humorist, and lecturer, he traveled throughout the United States and abroad. His most popular works for young people are *The Adventures of Tom Sawyer, The Adventures of Huckleberry Finn,* and "The Celebrated Jumping Frog of Calaveras County."

Language Arts Activity

Read the excerpt, focusing on what the dialogue tells you about the characters of Mark Twain and Mr. Bixby.

◆ What lesson does Mark Twain learn?

◆ How does Mr. Bixby feel about the Mississippi River? How can you tell?

Now, use dialogue to write an ending to this riverboat excerpt. Before you begin writing, think carefully about the characters, setting, and your conclusion.

Riverboat captains were licensed to navigate the river. ▶

Tie It Together

Celebrate the River

Plan a class fair featuring cities on the Mississippi River today, such as St. Louis (above). Set up a booth for each city and create a travel brochure to persuade people to visit.

As a team, choose a city to represent. Then divide up tasks so different members find information on the following topics:

◆ Interesting attractions and events that your city offers—zoos, museums, parks, sports events, music festivals, and so on.

◆ Influences of different groups on the city's food, customs, music, and architecture.

◆ Physical features of the area around the city.

◆ Famous people—writers, political figures, entertainers—who lived there.

◆ Historic places to visit, such as monuments, houses, battlefields, and statues.

◆ Illustrations and pictures of special attractions.

◆ Maps of walking tours and historic areas.

◆ Native plants and animals in the area.

Before starting your brochure, decide which attractions to highlight. Think of a slogan for your travel campaign. If you wish, make a poster. Celebrate life on the river today.

3 Assess

Activity Assessment

Let each student read his or her ending aloud to the rest of the class or role-play the dialogue with a partner. Evaluate students' written work based on the four points identified on the previous page.

Tie It Together

Time 1 week (2 days for research, 2 days for preparing the brochure and booth, 1 day for the fair)

Tips Have students work in groups of four or five. Encourage groups to choose a city that can be researched easily with readily available resource materials. If necessary, help each group divide up the tasks and work out a plan for researching and compiling information. Guide students through the writing process as follows:

◆ In the research stage, suggest that they narrow the topics by listing all their ideas and then selecting the ones that are most interesting.

◆ In the drafting stage, remind students to begin the brochure with a general introduction, followed by topic-specific sections such as Key Attractions, Famous People, and Historic Sites.

◆ In the editing stage, remind students to read the draft carefully, looking for errors and ways to improve the brochure.

Extend Groups could choose one cultural aspect to research across different cities. For example, one group could find out about (and possibly prepare for class tasting) foods representing different ethnic and regional groups—a Cajun dish for Louisiana, Scandinavian food for Minnesota, and so on. Another group could research the music in river cities, including jazz and ragtime in New Orleans, country and rock in Memphis, and bluegrass in Kentucky. Still another group could explore various types of arts and crafts characteristic of different cities and regions along the river.

Developing scientific thinking in students is important for a solid science education. To learn how to think scientifically, students need frequent opportunities to practice science process skills, critical thinking skills, as well as other skills that support scientific inquiry. The *Science Explorer* Skills Handbook introduces the following key science skills:

◆ Science Process Skills
◆ SI Measuring Skills
◆ Skills for Conducting a Scientific Investigation
◆ Critical Thinking Skills
◆ Information Organizing Skills
◆ Mapping Skills
◆ Data Table and Graphing Skills

The Skills Handbook is designed as a reference for students to use whenever they need to review a science skill. You can use the activities provided in the Skills Handbook to teach or reinforce the skills.

Think Like a Scientist

Observing

Remind students that an observation is only what they can see, hear, smell, taste, or feel. Ask: **Which senses will you use to make observations from this photograph?** *(Sight is the only sense that can be used to make observations from the photograph.)* **What are some observations you can make from the photograph?** *(Answers may vary. Sample answers: The boy is wearing sneakers, sport socks, shorts, and a tee shirt; the boy is sitting in the grass holding something blue against his knee; the boy is looking at his knee; there is a soccer ball lying beside the boy.)* List the observations on the chalkboard. If students make any inferences or predictions about the boy at this point, ask: **Can you be sure your statement is factual and accurate from just observing the photograph?** Help students understand how observations differ from inferences and predictions.

Explain to students that indirect evidence usually has to do with phenomena that cannot be observed firsthand. Scientists often rely on indirect evidence when investigating such topics

---

Think Like a Scientist

*A*lthough you may not know it, you think like a scientist every day. Whenever you ask a question and explore possible answers, you use many of the same skills that scientists do. Some of these skills are described on this page.

Observing

When you use one or more of your five senses to gather information about the world, you are **observing.** Hearing a dog bark, counting twelve green seeds, and smelling smoke are all observations. To increase the power of their senses, scientists sometimes use microscopes, telescopes, or other instruments that help them make more detailed observations.

An observation must be an accurate report of what your senses detect. It is important to keep careful records of your observations in science class by writing or drawing in a notebook. The information collected through observations is called evidence, or data. Evidence can be either direct or indirect.

Inferring

When you interpret an observation, you are **inferring,** or drawing an inference. For example, if you hear your dog barking, you may infer that someone is at your front door. To draw this inference, you combine the evidence—the barking dog—and your experience or knowledge—you know that your dog barks when strangers approach—to reach a logical conclusion.

Notice that an inference is not a fact; it is only one of many possible interpretations of an observation. For example, your dog may be barking because it wants to go for a walk. An inference may turn out to be incorrect even if it is based on accurate observations and logical reasoning. The only way to find out if an inference is correct is to investigate further.

Predicting

When you listen to the weather forecast, you may hear predictions about future weather—what the temperature will be, whether it will rain, and how windy it will be. Weather forecasters use observations and knowledge of weather patterns to predict the weather and weather trends. The skill of **predicting** involves making an inference about a future event based on current evidence.

Because a prediction is an inference, it may prove to be false. In science class, you can test some of your predictions by doing experiments. For example, suppose you predict that larger paper airplanes can fly farther than smaller airplanes. How could you test your prediction?

ACTIVITY Use the photograph to answer the questions below.

Observing Look closely at the photograph. List at least three observations.

Inferring Use your observations to make an inference about what has happened. What experience or knowledge did you use to make the inference?

Predicting Predict what will happen next. On what evidence or experience do you base your prediction?

---

as the conditions on other planets or the behavior of atoms in a chemical reaction, for example. Ask: **Suppose you fill your dog's food dish and leave the room. An hour later, the food is gone. Why is this indirect evidence that the dog ate the food?** *(The evidence is indirect because no one saw the dog eating the food.)*

Inferring

Review students' observations from the photograph. Then ask: **What inferences can you make from your observations?** *(Students may say that the boy hurt his knee playing soccer and is holding a coldpack against his injured knee.)* **What experience or knowledge helped you make this inference?** *(Students may have experienced knee injuries from playing soccer, and they may be familiar with coldpacks like the one the boy is using.)* **Can anyone suggest another possible**

Classifying

Could you imagine searching for a book in the library if the books were shelved in no particular order? Your trip to the library would be an all-day event! Luckily, librarians group together books on similar topics or by the same author. Grouping together items that are alike in some way is called **classifying.** You can classify items in many ways: by size, by shape, by use, and by other important characteristics.

Like librarians, scientists use the skill of classifying to organize information and objects. When things are sorted into groups, the relationships among them become easier to understand.

Classify the objects in the photograph into two groups based on any characteristic you choose. Then use another characteristic to classify the objects into three groups. **ACTIVITY**

Making Models

Have you ever drawn a picture to help someone understand what you were saying? Such a drawing is one type of model. A model is a picture, diagram, computer image, or other representation of a complex object or process. **Making models** helps people understand things that they cannot observe directly.

Scientists use models to represent very large or very small things, such as the planets in the solar system, or the parts of a cell. Such models are physical models—drawings or three-dimensional structures that look like the real thing. Other models are mental models—mathematical equations or words that describe how something works. All models have limitations.

This student is using a model to demonstrate what causes day and night on Earth. What do the flashlight and the tennis ball in the model represent? What are the model's limitations? **ACTIVITY**

Communicating

Whenever you talk on the phone, write a letter, or listen to your teacher at school, you are communicating. **Communicating** is the process of sharing ideas and information with other people. Communicating effectively requires many skills, including writing, reading, speaking, listening, and making models.

Scientists communicate to share results, information, and opinions. Scientists often communicate about their work in journals, over the telephone, in letters, and on the Internet. They also attend scientific meetings where they share their ideas with one another in person.

On a sheet of paper, write out clear, detailed directions for tying your shoe. Then exchange directions with a partner. Follow your partner's directions exactly. How successful were you at tying your shoe? How could your partner have communicated more clearly? **ACTIVITY**

581

Classifying

ACTIVITY

Encourage students to think of other common things that are classified. Then ask: **What things at home are classified?** (*Clothing might be classified by placing it in different dresser drawers; glasses, plates, and silverware are grouped in different parts of the kitchen; screws, nuts, bolts, washers, and nails might be separated into small containers.*) **What are some things that scientists classify?** (*Scientists classify many things they study, including organisms, geological features and processes, and kinds of machines.*) After students have classified the different fruits in the photograph, have them share their criteria for classifying them. (*Some characteristics students might use include shape, color, size, and where they are grown.*)

Making Models

ACTIVITY

Ask students: **What are some models you have used to study science?** (*Students may have used human anatomical models, solar system models, maps, stream tables.*) **How did these models help you?** (*Models can help you learn about things that are difficult to study, either because they are too big, too small, or complex.*) Be sure students understand that a model does not have to be three-dimensional. For example, a map in a textbook is a model. Ask: **What do the flashlight and tennis ball represent?** (*The flashlight represents the sun, and the ball represents Earth.*) **What are the limitations of this model?** (*Sizes and distances may not be to scale.*)

Communicating

ACTIVITY

Challenge students to identify the methods of communication they've used today. Then ask: **How is the way you communicate with a friend similar to and different from the way scientists communicate about their work to other scientists?** (*Both may communicate using various methods, but scientists must be very detailed and precise, whereas communication between friends may be less detailed and precise.*) Encourage students to communicate like a scientist as they carry out the activity. (*Students' directions should be detailed and precise enough for another person to successfully follow.*)

explanation for these observations? (*Answers may vary. Sample answer: The boy hurt his knee jogging, and he just happened to sit beside a soccer ball his sister left in the yard.*) **How can you find out whether an inference is correct?** (*by further investigation*)

Predicting

ACTIVITY

After coming to some consensus about the inference that the boy hurt his knee, encourage students to make predictions about what will happen next. (*Students' predictions may vary. Sample answers: The boy will go to the doctor. A friend will help the boy home.*)

On what did you base your prediction? (*Scientific predictions are based on knowledge and experience.*) Point out that in science, predictions can often be tested with experiments.

Making Measurements

Measuring in SI

Review SI units in class with students. Begin by providing metric rulers, graduated cylinders, balances, and Celsius thermometers. Use these tools to reinforce that the meter is the unit of length, the liter is the unit of volume, the gram is the unit of mass, and the degree Celsius is the unit for temperature. Ask: **If you want to measure the length and width of your classroom, which SI unit would you use?** *(meter)* **Which unit would you use to measure the amount of matter in your textbook?** *(gram)* **Which would you use to measure how much water a drinking glass holds?** *(liter)* **When would you use the Celsius scale?** *(To measure the temperature of something)* Then use the measuring equipment to review SI prefixes. For example, ask: **What are the smallest units on the metric ruler?** *(millimeters)* **How many millimeters are there in 1 cm?** *(10 mm)* **How many in 10 cm?** *(100 mm)* **How many centimeters are there in 1 m?** *(100 cm)* **What does 1,000 m equal?** *(1 km)*

Length (Students **ACTIVITY**
should state that the shell is 4.6 centimeters, or 46 millimeters, long.) If students need more practice measuring length, have them use meter sticks and metric rulers to measure various objects in the classroom.

Liquid Volume **ACTIVITY**
(Students should state that the volume of water in the graduated cylinder is 62 milliliters.) If students need more practice measuring liquid volume, have them use a graduated cylinder to measure different volumes of water.

Making Measurements

When scientists make observations, it is not sufficient to say that something is "big" or "heavy." Instead, scientists use instruments to measure just how big or heavy an object is. By measuring, scientists can express their observations more precisely and communicate more information about what they observe.

Measuring in SI

The standard system of measurement used by scientists around the world is known as the International System of Units, which is abbreviated as SI (in French, *Système International d'Unités*). SI units are easy to use because they are based on multiples of 10. Each unit is ten times larger than the next smallest unit and one tenth the size of the next largest unit. The table lists the prefixes used to name the most common SI units.

Common SI Prefixes		
Prefix	**Symbol**	**Meaning**
kilo-	k	1,000
hecto-	h	100
deka-	da	10
deci-	d	0.1 (one tenth)
centi-	c	0.01 (one hundredth)
milli-	m	0.001 (one thousandth)

Length To measure length, or the distance between two points, the unit of measure is the **meter (m).** The distance from the floor to a doorknob is approximately one meter. Long distances, such as the distance between two cities, are measured in kilometers (km). Small lengths are measured in centimeters (cm) or millimeters (mm). Scientists use metric rulers and meter sticks to measure length.

Common Conversions
1 km = 1,000 m
1 m = 100 cm
1 m = 1,000 mm
1 cm = 10 mm

The larger lines on the metric ruler in the picture show cen- **ACTIVITY** timeter divisions, while the smaller, unnumbered lines show millimeter divisions. How many centimeters long is the shell? How many millimeters long is it?

Liquid Volume To measure the volume of a liquid, or the amount of space it takes up, you will use a unit of measure known as the **liter (L).** One liter is the approximate volume of a medium-sized carton of milk. Smaller volumes are measured in milliliters (mL). Scientists use graduated cylinders to measure liquid volume.

Common Conversion
1 L = 1,000 mL

The graduated cylinder in the picture is marked in milliliter divisions. Notice that the water in the cylinder has a curved surface. This curved surface is called the *meniscus.* To measure the volume, you must read the level at the lowest point of the meniscus. What is the volume of water in this graduated cylinder? **ACTIVITY**

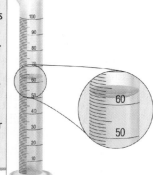

582

Mass To measure mass, or the amount of matter in an object, you will use a unit of measure known as the **gram (g).** One gram is approximately the mass of a paper clip. Larger masses are measured in kilograms (kg). Scientists use a balance to find the mass of an object.

Common Conversion

1 kg = 1,000 g

The mass of the apple in the picture is measured in kilograms. What is the mass of the apple? Suppose a recipe for applesauce called for one kilogram of apples. About how many apples would you need?

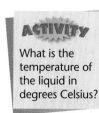
ACTIVITY

Temperature
To measure the temperature of a substance, you will use the **Celsius scale.** Temperature is measured in degrees Celsius (°C) using a Celsius thermometer. Water freezes at 0°C and boils at 100°C.

ACTIVITY
What is the temperature of the liquid in degrees Celsius?

Converting SI Units

To use the SI system, you must know how to convert between units. Converting from one unit to another involves the skill of **calculating,** or using mathematical operations. Converting between SI units is similar to converting between dollars and dimes because both systems are based on multiples of ten.

Suppose you want to convert a length of 80 centimeters to meters. Follow these steps to convert between units.

1. Begin by writing down the measurement you want to convert—in this example, 80 centimeters.

2. Write a conversion factor that represents the relationship between the two units you are converting. In this example, the relationship is *1 meter = 100 centimeters.* Write this conversion factor as a fraction, making sure to place the units you are converting from (centimeters, in this example) in the denominator.

3. Multiply the measurement you want to convert by the fraction. When you do this, the units in the first measurement will cancel out with the units in the denominator. Your answer will be in the units you are converting to (meters, in this example).

Example

80 centimeters = ___?___ meters

$$80 \text{ centimeters} \times \frac{1 \text{ meter}}{100 \text{ centimeters}} = \frac{80 \text{ meters}}{100}$$

$$= 0.8 \text{ meters}$$

ACTIVITY
Convert between the following units.
1. 600 millimeters = _?_ meters
2. 0.35 liters = _?_ milliliters
3. 1,050 grams = _?_ kilograms

583

Conducting a Scientific Investigation

Asking Questions

Before students do the activity on the next page, walk them through the steps of a typical scientific investigation. Begin by asking: **Why is a scientific question important to a scientific investigation?** *(It is the reason for conducting a scientific investigation and how every investigation begins.)* **What is the scientific question in the activity at the bottom of the next page?** *(Is a ball's bounce affected by the height from which it is dropped?)*

Formulating a Hypothesis

Emphasize that a hypothesis is a proposed explanation or suggested answer to a scientific question, but it is *not* just a guess. Ask: **On what information do scientists base their hypotheses?** *(Their observations and previous knowledge or experience)* Point out that a hypothesis does not always turn out to be correct. Ask: **In that case, do you think the scientist wasted his or her time? Explain your answer.** *(No, because the scientist probably learned from the investigation and maybe could develop another hypothesis that could be supported.)*

Designing an Experiment

Have a volunteer read the Experimental Procedure in the box. Then call on students to identify the manipulated variable *(amount of salt added to water)*, the variables that are kept constant *(amount and starting temperature of water, placing containers in freezer)*, the responding variable *(time it takes water to freeze)*, and the control *(Container 3)*.

Ask: **How might the experiment be affected if Container 1 had only 100 mL of water?** *(It wouldn't be a fair comparison with the containers that have more water.)* **What if Container 3 was not included in the experiment?** *(You wouldn't have anything to compare the other two containers to know if their freezing times were faster or slower than that of fresh water.)* Help students understand the importance of keeping all variables

Conducting a Scientific Investigation

In some ways, scientists are like detectives, piecing together clues to learn about a process or event. One way that scientists gather clues is by carrying out experiments. In an experiment, scientists test an idea in a careful, orderly manner. Although experiments do not all follow the same steps in the same order, many follow a pattern similar to the one described here.

Asking Questions

Experiments begin by asking a scientific question. A scientific question is one that can be answered by gathering evidence. For example, the question "Which freezes faster— fresh water or salt water?" is a scientific question because you can carry out an investigation and gather information to answer the question.

Formulating a Hypothesis

The next step is to form a hypothesis. A **hypothesis** is a possible explanation for a set of observations or answer to a scientific question. In science, a hypothesis must be something that can be tested. A hypothesis can be worded as an *If . . . then . . .* statement. For example, a hypothesis might be *"If I add salt to fresh water, then the water will take longer to freeze."* A hypothesis worded this way serves as a rough outline of the experiment you should perform.

584

constant except the manipulated variable. Also be sure they understand the role of the control. Then ask: **What operational definition is used in this experiment?** *("Frozen" means the time at which a wooden stick can no longer move in a container.)*

Background

Integrating Science The term *hypothesis* refers to a proposed explanation that can be tested. In science, many hypotheses are developed through logical thinking. But some hypotheses have been the results of imagination, creative leaps, chance events, even dreams. The key characteristic of a hypothesis is that it's a testable explanation.

Designing an Experiment

Next you need to plan a way to test your hypothesis. Your plan should be written out as a step-by-step procedure and should describe the observations or measurements you will make.

Two important steps involved in designing an experiment are controlling variables and forming operational definitions.

Controlling Variables In a well-designed experiment, you need to keep all variables the same except for one. A **variable** is any factor that can change in an experiment. The factor that you change is called the **manipulated variable.** In this experiment, the manipulated variable is the amount of salt added to the water. Other factors, such as the amount of water or the starting temperature, are kept constant.

The factor that changes as a result of the manipulated variable is called the responding variable. The **responding variable** is what you measure or observe to obtain your results. In this experiment, the responding variable is how long the water takes to freeze.

An experiment in which all factors except one are kept constant is a **controlled experiment.** Most controlled experiments include a test called the control. In this experiment, Container 3 is the control. Because no salt is added to Container 3, you can compare the results from the other containers to it. Any difference in results must be due to the addition of salt alone.

Forming Operational Definitions

Another important aspect of a well-designed experiment is having clear operational definitions. An **operational definition** is a statement that describes how a particular variable is to be measured or how a term is to be defined. For example, in this experiment, how will you determine if the water has frozen? You might decide to insert a stick in each container at the start of the experiment. Your operational definition of "frozen" would be that the stick can no longer move.

EXPERIMENTAL PROCEDURE

1. Fill 3 containers with 300 milliliters of cold tap water.

2. Add 10 grams of salt to Container 1; stir. Add 20 grams of salt to Container 2; stir. Add no salt to Container 3.

3. Place the 3 containers in a freezer.

4. Check the containers every 15 minutes. Record your observations.

Interpreting Data

The observations and measurements you make in an experiment are called data. At the end of an experiment, you need to analyze the data to look for any patterns or trends. Patterns often become clear if you organize your data in a data table, chart, or graph. Then think through what the data reveal. Do they support your hypothesis? Do they point out a flaw in your experiment? Do you need to collect more data?

Drawing Conclusions

A conclusion is a statement that sums up what you have learned from an experiment. When you draw a conclusion, you need to decide whether the data you collected support your hypothesis or not. You may need to repeat an experiment several times before you can draw any conclusions from it. Conclusions often lead you to pose new questions and plan new experiments to answer them.

Is a ball's bounce affected by the height from which it is dropped? Using the steps just described, plan a controlled experiment to investigate this problem. **ACTIVITY**

585

Interpreting Data

Emphasize the importance of collecting accurate and detailed data in a scientific investigation. Ask: **What if the students forgot to record the times that they made their observations in the experiment?** *(They wouldn't be able to completely analyze their data to draw valid conclusions.)* Then ask: **Why are data tables and graphs a good way to organize data?** *(They often make it easier to compare and analyze data.)* You may wish to have students review the Skills Handbook pages on Creating Data Tables and Graphs at this point.

Drawing Conclusions

Help students understand that a conclusion is not necessarily the end of a scientific investigation. A conclusion about one experiment may lead right into another experiment. Point out that in scientific investigations, a conclusion is a summary and explanation of the results of an experiment.

Tell students to suppose that for the Experimental Procedure described on this page, they obtained the following results: Container 1 froze in 45 minutes, Container 2 in 80 minutes, and Container 3 in 25 minutes. Ask: **What conclusions can you draw about this experiment?** *(Students might conclude that the more salt that is added to fresh water, the longer it takes the water to freeze. The hypothesis is supported, and the question of which freezes faster is answered—fresh water.)*

You might wish to have students work in pairs to plan the controlled experiment. *(Students should develop a hypothesis, such as "If I increase the height from which a ball is dropped, then the height of its bounce will increase." They can test the hypothesis by dropping balls from varying heights (the manipulated variable). All trials should be done with the same kind of ball and on the same surface (constant variables). For each trial, they should measure the height of the bounce (responding variable).)* After students have designed the experiment, provide rubber balls and invite them to carry out the experiment so they can collect and interpret data and draw conclusions. **ACTIVITY**

Thinking Critically

Comparing and Contrasting

Emphasize that the skill of comparing and contrasting often relies on good observation skills, as in this activity. *(Students' answers may vary. Sample answer: Similarities—both are dogs and have four legs, two eyes, two ears, brown and white fur, black noses, pink tongues; Differences—smooth coat vs. rough coat, more white fur vs. more brown fur, shorter vs. taller, long ears vs. short ears.)*

Applying Concepts

Point out to students that they apply concepts that they learn in school in their daily lives. For example, they learn to add, subtract, multiply, and divide in school. If they get a paper route or some other part-time job, they can apply those concepts. Challenge students to practice applying concepts by doing the activity. *(Antifreeze lowers the temperature at which the solution will freeze, and thus keeps the water in the radiator from freezing.)*

Interpreting Illustrations

Again, point out the need for good observation skills. Ask: **What is the difference between "interpreting illustrations" and "looking at the pictures"?** *("Interpreting illustrations" requires thorough examination of the illustration, caption, and labels, while "looking at the pictures" implies less thorough examination.)* Encourage students to thoroughly examine the diagram as they do the activity. *(Students' paragraphs may vary, but should describe the internal anatomy of an earthworm, including some of the organs in the earthworm.)*

Thinking Critically

Has a friend ever asked for your advice about a problem? If so, you may have helped your friend think through the problem in a logical way. Without knowing it, you used critical-thinking skills to help your friend. Critical thinking involves the use of reasoning and logic to solve problems or make decisions. Some critical-thinking skills are described below.

Comparing and Contrasting

When you examine two objects for similarities and differences, you are using the skill of **comparing and contrasting.** Comparing involves identifying similarities, or common characteristics. Contrasting involves identifying differences. Analyzing objects in this way can help you discover details that you might otherwise overlook.

> **ACTIVITY**
> Compare and contrast the two animals in the photo. First list all the similarities that you see. Then list all the differences.

Applying Concepts

When you use your knowledge about one situation to make sense of a similar situation, you are using the skill of **applying concepts.** Being able to transfer your knowledge from one situation to another shows that you truly understand a concept. You may use this skill in answering test questions that present different problems from the ones you've reviewed in class.

> **ACTIVITY**
> You have just learned that water takes longer to freeze when other substances are mixed into it. Use this knowledge to explain why people need a substance called antifreeze in their car's radiator in the winter.

Interpreting Illustrations

Diagrams, photographs, and maps are included in textbooks to help clarify what you read. These illustrations show processes, places, and ideas in a visual manner. The skill called **interpreting illustrations** can help you learn from these visual elements. To understand an illustration, take the time to study the illustration along with all the written information that accompanies it. Captions identify the key concepts shown in the illustration. Labels point out the important parts of a diagram or map, while keys identify the symbols used in a map.

Upper blood vessel
Reproductive organs
Arches
Brain
Mouth
Bristles
Digestive tract
Lower blood vessel
Nerve cord
Waste-removal organs
Intestine

▲ Internal anatomy of an earthworm

> **ACTIVITY**
> Study the diagram above. Then write a short paragraph explaining what you have learned.

586

Relating Cause and Effect

If one event causes another event to occur, the two events are said to have a cause-and-effect relationship. When you determine that such a relationship exists between two events, you use a skill called **relating cause and effect.** For example, if you notice an itchy, red bump on your skin, you might infer that a mosquito bit you. The mosquito bite is the cause, and the bump is the effect.

It is important to note that two events do not necessarily have a cause-and-effect relationship just because they occur together. Scientists carry out experiments or use past experience to determine whether a cause-and-effect relationship exists.

You are on a camping trip and your flashlight has stopped working. List some possible causes for the flashlight malfunction. How could you determine which cause-and-effect relationship has left you in the dark?

Making Generalizations

When you draw a conclusion about an entire group based on information about only some of the group's members, you are using a skill called **making generalizations.** For a generalization to be valid, the sample you choose must be large enough and representative of the entire group. You might, for example, put this skill to work at a farm stand if you see a sign that says, "Sample some grapes before you buy." If you sample a few sweet grapes, you may conclude that all the grapes are sweet—and purchase a large bunch.

A team of scientists needs to determine whether the water in a large reservoir is safe to drink. How could they use the skill of making generalizations to help them? What should they do?

Making Judgments

When you evaluate something to decide whether it is good or bad, or right or wrong, you are using a skill called **making judgments.** For example, you make judgments when you decide to eat healthful foods or to pick up litter in a park. Before you make a judgment, you need to think through the pros and cons of a situation, and identify the values or standards that you hold.

Should children and teens be required to wear helmets when bicycling? Explain why you feel the way you do.

Problem Solving

When you use critical-thinking skills to resolve an issue or decide on a course of action, you are using a skill called **problem solving.** Some problems, such as how to convert a fraction into a decimal, are straightforward. Other problems, such as figuring out why your computer has stopped working, are complex. Some complex problems can be solved using the trial and error method—try out one solution first, and if that doesn't work, try another. Other useful problem-solving strategies include making models and brainstorming possible solutions with a partner.

Relating Cause and Effect

Emphasize that not all events that occur together have a cause-and-effect relationship. For example, tell students that you went to the grocery and your car stalled. Ask: **Is there a cause-and-effect relationship in this situation? Explain your answer.** *(No, because going to the grocery could not cause a car to stall. There must be another cause to make the car stall.)* Have students do the activity to practice relating cause and effect. *(Students should identify that the malfunctioning flashlight is the effect. Some possible causes include dead batteries, a broken switch, or a burned-out bulb.)*

Making Generalizations

Point out the importance of having a large, representative sample before making a generalization. Ask: **If you went fishing at a lake and caught three catfish, could you make the generalization that all fish in the lake are catfish? Why or why not?** *(No, because there might be other kinds of fish you didn't catch because they didn't like the bait or they may be in other parts of the lake.)* **How could you make a generalization about the kinds of fish in the lake?** *(By having a larger sample)* Have students do the activity to practice making generalizations. *(The scientists should collect and test water samples from a number of different parts of the reservoir.)*

Making Judgments

Remind students that they make a judgment almost every time they make a decision. Ask: **What steps should you follow to make a judgment?** *(Gather information, list pros and cons, analyze values, make judgment)* Invite students to do the activity, and then to share and discuss the judgments they made. *(Students' judgments will vary, but should be supported by valid reasoning. Sample answer: Children and teens should be required to wear helmets when bicycling because helmets have been proven to save lives and reduce head injuries.)*

Problem Solving

Challenge student pairs to solve a problem about a soapbox derby. Explain that their younger brother is building a car to enter in the race. The brother wants to know how to make his soapbox car go faster. After student pairs have considered the problem, have them share their ideas about solutions with the class. *(Most will probably suggest using trial and error by making small changes to the car and testing the car after each change. Some students may suggest making and manipulating a model.)*

Organizing Information

Concept Maps

Challenge students to make a concept map with at least three levels of concepts to organize information about types of transportation. All students should start with the phrase *types of transportation* at the top of the concept map. After that point, their concept maps may vary. *(For example, some students might place* private transportation *and* public transportation *at the next level, while other students might have* human-powered *and* gas-powered. *Make sure students connect the concepts with linking words. Challenge students to include cross-linkages as well.)*

Compare/ Contrast Tables

Have students make their own compare/contrast tables using two or more different sports or other activities, such as playing musical instruments. Emphasize that students should select characteristics that highlight the similarities and differences between the activities. *(Students' compare/contrast tables should include several appropriate characteristics and list information about each activity for every characteristic.)*

Organizing Information

As you read this textbook, how can you make sense of all the information it contains? Some useful tools to help you organize information are shown on this page. These tools are called *graphic organizers* because they give you a visual picture of a topic, showing at a glance how key concepts are related.

Concept Maps

Concept maps are useful tools for organizing information on broad topics. A concept map begins with a general concept and shows how it can be broken down into more specific concepts. In that way, relationships between concepts become easier to understand.

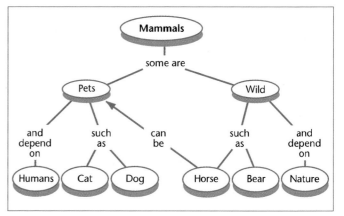

A concept map is constructed by placing concept words (usually nouns) in ovals and connecting them with linking words. Often, the most general concept word is placed at the top, and the words become more specific as you move downward. Often the linking words, which are written on a line extending between two ovals, describe the relationship between the two concepts they connect. If you follow any string of concepts and linking words down the map, it should read like a sentence.

Some concept maps include linking words that connect a concept on one branch of the map to a concept on another branch. These linking words, called cross-linkages, show more complex interrelationships among concepts.

Compare/Contrast Tables

Compare/contrast tables are useful tools for sorting out the similarities and differences between two or more items. A table provides an organized framework in which to compare items based on specific characteristics that you identify.

To create a compare/contrast table, list the items to be compared across the top of a table. Then list the characteristics that will form the basis of your comparison in the left-hand

Characteristic	Baseball	Basketball
Number of Players	9	5
Playing Field	Baseball diamond	Basketball court
Equipment	Bat, baseball, mitts	Basket, basketball

column. Complete the table by filling in information about each characteristic, first for one item and then for the other.

Venn Diagrams

Another way to show similarities and differences between items is with a Venn diagram. A Venn diagram consists of two or more circles that partially overlap. Each circle represents a particular concept or idea. Common characteristics, or similarities, are written within the area of overlap between the two circles. Unique characteristics, or differences, are written in the parts of the circles outside the area of overlap.

To create a Venn diagram, draw two overlapping circles. Label the circles with the names of the items being compared. Write the

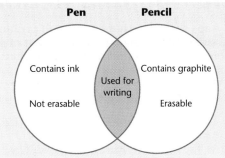

unique characteristics in each circle outside the area of overlap. Then write the shared characteristics within the area of overlap.

Flowcharts

A flowchart can help you understand the order in which certain events have occurred or should occur. Flowcharts are useful for outlining the stages in a process or the steps in a procedure.

To make a flowchart, write a brief description of each event in a box. Place the first event at the top of the page, followed by the second event, the third event, and so on. Then draw an arrow to connect each event to the one that occurs next.

Preparing Pasta

Boil water
↓
Cook pasta
↓
Drain water
↓
Add sauce

Cycle Diagrams

A cycle diagram can be used to show a sequence of events that is continuous, or cyclical. A continuous sequence does not have an end because, when the final event is over, the first event begins again. Like a flowchart, a cycle diagram can help you understand the order of events.

To create a cycle diagram, write a brief description of each event in a box. Place one event at the top of the page in the center. Then, moving in a clockwise direction around an imaginary circle, write each event in its proper sequence. Draw arrows that connect each event to the one that occurs next, forming a continuous circle.

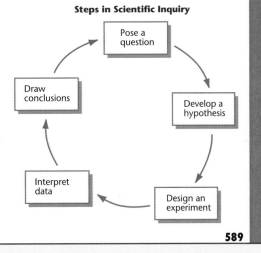

Steps in Scientific Inquiry

Pose a question → Develop a hypothesis → Design an experiment → Interpret data → Draw conclusions →

Venn Diagrams *ACTIVITY*

Students can use the same information from their compare/contrast tables to create a Venn diagram. Make sure students understand that the overlapping area of the circles is used to list similarities and the parts of the circles outside the overlap area are used to show differences. If students want to list similarities and differences among three activities, show them how to add a third circle that overlaps each of the other two circles and has an area of overlap for all three circles. (*Students' Venn diagrams will vary. Make sure they have accurately listed similarities in the overlap area and differences in the parts of the circles that do not overlap.*)

Flowcharts *ACTIVITY*

Encourage students to create a flowchart to show the things they did this morning as they got ready for school. Remind students that a flowchart should show the correct order in which events occurred or should occur. (*Students' flowcharts will vary somewhat. A typical flowchart might include: got up → ate breakfast → took a shower → brushed teeth → got dressed → gathered books and homework → put on jacket.*)

Cycle Diagrams *ACTIVITY*

Review that a cycle diagram shows a sequence of events that is continuous. Then challenge students to create a cycle diagram that shows how the weather changes with the seasons where they live. (*Students' cycle diagrams may vary, though most will include four steps, one for each season.*)

Making and Reading Maps

A Map's Scale

Before class, measure the basic dimensions of the classroom with a tape measure. Provide these measurements to students, and then challenge each student to make a map of the classroom on a piece of graph paper. Students should devise a scale, create a key, and include as many objects as possible in the map. A simple scale might be 3 squares equals 1 m.

ACTIVITY

Compass Rose

Challenge small groups to write a procedure by which a mapmaker could find north without using a compass, given this information: the sun is directly south at noon (or 1:00 P.M. during Daylight Savings Time). A typical procedure would involve sinking a stick into the ground and, then around noon, marking the length of its shadow with pebbles every few minutes. The shortest length between the base of the stick and a pebble points to true north.

ACTIVITY

Map Symbols

After students have examined the symbols, ask: **Which of these symbols could you recognize even without an explanation?** (*Students might mention the symbols for church, divided highway, and railroad tracks.*) Explain that the symbols were created to make sense even to those who have no specialized knowledge. Ask: **Is the symbol for woods always a rectangle?** (*No, this symbol shows what the color on the maps mean. Green is used for wooded areas.*)

Making and Reading Maps

Maps show the shape, size, and position of Earth's features. To understand the information that maps convey, you must learn about the symbols and other conventions that mapmakers use.

A Map's Scale

A map is a flat model that shows all or part of Earth's surface as it looks from above. Of course, the size of a feature on a map differs from the real size of the feature on Earth. The same is true of a globe, which is a sphere that represents Earth's entire surface. Both maps and globes include a **scale,** which relates distances on the map to the corresponding distances on Earth's surface.

A scale is sometimes given as a ratio. For example, one unit on a map may equal 100,000 units on the ground. This means that 1 centimeter on the map represents 100,000 centimeters, 1 kilometer, on Earth. Similarly, 1 inch on the map represents 100,000 inches, 1.58 miles, on Earth.

This scale, "one to one-hundred thousand" is written "1 : 100,000." The three types of map scales are shown below.

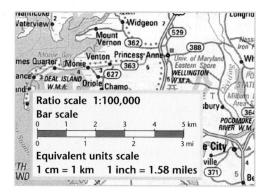

Compass Rose

Maps also include a compass rose. The compass rose relates directions on the map to directions on Earth. North is usually located at the top of a map.

Make a map of your classroom, school, or neighborhood. Be sure to include a scale, compass rose, and key explaining the symbols you used.

ACTIVITY

Map Symbols

Mapmakers use a variety of symbols to show where important landmarks and other features are located. The symbols are explained in a section of the map called the key, or legend. The table below shows some of the most common symbols often found on maps.

Commonly Used Map Symbols

Building	■ □ ▨ ▨	Primary highway	━━━	Airport	✈
School; church	♩ ♁	Secondary highway	━━━	Body of water	≈
Campground; picnic area	▲ ⊼	Divided highway	━━━	Waterfall or rapids	≋
Cemetery	Cem	Railroad tracks	┝━━┿	Woods or parks	▨

Latitude and Longitude

To find a point on Earth's surface, mapmakers use a reference system similar to the grid of squares on a checkerboard. The grid is made up of two types of imaginary lines. Lines of **latitude** run east-to-west around the globe, while lines of **longitude** run north-to-south.

Lines of latitude are sometimes called parallels because they run parallel to each other. In the middle of the globe is a parallel known as the equator. The **equator** divides Earth into two halves—the Northern and Southern hemispheres.

The equator is the starting line for measuring distances north or south. Distances are measured in units called degrees. The equator is 0° latitude. The farthest distance north of the equator is 90° north latitude, the location of the North Pole. The farthest distance south of the equator is 90° south latitude, the location of the South Pole.

If you look on a globe, you can see that, unlike lines of latitude, lines of longitude are not parallel lines. Lines of longitude run north-to-south and meet at the poles. The **prime meridian** is a line of longitude that passes through Greenwich, England. Places east of the prime meridian are in the Eastern hemisphere. Places west of the prime meridian are in the Western hemisphere.

The prime meridian is at 0° longitude, the starting line for measuring longitude. Longitude lines in each hemisphere are numbered up to 180°.

Every point on Earth's surface has a particular latitude and longitude. By finding the point where a latitude line crosses a longitude line, you can determine where a given place is located.

Where in the World? ACTIVITY

Using a globe, determine what city is found at each of the following points:
- **a.** 2° S, 80° W
- **b.** 38° N, 9° W
- **c.** 34° N, 135° E
- **d.** 34° S, 58° W
- **e.** 56° N, 3° W
- **f.** 1° N, 103° E

What word is spelled by the first letters of these city names?

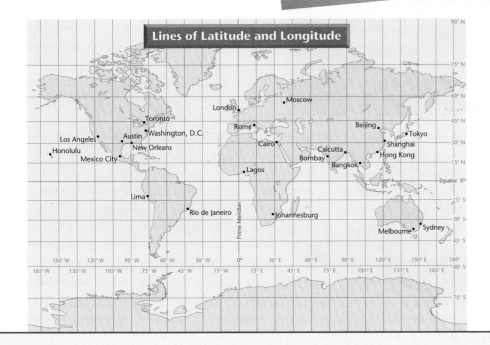

Lines of Latitude and Longitude

Latitude and Longitude

Draw a grid on the board to represent the intersections of several streets near the school. Label the streets, and then pose questions to students about stores or other buildings at or near prominent intersections. Direct students' attention to the map showing latitude and longitude. Ask: **What city is near the intersection of 45° N latitude and 15° E longitude?** *(Rome)* Explain that the imaginary grid on a map is as helpful in locating places as the grid of streets is.

In using the globe, students should find the approximate coordinates or the major city closest to the coordinates. The cities are, in order: Guayaquil, Ecuador; Lisbon, Portugal; Osaka, Japan; Buenos Aires, Argentina; Edinburgh, Scotland; Singapore, Singapore. The word spelled by the cities' first letters is GLOBES.

ACTIVITY

Topographic Maps

Call students's attention to the topographic map of Mt. Monadnock and ask: **How are the dark contour lines different from the lighter ones?** *(The dark contour lines, called index contours, are labeled with an elevation, while the lighter ones are not. They are also thicker than the other contour lines.)* **If the contour interval were not listed in the key, how could you tell what the contour interval was by looking at this map?** *(First, you could determine the difference in elevation between two dark contour lines. The difference between the contour line surrounding the summit and the next dark contour line is 1,000 ft. Then divide that number by the number of contour lines from one dark line to the next: 1,000 ft ÷ 5 = 200 ft.)*

Have students examine the map and ask any **ACTIVITY** initial questions before they try to respond to the problems. The White Arrow Trail is steeper. The difference in elevation between the Park Headquarters and the summit is more than 1,600 feet.

Topographic Maps

Some maps include information about a region's **topography,** or its physical features, such as mountains, hills, and valleys. These maps use symbols to show the land's elevation, or height above sea level.

A topographic map is a map that uses symbols known as contour lines to show the physical features of a region. On a topographic map, a **contour line** connects points of equal elevation. The change in elevation from one contour line to the next is called the **contour interval.** The contour interval for a given map is always the same. For example, the map below has a contour interval of 200 feet. If you start at one contour line and count up five contour lines, you have reached an elevation 1,000 feet above where you started. Usually every fifth contour line is darker and heavier than the others. This contour line is called the index contour. This line is labeled with the elevation in round units, such as 1,600 or 2,000 feet above sea level.

ACTIVITY

You are planning to hike up Mt. Monadnock. Use the topographic map to find the difference in elevation between the park headquarters and the summit. Also, determine which route is steeper: the White Arrow Trail or the Pumpelly Trail. How do you know?

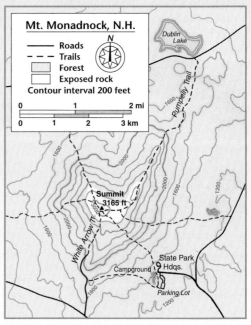

Mt. Monadnock, N.H.
Roads
Trails
Forest
Exposed rock
Contour interval 200 feet

Summit
3165 ft

State Park Hdqs.
Campground
Parking Lot

Dublin Lake

In addition to showing elevation, contour maps also show other features, such as bodies of water, roads, and buildings. The topographic map below, which shows part of Tennessee, was made by the United States Geological Survey (USGS). Note that contour maps, like all maps, include a scale. You can use the scale to figure out the size of the whole area or the distance between any two points on the map.

Call on students to read the descriptions of the various features on the USGS map and explain what the contour interval is. Students should practice finding high and low points on the map, steep and gentle slopes, and ridges and valleys. Also, have students use rulers to measure the scale and determine how much area the map covers.

To reinforce how a topographic map represents elevation and relief, divide students into small groups and provide each group with a topographic map. Then challenge each group to make a three-dimensional model of a section of the map that contains more than one feature.

ACTIVITY

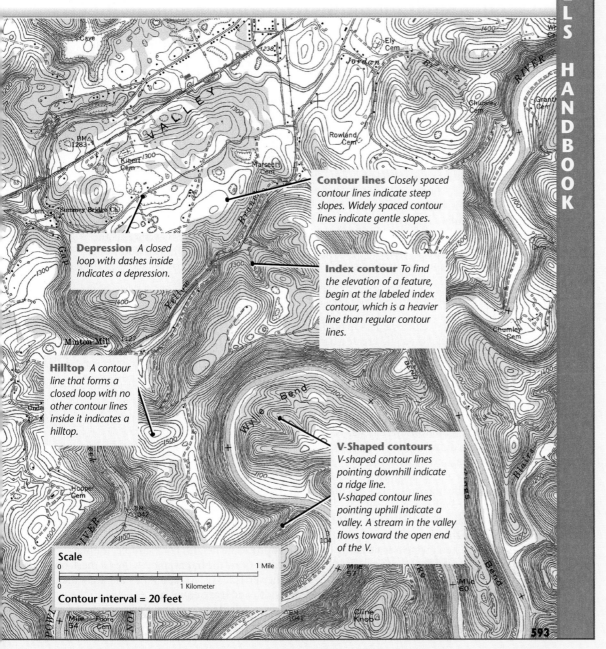

Contour lines *Closely spaced contour lines indicate steep slopes. Widely spaced contour lines indicate gentle slopes.*

Depression *A closed loop with dashes inside indicates a depression.*

Index contour *To find the elevation of a feature, begin at the labeled index contour, which is a heavier line than regular contour lines.*

Hilltop *A contour line that forms a closed loop with no other contour lines inside it indicates a hilltop.*

V-Shaped contours *V-shaped contour lines pointing downhill indicate a ridge line. V-shaped contour lines pointing uphill indicate a valley. A stream in the valley flows toward the open end of the V.*

Scale

0   1 Mile

0   1 Kilometer

Contour interval = 20 feet

593

Creating Data Tables and Graphs

Data Tables

Have students create a data table to show how much time they spend on different activities during one week. Suggest that students first list the main activities they do every week. Then they should determine the amount of time they spend on each activity each day. Remind students to give this data table a title. (*Students' data tables will vary. A sample data table is shown below.*)

Bar Graphs

Students can use the data from their data table above to make a bar graph showing how much time they spend on different activities during a week. The vertical axis should be divided into units of time, such as hours. Remind students to label both axes and give their graph a title. (*Students' bar graphs will vary. A sample bar graph is shown below.*)

Creating Data Tables and Graphs

How can you make sense of the data in a science experiment? The first step is to organize the data to help you understand them. Data tables and graphs are helpful tools for organizing data.

Data Tables

You have gathered your materials and set up your experiment. But before you start, you need to plan a way to record what happens during the experiment. By creating a data table, you can record your observations and measurements in an orderly way.

Suppose, for example, that a scientist conducted an experiment to find out how many Calories people of different body masses burn while doing various activities. The data table shows the results.

Notice in this data table that the manipulated variable (body mass) is the heading of one column. The responding

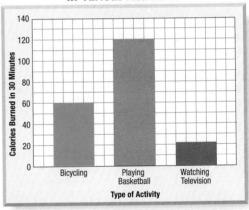

CALORIES BURNED IN 30 MINUTES OF ACTIVITY			
Body Mass	Experiment 1 Bicycling	Experiment 2 Playing Basketball	Experiment 3 Watching Television
30 kg	60 Calories	120 Calories	21 Calories
40 kg	77 Calories	164 Calories	27 Calories
50 kg	95 Calories	206 Calories	33 Calories
60 kg	114 Calories	248 Calories	38 Calories

variable (for Experiment 1, the number of Calories burned while bicycling) is the heading of the next column. Additional columns were added for related experiments.

Bar Graphs

To compare how many Calories a person burns doing various activities, you could create a bar graph. A bar graph is used to display data in a number of separate, or distinct, categories. In this example, bicycling, playing basketball, and watching television are three separate categories.

To create a bar graph, follow these steps.

1. On graph paper, draw a horizontal, or *x*-, axis and a vertical, or *y*-, axis.
2. Write the names of the categories to be graphed along the horizontal axis. Include an overall label for the axis as well.
3. Label the vertical axis with the name of the responding variable. Include units of measurement. Then create a scale along the axis by marking off equally spaced numbers that cover the range of the data collected.
4. For each category, draw a solid bar using the scale on the vertical axis to determine the

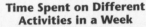

Calories Burned by a 30-kilogram Person in Various Activities

appropriate height. For example, for bicycling, draw the bar as high as the 60 mark on the vertical axis. Make all the bars the same width and leave equal spaces between them.
5. Add a title that describes the graph.

594

Hours Spent on Different Activities in a Week

	Going to Classes	Eating Meals	Playing Soccer	Watching Television
Monday	6	2	2	0.5
Tuesday	6	1.5	1.5	1.5
Wednesday	6	2	1	2
Thursday	6	2	2	1.5
Friday	6	2	2	0.5
Saturday	0	2.5	2.5	1
Sunday	0	3	1	2

Time Spent on Different Activities in a Week

Line Graphs

To see whether a relationship exists between body mass and the number of Calories burned while bicycling, you could create a line graph. A line graph is used to display data that show how one variable (the responding variable) changes in response to another variable (the manipulated variable). You can use a line graph when your manipulated variable is *continuous*, that is, when there are other points between the ones that you tested. In this example, body mass is a continuous variable because there are other body masses between 30 and 40 kilograms (for example, 31 kilograms). Time is another example of a continuous variable.

Line graphs are powerful tools because they allow you to estimate values for conditions that you did not test in the experiment. For example, you can use the line graph to estimate that a 35-kilogram person would burn 68 Calories while bicycling.

To create a line graph, follow these steps.

1. On graph paper, draw a horizontal, or *x*-, axis and a vertical, or *y*-, axis.
2. Label the horizontal axis with the name of the manipulated variable. Label the vertical axis with the name of the responding variable. Include units of measurement.
3. Create a scale on each axis by marking off equally spaced numbers that cover the range of the data collected.
4. Plot a point on the graph for each piece of data. In the line graph above, the dotted lines show how to plot the first data point (30 kilograms and 60 Calories). Draw an imaginary vertical line extending up from the horizontal axis at the 30-kilogram mark. Then draw an imaginary horizontal line extending across from the vertical axis at the 60-Calorie mark. Plot the point where the two lines intersect.

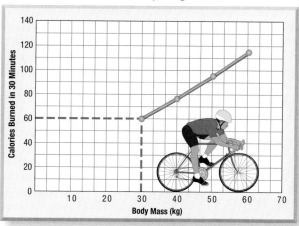

Effect of Body Mass on Calories Burned While Bicycling

5. Connect the plotted points with a solid line. (In some cases, it may be more appropriate to draw a line that shows the general trend of the plotted points. In those cases, some of the points may fall above or below the line. Also, not all graphs are linear. It may be more appropriate to draw a curve to connect the points.)
6. Add a title that identifies the variables or relationship in the graph.

> **Create line graphs to display the data from Experiment 2 and Experiment 3 in the data table.** ACTIVITY

> **You read in the newspaper that a total of 4 centimeters of rain fell in your area in June, 2.5 centimeters fell in July, and 1.5 centimeters fell in August. What type of graph would you use to display these data? Use graph paper to create the graph.** ACTIVITY

Line Graphs

Walk students through the steps involved in creating a line graph using the example illustrated on the page. For example, ask: **What is the label on the horizontal axis? On the vertical axis?** *(Body Mass (kg); Calories Burned in 30 Minutes)* **What scales are used on each axis?** *(3 squares per 10 kg on the x-axis and 2 squares per 20 calories on the y-axis)* **What does the second data point represent?** *(77 Calories burned for a body mass of 40 kg)* **What trend or pattern does the graph show?** *(The number of Calories burned in 30 minutes of cycling increases with body mass.)*

Have students follow the steps to carry out the first activity. *(Students should make a different graph for each experiment with different y-axis scales to practice making scales appropriate for data. See sample graphs below.)* ACTIVITY

Have students carry out the second activity. *(Students should conclude that a bar graph would be best to display the data. A sample bar graph for these data is shown below.)* ACTIVITY

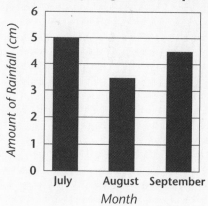

Rainfall in July, August, and September

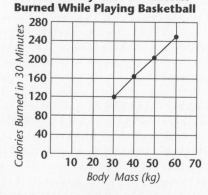

Effect of Body Mass on Calories Burned While Playing Basketball

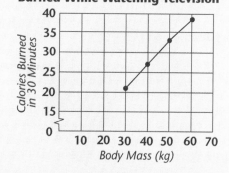

Effect of Body Mass on Calories Burned While Watching Television

Circle Graphs

Emphasize that a circle graph has to include 100 percent of the categories for the topic being graphed. For example, ask: **Could the data in the bar graph titled "Calories Burned by a 30-kilogram Person in Various Activities" (on the previous page) be shown in a circle graph? Why or why not?** *(No, because it does not include all the possible ways a 30-kilogram person can burn Calories.)* Then walk students through the steps for making a circle graph. Help students to use a compass and a protractor. Use the protractor to illustrate that a circle has 360 degrees. Make sure students understand the mathematical calculations involved in making a circle graph.

You might wish to have students work in pairs to complete the activity. *(Students' circle graphs should look like the graph below.)*

ACTIVITY

Circle Graphs

Like bar graphs, circle graphs can be used to display data in a number of separate categories. Unlike bar graphs, however, circle graphs can only be used when you have data for *all* the categories that make up a given topic. A circle graph is sometimes called a pie chart because it resembles a pie cut into slices. The pie represents the entire topic, while the slices represent the individual categories. The size of a slice indicates what percentage of the whole a particular category makes up.

The data table below shows the results of a survey in which 24 teenagers were asked to identify their favorite sport. The data were then used to create the circle graph at the right.

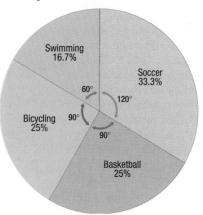

Sports That Teens Prefer

FAVORITE SPORTS	
Sport	Number of Students
Soccer	8
Basketball	6
Bicycling	6
Swimming	4

To create a circle graph, follow these steps.

1. Use a compass to draw a circle. Mark the center of the circle with a point. Then draw a line from the center point to the top of the circle.

2. Determine the size of each "slice" by setting up a proportion where x equals the number of degrees in a slice. (NOTE: A circle contains 360 degrees.) For example, to find the number of degrees in the "soccer" slice, set up the following proportion:

$$\frac{\text{students who prefer soccer}}{\text{total number of students}} = \frac{x}{\text{total number of degrees in a circle}}$$

$$\frac{8}{24} = \frac{x}{360}$$

Cross-multiply and solve for x.

$$24x = 8 \times 360$$
$$x = 120$$

The "soccer" slice should contain 120 degrees.

596

3. Use a protractor to measure the angle of the first slice, using the line you drew to the top of the circle as the 0° line. Draw a line from the center of the circle to the edge for the angle you measured.

4. Continue around the circle by measuring the size of each slice with the protractor. Start measuring from the edge of the previous slice so the wedges do not overlap. When you are done, the entire circle should be filled in.

5. Determine the percentage of the whole circle that each slice represents. To do this, divide the number of degrees in a slice by the total number of degrees in a circle (360), and multiply by 100%. For the "soccer" slice, you can find the percentage as follows:

$$\frac{120}{360} \times 100\% = 33.3\%$$

6. Use a different color to shade in each slice. Label each slice with the name of the category and with the percentage of the whole it represents.

7. Add a title to the circle graph.

ACTIVITY

In a class of 28 students, 12 students take the bus to school, 10 students walk, and 6 students ride their bicycles. Create a circle graph to display these data.

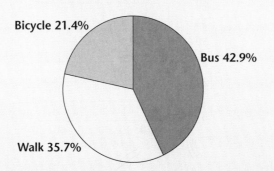

Ways Students Get to School

Bicycle 21.4%

Bus 42.9%

Walk 35.7%

Laboratory Safety

Safety Symbols

These symbols alert you to possible dangers in the laboratory and remind you to work carefully.

Safety Goggles Always wear safety goggles to protect your eyes in any activity involving chemicals, flames or heating, or the possibility of broken glassware.

Lab Apron Wear a laboratory apron to protect your skin and clothing from damage.

Breakage You are working with materials that may be breakable, such as glass containers, glass tubing, thermometers, or funnels. Handle breakable materials with care. Do not touch broken glassware.

Heat-resistant Gloves Use an oven mitt or other hand protection when handling hot materials. Hot plates, hot glassware, or hot water can cause burns. Do not touch hot objects with your bare hands.

Heating Use a clamp or tongs to pick up hot glassware. Do not touch hot objects with your bare hands.

Sharp Object Pointed-tip scissors, scalpels, knives, needles, pins, or tacks are sharp. They can cut or puncture your skin. Always direct a sharp edge or point away from yourself and others. Use sharp instruments only as instructed.

Electric Shock Avoid the possibility of electric shock. Never use electrical equipment around water, or when the equipment is wet or your hands are wet. Be sure cords are untangled and cannot trip anyone. Disconnect the equipment when it is not in use.

Corrosive Chemical You are working with an acid or another corrosive chemical. Avoid getting it on your skin or clothing, or in your eyes. Do not inhale the vapors. Wash your hands when you are finished with the activity.

Poison Do not let any poisonous chemical come in contact with your skin, and do not inhale its vapors. Wash your hands when you are finished with the activity.

Physical Safety When an experiment involves physical activity, take precautions to avoid injuring yourself or others. Follow instructions from your teacher. Alert your teacher if there is any reason you should not participate in the activity.

Animal Safety Treat live animals with care to avoid harming the animals or yourself. Working with animal parts or preserved animals also may require caution. Wash your hands when you are finished with the activity.

Plant Safety Handle plants in the laboratory or during field work only as directed by your teacher. If you are allergic to certain plants, tell your teacher before doing an activity in which those plants are used. Avoid touching harmful plants such as poison ivy, poison oak, or poison sumac, or plants with thorns. Wash your hands when you are finished with the activity.

Flames You may be working with flames from a lab burner, candle, or matches. Tie back loose hair and clothing. Follow instructions from your teacher about lighting and extinguishing flames.

No Flames Flammable materials may be present. Make sure there are no flames, sparks, or other exposed heat sources present.

Fumes When poisonous or unpleasant vapors may be involved, work in a ventilated area. Avoid inhaling vapors directly. Only test an odor when directed to do so by your teacher, and use a wafting motion to direct the vapor toward your nose.

Disposal Chemicals and other laboratory materials used in the activity must be disposed of safely. Follow the instructions from your teacher.

Hand Washing Wash your hands thoroughly when finished with the activity. Use antibacterial soap and warm water. Lather both sides of your hands and between your fingers. Rinse well.

General Safety Awareness You may see this symbol when none of the symbols described earlier appears. In this case, follow the specific instructions provided. You may also see this symbol when you are asked to develop your own procedure in a lab. Have your teacher approve your plan before you go further.

Laboratory Safety

Laboratory safety is an essential element of a successful science class. It is important for you to emphasize laboratory safety to students. Students need to understand exactly what is safe and unsafe behavior, and what the rationale is behind each safety rule.

Review with students the Safety Symbols and Science Safety Rules listed on this and the next two pages. Then follow the safety guidelines below to ensure that your classroom will be a safe place for students to learn science.

◆ Post safety rules in the classroom and review them regularly with students.

◆ Familiarize yourself with the safety procedures for each activity before introducing it to your students.

◆ Review specific safety precautions with students before beginning every science activity.

◆ Always act as an exemplary role model by displaying safe behavior.

◆ Know how to use safety equipment, such as fire extinguishers and fire blankets, and always have it accessible.

◆ Have students practice leaving the classroom quickly and orderly to prepare them for emergencies.

◆ Explain to students how to use the intercom or other available means of communication to get help during an emergency.

◆ Never leave students unattended while they are engaged in science activities.

◆ Provide enough space for students to safely carry out science activities.

◆ Keep your classroom and all science materials in proper condition. Replace worn or broken items.

◆ Instruct students to report all accidents and injuries to you immediately.

Laboratory Safety

Additional tips are listed below for the Science Safety Rules discussed on these two pages. Please keep these tips in mind when you carry out science activities in your classroom.

General Precautions

♦ For open-ended activities like Chapter Projects, go over general safety guidelines with students. Have students submit their procedures or design plans in writing and check them for safety considerations.

♦ In an activity where students are directed to taste something, be sure to store the material in clean, *nonscience* containers. Distribute the material to students in *new* plastic or paper dispensables, which should be discarded after the tasting. Tasting or eating should never be done in a lab classroom.

♦ During physical activity, make sure students do not overexert themselves.

♦ Remind students to handle microscopes and telescopes with care to avoid breakage.

Heating and Fire Safety

♦ No flammable substances should be in use around hot plates, light bulbs, or open flames.

♦ Test tubes should be heated only in water baths.

♦ Students should be permitted to strike matches to light candles or burners *only* with strict supervision. When possible, you should light the flames.

♦ Be sure to have proper ventilation when fumes are produced during a procedure.

♦ All electrical equipment used in the lab should have GFI switches.

Using Chemicals Safely

♦ When students use both chemicals and microscopes in one activity, microscopes should be in a separate part of the room from the chemicals so that when students remove their goggles to use the microscopes, their eyes are not at risk.

Science Safety Rules

To prepare yourself to work safely in the laboratory, read over the following safety rules. Then read them a second time. Make sure you understand and follow each rule. Ask your teacher to explain any rules you do not understand.

Dress Code

1. To protect yourself from injuring your eyes, wear safety goggles whenever you work with chemicals, burners, glassware, or any substance that might get into your eyes. If you wear contact lenses, notify your teacher.

2. Wear a lab apron or coat whenever you work with corrosive chemicals or substances that can stain.

3. Tie back long hair to keep it away from any chemicals, flames, or equipment.

4. Remove or tie back any article of clothing or jewelry that can hang down and touch chemicals, flames, or equipment. Roll up or secure long sleeves.

5. Never wear open shoes or sandals.

General Precautions

6. Read all directions for an experiment several times before beginning the activity. Carefully follow all written and oral instructions. If you are in doubt about any part of the experiment, ask your teacher for assistance.

7. Never perform activities that are not assigned or authorized by your teacher. Obtain permission before "experimenting" on your own. Never handle any equipment unless you have specific permission.

8. Never perform lab activities without direct supervision.

9. Never eat or drink in the laboratory.

10. Keep work areas clean and tidy at all times. Bring only notebooks and lab manuals or written lab procedures to the work area. All other items, such as purses and backpacks, should be left in a designated area.

11. Do not engage in horseplay.

First Aid

12. Always report all accidents or injuries to your teacher, no matter how minor. Notify your teacher immediately of any fires.

13. Learn what to do in case of specific accidents, such as getting acid in your eyes or on your skin. (Rinse acids from your body with lots of water.)

14. Be aware of the location of the first-aid kit, but do not use it unless instructed by your teacher. In case of injury, your teacher should administer first aid. Your teacher may also send you to the school nurse or call a physician.

15. Know the location of emergency equipment, such as the fire extinguisher and fire blanket, and know how to use it.

16. Know the location of the nearest telephone and whom to contact in an emergency.

Heating and Fire Safety

17. Never use a heat source, such as a candle, burner, or hot plate, without wearing safety goggles.

18. Never heat anything unless instructed to do so. A chemical that is harmless when cool may be dangerous when heated.

19. Keep all combustible materials away from flames. Never use a flame or spark near a combustible chemical.

20. Never reach across a flame.

21. Before using a laboratory burner, make sure you know proper procedures for lighting and adjusting the burner, as demonstrated by your teacher. Do not touch the burner. It may be hot. And never leave a lighted burner unattended!

22. Chemicals can splash or boil out of a heated test tube. When heating a substance in a test tube, make sure that the mouth of the tube is not pointed at you or anyone else.

23. Never heat a liquid in a closed container. The expanding gases produced may blow the container apart.

24. Before picking up a container that has been heated, hold the back of your hand near it. If you can feel heat on the back of your hand, the container is too hot to handle. Use an oven mitt to pick up a container that has been heated.

Using Glassware Safely

♦ Use plastic containers, graduated cylinders, and beakers whenever possible. If using glass, students should wear safety goggles.

♦ Use only nonmercury thermometers with anti-roll protectors.

♦ Check all glassware periodically for chips and scratches, which can cause cuts and breakage.

Using Chemicals Safely

25. Never mix chemicals "for the fun of it." You might produce a dangerous, possibly explosive, substance.

26. Never put your face near the mouth of a container that holds chemicals. Never touch, taste, or smell a chemical unless you are instructed by your teacher to do so. Many chemicals are poisonous.

27. Use only those chemicals needed in the activity. Read and double-check labels on supply bottles before removing any chemicals. Take only as much as you need. Keep all containers closed when chemicals are not being used.

28. Dispose of all chemicals as instructed by your teacher. To avoid contamination, never return chemicals to their original containers. Never simply pour chemicals or other substances into the sink or trash containers.

29. Be extra careful when working with acids or bases. Pour all chemicals over the sink or a container, not over your work surface.

30. If you are instructed to test for odors, use a wafting motion to direct the odors to your nose. Do not inhale the fumes directly from the container.

31. When mixing an acid and water, always pour the water into the container first, and then add the acid to the water. Never pour water into an acid.

32. Take extreme care not to spill any material in the laboratory. Wash chemical spills and splashes immediately with plenty of water. Immediately begin rinsing with water any acids that get on your skin or clothing, and notify your teacher of any acid spill at the same time.

Using Glassware Safely

33. Never force glass tubing or thermometers into a rubber stopper or rubber tubing. Have your teacher insert the glass tubing or thermometer if required for an activity.

34. If you are using a laboratory burner, use a wire screen to protect glassware from any flame. Never heat glassware that is not thoroughly dry on the outside.

35. Keep in mind that hot glassware looks cool. Never pick up glassware without first checking to see if it is hot. Use an oven mitt. See rule 24.

36. Never use broken or chipped glassware. If glassware breaks, notify your teacher and dispose of the glassware in the proper broken-glassware container. Never handle broken glass with your bare hands.

37. Never eat or drink from lab glassware.

38. Thoroughly clean glassware before putting it away.

Using Sharp Instruments

39. Handle scalpels or other sharp instruments with extreme care. Never cut material toward you; cut away from you.

40. Immediately notify your teacher if you cut your skin when working in the laboratory.

Animal and Plant Safety

41. Never perform experiments that cause pain, discomfort, or harm to mammals, birds, reptiles, fishes, or amphibians. This rule applies at home as well as in the classroom.

42. Animals should be handled only if absolutely necessary. Your teacher will instruct you as to how to handle each animal species brought into the classroom.

43. If you know that you are allergic to certain plants, molds, or animals, tell your teacher before doing an activity in which these are used.

44. During field work, protect your skin by wearing long pants, long sleeves, socks, and closed shoes. Know how to recognize the poisonous plants and fungi in your area, as well as plants with thorns, and avoid contact with them.

45. Never eat any part of an unidentified plant or fungus.

46. Wash your hands thoroughly after handling animals or the cage containing animals. Wash your hands when you are finished with any activity involving animal parts, plants, or soil.

End-of-Experiment Rules

47. After an experiment has been completed, clean up your work area and return all equipment to its proper place.

48. Dispose of waste materials as instructed by your teacher.

49. Wash your hands after every experiment.

50. Always turn off all burners or hot plates when they are not in use. Unplug hot plates and other electrical equipment. If you used a burner, check that the gas-line valve to the burner is off as well.

Using Sharp Instruments

♦ Always use blunt-tip safety scissors, except when pointed-tip scissors are required.

Animal and Plant Safety

♦ When working with live animals or plants, check ahead of time for students who may have allergies to the specimens.

♦ When growing bacteria cultures, use only disposable petri dishes. After streaking, the dishes should be sealed and not opened again by students. After the lab, students should return the unopened dishes to you. Students should wash their hands with antibacterial soap.

♦ Two methods are recommended for the safe disposal of bacteria cultures. *First method:* Autoclave the petri dishes and discard without opening. *Second method*: If no autoclave is available, carefully open the dishes (never have a student do this) and pour full-strength bleach into the dishes and let stand for a day. Then pour the bleach from the petri dishes down a drain and flush the drain with lots of water. Tape the petri dishes back together and place in a sealed plastic bag. Wrap the plastic bag with a brown paper bag or newspaper and tape securely. Throw the sealed package in the trash. Thoroughly disinfect the work area with bleach.

♦ To grow mold, use a new, sealable plastic bag that is two to three times larger than the material to be placed inside. Seal the bag and tape it shut. After the bag is sealed, students should not open it. To dispose of the bag and mold culture, make a small cut near an edge of the bag and cook in a microwave oven on high setting for at least 1 minute. Discard the bag according to local ordinance, usually in the trash.

♦ Students should wear disposable nitrile, latex, or food-handling gloves when handling live animals or nonliving specimens.

End-of-Experiment Rules

♦ Always have students use antibacterial soap for washing their hands.

Using the Microscope

The microscope is an essential tool in the study of life science. It allows you to see things that are too small to be seen with the unaided eye.

You will probably use a compound microscope like the one you see here. The compound microscope has more than one lens that magnifies the object you view.

Typically, a compound microscope has one lens in the eyepiece, the part you look through. The eyepiece lens usually magnifies 10 ×. Any object you view through this lens would appear 10 times larger than it is.

The compound microscope may contain one or two other lenses called objective lenses. If there are two objective lenses, they are called the low-power and high-power objective lenses. The low-power objective lens usually magnifies 10 ×. The high-power objective lens usually magnifies 40 ×.

To calculate the total magnification with which you are viewing an object, multiply the magnification of the eyepiece lens by the magnification of the objective lens you are using. For example, the eyepiece's magnification of 10 × multiplied by the low-power objective's magnification of 10 × equals a total magnification of 100 ×.

Use the photo of the compound microscope to become familiar with the parts of the microscope and their functions.

The Parts of the Compound Microscope

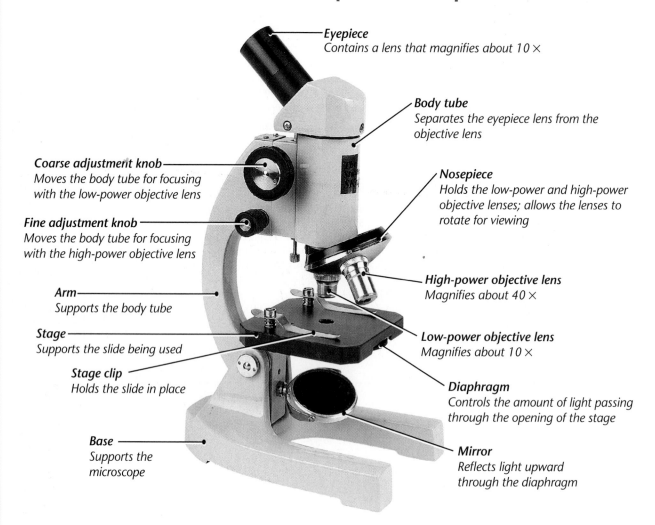

Eyepiece
Contains a lens that magnifies about 10 ×

Body tube
Separates the eyepiece lens from the objective lens

Coarse adjustment knob
Moves the body tube for focusing with the low-power objective lens

Nosepiece
Holds the low-power and high-power objective lenses; allows the lenses to rotate for viewing

Fine adjustment knob
Moves the body tube for focusing with the high-power objective lens

High-power objective lens
Magnifies about 40 ×

Arm
Supports the body tube

Stage
Supports the slide being used

Low-power objective lens
Magnifies about 10 ×

Stage clip
Holds the slide in place

Diaphragm
Controls the amount of light passing through the opening of the stage

Base
Supports the microscope

Mirror
Reflects light upward through the diaphragm

Using the Microscope

Use the following procedures when you are working with a microscope.

1. To carry the microscope grasp the microscope's arm with one hand. Place your other hand under the base.
2. Place the microscope on a table with the arm toward you.
3. Turn the coarse adjustment knob to raise the body tube.
4. Revolve the nosepiece until the low-power objective lens clicks into place.
5. Adjust the diaphragm. While looking through the eyepiece, also adjust the mirror until you see a bright white circle of light. **CAUTION:** *Never use direct sunlight as a light source.*
6. Place a slide on the stage. Center the specimen over the opening on the stage. Use the stage clips to hold the slide in place. **CAUTION:** *Glass slides are fragile.*
7. Look at the stage from the side. Carefully turn the coarse adjustment knob to lower the body tube until the low-power objective almost touches the slide.
8. Looking through the eyepiece, very slowly turn the coarse adjustment knob until the specimen comes into focus.
9. To switch to the high-power objective lens, look at the microscope from the side. Carefully revolve the nosepiece until the high-power objective lens clicks into place. Make sure the lens does not hit the slide.
10. Looking through the eyepiece, turn the fine adjustment knob until the specimen comes into focus.

Making a Wet-Mount Slide

Use the following procedures to make a wet-mount slide of a specimen.

1. Obtain a clean microscope slide and a coverslip. **CAUTION:** *Glass slides and coverslips are fragile.*
2. Place the specimen on the slide. The specimen must be thin enough for light to pass through it.
3. Using a plastic dropper, place a drop of water on the specimen.
4. Gently place one edge of the coverslip against the slide so that it touches the edge of the water drop at a 45° angle. Slowly lower the coverslip over the specimen. If air bubbles are trapped beneath the coverslip, tap the coverslip gently with the eraser end of a pencil.
5. Remove any excess water at the edge of the coverslip with a paper towel.

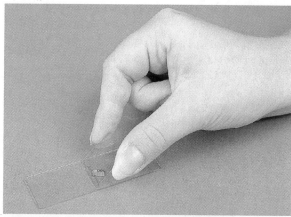

Using a Laboratory Balance

The laboratory balance is an important tool in scientific investigations. You can use a balance to determine the masses of materials that you study or experiment with in the laboratory.

Different kinds of balances are used in the laboratory. One kind of balance is the triple-beam balance. The balance that you may use in your science class is probably similar to the balance illustrated in this Appendix. To use the balance properly, you should learn the name, location, and function of each part of the balance you are using. What kind of balance do you have in your science class?

The Triple-Beam Balance

The triple-beam balance is a single-pan balance with three beams calibrated in grams. The back, or 100-gram, beam is divided into ten units of 10 grams each. The middle, or 500-gram, beam is divided into five units of 100 grams each. The front, or 10-gram, beam is divided into ten major units of 1 gram each. Each of these units is further divided into units of 0.1 gram. What is the largest mass you could find with a triple-beam balance?

The following procedure can be used to find the mass of an object with a triple-beam balance:

1. When no object is on the pan, and the riders are at zero, the pointer should be at zero.
2. Place the object on the pan.
3. Move the rider on the middle beam notch by notch until the horizontal pointer drops below zero. Move the rider back one notch.
4. Move the rider on the back beam notch by notch until the pointer again drops below zero. Move the rider back one notch.
5. Slowly slide the rider along the front beam until the pointer stops at the zero point.
6. The mass of the object is equal to the sum of the readings on the three beams.

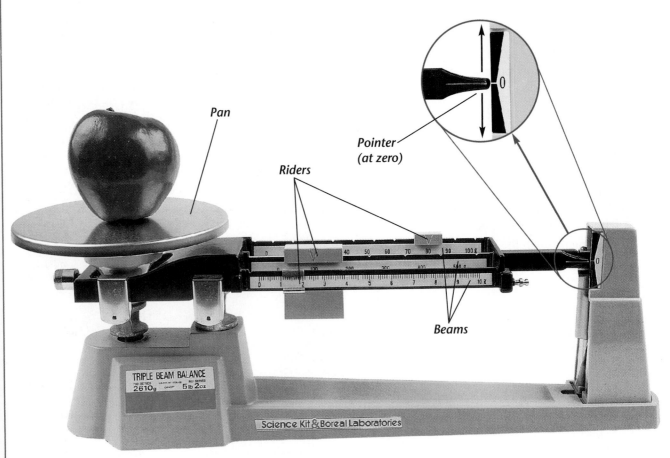

Pan

Riders

Pointer (at zero)

Beams

TRIPLE BEAM BALANCE
2610g   5 lb 2 oz

Science Kit & Boreal Laboratories

Triple-Beam Balance

List of Chemical Elements

Name	Symbol	Atomic Number	Atomic Mass[†]
Actinium	Ac	89	(227)
Aluminum	Al	13	26.982
Americium	Am	95	(243)
Antimony	Sb	51	121.75
Argon	Ar	18	39.948
Arsenic	As	33	74.922
Astatine	At	85	(210)
Barium	Ba	56	137.327
Berkelium	Bk	97	(247)
Beryllium	Be	4	9.012
Bismuth	Bi	83	208.980
Bohrium	Bh	107	(264)
Boron	B	5	10.811
Bromine	Br	35	79.904
Cadmium	Cd	48	112.411
Calcium	Ca	20	40.078
Californium	Cf	98	(251)
Carbon	C	6	12.011
Cerium	Ce	58	140.115
Cesium	Cs	55	132.905
Chlorine	Cl	17	35.453
Chromium	Cr	24	51.996
Cobalt	Co	27	58.933
Copper	Cu	29	63.546
Curium	Cm	96	(247)
Dubnium	Db	105	(262)
Dysprosium	Dy	66	162.50
Einsteinium	Es	99	(252)
Erbium	Er	68	167.26
Europium	Eu	63	151.965
Fermium	Fm	100	(257)
Fluorine	F	9	18.998
Francium	Fr	87	(223)
Gadolinium	Gd	64	157.25
Gallium	Ga	31	69.723
Germanium	Ge	32	72.61
Gold	Au	79	196.967
Hafnium	Hf	72	178.49
Hassium	Hs	108	(265)
Helium	He	2	4.003
Holmium	Ho	67	164.930
Hydrogen	H	1	1.008
Indium	In	49	114.818
Iodine	I	53	126.904
Iridium	Ir	77	192.22
Iron	Fe	26	55.847
Krypton	Kr	36	83.80
Lanthanum	La	57	138.906
Lawrencium	Lr	103	(262)
Lead	Pb	82	207.2
Lithium	Li	3	6.941
Lutetium	Lu	71	174.967
Magnesium	Mg	12	24.305
Manganese	Mn	25	54.938
Meitnerium	Mt	109	(268)
Mendelevium	Md	101	(258)
Mercury	Hg	80	200.659
Molybdenum	Mo	42	95.94

Name	Symbol	Atomic Number	Atomic Mass[†]
Neodymium	Nd	60	144.2
Neon	Ne	10	20.180
Neptunium	Np	93	(237)
Nickel	Ni	28	58.69
Niobium	Nb	41	92.906
Nitrogen	N	7	14.007
Nobelium	No	102	(259)
Osmium	Os	76	190.23
Oxygen	O	8	15.999
Palladium	Pd	46	106.42
Phosphorus	P	15	30.974
Platinum	Pt	78	195.08
Plutonium	Pu	94	(244)
Polonium	Po	84	(209)
Potassium	K	19	39.098
Praseodymium	Pr	59	140.908
Promethium	Pm	61	(145)
Protactinium	Pa	91	231.036
Radium	Ra	88	(226)
Radon	Rn	86	(222)
Rhenium	Re	75	186.207
Rhodium	Rh	45	102.906
Rubidium	Rb	37	85.468
Ruthenium	Ru	44	101.07
Rutherfordium	Rf	104	(261)
Samarium	Sm	62	150.36
Scandium	Sc	21	44.956
Seaborgium	Sg	106	(263)
Selenium	Se	34	78.96
Silicon	Si	14	28.086
Silver	Ag	47	107.868
Sodium	Na	11	22.990
Strontium	Sr	38	87.62
Sulfur	S	16	32.066
Tantalum	Ta	73	180.948
Technetium	Tc	43	(98)
Tellurium	Te	52	127.60
Terbium	Tb	65	158.925
Thallium	Tl	81	204.383
Thorium	Th	90	232.038
Thulium	Tm	69	168.934
Tin	Sn	50	118.710
Titanium	Ti	22	47.88
Tungsten	W	74	183.85
Ununbium	Uub	112	(277)
Ununhexium	Uuh	116	*
Ununnilium	Uun	110	(269)
Unununium	Uuu	111	(272)
Ununoctium	Uuo	118	*
Ununquadium	Uuq	114	*
Uranium	U	92	238.029
Vanadium	V	23	50.942
Xenon	Xe	54	131.29
Ytterbium	Yb	70	173.04
Yttrium	Y	39	88.906
Zinc	Zn	30	65.39
Zirconium	Zr	40	91.224

[†]Numbers in parentheses give the mass number of the most stable or common isotope.

*Newly discovered

Periodic Table of the Elements

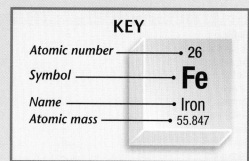

KEY

Atomic number —————• 26

Symbol ——————— **Fe**

Name ——————————• Iron

Atomic mass ——————• 55.847

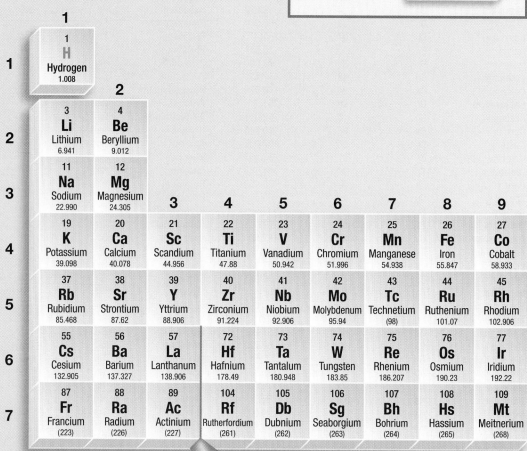

Lanthanide Series

Actinide Series

Mass numbers in parentheses are those of the most stable or common isotope.

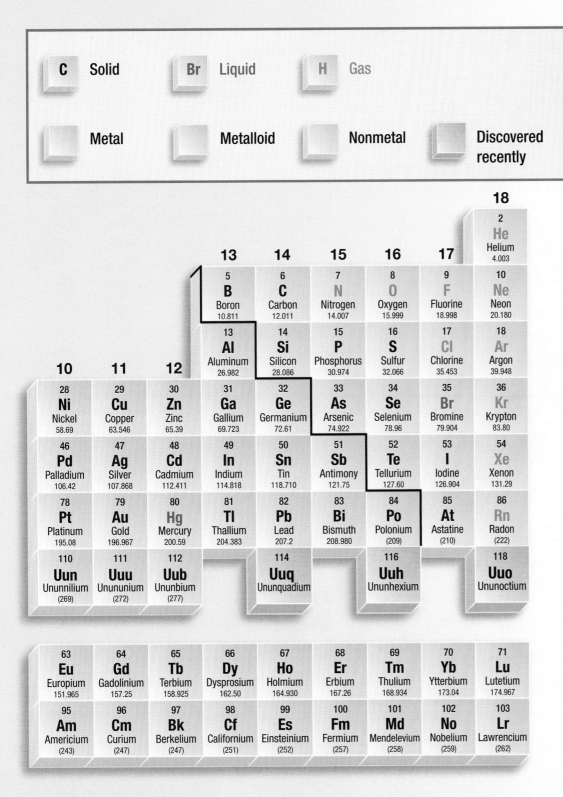

| C | Solid | | Br | Liquid | | H | Gas |
| Metal | | | Metalloid | | | Nonmetal | | | Discovered recently |

18

| | | | | | | | | | | | | **2**
He
Helium
4.003 |

| | | | **13** | **14** | **15** | **16** | **17** |
| **5**
B
Boron
10.811 | **6**
C
Carbon
12.011 | **7**
N
Nitrogen
14.007 | **8**
O
Oxygen
15.999 | **9**
F
Fluorine
18.998 | **10**
Ne
Neon
20.180 |

| | | | **13**
Al
Aluminum
26.982 | **14**
Si
Silicon
28.086 | **15**
P
Phosphorus
30.974 | **16**
S
Sulfur
32.066 | **17**
Cl
Chlorine
35.453 | **18**
Ar
Argon
39.948 |

10	**11**	**12**
28 **Ni** Nickel 58.69	**29** **Cu** Copper 63.546	**30** **Zn** Zinc 65.39	**31** **Ga** Gallium 69.723	**32** **Ge** Germanium 72.61	**33** **As** Arsenic 74.922	**34** **Se** Selenium 78.96	**35** **Br** Bromine 79.904	**36** **Kr** Krypton 83.80
46 **Pd** Palladium 106.42	**47** **Ag** Silver 107.868	**48** **Cd** Cadmium 112.411	**49** **In** Indium 114.818	**50** **Sn** Tin 118.710	**51** **Sb** Antimony 121.75	**52** **Te** Tellurium 127.60	**53** **I** Iodine 126.904	**54** **Xe** Xenon 131.29
78 **Pt** Platinum 195.08	**79** **Au** Gold 196.967	**80** **Hg** Mercury 200.59	**81** **Tl** Thallium 204.383	**82** **Pb** Lead 207.2	**83** **Bi** Bismuth 208.980	**84** **Po** Polonium (209)	**85** **At** Astatine (210)	**86** **Rn** Radon (222)
110 **Uun** Ununnilium (269)	**111** **Uuu** Unununium (272)	**112** **Uub** Ununbium (277)		**114** **Uuq** Ununquadium		**116** **Uuh** Ununhexium		**118** **Uuo** Ununoctium

| **63**
Eu
Europium
151.965 | **64**
Gd
Gadolinium
157.25 | **65**
Tb
Terbium
158.925 | **66**
Dy
Dysprosium
162.50 | **67**
Ho
Holmium
164.930 | **68**
Er
Erbium
167.26 | **69**
Tm
Thulium
168.934 | **70**
Yb
Ytterbium
173.04 | **71**
Lu
Lutetium
174.967 |
| **95**
Am
Americium
(243) | **96**
Cm
Curium
(247) | **97**
Bk
Berkelium
(247) | **98**
Cf
Californium
(251) | **99**
Es
Einsteinium
(252) | **100**
Fm
Fermium
(257) | **101**
Md
Mendelevium
(258) | **102**
No
Nobelium
(259) | **103**
Lr
Lawrencium
(262) |

The symbols shown for elements 110–118 are in use temporarily until names for these elements can be agreed upon.

Physical Map: Texas

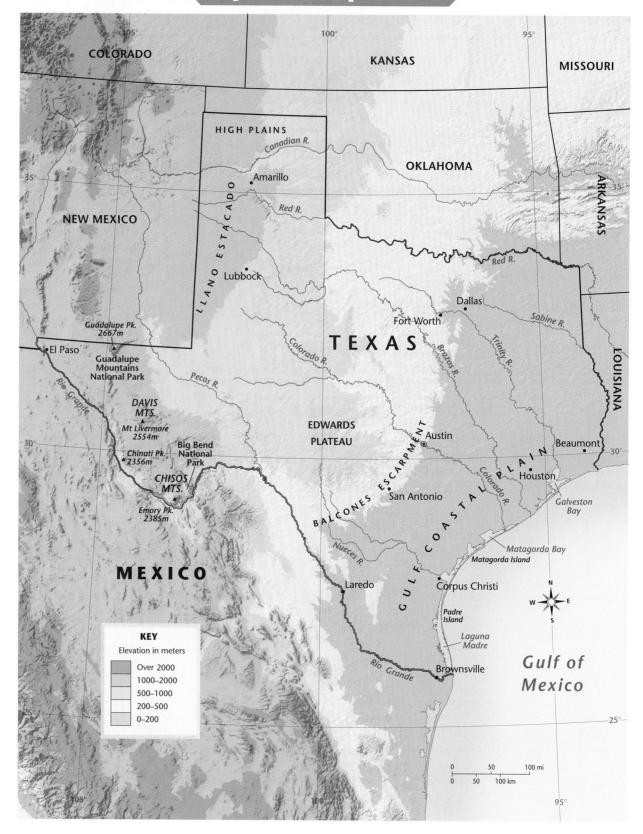

Identifying Common Minerals

GROUP 1
Metallic Luster, Mostly Dark-Colored

Mineral/Formula	Hardness	Density (g/cm³)	Luster	Streak	Color	Other Properties/Remarks
Pyrite FeS_2	6–6.5	5.0	Metallic	Greenish, brownish black	Light yellow	Harder than chalcopyrite and pyrrhotite; called "fool's gold," but harder than gold and very brittle
Magnetite Fe_3O_4	6	5.2	Metallic	Black	Iron black	Very magnetic; important iron ore; some varieties known as "lodestone"
Hematite Fe_2O_3	5.5–6.5	4.9–5.3	Metallic or earthy	Red or red brown	Reddish brown to black; also steel gray crystals	Most important ore of iron; known as "red ocher"; often used as red pigment in paint.
Pyrrhotite FeS	4	4.6	Metallic	Gray black	Brownish bronze	Less hard than pyrite: slightly magnetic
Sphalerite ZnS	3.5–4	3.9–4.1	Resinous	Brown to light yellow	Brown to yellow	Most important zinc ore
Chalcopyrite $CuFeS_2$	3.5–4	4.1–4.3	Metallic	Greenish black	Golden yellow, often tarnished	Most important copper ore; softer than pyrite and more yellow; more brittle than gold
Bornite Cu_5FeS_4	3	4.9–5.4	Metallic	Gray black	Copper, brown; turns to purple and black	Important copper ore; known as "peacock ore" because of iridescent purple color when exposed to air for a time
Copper Cu	2.5–3	8.9	Metallic	Copper red	Copper red to black	Can be pounded into various shapes and drawn into wires; used in making electrical wires, coins, pipes
Gold Au	2.5–3	19.3	Metallic	Yellow	Rich yellow	Can be pounded into various shapes and drawn into wires; does not tarnish; used in jewelry, coins, dental fillings
Silver Ag	2.5–3	10.0–11.0	Metallic	Silver to light gray	Silver white, tarnishes to black	Can be pounded into various shapes and drawn into wires; used in jewelry, coins, electrical wire
Galena PbS	2.5	7.4–7.6	Metallic	Lead gray	Lead gray	Main ore of lead; used in shields against radiation
Graphite C	1–2	2.3	Metallic to dull	Black	Black	Feels greasy; very soft; used as pencil "lead" and as a lubricant

GROUP 2
Nonmetallic Luster, Mostly Dark-Colored

Mineral/Formula	Hardness	Density (g/cm³)	Luster	Streak	Color	Other Properties/Remarks
Corundum Al_2O_3	9	3.9–4.1	Brilliant to glassy	White	Usually brown	Very hard; used as an abrasive; transparent crystals used as gems called "ruby" (red) and "sapphire" (blue and other colors)
Garnet $(Ca,Mg,Fe)_3 (Al,Fe,Cr)_2(SiO_4)_3$	7–7.5	3.5–4.3	Glassy to resinous	White, light brown	Red, brown, black, green	A group of minerals used in jewelry, as a birthstone, and as an abrasive
Olivine $(Mg,Fe)_2SiO_4$	6.5–7	3.3–3.4	Glassy	White or gray	Olive green	Found in igneous rocks; sometimes used as a gem
Augite $Ca(Mg,Fe,Al) (AlSi)_2O_6$	5–6	3.2–3.4	Glassy	Greenish gray	Dark green to black	Found in igneous rocks
Hornblende $NaCa_2(Mg,Fe,Al)_5 (Si,Al)_8O_{22}(OH)_2$	5–6	3.0–3.4	Glassy, silky	White to gray	Dark green to brown, black	Found in igneous and metamorphic rocks
Apatite $Ca_5(PO_4)_3F$	5	3.1–3.2	Glassy	White	Green, brown, red, blue, violet, yellow	Sometimes used as a gem; source of the phosphorus needed by plants
Azurite $Cu_3(CO_3)_2(OH)_2$	3.5–4	3.8	Glassy to dull	Pale blue	Intense blue	Ore of copper; used as a gem
Biotite $K(Mg,Fe)_3AlSiO_{10} (OH)_2$	2.5–3	2.8–3.4	Glassy or pearly	White to gray	Dark green, brown, or black	A type of mica, sometimes used as a lubricant
Serpentine $Mg_6Si_4O_{10}(OH)_8$	2–5	2.2–2.6	Greasy, waxy, silky	White	Usually green	Once used in insulation but found to cause cancer; used in fireproofing; can be in the form of asbestos
Limonite Mixture of hydrous iron oxides	1–5.5	2.8–4.3	Glassy to dull	Yellow brown	Brown black to brownish yellow	Ore of iron, also known as "yellow ocher," a pigment; a mixture that is not strictly a mineral
Bauxite Mixture of hydrous aluminum oxides	1–3	2.0–2.5	Dull to earthy	Colorless to gray	Brown, yellow, gray, white	Ore of aluminum, smells like clay when wet; a mixture that is not strictly a mineral

608

GROUP 3
Nonmetallic Luster, Mostly Light-Colored

Mineral/ Formula	Hardness	Density (g/cm³)	Luster	Streak	Color	Other Properties/Remarks
Diamond C	10	3.5	Brilliant	White	Colorless and varied	Hardest known substance; used in jewelry; as an abrasive; in cutting instruments
Topaz $Al_2SiO_4(F,OH)_2$	8	3.5–3.6	Glassy	White	Straw yellow, pink, bluish, greenish	Valuable gem
Quartz SiO_2	7	2.6	Glassy, greasy	White	Colorless, white; any color when not pure	The second most abundant mineral; many varieties are gems (amethyst, cat's-eye, bloodstone, agate, jasper, onyx); used in making glass
Feldspar (K,Na,Ca) $(AlSi_3O_8)$	6	2.6	Glassy	Colorless, white	Colorless, white, various colors	As a family, the most abundant of all minerals; the different types of feldspar make up over 60 percent of Earth's crust
Fluorite CaF_2	4	3.0–3.3	Glassy	Colorless	Purple, light, green, yellow, bluish green, other colors	Some types are fluorescent (glow when exposed to ultraviolet light); used in making steel
Dolomite $CaMg(CO_3)_2$	3.5–4	2.8	Glassy or pearly	White	Colorless, white, pinkish, or light tints	Used in making concrete and cement; fizzes slowly in dilute hydrochloric acid
Calcite $CaCO_3$	3	2.7	Glassy	White to grayish	Colorless, white, pale tints	Easily scratched; bubbles in dilute hydrochloric acid; frequently fluorescent
Halite NaCl	2.5	2.1–2.6	Glassy	White	Colorless or white	Occurs as perfect cubic crystals; has salty taste
Gypsum $CaSO_4 \cdot 2H_2O$	2	2.3	Glassy, pearly, silky	White	Colorless, white, light tints	Very soft; used in manufacture of plaster of Paris; form known as alabaster used for statues
Sulfur S	2	2.0–2.1	Resinous to greasy	White	Yellow to yellowish brown	Used in making many medicines, in production of sulfuric acid, and in vulcanizing rubber
Talc $Mg_3Si_4O_{10}(OH)_2$	1	2.7–2.8	Pearly to greasy	White	Gray, white, greenish	Very soft; used in talcum powder; found mostly in metamorphic rocks; also called "soapstone"

Glossary

A

aa A slow-moving type of lava that hardens to form rough chunks; cooler than pahoehoe. (p. 378)

abdomen The region of an organism, such as an insect, that contains its reproductive organs and part of its digestive tract. (p. 232)

abiotic factor A nonliving part of an ecosystem. (p. 268)

acceleration The rate at which velocity changes. (p. 102)

acid rain Rain that is more acidic than normal, caused by the release of molecules of sulfur dioxide and nitrogen oxide into the air. (p. 443)

active transport The movement of materials through a cell membrane using energy. (p. 161)

active Said of a volcano that is erupting or shows signs of eruption in the near future. (p. 380)

adaptation A characteristic that helps an organism survive in its environment and reproduce. (p. 219)

air mass A huge body of air that has similar temperature, pressure, and humidity throughout. (p. 496)

air pressure A force that is the result of the weight of a column of air pushing down on an area. (p. 446)

altitude Elevation above sea level. (p. 448)

amorphous solid A solid made up of particles that are not arranged in a regular pattern. (p. 58)

anemometer An instrument used to measure wind speed. (p. 473)

aneroid barometer An instrument that measures changes in air pressure without using a liquid. Changes in the shape of an airtight metal box cause a needle on the barometer dial to move. (p. 447)

anticline An upward fold in rock formed by compression of Earth's crust. (p. 364)

anticyclone A high-pressure center of dry air. (p. 502)

anus The opening at the end of an organism's digestive system through which wastes are eliminated. (p. 226)

aquifer An underground layer of rock or soil that holds water. (p. 414)

arachnid An arthropod with two body sections. (p. 234)

artesian well A well in which water rises because of pressure within the aquifer. (p. 415)

arthropod An invertebrate that has an external skeleton, a segmented body, and jointed attachments called appendages. (p. 230)

asexual reproduction The reproductive process that involves only one parent and produces offspring that are identical to the parent. (p. 150)

asteroid belt The region of the solar system between the orbits of Mars and Jupiter, where many asteroids are found. (p. 564)

asteroids Objects revolving around the sun that are too small and too numerous to be considered planets. (p. 564)

atmosphere The mixture of gases that surrounds Earth. The outermost of the four spheres into which scientists divide Earth. (p. 434)

atom The smallest particle of an element. (p. 42)

atrium Each of the two upper chambers of the heart that receives blood coming into the heart. (p. 241)

aurora borealis A colorful, glowing display in the sky caused when particles from the sun strike oxygen and nitrogen atoms in the ionosphere; also called the Northern Lights. (p. 456)

autotroph An organism that makes its own food. (p. 128)

B

balanced forces Equal forces acting on an object in opposite directions. (p. 100)

barometer An instrument used to measure changes in air pressure. (p. 446)

batholith A mass of rock formed when a large body of magma cooled inside the crust. (p. 387)

bilateral symmetry Line symmetry; the quality of being divisible into two halves that are mirror images. (p. 221)

binary fission A form of asexual reproduction in which one cell divides to form two identical cells. (p. 192)

binomial nomenclature The naming system for organisms in which each organism is given a two-part name—a genus name and a species name. (p. 185)

biomass The living or formerly living material in an ecosystem. (p. 286)

biomass fuel Fuel made from things that once were alive. (p. 303)

biotic factor A living part of an ecosystem. (p. 267)

bird An endothermic vertebrate that has feathers and a four-chambered heart, and lays eggs. (p. 247)

birth rate The number of births in a population in a certain amount of time. (p. 275)

boiling Vaporization that occurs on and below the surface of a liquid. (p. 77)

boiling point The temperature at which a substance changes from a liquid to a gas. (p. 77)

Boyle's law The relationship between the pressure and volume of a gas at constant temperature; when volume increases, pressure decreases. (p. 64)

budding A form of asexual reproduction in which a new organism grows out of the body of a parent. (p. 203)

C

caldera The large hole at the top of a volcano formed when the roof of a volcano's magma chamber collapses. (p. 390)

carnivore An animal that eats only other animals. (p. 219)

carrying capacity The largest population that an area can support. (p. 277)

cartilage A connective tissue that is more flexible than bone and that gives support to some parts of the body. (p. 239)

cell The basic unit of structure and function in organisms. (p. 123)

cell cycle The regular sequence of growth and division that cells undergo. (p. 171)

cell membrane The outside boundary of a cell; controls which substances can enter or leave the cell. (p. 139)

cell theory A widely accepted explanation of the relationship between cells and living things. (p. 134)

cell wall A rigid layer of nonliving material that surrounds the cells of plants and some other organisms. (p.139)

Celsius scale The temperature scale on which zero and 100 are the temperatures at which water freezes and boils, respectively. (p. 583)

Charles's law The relationship between the temperature and volume of a gas at constant pressure; when temperature increases, volume increases. (p. 66)

chemical bond The force that holds two atoms together. (p. 44)

chemical change A change in matter that produces new substances. (p. 31)

chemical property A characteristic that is observed when a substance interacts with another substance. (p. 26)

chemistry The study of the properties of matter and how matter changes. (p. 25)

chlorophyll A substance that gives chloroplasts their green color and captures light energy during photosynthesis. (p. 163)

chloroplast A structure in the cells of plants and some other organisms that captures energy from sunlight and uses it to produce food. (p. 144)

chromatid One of the pair of the identical rods of a chromosome. (p.172)

chromatin Material in cells that contains DNA and carries genetic information. (p.141)

chromosome A rod-shaped cellular structure made of condensed chromatin; contains DNA, which carries the genetic information that controls inherited characteristics such as eye color and blood type. (p. 141)

chromosphere The middle layer of the sun's atmosphere. (p. 539)

cilia The hairlike projections on the outside of cells that move in a wavelike manner. (p. 198)

cinder cone A steep, cone-shaped hill or mountain made of volcanic ash, cinders, and bombs piled up around a volcano's opening. (p. 388)

cirrus Wispy, feathery clouds made of mostly ice crystals that form at high levels, above about 6 kilometers. (p. 484)

classification The process of grouping things based on their similarities. (p. 184)

cleavage A mineral's ability to split easily along flat surfaces. (p. 335)

cnidarians Animals that use stinging cells to capture prey and defend themselves, and take food into a hollow central cavity. (p. 224)

combustion A rapid reaction between oxygen and fuel that produces thermal energy. (p. 293)

comet A ball of ice and dust whose orbit is a long, narrow ellipse. (p. 562)

community All the different populations that live together in an area. (p. 270)

composite volcano A tall, cone-shaped mountain in which layers of lava alternate with layers of ash and other volcanic materials. (p. 388)

composting The process by which the wastes and remains of living things decay in the soil. (p. 286)

compound A substance made of two or more elements chemically combined in a set ratio. (p. 28)

compound microscope A light microscope that has more than one lens. (p. 132)

compression Stress that squeezes rock until it folds or breaks. (p. 359)

condensation The change from the gaseous to the liquid state of matter; also, the process by which a gas, such as water vapor, changes to a liquid, such as water. (pp. 77, 483)

conduction The transfer of heat through direct physical contact. (p. 470)

conjugation The process in which a unicellular organism transfers some of its genetic material to another unicellular organism. (p. 192)

conservation The process of using a resource wisely so it will not be used up. (p. 425)

consumer An organism that obtains energy by feeding on other organisms. (p. 281)

continental (air mass) A dry air mass that forms over land. (p. 496)

contour line A line on a topographic map that connects points of equal elevation. (p. 592)

control rod Cadmium rod used in a nuclear reactor to absorb neutrons from fission. (p. 308)

controlled experiment An experiment in which all of the variables except for one remain the same. (p. 12)

convection The transfer of heat by movement of currents within a fluid. (p. 470)

convex lens A lens that is thicker in the center than at the edges. (p. 136)

core The central part of the sun, where nuclear fusion occurs. (p. 538)

Coriolis effect The way Earth's rotation makes winds in the Northern Hemisphere curve to the right and winds in the Southern Hemisphere curve to the left. (p. 477)

corona The outer layer of the sun's atmosphere. (p. 539)

cotyledon A seed leaf that stores food. (p. 208)

crater A bowl-shaped area that forms around a volcano's central opening. (p. 375)

crop A bird's internal storage tank that allows it to store food inside its body after swallowing the food. (p. 248)

crust The layer of rock that forms Earth's outer surface. (p. 326)

crustacean An arthropod that has two or three body sections, five or more pairs of legs, two pairs of antennae, and usually three pairs of appendages for chewing. (p. 234)

crystal A solid in which the atoms are arranged in a pattern that repeats again and again. (p. 332)

crystalline solid A substance that is made of crystals in which the particles are arranged in a regular, repeating pattern. (p. 58)

cumulus Clouds that form less than 2 kilometers above the ground and look like fluffy, rounded piles of cotton. (p. 484)

cyclone A swirling center of low air pressure. (p. 501)

cytokinesis The final stage of the cell cycle, in which the cell's cytoplasm divides, distributing the organelles into each of the two new cells. (p. 173)

cytoplasm The region of a cell located inside the cell membrane (in prokaryotes) or between the cell membrane and nucleus (in eukaryotes); contains a gel-like material and cell organelles. (p. 141)

············ **D** ············

data The facts, figures, and other evidence collected in an experiment. (p. 13)

death rate The number of deaths in a population in a certain amount of time. (p. 275)

decomposer An organism that breaks down the large molecules from wastes and the remains of dead organisms into small molecules and returns important materials to the soil and water. (pp. 193, 282)

deformation A change in the volume or shape of the Earth's crust. (p. 359)

delta A landform made of sediment that is deposited where a river flows into an ocean or lake. (p. 111)

density The measurement of how much mass of a sustance is contained in a given volume. (pp. 335, 445)

deposition The process by which sediment settles out of the water or wind that is carrying it, and is deposited in a new location. (pp. 108, 343)

desalination The process of obtaining fresh water from salt water by removing the salt. (p. 427)

dew point The temperature at which condensation begins. (p. 483)

diaphragm A large, dome-shaped muscle that has an important function in breathing. (p. 252)

diffusion The process by which molecules move from an area in which they are highly concentrated to an area in which they are less concentrated. (p. 159)

dike A slab of volcanic rock formed when magma forces itself across rock layers. (p. 387)

directly proportional A term used to describe the relationship between two variables whose graph is a straight line passing through the point (0,0). (p. 70)

divide A ridge of land that separates one drainage basin or watershed from another. (p. 405)

DNA (*DeoxyriboNucleic Acid*) The genetic material that carries information about an organism and is passed from parent to offspring. (p. 150)

dormant Said of a volcano that does not show signs of erupting in the near future. (p. 380)

drought A water shortage caused by long periods of low precipitation in a particular area. (p. 490)

············ ············

earthquake The shaking that results from the movement of rock beneath Earth's surface. (p. 358)

echinoderm A radially symmetrical invertebrate that lives on the ocean floor and has a spiny internal skeleton. (p. 235)

ecology The study of how living things interact with each other and with their environment. (p. 270)

ecosystem All the living and nonliving things that interact in an area. (p. 266)

ectotherm An animal whose body does not produce much internal heat. (p. 238)

efficiency The percentage of energy that is used by a device to perform work. (p. 314)

egg A female sex cell. (p. 150)

El Niño A warm water current that occurs every 2 to 7 years in the Pacific Ocean, causing changes in winds, currents, and weather patterns that can lead to dramatic climate changes. (pp. 503, 522)

electrode A metal strip that gains or loses electrons during electrolysis. (p. 48)

electrolysis A process by which an electric current breaks chemical bonds. (p. 48)

electromagnetic wave A form of energy that can travel through space. (p. 462)

element A substance that cannot be broken down into other substances by chemical or physical means. (p. 27)

ellipse An elongated circle, or oval shape; the shape of the planets' orbits. (p. 535)

embryo The young organism that develops from a zygote. (p. 208)

emigration Leaving a population. (p. 276)

endoplasmic reticulum A cell structure that forms a maze of passageways in which proteins and other materials are carried from one part of the cell to another. (p. 144)

endoskeleton An internal skeleton. (p. 235)

endospore A small, rounded, thick-walled, resting cell that forms inside a bacterial cell. (p. 192)

endotherm An animal whose body controls and regulates its temperature by controlling the internal heat it produces. (p. 238)

energy The ability to do work or cause change. (p. 25)

energy conservation The practice of reducing energy use. (p. 313)

energy transformation Any change from one form of energy to another. (p. 292)

epicenter The point on Earth's surface directly above an earthquake's focus. (p. 368)

equator An imaginary line halfway between the North and South poles that circles the Earth. (p. 591)

erosion The process by which water, ice, wind, or gravity moves fragments of rock and soil. (p. 108, 343)

estimate An approximation of a number, based on reasonable assumptions. (p. 274)

eukaryote An organism with cells that contain nuclei and other cell structures. (p. 145)

evacuate To move away temporarily. (p. 510)

evaporation The process that occurs when vaporization takes place only on the surface of a liquid; also, the process by which molecules at the surface of a liquid, such as water, absorb enough energy to change to a gaseous state, such as water vapor. (pp. 76, 398, 481)

exoskeleton An outer skeleton. (p. 230)

exosphere The outer layer of the thermosphere, extending outward into space. (p. 456)

external stimulus A change in an organism's surroundings that causes the organism to react. (p. 124)

extinct Describes a type of organism that no longer exists anywhere on Earth; also, a volcano that is unlikely to erupt again. (p. 380)

extrusive rock Igneous rock that forms from lava on Earth's surface. (p. 342)

fault A break or crack in Earth's lithosphere along which rocks move. (p. 360)

fault-block mountain A mountain that forms where a normal fault uplifts a block of rock. (p. 362)

fermentation The process by which cells break down molecules to release energy without using oxygen. (p. 167)

fertilization The joining of a sperm cell and an egg cell. (p. 208)

flagellum A long, whiplike structure that helps a unicellular organism move. (p. 191)

flash flood A sudden, violent flood that occurs within a few hours, or even minutes, of a heavy rainstorm. (p. 516)

flood The overflowing of a river's channel due to the increase of the volume of water in the river. (pp. 111, 406)

flood plain A broad, flat valley through which a river flows. (p. 109)

flower The reproductive structure of an angiosperm. (p. 209)

focus The point beneath Earth's surface where rock breaks under stress resulting in an earthquake. (p. 368)

fold A bend in rock that forms where part of Earth's crust is compressed. (p. 363)

food chain The series of events in which one organism eats another, resulting in a flow of energy among the organisms involved. (p. 282)

food web The pattern of overlapping food chains in an ecosystem. (p. 284)

footwall The block of rock that forms the lower half of a fault. (p. 360)

force A push or a pull exerted on an object. (p. 99)

fossil fuel An energy-rich substance (such as coal, oil, or natural gas) formed from the remains of organisms. (p. 295)

fracture The way a mineral looks when it breaks apart in an irregular way. (p. 335)

freezing The change in state from a liquid to a solid. (p. 76)

front The area where air masses meet and do not mix. (p. 499)

fruit The ripened ovary and other structures that enclose one or more seeds of an angiosperm. (p. 210)

fuel A material that releases energy when it burns. (p. 293)

fuel rod The uranium rod that undergoes fission in a nuclear reactor. (p. 308)

G

gas A state of matter with no definite shape or volume. (p. 59)

gas giants The name given to the first four outer planets: Jupiter, Saturn, Uranus, and Neptune. (p. 552)

gemstone A hard, colorful mineral that has a brilliant or glassy luster. (p. 336)

gene A segment of DNA on a chromosome that codes for a specific trait. (p. 150)

genus A classification grouping that consists of a number of similar, closely related species. (p. 185)

geocentric system A description of the solar system in which all of the planets revolve around Earth. (p. 533)

geologist A scientist who studies the forces that make and shape planet Earth. (p. 327)

geology The study of the solid Earth. (p. 327)

geosynchronous orbit The orbit of a satellite that revolves around Earth at the same rate that Earth rotates. (p. 568)

geothermal energy Heat energy in Earth's interior from water or steam that has been heated by magma. (pp. 303, 382)

gestation period The length of time between fertilization and the birth of a mammal. (p. 254)

geyser A type of hot spring that builds up pressure underground and erupts at regular intervals as a fountain of water and steam. (p. 382)

gill An organism's breathing organ that removes oxygen from water. (p. 228)

gizzard The thick-walled, muscular part of a bird's stomach that squeezes and grinds partially digested food. (p. 248)

global winds Winds that blow steadily from specific directions over long distances. (p. 477)

Golgi body A structure in a cell that receives proteins and other newly formed materials from the endoplasmic reticulum, packages them, and distributes them to other parts of the cell. (p. 144)

grain A particle of mineral or other rock that gives a rock its texture. (p. 341)

graph A diagram that shows how two variables are related. (p. 68)

gravity The force that pulls objects toward each other. (p. 535)

greenhouse effect The process by which heat is trapped in the atmosphere by water vapor, carbon dioxide, methane, and other gases that form a "blanket" around the earth. (pp. 465, 548)

H

habitat The place where an organism lives and that provides the things it needs to survive. (p. 267)

hanging wall The block of rock that forms the upper half of a fault. (p. 360)

headwaters The many small streams that come together at the source of a river. (p. 109)

heat The movement of thermal energy from one substance to another. (p. 469)

heliocentric system A description of the solar system in which all of the planets revolve around the sun. (p. 534)

herbivore An animal that eats only plants. (p. 219)

heredity The passing of traits from parents to offspring. (p. 149)

heterotroph An organism that cannot make its own food. (p. 128)

homeostasis The process by which an organism's internal environment is kept stable in spite of changes in its external environment. (p. 129)

hormone The chemical product of an endocrine gland that speeds up or slows down the activities of an organ or tissue; also, a chemical that affects a plant's growth and development. (p. 210)

host An organism that provides a source of energy or a suitable environment for a virus or for another organism to live. (p. 199)

humidity A measure of the amount of water vapor in the air. (p. 482)

hurricane A tropical storm that has winds of 119 kilometers per hour or higher; typically about 600 kilometers across. (p. 508)

hydrocarbon A compound that contains carbon and hydrogen atoms. (p. 295)

hydroelectric power Electricity produced by flowing water moving over a waterfall or dam. (p. 302)

hypothesis A possible explanation for a set of observations or answer to scientific question; must be testable. (p. 12)

I

igneous rock A type of rock that forms from the cooling of molten rock at or below the surface of Earth. (p. 342)

immigration Moving into a population. (p. 276)

impermeable Characteristic of materials through which water does not easily pass, such as clay or granite. (p. 413)

inertia The tendency of a moving object to continue in a straight line or a stationary object to remain in place. (p. 535)

inexhaustible resource Any living or nonliving thing in the environment of which there is a limitless supply. (p. 299)

inference An interpretation of an observation based on evidence and prior knowledge. (p. 11)

infrared radiation A form of energy with wavelengths that are longer than visible light. (p. 463)

inner core A dense sphere of solid iron and nickel in the center of Earth. (p. 328)

insect An arthropod with three body sections, six legs, one pair of antennae, and usually one or two pairs of wings. (p. 232)

insulation A building material that blocks heat transfer between the air inside and the air outside. (p. 315)

internal stimulus A change from within an organism, such as hunger and thirst, that causes the organism to respond. (p. 124)

International System of Units A system of measurement based on multiples of ten and on established measures of mass, length, and time. (p. 35)

interphase The stage of the cell cycle that takes place before cell division occurs; during this stage, the cell grows, copies its DNA, and prepares to divide. (p. 171)

intrusive rock Igneous rock that forms when magma hardens beneath Earth's surface. (p. 342)

invertebrate An animal without a backbone. (p. 220)

ionosphere The lower part of the thermosphere, where electrically charged particles called ions are found. (p. 456)

irrigation The process of supplying water to areas of land to make them suitable for growing crops. (p. 400)

isobars Lines on a map joining places that have the same air pressure. (p. 522)

isotherms Lines on a map joining places that have the same temperature. (p. 522)

jet streams Bands of high-speed winds about 10 kilometers above Earth's surface. (p. 480)

kidney A major organ of the excretory system; eliminates urea, excess water, and other waste materials from the body. (p. 243)

land breeze The flow of air from land to a body of water. (p. 476)

larva The immature form of an animal that looks very different from the adult. (p. 232)

latitude The distance north or south from the equator, measured in degrees. (p. 478)

lava Magma that reaches the surface; also the rock formed when liquid lava hardens. (p. 336)

lava flow The area covered by lava as it pours out of a volcano's vent. (p. 375)

leaf The organ of a vascular plant where photosynthesis occurs. (p. 205)

levee A long ridge formed by deposits of sediment alongside a river channel. (pp. 112, 407)

lightning A sudden spark, or energy discharge, caused when electrical charges jump between parts of a cloud or between a cloud and the ground. (p. 504)

limiting factor An environmental factor that prevents a population from increasing. (p. 277)

linear The term used to describe the relationship between variables whose graph is a straight line. (p. 105)

liquid A state of matter that has a definite volume but no definite shape. (p. 58)

lithosphere A rigid layer made up of the uppermost part of Earth's mantle and crust. One of four spheres into which scientists divide Earth. (p. 329)

local wind Wind that blows over short distances. (p. 474)

luster The way a mineral reflects light from its surface. (p. 334)

lysosome A small rounded cell structure that contains chemicals that break down large food particles into smaller ones. (p. 145)

magma The molten mixture of rock-forming substances, gases, and water that makes up part of Earth's mantle. (p. 336)

magma chamber The pocket beneath a volcano where magma collects. (p. 375)

magnification The ability to make things look larger than they are. (p. 136)

magnitude The measurement of an earthquake's strength based on seismic waves and movement along faults. (p. 371)

mammary gland The organ that produces the milk with which mammals feed their young. (p. 253)

manipulated variable The one factor that a scientist changes during an experiment; also called independent variable. (p. 12)

mantle The layer of hot, solid material between Earth's crust and core. (p. 329)

maritime (air mass) A humid air mass that forms over oceans. (p. 496)

marsupial A mammal whose young are born alive at an early stage of development, and then usually continue to develop in a pouch on their mother's body. (p. 254)

mass A measure of how much matter is in an object. (p. 35)

matter Anything that has mass and occupies space. (p. 24)

meander A looping curve formed in a river as it winds through its flood plain. (p. 111)

meltdown A dangerous condition caused by overheating inside a nuclear reactor. (p. 309)

melting The change from the solid to the liquid state of matter. (p. 75)

melting point The temperature at which a substance changes from a solid to a liquid. (p. 58)

Mercalli scale A scale that rates earthquakes according to their intensity and how much damage they cause. (p. 371)

mercury barometer An instrument that measures changes in air pressure, consisting of a glass tube partly filled with mercury, with its open end resting in a dish of mercury. Air pressure pushing on the mercury in the dish forces the mercury in the tube higher. (p. 446)

mesosphere The middle layer of Earth's atmosphere; the layer in which most meteoroids burn up. (p. 452)

metamorphic rock A type of rock that forms from an existing rock that is changed by heat, pressure, or chemical reactions. (p. 345)

metamorphosis A process in which an animal's body undergoes dramatic changes during its life cycle. (p. 232)

meteor A streak of light in the sky produced by the burning of a meteoroid in Earth's atmosphere. (p. 565)

meteorite A meteoroid that has hit Earth's surface. (p. 565)

meteoroid A chunk of rock or dust in space. (p. 565)

meteorologist A scientist who studies the causes of weather and tries to predict it. (p. 520)

microscope An instrument that makes small objects look larger. (p. 132)

mineral A naturally occurring inorganic solid that has a crystal structure and a definite chemical composition. (p. 331)

mitochondria Rod-shaped cell structures that produce most of the energy needed to carry out the cell's functions. (p. 141)

mitosis The stage of the cell cycle during which the cell's nucleus divides into two new nuclei and one copy of the DNA is distributed into each daughter cell. (p. 172)

mixture Two or more substances that are mixed together but not chemically combined. (p. 28)

molecule A particle made of two or more atoms bonded together. (p. 44)

mollusk An invertebrate with a soft, unsegmented body; most are protected by hard outer shells. (p. 227)

moment magnitude scale A scale that rates earthquakes by estimating the total energy released by an earthquake. (p. 372)

monotreme A mammal that lays eggs. (p. 254)

monsoons Sea and land breezes over a large region that change direction with the seasons. (p. 476)

motion The state in which one object's distance from another is changing. (p. 87)

mouth The point at which a river flows into another body of water. (p. 111)

net force The overall force on an object when all the individual forces acting on an object are added together. (p. 99)

nitrogen fixation The process of changing free nitrogen gas into a usable form. (p. 285)

nonlinear The term used to describe a relationship between variables whose graph is not a straight line. (p. 105)

nonrenewable resource A natural resource that is not replaced as it is used. (p. 295)

normal fault A type of fault where the hanging wall slides downward; caused by tension in the crust. (p. 360)

nuclear fission The splitting of an atom's nucleus into two smaller nuclei. (p. 307)

nuclear fusion The combining of two atomic nuclei to produce a single larger nucleus as when two hydrogen atoms join together to form helium, releasing energy. (pp. 310, 538)

nucleus The control center of the cell that directs the cells' activities and determines the cell's characteristics; also, the central core of an atom containing protons and usually neutrons. (pp. 140, 307)

nymph A stage of gradual metamorphosis that usually resembles the adult insect. (p. 232)

observation The process of using one or more senses to gather information. (p. 11)

occluded Cut off, as the warm air mass at an occluded front is cut off from the ground by cooler air beneath it. (p. 501)

omnivore An animal that eats both plants and animals. (p. 219)

organ A structure in the body that is composed of different kinds of tissue. (p. 146)

organ system A group of organs that work together to perform a major function in the body. (p. 147)

organelle A tiny cell structure that carries out a specific function within the cell. (p. 139)

organism A living thing. (p. 122)

osmosis The diffusion of water molecules through a selectively permeable membrane. (p. 160)

outer core A layer of molten iron and nickel that surrounds the inner core of Earth. (p. 328)

ovary An organ of the female reproductive system in which eggs and estrogen are produced; also, a protective structure in plants that encloses the developing seeds (p. 209)

ovule A plant structure in seed plants that contains an egg cell. (p. 209)

oxbow lake The crescent-shaped, cutoff body of water that remains after a river carves a new channel. (p. 111)

ozone A form of oxygen that has three oxygen atoms in each molecule instead of the usual two. (p. 436)

P wave A type of seismic wave that compresses and expands the ground. (p. 369)

pahoehoe A hot, fast-moving type of lava that hardens to form smooth, ropelike coils. (p. 378)

Pangaea The name of the single landmass that broke apart 225 million years ago and gave rise to today's continents. (p. 355)

parasite An organism that lives on or in a host and causes harm to the host. (p. 199)

passive transport The movement of materials through a cell membrane without using energy. (p. 161)

permeable Characteristic of materials such as sand and gravel which allow water to pass easily through them. (p. 413)

pesticide A chemical intended to kill insects and other organisms that damage crops. (p. 152)

petrochemical A compound made from oil. (p. 297)

petroleum Liquid fossil fuel; oil. (p. 296)

photochemical smog A brownish haze that is a mixture of ozone and other chemicals, formed when nitrogen oxides, hydrocarbons, and other pollutants react with one another in the presence of sunlight. (p. 442)

photosphere The inner layer of the sun's atmosphere. (p. 539)

photosynthesis The process by which plants and some other organisms capture light energy and use it to make food from carbon dioxide and water. (p. 163)

physical change A change that alters the form or appearance of a substance but does not make the material into another substance. (p. 30)

physical property A characteristic of a substance that can be observed without changing the substance into something else. (p. 26)

pipe A long tube through which magma moves from the magma chamber to Earth's surface. (p. 375)

placenta An organ that becomes the link between the developing embryo or fetus and the mother. (p. 255)

placental mammal A mammal that develops inside its mother's body until its body systems can function independently. (p. 255)

plate boundary A crack in the lithosphere where two of Earth's plates meet. (p. 356)

plate A section of the lithosphere that slowly moves, carrying pieces of continental and oceanic crust. (p. 354)

plateau A landform that has a more or less level surface and is elevated high above sea level. (p. 365)

polar (air mass) A cold air mass that forms north of 50° north latitude and south of 50° south latitude and has high air pressure. (p. 496)

pollen Tiny particles produced by plants that contain the microscopic cells that later become sperm cells. (p. 209)

pollutant A harmful substance in the air, water, or soil. (p. 440)

population All the members of one species in a particular area. (p. 269)

population density The number of individuals in a specific area. (p. 273)

pores Tiny openings in and between particles of rock and soil which may contain air or water. (p. 413)

precipitation Forms of water such as rain, snow, sleet, or hail that fall from clouds and reach Earth's surface. (pp. 398, 487)

predator A carnivore that hunts and kills other animals for food and has adaptations that help it capture the animals it preys upon. (p. 219)

pressure The force pushing on an area or surface; also, the force of a gas's outward push divided by the area of the walls of the container. (pp. 63, 445)

prey An animal that a predator feeds upon. (p. 219)

prime meridian The line that makes a half-circle from the North pole to the South pole, passing through Greenwich, England. (p. 591)

producer An organism that can make its own food. (p. 281)

prokaryote An organism whose cells lack a nucleus and some other cell structures. (p. 145)

prominence A loop of gas that protrudes from the sun's surface, linking parts of sunspot regions. (p. 542)

protozoan An animal-like protist. (p. 197)

pseudopod A "false foot" or temporary bulge of the cell membrane used for feeding and movement in some protozoans. (p. 197)

psychrometer An instrument used to measure relative humidity, consisting of a wet-bulb thermometer and a dry-bulb thermometer. (p. 482)

pupa The second stage of complete metamorphosis, in which an insect is enclosed in a protective covering and gradually changes from a larva to an adult. (p. 232)

pyroclastic flow The expulsion of ash, cinders, bombs, and gases during an explosive volcanic eruption. (p. 379)

radial symmetry The quality of having many lines of symmetry that all pass through a central point. (p. 221)

radiation The direct transfer of energy by electromagnetic waves. (p. 462)

radula A flexible ribbon of tiny teeth in mollusks. (p. 228)

rain gauge An instrument used to measure the amount of precipitation, consisting of an open-ended container topped by a collecting funnel and having a collecting tube and measuring scale inside. (p. 489)

reactor vessel The part of a nuclear reactor where nuclear fission occurs. (p. 308)

recharge New water that enters an aquifier from the surface. (p. 415)

reference point A place or object used for comparison to determine if an object is in motion. (p. 88)

refinery A factory where crude oil is separated into fuels and other products. (p. 297)

relative humidity The percentage of water vapor in the air compared to the maximum amount the air can hold at that temperature. (p. 482)

renewable resource A resource that is naturally replaced in a relatively short time. (p. 299)

replication The process by which a cell makes a copy of the DNA in its nucleus. (p. 171)

reproduce The production of offspring that are similar to the parents. (p. 125)

reserve A known deposit of fuels. (p. 298)

reservoir A natural or artificial lake that stores water for human use. (p. 410)

resolution The ability to clearly distinguish the individual parts of an object. (p. 137)

respiration The process by which cells break down simple food molecules to release the energy they contain. (p. 166)

responding variable The factor that changes as a result of changes to the manipulated variable in an experiment. (p. 12)

response An action or change in behavior that occurs as a result of a stimulus. (p. 125)

retrograde rotation The spinning motion of a planet from east to west, opposite to the direction of rotation of most planets and moons. (p. 547)

reverse fault A type of fault where the hanging wall slides upward; caused by compression in the crust. (p. 361)

revolution The movement of an object around another object. (p. 544)

ribosome A tiny structure in the cytoplasm of a cell where proteins are made. (p. 144)

Richter scale A scale that rates seismic waves as measured by a mechanical seismograph. (p. 371)

river A large stream. (p. 404)

rock The material that forms Earth's hard surface. (pp. 326, 340)

rock cycle A series of processes on the surface and inside earth that slowly changes rocks from one kind to another. (p. 346)

root The underground part of any plant which anchors the plant in the ground and absorbs water and nutrients from the soil. (p. 208)

rotation The spinning motion of a planet about its axis. (p. 544)

S waves A type of seismic wave that moves the ground up and down and side to side. (p. 369)

satellite Any object that revolves around another object in space. (p. 567)

saturated zone A layer of permeable rock or soil in which the cracks and pores are completely filled with water. (p. 413)

scale Relates distance on a map to the corresponding distance on Earth's surface. (p. 590)

scattering Reflection of light in all directions. (p. 464)

science A way of learning about the natural world. (p. 10)

scientific inquiry The diverse ways in which scientists study the natural world. (p. 16)

scientific law A statement that describes what scientists expect to happen every time under a particular set of conditions. (p. 16)

scientific theory A well-tested scientific concept that explains a wide range of observations. (p. 16)

sea breeze The flow of air from an ocean or lake to the land. (p. 476)

sediment Small, solid particles of material from rocks or organisms which are moved by water or wind, resulting in erosion and deposition. (pp. 108, 343)

sedimentary rock A type of rock that forms when particles from other rocks or the remains of plants and animals are pressed and cemented together. (p. 343)

seed The plant structure that contains a young plant inside a protective covering. (p. 208).

seismic wave A vibration that travels through Earth carrying the energy released during an earthquake. (pp. 327, 368)

seismograph A device that records ground movements caused by seismic waves as they move through Earth. (p. 370)

selective breeding The process of selecting a few organisms with desired traits to serve as parents of the next generation. (p. 151).

selectively permeable A property of cell membranes that allows some substances to pass through, while others cannot. (p. 158)

sexual reproduction The reproductive process that involves two parents whose genetic material is combined to produce a new organism, which differs from both parents. (p. 150)

shearing Stress that pushes a mass of rock in opposite directions. (p. 359)

shield volcano A wide, gently sloping mountain made of layers of lava and formed by quiet eruptions. (p. 388)

silica A material that is formed from the elements oxygen and silicon; silica is found in magma. (p. 377)

sill A slab of volcanic rock formed when magma squeezes between layers of rock. (p. 387)

solar energy Energy from the sun. (p. 299)

solar flare An explosion of hydrogen gas from the sun's surface that occurs when loops in sunspot regions suddenly connect. (p. 542)

solar system A large planetary system that consists of a combination of many smaller planetary systems and objects. (p. 534)

solar wind A stream of electrically charged particles produced by the sun's corona. (p. 540)

solid A state of matter that has a definite volume and a definite shape. (p. 57)

species A group of similar organisms whose members can mate with one another and produce fertile offspring. (p. 185)

speed The distance an object travels in one unit of time. (p. 90)

sperm cell A male sex cell. (p. 150)

spontaneous generation The mistaken idea that living things arise from nonliving sources. (p. 125)

spore A tiny cell that is able to grow into a new organism. (p. 201)

spring A place where groundwater bubbles or flows out of cracks in the rock. (p. 414)

stamen The male reproductive parts of a flower. (p. 209)

stem The stalk-like organ that supports a plant and that connects the roots to the leaves. (p. 208)

stimulus A change in an organism's surroundings that causes the organism to respond. (p. 124)

stomata The small openings on the undersides of most leaves through which oxygen and carbon dioxide can move. (p. 205)

storm A violent disturbance in the atmosphere. (p. 503)

storm surge A "dome" of water that sweeps across the coast where the hurricane lands. (p. 510)

stratosphere The second lowest layer of Earth's atmosphere; the ozone layer is located in the upper stratosphere. (p. 452)

stratus Clouds that form in flat layers. (p. 484)

streak The color of a mineral's powder. (p. 334)

stress A force that acts on rock to change its shape or volume. (p. 358)

strike-slip fault A type of fault where rocks on either side move past each other sideways with little up-or-down motion. (p. 360)

sublimation The change in state from a solid directly to a gas without passing through the liquid state. (p. 78)

substance A single kind of matter that has distinct physical and chemical properties. (p. 25)

sunspot A dark, cooler region on the surface of the sun. (p. 540)

surface waves A type of seismic wave that forms when P waves and S waves reach Earth's surface. (p. 370)

syncline A downward fold in rock formed by compression in Earth's crust. (p. 364)

taxonomy The scientific study of how living things are classified. (p. 185)

temperature The average amount of energy of motion in the molecules of a substance. (pp. 62, 469)

temperature inversion A phenomenon that results when a layer of warm air becomes trapped between two cooler layers, preventing the air close to Earth from escaping. (p. 442)

tension Stress that stretches rock so that it becomes thinner in the middle. (p. 359)

terrestrial planets The name given to the four inner planets: Mercury, Venus, Earth and Mars. (p. 544)

texture The size, shape, and pattern of a rock's grains. (p. 341)

theory of plate tectonics The theory that pieces of Earth's lithosphere are in constant motion, driven by convection currents in the mantle. (p. 356)

thermal energy The total energy of a substance's particles due to their movement or vibration; also, the energy of motion in the molecules of a substance. (pp. 74, 469)

thermometer An instrument used to measure temperature, consisting of a thin, glass tube with a bulb on one end that contains a liquid, usually mercury or alcohol. (p. 469)

thermosphere The outermost layer of Earth's atmosphere. (p. 455)

thorax An insect's mid-section, to which its wings and legs are attached. (p. 232)

tissue A group of similar cells that perform a specific function in an organism. (p. 146)

tornado A rapidly whirling, funnel-shaped cloud that reaches down from a storm cloud to touch Earth's surface, usually leaving a destructive path. (p. 505)

trait A characteristic that an organism can pass onto its offspring through its genes. (p. 149)

transpiration The process by which water is lost through a plant's leaves. (p. 398)

tributary A stream or small river that flows into a larger stream. (p. 404)

tropical (air mass) A warm air mass that forms in the tropics and has low air pressure. (p. 496)

tropism The growth response of a plant toward or away from a stimulus. (p. 210)

troposphere The lowest layer of Earth's atmosphere; where weather occurs. (p. 451)

ultraviolet radiation A form of energy with wavelengths that are shorter than visible light. (p. 463)

unbalanced force A nonzero net force that changes an object's motion. (p. 99)

unsaturated zone A layer of rocks and soil above the water table in which the pores contain air as well as water. (p. 413)

vacuole A water-filled sac inside a cell that acts as a storage area. (p. 145)

vaporization The change from the liquid to the gaseous state of matter. (p. 76)

vary inversely A term used to describe the relationship between two variables whose graph forms a curve that slopes downward from left to right. (p. 71)

vascular tissue The internal transporting tissue in some plants that is made up of tube-like structures. (p. 205)

vein A narrow band of a mineral that forms from solution underground; also a blood vessel that carries blood back to the heart. (p. 336)

velocity Speed in a given direction. (p. 93)

vent An opening through which molten rock and gas leave a volcano. (p. 375)

ventricle A lower chamber of the heart that pumps blood out to the lungs and body. (p. 241)

vertebrae The bones that make up the backbone of an animal. (p. 237)

vertebrate An animal with a backbone. (p. 220)

viscosity The resistance of a liquid to flowing. (p. 59)

volcanic neck A deposit of hardened magma in a volcano's pipe. (p. 387)

volume The amount of space that matter occupies. (p. 35)

water cycle The continuous process by which water moves from Earth's surface to the atmosphere and back passing through the living and nonliving parts of the environment. (p. 398)

water pollution The addition of any substance that has a negative effect on water or the living things that depend on the water. (p. 298)

water table The top of the saturated zone, or depth to the groundwater in an aquifer. (p. 413)

water vapor The invisible, gaseous form of water. (p. 437)

watershed The land area that supplies water to a river system. (p. 405)

weather The condition of Earth's atmosphere at a particular time and place. (p. 434)

weight A measure of the force of gravity on an object. (p. 35)

wind The horizontal movement of air from an area of high pressure to an area of lower pressure. (p. 472)

wind-chill factor Increased cooling caused by the wind. (p. 473)

zygote A fertilized egg, produced by the joining of a sperm cell and egg cell. (p. 208)

Spanish Glossary

A

aa/malpaís Tipo lento de lava que al solidificarse forma bloques ásperos; menos caliente que la lava cordada. (pág. 378)

abdomen/abdomen Región del cuerpo de algunos organismos, como los insectos, donde se encuentran los órganos reproductores y parte del canal digestivo. (pág. 232)

abiotic factor/factor abiótico Parte sin vida de un ecosistema. (pág. 268)

acceleration/aceleración Ritmo de cambio de velocidad. (pág. 102)

acid rain/lluvia ácida Lluvia más ácida de lo normal, producida por la liberación en el aire de moléculas de dióxido de azufre y óxido de nitrógeno. (pág. 443)

active/activo Se dice del volcán que entra en erupción o da señales de poder hacerlo en un futuro próximo. (pág. 380)

active transport/transporte activo Movimiento de materiales a través de la membrana celular, usando energía para ello. (pág. 61)

adaptation/adaptación Característica que ayuda a un organismo a sobrevivir en su entorno y a reproducirse. (pág. 219)

air mass/masa de aire Enorme volumen de aire cuya temperatura, presión y humedad son uniformes. (pág. 496)

air pressure/presión atmosférica Fuerza que ejerce el peso de una columna de aire sobre una zona. (pág. 446)

altitude/altitud Elevación sobre el nivel del mar. (pág. 448)

amorphous solid/sólido amorfo Sólido formado por partículas que no están ordenadas según un patrón regular. (pág. 58)

anemometer/anemómetro Instrumento usado para medir la velocidad del viento. (pág. 473)

aneroid barometer/barómetro aneroide Instrumento que mide los cambios en la presión atmosférica sin usar líquido. Las alteraciones en la forma de la caja metálica hermética hacen que se mueva la aguja indicadora de este aparato. (pág. 447)

anticline/anticlinal Pliegue hacia arriba de las rocas debido a la compresión de la corteza terrestre. (pág. 364)

anticyclone/anticiclón Centro de alta presión de aire seco. (pág. 502)

anus/ano Abertura al final del aparato digestivo por la cual se eliminan los desechos del organismo. (pág. 226)

aquifer/acuífero Capa subterránea de roca o tierra donde se acumula agua. (pág. 414)

arachnid/arácnido Artrópodo cuyo cuerpo tiene dos secciones. (pág. 234)

artesian well/pozo artesiano Pozo donde el agua sube debido a la presión del interior del acuífero. (pág. 415)

arthropod/artrópodo Invertebrado con esqueleto externo, cuerpo dividido en segmentos y apéndices articulados. (pág. 230)

asexual reproduction/reproducción asexual Proceso por el cual un solo organismo produce descendientes idénticos a él. (pág. 150)

asteroid belt/cinturón de asteroides Región del sistema solar situada entre las órbitas de Marte y Júpiter, donde se encuentran muchos asteroides. (pág. 564)

asteroids/asteroides Objetos que giran alrededor del Sol, demasiado pequeños y numerosos como para ser considerados planetas. (pág. 564)

atmosphere/atmósfera Mezcla de gases que rodea la Tierra; la más externa de las cuatro esferas en que los científicos dividen al planeta. (pág. 434)

atom/átomo La partícula más pequeña de un elemento. (pág. 42)

atrium/aurícula Cada una de las dos cavidades superiores del corazón que reciben la sangre que entra en él. (pág. 241)

aurora borealis/aurora boreal Despliegue brillante de colores en el cielo, provocado por el choque en la ionosfera de partículas solares con átomos de oxígeno y nitrógeno; también se le llama luces del norte. (pág. 456)

autotroph/autótrofo Organismo que elabora sus propios alimentos. (pág. 128)

B

balanced forces/fuerzas equilibradas Fuerzas iguales que actúan sobre un objeto en sentidos opuestos. (pág. 100)

barometer/barómetro Instrumento usado para medir los cambios en la presión atmosférica. (pág. 446)

batholith/batolito Masa rocosa que se forma al enfriarse un gran volumen de magma en el interior de la corteza. (pág. 387)

bilateral symmetry/simetría bilateral Simetría lineal; capacidad de ser divisible en dos mitades que son reflejos exactos entre sí. (pág. 221)

binary fission/fisión binaria Forma de reproducción asexual en la que una célula se divide en otras dos idénticas. (pág. 192)

binomial nomenclature/nomenclatura binomial Sistema de denominación en el que cada organismo recibe un nombre formado por dos palabras, una para el género y otra para la especie. (pág. 185)

biomass/biomasa Material vivo o sus restos que haya en un ecosistema. (pág. 286)

biomass fuel/combustible de biomasa Combustible formado a partir de lo que fueron seres vivos. (pág. 303)

biotic factor/factor biótico Parte viva de un ecosistema. (pág. 267)

bird/ave Vertebrado endotérmico con plumas y corazón de cuatro cavidades, y que pone huevos. (pág. 247)

birth rate/índice de natalidad Número de nacimientos ocurridos en una población durante un período de tiempo determinado. (pág. 275)

boiling/ebullición Vaporización que ocurre sobre y bajo la superficie de un líquido. (pág. 77)

boiling point/punto de ebullición Temperatura a la que una sustancia pasa del estado líquido al gaseoso. (pág. 77)

Boyle's law/ley de Boyle Relación entre la presión y el volumen de un gas, a una temperatura constante; al aumentar el volumen, disminuye la presión. (pág. 64)

budding/gemación Modo de reproducción asexual en el que un nuevo organismo se forma separándose del cuerpo del progenitor. (pág. 203)

caldera/caldera Depresión grande en la parte superior de un volcán, formada al colapsarse el techo de la cámara magmática. (pág. 390)

carnivore/carnívoro Animal que se alimenta sólo de otros animales. (pág. 219)

carrying capacity/capacidad portadora Población máxima que una zona puede soportar. (pág. 277)

cartilage/cartílago Tejido conjuntivo más elástico que el hueso y que sirve de soporte a ciertas partes del cuerpo. (pág. 239)

cell/célula Unidad básica de estructura y función de los organismos. (pág. 123)

cell cycle/ciclo celular Secuencia normal de crecimiento y división que experimentan las células. (pág. 171)

cell membrane/membrana celular Borde exterior de una célula; regula la entrada y salida de sustancias de la célula. (pág. 139)

cell theory/teoría celular Explicación ampliamente aceptada de las relaciones entre las células y los seres vivos. (pág. 134)

cell wall/pared celular Capa rígida de material no vivo que rodea las células vegetales y las de algunos otros organismos. (pág. 139)

Celsius scale/escala Celsius Escala de temperaturas donde cero y 100 son las temperaturas a las que el agua se congela o hierve, respectivamente. (pág. 583)

Charles's law/ley de Charles Relación entre la temperatura y el volumen de un gas, a una presión constante; al aumentar la temperatura, aumenta el volumen. (pág. 66)

chemical bond/enlace químico Fuerza que une dos átomos. (pág. 44)

chemical change/cambio químico Transformación en la materia que produce nuevas sustancias. (pág. 31)

chemical property/propiedad química Característica que se observa cuando una sustancia interactúa con otra. (pág. 26)

chemistry/química Estudio de las propiedades y las transformaciones de la materia. (pág. 25)

chlorophyll/clorofila Sustancia que da su color verde a los cloroplastos y atrapa energía luminosa durante la fotosíntesis. (pág. 163)

chloroplast/cloroplasto Estructura de las células de las plantas y de algunos otros organismos que atrapa la energía de la luz solar y la utiliza para producir el alimento. (pág. 144)

chromatid/cromátida Cada uno de los dos bastones idénticos de un cromosoma. (pág. 172)

chromatin/cromatina Material celular que contiene ADN y transmite información genética. (pág. 141)

chromosome/cromosoma Estructura celular en forma de bastones, compuesta de cromatina condensada; contiene ADN, portador de la información genética que controla las características heredadas como son el color de los ojos y el grupo sanguíneo. (pág. 141)

chromosphere/cromosfera Capa intermedia de la atmósfera del Sol. (pág. 539)

cilia/cilios Estructuras de forma capilar que se prolongan por el exterior de las células y se mueven por ondas. (pág. 198)

cinder cone/cono de escorias Colina o montaña inclinada de forma cónica, compuesta de cenizas, escorias y bombas acumuladas alrededor de la abertura de un volcán. (pág. 388)

cirrus/cirros Nubes tenues y plumosas compuestas principalmente de cristales de hielo y formadas a grandes alturas, aproximadamente a más de 6 kilómetros de la tierra. (pág. 484)

classification/clasificación Proceso de agrupar objetos basándose en sus semejanzas. (pág. 184)

cleavage/exfoliación Capacidad de un mineral para fracturarse fácilmente en superficies planas. (pág. 335)

cnidarians/cnidarios Animales que usan células urticantes para capturar sus presas y defenderse, e ingieren sus alimentos por una cavidad central hueca. (pág. 224)

combustion/combustión Reacción rápida entre el oxígeno y un combustible, la cual produce energía térmica. (pág. 293)

comet/cometa Bola de hielo y polvo cuya órbita es una elipse larga y estrecha. (pág. 562)

community/comunidad Todas las diferentes poblaciones que conviven en una zona. (pág. 270)

composite volcano/volcán compuesto Montaña elevada y de forma cónica en la que las capas de lava se alternan con las de cenizas y otros materiales volcánicos. (pág. 388)

composting/compostaje Proceso mediante el cual los desechos y restos de seres vivos se descomponen en el suelo. (pág. 286)

compound/compuesto Sustancia formada por dos o más elementos combinados químicamente según una razón establecida. (pág. 28)

compound microscope/microscopio compuesto Microscopio de luz dotado de más de una lente. (pág. 132)

compression/compresión Tipo de esfuerzo que oprime las rocas hasta doblarlas o fragmentarlas. (pág. 359)

condensation/condensación Paso de la materia del estado gaseoso al líquido; también, proceso por el cual un gas, como el vapor de agua, se transforma en un líquido, como el agua. (págs. 77, 483)

conduction/conducción Transferencia de calor mediante el contacto físico directo. (pág. 470)

conjugation/conjugación Proceso en el que un organismo unicelular transfiere a otro parte de su material genético. (pág. 192)

conservation/conservación Uso racional de un recurso para evitar que se agote. (pág. 425)

consumer/consumidor Organismo que obtiene energía alimentándose de otros organismos. (pág. 281)

continental (air mass)/masa de aire continental Masa de aire seco que se forma sobre la tierra. (pág. 496)

contour line/curva de nivel Línea que une en un mapa topográfico los puntos de igual elevación. (pág. 592)

control rod/barra de control Varilla de cadmio usada en los reactores nucleares para absorber los neutrones de la fisión. (pág. 308)

controlled experiment/experimento controlado Experimento donde todas las variables menos una se mantienen iguales. (pág. 12)

convection/convección Transferencia de calor mediante los movimientos de las corrientes de un fluido. (pág. 470)

convex lens/lente convexa Lente que tiene el centro más grueso que los bordes. (pág. 136)

core/núcleo Parte central del Sol donde se produce la fusión nuclear. (pág. 538)

Coriolis effect/efecto Coriolis Forma en que la rotación terrestre desvía hacia la derecha la dirección de los vientos del hemisferio norte y hacia la izquierda la de los vientos del hemisferio sur. (pág. 477)

corona/corona Capa externa de la atmósfera del Sol. (pág. 539)

cotyledon/cotiledón Hoja que sale de la semilla y en la que se almacena el alimento. (pág. 208)

crater/cráter Zona con forma de tazón que se origina alrededor de la abertura principal de un volcán. (pág. 375)

crop/buche Depósito interno de las aves donde almacenan los alimentos una vez tragados. (pág. 248)

crust/corteza Capa rocosa que forma la superficie externa de la Tierra. (pág. 326)

crustacean/crustáceo Artrópodo con dos o tres secciones corporales, cinco o más pares de patas, dos pares de antenas y normalmente tres pares de apéndices para masticar. (pág. 234)

crystal/cristal Sólido cuyos átomos están dispuestos según un patrón que se repite una y otra vez. (pág. 332)

crystalline solid/sólido cristalino Sustancia compuesta de cristales cuyas partículas están dispuestas según un patrón regular que se repite. (pág. 58)

cumulus/cúmulos Nubes que se forman a menos de 2 kilómetros de la tierra y parecen montones de algodón redondos y esponjosos. (pág. 484)

cyclone/ciclón Remolino de aire con centro de baja presión. (pág. 501)

cytokinesis/citocinesis Etapa final del ciclo celular en la que el citoplasma se divide y distribuye los organelos a cada una de las dos nuevas células. (pág. 173)

cytoplasm/citoplasma Región celular situada dentro de la membrana (en las procariotas) o bien entre ésta y el núcleo (en las eucariotas); contiene un material gelatinoso y los organelos. (pág. 141)

data/datos Hechos, cifras y otras evidencias recogidos en un experimento. (pág. 13)

death rate/índice de mortalidad Número de muertes ocurridas en una población durante un período determinado. (pág. 275)

decomposer/descomponedor Organismo que separa las moléculas grandes de los desechos y restos de los seres vivos, convirtiéndolas en moléculas más pequeñas, devolviendo a la tierra y al agua materiales importantes. (págs. 193, 282)

deformation/deformación Cambio en el volumen o la forma de la corteza terrestre. (pág. 359)

delta/delta Forma del relieve compuesta por los sedimentos que los ríos depositan al llegar a un océano o un lago. (pág. 111)

density/densidad Medida de la cantidad de masa de una sustancia que ocupa un volumen determinado. (págs. 335, 445)

deposition/sedimentación Proceso por el cual los sedimentos dejan el agua o el viento que los traslada, depositándose en un nuevo lugar. (págs. 108, 343)

desalination/desalinización Proceso de obtener agua dulce a partir del agua del mar extrayéndole la sal. (pág. 427)

dew point/punto de condensación Temperatura a la que se inicia la condensación. (pág. 483)

diaphragm/diafragma Músculo grande y con forma de bóveda que tiene una importante función en la respiración. (pág. 252)

diffusion/difusión Proceso por el que las moléculas pasan de una zona de alta concentración a otra de concentración menor. (pág. 159)

dike/dique Bloque de roca volcánica que se forma cuando el magma atraviesa los estratos rocosos. (pág. 387)

directly proportional/directamente proporcionales Término empleado para describir la relación entre dos variables cuya gráfica es una línea recta que pasa por el punto (0,0). (pág. 70)

divide/divisoria Elevación de tierra que separa un área de drenaje o cuenca hidrográfica de otra. (pág. 405)

DNA (*DeoxyriboNucleic Acid*)/ADN (*Acido DesoxirriboNucleico*) Material genético que contiene la información de un organismo y se transmite de padres a hijos. (pág. 150)

dormant/atenuado Se dice del volcán que no da señales de entrar en erupción en un futuro próximo. (pág. 380)

drought/sequía Escasez de agua ocasionada por períodos prolongados de bajas precipitaciones en una zona determinada. (pág. 490)

earthquake/terremoto Sacudidas producidas por los movimientos de las rocas debajo de la superficie terrestre. (pág. 358)

echinoderm/equinodermo Invertebrado de simetría radial y con esqueleto interno espinoso que vive en el fondo oceánico. (pág. 235)

ecology/ecología Estudio de las interacciones de los seres vivos entre sí y con su medio ambiente. (pág. 270)

ecosystem/ecosistema Todas las cosas vivas o no que interactúan en una zona. (pág. 266)

ectotherm/ectotermo Animal cuyo cuerpo no produce suficiente calor interno. (pág. 238)

efficiency/eficiencia Porcentaje de energía usada por un aparato para realizar un trabajo. (pág. 314)

egg/óvulo Célula sexual femenina. (pág. 150)

El Niño/el Niño Corriente de agua templada que tiene lugar en períodos de 2 a 7 años en el océano Pacífico, causando cambios en los vientos, las corrientes y los patrones meteorológicos que pueden dar origen a transformaciones climáticas dramáticas. (págs. 503, 522)

electrode/electrodo Lámina de metal que adquiere o pierde electrones durante la electrólisis. (pág. 48)

electrolysis/electrólisis Proceso por el cual una corriente eléctrica rompe los enlaces químicos. (pág. 48)

electromagnetic wave/onda electromagnética Forma de energía que puede propagarse a través del espacio. (pág. 462)

element/elemento Sustancia que no puede descomponerse en otras por medios químicos o físicos. (pág. 27)

ellipse/elipse Círculo alargado o de forma ovalada; forma de la órbita de los planetas. (pág. 535)

embryo/embrión Organismo en desarrollo que se forma a partir de un cigoto. (pág. 208)

emigration/emigración Abandono de una población. (pág. 276)

endoplasmic reticulum/retículo endoplásmico Estructura celular que forma un laberinto de pasadizos en el que las proteínas y otros materiales son trasladados de una parte de la célula a otra. (pág. 144)

endoskeleton/endoesqueleto Esqueleto interno. (pág. 235)

endospore/endospora Célula inactiva pequeña, redondeada y de paredes gruesas que se forma en el interior de las células de las bacterias. (pág. 192)

endotherm/endotermo Animal cuyo cuerpo regula su temperatura controlando el calor interno que produce. (pág. 238)

energy/energía Capacidad para realizar un trabajo o producir cambios. (pág. 25)

energy conservation/conservación de la energía Proceso de reducir el consumo de energía. (pág. 313)

energy transformation/transformación de la energía Cualquier cambio de una forma de energía a otra. (pág. 292)

epicenter/epicentro Lugar de la superficie terrestre situado exactamente sobre el foco de un terremoto. (pág. 368)

equator/ecuador Línea imaginaria que circunda la Tierra a medio camino entre los polos norte y sur. (pág. 591)

erosion/erosión Proceso por el cual el agua, el hielo, el viento o la gravedad desplazan fragmentos de roca y tierra. (págs. 108, 343)

estimate/estimación Cálculo aproximado de un número basándose en supuestos razonables. (pág. 274)

eukaryote/eucariota Organismo cuyas células contienen un núcleo y otras estructuras. (pág. 145)

evacuate/evacuar Abandonar temporalmente un lugar. (pág. 510)

evaporation/evaporación Proceso en el que la vaporización sólo ocurre en la superficie de un líquido; también, proceso por el cual las moléculas de la superficie de un líquido, como el agua, absorben suficiente energía como para pasar al estado gaseoso, como el vapor de agua. (págs. 76, 398, 481)

exoskeleton/exoesqueleto Esqueleto externo. (pág. 230)

exosphere/exosfera Capa exterior de la termosfera que se extiende hacia el espacio. (pág. 456)

external stimulus/estímulo externo Cambio producido en el entorno de un organismo, provocándole una reacción. (pág. 124)

extinct/extinto Se aplica al tipo de organismo que ya no existe en el planeta; también se dice del volcán que tiene pocas probabilidades de entrar de nuevo en erupción. (pág. 380)

extrusive rock/roca efusiva Roca ígnea que se forma a partir de la lava de la superficie terrestre. (pág. 342)

fault/falla Fractura o grieta en la litosfera terrestre a lo largo de la cual se desplazan las rocas. (pág. 360)

fault-block mountain/montaña de bloques fallados Montaña formada en el lugar donde una falla normal levanta un bloque rocoso. (pág. 362)

fermentation/fermentación Proceso por el cual las células degradan las moléculas para liberar energía sin usar oxígeno. (pág. 167)

fertilization/fecundación Unión de un espermatozoide y un óvulo. (pág. 208)

flagellum/flagelo Estructura larga y con forma de látigo que sirve a los organismos unicelulares para moverse. (pág. 191)

flash flood/inundación repentina Inundación súbita y violenta que ocurre a pocas horas o incluso minutos de una fuerte tormenta de lluvia. (pág. 516)

flood/inundación Desbordamiento del cauce de un río debido al aumento del volumen de sus aguas. (págs. 111, 406)

flood plain/llanura aluvial Valle extenso y plano por el cual discurre un río. (pág. 109)

flower/flor Estructura reproductora de las angiospermas. (pág. 209)

focus/foco Zona situada debajo de la superficie terrestre donde las rocas sometidas a esfuerzo se rompen, provocando un terremoto. (pág. 368)

fold/pliegue Doblez de las rocas que se produce en lugares donde se comprime parte de la corteza terrestre. (pág. 363)

food chain/cadena alimenticia Secuencia de sucesos en la que un organismo se alimenta de otro, dando lugar a un flujo de energía entre los organismos afectados. (pág. 282)

food web/red alimenticia Patrón de cadenas alimenticias superpuestas de un ecosistema. (pág. 284)

footwall/labio inferior Bloque rocoso que compone la mitad inferior de una falla. (pág. 360)

force/fuerza Impulso o atracción ejercido sobre un objeto. (pág. 99)

fossil fuel/combustible fósil Sustancia rica en energía (como el carbón, el petróleo o el gas natural), formada a partir de restos de organismos. (pág. 295)

fracture/fractura Aspecto de un mineral al romperse de forma irregular. (pág. 335)

freezing/congelación Paso del estado líquido al sólido. (pág. 76)

front/frente Zona donde dos masas de aire se encuentran sin mezclarse. (pág. 499)

fruit/fruto En las angiospermas, ovario maduro y otras estructuras que encierran una o más semillas. (pág. 210)

fuel/combustible Material que libera energía cuando arde. (pág. 293)

fuel rod/barra de combustible Varilla de uranio sometida a fisión en un reactor nuclear. (pág. 308)

gas/gas Estado de la materia que carece de forma y volumen definidos. (pág. 59)

gas giants/gigantes gaseosos Nombre dado a los primeros cuatro planetas exteriores: Júpiter, Saturno, Urano y Neptuno. (pág. 552)

gemstone/gema Mineral duro y colorido de brillo intenso o vítreo. (pág. 336)

gene/gen Segmento de ADN de un cromosoma que lleva codificado un rasgo específico. (pág. 150)

genus/género Agrupamiento clasificatorio que comprende varias especies semejantes y de parentesco cercano. (pág. 185)

geocentric system/sistema geocéntrico Descripción del sistema solar en la que todos los planetas giran alrededor de la Tierra. (pág. 533)

geologist/geólogo Científico que estudia las fuerzas que forman y configuran el planeta Tierra. (pág. 327)

geology/geología Estudio de la masa terrestre. (pág. 327)

geosynchronous orbit/órbita geosíncrona Órbita de un satélite que gira alrededor de la Tierra al ritmo de rotación de ésta. (pág. 568)

geothermal energy/energía geotérmica Energía del calor del interior de la Tierra traída por el agua o el vapor que ha sido calentado por el magma. (págs. 303, 382)

gestation period/período de gestación Lapso de tiempo transcurrido entre la fecundación y el nacimiento de un mamífero. (pág. 254)

geyser/géiser Tipo de manantial termal que, debido a que aumenta la presión subterránea, arroja de forma intermitente un surtidor de agua y vapor. (pág. 382)

gill/branquia Órgano respiratorio de ciertos organismos que extrae oxígeno del agua. (pág. 228)

gizzard/molleja Parte musculosa y de paredes gruesas del estómago de las aves donde se estrujan y trituran los alimentos parcialmente digeridos. (pág. 248)

global winds/vientos globales Vientos constantes que soplan desde direcciones específicas a través de largas distancias. (pág. 477)

Golgi body/aparato de Golgi Estructura celular que recibe del retículo endoplásmico proteínas y otras sustancias recién formadas, las empaqueta y las distribuye a otras partes de la célula. (pág. 144)

grain/grano Partícula de un mineral u otra roca que caracteriza su textura. (pág. 341)

graph/gráfica Diagrama que muestra la relación entre dos variables. (pág. 68)

gravity/gravedad Fuerza que atrae objetos entre sí. (pág. 535)

greenhouse effect/efecto invernadero Proceso mediante el cual el calor es atrapado en la atmósfera por el vapor de agua, el dióxido de carbono, el metano y otros gases que forman un "cobertor" alrededor de la Tierra. (págs. 465, 548)

habitat/hábitat Lugar donde vive un organismo y que le proporciona lo que necesita para sobrevivir. (pág. 267)

hanging wall/labio superior Bloque rocoso que compone la mitad superior de una falla. (pág. 360)

headwaters/cabecera Conjunto de los numerosos y pequeños cursos de agua que confluyen en el nacimiento de un río. (pág. 109)

heat/calor Desplazamiento de energía térmica de una sustancia a otra. (pág. 469)

heliocentric system/sistema heliocéntrico Descripción del sistema solar en la que todos los planetas giran alrededor del Sol. (pág. 534)

herbivore/herbívoro Animal que se alimenta sólo de plantas. (pág. 219)

heredity/herencia Transmisión de rasgos de padres a hijos. (pág. 149)

heterotroph/heterótrofo Organismo incapaz de sintetizar su propio alimento. (pág. 128)

homeostasis/homeostasis Proceso mediante el cual el entorno interno del organismo se mantiene estable a pesar de los cambios producidos en el ambiente externo. (pág. 129)

hormone/hormona Producto químico de una glándula endocrina que acelera o desacelera las actividades de un órgano o tejido; también, sustancia química que afecta al crecimiento y desarrollo de las plantas. (pág. 210)

host/huésped Organismo que proporciona una fuente de energía o un ambiente adecuado para la vida de un virus u otro organismo. (pág. 199)

humidity/humedad Medida de la cantidad de vapor de agua presente en el aire. (pág. 482)

hurricane/huracán Tormenta tropical con vientos mínimos de 119 kilómetros por hora y generalmente de unos 600 kilómetros de diámetro. (pág. 508)

hydrocarbon/hidrocarburo Compuesto que contiene átomos de carbono y de hidrógeno. (pág. 295)

hydroelectric power/energía hidroeléctrica Electricidad producida por el movimiento del agua al descender por una cascada o presa. (pág. 302)

hypothesis/hipótesis Explicación posible a una serie de observaciones o respuesta a una pregunta científica; capaz de ser verificada. (pág. 12)

igneous rock/roca ígnea Tipo de roca que se forma al enfriarse las rocas fundidas en o debajo de la superficie terrestre. (pág. 342)

immigration/inmigración Traslado a una población. (pág. 276)

impermeable/impermeable Característica del material que no puede ser atravesado fácilmente por el agua, como la arcilla o el granito. (pág. 413)

inertia/inercia Tendencia de un objeto en movimiento a avanzar en línea recta o de un objeto estacionario a quedarse en el mismo sitio. (pág. 535)

inexhaustible resource/recurso inagotable Cualquier cosa viva o no del medio ambiente que no puede agotarse. (pág. 299)

inference/inferencia Interpretación de una observación basándose en evidencias y conocimientos previos. (pág. 11)

infrared radiation/radiación infrarroja Forma de energía cuya longitud de onda es mayor que la de la luz visible. (pág. 463)

inner core/núcleo interior Densa esfera de hierro y níquel sólidos del centro de la Tierra. (pág. 328)

insect/insecto Artrópodo cuyo cuerpo tiene tres secciones, seis patas, un par de antenas y normalmente uno o dos pares de alas. (pág. 232)

insulation/aislante Material de construcción que impide la transferencia de calor entre el aire interior y el exterior. (pág. 315)

internal stimulus/estímulo interno Cambio producido en el interior de un organismo, como el hambre o la sed, que le provoca una reacción. (pág. 124)

International System of Units/Sistema Internacional de Unidades Sistema de medidas basado en múltiplos de diez y en medidas establecidas de masa, longitud y tiempo. (pág. 35)

interphase/interfase Etapa del ciclo celular que ocurre antes de la división; en ella, la célula crece, copia el ADN y se prepara para dividirse. (pág. 171)

intrusive rock/roca intrusiva Roca ígnea que se forma al solidificarse el magma bajo la superficie terrestre. (pág. 342)

invertebrate/invertebrado Animal sin columna vertebral. (pág. 220)

ionosphere/ionosfera Parte inferior de la termosfera donde se encuentran partículas cargadas eléctricamente llamadas iones. (pág. 456)

irrigation/riego Proceso de suministrar agua a la tierra para que sea apta para el cultivo agrícola. (pág. 400)

isobars/isobaras Líneas que unen en un mapa los lugares que tienen igual presión atmosférica. (pág. 522)

isotherms/isotermas Líneas que unen en un mapa los lugares que tienen igual temperatura. (pág. 522)

jet streams/corrientes de chorro Bandas de vientos de alta velocidad a unos 10 kilómetros de la superficie terrestre. (pág. 480)

kidney/riñón Órgano principal del aparato excretor; elimina del cuerpo la urea, el exceso de agua y algunos otros materiales de desecho. (pág. 243)

land breeze/brisa terrestre Corriente de aire que va desde la tierra hasta una masa de agua. (pág. 476)

larva/larva Forma inmadura de un animal de aspecto muy distinto al del adulto. (pág. 232)

latitude/latitud Distancia expresada en grados al norte o al sur del ecuador. (pág. 478)

lava/lava Magma que llega a la superficie; también, rocas formadas al solidificarse la lava líquida. (pág. 336)

lava flow/colada de lava Zona que cubre la lava al salir de la boca de un volcán. (pág. 375)

leaf/hoja Órgano de las plantas vasculares donde se realiza la fotosíntesis. (pág. 205)

levee/dique Muro alargado formado por los sedimentos depositados junto al cauce de un río. (págs. 112, 407)

lightning/rayo Chispa repentina o descarga de energía provocada por cargas eléctricas que saltan entre distintas partes de una nube o entre una nube y la tierra. (pág. 504)

limiting factor/factor limitante Elemento ambiental que impide el crecimiento de una población. (pág. 277)

linear/lineal Término empleado para describir la relación entre variables cuya gráfica es una línea recta. (pág. 105)

liquid/líquido Estado de la materia que tiene su volumen definido, pero no su forma. (pág. 58)

lithosphere/litosfera Capa rígida formada por la parte superior del manto y la corteza terrestres; una de las cuatro esferas en que los científicos dividen la Tierra. (pág. 329)

local wind/viento local Viento que recorre distancias cortas. (pág. 474)

luster/brillo Forma en que un mineral refleja la luz que recibe sobre su superficie. (pág. 334)

lysosome/lisosoma Estructura celular pequeña y esférica que contiene sustancias químicas capaces de separar grandes partículas de alimento en otras más pequeñas. (pág. 145)

magma/magma Mezcla fundida de gases, agua y sustancias que forman las rocas; compone parte del manto terrestre. (pág. 336)

magma chamber/cámara magmática Cavidad del interior de un volcán donde se acumula el magma. (pág. 375)

magnification/aumento Capacidad de hacer que los objetos parezcan más grandes de lo que son. (pág. 136)

magnitude/magnitud Medida de la fuerza de un terremoto según las ondas sísmicas y los movimientos a lo largo de las fallas. (pág. 371)

mammary gland/glándula mamaria Órgano que produce la leche con la que los mamíferos alimentan a sus crías. (pág. 253)

manipulated variable/variable manipulada Único factor que un científico cambia durante un experimento; también se llama variable independiente. (pág. 12)

mantle/manto Capa de material sólido y caliente situada entre la corteza y el núcleo de la Tierra. (pág. 329)

maritime (air mass)/masa de aire marítimo Masa de aire húmedo que se forma sobre los océanos. (pág. 496)

marsupial/marsupial Mamífero cuyas crías nacen en un estado de desarrollo temprano que normalmente completan en una bolsa del cuerpo de la madre. (pág. 254)

mass/masa Medida de la cantidad de materia que hay en un objeto. (pág. 35)

matter/materia Todo lo que tiene masa y ocupa un sitio. (pág. 24)

meander/meandro Curva muy cerrada formada en el curso sinuoso de un río en la llanura aluvial. (pág. 111)

meltdown/fusión del núcleo de un reactor Estado peligroso ocasionado por el sobrecalentamiento del interior de un reactor nuclear. (pág. 309)

melting/fusión Paso de la materia del estado sólido al líquido. (pág. 75)

melting point/punto de fusión Temperatura a la cual una sustancia pasa de sólida a líquida. (pág. 58)

Mercalli scale/escala de Mercalli Escala que evalúa los terremotos según la intensidad y los daños causados. (pág. 371)

mercury barometer/barómetro de mercurio Instrumento que mide los cambios en la presión atmosférica. Consta de un tubo de cristal cerrado en uno de sus extremos y parcialmente lleno de mercurio, y en el que el extremo abierto se encuentra inmerso en un plato con mercurio. La presión atmosférica empuja al mercurio del plato, haciendo que suba por el tubo. (pág. 446)

mesosphere/mesosfera Capa intermedia de la atmósfera terrestre en la que la mayoría de los meteoroides se consumen. (pág. 452)

metamorphic rock/roca metamórfica Tipo de roca que se forma a partir de otra roca preexistente modificada por el calor, la presión o las reacciones químicas. (pág. 345)

metamorphosis/metamorfosis Proceso en el cual el cuerpo de un animal sufre cambios radicales durante su ciclo vital. (pág. 232)

meteor/meteoro Rayo de luz en el cielo, producto de la combustión de un meteoroide en la atmósfera terrestre. (pág. 565)

meteorite/meteorito Meteoroide que alcanza la superficie terrestre. (pág. 565)

meteoroid/meteoroide Pedazo de roca o polvo en el espacio. (pág. 565)

meteorologist/meteorólogo Científico que estudia las causas del estado del tiempo y trata de predecirlo. (pág. 520)

microscope/microscopio Instrumento que amplifica la imagen de objetos pequeños. (pág. 132)

mineral/mineral Sólido inorgánico de origen natural que tiene estructura de cristal y composición química definida. (pág. 331)

mitochondria/mitocondrias Estructuras celulares con forma de bastón que producen gran parte de la energía necesaria para efectuar las funciones celulares. (pág. 141)

mitosis/mitosis Etapa del ciclo celular durante la cual el núcleo se divide en dos y una copia del ADN se reparte a cada célula hija. (pág. 172)

mixture/mezcla Asociación de dos o más sustancias pero sin combinarlas químicamente. (pág. 28)

molecule/molécula Partícula formada por dos o más átomos unidos entre sí. (pág. 44)

mollusk/molusco Invertebrado de cuerpo blando y no segmentado; la mayoría se protege con conchas exteriores duras. (pág. 227)

moment magnitude scale/escala de magnitud de momento sísmico Escala que evalúa los terremotos estimando la energía total que liberan. (pág. 372)

monotreme/monotrema Mamífero que pone huevos. (pág. 254)

monsoons/monzones Brisas marinas y terrestres que soplan sobre una región extensa y cambian de dirección según las estaciones. (pág. 476)

motion/movimiento Estado en el que cambia la distancia entre un objeto y otro. (pág. 87)

mouth/desembocadura Lugar donde un río se encuentra con otra masa de agua. (pág. 111)

net force/fuerza neta Fuerza total ejercida sobre un objeto cuando se suman todas las fuerzas individuales que actúan sobre él. (pág. 99)

nitrogen fixation/fijación del nitrógeno Proceso de conversión del gas nitrógeno libre en una forma aprovechable. (pág. 285)

nonlinear/no lineal Término empleado para describir la relación entre variables cuya gráfica no es una línea recta. (pág. 105)

nonrenewable resource/recurso no renovable Recurso natural que no es reemplazado una vez utilizado. (pág. 295)

normal fault/falla normal Tipo de falla donde el labio superior se desliza hacia abajo; está provocada por la tensión de la corteza. (pág. 360)

nuclear fission/fisión nuclear División del núcleo de un átomo en dos más pequeños. (pág. 307)

nuclear fusion/fusión nuclear Unión de dos núcleos atómicos para producir uno más grande, como ocurre al unirse dos átomos de hidrógeno para formar helio, liberando energía. (págs. 310, 538)

nucleus/núcleo Centro de control que dirige las actividades de la célula y determina las características de ésta; también, parte central del átomo que contiene protones y normalmente neutrones. (págs. 140, 307)

nymph/ninfa Etapa de la metamorfosis gradual en la que el organismo normalmente se parece al insecto adulto. (pág. 232)

observation/observación Uso de al menos uno de los cinco sentidos para obtener información. (pág. 11)

occluded/ocluido Aislado o cerrado, como cuando la masa de aire cálido de un frente ocluido queda aislada de la tierra por el aire inferior más fresco. (pág. 501)

omnivore/omnívoro Animal que se alimenta tanto de plantas como de animales. (pág. 219)

organ/órgano Estructura corporal compuesta por diferentes clases de tejidos. (pág. 146)

organ system/sistema de órganos Grupo de órganos que realizan conjuntamente una función principal del cuerpo. (pág. 147)

organelle/organelo Estructura celular minúscula que efectúa una función determinada en la célula. (pág. 139)

organism/organismo Ser vivo. (pág. 122)

osmosis/ósmosis Difusión de moléculas del agua a través de una membrana selectivamente permeable. (pág. 160)

outer core/núcleo exterior Capa de hierro y níquel fundidos que rodea el núcleo interior de la Tierra. (pág. 328)

ovary/ovario Órgano del sistema reproductor femenino donde se producen los óvulos y el estrógeno; también en las plantas, estructura protectora que contiene las semillas en desarrollo. (pág. 209)

ovule/óvulo Estructura de las plantas con semillas que contiene una célula sexual femenina. (pág. 209)

oxbow lake/meandro abandonado Masa de agua aislada y de forma semilunar que permanece tras crear un río un nuevo cauce. (pág. 111)

ozone/ozono Forma de oxígeno que tiene tres átomos en cada molécula en lugar de los dos habituales. (pág. 436)

P wave/onda P Tipo de onda sísmica que comprime y expande el suelo. (pág. 369)

pahoehoe/cordada Tipo caliente y rápido de lava que al solidificarse forma tubos lisos con forma de cuerda. (pág. 378)

Pangaea/Pangea Nombre de una única masa continental que se fragmentó hace 225 millones de años, dando origen a los continentes actuales. (pág. 355)

parasite/parásito Organismo que vive en la superficie o en el interior de un huésped, provocándole daños. (pág. 199)

passive transport/transporte pasivo Movimiento de materiales a través de la membrana celular sin usar energía. (pág. 161)

permeable/permeable Característica del material que deja pasar el agua con facilidad, como la arena o la grava. (pág. 413)

pesticide/pesticida Sustancia química cuyo fin es destruir insectos y otros organismos que dañan los cultivos. (pág. 152)

petrochemical/producto petroquímico Compuesto obtenido del petróleo. (pág. 297)

petroleum/petróleo Combustible fósil líquido. (pág. 296)

photochemical smog/smog fotoquímico Bruma pardusca, mezcla de ozono y otras sustancias químicas, que se forma cuando los óxidos de nitrógeno, los hidrocarburos y otros contaminantes reaccionan entre sí en presencia de luz solar. (pág. 442)

photosphere/fotosfera Capa interior de la atmósfera del Sol. (pág. 539)

photosynthesis/fotosíntesis Proceso por el cual las plantas y algunos otros organismos atrapan la energía luminosa y la utilizan para elaborar su alimento a partir del dióxido de carbono y del agua. (pág. 163)

physical change/cambio físico Cambio que altera la forma o el aspecto de un material, pero sin transformarlo en otra sustancia. (pág. 30)

physical property/propiedad física Característica de un material que puede observarse sin necesidad de transformarlo en otra sustancia. (pág. 26)

pipe/chimenea Tubo alargado por el que se desplaza el magma desde la cámara magmática hasta la superficie terrestre. (pág. 375)

placenta/placenta Órgano que representa el nexo entre el embrión o feto en desarrollo y la madre. (pág. 255)

placental mammal/mamífero placentario Mamífero que se desarrolla en el cuerpo de la madre hasta que sus sistemas corporales pueden funcionar independientemente. (pág. 255)

plate/placa Sección de la litosfera que se desplaza lentamente, llevando consigo fragmentos de la corteza continental y oceánica. (pág. 354)

plate boundary/borde de placas Grieta en la litosfera donde dos placas terrestres se cruzan. (pág. 356)

plateau/meseta Forma del relieve que tiene una superficie bastante llana y se encuentra muy por encima del nivel del mar. (pág. 365)

polar (air mass)/masa de aire polar Masa de aire frío de alta presión atmosférica que se forma al norte de los 50° de latitud norte o al sur de los 50° de latitud sur. (pág. 496)

pollen/polen Partículas diminutas producidas por las plantas y que contienen las células microscópicas que posteriormente se convierten en células sexuales masculinas. (pág. 209)

pollutant/contaminante Sustancia dañina del aire, agua o suelo. (pág. 440)

population/población Todos los miembros de una especie de una zona determinada. (pág. 269)

population density/densidad de población Número de individuos que habitan un lugar específico. (pág. 273)

pores/poros Aberturas diminutas en o entre las partículas de roca y tierra que pueden contener aire o agua. (pág. 413)

precipitation/precipitación Formas del agua como lluvia, nieve, aguanieve o granizo que proceden de las nubes y llegan a la superficie terrestre. (págs. 398, 487)

predator/depredador Carnívoro que caza y mata otros animales para alimentarse de ellos y que cuenta con adaptaciones que le ayudan a capturar sus presas. (pág. 219)

pressure/presión Fuerza que se ejerce sobre una zona o superficie; también, fuerza del empuje de un gas hacia el exterior dividida entre el área de las paredes del recipiente. (págs. 63, 445)

prey/presa Animal del que se alimenta un depredador. (pág. 219)

prime meridian/primer meridiano Línea que traza un medio círculo desde el polo norte al polo sur pasando por Greenwich, Inglaterra. (pág. 591)

producer/productor Organismo que puede elaborar su propio alimento. (pág. 281)

prokaryote/procariota Organismo cuyas células carecen de núcleo y de otras estructuras. (pág. 145)

prominence/protuberancia Arco de gas que sobresale de la superficie solar, enlazando diferentes zonas de las regiones con manchas solares. (pág. 542)

protozoan/protozoario Protista con características animales. (pág. 197)

pseudopod/pseudópodo "Pie falso" o proyección temporal de la membrana celular que emplean algunos protozoarios para desplazarse y alimentarse. (pág. 197)

psychrometer/psicrómetro Instrumento usado para medir la humedad relativa; consta de un termómetro de cubeta húmeda y otro de cubeta seca. (pág. 482)

pupa/pupa Segunda etapa de la metamorfosis completa en la que el insecto, envuelto en una cubierta protectora, se transforma gradualmente de larva en adulto. (pág. 232)

pyroclastic flow/flujo piroclástico Expulsión de cenizas, escorias, bombas y gases durante una erupción volcánica explosiva. (pág. 379)

radial symmetry/simetría radial Cualidad de poseer muchos ejes de simetría que pasan por un punto central. (pág. 221)

radiation/radiación Transferencia directa de energía por medio de ondas electromagnéticas. (pág. 462)

radula/rádula Cinta flexible de dientes minúsculos de los moluscos. (pág. 228)

rain gauge/pluviómetro Instrumento usado para medir la cantidad de precipitaciones; consta de una lata que tiene en su extremo abierto un embudo colector y en su interior un tubo de acumulación y una escala medidora. (pág. 489)

reactor vessel/nave del reactor Parte del reactor nuclear donde tiene lugar la fisión. (pág. 308)

recharge/recarga Nueva aportación de agua que recibe el acuífero desde la superficie. (pág. 415)

reference point/punto de referencia Objeto o lugar que se usa como punto de comparación para determinar si un objeto está en movimiento. (pág. 88)

refinery/refinería Planta donde el petróleo bruto se separa en combustibles y otros productos. (pág. 297)

relative humidity/humedad relativa Porcentaje de vapor de agua que hay en el aire frente a la cantidad máxima que éste puede contener a esa temperatura. (pág. 482)

renewable resource/recurso renovable Recurso restituido de manera natural en un período de tiempo relativamente corto. (pág. 299)

replication/replicación Proceso por el cual una célula hace una copia del ADN de su núcleo. (pág. 171)

reproduce/reproducir Procrear descendientes parecidos a los progenitores. (pág. 125)

reserve/reserva Depósito conocido de combustibles. (pág. 298)

reservoir/embalse Lago natural o artificial donde se almacena agua para el aprovechamiento humano. (pág. 410)

resolution/resolución Capacidad de diferenciar con claridad cada una de las partes de un objeto. (pág. 137)

respiration/respiración Proceso por el cual las células degradan las moléculas simples de los alimentos para liberar la energía que contienen. (pág. 166)

responding variable/variable de respuesta Factor que se altera como resultado de los cambios producidos en la variable manipulada de un experimento. (pág. 12)

response/respuesta Acto o cambio de conducta que siguen a un estímulo. (pág. 125)

retrograde rotation/rotación retrógrada Movimiento giratorio de un planeta de este a oeste, en sentido opuesto al de la rotación de la mayoría de los planetas y las lunas. (pág. 547)

reverse fault/falla inversa Tipo de falla donde el labio superior se desliza hacia arriba; está provocada por la compresión de la corteza. (pág. 361)

revolution/revolución Movimiento de un objeto alrededor de otro. (pág. 544)

ribosome/ribosoma Estructura diminuta del citoplasma celular en la que se elaboran las proteínas. (pág. 144)

Richter scale/escala de Richter Escala que evalúa las ondas sísmicas según las mediciones de un sismógrafo mecánico. (pág. 371)

river/río Corriente grande de agua. (pág. 404)

rock/roca Material que forma la superficie dura de la Tierra. (págs. 326, 340)

rock cycle/ciclo de las rocas Serie de procesos ocurridos en la superficie y en el interior de la Tierra que transforman lentamente rocas de una clase en otra. (pág. 346)

root/raíz Parte vegetal subterránea que fija las plantas al suelo y absorbe agua y nutrientes de éste. (pág. 208)

rotation/rotación Movimiento giratorio de un planeta alrededor de su eje. (pág. 544)

⸺⸺ Ⓢ ⸺⸺

S waves/ondas S Tipo de ondas sísmicas que mueven el suelo de arriba a abajo y de un lado a otro. (pág. 369)

satellite/satélite Cualquier objeto que gira alrededor de otro en el espacio. (pág. 567)

saturated zone/zona saturada Capa de roca o tierra permeables en la que las grietas y los poros están totalmente llenos de agua. (pág. 413)

scale/escala Relaciona la distancia en el mapa con la correspondiente de la superficie terrestre. (pág. 590)

scattering/dispersión Reflexión de la luz en todas las direcciones. (pág. 464)

science/ciencia Estudio del mundo natural. (pág. 10)

scientific inquiry/investigación científica Diversidad de métodos con los que los científicos estudian el mundo natural. (pág. 10)

scientific law/ley científica Afirmación que describe lo que los científicos esperan que ocurra cada vez que se dan una serie determinada de condiciones. (pág. 16)

scientific theory/teoría científica Concepto científico comprobado que explica una gran variedad de observaciones. (pág. 16)

sea breeze/brisa marina Corriente de aire que va desde un océano o lago hasta la tierra. (pág. 476)

sediment/sedimentos Partículas sólidas y pequeñas de material procedente de rocas u organismos que son trasladadas por el agua o el viento, dando origen a la erosión y la sedimentación. (págs. 108, 343)

sedimentary rock/roca sedimentaria Tipo de roca que se forma cuando las partículas de otras rocas o los restos vegetales y animales se comprimen y cementan entre sí. (pág. 343)

seed/semilla Estructura vegetal que contiene una planta en desarrollo envuelta en una cubierta protectora. (pág. 208)

seismic wave/onda sísmica Vibración que se propaga por la Tierra llevando consigo la energía liberada durante un terremoto. (págs. 327, 368)

seismograph/sismógrafo Aparato que registra los movimientos que producen en el suelo las ondas sísmicas al desplazarse por la Tierra. (pág. 370)

selective breeding/apareamiento dirigido Proceso de seleccionar algunos organismos con rasgos deseables para usarlos como progenitores de la siguiente generación. (pág. 151)

selectively permeable/selectivamente permeable Propiedad de la membrana celular que permite el paso de ciertas sustancias e impide el paso de otras. (pág. 158)

sexual reproduction/reproducción sexual Proceso en el que se combina el material genético de dos progenitores para originar un nuevo organismo diferente a ambos. (pág. 150)

shearing/cizallamiento Tipo de esfuerzo que empuja una masa rocosa en sentidos opuestos. (pág. 359)

shield volcano/volcán en escudo Montaña ancha, de pendiente suave y compuesta por capas de lava procedentes de erupciones no explosivas. (pág. 388)

silica/sílice Material compuesto de dos elementos, silicio y oxígeno; se encuentra en el magma. (pág. 377)

sill/reborde Bloque de rocas volcánicas que se forma al introducirse el magma entre las capas rocosas. (pág. 387)

solar energy/energía solar Energía del Sol. (pág. 299)

solar flare/erupción solar Explosión de gas hidrógeno de la superficie del Sol que ocurre al unirse repentinamente arcos de las regiones con manchas solares. (pág. 542)

solar system/sistema solar Gran sistema planetario que consta de la combinación de muchos objetos y sistemas planetarios más pequeños. (pág. 534)

solar wind/viento solar Corriente de partículas cargadas eléctricamente, producida por la corona del Sol. (pág. 540)

solid/sólido Estado de la materia que tiene volumen y forma definidos. (pág. 57)

species/especie Grupo de organismos parecidos cuyos miembros pueden aparearse entre sí y tener descendencia fértil. (pág. 185)

speed/rapidez Distancia que recorre un objeto durante una unidad de tiempo. (pág. 90)

sperm cell/espermatozoide Célula sexual masculina. (pág. 150)

spontaneous generation/generación espontánea Idea errónea de que los seres vivos surgen de fuentes no vivientes. (pág. 125)

spore/espora Célula diminuta capaz de crecer y convertirse en un nuevo organismo. (pág. 201)

spring/manantial Lugar donde el agua subterránea sale a borbotones o emana por las grietas de las rocas. (pág. 414)

stamen/estambre Parte reproductora masculina de las flores. (pág. 209)

stem/tallo Órgano que sostiene las plantas y une las raíces a las hojas. (pág. 208)

stimulus/estímulo Cambio en el entorno del organismo que le hace reaccionar. (pág. 124)

stomata/estomas Pequeños orificios en el envés de la mayoría de las hojas a través de los cuales pueden pasar el oxígeno y el dióxido de carbono. (pág. 205)

storm/tormenta Violenta alteración en la atmósfera. (pág. 503)

storm surge/marejada de tormenta "Bóveda" de agua que se desplaza por la costa donde toca tierra el huracán. (pág. 510)

stratosphere/estratosfera Segunda capa inferior de la atmósfera terrestre; la capa de ozono se encuentra en la estratosfera superior. (pág. 452)

stratus/estratos Nubes en forma de capas planas. (pág. 484)

streak/raya Se aplica al color del polvo de un mineral. (pág. 334)

stress/tensión Fuerza que hace que una roca cambie de forma o volumen. (pág. 358)

strike-slip fault/falla transcurrente Tipo de falla donde las rocas de cada lado se desplazan en sentido horizontal, sin apenas movimientos verticales. (pág. 360)

sublimation/sublimación Cambio del estado sólido directamente al gaseoso, sin pasar por el estado líquido. (pág. 78)

substance/sustancia El tipo de materia que presenta propiedades físicas y químicas concretas. (pág. 25)

sunspot/mancha solar Región oscura y menos caliente de la superficie del Sol. (pág. 540)

surface waves/ondas superficiales Tipo de ondas sísmicas que se forman cuando las ondas P y S llegan a la superficie terrestre. (pág. 370)

syncline/sinclinal Pliegue hacia abajo de las rocas debido a la compresión de la corteza terrestre. (pág. 364)

taxonomy/taxonomía Estudio científico de la clasificación de los seres vivos. (pág. 185)

temperature/temperatura Cantidad media de energía de movimiento que hay en las moléculas de una sustancia. (págs. 62, 469)

temperature inversion/inversión térmica Fenómeno que ocurre cuando una capa de aire templado queda atrapada entre dos capas de aire frío, impidiendo que escape el aire cercano a la Tierra. (pág. 442)

tension/tensión Tipo de esfuerzo que estira las rocas de modo que se alarguen en el centro. (pág. 359)

terrestrial planets/planetas telúricos Nombre que se les da a los cuatro planetas interiores: Mercurio, Venus, Tierra y Marte. (pág. 544)

texture/textura Tamaño, forma y patrón de los granos de una roca. (pág. 341)

Theory of Plate Tectonics/Teoría de la tectónica de placas Teoría que expone que los fragmentos de la litosfera terrestre se desplazan de forma constante, impulsados por las corrientes de convección del manto. (pág. 356)

thermal energy/energía térmica Energía total de las partículas de una sustancia debida a sus movimientos o vibraciones; también, energía del movimiento de las moléculas de una sustancia. (págs. 74, 469)

thermometer/termómetro Instrumento usado para medir la temperatura; consta de un delgado tubo de vidrio que tiene en uno de sus extremos una cubeta de líquido, el cual suele ser mercurio o alcohol. (pág. 469)

thermosphere/termosfera Capa exterior de la atmósfera terrestre. (pág. 455)

thorax/tórax Sección media de un insecto a la cual están sujetas las alas y las patas. (pág. 232)

tissue/tejido Grupo de células similares que desempeñan una función determinada en un organismo. (pág. 146)

tornado/tornado Nube con forma de embudo que girando velozmente sale de una nube de tormenta y toca la superficie terrestre, produciendo por lo general una trayectoria destructiva. (pág. 505)

trait/rasgo Característica que un organismo puede transmitir a través de sus genes a su descendencia. (pág. 149)

transpiration/transpiración Proceso por el cual se libera agua a través de las hojas de las plantas. (pág. 398)

tributary/tributario Corriente o río pequeño que desemboca en otra corriente más grande. (pág. 404)

tropical (air mass)/masa de aire tropical Masa de aire templado de baja presión atmosférica que se forma en los trópicos. (pág. 496)

tropism/tropismo Respuesta de crecimiento de las plantas, dirigiéndose hacia un estímulo o alejándose de él. (pág. 210)

troposphere/troposfera Capa inferior de la atmósfera terrestre; zona donde se producen los cambios de tiempo. (pág. 451)

ultraviolet radiation/radiación ultravioleta Forma de energía cuya longitud de onda es más corta que la de la luz visible. (pág. 463)

unbalanced force/fuerza desequilibrada Fuerza neta distinta a cero que cambia el movimiento de un objeto. (pág. 99)

unsaturated zone/zona no saturada Capa de rocas y tierra situada por encima del nivel freático en la que los poros contienen tanto aire como agua. (pág. 413)

vacuole/vacuola Bolsa llena de agua del interior de las células que hace de zona de almacenamiento. (pág. 145)

vaporization/vaporización Paso de la materia del estado líquido al gaseoso. (pág. 76)

vary inversely/varían inversamente Término empleado para describir la relación entre dos variables cuya gráfica forma una curva que se inclina hacia abajo y de izquierda a derecha. (pág. 71)

vascular tissue/tejido vascular En algunas plantas, tejido interno compuesto por estructuras tubulares y dedicado al transporte. (pág. 205)

vein/vena Filón de metal que se forma a partir de una solución subterránea; tambien un vaso sanguíneo por donde vuelve la sangre al corazón. (pág. 336)

velocity/velocidad Rapidez en una dirección dada. (pág. 93)

vent/boca Abertura por donde las rocas fundidas y el gas salen del volcán. (pág. 375)

ventricle/ventrículo Cavidad inferior del corazón que bombea sangre a los pulmones y al resto del cuerpo. (pág. 241)

vertebrae/vértebras Huesos que forman la columna vertebral de los animales. (pág. 237)

vertebrate/vertebrado Animal que tiene columna vertebral. (pág. 220)

viscosity/viscosidad Resistencia de un líquido a fluir. (pág. 59)

volcanic neck/cuello volcánico Depósito de magma solidificado en la chimenea de un volcán. (pág. 387)

volume/volumen Cantidad de espacio que ocupa la materia. (pág. 35)

water cycle/ciclo del agua Proceso constante mediante el cual el agua va de la superficie terrestre a la atmósfera y después regresa al suelo, pasando por los componentes vivos o no del medio ambiente. (pág. 398)

water pollution/contaminación del agua Incorporación al agua de cualquier sustancia que tenga efectos negativos para ella o para los seres vivos que de ella dependen. (pág. 298)

water table/nivel freático Parte superior de la zona saturada, o profundidad a la que está el agua subterránea en un acuífero. (pág. 413)

water vapor/vapor de agua Forma gaseosa e invisible del agua. (pág. 437)

watershed/cuenca hidrográfica Extensión de tierra que suministra el agua a un sistema fluvial. (pág. 405)

weather/tiempo Estado de la atmósfera terrestre en un lugar y momento determinados. (pág. 434)

weight/peso Medida de la fuerza de gravedad ejercida sobre un objeto. (pág. 35)

wind/viento Movimiento horizontal del aire desde una zona de presión alta a otra de presión baja. (pág. 472)

wind-chill factor/factor de enfriamiento por viento Incremento del frío causado por el viento. (pág. 473)

zygote/cigoto Óvulo fecundado tras la unión de una célula sexual masculina y otra femenina. (pág. 208)

Index

Index

fuels 293, 295–298
  biomass, 303
  fossil, 295–298, 313, 441, 442
Fuji, Mt. 386
function. *See* structure and function
fungi 189, 201–203
fungus-like protists 201
fur 251
fusion, nuclear 310–311, 538–539

Gagarin, Yuri 567
Galileo Galilei 534, 537, 554, 555
Galileo (spacecraft), 552
Ganymede 554, 555
gas(es) 59–60
  in atmosphere, 435–437
  change of state between liquids and, 76–77, 78
  change of state between solids and, 78–79
  measuring, 62–63
  trace, 437
gas behavior 61–73
  graphing, 68–71
  pressure and temperature, relating, 64–65
  pressure and volume, relating, 63–64, 70–71
  volume and temperature, relating, 66–67, 69–70
gas giants 552–558
gasohol 303
Gay-Lussac, Joseph-Louis 454
gemstone 336
generalizations, making 587
genes, role in inheritance of 150
genetic engineering 260–263
genetic material 123, 141, 149–152, 171
  in bacterial cell, 145, 190, 191, 192
  DNA, 150, 175, 186, 262
genetics 149–152
genus 185, 186
geocentric system 533, 534
geologists 327
geology 327
geosynchronous orbits 568
geothermal energy 303, 382
gestation period 254
geyser 382
gills 228, 238–239, 240
gizzard 249
glaciers 11–15, 411
Global Positioning Satellites 568
global wind belts 478–480, 499
global winds 477, 479
glucose 164, 165, 166
gneiss 345
Goddard, Robert H. 567
Golgi body 143, 144
gradual metamorphosis 233, 234
graduated cylinder 37, 40, 169, 397, 582
grain of rock 341
gram (g), 35, 583
granite 342, 345, 346

graph(s) 68
  axes of, 69–70
  bar, 594
  circle, 596
  line, 595
  motion, 94, 95
graphic organizers 588–589
gravity or gravitational force 101
  orbit of planets and, 535, 536
  responses of organisms to, 210, 212
  weight and, 35
greenhouse effect 465, 548
groundwater 397, 412–417
  brought to surface, 414–415
  relationship to surface water, 397, 398, 407, 414, 415, 424–425
  underground layers of rock and, 412–414
growth 124
  in cell cycle, 171
  plant, 210
guanine 176
gymnosperms 207, 209
gypsum 337

habitats 267
  lake, 410–411
  pond, 408–409
hail 488
hair 251
Halley, Edmond 563
hanging wall 360, 361, 363
hardness of mineral 333
headwaters 109, 110
heat 32, 294, 469. *See also* thermal energy
  solar heating system, 301
  transformation of electrical energy to, 33, 292
  transformation to electrical energy, 308–309
heat exchanger 309
heat transfer 469–471
heliocentric system 534
herbivores 219, 281
heredity 149–152
Herschel, William 557
heterotrophs 128, 163, 165, 188, 189, 191, 197, 201, 218, 219, 280, 281
homeostasis 129
Hooke, Robert 132, 134
hormones 210
horse latitudes 478, 479
host 199
hot plate 468
hot spring 382
humidity 482–483, 496
hunger, responses of organisms to 218, 248
hurricanes 508–510, 512–514
hydrocarbons 295, 442
hydroelectric power 302
hydroelectric power plants 302, 304, 306
hydrogen power 304
hyphae 202
hypothesis 12, 584

ice 397
icebergs 411, 427
igneous rock 342, 346, 347
illustrations, interpreting 586
immigration 276
index contour 592, 593
indirect observation 274
inequalities 276
inertia 535, 536
inexhaustible resource 299, 304
inference 11, 253, 580
infrared radiation 463, 465, 469
inner core 328, 329, 545
inner planets 544–551
  Earth, 544–545
  Mars, 549–551
  Mercury, 546
  Venus, 547–549
insects 232–234
insulation 256, 315
  fiberglass, 314, 315
  in mammals, 251
insulin 261, 262–263
interactions between matter and energy
  compost bins, 286
  decay of biomass, 286
  water cycle, 398–399
internal stimuli 124
  hormones, 210
  hunger, 218, 248
  responses of organisms to, 124, 125, 210, 218, 248
  thirst, 125, 218
International System of Units (SI), 13, 35, 89, 582
  converting SI units, 89, 583
Internet 19, 581
interphase 171–172, 174
interstate highway system 93
intrusive rock 342
inversely varied relationship 71
invertebrates 220
Io 554, 555
ionosphere 453, 456
ions 456
irrigation 400, 401, 426, 428
isobars 522
isotherms 522

Janssen, Hans 134
jawless fishes 239
jet streams 480
judgments, making 587
Jupiter 554–555

Kepler, Johannes 535
kidneys 243
kilogram (kg), 35
kilopascals (kPa), 63
kingdom (level of classification), 186, 188–189

Index

Index

Acknowledgments

Staff Credits

The people who made up the *Texas Science Explorer* team—representing design services, editorial, editorial services, electronic publishing technology, manufacturing & inventory planning, market research, marketing services, online services & multimedia development, planning & budgeting, product planning, production services, project office, and publishing processes—are listed below. Bold type denotes the core team members.

Scott Andrews, **Carolyn Belanger,** Barbara A. Bertell, Suzanne Biron, **Peggy Bliss,** Kristen Braghi, Dan Breslin, Jonathan Cheney, **Lisa J. Clark,** Robin Clark, Ed Cordero, Bob Craton, Christine Cuccio, **Patricia Cully,** Gabriella Della Corte, Kathleen J. Dempsey, Emily Ellen, Barnard Gage, Jane P. Gardner, **Julie Gecha,** Adam Goldberg, Kerri Hoar, Joanne Hudson, Alan Hull, Anne Jones, Toby Klang, Carolyn Langley, Carolyn Lock, Diahanne Lucas, Don Manning, Jeanne Y. Maurand, **Tim McDonald,** Carolyn McGuire, Karen McHugh, Natania Mlawer, Paul Murphy, Judi Pinkham, **Robin L. Santel,** Suzanne Schineller, **Diane Walsh,** Jane Willan, Pat Williams, Char Lyn Yeakley, Helen Young

Illustrations

AccuWeather: 524, 525
Sally Bensusen: 233
Suzanne Biron: 130, 148
Peter Brooks: 35, 48, 72, 80, 431, 543, 560
Patrice Rossi Calkin: 111, 198, 199, 244
Warren Cutler: 249, 408–409, 420–421
Kathleen Dempsey: 366, 384
John Edwards & Associates: 205, 283, 284, 293, 301, 303, 309, 329, 356–357, 450, 464, 476, 501, 509, 536, 545, 553
Julia Gecha: 526
Andrea Golden: 229, 403, 414
Biruta Hansen: 270
Keith Kasnot: 141, 142, 143, 144, 200
MapQuest.com, Inc.: 321, 355, 362, 373, 405, 422, 508, 511, 512, 523
Martucci Studio: 68, 69, 70, 71, 78, 94, 105, 166, 313, 397, 435, 463, 523, 543
Matt Mayerchak: 51, 113, 153, 174, 429, 457
Fran Milner: 147, 232, 240, 242
Morgan Cain & Associates: 49, 57, 57, 58, 60, 63, 64, 69, 70, 123, 126, 127, 136, 155, 159, 161, 169, 174, 215, 256, 262, 289, 294, 297, 308, 310, 312, 343, 364, 369, 370, 376, 387, 389, 425, 442, 446, 447, 448, 459, 465, 468, 470, 474, 477, 479, 487, 489, 493, 541, 545, 563, 566, 567, 573, 600–601
Ortelius Design Inc.: 3, 7, 36, 37, 355, 380, 381, 400, 401, 428, 437, 476, 502, 506, 507, 529, 606
Matthew Pippin: 110, 302, 369, 399, 413, 431, 446, 453, 481, 485, 516
John Sanderson: 498
Walter Stuart: 202
Cynthia Turner: 208
Roberta Warshaw: 40, 171, 285, 287, 349, 601tr
J/B Woolsey Associates: 53, 117, 119, 124, 164, 200, 209, 212, 215, 226, 231, 239, 241, 248, 276, 285, 332, 351, 393, 484, 517, 600–601

Photography

Cover Design: Studio Montage

Cover Image: NASA

Front Matter
Page i, NASA; **ii,** NASA; **iii l,** Courtesy of Michael J. Padilla, Ph.D; **iii r,** Courtesy of Martha Cyr, Ph.D. and Ioannis Miaoulis, Ph.D; **viii t,** Ken Lucas/Visuals Unlimited; **viii b,** John Kelly/Image Bank; **ix l,** M. Abbey/Visuals Unlimited; **ix m,** Dr. David Scott/CNRI/Phototake; **ix r,** Dr. Dennis Kunkel/Phototake; **x t,** Bas van Beek/Leo de Wys; **x m,** Patti Murray/Animals Animals; **x b,** Stone/Richard A Cooke III; **xi t,** Superstock; **xi top inset,** Wernher Krutein/Liaison Agency; **xi bl,** Ralph A. Clevenger/Corbis Westlight; **xi bm,** Calvin Larsen/Photo Researchers, Inc.; **xi br,** Tim Olive/SharpShooters; **xii t,** Biophoto Associates/Photo Researchers, Inc.; **xii bl,** NASA/Photo Researchers, Inc.; **xii br,** Steve Vidler/Superstock; **xiii tl,** Dan Sudia/Photo Researchers, Inc.; **xiii tr,** NASA Goddard Laboratory for Atmospheres; **xiii bl,** Russ Lappa; **xiii br,** NOAA; **xiv t,** Richard Haynes; **xiv m,** Renee Lynn/Photo Researchers; **xiv b,** Paul Rezendes; **xv t,** Richard Haynes; **xv b,** Superstock; **xvi t,** A. T. Willet/Image Bank; **xvi b,** Doug Martin/Photo Researchers, Inc.; **xvii t,** Robert Maier/Animals Animals; **xvii b,** Richard Haynes; **xviii t,** NASA; **xviii b,** Stone/Mark Lewis; **xix l,** Norbert Rosing/Animals Animals/Earth Scenes; **xix r,** PhotoDisc, Inc.; **xx tl,** Richard Megna/Fundamental Photographs; **xx tml,** Goivaux Communication/Phototake; **xx tmr,** Charles D. Winters/Photo Researchers, Inc.; **xx tr,** Ken Lucas/Visuals Unlimited; **xx bl,** Marc Romanelli/Image Bank; **xx br,** Tim DeFrisco/Allsport; **xxi,** Richard Haynes.

Texas Field Trip
Pages 2 tl, Courtesy of Rosenberg Library, Galveston, Texas; **2 tr,** National Oceanic and Atmospheric Administration/Department of Commerce; **2 bl, 2 br,** Courtesy of Rosenberg Library, Galveston, Texas; **2–3,** NOAA/Science Photo Library/Photo Researchers; **3 t,** Mark Perlstein/Black Star; **4 l,** National Oceanic and Atmospheric Administration/Department of Commerce; **4 m,** Gamma Liaison; **4 r,** AP Photo/David J. Phillip; **5 both,** Courtesy of Wind Engineering Research Center, Texas Tech University.

Nature of Science
Page 6 m, Courtesy of Wind Engineering Research Center, Texas Tech University; **6–7,** Annie Griffiths Belt/National Geographic; **7 t, 7 b, 8, 9 all,** Courtesy of Wind Engineering Research Center, Texas Tech University.

What Is Science?
Page 10 t, Stone/Dave Bjorn; **10 b,** Nancy Sheehan Photography; **11,** Manfred Gottschalk/Tom Stack & Associates; **15,** Tsado/NCDC/NOAA/Tom Stack & Associates; **16, 17,** Richard Haynes; **18 l,** Paula Lerner/Index Stock Imagery; **18 r,** Peter Menzel/Stock Boston; **19 t,** Frank Pederick/The Image Works; **19 b,** Kim Steele/PhotoDisc; **20,** Tsado/NCDC/NOAA/Tom Stack & Associates.

Chapter 1
Pages 22–23, Superstock; **24 both,** Russ Lappa; **25,** Thomas H. Ives/The Stock Market; **26,** PhotoDisc, Inc.; **27 l,** Stone/Cathlyn Melloan; **27 m,** Bernard Roussel/The Image Bank; **27 r,** Bob Firth/International Stock; **28 l,** Ken Lucas/Visuals Unlimited; **28 r,** Yoav Levy/Phototake; **29 t,** David D. Keaton/The Stock Market; **29 tl,** Michael Fogden/DRK Photo; **29 tr,** Glenn M. Oliver/Visuals Unlimited; **29 bl,** Richard Megna/Fundamental Photographs; **29 bml,** Goivaux Communication/PhotoTake; **29 bmr,** Charles D. Winters/Photo Researchers, Inc.; **29 br,** Ken Lucas/Visuals Unlimited; **30 t,** Micheal P Gadomski/Photo Researchers, Inc.; **30 b,** Stone/Lawrence Migdale; **31,** John M. Roberts/The Stock Market; **32,** Stone/Alan R Moller; **33 t,** James Dwyer/Stock Boston; **33 b,** Tony Freeman/PhotoEdit; **34 t,** Richard Haynes; **34 b,** SuperStock; **35 l,** Russ Lappa; **35 r,** Richard Haynes; **36, 37 t,** Corbis-Bettmann; **37 b,** The Granger Collection, NY; **38,** Stone/Mark Lewis; **41 both,** 1998, The Art Institute of Chicago; **42,** Rich Treptow/Visuals Unlimited; **43,** Chuck Feil/Uniphoto; **44,** SCI-VU-IBMRL/Visuals Unlimited; **45,** Ken Eward/Science Source/Photo Researchers, Inc.; **46 t,** Russ Lappa; **46 b,** Corbis-Bettmann; **47 t,** Helga Lade/Peter Arnold, Inc.; **47 bl,** E. R. Degginger/Animals Animals/Earth Scenes; **47 br,** Charles D. Winters/Photo Researchers, Inc.; **48,** Aron Haupt/ David R. Frazier Photo Library; **50,** Heine Schneebeli/Science Photo Library/Photo Researchers, Inc.; **51,** Corbis-Bettmann.

Chapter 2
Pages 54–55, Milton Rand/Tom Stack & Associates; **56 t,** Richard Haynes; **56 b,** Shambroom/Photo Researchers, Inc.; **57,** Stone/Darryl Torckler; **58 t,** Rivera Collection/Superstock; **58 b,** Russ Lappa; **59,** Tsutomu Nakayama/Uniphoto; **60,** Tomas Muscionoco/The Stock Market; **61,** A. Ramey/Stock Boston; **62,** John D. Cunningham/Visuals Unlimited; **63, 64,** Richard Haynes; **65,** Ken Ross/FPG International; **67 both,** Ken Karp; **72,** Russ Lappa; **73, 74 t,** Richard Haynes; **74 b,** Russ Lappa; **75,** Doug Martin/Photo Researchers, Inc.; **76,** The Granger Collection, NY; **77,** Martin Dohrn/Science Photo Library/Photo Researchers, Inc.; **79,** Charles D. Winters/Photo Researchers, Inc.; **80,** Russ Lappa; **81,** Stone/Darryl Torckler.

Chapter 3
Pages 84–85, Frans Lanting/Minden Pictures; **86 t,** Richard Haynes; **86 b,** Roy Morsch/The Stock Market; **87 t,** D. Roundtree/Image Bank; **87 b,** Steve Maslowshi/Photo Researchers, Inc.; **88,** NASA; **89 l,** Chuck Zsymanski/International Stock; **89 r,** Robert Maier/Animals Animals; **90,** Mike Agliolo/International Stock; **91,** John Kelly/Image Bank; **92,** National Motor Museum, Beaulieu, England; **93 t,** Topham/The Image Works; **93 b,** David Barnes/The Stock Market; **94,** Marc Romanelli/Image Bank; **95,** A.T. Willet/Image Bank; **97, 98 t,** Richard Haynes; **98 b,** Mike Hewitt/Allsport; **99 t,** Russ Lappa; **99 b,** The Stock Market; **100,** Bob Daemmrich/The Image Works; **101 bl,** Mark C. Burnett/Photo Researchers, Inc.; **101 br,** Tony Freeman/PhotoEdit; **102 t,** Yann Guichaoua/Agence Vandystadt/Allsport; **102 m,** Tim DeFrisco/Allsport; **102 b,** Tracy Frankel/Image Bank; **103,** Addison Geary/Stock Boston; **106,** Richard Haynes; **107,** Lou Jones/Image Bank; **108,** Russ Lappa; **109,** Stone/Jacques Jangoux; **112,** Bill Gillette/Liaison Agency; **112 inset,** Gregory Foster/Liaison Agency; **116,** Brian Smale/Discover Magazine; **117,** Stephen G.

Maka/DRK Photo; **118,** Brian Smale/Discover Magazine; **118 inset,** Helen Ghiradella/Discover Magazine.

Chapter 4
Pages 120–121, Joe McDonald/DRK Photo; **122 t,** Russ Lappa; **122 b,** Beatty/Visuals Unlimited; **123,** John Pontier/Animals Animals; **125,** Michael Quinton/Minden Pictures; **126, 127,** The Granger Collection, NY; **128 l,** James Dell/Science Source/Photo Researchers, Inc.; **128 r,** Zig Leszcynski/Animals Animals; **129,** Jim Brandenburg/Minden Pictures; **131 t,** Richard Haynes; **131 b,** John Coletti/Stock Boston; **131 inset,** Joseph Nettis/Photo Researchers, Inc.; **132, 133 l,** The Granger Collection, NY; **133 r,** Caroline Biological Supply Company/Phototake; **134 both,** The Granger Collection, NY; **135 t,** H. R. Bramaz/Peter Arnold, Inc.; **135 bl,** Corbis-Bettmann; **135 br,** Lawrence Migdale/Stock Boston; **137,** CNRI/Science Photo Library/Photo Researchers, Inc.; **138 t,** Runk/Schoenberger/Grant Heilman Photography; **138 b,** Doug Wilson/Corbis Westlight; **139 l,** M. Abbey/Visuals Unlimited; **139 r,** Runk/Schoenberger/Grant Heilman Photography; **140,** Dr. Dennis Kunkel/Phototake; **141,** Bill Longcore/Photo Researchers, Inc.; **144,** K. G. Murtis/Visuals Unlimited; **145,** Stone/John Cardamone; **146 l,** Dr. David Scott/CNRI/Phototake; **146 r,** Dr. Dennis Kunkel/Phototake; **148,** Runk/Schoenberger/Grant Heilman Photography; **149 both,** Richard Haynes; **150 t,** Stephen J. Krasemann/DRK Photo; **150 m,** PhotoDisc, Inc.; **150 bl,** Stone/Andrew Olney; **150 br,** Brian Parker/Tom Stack & Associates; **151,** Stone/Gary Bumgarner; **152,** Santa Gertudis Association.

Chapter 5
Pages 156–157, Julie Habel/Corbis Westlight; **158,** NASA; **160 l,** Stanley Flegler/Visuals Unlimited; **160 m,** David M. Phillips/Visuals Unlimited; **160 r,** David M. Phillips/Visuals Unlimited; **162,** M. Abbey/Visuals Unlimited; **163 t,** Russ Lappa; **163 bl,** Stone/Cosmo Condina; **163 br,** Biophoto Associates/Photo Researchers, Inc.; **165 l,** Frans Lanting/Minden Pictures; **165 r,** Tom J. Ulrich/Visuals Unlimited; **166 l,** Stephen Dalton/Photo Researchers, Inc.; **166 r,** Phil Dotson/Photo Researchers, Inc.; **167,** Mark Newman/Visuals Unlimited; **168,** Terje Rakke/Image Bank; **170 t,** David Scharf/Peter Arnold, Inc.; **170 b,** Larry Lefever/Grant Heilman Photography; **171,** Stone/Art Wolfe; **172,** Biophoto Associates/Science Source/Photo Researchers, Inc.; **174, 175 all,** M. Abbey/Photo Researchers, Inc.; **178,** Robert Knauft/Biology Media.

Chapter 6
Pages 182–183, J. Lotter Gurling/Tom Stack & Associates; **184 t** Russ Lappa; **184 b,** Inga Spence/The Picture Cube; **185 l,** Gerard Lacz/Animals Animals **185 m,** Tom Brakefield/DRK Photo; **185 r,** Ron Kimball; **186–187,** Thomas Kitchin/Tom Stack & Associates; **188 t,** Alan L. Detrick/Photo Researchers; **188 bl,** Oliver Meckes/Photo Researchers; **188 br,** David M. Phillips/Visuals Unlimited; **189,** Ray Coleman/Photo Researchers; **190 t,** Richard Haynes; **190 b,** Science Photo Library/Photo Researchers; **191,** Dr. Rony Brain/Science Photo Library/Photo Researchers; **192 bl,** Dr. K. S Kim/Peter Arnold; **192 br,** Dr. Ennis Kunkel/Phototake; **193 l,** Stone/Ben Osborne; **193 r,** Michael Abbey/Photo Researchers; **195,** Richard Haynes; **196 t,** Science VU/Visuals Unlimited; **196 b,** Jan Hinsch/Science Photo Library/Photo Researchers; **197 tl,** O.S.F./Animals Animals; **197 tr,** A. Le Toquin/Photo Researchers; **197 b,** Gregory G. Dimijian/Photo Researchers; **198,** Astrid & Hanns-Frieder Michler/Science Photo Library/Photo Researchers; **199,** Eric Grave/Science Source/Photo Researchers; **200,** Sinclair Stammers Oxford Scientific Films; **201 t,** Dwight R. Kuhn; **201 b,** Michael Fogden/Animals Animals; **202,** Fred Unverhau/Animals Animals/Earth Scenes; **203,** David Scharf/Peter Arnold; **204,** Joanne Lotter/Tom Stack & Associates; **206 tl,** Runk/Schoenberger/Grant Heilman Photography; **206 tr, 206 bl,** Runk/Schoenberger/Grant Heilman Photography, Inc.; **206 br,** Rod Planck/Tom Stack & Associates; **207 l,** Runk/Schoenberger/Grant Heilman Photography; **207 inset,** Breck P. Kent; **207 ml,** Thomas Kitchin/Tom Stack & Associates; **207 mr,** David Forbert/Superstock; **209,** E. R. Degginger; **210,** Porterfield-Chickering/Photo Researchers; **211 tl,** E. R. Degginger; **211 tr,** Mark E. Gibson/The Stock Market; **211 b,** Larry Lefever/Grant Heilman Photography.

Chapter 7
Pages 216–217, Norbert Wu/DRK Photo; **218 t,** Richard Haynes; **218 b,** Leonard Lee Rue III/Animals Animals/Earth Scenes; **219 l,** Stone/Oliver Strewe; **219 r,** Frans Lanting/Minden Pictures; **220 l,** Dave B. Fleetham/Visuals Unlimited; **220 r,** Stone/David Tipling; **221,** Corel Corp.; **222,** William C Jorgensen/Visuals Unlimited; **223 t,** Russ Lappa; **223 b,** Gregory Ochocki/Photo Researchers, Inc.; **224 l,** Stone/Charles Seaborn; **224 r,** Biophoto Associates/Photo Researchers, Inc.; **225,** David M. Dennis/Tom Stack & Associates; **226,** Sinclair Stammers/Science Photo Library/Photo Researchers, Inc.; **228 l,** Stone/Kevin & Cat Sweeney; **228 r,** Bruce Watkins/Animals Animals; **230 t,** Richard Haynes; **230 b,** Patti Murray/Animals Animals; **231 l,** John Gerlach/Tom Stack & Associates; **231 r,** Donald Specker/Animals Animals; **232,** CNRI/Science Photo Library/Photo Researchers, Inc.; **234,** The G. R. 'Dick' Roberts Photo Library; **235 tl,** Simon D. Pollard/Photo Researchers, Inc.; **235 tr,** Stone/Tim Flach; **235 b,** Stone/Christoph Burki; **236 l,** Brian Parker/Tom Stack & Associates; **236 m,** Stone/Darryl Torckler **236 r,** Fred Whitehead/Animals Animals; **237 t,** Russ Lappa; **237**

b, Phil Dotson/Photo Researchers, Inc.; **238 l,** Larry Lipsky/DRK Photo; **238 r,** John d. Cummingham/Visuals Unlimited; **239 l,** Jeff Rotman; **239 r,** Herve Berthoule Jacana/Photo Researchers, Inc.; **241,** Suzanne L. Collins & Joseph T. Collins/Photo Researchers, Inc.; **243,** Tom Stack and Associates; **244,** Zig Leszcynski/Animals Animals; **245 l,** Brian Kenney/Natural Selection; **245 r,** M. C. Chamberlain/DRK Photo; **246,** Colin Milkins/Animals Animals; **247 t,** Richard Haynes; **247 b,** Wayne Lankinen/DRK Photo; **248,** Stephen Krasemann/DRK Photo; **250,** Stone/Manfred Danegger; **251 l,** Henry Ausloos/Animals Animals/Earth Scenes; **251 r,** Stone/Art Wolfe; **252 t,** Hilary Pooley/Animals Animals; **252–253 b,** Michael Fogden/DRK Photo; **253 t,** Johnny Johnson/DRK Photo; **254 l,** Tom McHugh/Photo Researchers, Inc.; **254 r,** Jack Dermid; **255 t,** Roger Aitkenhead/Animals Animals; **255 b,** Stone/Chuck Davis; **260,** Courtesy of Lydia Villa-Komaroff; **261,** Courtesy of Lydia Villa-Komaroff; **262 t,** Biophoto Associates/Science Source/Photo Researchers, Inc.; **262 b,** Howard Sochurek/The Stock Market; **263,** Will & Deni McIntyre/Photo Researchers, Inc.

Chapter 8
Pages 264–265, Stone/Tony Craddock; **266 t,** Richard Haynes; **266-267 b,** Shin Yoshino/Minden Pictures; **267 t,** Carr Clifton/Minden Pictures; **267 t inset,** Corel Corp.; **267 b inset,** S. Nielsen/DRK Photo; **268,** John Cancalosi/Tom Stack & Associates; **269,** Patti Murray/Animals Animals; **273 t,** Richard Haynes; **273 b,** Michlo Hoshino/Minden Pictures; **274,** C. Allan Morgan/DRK Photo; **275 t,** Rob Simpson/Visuals Unlimited; **275 b,** Bas van Beek/Leo de Wys; **277,** Mitsuaki Iwago/Minden Pictures; **278 t,** Dan Budnick/Woodfin Camp & Associates; **278 b,** Russ Lappa; **280,** The Stock Market; **281,** Stone/Frans Lanting; **282 tl,** David Davis/Index Stock; **282 tr,** Gail Shumway/FPG International; **282 b,** Nobel Proctor/Science Source/Photo Researchers, Inc.; **286,** Larry Lefever/Grant Heilman Photography.

Chapter 9
Pages 290–291, Stone/Yamada Toshiro; **292,** M. L. Sinibaldi/The Stock Market; **295,** Stone/Richard A Cooke III; **296,** Stone/Keith Wood; **298,** Stone/Mike Abrahams; **299,** Chad Ehlers/International Stock; **300,** Stone/Nadia MacKenzie; **302,** Robert K. Grubbs/Photo Network; **304,** NASA; **305,** Richard Haynes; **306,** Herb Swanson; **307 t,** Russ Lappa; **307 b,** Photograph by Johan Hagemeyer, courtesy AIP Emilio Segre Visual Archives; **310,** Y. Arthus-Bertrand/Peter Arnold, Inc.; **311,** U.S. Dept. of Energy/Science Photo Library/Photo Researchers, Inc.; **313,** Richard Haynes; **314 t,** Stone/Mitch Kezar; **314 b,** Leonard Lessin/Peter Arnold, Inc.; **315,** Stone/Yves Marcoux; **316,** Wolf/Monkmeyer; **317,** Stone/Nadia MacKenzie; **320 t,** Jeff Foott/Tom Stack & Associates; **320 b,** Courtesy of Elroy Masters; **321 t,** Courtesy of Elroy Masters; **321 b,** Pat O'Hara/DRK Photo; **322–323 b,** M. Collier/DRK Photo; **322 t inset,** Vireo; **322 b inset,** Jeff Foott/Tom Stack & Associates; **323 t,** Gilbert Grant/Photo Researchers, Inc.

Chapter 10
Pages 324–325, Hubertus Kanus/Superstock; **326,** ESA/PLI/The Stock Market; **327 l,** Peter Arnold, Inc.; **327 r,** Stone/G. Brad Lewis; **328,** John Eastcott/Yva Momatiuk/The Image Works; **330 t,** Richard Haynes; **330 b,** Barry L. Runk/Grant Heilman Photography; **331 l,** Mark A. Schneider/Visuals Unlimited; **331 m, 331 r, 332 l,** Breck P. Kent; **332 r,** E.R. Degginger; **334 tl,** Paul Silverman/Fundamental Photographs; **334 tr,** Breck P. Kent; **334 bl,** Charles D. Winters/Photo Researchers, Inc; **334 bm,** Runk/Schoenberger/Grant Heilman Photography; **334 br,** William Ferguson; **335 l,** Runk/Schoenberger/Grant Heilman Photography; **335 r,** Paul Silverman/Fundamental Photographs; **336 t,** Runk/Schoenberger/Grant Heilman Photography; **336 b,** Gemological Institute of America; **337 tl,** Bill Pierce/Rainbow; **337 tr,** Pearson Education/PH College/Prentice Hall; **337 m,** Laurence Parent; **337 b,** Michael Newman/PhotoEdit; **339,** Richard Haynes; **340,** Tom Bean; **341 tl,** E. R. Degginger; **341 tm, 341 tr, 341 m, 341 b, 342 r,** Breck P. Kent; **342 l,** E.R. Degginger; **343,** Breck P. Kent; **344 t,** David Welling/Animals Animals/Earth Scenes; **344 m,** Barry Runk/Grant Heilman Photography; **344 b,** PhotoDisc, Inc.; **345 tl,** Barry L. Runk/Grant Heilman Photography; **345 tr,** Andrew J. Martinez/Photo Researchers, Inc.; **345 m,** Jeff Scovil; **345 b,** Jeff Scovil; **346,** David Muench Photography.

Chapter 11
Pages 352–353, Soames Summerhays/Photo Researchers, Inc.; **354 t,** Russ Lappa; **354 b,** Simon Fraser/Science Photo Library/Photo Reseachers, Inc.; **358,** Ben S. Kwiatkowski/Fundamental Photographs; **360 t,** David Parker/Science Photo Library/Photo Researchers, Inc.; **360 b,** David Muench Photography; **361,** Sharon Gerig/Tom Stack & Associates; **362,** Stone/Stan Osolinski; **363,** Phillips Petroleum; **364, 365,** Tom Bean; **367 both, 368, 370 t,** Richard Haynes; **370 b,** Russell D. Curtis/Photo Researchers, Inc.; **371,** AP Photo/Leonetto Medici; **372,** EERC/Berkeley; **374 t, 374 b,** Breck P. Kent; **374 m, 375, 377 b,** E. R. Degginger; **377 t,** Ed Reschke/Peter Arnold, Inc.; **378 t,** William Felger/Grant Heilman Photography; **378 b,** Dave B. Fleetham/Tom Stack & Associates; **379 all,** Alberto Garcia/Saba Press; **380, tl,** North Wind Picture Archives; **380 tr,** Kim Heacox/Peter Arnold, Inc.; **380 b,** Robert Fried Photography; **381,** Alberto Garcia/Saba Press; **382,** Norbert Rosing/Animals Animals/Earth Scenes; **383 l,** AP Photo/Pat Roqua; **383 r,** Antonio Emerito/Sipa Press; **385, 386 t,** Richard Haynes; **386 b,** Brownie Harris/The Stock Market; **387 l,** Tom

Bean/DRK Photo; **387 r,** David Hosking/Photo Researchers, Inc.; **388,** Betty Crowell/Faraway Places; **389 t,** Picture Perfect; **389 m,** Manfred Gottschalk/Tom Stack & Associates; **389 b,** Chris Hamilton/The Stock Market; **390,** Greg Vaughn/Tom Stack & Associates.

Chapter 12
Pages 394–395, Randy Linchs/Sharpshooters; **396,** Richard Haynes; **400 t,** O. Louis Mazzatenta/National Geographic Image Collection; **400 b,** Liba Taylor/Corbis; **401 t,** Stone/Tom Bean; **401 b,** Gianni Dagli Orti/Corbis; **404 t,** Russ Lappa; **404 b,** Superstock; **404 inset,** Wernher Krutein/Liaison Agency; **406,** Les Stone/Corbis Sygma; **407,** Stone/Doug McKay; **410 l,** David L. Brown/The Stock Market; **410 r,** John Shaw/Tom Stack & Associates; **411,** Ralph A. Clevenger/Corbis Westlight; **412 t,** Richard Haynes; **412 b,** Tim Olive/SharpShooters; **417,** Mark Thayer; **418 t,** Russ Lappa; **418 b,** Greg Vaughn/Tom Stack & Associates; **419 l,** PhotoDisc, Inc.; **419 r,** Breck P. Kent/Animals Animals/Earth Scenes; **423 t,** Russ Lappa; **423 b,** Laura Sikes/Corbis Sygma; **424,** Calvin Larsen/Photo Researchers, Inc.; **426,** Russ Lappa; **427 t,** Peter Skinner/Photo Researchers, Inc.; **427 b,** Russ Lappa.

Chapter 13
Pages 432–433, Stone/Jay Simon; **434 t,** Russ Lappa; **434 b,** NASA/Photo Researchers, Inc.; **436 t,** Richard Haynes; **436 b,** Russ Lappa; **437,** George G. Dimijian/Photo Researchers, Inc; **438,** Eric Horan/Liaison Agency; **439,** Richard Haynes; **440 t,** Russ Lappa; **440 b,** Aaron Haupt/Photo Researchers, Inc.; **441 t,** Biophoto Associates/Photo Researchers, Inc.; **441 b,** Paul Lowe/Magnum Photos; **443,** Will McIntyre/Photo Researchers, Inc.; **444,** Steve Casimiro/Liaison Agency; **445 t,** Russ Lappa; **445 b,** Eric A. Kessler; **447,** Ivan Bucher/Photo Researchers, Inc.; **449, 451 t,** Russ Lappa; **451 b,** Steve Vidler/Superstock; **452,** Mark C. Burnett/Photo Researchers, Inc.; **454 t,** The Granger Collection, NY; **454 b,** Corbis-Bettmann; **455 t,** The National Archives/Corbis; **455 b,** NASA; **456;** Jack Finch/Science Photo Library/Photo Researchers, Inc.

Chapter 14
Pages 460–461, William Johnson/Stock Boston; **462–463,** Photo Researchers, Inc.; **467,** Richard Haynes; **468, 469, 472 t,** Russ Lappa; **472 b,** Victoria Hurst/Tom Stack & Associates; **473 t,** Richard Haynes; **473 b,** Gary Retherford/Photo Researchers, Inc.; **475,** Richard Haynes; **476,** Steve McCurry/Magnum Photos; **478,** Scala/Art Resource, NY; **480,** Stone/Ken McVey; **481,** Russ Lappa; **482,** E.J. Tarbuck; **483,** Peter Arnold, Inc.; **485 t,** Michael Gadomski/GADOM/Bruce Coleman; **485 tm,** Phil Degginger/Bruce Coleman, Inc.; **485 bm,** E.R. Degginger; **485 b,** John Shaw/Bruce Coleman, Inc.; **486,** Wendy Shattil/Bob Rozinski/Tom Stack & Associates; **487,** Richard Haynes; **488 t,** AP/Wide World Photos; **488 inset,** Stone/Gerben Oppermans Stone; **488 b,** Nuridsany et Perennou/Photo Researchers, Inc.; **490,** Stone/Bill Frantz; **491,** Stone/Gerben Oppermans.

Chapter 15
Pages 494–495, Pete Turner/Image Bank; **496 both,** Russ Lappa; **497,** Stone/Jim Corwin; **503 t,** Russ Lappa; **503 b,** Dirck Halstead/Liaison Agency; **504,** Dan Sudia/Photo Researchers, Inc.; **505,** Schuster Catalog/Superstock; **506 both,** The Granger Collection, NY; **507,** North Wind Picture Archives; **508,** Sheila Beougher/Liaison Agency; **509,** NASA Goddard Laboratory for Atmospheres; **510,** Clore Collection, Tate Gallery, London/Art Resource, NY; **512,** NOAA; **514,** Tony Freeman/PhotoEdit; **515 t,** Richard Haynes; **515 bl,** Keith Kent/Science Photo Library/Photo Researchers, Inc.; **515 br,** Grant V. Faint/Image Bank; **518,** AP Photos/David J. Phillip; **519 t,** Larry Lawfer, **519 b,** Corel Corp.; **520,** AP Photo/David Umberger; **521,** NOAA; **527,** Schuster Catalog/Superstock.

Chapter 16
Pages 530–531, NASA; **532 t,** Russ Lappa; **532 b,** Anglo-Australian Observatory, photograph by David Malin; **533, 534,** The Granger Collection, NY; **535 t,** Richard Haynes; **535 b,** The Granger Collection, NY; **538,** Richard Haynes; **539,** Digital Vision; **540,** National Solar Observatory; **540 inset,** Space Telescope Science Institute; **542 t,** Space Telescope Science Institute; **542 b,** National Solar Observatory; **546,** NASA; **546 inset,** A.S.P./Science Source/Photo Researchers, Inc.; **547,** Digital Vision; **548,** Digital Vision; **549,** NASA; **550,** Jet Propulsion Laboratory; **551 both,** NASA; **552,** Stone; **554 both,** NASA; **555, 556 t,** Jet Propulsion Laboratory; **556 inset,** Digital Vision; **556 b, 557, 558 both, 559,** NASA; **560, 561, 562 t,** Richard Haynes; **562 b,** Space Telescope Science Institute; **564,** Jet Propulsion Laboratory; **565 l,** U.S. Geological Survey; **565 r,** Jerry Schad/Photo Researchers, Inc.; **566,** Richard Haynes; **567,** NASA/Roger Ressmeyer/CORBIS; **568, 569,** NASA; **570, 571 t,** Jet Propulsion Laboratory; **571 b, 575 t,** The Granger Collection, NY; **575 m,** 1998 North Wind Picture Archives; **575 b,** Hippolyte Sebron (born France 1801–1879) Giant Steamboats on the Levee at New Orleans, 1853. Oil on canvas, Tulane. University Art Collection, Gift of D. H. Holmes Company.; **577,** Richard Pasley/Liaison Agency; **578,** National Portrait Gallery, Smithsonian Institution/Art Resource, NY; **579 t,** 1998 North Wind Picture Archives; **579 b,** Chromo Sohm/Sohm/Photo Researchers, Inc.

Skills Handbook
Page 580, Mike Moreland/Photo Network; **581 t,** FoodPix; **581 m,** Richard Haynes; **581 b,** Russ Lappa; **584,** Richard Haynes; **586,** Ron Kimball; **587,** Renee Lynn/Photo Researchers; **592,** Paul Rezendes.

Appendix
Page 600, 601 both, 602 both, Russ Lappa.